W. H. HUDSON'S
SOUTH AMERICAN ROMANCES

W. H. HUDSON'S

SOUTH AMERICAN ROMANCES

THE PURPLE LAND; GREEN MANSIONS; EL OMBÚ

DUCKWORTH
8 HENRIETTA STREET
LONDON W.C.

First Published 1930

Made and Printed in Great Britain by
The Camelot Press Limited,
London and Southampton

CONTENTS

THE PURPLE LAND

Being the Narrative of one Richard Lamb's Adventures in the Banda Oriental, in South America, as told by Himself

CHAPTER I

RAMBLES IN MODERN TROY

THREE chapters in the story of my life—three periods, distinct and well defined, yet consecutive—beginning when I had not completed twenty-five years and finishing before thirty, will probably prove the most eventful of all. To the very end they will come back oftenest to memory and seem more vivid than all the other years of existence—the four-and-twenty I had already lived, and the, say, forty or forty-five—I hope it may be fifty or even sixty—which are to follow. For what soul in this wonderful various world would wish to depart before ninety! The dark as well as the light, its sweet and its bitter, make me love it.

Of the first of these three a word only need be written. This was the period of courtship and matrimony; and though the experience seemed to me then something altogether new and strange in the world, it must nevertheless have resembled that of other men, since all men marry. And the last period, which was the longest of the three, occupying fully three years, could not be told. It was all black disaster. Three years of enforced separation and the extremest suffering which the cruel law of the land allowed an enraged father to inflict on his child and the man who had ventured to wed her against his will. Even the wise may be driven mad by oppression, and I that was never wise, but lived in and was led by the passions and illusions and the unbounded self-confidence of youth, what must it have been for me when we were cruelly torn asunder; when I was cast into prison to lie for long months in the company of felons, ever thinking of her who was also desolate and breaking her heart! But it is ended—the abhorred restraint, the anxiety, the broodings over a thousand possible and impossible schemes of revenge. If it is any consolation to know that in breaking her heart he, at the same time, broke his own and made haste to join her in that silent place, I have it. Ah no! it is no comfort to me, since I cannot but reflect that before he shattered my life I had shattered his by taking her from him, who was his idol. We are quits then, and I can even say, "Peace to his ashes!" But I could not say it then in my frenzy and grief, nor could it be said in that fatal country which I had inhabited from boyhood and had learned to love like my own, and had hoped never to leave. It was grown hateful to me, and, flying from it, I found myself once more in that Purple Land where we had formerly taken refuge together, and which now seemed to my distracted mind a place of pleasant and peaceful memories.

During the months of quietude after the storm, mostly

spent in lonely rambles by the shore, these memories were more and more with me. Sometimes sitting on the summit of that great solitary hill, which gives the town its name, I would gaze by the hour on the wide prospect towards the interior, as if I could see and never weary of seeing all that lay beyond—plains and rivers and woods and hills, and cabins where I had rested, and many a kindly human face. Even the faces of those who had ill-treated or regarded me with evil eyes now appeared to have a friendly look. Most of all did I think of that dear river, the unforgettable Yí, the shaded white house at the end of the little town, and the sad and beautiful image of one whom I, alas! had made unhappy.

So much was I occupied towards the end of that vacant period with these recollections that I remembered how, before quitting these shores, the thought had come to me that during some quiet interval in my life I would go over it all again, and write the history of my rambles for others to read in the future. But I did not attempt it then, nor until long years afterwards. For I had no sooner begun to play with the idea than something came to rouse me from the state I was in, during which I had been like one that has outlived his activities, and is no longer capable of a new emotion, but feeds wholly on the past. And this something new, affecting me so that I was all at once myself again, eager to be up and doing, was nothing more than a casual word from a distance, the cry of a lonely heart, which came by chance to my ear; and hearing it I was like one who opening his eyes from a troubled doze unexpectedly sees the morning star in its unearthly lustre above the wide, dark plain where night overtook him—the star of day and everlasting hope, and of passion and strife and toil and rest and happiness.

I need not linger on the events which took us to the Banda—our nocturnal flight from Paquíta's summer home on the pampas; the hiding and clandestine marriage in the capital and subsequent escape northwards into the province of Santa Fé; the seven to eight months of somewhat troubled happiness we had there; and finally, the secret return to Buenos Ayres in search of a ship to take us out of the country. Troubled happiness! Ah yes, and my greatest trouble was when I looked on her, my partner for life, when she seemed loveliest, so small, so exquisite in her dark blue eyes that were like violets, and silky black hair and tender pink and olive complexion—so frail in appearance! And I had taken her—stolen her—from her natural protectors, from the home where she had been worshipped—I of an alien race and another religion, without means, and, because I had stolen her, an offender against the law. But of this no more. I begin my itinerary where, safe on our little ship, with the towers of Buenos Ayres fast fading away in the west, we began to feel free from apprehension and to give ourselves up to the contemplation of the delights before us. Winds and waves presently interfered with our raptures, Paquíta proving a very indifferent sailor, so that for some hours we had a very trying time of it. Next day a favourable north-west breeze sprang up to send us flying like a bird over those unlovely red billows, and in the evening we disembarked in Montevideo, the city of refuge.

We proceeded to an hotel, where for several days we lived very happily, enchanted with each other's society; and when we strolled along the beach to watch the setting sun, kindling with mystic fire heaven, water, and the great hill that gives the city its name, and remembered that we were looking towards the shores of Buenos Ayres, it was pleasant to reflect that the widest river in the world rolled between us and those who probably felt offended at what we had done.

This charming state of things came to an end at length in a somewhat curious manner. One night, before we had been a month in the hotel, I was lying wide awake in bed. It was late; I had already heard the mournful, long-drawn voice of the watchman under my window calling out, "Half-past one and cloudy."

Gil Blas relates in his biography that one night while lying awake he fell into practising a little introspection, an unusual thing for him to do, and the conclusion he came to was that he was not a very good young man. I was having a somewhat similar experience that night when, in the midst of my unflattering thoughts about myself, a profound sigh from Paquíta made me aware that she too was lying wide awake and also, in all probability, chewing the cud of reflection. When I questioned her concerning that sigh, she endeavoured in vain to conceal from me that she was beginning to feel unhappy. What a rude shock the discovery gave me! And we so lately married! It is only just to Paquíta, however, to say that had I not married her she would have been still more unhappy. Only the poor child could not help thinking of father and mother; she yearned for reconciliation, and her present sorrow rose from her belief that they would never, never, never forgive her. I endeavoured, with all the eloquence I was capable of, to dispel these gloomy ideas, but she was firm in her conviction that precisely because they had loved her so much they would never pardon this first great offence. My poor darling might have been reading "Christabel," I thought, when she said that it is toward those who have been most deeply loved the wounded heart cherishes the greatest bitterness. Then, by way of illustration, she told me of a quarrel between her mother and a till then dearly loved sister. It had happened many years ago, when she, Paquíta, was a mere child; yet the sisters had never forgiven each other.

"And where," I asked, "is this aunt of yours, of whom I have never heard you speak until this minute?"

"Oh," answered Paquíta, with the greatest simplicity imaginable, "she left this country long, long ago, and you never heard of her because we were not even allowed to mention her name in the house. She went to live in Montevideo, and I believe she is there still, for several years ago I heard some person say that she had bought herself a house in that city."

"Soul of my life," said I, "you have never left Buenos Ayres in heart, even to keep your poor husband company! Yet I know, Paquíta, that corporeally you are here in Montevideo conversing with me at this very moment."

"True," said Paquíta; "I had somehow forgotten that we were in Montevideo. My thoughts were wandering—perhaps it is sleepiness."

"I swear to you, Paquíta," I replied, "that you shall see this aunt of yours to-morrow before set of sun; and I am positive, sweetest, that she will be delighted to receive so near and lovely a relation. How glad she will be of an opportunity of relating that ancient quarrel with her sister and ventilating her mouldy grievances! I know these old dames—they are all alike."

Paquíta did not like the idea at first, but when I assured her that we were getting to the end of our money, and that her aunt might be able to put me in the way of obtaining employment, she consented, like the dutiful little wife she was.

Next day I discovered her relation without very much trouble, Montevideo not being a large city. We found Doña Isidora—for that was the lady's name—living in a somewhat mean-looking house at the eastern extremity of the town, furthest away from the water. There was an air of poverty about the place, for the good dame, though well provided with means to live comfortably, made a pet of her gold. Nevertheless, she received us very kindly when we introduced ourselves and related our mournful and romantic story; a room was prepared for our immediate reception, and she even made me some vague promises of assistance. On a more intimate acquaintance with our hostess we found that I had not been very far out in guessing her character. For several days she could talk of nothing except her immemorial quarrel with her sister and her sister's husband, and we were bound to listen attentively and to sympathise with her, for that was the only return we could make for her hospitality.

Paquíta had more than her share of it, but was made no wiser as to the cause of this feud of long standing; for, though Doña Isidora had evidently been nursing her wrath all those years to keep it warm, she could not, for the life of her, remember how the quarrel originated.

After breakfast each morning I would kiss her and hand her over to the tender mercies of her Isidora, then go forth on my fruitless perambulations about the town. At first I only acted the intelligent foreigner, going about staring at the public buildings, and collecting curios—strangely marked pebbles, and a few military brass buttons, long shed by the garments they once made brave; rusty misshapen bullets, mementoes of the immortal nine or ten years' siege which had won for Montevideo the mournful appellation of modern Troy. When I had fully examined from the outside the scene of my future triumphs—for I had now resolved to settle down and make my fortune in Montevideo—I began seriously to look out for employment. I visited in turn every large mercantile establishment in the place, and, in fact, every house where I thought there might be a chance of lighting on something to do. It was necessary to make a beginning, and I would not have turned up my nose at anything, however small, I was so heartily sick of being poor, idle, and dependent. Nothing could I find. In one house I was told that the city had not yet recovered from the effects of the late revolution, and that business was, in consequence, in a complete state of paralysis; in another that the city was on the eve of a revolution, and that business was, in consequence, in a complete state of paralysis. And everywhere it was the same story—the political state of the country made it impossible for me to win an honest dollar.

Feeling very much dispirited, and with the soles nearly worn off my boots, I sat down on a bench beside the sea, or river—for some call it one thing, some the other, and the muddied hue and freshness of the water, and the uncertain words of geographers, leave one in doubt as to whether Montevideo is situated on the shores of the Atlantic, or only near the Atlantic and on the shores of a river one hundred and fifty miles wide at its mouth. I did not trouble my head about it; I had other things that concerned me more nearly to think of. I had a quarrel with this Oriental nation, and that was more to me than the greenness or the saltness of the vast estuary that washes the dirty feet of its queen—for this modern Troy, this city of battle, murder, and sudden death, also calls itself Queen of the Plata. That it was a very just quarrel on my part I felt well assured. Now, to be even with every human being who despitefully uses me has ever been a principle of action with me. Nor let it be said that it is an unchristian principle; for when I have been smitten on the right or left cheek (the pain is just the same in either case), before I am prepared to deliver the return blow so long a time has often elapsed that all wrathful or revengeful thoughts are over. I strike in such a case more for the public good than for my own satisfaction, and am therefore right in calling my motive a principle of action, not an impulse. It is a very valuable one too, infinitely more effective than the fantastical code of the duellist, which favours the person who inflicts the injury, affording him facilities for murdering or maiming the person injured. It is a weapon invented for us by Nature before Colonel Colt ever lived, and it has this advantage, that one is permitted to wear it in the most law-abiding communities as well as amongst miners and backwoodsmen. If inoffensive people were ever to cast it aside, then wicked men would have everything their own way and make life intolerable. Fortunately the evil-doers always have the fear of this intangible six-shooter before them; a wholesome feeling, which restrains them more than reasonableness or the law courts, and to which we owe it that the meek are permitted to inherit the earth. But now this quarrel was with a whole nation, though certainly not with a very great one, since the population of the Banda Orientál numbers only about a quarter of a million. Yet in this sparsely settled country, with its bountiful soil and genial climate, there was apparently no place for me, a muscular and fairly intelligent young man, who only asked to be allowed to work to live! But how was I to make them smart for this injustice? I could not take the scorpion they gave me when I asked them for an egg, and make it sting every individual composing the nation. I was powerless, utterly powerless, to punish them, and therefore the only thing that remained for me to do was to curse them.

Looking around me, my eyes rested on the famous hill across the bay, and I all at once resolved to go up to its summit. and, looking down on the Banda Orientál, pronounce my imprecation in the most solemn and impressive manner.

The expedition to the *cerro*, as it is called, proved agreeable enough. Notwithstanding the excessive heats we were just then having, many wild flowers were blooming on its slopes, which made it a perfect garden. When I reached the old ruined fort which crowns the summit, I got upon a wall and rested for half an hour, fanned by a fresh breeze from the river and greatly enjoying the prospect before me. I had not left out of sight the serious object of my visit to that commanding spot, and only wished that the malediction I was about to utter could be rolled down in the shape of a stupendous rock, loosed from its hold, which would go bounding down the mountain, and, leaping clear over the bay, crash through the iniquitous city beyond, filling it with ruin and amazement.

"Whichever way I turn," I said, "I see before me one of the fairest habitations God has made for man: great plains smiling with everlasting spring; ancient woods; swift beautiful rivers; ranges of blue hills stretching away to the dim horizon. And beyond those fair slopes, how many leagues of pleasant wilderness are sleeping in the sunshine, where the wild flowers waste their sweetness and no plough turns the fruitful soil, where deer and ostrich roam fearless of the hunter, while over all bends a blue sky without a cloud to stain its exquisite beauty? And the people dwelling in yon city—the key to a continent—they are the possessors of it all. It is theirs, since the world, out of which the old spirit is fast dying, has suffered them to keep it. What have they done with this their heritage? What are they doing even now? They are sitting dejected in their houses, or standing in their doorways with folded arms and anxious, expectant faces. For a change is coming: they are on the eve of a tempest. Not an atmospheric change; no blighting simoom will sweep over their fields, nor will any volcanic eruption darken their crystal heavens. The earthquakes that shake the Andean cities to their foundations they have never known and can never know. The expected change and tempest is a political one. The plot is ripe, the daggers sharpened, the contingent of assassins hired, the throne of human skulls, styled in their ghastly facetiousness a Presidential Chair, is about to be assaulted. It is long, weeks or even months, perhaps, since the last wave, crested with bloody froth, rolled its desolating flood over the country; it is high time, therefore, for all men to prepare themselves for the shock of the succeeding wave. And we consider it right to root up thorns and thistles, to drain malarious marshes, to extirpate rats and vipers; but it would be immoral, I suppose, to stamp out these people because their vicious natures are disguised in human shape; this people that in crimes have surpassed all others, ancient or modern, until because of them the name of a whole continent has grown to be a byword of scorn and reproach throughout the earth, and to stink in the nostrils of all men!

"I swear that I, too, will become a conspirator if I remain long on this soil. Oh, for a thousand young men of Devon and Somerset here with me, every one of them with a brain on fire with thoughts like mine! What a glorious deed would be done for humanity! What a mighty cheer we would raise for the glory of the old England that is passing away! Blood would flow in yon streets as it never flowed before, or, I should say, as it only flowed in them once, and that was when they were swept clean by British bayonets. And afterwards there would be peace, and the grass would be greener and the flowers brighter for that crimson shower.

"Is it not then bitter as wormwood and gall to think that over these domes and towers beneath my feet, no longer than half a century ago, fluttered the holy cross of St. George! For never was there a holier crusade undertaken, never a nobler conquest planned, than that which had for its object the wresting this fair country from unworthy hands, to make it for all time part of the mighty English kingdom. What would it have been now—this bright, winterless land, and this city commanding the entrance to the greatest river in the world? And to think that it was won for England, not treacherously, or bought with gold, but in the old Saxon fashion with hard blows, and climbing over heaps of slain defenders; and after it was thus won, to think that it was lost—will it be believed?—not fighting, but yielded up without a stroke by craven wretches unworthy of the name of Britons! Here, sitting alone on this mountain, my face burns like fire when I think of it—this glorious opportunity lost for ever! 'We offer you your laws, your religion, and property under the protection of the British Government,' loftily proclaimed the invaders—Generals Beresford,

Achmuty, Whitelocke, and their companions; and presently, after suffering one reverse, they (or one of them) lost heart and exchanged the country they had drenched in blood, and had conquered, for a couple of thousand British soldiers made prisoners in Buenos Ayres across the water; then, getting into their ships once more, they sailed away from the Plata for ever! This transaction, which must have made the bones of our Viking ancestors rattle with indignation in their graves, was forgotten later on when we seized the rich Falklands. A splendid conquest and a glorious compensation for our loss! When yon queen city was in our grasp, and the regeneration, possibly even the ultimate possession, of this green world before us, our hearts failed us and the prize dropped from our trembling hands. We left the sunny mainland to capture the desolate haunt of seals and penguins; and now let all those who in this quarter of the globe aspire to live under that 'British Protection' of which Achmuty preached so loudly at the gates of yon capital, transport themselves to those lonely antarctic islands to listen to the thunder of the waves on the grey shores and shiver in the bleak winds that blow from the frozen south!"

After delivering this comminatory address I felt greatly relieved, and went home in a cheerful frame of mind to supper, which consisted that evening of mutton scrag, boiled with pumpkin, sweet potatoes, and milky maize—not at all a bad dish for a hungry man.

CHAPTER II

PEASANT HOMES AND HEARTS

SEVERAL days passed, and my second pair of boots had been twice resoled before Doña Isidora's schemes for advancing my fortunes began to take form. Perhaps she was beginning to think us a burden on her somewhat niggardly establishment; anyway, hearing that my preference was for a country life, she gave me a letter containing half a dozen lines of commendation addressed to the Mayordomo of a distant cattle-breeding establishment, asking him to serve the writer by giving her *nephew*—as she called me—employment of some kind on the estancia. Probably she knew that this letter would really lead to nothing, and gave it merely to get me away into the interior of the country, so as to keep Paquíta for an indefinite time to herself, for she had become extremely attached to her beautiful niece. The estancia was on the borders of the Paysandù department, and not less than two hundred miles from Montevideo. It was a long journey, and I was advised not to attempt it without a *tropilla*, or troop of horses. But when a native tells you that you cannot travel two hundred miles without a dozen horses, he only means that you cannot do the distance in two days; for it is hard for him to believe that one may be satisfied with less than one hundred miles a day. *I* travelled on one horse, and it therefore took me several days to accomplish the journey. Before I reached my destination, called *Estancia de la Virgen de los Desamparados*, I met with some adventures worth relating, and began to feel as much at home with the *Orientales* as I had long been with the *Argentinos*.

Fortunately, after I left the town, a west wind continued blowing all day, bringing with it many light flying clouds to mitigate the sun, so that I was able to cover a good number of leagues before the evening. I took the road northwards through Camelones department, and was well on into the Florida department when I put up for the night at the solitary mud rancho of an old herdsman, who lived with his wife and children in a very primitive fashion. When I rode up to the house, several huge dogs rushed out to attack me: one seized my horse by the tail, dragging the poor beast about this way and that, so that he staggered and could scarcely keep his legs; another caught the bridle-reins in his mouth; while a third fixed his fangs in the heel of my boot. After eyeing me for some moments, the grizzled old herdsman, who wore a knife a yard long at his waist, advanced to the rescue. He shouted at the dogs, and finding that they would not obey, sprang forward and with a few dexterous blows, dealt with his heavy whip-handle, sent them away howling with rage and pain. Then he welcomed me with great courtesy, and very soon, when my horse had been unsaddled and turned loose to feed, we were sitting together enjoying the cool evening air and imbibing the bitter and refreshing maté his wife served to us. While we conversed I noticed numberless fireflies flitting about; I had never seen them so numerous before, and they made a very lovely show. Presently one of the children, a bright little fellow of seven or eight, came running to us with one of the sparkling insects in his hand, and cried—

"Look, tatita, I have caught a *linterna*. See how bright it is!"

"The Saints forgive you, my child," said the father. "Go, little son, and put it back on the grass, for if you should hurt it, the spirits would be angry with you, for they go about by night and love the *linterna* that keeps them company."

What a pretty superstition, I thought; and what a mild, merciful heart this old Oriental herdsman must possess to show so much tenderness towards one of God's tiny creatures. I congratulated myself on my good fortune in having fallen in with such a person in this lonely place.

The dogs, after their rude behaviour to me and the sharp punishment they had suffered in consequence, had returned, and were now gathered around us lying on the ground. Here I noticed, not for the first time, that the dogs belonging to these lonely places are not nearly so fond of being noticed and caressed as are those of more populous and civilised districts. On attempting to stroke one of these surly brutes on the head, he displayed his teeth and growled savagely at me. Yet this animal, though so truculent in temper, and asking for no kindness from his master, is just as faithful to man as his better-mannered brother in the more settled country. I spoke on that subject to my gentle herdsman.

"What you say is true," he replied. "I remember once during the siege of Montevideo, when I was with a small detachment sent to watch the movements of General Rivera's army, we one day overtook a man on a tired horse. Our officer, suspecting him to be a spy, ordered him to be killed, and after cutting his throat we left his body lying on the open ground at a distance of about two hundred and fifty yards from a small stream of water. A dog was with him, and when we rode off we called it to follow us, but it would not stir from its dead master's side.

"Three days later we returned to the same spot, to find the corpse lying just where we had left it. The foxes and birds had not touched it, for the dog was still there to defend it. Many vultures were near, waiting for a chance to begin their feast. We alighted to refresh ourselves at the stream, then stood there for half an hour watching the dog. He seemed to be half-famished with thirst, and came towards the stream to drink; but before he got half-way to it the vultures, by twos and threes, began to advance, when back he flew and chased them away barking. After resting a few minutes beside the corpse, he came again towards the stream, till, seeing the hungry birds advance once more, he again flew back at them, barking furiously and foaming at the mouth. This we saw repeated many times, and at last, when we left, we tried once more to entice the dog to follow us, but he would not. Two days after that we had occasion to pass by that spot again, and there we saw the dog lying dead beside his dead master."

"Good God," I exclaimed, "how horrible must have been the feelings you and your companions experienced at such a sight!"

"No, señor, not at all," replied the old man. "Why, señor, I myself put the knife into that man's throat. For if a man did not grow accustomed to shed blood in this world, his life would be a burden to him."

What an inhuman old murderer! I thought. Then I asked him whether he had ever in his life felt remorse for shedding blood.

"Yes," he answered; "when I was a very young man, and had never before dipped weapon in human blood; that was when the siege began. I was sent with half a dozen men in pursuit of a clever spy, who had passed the lines with letters from the besieged. We came to a house where, our officer had been informed, he had been lying concealed. The master of the house was a young man about twenty-two years old. He would confess nothing. Finding him so stubborn, our officer became enraged, and bade him step out, and then ordered us to lance him. We galloped forty yards off, then wheeled back. He stood silent, his arms folded on his breast, a smile on his lips. Without a cry, without a groan, with that smile still on his lips, he fell pierced through with our lances. For days afterwards his face was ever present to me. I could not eat, for my food choked me. When I raised a jug of water to my lips I could, señor, distinctly see his eyes looking at me from the water. When I lay down to sleep, his face was again before me, always with that smile that seemed to mock me on the lips. I could not under stand it. They told me it was remorse, and that it would soon leave me, for there is no ill that time will not cure. They spoke truth, and when that feeling left me I was able to do all things."

The old man's story so sickened me that I had little appetite for supper, and passed a bad night thinking, waking or sleeping, of that young man in this obscure corner of the world who folded his arms and smiled on his slayers when they were slaying him. Very early next morning I bade my host good-bye, thanking him for his hospitality, and devoutly hoping that I should never look upon his abhorred face again.

I made little progress that day, the weather proving hot, and my horse lazier than ever. After riding about five leagues, I rested for a couple of hours, then proceeded again at a gentle trot till about the middle of the afternoon, when I dismounted at a wayside *pulpería*, or store and public-house all in one, where several natives were sipping rum and conversing. Standing before them was a brisk-looking old man—old, I say, because he had a dark dry skin, though his hair and moustache were black as jet —who paused in the discourse he appeared to be delivering, to salute me; then, after bestowing a searching glance on me out of his dark hawk-like eyes, he resumed his talk. After calling for rum and water, to be in the fashion, I sat down on a bench, and, lighting a cigarette, prepared to listen. He was dressed in shabby gaucho habiliments—cotton shirt, short jacket, wide cotton drawers and *chiripà*, a shawl-like garment fastened at the waist with a sash, and reaching down half-way between the knees and ankles. In place of a hat he wore a cotton handkerchief tied carelessly about his head; his left foot was bare, while the right one was cased in a colt's-skin stocking, called *bota-de-potro*, and on this distinguished foot was buckled a huge iron spur, with spikes two inches long. One spur of the kind would be quite sufficient, I should imagine, to get out of a horse all the energy of which he was capable. When I entered he was holding forth on the pretty well-worn theme of fate *versus* free will; his arguments were not, however, the usual dry philosophical ones, but took the form of illustration, chiefly personal reminiscences and strange incidents in the lives of people he had known, while so vivid and minute were his descriptions—sparkling with passion, satire, humour, pathos, and so dramatic his action, while wonderful story followed story—that I was fairly astonished, and pronounced this old *pulpería* orator a born genius.

His argument over, he fixed his keen eyes on me and said—

"My friend, I perceive you are a traveller from Montevideo: may I ask what news there is from that city?"

"What news do you expect to hear?" said I; then it came into my thought that it was scarcely proper to confine myself to mere commonplace phrases in replying to this curious old Oriental bird, with such ragged plumage, but whose native woodnotes wild had such a charm in them. "It is only the old story over again!" I continued. "They say there will be a revolution some day. Some of the people have already retired into their houses, after chalking in very big letters on their front doors, 'Please come into this house and cut the owner's throat for him, so that he may rest at peace, and have no fear of what may happen.' Others have climbed on to their roofs and occupy themselves there looking at the moon through spy-glasses, thinking that the conspirators are concealed in that luminary, and only waiting for a cloud to obscure it, in order to descend upon the city unobserved."

"Hear!" cried the old man, rapping delighted applause on the counter with his empty glass.

"What do you drink, friend?" I asked, thinking his keen appreciation of my grotesque speech deserved a treat, and wishing to draw him out a little more.

"Rum, friend, thank you. They say it warms you in winter, and cools you in summer—what can you have better?"

"Tell me," said I, when his glass had been refilled by the storekeeper, "what I shall say when I return to Montevideo, and am asked what news there is in the country?"

The old fellow's eyes twinkled, while the other men ceased talking, and looked at him as if anticipating something good in reply to my question.

"Say to them," he answered, "that you met an old man—a horse-tamer named Lucero—and that he told you this fable for you to repeat to the townspeople: Once there was a great tree named Montevideo growing in this country, and in its branches lived a colony of monkeys. One day one of the monkeys came down from the tree

"Señora," I said when he had finished, "you must not give me credit for all you have heard from your husband. I only gave him brute wool, and he has woven it for your delight into beautiful cloth."

"Hear him! Did I not tell you what to expect, Juana?" cried the old man, which made me blush still more.

We then settled down to maté and quiet conversation. Sitting in the kitchen on the skull of a horse—a common article of furniture in an Oriental rancho—was a boy about twelve years old, one of Lucero's grandchildren, with a very beautiful face. His feet were bare and his clothes very poor, but his soft dark eyes and olive face had that tender half-melancholy expression often seen in children of Spanish origin, which is always so strangely captivating.

"Where is your guitar, Cipriano?" said his grandfather, addressing him, whereupon the boy rose and fetched a guitar which he first politely offered to me.

When I had declined it, he seated himself once more on his polished horse skull and began to play and sing. He had a sweet boy's voice, and one of his ballads took my fancy so much that I made him repeat the words to me while I wrote them down in my notebook, which greatly gratified Lucero, who seemed proud of the boy's accomplishment. Here are the words translated almost literally, therefore without rhymes, and I only regret that I cannot furnish my musical readers with the quaint, plaintive air they were sung to:—

and ran full of excitement across the plain, now scrambling along like a man on all fours, then erect like a dog running on its hind legs, while its tail with nothing to catch hold of wriggled about like a snake when its head is under foot. He came to a place where a number of oxen were grazing, and some horses, ostriches, deer, goats, and pigs. 'Friends all,' cried the monkey, grinning like a skull, and with staring eyes round as dollars, 'great news! great news! I come to tell you that there will shortly be a revolution.' 'Where?' said an ox. 'In the tree—where else?' said the monkey. 'That does not concern us,' said the ox. 'Oh, yes it does!' cried the monkey, 'for it will presently spread about the country and you will all have your throats cut.' Then the ox replied, 'Go back, monkey, and do not molest us with your news, lest we get angry and go to besiege you in your tree, as we have often had to do since the creation of the world; and then, if you and the other monkeys come down to us, we will toss you on our horns.'"

This apologue sounded very well, so admirably did the old man picture to us with voice and gesture the chattering excitement of the monkey and the majestic *àplomb* of the ox.

"Señor," he continued, after the laugh had subsided, "I do not wish any of my friends and neighbours here present to fly to the conclusion that I have spoken anything offensive. Had I seen in you a Montevidean I should not have spoken of monkeys. But, señor, though you speak as we do, there is yet in the pepper and salt on your tongue a certain foreign flavour."

"You are right," I said; "I am a foreigner."

"A foreigner in some things, friend, for you were doubtless born under other skies; but in that chief quality, which we think was given by the Creator to us and not to the people of other lands—the ability to be one in heart with the men you meet, whether they are clothed in velvet or in sheep skins—in that you are one of us, a pure Oriental."

I smiled at his subtle flattery; possibly it was only meant in payment of the rum I had treated him to, but it pleased me none the less, and to his other mental traits I was now inclined to add a marvellous skill in reading character.

After a while he invited me to spend the night under his roof. "Your horse is fat and lazy," he said with truth, "and unless you are a relation of the owl family, you cannot go much further before to-morrow. My house is a humble one, but the mutton is juicy, the fire warm, and the water cool there, the same as in another place."

I readily accepted his invitation, wishing to see as much as I could of so original a character, and before starting I purchased a bottle of rum, which made his eyes sparkle so that I thought his name—Lucero—rather an appropriate one. His rancho was about two miles from the store, and our ride thither was about as strange a gallop as I ever took. Lucero was a *domador*, or horse-tamer, and the beast he rode was quite unbroken and vicious as it could be. Between horse and man a fierce struggle for mastery raged the whole time, the horse rearing, plunging, buck-jumping, and putting into practice

every conceivable trick to rid itself of its burden; while Lucero plied whip and spur with tremendous energy and poured out torrents of strange adjectives. At one moment he would come into violent collision with my old sober beast, at another there would be fifty yards of ground between us; still Lucero would not stop talking, for he had begun a very interesting story at starting and he stuck to his narrative through everything, resuming the thread after each tempest of execration vented on his horse, and raising his voice almost to a shout when we were far apart. The old fellow's staying powers were really extraordinary, and when we arrived at the house he jumped airily to the ground and seemed fresh and calm as possible.

In the kitchen were several people sipping maté, Lucero's children and grandchildren, also his wife, a grey old dame with dim-looking eyes. But then my host was old in years himself, only, like Ulysses, he still possessed the unquenched fire and energy of youth in his soul, while time bestowed infirmities together with wrinkles and white hairs on his helpmate.

He introduced me to her in a manner that brought the modest flame to my cheek. Standing before her, he said that he had met me at the *pulpería* and had put to me the question which a simple old countryman must ask of every traveller from Montevideo—What the news was? Then, assuming a dry satirical tone, which years of practice would not enable me to imitate, he proceeded to give my fantastical answer, garnished with much original matter of his own.

O let me go—O let me go,
Where high are born amidst the hills
The streams that gladden all the south,
And o'er the grassy desert wide,
Where slakes his thirst the antlered deer,
Hurry towards the great green ocean.

The stony hills—the stony hills,
With azure air-flowers on their crags,
Where cattle stray unowned by man ;
The monarch of the herd there seems
No bigger than my hand in size,
Roaming along the tall, steep summit.

I know them well—I know them well,
Those hills of God, and they know me ;
When I go there they are serene,
But when the stranger visits them
Dark rain-clouds gather round their tops—
Over the earth goes forth the tempest.

Then tell me not—then tell me not
'Tis sorrowful to dwell alone :
My heart within the city pent
Pines for the desert's liberty ;
The streets are red with blood, and fear
Makes pale the mournful women's faces.

O bear me far—O bear me far,
On swift, sure feet, my trusty steed :
I do not love the burial-ground,
But I shall sleep upon the plain,
Where long green grass shall round me wave—
Over me graze wild herds of cattle.

CHAPTER III

MATERIALS FOR A PASTORAL

LEAVING the eloquent old horse-tamer's rancho early next morning, I continued my ride, jogging quietly along all day and, leaving the Florida department behind me, entered upon that of the Durazno. Here I broke my journey at an estancia where I had an excellent oppor tunity of studying the manners and customs of the Orientals, and where I also underwent experiences of a mixed character and greatly increased my knowledge of the insect world. This house, at which I arrived an hour before sunset to ask for shelter ("permission to unsaddle" is the expression the traveller uses), was a long, low structure, thatched with rushes, but the low, enormously thick walls were built of stone from the neighbouring sierras, in pieces of all shapes and sizes, and presenting, outwardly, the rough appearance of a stone fence. How these rudely piled-up stones, without cement to hold them together, had not fallen down was a mystery to me; and it was more difficult still to imagine why the rough interior, with its innumerable dusty holes and interstices, had never been plastered.

I was kindly received by a very numerous family, consisting of the owner, his hoary-headed old mother-in-law his wife. three sons, and five daughters, all grown up. There were also several small children, belonging, I believe, to the daughters, notwithstanding the fact that they were unmarried. I was greatly amazed at hearing the name of one of these youngsters. Such Christian names as Trinity, Heart of Jesus, Nativity, John of God, Conception, Ascension, Incarnation, are common enough, but these had scarcely prepared me to meet with a fellow-creature named—well, Circumcision! Besides the people, there were dogs, cats, turkeys, ducks, geese, and fowls without number. Not content with all these domestic birds and beasts, they also kept a horrid, shrieking paroquet, which the old woman was incessantly talking to, explaining to the others all the time, in little asides, what the bird said or wished to say, or, rather, what she imagined it wished to say. There were also several tame young ostriches, always hanging about the big kitchen or living-room on the look-out for a brass thimble, or iron spoon, or other little metallic *bonne bouche* to be gobbled up when no one was looking. A pet armadillo kept trotting in and out, in and out, the whole evening, and a lame gull was always standing on the threshold in everybody's way, perpetually wailing for something to eat—the most persistent beggar I ever met in my life.

The people were very jovial and rather industrious for so indolent a country. The land was their own, the men tended the cattle, of which they appeared to have a large number, while the women made cheeses, rising before daylight to milk the cows.

During the evening two or three young men—neighbours, I imagine, who were paying their addresses to the young ladies of the establishment—dropped in; and after a plentiful supper we had singing and dancing to the music of the guitar, on which every member of the family—excepting the babies—could strum a little.

About eleven o'clock I retired to rest, and stretching myself on my rude bed of rugs, in a room adjoining the kitchen, I blessed these simple-minded hospitable people. Good heavens, thought I to myself, what a glorious field is waiting here for some new Theocritus! How unutterably worn out, stilted, and artificial seems all the so-called pastoral poetry ever written when one sits down to supper and joins in the graceful *Cielo* or *Pericon* in one of these remote semi-barbarous South American estancias! I swear I will turn poet myself, and go back some day to astonish old *blasé* Europe with something so—so—— What the deuce was that? My sleepy soliloquy was suddenly brought to a most lame and impotent conclusion, for I had heard a sound of terror—the unmistakable *zz-zzing* of an insect's wings. It was the hateful vinchuca. Here was an enemy against which British pluck and six-shooters are of no avail, and in whose presence one begins to experience sensations which are not usually supposed to enter into the brave man's breast. Naturalists tell us that it is the *Connorhinus infestans*, but as that information leaves something to be desired, I will proceed in a few words to describe the beast. It inhabits the entire Chilian, Argentine, and Oriental countries, and to all the dwellers in this vast territory it is known as the vinchuca; for, like a few volcanoes, deadly vipers, cataracts, and other sublime natural objects, it has been permitted to keep the ancient name bestowed on it by the aborigines. It is all over of a blackish-brown colour, as broad as a man's thumb-nail, and flat as the blade of a table-knife—when fasting. By day it hides, bug-like, in holes and chinks, but no sooner are the candles put out, than forth it comes to seek whom it may devour; for, like the pestilence, it walks in darkness. It can fly, and in a dark room knows where you are and can find you. Having selected a nice tender part, it pierces the skin with its proboscis or rostrum, and sucks vigorously for two or three minutes, and, strange to say, you do not feel the operation, even when lying wide awake. By that time the creature, so attenuated before, has assumed the figure, size, and general appearance of a ripe gooseberry, so much blood has it drawn from your veins. Immediately after it has left you the part begins to swell up and burn as if stung by nettles. That the pain should come after and not during the operation is an arrangement very advantageous to the vinchuca, and I greatly doubt whether any other blood-sucking parasite has been equally favoured by nature in this respect.

Imagine then my sensations when I heard the sound of not one, but two or three pairs of wings! I tried to forget the sound and go to sleep. I tried to forget about those rough old walls full of interstices—a hundred years old they were, my host had informed me. Most interesting old house, thought I; and then very suddenly a fiery itching took possession of my great toe. There it is! said I; heated blood, late supper, dancing, and all that.

I can almost imagine that something has actually bitten me, when of course nothing of that kind has happened. Then, while I was furiously rubbing and scratching it, feeling a badger-like disposition to gnaw it off, my left arm was pierced with red-hot needles. My attentions were quickly transferred to that part; but soon my busy hands were called elsewhere, like a couple of hard-worked doctors in a town afflicted with an epidemic; and so all night long, with only occasional snatches of miserable sleep, the contest went on.

I rose early, and going to a wide stream, a quarter of a mile from the house, took a plunge which greatly refreshed me and gave me strength to go in quest of my horse. Poor brute! I had intended giving him a day's rest, so pleasant and hospitable had the people shown themselves; but now I shuddered at the thought of spending another night in such a purgatory. I found him so lame that he could scarcely walk, and so returned to the house on foot and very much cast down. My host consoled me by assuring me that I would sleep the siesta all the better for having been molested by those "little things that go about," for in this very mild language he described the affliction. After breakfast, at noon, acting on his hint, I took a rug to the shade of a tree and, lying down, quickly fell into a profound sleep which lasted till late in the afternoon.

That evening visitors came again and we had a repetition of the singing, dancing, and other pastoral amusements, till near midnight; then, thinking to cheat my bedfellows of the night before, I made my simple bed in the kitchen. But here also the vile vinchucas found me, and there were, moreover, dozens of fleas that waged a sort of guerilla warfare all night, and in this way exhausted my strength and distracted my attention, while the more formidable adversary took up his position. My sufferings were so great that before daybreak I picked up my rugs and went out a distance from the house to lie down on the open plain, but I carried with me a smarting body and got but little rest. When morning came I found that my horse had not yet recovered from his lameness.

"Do not be in a hurry to leave us," said my host, when I spoke of it; "I perceive that the little animals have again fought with and defeated you. Do not mind it; in time you will grow accustomed to them."

How *they* contrived to endure it, or even to exist, was a puzzle to me; but possibly the vinchucas respected them, and only dined when, like the giant in the nursery rhyme, they "smelt the blood of an Englishman."

I again enjoyed a long siesta, and when night came resolved to place myself beyond the reach of the vampires, and so, after supper, went out to sleep on the plain. About midnight, however, a sudden storm of wind and rain drove me back to the shelter of the house, and the next morning I rose in such a deplorable state that I deliberately caught and saddled my horse, though the poor beast could scarcely put one foot on the ground. My friends laughed good-humouredly when they saw me making these resolute preparations for departure. After partaking of bitter maté, I rose and thanked them for their hospitality.

"You surely do not intend leaving us on that animal!" said my host. "He is unfit to carry you."

"I have no other," I replied, "and am anxious to reach my destination."

"Had I known this I should have offered you a horse before," he returned, and then he sent one of his sons to drive the horses of the estancia into the corral.

Selecting a good-looking animal from the herd, he presented it to me, and as I did not have money enough to buy a fresh horse whenever I wanted one, I accepted the gift very gladly. The saddle was quickly transferred to my new acquisition, and once more thanking these good people and bidding adieu, I resumed my journey.

When I gave my hand before leaving to the youngest, and also, to my mind, the prettiest of the five daughters of the house, instead of smiling pleasantly and wishing me a prosperous journey, like the others, she was silent, and darted a look at me, which seemed to say, "Go, sir; you have treated me badly, and you insult me by offering your hand; if I take it, it is not because I feel disposed to forgive you, but only to save appearances."

At the same moment, when she bestowed that glance on me which said so much, a look of intelligence passed over the faces of the other people in the room. All this revealed to me that I had just missed a very pretty little idyllic flirtation, conducted in very novel circumstances. Love cometh up as a flower, and men and charming women naturally flirt when brought together. Yet it was hard to imagine how I could have started a flirtation and carried it on to its culminatory point in that great public room, with all those eyes on me; dogs, babes, and cats tumbling about my feet; ostriches staring covetously at my buttons with great vacant eyes; and that intolerable paroquet perpetually reciting "How the waters came down at Lodore," in its own shrieky, beaky, birdy, hurdy-gurdy, parrot language. Tender glances, soft whispered words, hand-touchings, and a thousand little personal attentions, showing which way the emotions tend, would scarcely have been practicable in such a place and in such conditions, and new signs and symbols would have to be invented to express the feelings of the heart. And doubtless these Orientals, living all together in one great room, with their children and pets, like our very ancient ancestors, the pastoral Aryans, do possess such a language. And this pretty language I should have learnt from the most willing of teachers, if those venomous vinchucas had not dulled my brain with their persecutions and made me blind to a matter which had not escaped the observation of even unconcerned lookers-on. Riding away from the estancia, the feeling I experienced at having finally escaped from these execrable "little things that go about" was not one of unmixed satisfaction.

CHAPTER IV

VAGABONDS' REST

CONTINUING my journey through the Durazno district, I forded the pretty River Yí and entered the Tacuarembó department, which is immensely long, extending right away to the Brazilian frontier. I rode over its narrowest part, however, where it is only about twenty-five miles wide; then crossing two very curiously named rivers, Rios Salsipuedes Chico and Salsipuedes Grande, which mean Get-out-if-you-can Rivers, Little and Big, I at length reached the termination of my journey in the province or department of Paysandù. The *Estancia de la Virgen de los Desamparados*, or, to put it very shortly, Vagabonds' Rest, was a good-sized square brick house built on very high ground, which overlooked an immense stretch of grassy undulating country. There was no plantation about the house, not even a shade tree or cultivated plant of any description, but only some large *corrales*, or enclosures, for the cattle, of which there were six or seven thousand head on the land. The absence of shade and greenery gave the place a desolate, uninviting aspect, but if I was ever to have any authority here this would soon be changed. The Mayordomo, or manager, Don Policarpo Santierra de Peñalosa, which, roughly done into English, means Polycarp of the Holy Land abounding in Slippery Rocks, proved to be a very pleasant, affable person. He welcomed me with that quiet Oriental politeness which is never cold and never effusive, and then perused the letter from Doña Isidora. Finally he said, "I am willing, my friend, to supply you with all the conveniences procurable at this elevation; and, for the rest, you know, doubtless, what I can say to you. A ready understanding requires few words. Nevertheless, there is here no lack of good beef, and, to be short, you will do me a great favour by making this house with everything it contains your own, while you honour us by remaining in it."

After delivering himself of these kindly sentiments, which left me rather in a mist as to my prospects, he mounted his horse and rode off, probably on some very important affair, for I saw no more of him for several days.

I at once proceeded to establish myself in the kitchen. No person in the house appeared ever to pay even a casual visit to any other room. This kitchen was vast and barn-like, forty feet long at least, and proportionately wide; the roof was of reeds, and the hearth, placed in the centre of the floor, was a clay platform, fenced round with cows' shank-bones, half buried and standing upright. Some trivets and iron kettles were scattered about, and from the centre beam, supporting the roof, a chain and hook were suspended to which a vast iron pot was fastened. One more article, a spit about six feet long for roasting meat, completed the list of cooking utensils.

There were no chairs, tables, knives, or forks; everyone carried his own knife, and at meal-time the boiled meat was emptied into a great tin dish, whilst the roast was eaten from the spit, each one laying hold with his fingers and cutting his slice. The seats were logs of wood and horse-skulls. The household was composed of one woman, an ancient, hideously ugly, grey-headed negress, about seventy years old, and eighteen or nineteen men of all ages and sizes, and of all colours from parchment-white to very old oak. There was a *capatas*, or overseer, and seven or eight paid *peones*, the others being all *agregados* —that is, supernumeraries without pay, or, to put it plainly, vagabonds who attach themselves like vagrant dogs to establishments of this kind, lured by the abundance of flesh, and who occasionally assist the regular *peones* at their work, and also do a little gambling and stealing to keep themselves in small change. At break of day everyone was up sitting by the hearth sipping bitter maté and smoking cigarettes; before sunrise all were mounted and away over the surrounding country to gather up the herds; at midday they were back again to breakfast. The consumption and waste of meat was something frightful. Frequently, after breakfast, as much as twenty or thirty pounds of boiled and roast meat would be thrown into a wheelbarrow and carried out to the dust-heap, where it served to feed scores of hawks, gulls, and vultures, besides the dogs.

Of course, I was only an *agregado*, having no salary or regular occupation yet. Thinking, however, that this would only be for a time, I was quite willing to make the best of things, and very soon became fast friends with my fellow *agregados*, joining heartily in all their amusements and voluntary labours.

In a few days I got very tired of living exclusively on flesh, for not even a biscuit was "procurable at this elevation"; and as for a potato, one might as well have asked for a plum-pudding. It occurred to my mind at last that, with so many cows, it might be possible to procure some milk and introduce a little change into our diet. In the evening I broached the subject, proposing that on the following day we should capture a cow and tame her. Some of the men approved of the suggestion, remarking that they had never thought of it themselves; but the old negress, who, being the only representative of the fair sex present, was always listened to with all the deference due to her position, threw herself with immense zeal into the opposition. She affirmed that no cow had been milked at that establishment since its owner had paid it a visit with his young wife twelve years before. A milch-cow was then kept, and on the señora partaking of a large quantity of milk "before breaking her fast," it produced such an indigestion in her that they were obliged to give her powdered ostrich stomach, and finally to convey her, with great trouble, in an ox-cart to Paysandù and thence by water to Montevideo. The owner ordered the cow to be released, and never, to her certain knowledge, had cow been milked since at La Virgen de los Desamparados.

These ominous croakings produced no effect on me, and the next day I returned to the subject. I did not possess a lasso, and so could not undertake to capture a half-wild cow without assistance. One of my fellow *agregados* at length volunteered to help me, observing that he had not tasted milk for several years, and was inclined to renew his acquaintance with that singular beverage. This new-found friend in need merits being formally introduced to the reader. His name was Epifanio Claro. He was tall and thin, and had an idiotic expression on his long, sallow face. His cheeks were innocent of whiskers, and his lank, black hair, parted in the middle, fell to his shoulders, enclosing his narrow face between a pair of raven's wings. He had very large, light-coloured, sheepish-looking eyes, and his eyebrows bent up like a couple of Gothic arches, leaving a narrow strip above them that formed the merest apology for a forehead. This facial peculiarity had won for him the nickname of Cejas (Eyebrows), by which he was known to his intimates. He spent most of his time strumming on a wretched old cracked guitar, and singing amorous ballads in a lugubrious whining falsetto, which reminded me not a little of that hungry, complaining gull I had met at the estancia in Durazno. For though poor Epifanio had an absorbing passion for music, Nature had unkindly withheld from him the power to express it in a manner pleasing to others. I must, however, in justice to him, allow that he gave a preference to ballads or compositions of a thoughtful, not to say metaphysical, character. I took the trouble of translating the words of one literally, and here they are :—

Yesterday my senses opened,
At a rap-a-tap from Reason,

Inspiring in me an intention
Which I never had before,
Seeing that through all my days
My life has been just what it is.
Therefore when I rose I said,
To-day shall be as yesterday,
Since Reason tells me I have been
From day to day the self-same thing.

This is very little to judge from, being only a fourth part of the song; but it is a fair specimen, and the rest is no clearer. Of course it is not to be supposed that Epifanio Claro, an illiterate person, took in the whole philosophy of these lines; still it is probable that a subtle ray or two of their deep meaning touched his intellect, to make him a wiser and a sadder man.

Accompanied by this strange individual, and with the grave permission of the *capatas*, who declined, however, in words of many syllables all *responsabilidad* in the matter, we went out to the grazing grounds in quest of a promising-looking cow. Very soon we found one to our liking. She was followed by a small calf, not more than a week old, and her distended udder promised a generous supply of milk; but unfortunately she was fierce-tempered, and had horns as sharp as needles.

"We will cut them by-and-by," shouted Eyebrows.

He then lassoed the cow, and I captured the calf, and lifting it into the saddle before me, started homewards. The cow followed me at a furious pace, and behind came Claro at a swinging gallop. Possibly he was a little too confident, and carelessly let his captive pull the line that held her; anyhow, she turned suddenly on him, charged with amazing fury, and sent one of her horrid horns deep into the belly of his horse. He was, however, equal to the occasion, first dealing her a smart blow on the nose, which made her recoil for a moment; he then severed the lasso with his knife, and shouting to me to drop the calf, made his escape. We pulled up as soon as we had reached a safe distance, Claro drily remarking that the lasso had been borrowed, and that the horse belonged to the estancia, so that we had lost nothing. He alighted, and stitched up the great gash in the poor brute's belly, using for a thread a few hairs plucked from its tail. It was a difficult task, or would have been so to me, as he had to bore holes in the animal's hide with his knife-point, but it seemed quite easy to him. Taking the remaining portion of the severed lasso, he drew it round the hind and one of the fore feet of his horse, and threw him to the ground with a dexterous jerk; then, binding him there, performed the operation of sewing up the wound in about two minutes.

"Will he live?" I asked.

"How can I tell," he answered indifferently. "I only know that now he will be able to carry me home; if he dies afterwards what will it matter?"

We then mounted and rode quietly home. Of course we were chaffed without mercy, especially by the old negress, who had foreseen all along, she told us, just how it would be. One would have imagined, to hear this old black creature talk, that she looked on milk-drinking as one of the greatest moral offences man could be guilty of, and that in this case Providence had miraculously interposed to prevent us from gratifying our depraved appetites.

Eyebrows took it all very coolly.

"Do not notice them," he said to me. "The lasso was not ours, the horse was not ours, what does it matter what they say?"

The owner of the lasso, who had good-naturedly lent it to us, roused himself on hearing this. He was a very big, rough-looking man, his face covered with an immense shaggy black beard. I had taken him for a good-humoured specimen of the giant kind before, but I now changed my opinion of him when his angry passions began to rise. Blas, or Barbudo, as we called the giant, was seated on a log sipping maté.

"Perhaps you take me for a sheep, sirs, because you see me wrapped in skins," he observed; "but let me tell you this, the lasso I lent you must be returned to me."

"These words are not for us," remarked Eyebrows, addressing me, "but for the cow that carried away his lasso on her horns—curse them for being so sharp!"

"No, sir," returned Barbudo, "do not deceive yourself; they are not for the cow, but for the fool that lassoed the cow. And I promise you, Epifanio, that if it is not restored to me, this thatch over our heads will not be broad enough to shelter us both."

"I am pleased to hear it," said the other, "for we are short of seats; and when you leave us, the one you now encumber with your carcass will be occupied by some more meritorious person."

"You can say what you like, for no one has yet put a

padlock on your lips," said Barbudo, raising his voice to a shout; "but you are not going to plunder me; and if my lasso is not restored to me, then I swear I will make myself a new one out of a human hide."

"Then," said Eyebrows, "the sooner you provide yourself with a hide for the purpose, the better, for I will never return the lasso to you; for who am I to fight against Providence, that took it out of my hands?"

To this Barbudo replied furiously—

"Then I will have it from this miserable starved foreigner, who comes here to learn to eat meat and put himself on an equality with men. Evidently he was weaned too soon; but if the starveling hungers for infant's food, let him in future milk the cats that warm themselves beside the fire, and can be caught without a lasso, even by a Frenchman!"

I could not endure the brute's insults, and sprang up from my seat. I happened to have a large knife in my hand, for we were just preparing to make an assault on the roasted ribs of a cow, and my first impulse was to throw down the knife and give him a blow with my fist. Had I attempted it I should most probably have paid dearly for my rashness. The instant I rose Barbudo was on me, knife in hand. He aimed a furious blow, which luckily missed me, and at the same moment I struck him, and he reeled back with a dreadful gash on his face. It was all done in a second of time, and before the others could interpose; in another moment they disarmed us, and set about bathing the barbarian's wound. During the operation, which I daresay was very painful, for the old negress insisted on having the wound bathed with rum instead of water, the brute blasphemed outrageously, vowing that he would cut out my heart and eat it stewed with onions and seasoned with cummin seed and various other condiments.

I have often since thought of that sublime culinary conception of Blas the barbarian. There must have been a spark of wild Oriental genius in his bovine brains.

When the exhaustion caused by rage, pain, and loss of blood had at length reduced him to silence, the old negress turned on him, exclaiming that he had been rightly punished, for had he not, in spite of her timely warnings, lent his lasso to enable these two heretics (for that is what she called us) to capture a cow? Well, his lasso was lost; then his friends, with the gratitude only to be expected from milk-drinkers, had turned round and well-nigh killed him.

After supper the *capatas* got me alone, and with excessive friendliness of manner, and an abundance of circumlocutory phrases, advised me to leave the estancia, as it would not be safe for me to remain. I replied that I was not to blame, having struck the man in self-defence; also, that I had been sent to the estancia by a friend of the Mayordomo, and was determined to see him and give him my version of the affair.

The *capatas* shrugged his shoulders and lit a cigarette.

At length Don Policarpo returned, and when I told him my story he laughed slightly, but said nothing. In the evening I reminded him of the subject of the letter I had brought from Montevideo, asking him whether it was his intention to give me some employment on the estancia.

"You see, my friend," he replied, "to employ you now would be useless, however valuable your services might be, for by this time the authorities will have information of your fight with Blas. In the course of a few days you may expect them here to make inquiries into that affair, and it is probable that you and Blas will both be taken into custody."

"What then would you advise me to do?" I asked.

His answer was, that when the ostrich asked the deer what he would advise him to do when the hunters appeared, the deer's reply was, "Run away."

I laughed at his pretty apologue, and answered that I did not think the authorities would trouble themselves about me—also that I was not fond of running away.

Eyebrows, who had hitherto been rather inclined to patronise me and take me under his protection, now became very warm in his friendship, which was, however, dashed with an air of deference when we were alone together, but in company he was fond of parading his familiarity with me. I did not quite understand this change of manner at first, but by-and-by he took me mysteriously aside and became extremely confidential.

"Do not distress yourself about Barbudo," he said. 'He will never again presume to lift his hand against you; and if you will only condescend to speak kindly to him, he will be your humble slave, and proud to have you wipe your greasy fingers on his beard. Take no notice of what the Mayordomo says, he also is afraid of you. If the authorities take you, it will only be to see what you can give them: they will not keep you long, for you are a foreigner, and cannot be made to serve in the army. But when you are again at liberty it will be necessary for you to kill someone."

Very much amazed, I asked him why.

"You see," he replied, "your reputation as a fighter is now established in this department, and there is nothing men envy more. It is the same as in our old game of *Pato*, where the man that carries the duck away is pursued by all the others, and before they give up chasing him he must prove that he can keep what he has taken. There are several fighters you do not know, who have resolved to pick quarrels with you in order to try your strength. In your next fight you must not wound but kill, or you will have no peace."

I was greatly disturbed at this result of my accidental victory over Blas the Bearded, and did not at all appreciate the kind of greatness my officious friend Claro seemed so determined to thrust upon me. It was certainly flattering to hear that I had already established my reputation as a good fighter in so warlike a department as Paysandù, but then the consequences entailed were disagreeable, to say the least of it; and so, while thanking Eyebrows for his friendly hint, I resolved to quit the estancia at once. I would not run away from the authorities, since I was not an evil-doer, but from the necessity of killing people for the sake of peace and quietness I certainly would depart. And early next morning, to my friend's intense disgust, and without telling my plans to anyone, I mounted my horse and quitted Vagabonds' Rest to pursue my adventures elsewhere.

CHAPTER V

A COLONY OF ENGLISH GENTLEMEN

FAITH in the estancia as a field for my activities had been weak from the first; the Mayordomo's words on his return had extinguished it altogether; and after hearing that ostrich parable I had only remained from motives of pride. I now determined to go back towards Montevideo, not, however, over the route I had come by, but making a wide circuit into the interior of the country, where I would explore a new field and perhaps meet with some occupation at one of the estancias on the way. Riding in a south-westerly direction towards the Rio Malo in the Tacuarembó department, I soon left the plains of Paysandù behind me, and being anxious to get well away from a neighbourhood where I was expected to kill some-one, I did not rest till I had ridden about twenty-five miles. At noon I stopped to get some refreshment at a little roadside *pulpería*. It was a wretched-looking place, and behind the iron bars protecting the interior, giving it the appearance of a wild beast's cage, lounged the store-keeper smoking a cigar. Outside the bar were two men with English-looking faces. One was a handsome young fellow with a somewhat worn and dissipated look on his bronzed face; he was leaning against the counter, cigar in mouth, looking slightly tipsy, I thought, and wore a large revolver slung ostentatiously at his waist. His companion was a big, heavy man, with immense whiskers sprinkled with grey, who was evidently very drunk, for he was lying full-length on a bench, his face purple and swollen, snoring loudly. I asked for bread, sardines, and wine, and careful to observe the custom of the country I was in, duly invited the tipsy young man to join in the repast. An omission of this courtesy might, amongst proud and sensitive Orientals, involve one in a sanguinary quarrel, and of quarrelling I had just then had enough.

He declined with thanks, and entered into conversation with me; then the discovery, quickly made, that we were compatriots gave us both great pleasure. He at once offered to take me to his house with him, and gave a glowing account of the free, jovial life he led in company with several other Englishmen—sons of gentlemen, every one of them, he assured me—who had bought a piece of land and settled down to sheep-farming in this lonely district. I gladly accepted the invitation, and when we had finished our glasses he proceeded to wake the sleeper.

"Hullo, I say, Cap, wake up, old boy," shouted my new friend. "Quite time to go home, don't you know. That's right—up you come. Now let me introduce you to Mr. Lamb. I'm sure he's an acquisition. What, off again! Damn it, old Cloud, that's unreasonable, to say the least of it."

At length, after a great deal of shouting and shaking, he succeeded in rousing his drunken companion, who staggered up and stared at me in an imbecile manner.

"Now let me introduce you," said the other. "Mr. Lamb. My friend, Captain Cloudesley Wriothesley. Bravo! Steady, old cock—now shake hands."

The Captain said nothing, but took my hand, swaying forwards as if about to embrace me. We then with considerable difficulty got him on to his saddle and rode off together, keeping him between us to prevent him from falling off. Half an hour's ride brought us to my host Mr. Vincent Winchcombe's house. I had pictured to myself a charming little homestead, buried in cool greenery and flowers, and filled with pleasant memories of dear old England; I was, therefore, grievously disappointed to find that his "home" was only a mean-looking rancho, with a ditch round it, protecting some ploughed or dug-up ground, on which not one green thing appeared. Mr. Winchcombe explained, however, that he had not yet had time to cultivate much. "Only vegetables and such things, don't you know," he said.

"I don't see them," I returned.

"Well, no; we had a lot of caterpillars and blister beetles and things, and they ate everything up, don't you know," said he.

The room into which he conducted me contained no furniture except a large deal table and some chairs; also a cupboard, a long mantelpiece, and some shelves against the walls. On every available place were pipes, pouches, revolvers, cartridge boxes, and empty bottles. On the table were tumblers, cups, a sugar-basin, a monstrous tin teapot, and a demijohn, which I soon ascertained was half-full of Brazilian rum, or caña. Round the table five men were seated smoking, drinking tea and rum and talking excitedly, all of them more or less intoxicated. They gave me a hearty welcome, making me join them at the table, pouring out tea and rum for me, and generously pushing pipes and pouches towards me.

"You see," said Mr. Winchcombe, in explanation of this convivial scene, "there are, altogether, ten of us settlers here going in for sheep-farming and that sort of thing. Four of us have already built houses and bought sheep and horses. The other six fellows live with us from house to house, don't you know. Well, we've made a jolly arrangement — old Cloud — Captain Cloud, don't you know, first suggested it—and it is that every day one of the four—the Glorious Four we are called—keeps open house; and it's considered the right thing for the other nine fellows to drop in on him some time during the day, just to cheer him up a bit. Well, we soon made the discovery—old Cloud, I fancy, made it—that tea and rum were about the best things to have on these occasions. To-day it was my day and to-morrow it will be some other fellow's, don't you know. And, by Jove, how lucky I was to meet you at the *pulpería!* It will be ever so much jollier now."

I had certainly not stumbled upon a charming little English paradise in this Oriental wilderness, and as it always makes me uncomfortable to see young men drifting into intemperate habits and making asses of themselves generally, I was not rapturously delighted with "old Cloud's" system. Still I was glad to find myself with Englishmen in this distant country, and in the end I succeeded in making myself tolerably happy. The discovery that I had a voice pleased them greatly, and when, somewhat excited from the effects of strong cavendish, rum, and black tea, I roared out—

> And may his soul in heaven dwell,
> Who first found out the leather botél,

they all got up and drank my health in big tumblers, and declared they would never let me leave the colony.

Before evening the guests departed, all except the Captain. He had sat with us at the table, but was too far gone in his cups to take part in the boisterous fun and conversation. Once in about every five minutes he had implored someone in a husky voice to give him a light for his pipe, then, after two or three ineffectual puffs, he would let it go out again. He had also attempted two or three times to join in the chorus of a song, but soon relapsed again into his imbecile condition.

Next day, however, when he sat down refreshed by a night's sleep to breakfast, I found him a very agreeable fellow. He had no house of his own yet, not having received his money from home, he confidentially informed me, but lived about, breakfasting in one house, dining in a second, and sleeping in a third. "Never mind," he would say, "by-and-by it will be my turn; then I will receive you all every day for six weeks to make it all square."

None of the colonists did any work, but all spent their time lounging about and visiting each other, trying to make their dull existence endurable by perpetual smoking and tea and rum drinking. They had tried. they told me, ostrich-hunting, visiting their native neighbours, partridge-shooting, horse-racing, etc.; but the partridges were too tame for them, they could never catch the ostriches, the natives didn't understand them, and they had finally given up all these so-called amusements. In each house a peon was kept to take care of the flock and to cook, and as the sheep appeared to take care of themselves, and the cooking merely meant roasting a piece of meat on a spit, there was very little for the hired men to do.

"Why don't you do these things for yourselves?" I innocently asked.

"I fancy it wouldn't quite be the right thing, don't you know," said Mr. Winchcombe.

"No," said the Captain gravely, "we haven't quite come down to that yet."

I was greatly surprised to hear them. I had seen Englishmen sensibly roughing it in other places, but the lofty pride of these ten rum-drinking gentlemen was quite a new experience to me.

Having spent a somewhat listless morning, I was invited to accompany them to the house of Mr. Bingley, one of the Glorious Four. Mr. Bingley was really a very nice young fellow, living in a house far more worthy of the name than the slovenly rancho tenanted by his neighbour Winchcombe. He was the favourite of the colonists, having more money than the others, and keeping two servants. Always on his reception-day he provided his guests with hot bread and fresh butter, as well as with the indispensable rum-bottle and teapot. It therefore happened that, when his turn came round to keep open house, not one of the other nine colonists was absent from his table.

Soon after our arrival at Bingley's, the others began to appear, each one on entering taking a seat at the hospitable board, and adding another cloud to the dense volume of tobacco smoke obscuring the room. There was a great deal of hilarious conversation; songs were sung, and a vast amount of tea, rum, bread and butter, and tobacco consumed; but it was a wearisome entertainment, and by the time it was over, I felt heartily sick of this kind of life.

Before separating, after "John Peel" had been sung with great enthusiasm, someone proposed that we should get up a fox-hunt in real English style. Everyone agreed, glad of anything, I suppose, to break the monotony of such an existence, and next day we rode out, followed by about twenty dogs, of various breeds and sizes, brought together from all the houses. After some searching about in the most likely places, we at length started a fox from a bed of dark-leafed Mio-mio bushes. He made straight away for a range of hills about three miles distant, and over a beautifully smooth plain, so that we had a very good prospect of running him down. Two of the hunters had provided themselves with horns, which they blew incessantly, while the others all shouted at the top of their lungs, so that our chase was a very noisy one. The fox appeared to understand his danger and to know that his only chance of escape lay in keeping up his strength till the refuge of the hills was reached. Suddenly, however, he changed his course, this giving us a great advantage, for by making a short cut we were all soon close at his heels, with only the wide level plain before us. But reynard had his reasons for what he did; he had spied a herd of cattle, and in a very few moments had overtaken and mixed with them. The herd, struck with terror at our shouts and horn-blowing, instantly scattered and flew in all directions, so that we were able still to keep our quarry in sight. Far in advance of us the panic in the cattle ran on from herd to herd, swift as light, and we could see them miles away fleeing from us, while their hoarse bellowings and thundering tread came borne by the wind faintly to our ears. Our fat lazy dogs ran no faster than our horses, but still they laboured on, cheered by incessant shouts, and at last ran into the first fox ever properly hunted in the Banda Orientál.

The chase, which had led us far from home, ended close to a large estancia house, and while we stood watching the dogs worrying their victim to death, the *capatas* of the establishment, accompanied by three men, rode out to inquire who we were, and what we were doing. He was a small dark native, wearing a very picturesque costume, and addressed us with extreme politeness.

"Will you tell me, señores, what strange animal you have captured?" he asked.

"A fox!" shouted Mr. Bingley, triumphantly waving the brush, which he had just cut off, over his head. "In our country—in England—we hunt the fox with dogs, and we have been hunting after the manner of our country."

The *capatas* smiled, and replied that if we were disposed to join him, it would afford him great pleasure to show us a hunt after the manner of the Banda Orientál.

We consented gladly, and mounting our horses, set off at a swinging gallop after the *capatas* and his men. We soon came to a small herd of cattle; the *capatas* dashed after them, and unloosening the coils of his lasso, flung the noose dexterously over the horns of a fat heifer he had singled out, then started homewards at a tremendous pace. The cow, urged forward by the men, who rode close behind and pricked it with their knives, rushed on, bellowing with rage and pain, trying to overtake the *capatas*, who kept just out of reach of its horns; and in this way we quickly reached the house. One of the men now flung his lasso and caught the beast's hind leg; pulled in two opposite directions, it quickly came to a standstill; the other men now dismounting, first hamstrung, then ran a long knife into its throat. Without removing the hide, the carcass was immediately cut up, and the choice pieces flung on to a great fire of wood, which one of the men had been making. In an hour's time we all sat down to a feast of *carne con cuero*, or meat roasted in the hide, juicy, tender, and exquisitely flavoured. I must tell the English reader who is accustomed to eat meat and game which has been kept till it is tender, that before the tender stage is reached, it has been permitted to get tough. Meat, game included, is never so tender or deliciously flavoured as when cooked and eaten immediately after it is killed. Compared with meat at any subsequent stage, it is like a new-laid egg or a salmon with the cream on, compared with an egg or a salmon after a week's keeping.

We enjoyed the repast immensely, though Captain Cloud bitterly lamented that we had neither rum nor tea to wash it down. When we had thanked our entertainer and were about to turn our horses' heads homewards, the polite *capatas* once more stepped out and addressed us.

"Gentlemen," he said, "whenever you feel disposed to hunt, come to me and we will lasso and roast a heifer in the hide. It is the best dish the republic has to offer the stranger, and it will give me great pleasure to entertain you; but I beg you will hunt no more foxes over the ground belonging to this estancia, for you have caused so great a commotion amongst the cattle I am placed here in charge of, that it will take my men two or three days to find them all and bring them back again."

We gave the desired promise, plainly perceiving that fox-hunting in the English fashion is not a sport adapted to the Oriental country. Then we rode back, and spent the remaining hours at the house of Mr. Girling, of the Glorious Four, drinking rum and tea, smoking unlimited pipes of cavendish, and talking over our hunting experience.

CHAPTER VI

THE COLONY UNDER A CLOUD

I SPENT several days at the colony; and I suppose the life I led there had a demoralising effect on me, for unpleasant as it was, every day I felt less inclined to break loose from it, and sometimes I even thought seriously of settling down there myself. This crazy idea, however, would usually come to me late in the day, after a great deal of indulgence in rum and tea, a mixture that would very soon drive any man mad.

One afternoon, at one of our convivial meetings, it was resolved to pay a visit to the little town of Tolosa, about eighteen miles to the east of the colony. Next day we set out, every man wearing a revolver slung at his waist and provided with a heavy poncho for covering; for it was the custom of the colonists to spend the night at Tolosa when they visited it. We put up at a large public-house in the centre of the miserable little town, where there was accommodation for man and beast, the last always faring rather better than the first. I very soon discovered that the chief object of our visit was to vary the entertainment of drinking rum and smoking at the "Colony," by drinking rum and smoking at Tolosa. The bibulous battle raged till bedtime, when the only sober member of our party was myself; for I had spent the greater part of the afternoon walking about talking to the townspeople, in the hope of picking up some information useful to me in my search for occupation. But the women and old men I met gave me little encouragement. They seemed to be a rather listless set in Tolosa, and when I asked them what they were doing to make a livelihood, they said they were *waiting*. My fellow-countrymen and their visit to the town was the principal topic of conversation. They regarded their English neighbours as strange and dangerous creatures, who took no solid food, but subsisted on a mixture of rum and gunpowder (which was the truth), and who were armed with deadly engines called revolvers, invented specially for them by their father the devil. The day's experience convinced me that the English colony had some excuse for its existence, since its periodical visits gave the good people of Tolosa a little wholesome excitement during the stagnant intervals between the revolutions.

At night we all turned into a large room with a clay floor, in which there was not a single article of furniture. Our saddles, rugs, and ponchos had all been thrown together in a corner, and anyone wishing to sleep had to make himself a bed with his own horse-gear and toggery as best he could. The experience was nothing new to me, so I soon made myself a comfortable nest on the floor, and, pulling off my boots, coiled myself up like an opossum that knows nothing better and is friendly with fleas. My friends, however, were evidently bent on making a night of it, and had taken care to provide themselves with three or four bottles of rum. After conversation, with an occasional song, had been going on for some time, one of them—a Mr. Chillingworth—rose to his feet and demanded silence.

"Gentlemen," he said, advancing into the middle of the room, where, by occasionally throwing out his arms to balance himself, he managed to maintain a tolerably erect position, "I am going to make a what-d'ye-call-it."

Furious cheers greeted this announcement, while one of the hearers, carried away with enthusiasm at the prospect of listening to his friend's eloquence, discharged his revolver at the roof, scattering confusion amongst a legion of long-legged spiders that occupied the dusty cobwebs above our heads.

I was afraid the whole town would be up in arms at our carryings on, but they assured me that they all fired off their revolvers in that room and that nobody came near them, as they were so well known in the town.

"Gentlemen," continued Mr. Chillingworth, when order had been at length restored, "I've been thinking, that's what I've been doing. Now let's review the situation. Here we stand, a colony of English gentlemen: here we are, don't you know, far from our homes and country and all that sort of thing. What says the poet? I daresay some of you fellows remember the passage. But what for, I ask! What, gentlemen, is the object of our being here? That's just what I'm going to tell you, don't you know. We are here, gentlemen, to infuse a little of our Anglo-Saxon energy, and all that sort of thing, into this dilapidated old tin-pot of a nation."

Here the orator was encouraged by a burst of applause.

"Now, gentlemen," he continued, "isn't it hard—devilish hard, don't you know, that so little is made of us? I feel it—I feel it, gentlemen; our lives are being frittered away. I don't know whether you fellows feel it. You see we ain't a melancholy lot. We're a glorious combination against the blue devils, that's what we are. Only sometimes I feel, don't you know, that all the rum in the place can't quite kill them. I can't help thinking of jolly days on the other side of the water. Now don't you fellows look at me as if you thought I was going to blubber. I'm not going to make such a confounded ass of myself, don't you know. But what I want you fellows to tell me is this: Are we to go on all our lives making beasts of ourselves, guzzling rum—I—I beg your pardon, gentlemen. I didn't mean to say that, really. Rum is about the only decent thing in this place. Rum keeps us alive. If any man says a word against rum, I'll call him an infernal ass. I meant to say the country, gentlemen—this rotten old country, don't you know. No cricket, no society, no Bass, no anything. Supposing we had gone to Canada with our —our capital and energies, wouldn't they have received us with open arms? And what's the reception we get here? Now, gentlemen, what I propose is this: let's protest. Let's get up a what-d'you-call-it to the thing they call a government. We'll state our case to the thing, gentlemen; and we'll insist on it and be very firm; that's what we'll do, don't you know. Are we to live amongst these miserable monkeys and give them the benefit of our—our—yes, gentlemen, our capital and energies, and get nothing in return? No, no; we must let them know that we are not satisfied, that we will be very angry with them. That's about all I have to say, gentlemen."

Loud applause followed, during which the orator sat down rather suddenly on the floor. Then followed "Rule Britannia," everyone assisting with all the breath in his lungs to make night hideous.

When the song was finished the loud snoring of Captain Wriothesley became audible. He had begun to spread some rugs to lie on, but becoming hopelessly entangled in his bridle-reins, surcingle, and stirrup-straps, had fallen to sleep with his feet on his saddle and his head on the floor.

"Hallo, we can't have this!" shouted one of the fellows. "Let's wake old Cloud by firing at the wall over him and knocking some plaster on to his head. It'll be awful fun, you know."

Everybody was delighted with the proposal, except poor Chillingworth, who after delivering his speech had crept away on all fours into a corner, where he was sitting alone and looking very pale and miserable.

The firing now began, most of the bullets hitting the wall only a few inches above the recumbent Captain's head, scattering dust and bits of plaster over his purple face. I jumped up in alarm and rushed amongst them, telling them in my haste that they were too drunk to hold their revolvers properly, and would kill their friend. My interference raised a loud, angry remonstrance, in the midst of which the Captain, who was lying in a most uncomfortable position, woke, and, struggling into a sitting posture, stared vacantly at us, his reins and straps wound like serpents about his neck and arms.

"What's all the row 'bout?" he demanded huskily. "Getting up rev'lution, I s'pose. A'right; only thing to do in this country. Only don't ask me to be pres'dent. Nor good enough. Goo' night, boys; don't cur my throat by mistake. Gor bless you all."

"No, no, don't go to sleep, Cloud," they shouted. "Lamb's the cause of all this. He says we're drunk—that's the way Lamb repays our hospitality. We were firing to wake you up, old Cap, to have a drink——"

"A drink—yes," assented the Captain hoarsely.

"And Lamb was afraid we would injure you. Tell him, old Cloud, whether you're afraid of your friends. Tell Lamb what you think of his conduct."

"Yes, I'll tell him," returned the Captain in his thick tones. "Lamb shan't interfere, gentlemen. But you know you took him in, didn't you now? And what was my opinion of him? It wasn't right of you fellows, was it, now? He couldn't be one of us, you know, could he now? I'll leave it to you, gentlemen; didn't I say the fellow was a cad? Why the devil doesn't he leave me alone then? I'll tell you what I'll do with Lamb, I'll punch his damned nose, don't you know."

And here the gallant gentleman attempted to rise, but his legs refused to assist him, and, tumbling back against the wall, he was only able to glare at me out of his watery eyes.

I went up to him intending, I suppose, to punch *his* nose, but suddenly changing my mind I merely picked up my saddle and things, then left the room with a hearty curse on Captain Cloudesley Wriothesley, the evil genius, drunk or sober, of the colony of English gentlemen. I was no sooner outside the door than the joy they felt at being rid of me was expressed in loud shouts, clapping of hands, and a general discharge of firearms into the roof.

I spread my rugs out of doors and soliloquised myself to sleep. "And so ends," said I, fixing my somewhat drowsy eyes on the constellation of Orion, "adventure the second, or twenty-second—little does it matter about the exact number of them, since they all alike end in smoke—revolver smoke—or a flourish of knives and the shaking of dust from off my feet. And, perhaps, at this very moment Paquíta, roused from light slumbers by the droning cry of the night-watchman under her window, puts out her arms to feel me, and sighs to find my place still vacant. What must I say to her? That I must change my name to Ernandes or Fernandes, or Blas or Chas, or Sandariaga, Gorostiaga, Madariaga, or any other *aga*, and conspire to overthrow the existing order of things. There is nothing else for me to do, since this Oriental world is indeed an oyster only a sharp sword will serve to open. As for arms and armies and military training, all that is quite unnecessary. One has only got to bring together a few ragged, dissatisfied men, and, taking horse, charge pell-mell into poor Mr. Chillingworth's dilapidated old tin-pot. I almost feel like that unhappy gentleman to-night, ready to blubber. But, after all, my position is not quite so hopeless as his; I have no brutalised, purple-nosed Briton sitting like a nightmare on my chest, pressing the life out of me."

The shouts and choruses of the revellers grew fainter and fewer, and had almost ceased when I sank to sleep, lulled by a solitary tipsy voice droning out in a lugubrious key:—

We won't go—gome till morring.

CHAPTER VII

LOVE OF THE BEAUTIFUL

EARLY next morning I left Tolosa and travelled the whole day in a south-westerly direction. I did not hurry, but frequently dismounted to give my horse a sip of clear water and a taste of green herbage. I also called during the day at three or four estancia houses, but failed to hear anything that could be advantageous to me. In this way I covered about thirty-five miles of road, going always towards the eastern part of the Florida district in the heart of the country. About an hour before sunset I resolved to go no further that day; and I could not have hoped to find a nicer resting-place than the one now before me—a neat rancho with a wide corridor supported by wooden pillars, standing amidst a bower of fine old weeping willows. It was a calm, sunshiny afternoon, peace and quiet resting on everything, even bird and insect, for they were silent, or uttered only soft, subdued notes; and that modest lodge, with its rough stone walls and thatched roof, seemed to be in harmony with it all. It looked like the home of simple-minded pastoral people that had for their only world the grassy wilderness, watered by many clear streams. bounded ever by that far-off unbroken ring of the horizon, and arched over with blue heaven, starry by night and filled by day with sweet sunshine.

On approaching the house I was agreeably disappointed at having no pack of loud-mouthed, ferocious dogs rushing forth to rend the presumptuous stranger to pieces, a thing one always expects. The only signs of life visible were a white-haired old man seated within the corridor smoking, and a few yards from it a young girl standing under a willow tree. But that girl was a picture for one to gaze long upon and carry about in his memory for a lifetime. Never had I beheld anything so exquisitely beautiful. It was not that kind of beauty so common in these countries, which bursts upon you like the sudden south-west wind called *pampero*, almost knocking the breath out of your body, then passing as suddenly away, leaving you with hair ruffled up and mouth full of dust. Its influence was more like that of the spring wind, which blows softly, scarcely fanning your cheek, yet infusing through all your system a delicious magical sensation like—like nothing else in earth or heaven. She was, I fancy, about fourteen years old, slender and graceful in figure, and with a marvellously clear white skin, on which this bright Oriental sun had not painted one freckle. Her features were, I think, the most perfect I have ever seen in any human being, and her golden brown hair hung in two heavy braids behind, almost to her knees. As I approached, she looked up to me out of sweet, grey-blue eyes; there was a bashful smile on her lips, but she did not move or speak. On the willow branch over her head were two young doves: they were, it appeared, her pets, unable yet to fly, and she had placed them there. The little things had crept up just beyond her reach, and she was trying to get them by pulling the branch down towards her.

Leaving my horse I came to her side.

"I am tall, señorita," I said, "and can perhaps reach them."

She watched me with anxious interest while I gently pulled her birds from their perch and transferred them to her hands. Then she kissed them, well pleased, and with a gentle hesitation in her manner asked me in.

Under the corridor I made the acquaintance of her grandfather, the white-haired old man, and found him a person it was very easy to get on with, for he agreed readily with everything I said. Indeed, even before I could get a remark out he began eagerly assenting to it. There, too, I met the girl's mother, who was not at all like her beautiful daughter, but had black hair and eyes, and a brown skin, as most Spanish-American women have. Evidently the father is the white-skinned, golden-haired one, I thought. When the girl's brother came in, by-and-by, he unsaddled my horse and led him away to pasture; this boy was also dark, darker even than his mother.

The simple spontaneous kindness with which these people treated me had a flavour about it, the like of which I have seldom experienced elsewhere. It was not the common hospitality usually shown to a stranger, but a natural, unstrained kindness, such as they might be expected to show to a beloved brother or son who had gone out from them in the morning and was now returned.

By-and-by the girl's father came in, and I was extremely surprised to find him a small, wrinkled, dark specimen, with jet-black, bead-like eyes and podgy nose, showing plainly enough that he had more than a dash of aboriginal Charrua blood in his veins. This upset my theory about the girl's fair skin and blue eyes; the little dark man was, however, quite as sweet-tempered as the others, for he came in, sat down and joined in the conversation, just as if I had been one of the family whom he had expected to find there. While I talked to these good people on simple pastoral matters, all the wickedness of Orientals—the throat-cutting war of Whites and Reds, and the unspeakable cruelties of the ten years' siege—were quite forgotten; I wished that I had been born amongst them and was one of them, not a weary, wandering Englishman, overburdened with the arms and armour of civilisation, and staggering along, like Atlas, with the weight of a kingdom on which the sun never sets on his shoulders.

By-and-by this good man, whose real name I never discovered, for his wife simply called him Batata (sweet potato), looking critically at his pretty girl, remarked: "Why have you decked yourself out like this, my daughter—it is not a Saint's day?"

His daughter indeed! I mentally ejaculated; she is more like the daughter of the evening star than of such a man. But his words were unreasonable, to say the least of it; for the sweet child, whose name was Margarita, though wearing shoes, had no stockings on, while her dress—very clean, certainly—was a cotton print so faded that the pattern was quite undistinguishable. The only pretence of finery of any description was a narrow bit of blue ribbon tied about her lily-white neck. And yet had she been wearing richest silks and costliest gems she could not have blushed and smiled with a prettier confusion.

"We are expecting Uncle Anselmo this evening, papita," she replied.

"Leave the child, Batata," said the mother. "You know what a craze she has for Anselmo; when he comes she is always prepared to receive him like a queen."

This was really almost too much for me, and I was powerfully tempted to jump up and embrace the whole family on the spot. How sweet was this primitive simplicity of mind! Here, doubtlesss, was the one spot on the wide earth where the golden age still lingered, appearing like the last beams of the setting sun touching some prominent spot, when elsewhere all things are in shadow. Ah, why had fate led me into this sweet Arcadia, since I must presently leave it to go back to the dull world of toil and strife,

> That vain low strife
> Which makes men mad, the tug for wealth and power,
> The passions and the cares that wither life
> And waste its little hour?

Had it not been for the thought of Paquíta waiting for me over there in Montevideo I could have said, "O good friend Sweet Potato, and good friends all, let me remain for ever with you under this roof, sharing your simple pleasures, and, wishing for nothing better, forget that great crowded world where all men are striving to conquer nature and death and to win fortune; until, having wasted their miserable lives in their vain endeavours, they drop down and the earth is shovelled over them!"

Shortly after sunset the expected Anselmo arrived to spend the night with his relations, and scarcely had he got down from his horse before Margarita was at his side to ask the avuncular blessing, at the same time raising his hand to her delicate lips. He gave his blessing, touching her golden hair; then she lifted her face bright with new happiness.

Anselmo was a fine specimen of the Oriental gaucho, dark and with good features, his hair and moustache intensely black. He wore costly clothes, while his whip-handle, the sheath of his long knife, and other things about him were of massive silver. Of silver also were his heavy spurs, the pommel of his saddle, his stirrups and the headstall of his bridle. He was a great talker; never, in fact, in the whole course of my varied experience have I encountered anyone who could pour out such an incessant stream of talk about small matters as this man. We all sat together in the social kitchen, sipping maté; I taking little part in the conversation, which was all about horses, scarcely even listening to what the others were saying. Reclining against the wall, I occupied myself agreeably watching the sweet face of Margarita, which in her happy excitement had become suffused with a delicate rosy colour. I have always had a great love for the beautiful: sunsets, wild flowers, especially verbenas, so prettily called margaritas in this country; and beyond everything the rainbow spanning the vast gloomy heavens with its green and violet arch when the storm-cloud passes eastward over the wet sun-flushed earth. All these things have a singular fascination for my soul. But beauty when it presents itself in the human form is even more than these things. There is in it a magnetic power drawing my heart; a something that is not love, for how can a married man have a feeling like that towards anyone except his wife? No, it is not love, but a sacred ethereal kind of affection, resembling love only as the fragrance of violets resembles the taste of honey and the honey-comb.

At length, some time after supper, Margarita to my sorrow rose to retire, though not without first once more asking her uncle's blessing. After her departure from the kitchen, finding that the inexhaustible talking-machine Anselmo was still holding forth fresh as ever, I lit a cigar and prepared to listen.

CHAPTER VIII

MANUEL, ALSO CALLED THE FOX

WHEN I began to listen, it was a surprise to find that the subject of conversation was no longer the favourite one of horse-flesh, which had held undisputed sway the whole evening. Uncle Anselmo was just now expatiating on the merits of gin, a beverage for which he confessed to a special liking.

"Gin is, without doubt," said he, "the flower of all strong drinks. I have always maintained that it is incomparable. And for this reason I always keep a little of it in the house in a stone bottle; for, when I have taken my maté in the morning, and, after it, one or two or three or four sips of gin, I saddle my horse and go out with a tranquil stomach, feeling at peace with the whole world.

"Well, sirs, it happened that on the morning in question, I noticed that there was very little gin left in the bottle; for, though I could not see how much it contained, owing to its being of stone and not of glass, I judged from the manner in which I had to tip it upwards when pouring it out. In order to remember that I had to bring home some with me that day I tied a knot in my handkerchief; then, mounting my horse, I rode out towards the side on which the sun sets, little expecting that anything unusual was going to happen to me that day. But thus it often is; for no man, however learned he may be and able to read the almanac, can tell what a day will bring forth."

Anselmo was so outrageously prosy, I felt strongly inclined to go to bed to dream of beautiful Margarita; but politeness forbade, and I was also somewhat curious to hear what extraordinary thing had happened to him on that very eventful day.

"It fortunately happened," continued Anselmo, "that I had that morning saddled the best of my cream-noses; for on that horse I could say without fear of contradiction, I am on horseback and not on foot. I called him Chingolo, a name which Manuel, also called the Fox, gave him, because he was a young horse of promise, able to fly with his rider. Manuel had nine horses—cream-noses every one—and how from being Manuel's they came to be mine I will tell you. He, poor man, had just lost all his money at cards—perhaps the money he lost was not much, but how he came to have any was a mystery to many. To me, however, it was no mystery, and when my cattle were slaughtered and had their hides stripped off by night, perhaps I could have gone to Justice—feeling like a blind man for something in the wrong place—and led her in the direction of the offender's house; but when one has it in his power to speak, knowing at the same time that his words will fall like a thunderbolt out of a blue sky upon a neighbour's dwelling, consuming it to ashes and killing all within it, why, sirs, in such a case the good Christian prefers to hold his peace. For what has one man more than another that he should put himself in the place of Providence? We are all of flesh. True, some of us are only dog's flesh, fit for nothing; but to all of us the lash is painful, and where it rains blood will sprout. This, I say; but, remember, I say not that Manuel the Fox robbed me—for I would sully no man's reputation, even a robber's, or have anyone suffer on my account.

"Well, sirs, to go back to what I was saying, Manuel lost everything; then his wife fell ill with fever; and what was there left for him but to turn his horses into money? In this way it came about that I bought the cream-noses and paid him fifty dollars for them. True, the horses were young and sound, nevertheless it was a great price, and I paid it not without first weighing the matter well in my own mind. For in things of this nature if a person makes not his reckoning beforehand, where, let me ask, sirs, will he find himself at the year's end? The devil will take him with all the cattle he inherited from his fathers, or got together by his own proper abilities and industry.

"For you see the thing is this. I have a poor head for figures; all other kinds of knowledge come easy to me, but how to calculate readily has never yet found an entrance into my head. At the same time, whenever I find it impossible to make out my accounts, or settle what to do. I have only to take the matter to bed with me and lie awake thinking it over. For when I do that, I rise next morning feeling free and refreshed, like a man that has just eaten a water-melon; for what I have to do and how it is to be done is all as plain to my sight as this maté-cup I hold in my hand.

"In this difficulty I therefore resolved to take the subject of the horses to bed with me, and to say, 'Here I have you and you shall not escape from me.' But about supper-time Manuel came in to molest me, and sat in the kitchen with a sad face, like a prisoner under sentence of death.

"'If Providence is angry against the entire human race,' said he, 'and is anxious to make an example, I know not for what reason so harmless and obscure a person as I am should have been selected.'

"'What would you have, Manuel?' I replied. 'Wise men tell us that Providence sends us misfortunes for our good.'

"'True, I agree with you,' he said. 'It is not for me to doubt it, for what can be said of that soldier who finds fault with the measures of his commander? But you know, Anselmo, the man I am, and it is bitter that these troubles should fall on one who has never offended except in being always poor.'

"'The vulture,' said I, 'ever preys on the weak and ailing.'

"'First I lose everything,' he continued, 'then this woman must fall ill of a calenture; and now I am forced to believe that even my credit is gone, since I cannot borrow the money I require. Those who knew me best have suddenly become strangers.'

"'When a man is down,' said I, 'the very dogs will scratch up the dust against him.'

"'True,' said Manuel; 'and since these calamities fell on me, what has become of the friendships that were so many? For nothing has a worse smell, or stinks more, than poverty, so that all men when they behold it cover up their faces or fly from such a pestilence.'

"'You speak the truth, Manuel,' I returned; 'but say not all men, for who knows—there being so many souls in the world—whether you may not be doing injustice to someone.'

"'I say it not of you,' he replied. 'On the contrary, if any person has had compassion on me it is you; and this I say, not in your presence only, but publicly proclaim it to all men.'

"Words only were these. 'And now,' he continued, 'my cards oblige me to part with my horses for money; therefore I come this evening to learn your decision.'

"'Manuel,' said I, 'I am a man of few words, as you know, and straightforward, therefore you need not have used compliments, and before saying this to have said so many things; for in this you do not treat me as a friend.'

"'You say well,' he replied; 'but I love not to dismount before checking my horse and taking my toes from the stirrups.'

"'That is only as it should be,' said I; 'nevertheless, when you come to a friend's house, you need not alight at such a distance from the gate.'

"'For what you say, I thank you,' he answered. 'My faults are more numerous than the spots on the wild cat, but not amongst them is precipitancy.'

"'That is what I like,' said I; 'for I do not love to go

about like a drunk man embracing strangers. But our acquaintance is not of yesterday, for we have looked into and know each other, even to the bowels and to the marrow in the bones. Why, then, should we meet as strangers, since we have never had a difference, or any occasion to speak ill of each other?'

"'And how should we speak ill,' replied Manuel, 'since it has never entered into either of us, even in a dream, to do the other an injury? Some there are, who, loving me badly, would blow up your head like a bladder with lies if they could, laying I know not what things to my charge, when—heaven knows—they themselves are perhaps the authors of all they so readily blame me for.'

"'If you speak,' said I, 'of the cattle I have lost, trouble not yourself about such trifles; for if those who speak evil of you, only because they themselves are evil, were listening, they might say, This man begins to defend himself when no one has so much as thought of drawing against him.'

"'True, there is nothing they will not say of me,' said Manuel; 'therefore I am dumb, for nothing is to be gained by speaking. They have already judged me, and no man wishes to be made a liar.'

"'As for me,' I said, 'I never doubted you, knowing you to be a man, honest, sober, and diligent. If in anything you had given offence I should have told you of it, so great is my frankness towards all men.'

"'All that you tell me I firmly believe,' said he, 'for I know that you are not one that wears a mask like others. Therefore, relying on your great openness in all things, I come to you about these horses; for I love not dealing with those who shake you out a whole bushel of chaff for every grain of corn.'

"'But, Manuel,' said I, 'you know that I am not made of gold, and that the mines of Peru were not left to me for an inheritance. You ask a high price for your horses.'

"'I do not deny it,' he replied. 'But you are not one to stop your ears against reason and poverty when they speak. My horses are my only wealth and happiness, and I have no glory but them.'

"'Frankly then,' I answered, 'to-morrow I will tell you yes or no.'

"'Let it be as you say; but, friend, if you will close with me to-night I will abate something from the price.'

"'If you wish to abate anything,' said I, 'let it be to-morrow, for I have accounts to make up to-night and a thousand things to think of.'

"After that Manuel got on to his horse and rode away. It was black and rainy, but he had never needed moon or lantern to find what he sought by night, whether his own house, or a fat cow—also his own, perhaps.

"Then I went to bed. The first question I asked myself, when I had blown out the candle, was, Are there fat wethers enough in my flock to pay for the cream-noses? Then I asked, How many fat wethers will it take at the price Don Sebastian—a miserly cheat be it said in passing—offers me a head for them to make up the amount I require?

"That was the question; but you see, friends, I could not answer it. At length, about midnight, I resolved to light the candle and get an ear of maize; for by putting the grains into small heaps, each heap the price of a wether, then counting the whole, I could get to know what I wanted.

"The idea was good. I was feeling under my pillow for the matches to strike a light when I suddenly remembered that all the grain had been given to the poultry. No matter, said I to myself, I have been spared the trouble of getting out of bed for nothing. Why, it was only yesterday, said I, still thinking about the maize, that Pascuala, the cook, said to me when she put my dinner before me, 'Master, when are you going to buy some grain for the fowls? How can you expect the soup to be good when there is not even an egg to put in it? Then there is the black cock with the twisted toe—one of the second brood the spotted hen raised last summer, though the foxes carried off no less than three hens from the very bushes where she was sitting—he has been going round with drooping wings all day, so that I verily believe he is going to have the pip. And if any epidemic comes amongst the fowls, as there was in neighbour Gumesinda's the year before last, you may be sure it will only be for want of corn. And the strangest thing is, and it is quite true, though you may doubt it, for neighbour Gumesinda told me only yesterday when she came to ask me for some parsley, because, as you know very well, her own was all rooted up when the pigs broke into her garden last October; well, sir, she says the epidemic which swept off twenty-seven of her best fowls in one week began by a black cock with a broken toe, just like ours, beginning to droop its wings as if it had the pip.'

"'May all the demons take this woman!' I cried, throwing down the spoon I had been using, 'with her chatter about eggs and pip and neighbour Gumesinda, and I know not what besides! Do you think I have nothing to do but to gallop about the country looking for maize, when it is not to be had for its weight in gold at this season, and all because a sickly spotted hen is likely to have the pip?'

"'I have said no such thing,' retorted Pascuala, raising her voice as women do. 'Either you are not paying proper attention to what I am telling you, or you pretend not to understand me. For I never said the spotted hen was likely to have the pip; and if she is the fattest fowl in all this neighbourhood you may thank me, after the Virgin, for it, as neighbour Gumesinda often says, for I never fail to give her chopped meat three times a day; and that is why she is never out of the kitchen, so that even the cats are afraid to come into the house, for she flies like a fury into their faces. But you are always laying hold of my words by the heels; and if I said anything at all about pip, it was not the spotted hen, but the black cock with the twisted toe, I said was likely to have it.'

"'To the devil with your cock and your hen!' I shouted, rising in haste from my chair, for my patience was all gone and the woman was driving me crazy with her story of a twisted toe and what neighbour Gumesinda said. 'And may all the curses fall on that same woman, who is always full as a gazette of her neighbours' affairs! I know well what the parsley is she comes to gather in my garden. It is not enough that she goes about the country giving importance to the couplets I sang to Montenegro's daughter, when I danced with her at Cousin Teodoro's dance after the cattle-marking, when, heaven knows, I never cared the blue end of a finger-nail for that girl. But things have now come to a pretty pass when even a chicken with a broken toe cannot be indisposed in my house without neighbour Gumesinda thrusting her beak into the matter!'

"Such anger did I feel at Pascuala when I remembered these things and other things besides, for there is no end to that woman's tongue, that I could have thrown the dish of meat at her head.

"Just then, while occupied with these thoughts, I fell asleep. Next morning I got up, and without heating my head any more I bought the horses and paid Manuel his price. For there is in me this excellent gift, when I am puzzled in mind and in doubt about anything, night makes everything plain to me and I rise refreshed and with my determination formed."

Here ended Anselmo's story, without one word about those marvellous matters he had set out to tell. They had all been clean forgotten. He began to make a cigarette, and, fearing that he was about to launch forth on some fresh subject, I hastily bade good night and retreated to my bed.

CHAPTER IX

THE BOTANIST AND THE SIMPLE NATIVE

EARLY next morning Anselmo took his departure, but I was up in time to say good-bye to the worthy spinner of interminable yarns leading to nothing. I was, in fact, engaged in performing my morning ablutions in a large wooden bucket under the willows when he placed himself in the saddle ; then, after carefully arranging the drapery of his picturesque garments, he trotted gently away, the picture of a man with a tranquil stomach and at peace with the whole world, even neighbour Gumesinda included.

I had spent a somewhat restless night, strange to say, for my hospitable hostess had provided me with a deliciously soft bed, a very unusual luxury in the Banda Orientál, and when I plunged into it there were no hungry bedfellows waiting my advent within its mysterious folds. I thought about the pastoral simplicity of the lives and character of the good people slumbering near me; and that inconsequent story of Anselmo's about Manuel and Pascuala caused me to laugh several times. Finally my thoughts, which had been roaming around in a wild, uncertain manner, like rooks "blown about the windy skies," settled quietly down to the consideration of that beautiful anomaly, that mystery of mysteries, the white-faced Margarita. For how, in the name of heredity, had she got there? Whence that pearly skin and lithesome form; the proud sweet mouth, the nose that Phidias might have taken for a model; the clear, spiritual, sapphire eyes, and the wealth of silky hair, that if unbound would cover her as with a garment of surpassing beauty? With such a problem vexing my curious brain, what sleep could a philosopher get?

When Batata saw me making preparations for departure, he warmly pressed me to stay to breakfast. I consented at once, for, after all, the more leisurely one does a thing the sooner will it be accomplished—especially in the Banda Orientál. One breakfasts here at noon, so that I had plenty of time to see, and renew my pleasure in seeing, pretty Margarita.

In the course of the morning we had a visitor; a traveller who arrived on a tired horse, and who slightly knew my host Batata, having, I was told, called at the house on former occasions. Marcos Marcó was his name; a tall sallow-faced individual about fifty years old, slightly grey, very dirty, and wearing threadbare gaucho garments. He had a slouching gait and manner, and a patient, waiting hungry animal expression of face. Very, very keen were his eyes, and I detected him several times watching me narrowly.

Leaving this Oriental tramp in conversation with Batata, who with misplaced kindness had offered to provide him with a fresh horse, I went out for a walk before breakfast. During my walk, which was along a tiny stream at the foot of the hill on which the house stood, I found a very lovely bell-shaped flower of a delicate rose-colour. I plucked it carefully and took it back with me, thinking it just possible that I might give it to Margarita should she happen to be in the way. On my return to the house I found the traveller sitting by himself under the corridor, engaged in mending some portion of his dilapidated horse-gear, and sat down to have a chat with him. A clever bee will always be able to extract honey enough to reward him from any flower, and so I did not hesitate tackling this outwardly very unpromising subject.

"And so you are an Englishman," he remarked, after we had had some conversation; and I, of course, replied in the affirmative.

"What a strange thing!" he said. "And you are fond of gathering pretty flowers?" he continued, with a glance at my treasure.

"All flowers are pretty," I replied.

"But surely, señor, some are prettier than others. Perhaps you have observed a particularly pretty one growing in these parts—the white margarita?"

Margarita is the Oriental vernacular for verbena; the fragrant white variety is quite common in the country; so that I was justified in ignoring the fellow's rather impudent meaning. Assuming as wooden an expression as I could, I replied, "Yes, I have often observed the flower you speak of; it is fragrant, and to my mind surpasses in beauty the scarlet and purple varieties. But you must know, my friend, that I am a botanist, that is, a student of plants, and they are all equally interesting to me."

This astonished him; and pleased with the interest he appeared to take in the subject, I explained, in simple language, the principles on which a classification of plants is founded, telling him about that *lingua franca* by means of which all the botanists in the world of all nations are able to converse together about plants. From this somewhat dry subject I launched into the more fascinating one of the physiology of plants. "Now look at this," I continued, and with my penknife I carefully dissected the flower in my hand, for it was evident that I could not now give it to Margarita without exposing myself to remarks. I then proceeded to explain to him the beautiful complex structure by means of which this campanula fertilises itself.

He listened in wonder, exhausting all the Spanish and Oriental equivalents of such expressions as "Dear me!" "How extraordinary!" "Lawks a mussy!" "You don't say so!" I finished my lecture, satisfied that my superior intellect had baffled the rude creature; then, tossing away the fragments of the flower I had sacrificed, I restored the penknife to my pocket.

"These are matters we do not often hear about in the Banda Orientál," he said. "But the English know everything—even the secrets of a flower. They are also able to do most things. Did you ever, sir botanist, take part in acting a comedy?"

After all, I had wasted my flower and scientific knowledge on the animal for nothing! "Yes, I have!" I replied rather angrily; then, suddenly remembering Eyebrows' teaching, I added, "and in tragedy also."

"Is that so?" he exclaimed. "How amused the spectators must have been! Well, we can all have our fill of fighting presently, for I see the *White Flower* coming this way to tell us that breakfast is ready. Batata's roast beef will give something for our knives to do; I only wish we had one of his own floury namesakes to eat with it."

I swallowed my resentment, and when Margarita came to us looked up into her matchless face with a smile, then rose to follow her into the kitchen.

CHAPTER X

MATTERS RELATING TO THE REPUBLIC

AFTER breakfast I bade a reluctant good-bye to my kind entertainers, took a last longing lingering look at lovely Margarita, and mounted my horse. Scarcely was I in the saddle before Marcos Marcó, who was alsc about to resume his journey on the fresh horse he had borrowed, remarked—

"You are travelling to Montevideo, good friend; I am also going in that direction, and will take you the shortest way."

"The road will show me the way," I rejoined curtly.

"The road," he said, "is like a lawsuit; round-about, full of puddles and pitfalls, and long to travel. It is only meant to be used by old half-blind men and drivers of bullock carts."

I hesitated about accepting the guidance of this strange fellow, who appeared to have a ready wit under his heavy slouching exterior. The mixed contempt and humility in his speech every time he addressed me gave me an uncomfortable sensation; then his poverty-stricken appearance and his furtive glances filled me with suspicion. I looked at my host, who was standing near, thinking to take my cue from the expression of his face; but it was only a stolid Oriental face that revealed nothing. An ancient rule in whist is to play trumps when in doubt; now my rule of action is, when two courses are open to me and I am in doubt, to take the bolder one. Acting on this principle, I determined to go with Marcos, and accordingly we rode forth together.

My guide soon struck away across country, leading me wide of the public road, through such lonely places that I at length began to suspect him of some sinister design against my person, since I had no property worth taking. Presently he surprised me by saying—"You were right, my young friend, in casting away idle fears when you accepted my company. Why do you let them return to trouble your peace? Men of your blood have never inflicted injuries on me that cry out for vengeance. Can I make myself young again by shedding your life, or would there be any profit in changing these rags I now wear for your garments, which are also dusty and frayed? No, no, sir Englishman, this dress of patience and suffering and exile, my covering by day and my bed by night, must soon be changed for brighter garments than you are wearing."

This speech relieved me sensibly, and I smiled at the poor devil's ambitious dream of wearing a soldier's greasy red jacket; for I supposed that that was what his words meant. Still, his "shortest way" to Montevideo continued to puzzle me considerably. For two or three hours we had been riding nearly parallel to a range of hills, or cuchilla, extending away on our left hand towards the south-east. But we were gradually drawing nearer to it, and apparently going purposely out of our way only to traverse a most lonely and difficult country. The few estancia-houses we passed, perched on the highest points of the great sweep of moor-like country on our right, appeared to be very far away. Where we rode there were no habitations, not even a shepherd's hovel; the dry, stony soil was thinly covered with a forest of dwarf thorn trees, and a scanty pasturage burnt to a rust-brown colour by the summer heats; and out of this arid region rose the hills, their brown, woodless sides looking strangely gaunt and desolate in the fierce noonday sun.

Pointing to the open country on our right, where the blue gleam of a river was visible, I said—"My friend, I assure you, I fear nothing, but I cannot understand why you keep near these hills when the valley over there would have been pleasanter for ourselves, and easier for our horses."

"I do nothing without a reason," he said, with a strange smile. "The water you see over there is the Rio de las Canas (River of grey hairs), and those who go down into its valley grow old before their time."

Occasionally talking, but oftener silent, we jogged on till about three o'clock in the afternoon, when suddenly as we were skirting a patch of scraggy woodland, a troop of six armed men emerged from it, and wheeling about came directly towards us. A glance was enough to tell us that they were soldiers or mounted policemen, scouring the country in search of recruits, or, in other words, of deserters, skulking criminals, and vagabonds of all descriptions. I had nothing to fear from them, but an exclamation of rage escaped my companion's lips, and turning to him I perceived that his face was of the whiteness of ashes. I laughed, for revenge is sweet, and I still smarted a little at his contemptuous treatment of me earlier in the day.

"Is your fear so great?" I said.

"You do not know what you say, boy!" he returned fiercely. "When you have passed through as much hell-fire as I have and have rested as sweetly with a corpse for a pillow, you will learn to curb your impertinent tongue when you address a man."

An angry retort was on my lips, but a glance at his face prevented me from uttering it—it was, in its expression, the face of a wild animal worried by dogs.

In another moment the men had cantered up to us, and one, their commander, addressing me, asked to see my passport.

"I carry no passport," I replied. "My nationality is a sufficient protection, for I am an Englishman as you can see."

"We have only your word for that," said the man. "There is an English consul in the capital, who provides English subjects with passports for their protection in this country. If you have not got one you must suffer for it, and no one but yourself is to blame. I see in you only a young man complete in all his members, and of such the republic is in need. Your speech is also like that of one who came into the world under this sky. You must go with us."

"I shall do nothing of the sort," I returned.

"Do not say such a thing, master," said Marcos, astonishing me very much with the change in his tone and manner. "You know I warned you a month ago that it was imprudent to leave Montevideo without our passports. This officer is only obeying the orders he has received; still he might see that we are only what we represent ourselves to be."

"Oh!" exclaimed the officer, turning to Marcos, "you are also an Englishman unprovided with a passport, I suppose? You might at least have supplied yourself with a couple of blue crockery eyes and a yellow beard for your greater safety."

"I am only a poor son of the soil," said Marcos meekly. "This young Englishman is looking for an estancia to buy, and I came as his attendant from the capital. We were very careless not to get our passports before starting."

"Then, of course, this young man has plenty of money in his pocket?" said the officer.

I did not relish the lies Marcos had taken upon himself to tell about me, but did not quite know what the consequences of contradicting them might be. I therefore replied that I was not so foolish as to travel in a country like the Banda Orientál with money on my person. "To pay for bread and cheese till I reach my destination is about as much as I have," I added.

"The government of this country is a generous one," said the officer sarcastically, "and will pay for all the bread and cheese you will require. It will also provide you with beef. You must now come with me to the Juzgado de las Cuevas. both of you."

Seeing no help for it, we accompanied our captors at a swinging gallop over a rough, undulating country, and in about an hour and a half reached Las Cuevas, a dirty, miserable-looking village, composed of a few ranchos built round a large plaza overgrown with weeds. On one side stood the church, on the other a square stone building with a flagstaff before it. This was the official building of the Juez de Paz, or rural magistrate; just now, however, it was closed, and with no sign of life about it except an old dead-and-alive-looking man sitting against the closed door, with his bare, mahogany-coloured legs stretched out in the hot sunshine.

"This is a very fine thing!" exclaimed the officer with a curse. "I feel very much inclined to let the men go."

"You will lose nothing by doing so, except, perhaps, a headache," said Marcos.

"Hold your tongue till your advice is asked!" retorted the officer, thoroughly out of temper.

"Lock them up in the calaboso till the Juez comes to-morrow, Lieutenant," suggested the old man by the door, speaking through a bushy white beard and a cloud of tobacco smoke.

"Do you not know that the door is broken, old fool?" said the officer. "Lock them up! Here I am neglecting my own affairs to serve the state, and this is how I am treated. We must now take them to the Juez at his own house and let him look after them. Come on, boys."

We were then conducted out of Las Cuevas to a distance of about two miles, where the Señor Juez resided in the bosom of his family. His private residence was a very dirty, neglected-looking estancia-house, with a great many dogs, fowls, and children about. We dismounted and were immediately taken into a large room, where the magistrate sat at a table on which lay a great number of papers—goodness knows what they were about. The Juez was a little hatchet-faced man, with bristly grey whiskers, standing out like a cat's moustache, and angry eyes—or, rather, with one angry eye, for over the other a cotton handkerchief was tied. No sooner had we all entered than a hen, leading a brood of a dozen half-grown chickens, rushed into the room after us, the chickens instantly distributing themselves about the floor in quest of crumbs, while the mother, more ambitious, flew on the table, scattering the papers right and left with the wind she created.

"A thousand demons take the fowls!" cried the Juez, starting up in a fury. "Man, go and bring your mistress here this instant. I command her to come."

This order was obeyed by the person who had ushered us in, a greasy-looking, swarthy-faced individual, in threadbare military clothes; and in two or three minutes he returned, followed by a very fat, slatternly woman, looking very good-tempered, however, who immediately subsided, quite exhausted, into a chair.

"What is it, Fernando?" she panted.

"What is it? How can you have the courage to ask such a question, Toribia? Look at the confusion your pestilent fowls are creating amongst my papers—papers that concern the safety of the republic! Woman, what measures are you going to take to stop this before I have your fowls all killed on the spot?"

"What can I do, Fernando?—they are hungry, I suppose. I thought you wanted to ask my advice about these prisoners—poor fellows! and here you are with your hens."

Her placid manner acted like oil on the fire of his wrath. He stormed about the room, kicking over chairs, and hurling rulers and paper-weights at the birds, apparently with the most deadly intentions, but with shockingly bad aim—shouting, shaking his fist at his wife, and even threatening to commit her for contempt of court when she laughed. At last, after a great deal of trouble, the fowls were all got out, and the servant placed to guard the door, with strict orders to decapitate the first chicken that should attempt to enter and disturb the proceedings.

Order being restored, the Juez lit a cigarette and began to smooth his ruffled feathers. "Proceed," he said to the officer, from his seat at the table.

"Sir," said the officer, "in pursuance of my duty I have taken in charge these two strangers, who are unprovided with passports or documents of any description to corroborate their statements. According to their story, the young man is an English millionaire going about the country buying up estates, while the other man is his servant. There are twenty-five reasons for disbelieving their story, but I have not sufficient time to impart them to you now. Having found the doors of the Juzgado closed, I have brought these men here with great inconvenience to myself; and I am now only waiting to have this business despatched without further delay, so that I may have a little time left to devote to my private affairs."

"Address not me in this imperative manner, sir officer!" exclaimed the Juez, his anger blazing out afresh. "Do you imagine, sir, that I have no private interests; that the state feeds and clothes my wife and children? No, sir, I am the servant of the republic, not the slave; and I beg to remind you that official business must be transacted during the proper hours and at the proper place."

"Sir Juez," said the officer, "it is my opinion that a civil magistrate ought never to have any part in matters which more properly come under the military authorities. However, since these things are differently arranged, and I am compelled to come with my reports to you in the first place, I am only here to know, without entering into any discussion concerning your position in the republic, what is to be done with these two prisoners I have brought before you."

"Done with them! Send them to the devil! cut their throats; let them go; do what you like, since you are responsible, not I. And be sure, sir officer, I shall not fail to report your insubordinate language to your superiors."

"Your threats do not alarm me," said the officer; "for one cannot be guilty of insubordination towards a person one is not bound to obey. And now, sirs," he added, turning to us, "I have been advised to release you; you are free to continue your journey."

Marcos rose with alacrity.

"Man, sit down!" yelled the irate magistrate, and poor Marcos, thoroughly crestfallen, sat down again. "Sir Lieutenant," continued the fierce old man, "you are dismissed from further attendance here. The republic you profess to serve would perhaps be just as well off without your valuable aid. Go, sir, to attend to your private affairs, and leave your men here to execute my commands."

The officer rose, and having made a profound and sarcastic bow, turned on his heel and left the room.

"Take these two prisoners to the stocks," continued the little despot. "I will examine them to-morrow."

Marcos was first marched out of the room by two of the soldiers; for it happened that an outhouse on the place was provided with the usual wooden arrangement to make captives secure for the night. But when the other men took me by the arms, I recovered from the astonishment the magistrate's order had produced in me, and shook them roughly aside. "Señor Juez," I said, addressing him, "let me beg you to consider what you are doing. Surely my accent is enough to satisfy any reasonable person that I am not a native of this country. I am willing to remain in your custody, or to go wherever you like to send me; but your men shall tear me to pieces before making me suffer the indignity of the stocks. If you maltreat me in any way, I warn you that the government you serve will only censure, and perhaps ruin you, for your imprudent zeal."

Before he could reply, his fat spouse, who had apparently

taken a great fancy to me, interposed on my behalf, and persuaded the little savage to spare me.

"Very well," he said, "consider yourself a guest in my house for the present; if you are telling the truth about yourself, a day's detention cannot hurt you."

I was then conducted by my kind intercessor into the kitchen, where we all sat down to partake of maté and talk ourselves into good humour.

I began to feel rather sorry for poor Marcos, for even a worthless vagabond, such as he appeared to be, becomes an object of compassion when misfortune overtakes him, and I asked permission to see him. This was readily granted. I found him confined in a large empty room built apart from the house; he had been provided with a maté-cup and a kettle of hot water, and was sipping his bitter beverage with an air of stoical indifference. His legs, confined in the stocks, were thrust straight out before him; but I suppose he was accustomed to uncomfortable positions, for he did not seem to mind it much. After sympathising with him in a general way, I asked him whether he could really sleep in that position.

"No," he replied with indifference. "But do you know I do not mind about being taken. They will send me to the comandancia, I suppose, and after a few days liberate me. I am a good workman on horseback, and there will not be wanting some estanciero in need of hands to get me out. Will you do me one small service, friend, before you go to your bed?"

"Yes, certainly, if I can," I answered.

He laughed slightly and looked at me with a strange keen glitter in his eyes; then, taking my hand, he gave it a powerful grip. "No, no, my friend, I am not going to trouble you to do anything for me," he said. "I have the devil's temper, and to-day, in a moment of rage, I insulted you. It therefore surprised me when you came here and spoke kindly to me. I desired to know whether that feeling was only on the surface; since the men one meets with are often like horned cattle. When one falls, his companions of the pasture-ground remember only his past offences, and make haste to gore him."

His manner surprised me; he did not now seem like the Marcos Marcó I had travelled with that day. Touched with his words, I sat down on the stocks facing him, and begged him to tell me what I could do for him.

"Well, friend," said he, "you see the stocks are fastened with a padlock. If you will get the key, and take me out, I will sleep well; then in the morning, before the old one-eyed lunatic is up, you can come and turn the key in the lock again. Nobody will be the wiser."

"And you are not thinking of escaping?" I said.

"I have not even the faintest wish to escape," he replied.

"You could not escape if you did," I said, "for the room would be locked, of course. But if I were disposed to do what you ask, how could I get the key?"

"That is an easy matter," said Marcos. "Ask the good señora to let you have it. Did I not notice her eyes dwelling lovingly on your face—for, doubtless, you reminded her of some absent relative, a favourite nephew, perhaps. She would not deny you anything in reason; and a kindness, friend, even to the poorest man, is never thrown away."

"I will think about it," I said, and shortly after that I left him.

It was a sultry evening, and the close, smoky atmosphere of the kitchen becoming unendurable, I went out and sat down on a log of wood out of doors. Here the old Juez, in his character of amiable host, came and discoursed for half an hour on lofty matters relating to the republic. Presently his wife came out, and, declaring that the evening air would have an injurious effect on his inflamed eye, persuaded him to go indoors. Then she subsided into a place at my side, and began to talk about Fernando's dreadful temper and the many cares of her life.

"What a very serious young man you are!" she remarked, changing her tone somewhat abruptly. "Do you keep all your gay and pleasant speeches for the young and pretty señoritas?"

"Ah, señora, you are yourself young and beautiful in my eyes," I replied; "but I have no heart to be gay when my poor fellow-traveller is fastened in the stocks, where your cruel husband would also have confined me but for your timely intervention. You are so kind-hearted, cannot you have his poor tired legs taken out in order that he may also rest properly to-night?"

"Ah, little friend," she returned, "I could not attempt such a thing. Fernando is a monster of cruelty, and would immediately put out my eyes without remorse.

Poor me, what I have to endure!"—and here she placed her fat hand on mine.

I drew my hand away somewhat coldly; a born diplomatist could not have managed the thing better.

"Madam," I said, "you are amusing yourself at my expense. When you have done me a great favour, will you now deny me this small thing? If your husband is so terrible a despot, surely you can do this without letting him know! Let me get my poor Marcos out of the stocks, and I give you my word of honour that the Juez will never hear of it, for I will be up early to turn the key in the lock before he is out of his bed."

"And what will my reward be?" she asked, again putting her hand on mine.

"The deep gratitude and devotion of my heart," I returned, this time without withdrawing my hand.

"Can I refuse anything to my sweet boy?" said she. "After supper I shall slip the key into your hand; I am going now to get it from his room. Before Fernando retires, ask to see your Marcos, to take him a rug, or some tobacco or something; and do not let the servant see what you do, for he will be at the door waiting to lock it when you come out."

After supper the promised key was secretly conveyed to me, and I had not the least difficulty in liberating my friend in misfortune. Luckily the man who took me to Marcos left us alone for some time, and I related my conversation with the fat woman.

He jumped up, and, seizing my hand, wrung it till I almost screamed with pain.

"My good friend," he said, "you have a noble, generous soul, and have done me the greatest service it is possible for one man to render to another. You have, in fact, now placed me in a position to—enjoy my night's rest. Good night, and may Heaven's angels put it in my power to reward you at some future time!"

The fellow was overdoing it a little, I thought; then, when I had seen him safely locked up for the night, I walked back to the kitchen slowly and very thoughtfully.

CHAPTER XI

THE WOMAN AND THE SERPENT

I WALKED thoughtfully back because, after rendering that unimportant service to Marcos, I began to experience sundry qualms of conscience and inward questionings concerning the strict morality of the whole proceeding. Allowing that I had done something very kind, charitable, and altogether praiseworthy in getting the poor fellow's unfortunate feet out of the stocks, did all that justify the cajolery I had practised to attain my object? Or, to put it briefly in the old familiar way, Does the end sanctify the means? Assuredly it does in some cases, very easy to be imagined. Let us suppose that I have a beloved friend, an ailing person of a nervous, delicate organisation, who has taken it into his poor cracked brains that he is going to expire at the stroke of twelve on a given night. Without consulting the authorities on ethical questions I should, in such a case, flit about his room secretly manipulating his timepieces, till I had advanced them a whole hour, and then, just before the stroke of midnight, triumphantly produce my watch and inform him that death had failed to keep the appointment. Such an acted lie as that would weigh nothing on the conscience of any man. The fact of the matter is, the circumstances must always be considered and every case judged on its own particular merits. Now this affair of getting the key was not one for me to judge, since I had been a chief actor in it, but rather for some acute and learned casuist. I therefore made a mental note of it with the intention of putting it impartially before the first person of that description I should meet. Having thus disposed of a troublesome matter, I felt greatly relieved in mind and turned into the kitchen once more. I had scarcely sat down, however, before I found that one disagreeable consequence of my performance—the fat señora's claim on my undying devotion and gratitude—had yet to be faced. She greeted my entrance with an effusive smile; and the sweetest smiles of some people one meets are less endurable than their black looks. In self-defence I assumed as drowsy and vacant an expression as I could summon on the instant to a countenance by nature almost too ingenuous. I pretended not to hear or to misunderstand everything that was said to me; finally I grew so sleepy that I was several times on the point of falling off my chair, then, after each extravagant nod, I would start up and stare vacantly around me. My grim little host could scarcely conceal a quiet smile, for never had he seen a person so outrageously sleepy before. At length he mercifully remarked that I seemed fatigued and advised me to retire. Very gladly I made my exit, followed in my retreat from the kitchen by a pair of sad, reproachful eyes.

I slept soundly enough in the comfortable bed, which my obese Gulnare had provided for me, until the numerous cocks of the establishment woke me shortly after daybreak with their crowing. Remembering that I had to secure Marcos in the stocks before the irascible little magistrate should appear on the scene, I rose and hastily dressed myself. I found the greasy man of the brass buttons already in the kitchen sipping his matutinal maté-amargo, and asked him to lend me the key of the prisoner's room; for this was what I had been instructed to do by the señora. He got up and went with me to open the door himself, not caring, I suppose, to trust me with the key. When he threw the door open we stood silently gazing for some time into the empty apartment. The prisoner had vanished, and a large hole cut in the thatch of the roof showed how and where he had made his exit. I felt very much exasperated at the shabby trick the fellow had played on us, on me especially, for I was in a measure responsible for him. Fortunately the man who opened the door never suspected me of being an accomplice, but merely remarked that the stocks had evidently been left unlocked by the soldiers the evening before, so that it was not strange the prisoner had made his escape.

When the other members of the household got up the matter was discussed with little excitement or even interest, and I soon concluded that the secret of the escape would remain between the lady of the house and myself. She watched for an opportunity to speak to me alone, then, shaking her fat forefinger at me in playful anger, whispered, "Ah, deceiver, you planned it all with him last evening and only made me your instrument!"

"Señora," I protested with dignity, "I assure you, on the word of honour of an Englishman, I never suspected the man had any intention of escaping. I am very angry it has happened."

"What do you suppose I care about his escaping?" she replied laughingly. "For your sake, sweet friend, I would gladly open the doors of every prison in the Banda if I had the power."

"Ah, how you flatter! But I must now go to your husband to learn from him what he intends doing with the prisoner who has not attempted to escape."

With this excuse I got away from her.

The wretched little Juez, when I spoke to him, put me off with a number of vague, meaningless phrases about his responsible position, the peculiar nature of his functions, and the unsettled state of the republic—as if it had ever known or was ever likely to know any other state! He then mounted his horse and rode away to Las Cuevas, leaving me with that dreadful woman; and I verily believe that in doing so he was only carrying out her private instructions. The only comfort he gave me was the promise he made before going that a communication respecting me would be forwarded to the Comandante of the district in the course of the day, which would probably result in my being passed on to that functionary. In the meanwhile he begged me to make free use of his house and everything in it. Of course, the misguided little wretch had no intention of throwing his fat wife at my head; still I had no doubt that it was she who inspired these complimentary phrases, telling him, perhaps, that he would lose nothing by a courteous treatment of the "English millionaire."

When he rode away he left me sitting on the gate, feeling very much disgusted, and almost wishing that, like Marcos Marcó, I had run away during the night. Never had I taken so sudden and violent a dislike to anything as I then and there did to that estancia, where I was an honoured, albeit a compulsory guest. The hot, brilliant morning sun shone down on the discoloured thatch and mud-plastered walls of the sordid-looking building, while all about wherever I cast my eyes they rested on weeds, old bones, broken bottles, and other rubbish, eloquent witnesses of the dirty, idle, thriftless character of the inmates. Meanwhile my sweet, angelic child-wife, with her violet eyes dim with tears, was waiting for me far away in Montevideo, wondering at my long absence, and even now perhaps shading her face with her lily hand and looking out on the white dusty road watching for my arrival! And here I was compelled to sit, idly swinging my legs on the gate, because that abominable fat woman had taken a fancy to keep me by her! Feeling mad with indignation, I suddenly jumped down from the gate with an exclamation not intended for ears polite, causing my hostess to jump also and utter a scream; for there she was (confound her!) standing just behind me.

"The Saints defend me!" she exclaimed, recovering herself and laughing; "what made you startle me so?"

I apologised for the strong expression I had used; then added, "Señora, I am a young man full of energy and accustomed to take a great deal of exercise every day, and

I am getting very impatient sitting here basking in the sunshine, like a turtle on a bank of mud."

"Why then do you not take a walk?" she said, with kind concern.

I said I would gladly do so, and thanked her for the permission; then she immediately offered to accompany me. I protested very ungallantly that I was a fast walker, and reminded her that the sun was excessively hot, and I should also have liked to add that she was excessively fat. She replied that it did not matter; so polite a person as myself would know how to accommodate his pace to that of his companion. Unable to shake her off, I started for my walk in a somewhat unamiable mood, the stout lady resolutely trudging on at my side, perspiring abundantly. Our path led us down to a little cañada, or valley, where the ground was moist and abounding with numerous pretty flowers and feathery grasses, very refreshing to look at after leaving the parched yellow ground about the estancia house.

"You seem to be very fond of flowers," observed my companion. "Let me help you gather them. To whom will you give your nosegay when it is made?"

"Señora," I replied, vexed at her trivial chatter, "I will give it to the——" I had almost said to the devil, when a piercing scream she uttered suddenly arrested the rude speech on my lips.

Her fright had been caused by a pretty little snake, about eighteen inches long, which she had seen gliding away at her feet. And no wonder it glided away from her with all the speed it was capable of, for how gigantic and deformed a monster that fat woman must have seemed to it! The terror of a timid little child at the sight of a hippopotamus, robed in flowing bed-curtains and walking erect on its hind legs, would perhaps be comparable to the panic possessing the shallow brain of the poor speckled thing when that huge woman came striding over it.

First I laughed, and then, seeing that she was about to throw herself for protection like a mountain of flesh upon me, I turned and ran after the snake—for I had observed that it belonged to a harmless species, one of the innocuous Coronella genus—and I was anxious to annoy the woman. I captured it in a moment; then, with the poor frightened creature struggling in my hand and winding itself about my wrist, I walked back to her.

"Did you ever see such lovely colours?" I cried. "Look at the delicate primrose yellow on its neck, deepening into vivid crimson on the belly. Talk of flowers and butterflies! And its eyes are bright as two small diamonds—look closely at them, señora, for they are well worth your admiration."

But she only turned and fled away screaming at my approach, and at last finding that I would not obey her and drop the terrible reptile, she left me in a towering rage and went back to the house by herself.

After that I continued my walk in peace amongst the flowers; but my little speckled captive had served me so well that I would not release it. It occurred to me that if I kept it on my person it might serve as a sort of talisman to protect me from the disagreeable attentions of the señora. Finding that it was a very sly little snakey, and, like Marcos Marcó in captivity, full of subtle deceit, I put it into my hat, which, when firmly pressed on to my head, left no opening for the little arrowy head to insinuate itself through. After spending two or three hours botanising in the cañada I returned to the house. I was in the kitchen refreshing myself with a bitter maté, when my hostess came in beaming with smiles, for she had, I suppose, forgiven me by this time. I politely rose and removed my hat. Unfortunately I had forgotten the snake, when out it dropped on the floor; then followed screams, confusion, and scuttling out of the kitchen by madame, children, and servants. After that I was compelled to carry the snake out and give it back its liberty, which no doubt tasted very sweet to it after its close confinement. On my return to the house, one of the servants informed me that the señora was too much offended to sit in the same room with me again, so that I was obliged to have my breakfast alone; and for the remainder of the time during which I was a prisoner, I was avoided by everyone (except Brass Buttons, who appeared indifferent to everything on earth), as if I had been a leper or a dangerous lunatic. They thought, perhaps, that I still had other reptiles concealed about my person.

Of course, one always expects to find a cruel, unreasoning prejudice against snakes amongst ignorant people, but I never knew before to what ridiculous lengths it will carry them. The prejudice makes me angry, but on this occasion it had a use, for it enabled me to pass the day unmolested.

In the evening the Juez returned, and I soon heard him loud in a stormy altercation with his wife. Perhaps she wanted him to have me decapitated. How it ended I cannot say; but when I saw him his manner towards me was freezing, and he retired without giving me an opportunity of speaking to him.

Next morning I got up resolved not to be put off any longer. Something would have to be done, or I would know the reason why. On stepping out I was very much surprised to see my horse standing saddled at the gate. I went into the kitchen and asked Brass Buttons, the only person up, what it meant.

"Who knows?" he returned, giving me a maté. "Perhaps the Juez desires you to leave the house before he is up."

"What did he say?" I demanded.

"Say? Nothing—what should he say?"

"But you saddled the horse, I suppose?"

"Of course. Who else would do it?"

"Were you told to do so by the Juez?"

"Told? Why should he tell me?"

"How then am I to know that he wishes me to leave his beautiful house?" I asked, getting angry.

"The question!" he returned, shrugging his shoulders. "How do you know when it is going to rain?"

Finding there was nothing more to be got out of the fellow, I finished taking maté, lit a cigar, and left the house. It was a lovely morning, without a cloud, and the heavy dew sparkled on the grass like drops of rain. What a pleasant thing it was to be able to ride forth again free to go where I liked!

And so ends my snake-story, which is perhaps not very interesting; but it is true, and therefore has one advantage over all other snake-stories told by travellers.

CHAPTER XII

CHILDREN IN THE FOREST

BEFORE leaving the magistrate's estancia I had made up my mind to return by the shortest route, and as quickly as possible, to Montevideo; and that morning, mounted on a well-rested horse, I covered a great deal of ground. By twelve o'clock, when I stopped to rest my horse and get some refreshment at a wayside *pulpería*, I had got over about eight leagues. This was travelling at an imprudent pace, of course; but in the Banda Oriental it is so easy to pick up a fresh horse that one becomes somewhat reckless. My journey that morning had taken me over the eastern portion of the Durazno district, and I was everywhere charmed with the beauty of the country, though it was still very dry, the grass on the higher lands being burnt to various shades of yellow and brown. Now, however, the summer heats were over, for the time was near the end of February; the temperature, without being oppressive, was deliciously warm, so that travelling on horseback was delightful. I might fill dozens of pages with descriptions of pretty bits of country I passed that day, but must plead guilty of an unconquerable aversion to this kind of writing. After this candid confession, I hope the reader will not quarrel with me for the omission;

besides, anyone who cares for these things, and knows how evanescent are the impressions left by word pictures on the mind, can sail the seas and gallop round the world to see them all for himself. It is not, however, every wanderer from England—I blush while saying it—who can make himself familiar with the home habits, the ways of thought and speech, of a distant people. Bid me discourse of lowly valley, lofty height, of barren waste, shady wood, or cooling stream where I have drunk and been refreshed; but all these places, pleasant or dreary, must be in the kingdom called the heart.

After getting some information about the country I had to traverse from the *pulpero*, who told me that I would probably reach the river Yí before evening, I resumed my journey. About four o'clock in the afternoon I came to an extensive wood of thorn trees, of which the *pulpero* had spoken, and, in accordance with his instructions, I skirted it on the eastern side. The trees were not large, but there was an engaging wildness about this forest, full of the musical chatter of birds, which tempted me to alight from my horse and rest for a hour in the shade. Taking the bit from his mouth to let him feed, I threw myself down on the dry grass under a clump of shady thorns, and for half an hour watched the sparkling sunlight falling through the foliage overhead, and listened to the feathered people that came about me, loudly chirping, apparently curious to know what object had brought me to their haunts. Then I began to think of all the people I had recently mixed with; the angry magistrate and his fat wife—horrid woman!—and Marcos

Marcó, that shabby rascal, rose up before me to pass quickly away, and once more I was face to face with that lovely mystery Margarita. In imagination I put forth my hands to take hers and drew her towards me so as to look more closely into her eyes, vainly questioning them as to their pure sapphire hue. Then I imagined, or dreamt, that with trembling fingers I unbraided her hair to let it fall like a splendid golden mantle over her mean dress, and asked her how she came to possess that garment of glory. The sweet, grave, child lips smiled, but returned no answer. Then a shadowy face seemed to shape itself dimly against the green curtain of foliage, and, looking over the fair girl's shoulder, gaze sadly into my eyes. It was the face of Paquíta. Ah, sweet wife, never let the green-eyed monster trouble the peace of your heart! Know that the practical Saxon mind of your husband is puzzling itself over a purely scientific problem, that this surpassingly fair child interests me only because her fairness seems to upset all physiological laws. I was, in fact, just sinking to sleep at this moment when the shrill note of a trumpet blown close by and followed by loud shouts from several voices made me spring instantly to my feet. A storm of answering shouts came from another quarter of the wood, then followed profound silence. Presently the trumpet sounded again, making me feel very much alarmed. My first impulse was to spring on to my horse and ride away for dear life; but, on second thoughts, I concluded that it would be safer to remain concealed amongst the trees, as by leaving them I should only reveal myself to the robbers or rebels. or whatever they were. I bridled my horse so as to be ready to run, then drew him into a close thicket of dark-foliaged bushes and fastened him there. The silence that had fallen on the wood continued, and at last, unable to bear the suspense longer, I began to make my way cautiously, revolver in hand, towards the point the sounds had proceeded from. Stealing softly through the bushes and trees where they grew near together, I came at length in sight of an open piece of ground, about two or three hundred yards wide, and overgrown with grass. Near its border on one side I was amazed to see a group of about a dozen boys, their ages ranging from about ten to fifteen, all standing perfectly motionless. One of them held a trumpet in his hand, and they all wore red handkerchiefs or rags tied round their heads. Suddenly, while I crouched amongst the leafage watching them, a shrill note sounded from the opposite side of the open space, and another troop of boys wearing white on their heads burst from the trees and advanced with loud shouts of *vivas* and *mueras* towards the middle of the ground. Again the red heads sounded their trumpet and went out boldly to meet the new-comers. As the two bands approached each other, each led by a big boy, who turned at intervals, and with many wild gestures addressed his followers, apparently to encourage them, I was amazed to see them all suddenly draw out long knives, such as the native horsemen usually wear, and rush furiously together. In a moment they were mingled together in a desperate fight, uttering the most horrible yells, their long weapons glittering in the sunshine as they brandished them about.

With such fury did they fight that in a few moments all the combatants lay stretched out on the grass, excepting three boys wearing the red badges. One of these bloodthirsty young miscreants then snatched up the trumpet and blew a victorious blast, while the other two shrieked an accompaniment of *vivas* and *mueras*. While they were thus occupied one of the white-headed boys struggled to his feet, and, snatching up a knife, charged the three reds with desperate courage. Had I not been perfectly paralysed with amazement at what I had witnessed, I should then have rushed out to aid this boy in his forlorn attempt; but in an instant his three foes were on him and dragged him down to the ground. Two of them then held him fast by the legs and arms, the other raised his long knife and was just about to plunge it in the struggling captive's breast, when, uttering a loud yell, I sprang up and rushed at them. Instantly they started up and fled screaming towards the trees in the greatest terror; and then, most wonderful thing of all, the dead boys all came to life, and, springing to their feet, fled from me after the others. This brought me to a stand, when, seeing that one of the boys limped painfully after his companions, hopping on one leg, I made a sudden dash and captured him before he could reach the shelter of the trees.

"O señor, do not kill me!" he pleaded, bursting into tears.

"I have no wish to kill you, you unspeakable young miscreant, but I think I ought to thrash you," I answered, for, though greatly relieved at the turn things had taken,

I was excessively annoyed at having experienced all those sensations of blood-curdling horror for nothing.

"We were only playing at Whites and Reds," he pleaded.

I then made him sit down and tell me all about this singular game.

None of the boys lived very near, he said; some of them came a distance of several leagues, and they had selected this locality for their sports on account of its seclusion, for they did not like to be found out. Their game was a mimic war of Whites and Reds, manœuvres, surprises, skirmishes, throat-cutting, and all.

I pitied the young patriot at the last, for he had sprained his ankle badly and could scarcely walk, and so assisted him to the spot where his horse was hidden; then having helped him to mount and given him a cigarette, for which he had the impudence to ask me, I laughingly bade him good-bye. I went back to look for my own horse after that, beginning to feel very much amused at the whole thing; but alas! my steed was gone. The young scoundrels had stolen him, to revenge themselves on me, I suppose, for disturbing them; and to relieve me from all doubt in the matter they left two bits of rag, one white and the other red, attached to the branch I had fastened the bridle to. For some time I wandered about the wood, and even shouted aloud in the wild hope that the young fiends were not going to carry things so far as to leave me without a horse in that solitary place. Nothing could I see or hear of them, however, and as it was getting late and I was becoming desperately hungry and thirsty, I resolved to go in search of some habitation.

On emerging from the forest I found the adjacent plain covered with cattle quietly grazing. Any attempt to pass through the herd would have been almost certain death, as these more than half-wild beasts will always take revenge on their master man when they catch him dismounted in the open. As they were coming up from the direction of the river, and were slowly grazing past the wood, I resolved to wait for them to pass on before leaving my concealment. I sat down and tried to be patient, but the brutes were in no hurry, and went on skirting the wood at a snail's pace. It was about six o'clock before the last stragglers had left, and then I ventured out from my hiding-place, hungry as a wolf and afraid of being overtaken by night before finding any human habitation. I had left the trees half a mile behind me and was walking hurriedly along towards the valley of the Yí, when passing over a hillock, I suddenly found myself in sight of a bull resting on the grass and quietly chewing his cud. Unfortunately the brute saw me at the same moment and immediately stood up. He was, I think, about three or four years old, and a bull of that age is even more dangerous than an older one; for he is quite as truculent as the other and far more active. There was no refuge of any kind near, and I knew very well that to attempt to escape by running would only increase my danger, so after gazing at him for a few moments I assumed an easy unconcerned manner and walked on; but he was not going to be taken in that way and began to follow me. Then for the first, and I devoutly hope for the last, time in my life I was compelled to resort to the gaucho plan, and casting myself face downwards on the earth, lay there simulating death. It is a miserable, dangerous expedient, but in the circumstances I found myself, the only one offering a chance of escape from a very terrible death. In a few moments I heard his heavy tramp, then felt him sniffing me all over. After that he tried unsuccessfully to roll me over, in order to study my face, I suppose. It was horrible to endure the prods he gave me and lie still, but after a while he grew quieter and contented himself by simply keeping guard over me; occasionally smelling at my head, then turning round to smell at my heels. Probably his theory was, if he had one, that I had fainted with fear at the sight of him and would recover presently, but he was not quite sure at which end of me returning life would first show itself. About once in every five or six minutes he seemed to get impatient, and then he would paw me with his heavy hoof, uttering a low hoarse moaning, spattering me with froth from his mouth; but as he showed no disposition to leave, I at last resolved to try a very bold experiment, for my position was becoming unendurable. I waited till the brute's head was turned from me, then worked my hand cautiously down to my revolver; but before I had quite drawn it, he noticed the movement and wheeled swiftly round, kicking my legs as he did so. Just as he brought his head round close to mine, I discharged the weapon in his face, and the sudden explosion so terrified him that he turned tail and fled, never pausing in his lumbering gallop till he was out of sight. It was a glorious victory; and though I could scarcely stand on my legs at first, so stiff and bruised did I feel all over, I laughed with joy, and even sent another bullet whizzing after the retreating monster, accompanying the discharge with a wild yell of triumph.

After that I proceeded without further interruption on my walk, and, had I not felt so ravenously hungry and so sore where the bull had trod on me or prodded me with his horns, the walk would have been very enjoyable, for I was now approaching the Yí. The ground grew moist and green, and flowers abounded, many of them new to me and so lovely and fragrant that in my admiration for them I almost forgot my pain. The sun went down, but no house appeared in sight. Over the western heavens flamed the brilliant hues of the afterglow, and from the long grass came the sad monotonous trill of some night insect. Troops of hooded gulls flew by me on their way from their feeding grounds to the water, uttering their long hoarse laughter-like cries. How buoyant and happy they seemed, flying with their stomachs full to their rest; while I, dismounted and supperless, dragged painfully on like a gull that had been left behind with a broken wing. Presently, through the purple and saffron-hued vapours in the western sky, the evening star appeared, large and luminous, the herald of swift-coming darkness; and then, weary, bruised, hungry, baffled, and despondent, I sat down to meditate on my forlorn position.

CHAPTER XIII

BARKING DOGS AND SHOUTING REBELS

I SAT there till it was very dark, and the longer I sat the colder and stiffer I grew, yet I felt no disposition to walk further. At length a large owl, flapping down close to my head, gave utterance to a long hiss, followed by a sharp clicking sound, ending with a sudden loud, laugh-like cry. The nearness of it startled me, and looking up, I saw a twinkling yellow light gleam for a moment across the wide, black plain, then disappear. A few fireflies were flitting about the grass, but I felt sure the gleam just witnessed proceeded from a fire; and after vainly trying to catch sight of it again from my seat on the ground, I rose and walked on, keeping before me a particular star shining directly over the spot where that transient glimmer had appeared. Presently, to my great joy, I spied it again in the same place, and felt convinced that it was the gleam of firelight shining from the open door or window of some rancho or estancia house. With renewed hope and energy I hastened on, the light increasing in brightness as I progressed; and, after half an hour's brisk walking, I found myself approaching a human dwelling of some kind. I could make out a dark mass of trees and bushes, a long, low house, and, nearer to me, a corral, or cattle-pen, of tall upright posts. Now, however, when a refuge seemed so close, the fear of the terrible, savage dogs kept on most of these cattle-breeding establishments made me hesitate. Unless I wished to run the risk of being shot, it was necessary to shout loudly to make my approach known, yet by shouting I would inevitably bring a pack of huge, frantic dogs upon me; and the horns of the angry bull I had encountered were less terrible to contemplate than the fangs of these powerful truculent brutes. I sat down on the ground to consider the position, and presently heard the clatter of approaching hoofs. Immediately afterwards three men rode past me, but did not see me, for I was crouching down behind some scrubby bushes. When the horsemen approached the house the dogs rushed forth to assail them, and their loud, fierce barking, and the wild shouts of some person from the house calling them off, were enough to make a dismounted man nervous. However, now was my only chance, and, starting up, I hurried on towards the noise. As I passed the corral the brutes became aware of my approach, and instantly turned their attention on me. I wildly shouted "*Ave Maria*," then, revolver in hand, stood awaiting the onset; but when they were near enough for me to see that the pack was composed of eight or ten huge yellow mastiff-like brutes my courage failed, and I fled to the corral, where, with an agility surpassing that of a wild cat, so great was my terror, I climbed up a post and placed myself beyond their reach. With the dogs furiously barking under me, I renewed my shouts of "*Ave Maria*" —the proper thing to do when you approach a strange house in these pious latitudes. After some time the men approached—four of them—and asked me who I was and what I did there. I gave an account of myself, then asked whether it would be safe for me to descend. The master of the house took the hint, and drove his faithful protectors off, after which I came down from my uncomfortable perch.

He was a tall, well-made, but rather fierce-looking gaucho, with keen black eyes, and a heavy black beard. He seemed suspicious of me—a very unusual thing in a native's house, and asked me a great many searching questions; and finally, still with some reluctance in his manner, he invited me into the kitchen. There I found a big fire blazing merrily on the raised clay hearth in the centre of the large room, and seated near it an old grey-haired woman, a middle-aged, tall, dark-skinned dame in a purple dress—my host's wife; a pale, pretty young woman, about sixteen years old, and a little girl. When I sat down my host began once more questioning me; but he apologised for doing so, saying that my arrival on foot seemed a very extraordinary circumstance. I told them how I had lost my horse, saddle, and poncho in the wood, and then related my encounter with the bull. They listened to it all with very grave faces, but I am sure it was as good as a comedy to them. Don Sinforiano Alday, the owner of the place and my questioner, made me take off my coat to exhibit the bruises the bull's hoofs had inflicted on my arms and shoulders. He was anxious, even after that, to know something more about me, and so to satisfy him I gave him a brief account of some of my adventures in the country, down to my arrest with Marcos Marcó, and how that plausible gentleman had made his escape from the magistrate's house. That made them all laugh, and the three men I had seen arrive, and who appeared to be casual visitors, became very friendly, frequently passing me the rum bottle with which they were provided.

After sipping maté and rum for half an hour we settled down to discuss a plentiful supper of roast and boiled beef and mutton, with great basins of well-seasoned broth to wash it down. I consumed an amazing quantity of meat, as much, in fact, as any gaucho there; and to eat as much as one of these men at a sitting is a feat for an Englishman to boast about. Supper done, I lit a cigar and leant back against the wall enjoying many delightful sensations all together—warmth, rest, and hunger satisfied, and the subtle fragrance of that friend and comforter, divine tobacco. On the further side of the room my host was meanwhile talking to the other men in low tones. Occasional glances in my direction seemed to show that they still harboured some suspicion of me, or that they had some grave matters to converse about unsuitable for a stranger to hear.

At length Alday rose and addressed me. "Señor, if you are ready to rest I will now conduct you to another room, where you can have some rugs and ponchos to make a bed with."

"If my presence here is not inconvenient," I returned, "I would rather remain and smoke by the fire."

"You see, señor," he said, "I have arranged to meet

some neighbours and friends, who are coming here to discuss matters of importance with me. I am even now expecting their arrival, and the presence of a stranger would scarcely allow us to talk freely over our affairs."

"Since you wish it, I will go to any part of the house you may think proper to put me in," I returned.

I rose, not very cheerfully, I must say, from my comfortable seat before the fire, to follow him out, when the tramp of galloping horses came to our ears.

"Follow me this way—quick," exclaimed my impatient conductor; but just as I reached the door about a dozen mounted men dashed up close to us and burst forth in a perfect storm of yells. Instantly all those who were in the kitchen sprang to their feet uttering loud exclamations and looking greatly excited. Then came from the mounted men another wild outburst as they all yelled together, "*Viva el General Santa Coloma—viv—a.*"

The other three men then rushed from the kitchen, and in excited tones began to ask if anything fresh had happened. Meanwhile, I was left standing at the door by myself. The women appeared almost as excited as the men, except the girl, who had glanced at me with shy compassion in her large, dark eyes when I had been roused from my seat by the fire. Taking advantage of the general excitement, I now repaid that kindly look with one of admiration. She was a quiet, bashful girl, her pale face crowned with a profusion of black hair; and while she stood there waiting, apparently unconcerned by the hubbub outside, she looked strangely pretty, her home-made cotton gown, of limp and scanty material, clinging closely to her limbs so as to display her slender, graceful form to the best advantage. Presently, seeing me looking at her she came near, and touching my arm in passing told me in a whisper to go back to my seat by the fire. I gladly obeyed her, for my curiosity was now thoroughly aroused, and I wished to know the meaning of this outcry which had thrown these phlegmatic gauchos into such a frenzied state of excitement. It looked rather like a political row—but of General Santa Coloma I had never heard, and it seemed curious that a name so seldom mentioned should be the rallying cry of revolutionists.

In a few minutes the men all streamed back into the kitchen. Then the master of the house, Alday, his face on fire with emotion, thrust himself into the midst of the crowd.

"Boys, are you mad!" he cried. "Do you not see a stranger here? What is the meaning of all this outcry if nothing new has happened?"

A roar of laughter from the new-comers greeted this outburst, after which they raised another yell of "*Viva Santa Coloma!*"

Alday became furious. "Speak, madmen!" he shouted; "tell me, in God's name, what has happened—or do you wish to ruin everything with your imprudence?"

"Listen, Alday," replied one of the men, "and know how little we need fear the presence of a stranger. Santa Coloma, the hope of Uruguay, the saviour of his country, who will shortly deliver us out of the power of Colorado assassins and pirates—Santa Coloma has come! He is here in our midst; he has seized on El Molino del Yí, and has raised the standard of revolt against the infamous government of Montevideo! *Viva Santa Coloma!*"

Alday flung his hat off and, falling on his knees, remained for some moments in silent prayer, his hands clasped before him. The others all snatched off their hats and stood silent, grouped about him. Then he stood up, and all together joined in a *viva*, which far surpassed in its deafening power their previous performances.

My host now appeared to be almost beside himself with excitement.

"What," he cried, "my General come! Do you tell me that Santa Coloma has come? O, friends, the great God has remembered our suffering country at last! He has grown weary of looking on man's injustice, the persecutions, the bloodshed, the cruelties that have almost driven us mad. I cannot realise it! Let me go to my General that these eyes that have watched for his coming may see him and rejoice. I cannot wait for daylight—this very night must I ride to El Molino, that I may see him and touch him with my hands, and know that it is not a dream."

His words were welcomed with a shout of applause, and the other men all immediately announced their intention to accompany him to El Molino, a small town on the Yí some leagues distant.

Some of the men now went out to catch fresh horses, while Alday busied himself in bringing out a store of old broadswords and carbines from their concealment in some other part of the house. The men, talking excitedly together, occupied themselves in scouring and sharpening the rusty weapons, while the women cooked a fresh supply of meat for the last comers; and in the meantime I was permitted to remain unnoticed by the fire, smoking peacefully.

CHAPTER XIV

MAIDS OF FANCY: MAIDS OF YÏ

THE girl I have mentioned, whose name was Monica, and the child, called Anita, were the only persons there besides myself who were not carried away by the warlike enthusiasm of the moment. Monica, silent, pale, almost apathetic, was occupied serving maté to the numerous guests; while the child, when the shouting and excitement was at its height, appeared greatly terrified, and clung to Alday's wife, trembling and crying piteously. No notice was taken of the poor little thing, and at length she crept away into a corner to conceal herself behind a faggot of wood. Her hiding-place was close to my seat, and after a little coaxing I induced her to leave it and come to me. She was a most forlorn little thing, with a white, thin face and large, dark, pathetic eyes. Her mean little cotton frock only reached to her knees, and her little legs and feet were bare. Her age was seven or eight; she was an orphan, and Alday's wife, having no children of her own, was bringing her up, or rather permitting her to grow up under her roof. I drew her to me, and tried to soothe her tremors and get her to talk. Little by little she gained confidence, and began to reply to my questions; then I learnt that she was a little shepherdess, although so young, and spent most of the time every day in following the flock about on her pony. Her pony and the girl Monica, who was some relation—cousin, the child called her—were the two beings she seemed to have the greatest affection for.

"And when you slip off, how do you get on again?" I asked.

"Little pony is tame, and I never fall off," she said. "Sometimes I get off, then I climb on again."

"And what do you do all day long—talk and play?"

"I talk to my doll; I take it on the pony when I go with the sheep."

"Is your doll very pretty, Anita?"

No answer.

"Will you let me see your doll, Anita? I know I shall like your doll, because I like you."

She gave me an anxious look. Evidently doll was a very precious being and had not met with proper appreciation. After a little nervous fidgeting she left me and crept out of the room; then presently she came back, apparently trying to screen something from the vulgar gaze in her scanty little dress. It was her wonderful doll—the dear companion of her rambles and rides. With fear and trembling she allowed me to take it into my hands. It was, or consisted of, the fore-foot of a sheep, cut off at the knee; on the top of the knee part a little wooden ball wrapped in a white rag represented the head, and it was dressed in a piece of red flannel—a satyr-like doll with one hairy leg and a cloven foot. I praised its pleasing countenance, its pretty gown and dainty little boots; and all I said sounded very precious to Anita, filling her with emotions of the liveliest pleasure.

"And do you never play with the dogs and cats and little lambs?" I asked.

"Not with the dogs and cats. When I see a very little lamb asleep, I get down and go softly, softly and catch it. It tries to get away; then I put my finger in its mouth, and it sucks, and sucks; then it runs away."

"And what do you like best to eat?"

"Sugar. When uncle buys sugar, aunt gives me a lump. I make doll eat some, and bite off one small piece and put it in pony's mouth."

"Which would you rather have, Anita—a great many lumps of sugar, or a beautiful string of beads, or a little girl to play with?"

This question was rather too much for her neglected little brain, which had fed itself with such simple fare; so I was obliged to put it in various ways, and at last, when she understood that only one of the three things could be chosen, she decided in favour of a little girl to play with.

Then I asked her if she liked to hear stories; this also puzzled her, and after some cross-questioning I discovered that she had never heard a story, and did not know what it meant.

"Listen, Anita, and I will tell you a story," I said. "Have you seen the white mist over the Yí in the morning—a light white mist that flies away when the sun gets hot?"

Yes, she often saw the white mist in the morning, she told me.

"Then I will tell you a story about the white mist and a little girl named Alma.

"Little Alma lived close to the river Yí, but far, far from here, beyond the trees and beyond the blue hills, for the Yí is a very long river. She lived with her grandmother and with six uncles, all big tall men with long beards; and they always talked about wars, and cattle, and horse-racing, and a great many other important things that Alma could not understand. There was no one to talk to Alma and for Alma to talk to or to play with. And when she went out of the house where all the big people were talking, she heard the cocks crowing, the dogs barking, the birds singing, the sheep bleating, and the trees rustling their leaves over her head, and she could not understand one word of all they said. At last, having no one to play with or talk to, she sat down and began to cry. Now, it happened that near the spot where she sat there was an old black woman wearing a red shawl, who was gathering sticks for the fire, and she asked Alma why she cried.

"'Because I have no one to talk to and play with,' said Alma. Then the old black woman drew a long brass pin out of her shawl and pricked Alma's tongue with it, for she made Alma hold it out to be pricked.

"'Now,' said the old woman, 'you can go and play and talk with the dogs, cats, birds, and trees, for you will understand all they say, and they will understand all you say.'

"Alma was very glad, and ran home as fast as she could to talk to the cat.

"'Come, cat, let us talk and play together,' she said.

"'Oh no,' said the cat. 'I am very busy watching a little bird, so you must go away and play with little Niebla down by the river.'

"Then the cat ran away among the weeds and left her. The dogs also refused to play when she went to them; for they had to watch the house and bark at strangers. Then they also told her to go and play with little Niebla down by the river. Then Alma ran out and caught a little duckling, a soft little thing that looked like a ball of yellow cotton, and said—

"'Now, little duck, let us talk and play.'

"But the duckling only struggled to get away and screamed, 'Oh, mamma, mamma, come and take me away from Alma!'

"Then the old duck came rushing up, and said—

"'Alma, let my child alone: and if you want to play, go and play with Niebla down by the river. A nice thing to catch my duckie in your hands—what next, I wonder!'

"So she let the duckling go, and at last she said, 'Yes, I will go and play with Niebla down by the river.'

"She waited till she saw the white mist, and then ran all the way to the Yí, and stood still on the green bank close by the water with the white mist all round her. By-and-by she saw a beautiful little child come flying towards her in the white mist. The child came and stood on the green bank and looked at Alma. Very, very pretty she was; and she wore a white dress—whiter than milk, whiter than foam, and all embroidered with purple flowers; she had also white silk stockings and scarlet shoes, bright as scarlet verbenas. Her hair was long and fluffy, and shone like gold, and round her neck she had a string of big gold beads. Then Alma said, 'Oh, beautiful little girl, what is your name?' to which the little girl answered—

"'Niebla.'

"'Will you talk to me and play with me?' said Alma.

"'Oh no,' said Niebla, 'how can I play with a little girl dressed as you are and with bare feet?'

"For you know poor Alma only wore a little old frock that came down to her knees, and she had no shoes and stockings on. Then little Niebla rose up and floated away, away from the bank and down the river, and at last, when she was quite out of sight in the white mist, Alma began to cry. When it got very hot she went and sat down, still crying, under the trees; there were two very big willow trees growing near the river. By-and-by the leaves rustled in the wind and the trees began talking to each other, and Alma understood everything they said.

"'Is it going to rain, do you think?' said one tree.

"'Yes, I think it will—some day,' said the other.

"'There are no clouds,' said the first tree.

"'No, there are no clouds to-day, but there were some the day before yesterday,' said the other.

"'Have you got any nests in your branches?' said the first tree.

"'Yes, one,' said the other. 'It was made by a little yellow bird, and there are five speckled eggs in it.'

"Then the first tree said, 'There is little Alma sitting in our shade; do you know why she is crying, neighbour?'

"The other tree answered, 'Yes, it is because she has no one to play with. Little Niebla by the river refused to play with her because she is not beautifully dressed.'

"Then the first tree said, 'Ah, she ought to go and ask the fox for some pretty clothes to wear. The fox always keeps a great store of pretty things in her hole.'

"Alma had listened to every word of this conversation. She remembered that a fox lived on the hillside not far off; for she had often seen it sitting in the sunshine with its little ones playing round it and pulling their mother's tail in fun. So Alma got up and ran till she found the hole, and putting her head down it she cried out, 'Fox! Fox!' But the fox seemed cross and only answered without coming out, 'Go away, Alma, and talk to little Niebla. I am busy getting dinner for my children and have no time to talk to you now.'

"Then Alma cried, 'Oh, Fox, Niebla will not play with me because I have no pretty things to wear. Oh, Fox, will you give me a nice dress and shoes and stockings and a string of beads?'

"After a little while the fox came out of its hole with a big bundle done up in a red cotton handkerchief, and said, 'Here are the things, Alma, and I hope they will fit you. But you know, Alma, you really ought not to come at this time of day, for I am very busy just now cooking the dinner—an armadillo roasted and a couple of partridges stewed with rice, and a little omelette of turkeys' eggs. I mean plovers' eggs, of course; I never touch turkeys' eggs.'

"Alma said she was very sorry to give so much trouble.

"'Oh, never mind,' said the fox. 'How is your grandmother?'

"She is very well, thank you,' said Alma, 'but she has a bad headache.'

"'I am very sorry to hear it,' said the fox. 'Tell her to stick two fresh dock leaves on her temples, and to drink a little weak tea made of knot-grass, and on no account to go out in the hot sun. I should like to go and see her, only I do not like the dogs being always about the house. Give her my best respects. And now run home, Alma, and try on the things, and when you are passing this way you can bring me back the handkerchief, as I always tie my face up in it when I have the toothache.'

"Alma thanked the fox very much and ran home as fast as she could, and when the bundle was opened she found in it a beautiful white dress, embroidered with purple flowers, a pair of scarlet shoes, silk stockings, and a string of great golden beads. They all fitted her very well; and next day when the white mist was on the Yí she dressed herself in her beautiful clothes and went down to the river. By-and-by little Niebla came flying along, and when she saw Alma she came and kissed her and took her by the hand. All the morning they played and talked together, gathering flowers and running races over the green sward; and at last Niebla bade her good-bye and flew away, for all the white mist was floating off down the river. But every day after that Alma found her little companion by the Yí, and was very happy, for now she had someone to talk to and to play with."

After I had finished the story Anita continued gazing into my face with an absorbed expression in her large wistful eyes. She seemed half scared, half delighted at what she had heard; but presently, before the little thing had said a word, Monica, who had been directing shy and wondering glances towards us for some time, came, and taking her by the hand led her away to bed.

I was getting sleepy then, and as the clatter of talk and warlike preparation showed no signs of abating, I was glad to be shown into another room, where some sheep-skins, rugs, and a couple of ponchos were given to me for a bed.

During the night all the men took their departure, for in the morning, when I went into the kitchen, I only found the old woman and Alday's wife sipping bitter maté. The child, they informed me, had disappeared from the house an hour before, and Monica had gone out to look for her. Alday's wife was highly indignant at the little one's escapade, for it was high time for Anita to go out with the flock. After taking maté I went out, and looking towards the Yí veiled in a silvery mist, I spied Monica leading the culprit home by the hand, and went to meet them. Poor little Anita! her face stained with tears, her little legs and feet covered with clay and scratched by sharp reeds in fifty places, her dress soaking wet with the heavy mist, looked a most pitiful object.

"Where did you find her?" I asked the girl, beginning

to fear that I had been the indirect cause of the poor child's misfortunes.

"Down by the river looking for little Niebla. I knew she would be there when I missed her this morning."

"How did you know that?" I asked. "You did not hear the story I told her."

"I made her repeat it all to me last night," said Monica.

After that little Anita was scolded, shaken, washed and dried, then fed and finally lifted on to the back of her pony and sent to take care of the sheep. While undergoing this treatment she maintained a profound silence, her little face puckered up into an expression that boded tears. They were not for the public, however, and only after she was on the pony with the reins in her little mites of hands and her back towards us did she give way to her grief and disappointment at having failed to find the beautiful child of the mist.

I was astonished to find that she had taken the fantastic little tale invented to amuse her as truth; but the poor babe had never read books or heard stories, and the fairy tale had been too much for her starved little imagination. I remember that once on another occasion I told a pathetic story of a little child, lost in a great wilderness, to a girl about Anita's age. and just as unaccustomed to this kind of mental fare. Next morning her mother informed me that my little listener had spent half the night sobbing and begging to be allowed to go and look for that lost child I had told her about.

Hearing that Alday would not return till evening or till the following day, I asked his wife to lend or give me a horse to proceed on my journey. This, however, she could not do ; then she added, very graciously, that while all the men were away my presence in the house would be a comfort to her, a man always being a great protection. The arrangement did not strike me as one very advantageous to myself, but as I could not journey very well to Montevideo on foot, I was compelled to sit still and wait for Alday's return.

It was dull work talking to those two women in the kitchen. They were both great talkers, and had evidently come to a tacit agreement to share their one listener fairly between them, for first one, then the other would speak with a maddening monotony. Alday's wife had six favourite, fine-sounding words—*elements*, *superior*, *division*, *prolongation*, *justification*, and *disproportion*. One of these she somehow managed to drag into every sentence, and sometimes she succeeded in getting in two. Whenever this happened the achievement made her so proud that she would in the most deliberate cold-blooded way repeat the sentence again, word for word. The strength of the old woman lay in dates. Not an occurrence did she mention, whether it referred to some great public event or to some trivial domestic incident in her own rancho, without giving the year, the month, and the day. The duet between these two confounded barrel-organs, one grinding out rhetoric, the other chronology, went on all the morning, and often I turned to Monica, sitting over her sewing, in hopes of a different tune from her more melodious instrument, but in vain, for never a word dropped from those silent lips. Occasionally her dark luminous eyes were raised for a moment, only to sink abashed again when they encountered mine. After breakfast I went for a walk along the river, where I spent several hours hunting for flowers and fossils, and amusing myself as best I could. There were legions of duck, coot, rosy spoonbills, and black-necked swans disporting themselves in the water, and I was very thankful that I had no gun with me, and so was not tempted to startle them with rude noises, and send any of them away to languish wounded amongst the reeds. At length, after having indulged in a good swim, I set out to walk back to the estancia.

When still about a mile from the house as I walked on, swinging my stick and singing aloud in lightness of heart, I passed a clump of willow trees, and looking up saw Monica under them watching my approach. She was standing perfectly motionless, and when I caught sight of her cast her eyes demurely down, apparently to contemplate her bare feet, which looked very white on the deep green turf. In one hand she held a cluster of stalks of the large, crimson autumnal lilies which had just begun to blossom. My singing ceased suddenly, and I stood for some moments gazing admiringly at the shy, rustic beauty.

"What a distance you have walked to gather lilies, Monica!" I said, approaching her. "Will you give me one of your stalks?"

"They were gathered for the Virgin, so I cannot give away any of these," she replied. "If you will wait here under the trees I will find one to give you."

I agreed to wait for her; then placing the cluster she had gathered on the grass she left me. Before long she returned with a stalk, round, polished, slender, like a pipe stem, and crowned with its cluster of three splendid crimson flowers.

When I had sufficiently thanked her and admired it, I said, "What boon are you going to ask from the Virgin, Monica, when you offer her these flowers—safety for your lover in the wars?"

"No, señor; I have no offering to make, and no boon to ask. They are for my aunt; I offered to gather them for her, because—I wished to meet you here."

"To meet me, Monica—what for?"

"To ask for a story, señor," she replied, colouring, and with a shy glance at my face.

"Ah, we have had stories enough," I said. "Remember poor Anita running away this morning to look for a playmate in the wet mist."

"She is a child; I am a woman."

"Then, Monica, you must have a lover who will be jealous if you listen to stories from a stranger's lips in this lonely spot."

"No person will ever know that I met you here," she returned—so bashful, yet so persistent.

"I have forgotten all my stories," I said.

"Then, señor, I will go and find you another *ramo* of lilies while you think of one to tell me."

"No," I said, "you must get no more lilies for me. Look, I will give you back these you gave me." And saying that, I fastened them in her black hair, where by contrast they looked very splendid, and gave the girl a new grace. "Ah, Monica, they make you look too pretty—let me take them out again."

But she would not have them taken. "I will leave you now to think of a story for me," she said, blushing and turning away.

Then I took her hands and made her face me. "Listen, Monica," I said. "Do you know that these lilies are full of strange magic? See how crimson they are; that is the colour of passion, for they have been steeped in passion, and turn my heart to fire. If you bring me any more of them, Monica, I shall tell you a story that will make you tremble with fear—tremble like the willow leaves and turn pale as the mists over the Yí."

She smiled at my words; it was like a ray of sunlight falling through the foliage on her face. Then, in a voice that was almost a whisper, she said, "What will the story be about, señor? Tell me, then I shall know whether to gather lilies for you or not."

"It will be about a stranger meeting a sweet, pale girl standing under the trees, her dark eyes cast down, and red lilies in her hand; and how she asked him for a story, but he could speak to her of nothing but love, love, love."

When I finished speaking she gently withdrew her hands from mine and turned away amongst the trees, doubtless to fly from me, trembling at my words, like a frightened young fawn from the hunter.

So for a moment I thought. But no, there lay the lilies gathered for a religious purpose at my feet, and there was nothing reproachful in the shy dark eyes when they glanced back for a moment at me; for in spite of those warning words she had only gone to find more of those perilous crimson flowers to give me.

Not then, while I waited for her return with palpitating heart, but afterwards in calmer moments, and when Monica had become a pretty picture in the past, did I compose the following lines. I am not so vain as to believe that they possess any great poetical merit, and introduce them principally to let the reader know how to pronounce the pretty name of that Oriental river, which it still keeps in remembrance of a vanished race.

Standing silent, pale her face was,
  Pale and sweet to see:
'Neath the willows waiting for me,
  Willow-like was she,
Smiling, blushing, trembling, bashful
  Maid of Yí.

Willow-like she trembled, yet she
  Never fled from me;
But her dove-like eyes were downcast,
  On the grass to see
White feet standing: white thy feet were,
  Maid of Yí.

Stalks of lilies in her hands were:
  Crimson lilies three,
Placed I in her braids of black hair—
  They were bright to see!
Lift thy dark eyes, for I love thee,
  Maid of Yí!

CHAPTER XV

WHEN THE TRUMPET CALLS TO BATTLE

IN the evening Alday returned with a couple of his friends, and as soon as an opportunity offered, I took him aside and begged him to let me have a horse to continue my journey to Montevideo. He answered evasively that the horse I had lost in the neighbouring forest would probably be recovered in the course of two or three days. I replied that if he would let me have a horse, the one I had lost, together with saddle, poncho, etc., could be claimed by him whenever they turned up. He then said that he could not very well give me a horse, "with saddle and bridle also." It looked as if he wanted to keep me in his house for some purpose of his own, and this made me all the more determined to leave it immediately, in spite of the tender, reproachful glances which Monica flashed on me from under her long, drooping eyelashes. I told him that if I could not have a horse I would leave his estancia on foot. That rather put him in a corner; for in this country, where horse-stealing and cheating at cards are looked on as venial offences, to let a man leave your estancia on foot is considered a very dishonourable thing. He pondered over my declaration for some minutes, then, after conferring with his friends, he promised to provide me with all I required next day. I had heard nothing more about the revolution, but after supper Alday suddenly became very confidential, and said that the whole country would be up in arms in the course of a very few days, and that it would be highly dangerous for me to attempt travelling by myself to the capital. He expatiated on the immense prestige of General Santa Coloma, who had just taken up arms against the Colorado party then in power, and concluded by saying that my safest plan would be to join the rebels and accompany them on their march to Montevideo, which would begin almost immediately. I replied that I took no interest in the dissensions of the Banda Orientál, and did not wish to compromise myself by joining a military expedition of any kind. He shrugged his shoulders, and renewing his promise of a horse next day, retired to rest.

On rising next morning I found that the others were already up. The horses were standing saddled at the door, and Alday, pointing out a very fair-looking animal, informed me that it had been saddled for me, and then added that he and his friends would ride one or two leagues with me to put me on the right road to Montevideo. He had suddenly become almost too kind, but in the simplicity of my heart I believed that he was only making amends for the slight inhospitality of the day before.

After partaking of bitter maté I thanked my hostess, looked my last into Monica's dark, sorrowful eyes, lifted for one moment to mine, and kissed little Anita's pathetic face, by so doing filling the child with astonishment and causing considerable amusement to the other members of the family. After we had ridden about four miles, keeping nearly parallel with the river, it struck me that we were not going in the right direction—the right one for me, at any rate. I therefore checked my horse and told my companions that I would not trouble them to ride with me any farther.

"My friend," said Alday, approaching me, "you will, if you leave us now, infallibly fall into the hands of some *partida*, who, finding you without a passport, will take you to El Molino, or to some other centre. Though it would make no difference if you had a passport, for they would only tear it up and take you all the same. In these circumstances it is your safest plan to go with us to El Molino, where General Santa Coloma is collecting his forces, and you will then be able to explain your position to him."

"I refuse to go to El Molino," I said angrily, exasperated at his treachery.

"You will then compel us to take you there," he returned.

I had no wish to become a prisoner again so soon, and seeing that a bold stroke was necessary to keep my liberty, I suddenly reined up my horse and drew my revolver. "My friends," I said, "your road lies in that direction; mine in this. I wish you good morning."

I had scarcely finished speaking before a blow of a heavy whip-handle descended on my arm below the elbow, almost breaking it, and sending me off my horse, while the revolver went spinning away a dozen yards. The blow had been dealt by one of Alday's two followers who had just dropped a little to the rear, and the rascal certainly showed a marvellous quickness and dexterity in disabling me.

Wild with rage and pain, I scrambled to my feet, and drawing my knife, threatened to stab the first man who approached me; and then, in unmeasured language, I abused Alday for his cowardice and brutality. He only smiled and replied that he considered my youth, and therefore felt no resentment against me for using such intemperate words.

"And now, my friend," he continued, after picking up my revolver and remounting his horse, "let us waste no more time, but hasten on to El Molino, where you can state your case to the General."

As I did not wish to be tied on to my horse and carried in that unpleasant and ignominious manner, I had to obey. Climbing into the saddle with some difficulty, we set out towards the village of El Molino at a swinging gallop. The rough motion of the horse I rode increased the pain in my arm till it became intolerable; then one of the men mercifully bound it up in a sling, after which I was able to travel more comfortably, though still suffering a great deal.

The day was excessively warm, and we did not reach our destination till about three o'clock in the afternoon. Just before entering the town we rode through a little army of gauchos encamped on the adjacent plain. Some of them were engaged cooking meat, others were saddling horses, while others in bodies of twenty or thirty were going through cavalry exercises, the whole making a scene of wonderful animation. Very nearly all the men wore the ordinary gaucho costume, and those who were exercising carried lances, to which were attached little white fluttering bannerets. Passing through the encampment, we clattered into the town, composed of about seventy or eighty houses of stone or mud, some thatched, others with tiled roofs, and every house with a large garden attached to it. At the official building facing the plaza a guard of ten men, armed with carbines, was stationed. We dismounted and went into the building, only to hear that the General had just left the town, and was not expected back till the following day.

Alday spoke to an officer sitting at a table in the room we were shown into, addressing him as Major. He was a thin, elderly man, with calm grey eyes and a colourless face, and looked like a gentleman. After hearing a few words from Alday, he turned to me and said courteously that he was sorry to tell me I should have to remain in El Molino till the General's return, when I could give an account of myself to him.

"We do not," he said in conclusion, "wish to compel any foreigner, or any Oriental even, to join our forces; but we are naturally suspicious of strangers, having already caught two or three spies in the neighbourhood. Unfortunately you are not provided with a passport, and it is best that the General should see you."

"Sir officer," I replied, "by ill-treating and detaining an Englishman you are doing your cause no good."

He answered that he was grieved that his people had

found it necessary to treat me roughly, for he put it in that mild way. Everything, he said, short of liberating me, would be done to make my sojourn in El Molino pleasant.

"If it is necessary that the General should see me himself before I can have my liberty, pray let these men take me to him at once," I said.

"He has not yet left El Molino," said an orderly standing in the room. "He is at the end of the town at the Casa Blanca, and does not leave till half-past three."

"It is nearly that now," said the officer, consulting his watch. "Take him to the General at once, Lieutenant Alday."

I thanked the officer, who had looked and spoken so unlike a revolutionary bandit, and as soon as I had succeeded in clambering on to my horse we were once more dashing along the main street at a fast gallop. We drew up before a large old-looking stone house at the end of the town, standing some distance back from the road, and screened from it by a double row of tall Lombardy poplars. The back of the house was towards the road, and passing round to the front after leaving our horses at the gate, we entered a spacious *patio*, or yard. Running along the front of the dwelling was a wide corridor, supported by wooden pillars, painted white, while the whole of the *patio* was shaded by an immense grape-vine. This was evidently one of the best houses in the place, and coming directly from the glaring sun and the white dusty road the vine-shaded *patio* and corridor looked delightfully cool and inviting. A gay company of twelve or fifteen people were gathered under the corridor, some sipping maté, others sucking grapes; and when we came on the scene a young lady was just finishing a song she was singing. I at once singled out General Santa Coloma, sitting by the young lady with the guitar—a tall, imposing man, with somewhat irregular features, and a bronzed, weather-beaten face. He was booted and spurred, and over his uniform wore a white silk poncho with purple fringe. I judged from his countenance that he was not a stern or truculent man, as one expects a Caudillo—a leader of men—in the Banda Orientál to be: and remembering that in a few minutes he would be leaving the house, I was anxious to push forward and state my case to him. The others, however, prevented me, for the General just then happened to be engaged in a vivacious conversation with the young lady sitting by him. When I had once looked attentively at this girl I had eyes for no other face there. The type was Spanish, and I have never seen a more perfect face of the kind; a wealth of blue-black hair shading the low broad forehead, straight nose, dark luminous eyes, and crimson pouting lips. She was tall, perfect in her figure as in her face, and wore a white dress with a deep red China rose on her bosom for only ornament. Standing there unnoticed at the end of the corridor I gazed with a kind of fascination on her, listening to her light rippling laughter and lively talk, watching her graceful gestures, her sparkling eyes and damask cheeks flushed with excitement. Here is a woman, I thought with a sigh—I felt a slight twinge at that disloyal sigh—I could have worshipped. She was pressing the guitar on the General.

"You have promised to sing one song before you go, and I cannot let you off," she exclaimed.

At length he took the instrument, protesting that his voice was a very bad one; then, sweeping the strings, began that fine old Spanish song of love and war—

Cuando suena la trompa guerrera.

His voice was uncultivated and somewhat harsh, but there was a good deal of fire and expression in the performance, and it was rapturously applauded.

The moment the song was over he handed her back the guitar, and starting up hastily, bade the company adieu. and turned to go.

Coming forward, I placed myself before him and began to speak.

"I am pressed for time and cannot listen to you now," he said quickly, scarcely glancing at me. "You are a prisoner—wounded, I see; well, when I return——" Suddenly he stopped, caught hold of my wounded arm, and said, "How did you get hurt? Tell me quickly."

His sharp impatient manner, and the sight of twenty people all standing round staring at me, quite upset me, and I could only stammer out a few unintelligible words, feeling that my face was blushing scarlet to the very roots of my hair.

"Let me tell you, General," said Alday, advancing.

"No, no," said the General; "he shall speak."

The sight of Alday so eager to give his version of the

affair first restored my anger to me, and with that came back the power of speech and the other faculties which I had lost for a moment.

"Sir General, all I have to say is this," I said; "I came to this man's house at night, a stranger, lost, on foot, for my horse had been stolen from me. I asked him for shelter in the belief that at least the one virtue of hospitality still survives in this country. He, assisted by these two men, treacherously disabled me with a blow on my arm and dragged me here a prisoner."

"My good friend," said the General, "I am extremely sorry that you have been hurt through an excess of zeal on the part of one of my people. But I can scarcely regret this incident, painful as it seems, since it enables me to assure you that one other virtue besides hospitality still survives in the Banda Orientál—I mean gratitude."

"I do not understand you," I said.

"We were companions in misfortune a very short time ago," he returned. "Have you forgotten the service you did me then?"

I stared at him, astonished at his words; and while I looked into his face suddenly that scene at the magistrate's estancia, when I went with the key to let my fellow-traveller out of the stocks, and he jumped up and seized my hand, flashed on me. Still I was not quite sure, and half whispered tentatively, "What, Marcos Marcó?"

"Yes," he returned, smiling, "that was my name at that moment. My friends," he continued, resting a hand on my shoulder, and speaking to the others, "I have met this young Englishman before. A few days ago, when

I was on my way hither, I was arrested at Las Cuevas in his company; it was by means of his assistance that I succeeded in making my escape. He did this good deed, believing at the time that he was helping a poor peasant, and not expecting any return."

I might have reminded him that only after he had given me a solemn assurance that he did not intend attempting to make his escape, did I consent to get his legs out of the stocks. However, as he thought proper to forget that part of the affair I was not going to recall it to him.

There were many surprised exclamations from the bystanders, and glancing at that beautiful girl, who was standing near with the others, I found her dark eyes fixed on my face with an expression of tenderness and sympathy in them that sent the blood rushing to my heart.

"They have hurt you badly, I fear," said the General, addressing me again. "To continue your journey now would be imprudent. Let me beg of you to remain where you are, in this house, till your arm is better." Then, turning to the young lady, he said, "Dolores, will you and your mother take charge of my young friend till I return, and see that his injured arm is attended to?"

"My General, you will make us happy by leaving him in our care," she replied, with a bright smile.

He then introduced me as Don Ricardo simply, for he did not know my surname, to the lovely señorita—Dolores Zelaya; after which he again bade us adieu and hurried away.

When he had gone Alday advanced, hat in hand, and

gave me back my revolver, which I had forgotten all about. I took it with my left hand, and put it in my pocket. He then apologised for having treated me roughly—the Major had taught him that word—but without the faintest trace of servility in his speech or manner; and after that he offered me his hand.

"Which will you have," I said, "the hand you have injured or the left hand?"

He immediately dropped his own hand to his side, then bowing, said he would wait till I had recovered the use of my right hand. Turning to go, he added with a smile that he hoped the injury would soon heal, so that I would be able to wield a sword in my friend Santa Coloma's cause.

His manner, I thought, was a little too independent. "Pray take back your horse now," I said, "as I have no further use for it, and accept my thanks for conducting me thus far on my journey."

"Do not mention it," he replied, with a dignified wave of his hand, "I am pleased to have been able to render you this small service."

CHAPTER XVI

ROMANCE OF THE WHITE FLOWER

WHEN Alday had left us, the charming señorita, in whose care I was well pleased to find myself, led me into a cool spacious room, dimly lighted, scantily furnished, and with a floor of red tiles. It was a great relief to drop into a sofa there, for I now felt fatigued and suffered great pain from my arm. In a few moments I had the señorita, her mother, Doña Mercedes, and an old serving-woman all round me. Gently drawing off my coat, they subjected my wounded arm to a minute examination; their compassionate finger-tips—those of the lovely Dolores especially—feeling like a soft cooling rain on the swollen inflamed part, which had become quite purple.

"Ah, how barbarous of them to hurt you like that! a friend, too, of our General!" exclaimed my beautiful nurse; which made me think that I had involuntarily become associated with the right political party in the state.

They rubbed the arm with sweet oil; while the old servant brought in a bundle of rue from the garden, which being bruised in a mortar, filled the room with a fresh aromatic smell. With this fragrant herb she made a cooling cataplasm. Having dressed my arm they placed it in a sling, then in place of my coat a light Indian poncho was brought for me to wear.

"I think you are feverish," said Doña Mercedes, feeling my pulse. "We must send for the doctor—we have a doctor in our little town, a very skilful man."

"I have little faith in doctors, señora," I said, "but great faith in women and grapes. If you will give me a cluster from your vine to refresh my blood I promise to be well very soon."

Dolores laughed lightly and left the room, only to return in a few minutes with a dish full of ripe purple clusters. They were delicious and did seem to allay the fever I felt, which had probably been caused as much by angry passions as by the blow I had received.

While I reclined luxuriously, sucking my grapes, the two ladies sat on each side of me, ostensibly fanning themselves, but only, I think, trying to make the air cooler for me. Very cool and pleasant they made it, certainly, but the gentle attentions of Dolores were at the same time such as might well create a subtler kind of fever in a man's veins—a malady not to be cured by fruit, fans, or phlebotomy.

"Who would not suffer blows for such compensation as this!" I said.

"Do not say such a thing!" exclaimed the señorita, with wonderful animation. "Have you not rendered a great service to our dear General—to our beloved country! If we had it in our power to give you everything your heart might desire it would be nothing, nothing. We must be your debtors for ever."

I smiled at her extravagant words, but they were very sweet to hear, none the less.

"Your ardent love of your country is a beautiful sentiment," I remarked somewhat indiscreetly, "but is General Santa Coloma so necessary to its welfare?"

She looked offended and did not reply. "You are a stranger in our country, señor, and do not quite understand these things," said the mother gently. "Dolores must not forget that. You know nothing of the cruel wars we have seen and how our enemies have conquered only by bringing in the foreigner to their aid. Ah, señor, the bloodshed, the proscriptions, the infamies which they have brought on this land! But there is one man they have never yet succeeded in crushing: always from boyhood he has been foremost in the fight, defying their bullets, and not to be corrupted by their Brazilian gold. Is it strange that he is so much to us, who have lost all our relations, and have suffered many persecutions, being deprived almost of the means of subsistence that hirelings and traitors might be enriched with our property? To us in this house he is even more than to others. He was my husband's friend and companion in arms. He has done us a thousand favours, and if he ever succeeds in overthrowing this infamous government he will restore to us all the property we have lost. But *ai de mi*, I cannot see deliverance yet."

"Mamita, do not say such a thing!" exclaimed her daughter. "Do you begin to despair now when there is most reason to hope?"

"Child, what can he do with this handful of ill-armed

men?" returned the mother sadly. "He has bravely raised the standard, but the people do not flock to it. Ah, when this revolt is crushed, like so many others, we poor women will only have to lament for more friends slain and fresh persecutions." And here she covered her eyes with her handkerchief.

Dolores tossed her head back and made a sudden gesture of impatience.

"Do you then expect to see a great army formed before the ink is dry on the General's proclamation? When Santa Coloma was a fugitive without a follower you hoped; now when he is with us, and actually preparing for a march on the capital, you begin to lose heart —I cannot understand it!"

Doña Mercedes rose without replying, and left the room. The lovely enthusiast dropped her head on her hand, and remained silent, taking no notice of me, a cloud of sorrow on her countenance.

"Señorita," I said, "it is not necessary for you to remain longer here. Only tell me before going that you forgive me, for it makes me very unhappy to think that I have offended you."

She turned to me with a very bright smile and gave me her hand.

"Ah, it is for you to forgive me for hastily taking offence at a light word," she said. "I must not allow anything you say in future to spoil my gratitude. Do you know I think you are one of those who like to laugh at most things, señor—no, let me call you Richard, and you shall call me Dolores, for we must remain friends always. Let us make a compact, then it will be impossible for us to quarrel. You shall be free to doubt, question, laugh at everything, except one thing only—my faith in Santa Coloma."

"Yes, I will gladly make that agreement," I replied. "It will be a new kind of paradise, and of the fruit of every tree I may eat except of this tree only."

She laughed gaily.

"I will now leave you," she said. "You are suffering pain, and are very tired. Perhaps you will be able to sleep." While speaking she brought a second cushion for my head, then left me, and before long I fell into a refreshing doze.

I spent three days of enforced idleness at the Casa Blanca, as the house was called, before Santa Coloma returned, and after the rough experience I had undergone, during which I had subsisted on a flesh diet untempered by bread or vegetables, they were indeed like days spent in paradise to me. Then the General came back. I was sitting alone in the garden when he arrived and coming out to me he greeted me warmly.

"I greatly feared from my previous experience of your impatience under restraint that you might have left us," he said kindly.

"I could not do that very well yet without a horse to ride on," I returned.

"Well, I came here just now to say I wish to present you with a horse and saddle. The horse is standing at the gate now, I believe; but if you are only waiting for a horse to leave us I shall have to regret making you this present. Do not be in a hurry; you have yet many years to live in which to accomplish all you wish to do, and let us have the pleasure of your company a few days longer. Doña Mercedes and her daughter desire nothing better than to keep you with them."

I promised him not to run away immediately, a promise which was not hard to make; then we went to inspect my horse, which proved to be a very fine bay, saddled with a dashing native *recado*.

"Come with me and try him," he said. "I am going to ride out to the Cerro Solo."

The ride proved an extremely pleasant one, as I had not mounted a horse for some days, and had been longing to spice my idle hours with a little exhilarating motion. We went at a swinging gallop over the grassy plain, the General all the time discoursing freely of his plans and of the brilliant prospects awaiting all those timely wise individuals who should elect to link their fortunes with his at this early stage of the campaign.

The Cerro, three leagues distant from the village of El Molino, was a high conical hill standing quite alone and overlooking the country for a vast distance around. A few well-mounted men were stationed on the summit, keeping watch; and after talking with them for a while the General led me to a spot a hundred yards away, where there was a large mound of sand and stone, up which we made our horses climb with some difficulty. While we stood here he pointed out the conspicuous objects on the surface of the surrounding country, telling me the names of the estancias, rivers, distant hills, and other things. The whole country about us seemed very familiar to him. He ceased speaking at length, but continued gazing over the wide sunlit prospect with a strange far-off look on his face. Suddenly dropping the reins on the neck of his horse, he stretched out his arms towards the south and began to murmur words which I could not catch, while an expression of mingled fury and exultation transformed his face. It passed away as suddenly as it came. Then he dismounted, and stooping till his knee touched the ground he kissed the rock before him, after which he sat down and quietly invited me to do the same. Returning to the subject he had talked about during our ride, he began openly pressing me to join him in his march to Montevideo, which, he said, would begin almost immediately, and would infallibly result in a victory, after which he would reward me for the incalculable service I had rendered him in assisting him to escape from the Juez of Las Cuevas. These tempting offers, which would have fired my brain in other circumstances—the single state, I mean—I felt compelled to decline, though I did not state my real reasons for doing so. He shrugged his shoulders in the eloquent Oriental fashion, remarking that it would not surprise him if I altered my resolution in a few days.

"Never!" I mentally ejaculated.

Then he recalled our first meeting again, spoke of Margarita, that marvellously beautiful child, asking if I had not thought it strange so fair a flower as that should have sprung from the homely stalk of a sweet potato? I answered that I had been surprised at first, but had ceased to believe that she was a child of Batata's, or of any of his kin. He then offered to tell me Margarita's history; and I was not surprised to hear that he knew it.

"I owe you this," he said, "in expiation of the somewhat offensive remarks I addressed to you that day in reference to the girl. But you must remember that I was then only Marcos Marcó, a peasant, and having some slight knowledge of acting it was only natural that my speech should be, as you find it in our common people, somewhat dry and ironical.

"Many years ago there lived in this country one Basilio de la Barca, a person of so noble a figure and countenance that to all those who beheld him he became the type of perfect beauty, so that a 'Basilio de la Barca' came to be a proverbial expression in Montevidean society when anyone surpassingly handsome was spoken of. Though he had a gay, light-hearted disposition and loved social pleasures, he was not spoilt by the admiration his beauty excited. Simple-minded and modest he remained always; though perhaps not capable of any very strong passion, for though he won, without seeking it, the hearts of many fair women, he did not marry. He might have married some rich woman to improve his position had he been so minded, but in this, as in everything else in his life, Basilio appeared to be incapable of doing anything to advance his own fortunes. The de la Barcas had once possessed great wealth in land in the country, and, I have heard, descended from an ancient noble family of Spain During the long, disastrous wars this country has suffered, when it was conquered in turn by England, Portugal,

Spain, Brazil, and the Argentines, the family became impoverished and at last appeared to be dying out. The last of the de la Barcas was Basilio, and the evil destiny which had pursued all of that name for so many generations did not spare him. His whole life was a series of calamities. When young he entered the army, but in his first engagement he received a terrible wound which disabled him for life and compelled him to abandon the military career. After that he embarked all his little fortune in commerce and was ruined by a dishonest partner. At length when he had been reduced to great poverty, being then about forty years old, he married an old woman out of gratitude for the kindness she had shown to him; and with her he went to live on the sea-coast, several leagues east of Cabo Santa Maria. Here in a small rancho in a lonely spot called Barranca del Peregrino, and with only a few sheep and cows to subsist on, he spent the remainder of his life. His wife, though old, bore him one child, a daughter, named Transita. They taught her nothing; for in all respects they lived like peasants and had forgotten the use of books. The situation was also wild and solitary, and they very seldom saw a strange face. Transita spent her childhood in rambling over the dunes on that lonely coast, with only wild flowers, birds, and the ocean waves for playmates. One day, her age being then about eleven, she was at her usual pastimes, her golden hair blowing in the wind, her short dress and bare legs wet with the spray, chasing the waves as they retired, or flying with merry shouts from them as they hurried back towards the shore, flinging a cloud of foam over her retreating form, when a youth, a boy of fifteen, rode up and saw her there. He was hunting ostriches, when, losing sight of his companions, and finding himself near the ocean, he rode down to the shore to watch the tide coming in.

"Yes, I was that boy, Richard—you are quick in making conclusions." This he said not in reply to any remark I had made, but to my thoughts, which he frequently guessed very aptly.

"The impression this exquisite child made on me it would be impossible to convey in words. I had lived much in the capital, had been educated in our best college, and was accustomed to associate with pretty women. I had also crossed the water and had seen all that was most worthy of admiration in the Argentine cities. And remember, that with us a youth of fifteen already knows something of life. This child, playing with the waves, was like nothing I had seen before. I regarded her not as a mere human creature; she seemed more like some being from I know not what far-off celestial region who had strayed to earth, just as a bird of white and azure plumage and unknown to our woods, sometimes appears, blown hither from a distant tropical country or island, filling those who see it with wonder and delight. Imagine, if you can, Margarita with her shining hair loose to the winds, swift and graceful in her motions as the waves she plays with, her sapphire eyes sparkling like sunlight on the waters, the tender tints of the sea-shell in her ever-changing countenance, with a laughter that seems to echo the wild melody of the sandpiper's note.

Margarita has inherited the form, not the spirit, of the child Transita. She is an exquisite statue endowed with life. Transita, with lines equally graceful and colours just as perfect, had caught the spirit of the wind and sunshine and was all freedom, motion, fire—a being half human, half angelic. I saw her only to love her; nor was it a common passion she inspired in me. I worshipped her, and longed to wear her on my bosom; but I shrank then and for a long time after from breathing the hot breath of love on so tender and heavenly a blossom. I went to her parents and opened my heart to them. My family being well known to Basilio, I obtained his consent to visit their lonely rancho whenever I could; and I, on my part, promised not to speak of love to Transita till her sixteenth year. Three years after I had found Transita, I was ordered to a distant part of the country, for I was already in the army then, and fearing that it would not be possible for me to visit them for a long time, I persuaded Basilio to let me speak to his daughter, who was now fourteen. She had by this time grown extremely fond of me, and she always looked forward with delight to my visits, when we would spend days together rambling along the shore, or seated on some cliff overlooking the sea, talking of the simple things she knew, and of that wonderful, far-away city life of which she was never tired of hearing. When I opened my heart to her she was at first frightened at these new strange emotions I spoke of. Soon, however, I was made happy by seeing her fear grow less. In one day she ceased to be a child; the rich blood mantled her cheeks to leave her the next moment pale and tremulous; her tender lips were toying with the rim of the honeyed cup. Before I left her she had promised me her hand, and at parting even clung to me, with her beautiful eyes wet with tears.

"Three years passed before I returned to seek her. During that time I sent scores of letters to Basilio, but received no reply. Twice I was wounded in fight, once very seriously. I was also a prisoner for several months. I made my escape at last, and returning to Montevideo obtained leave of absence. Then, with heart afire with sweet anticipations, I sought that lonely sea-coast once more, only to find the weeds growing on the spot where Basilio's rancho had stood. In the neighbourhood I learnt that he had died two years before, and that after his death the widow had returned to Montevideo with Transita. After long inquiry in that city I discovered that she had not long survived her husband, and that a foreign señora had taken Transita away, no one knew whither. Her loss cast a great shadow on my life. Poignant grief cannot endure for ever, nor for very long; only the memory of grief endures. To this memory, which cannot fade, it is perhaps due that in one respect at least I am not like other men. I feel that I am incapable of passion for any woman. No, not if a new Lucrezia Borgia were to come my way, scattering the fiery seeds of adoration upon all men, could they blossom to love in this arid heart. Since I lost Transita I have had one thought, one love, one religion, and it is all told in one word—*Patria*.

"Years passed. I was captain in General Oribe's army at the siege of my own city. One day a lad was captured in our lines, and came very near being put to death as a spy. He had come out from Montevideo, and was looking for me. He had been sent, he said, by Transita de la Barca, who was lying ill in the town, and desired to speak to me before she died. I asked and obtained permission from our General, who had a strong personal friendship for me, to penetrate into the town. This was, of course, dangerous, and more so for me, perhaps, than it would have been for many of my brother officers, for I was very well known to the besieged. I succeeded, however, by persuading the officers of a French sloop of war stationed in the harbour to assist me. These foreigners at that time had friendly relations with the officers of both armies, and three of them had at one time visited our General to ask him to let them hunt ostriches in the interior. He passed them on to me, and taking them to my own estancia, I entertained them and hunted with them for several days. For this hospitality they had expressed themselves very grateful, inviting me repeatedly to visit them on board, and also saying that they would gladly do me any personal service in the town, which they visited constantly. I love not the French, believing them to be the most vain and egotistical, consequently the least chivalrous, of mankind; but these officers were in my debt, and I resolved to ask them to help me. Under cover of night I went on board their ship; I told them my story, and asked them to take me on shore with them disguised as one of themselves. With some difficulty they consented, and I was thus enabled next day to be in Montevideo and with my long-lost Transita. I found her lying on her bed, emaciated and white as death, in the last stage of some fatal pulmonary complaint. On the bed with her was a child between two and three years old, exceedingly beautiful like her mother, for one glance was sufficient to tell me it was Transita's child. Overcome with grief at finding her in this pitiful condition, I could only kneel at her side pouring out the last tender tears that have fallen from these eyes. We Orientals are not tearless men, and I have wept since then, but only with rage and hatred. My last tears of tenderness were shed over unhappy, dying Transita.

"Briefly she told me her story. No letter from me had ever reached Basilio; it was supposed that I had fallen in battle, or that my heart had changed. When her mother lay dying in Montevideo she was visited by a wealthy Argentine lady named Romero, who had heard of Transita's singular beauty, and wished to see her merely out of curiosity. She was so charmed with the girl that she offered to take her and bring her up as her own daughter. To this the mother, who was reduced to the greatest poverty and was dying, consented gladly. Transita was in this way taken to Buenos Ayres, where she had masters to instruct her, and lived in great splendour. The novelty of this life charmed her for a time; the pleasures of a large city, and the universal admiration her beauty excited, occupied her mind and made her happy. When she was seventeen the Señora Romero bestowed her hand on a young man of that city, named Andrada, a wealthy person. He was a fashionable man, a gambler, and a Sybarite, and having conceived a violent passion for the girl, he succeeded in winning over the señora to aid his suit. Before marrying him Transita told him frankly that she felt incapable of great affection for him; he cared nothing for that, he only wished, like the animal he was, to possess her for her beauty. Shortly after marrying her he took her to Europe, knowing very well that a man with a full purse, and whose spirit is a compound of swine and goat, finds life pleasanter in Paris than in the Plata. In Paris Transita lived a gay, but an unhappy life. Her husband's passion for her soon passed away, and was succeeded by neglect and insult. After three miserable years he abandoned her altogether to live with another woman, and then, in broken health, she returned with her child to her own country. When she had been several months in Montevideo she heard casually that I was still alive and in the besieging army; and anxious to impart her last wishes to a friend, had sent for me.

"Could you, my friend, could any man, divine the nature of that dying request Transita wished to make?

"Pointing to her child, she said, 'Do you not see that Margarita inherits that fatal gift of beauty which won for me a life of splendour, with extreme bitterness of heart and early death? Soon, before I die, perhaps, there will not be wanting some new Señora Romero to take charge of her, who will at last sell her to some rich, cruel man, as I was sold; for how can her beauty remain long concealed? It was with very different views for her that

I secretly left Paris and returned here. During all the miserable years I spent there I thought more and more of my childhood on that lonely coast, until, when I fell ill, I resolved to go back there to spend my last days on that beloved spot where I had been so happy. It was my intention to find some peasant family there who would be willing to take Margarita and bring her up as a peasant's child, with no knowledge of her father's position and of the life men live in towns. The siege and my failing health made it impossible for me to carry out that plan. I must die here, dear friend, and never see that lonely coast where we have sat together so often watching the waves. But I think only of poor little Margarita now, who will soon be motherless: will you not help me to save her? Promise me that you will take her away to some distant place, where she will be brought up as a peasant's child, and where her father will never find her. If you can promise me this, I will resign her to you now, and face death without even the sad consolation of seeing her by me to the last.'

"I promised to carry out her wishes, and also to see the child as often as circumstances would allow, and when she grew up to find her a good husband. But I would not deprive her of the child then. I told her that if she died, Margarita would be conveyed to the French ship in the harbour, and afterwards to me, and that I knew where to place her with good-hearted, simple peasants who loved me, and would obey my wishes in all things.

"She was satisfied, and I left her to make the necessary arrangements to carry out my plans. A few weeks later

Transita expired, and the child was brought to me. I then sent her to Batata's house, where, ignorant of the secret of her birth, she has been brought up as her mother wished her to be. May she never, like the unhappy Transita, fall into the power of a ravening beast in man's shape."

"Amen!" I exclaimed. "But surely, if this child will be entitled to a fortune some day, it will only be right that she should have it."

"We do not worship gold in this country," he replied. "With us the poor are just as happy as the rich, their wants are so few, and easily satisfied. It would be too much to say that I love the child more than I love anyone else; I think only of Transita's wishes; that for me is the only right in the matter. Had I failed to carry them out to the letter, then I should have suffered a great remorse. Possibly I may encounter Andrada some day, and pass my sword through his body; that would give me no remorse."

After some moments of silence he looked up and said, "Richard, you admired and loved that beautiful girl when you first saw her. Listen, if you wish it you shall have her for a wife. She is simple-minded, ignorant of the world, affectionate, and where she is told to love she will love. Batata's people will obey my wishes in everything."

I shook my head, smiling somewhat sorrowfully when I thought that the events of the last few days had already half obliterated Margarita's fair image from my mind. This unexpected proposition had, moreover, forced on me, with a startling suddenness, the fact that by once performing the act of marriage a man has for ever used up the most glorious privilege of his sex—of course, I mean in countries where he is only allowed to have one wife. It was no longer in my power to say to any woman, however charming I might find her, "Be my wife." But I did not explain all this to the General.

"Ah, you are thinking of conditions," said he; "there will be none."

"No, you have guessed wrong—for once," I returned. "The girl is all you say; I have never seen a being more beautiful, and I have never heard a more romantic story than the one you have just told me about her birth. I can only echo your prayer that she may not suffer as her mother did. In name she is not a de la Barca, and perhaps destiny will spare her on that account."

He glanced keenly at me and smiled. "Perhaps you are thinking more of Dolores than of Margarita just now," he said. "Let me warn you of your danger there, my young friend. She is already promised to another."

Absurdly unreasonable as it may seem, I felt a jealous pang at that information; but then, of course, we are *not* reasonable beings, whatever the philosophers say.

I laughed, not very gaily, I must confess, and answered that there was no need to warn me, as Dolores would never be more to me than a very dear friend.

Even then I did not tell him that I was a married man; for often in the Banda Orientál I did not quite seem to know how to mix my truth and lies, and so preferred to hold my tongue. In this instance, as subsequent events proved, I held it not wisely but too well. The open man, with no secrets from the world, often enough escapes disasters which overtake your very discreet person, who acts on the old adage that speech was given to us to conceal our thoughts

CHAPTER XVII

PASSION VERSUS PATRIOTISM

WITH a horse to travel on, and my arm so much better that the sling supporting it was worn rather for ornament than use, there was nothing except that promise not to run away immediately to detain me longer in the pleasant retreat of the Casa Blanca; nothing, that is, had I been a man of gutta-percha or cast-iron; being only a creature of clay—very impressionable clay as it happened—I could not persuade myself that I was quite well enough to start on that long ride over a disturbed country. Besides, my absence from Montevideo had already lasted so long that a few days more could not make much difference one way or the other; thus it came to pass that I still stayed on enjoying the society of my new friends, while every day, every hour in fact, I felt less able to endure the thought of tearing myself away from Dolores.

Much of my time was spent in the pleasant orchard adjoining the house. Here, growing in picturesque irregularity, were fifty or sixty old peach, nectarine, apricot, plum, and cherry trees, their boles double the thickness of a man's thigh; they had never been disfigured by the pruner's knife or saw, and their enormous size and rough bark overgrown with grey lichen gave them an appearance of great antiquity. All about the ground, tangled together in a pretty confusion, flourished many of those dear familiar Old World garden flowers that spring up round the white man's dwelling in all temperate regions of the earth. Here were immemorial wallflowers, stocks and marigolds, tall hollyhock, gay poppy, brilliant bachelor's button; also, half hid amongst the grass, pansy and forget-me-not. The larkspur, red, white, and blue, flaunted everywhere; and here, too, was the unforgotten sweet-william, looking bright and velvety as of yore, yet, in spite of its brightness and stiff, green collar, still wearing the old shame-faced expression, as if it felt a little ashamed of its own pretty name. These flowers were not cultivated, but grew spontaneously from the seed they shed year by year on the ground, the gardener doing nothing for them beyond keeping the weeds down and bestowing a little water in hot weather. The solstitial heats being now over, during which European garden flowers cease to bloom for a season, they were again in gayest livery to welcome the long second spring of autumn, lasting from February to May. At the further end of this wilderness of flowers and fruit trees was an aloe hedge, covering a width of twenty to thirty yards with its enormous, disorderly, stave-like leaves. This hedge was like a strip of wild nature placed alongside of a plot of man's improved nature; and here, like snakes hunted from the open, the weeds and wildings which were not permitted to mix with the flowers had taken refuge. Protected by that rude bastion of spikes, the hemlock opened feathery clusters of dark leaves and whitish umbels wherever it could reach up to the sunshine. There also grew the nightshade, with other solanaceous weeds, bearing little clusters of green and purple berries, wild oats, fox-tail grass, and nettles. The hedge gave them shelter, but no moisture, so that all these weeds and grasses had a somewhat forlorn and starved appearance, climbing up with long stringy stems among the powerful aloes. The hedge was also rich in animal life. There dwelt mice, cavies, and elusive little lizards; crickets sang all day long under it, while in every open space the green epeiras spread their geometric webs. Being rich in spiders it was a favourite hunting-ground of those insect desperadoes, the mason-wasps, that flew about loudly buzzing in their splendid gold and scarlet uniform. There were also many little shy birds here, and my favourite was the wren, for in its appearance and its scolding, jerky, gesticulating ways it is precisely like our house-wren, though it has a richer and more powerful song than the English bird. On the other side of the hedge was the *potrero*, or paddock, where a milch-cow with two or three horses were kept. The man-servant, whose name was Nepomucino, presided over orchard and paddock, also to some extent over the entire establishment. Nepomucino was a pure negro, a little old round-headed, blear-eyed man, about five feet four in height, the short, lumpy wool on his head quite grey; slow in speech and movements, his old black or chocolate-coloured fingers all crooked, stiff-jointed, and pointing spontaneously in different directions. I have never seen anything in the human subject to equal the dignity of Nepomucino, the profound gravity of his bearing and expression forcibly reminding one of an owl. Apparently he had come to look upon himself as the sole head and master of the establishment, and the sense of responsibility had more than steadied him. The negrine propensity to frequent explosions of inconsequent laughter was not, of course, to be expected in such a sober-minded person; but he was, I think, a little too sedate for a black, for although his face would shine on warm days like polished ebony, it did not smile. Everyone in the house conspired to keep up the fiction of Nepomucino's importance; they had, in fact, conspired so long and so well, that it had very nearly ceased to be a fiction. Everybody addressed him with grave respect. Not a syllable of his long name was ever omitted—what the consequences of calling him Nepo, or Cino, or Cinito, the affectionate diminutive, would have been I am unable to say, since I never had the courage to try the experiment. It often amused me to hear Doña Mercedes calling to him from the house, and throwing the whole emphasis on the last syllable in a long, piercing crescendo—"Ne—po—mu—ci—no—o." Sometimes, when I sat in the orchard, he would come, and placing himself before me, discourse gravely about things in general, clipping his words and substituting r for l in the negro fashion, which made it hard for me to repress a smile. After winding up with a few appropriate moral reflections he would finish with the remark—"For though I am black on the surface, señor, my heart is white"; and then he would impressively lay one of his old crooked fingers on the part where the physiological curiosity was supposed to be. He did not like being told to perform menial offices, preferring to anticipate all requests of that kind and do whatever was necessary by stealth. Sometimes I would forget this peculiarity of the old black, and tell him that I wanted him to polish my boots. He would ignore the request altogether, and talk for a few minutes of political matters, or on the uncertainty of all things mundane, and by-and-by, glancing at my boots, would remark incidentally that they required polishing, offering somewhat ostentatiously to have them done for me. Nothing would make him admit that he did these things himself. Once I tried to amuse Dolores by mimicking his speech to her, but she quickly silenced me, saying that she loved Nepomucino too well to allow even her best friend to laugh at him. He had been born when blacks were slaves in the service of her family, had carried her in his arms when she was an infant, and had seen all the male members of the house of Zelaya swept away in the wars of Reds and Whites; but in the days of their adversity his faithful dog-like affection had never failed them. It was beautiful to see her manner towards him. If she wanted a rose for her hair or dress she would not pluck it herself or allow me to get it for her, but Nepomucino must be asked to get it. Then every day she would find time to sit down in the garden by his side to tell him all the news of the village and of the country at large, discuss the position of affairs with him, and ask his advice about everything in the house.

In doors or out I generally had Dolores for a companion, and I could certainly not have had a more charming one. The civil war—though the little splutter on the Yí scarcely deserved that name yet—was her unfailing theme. She was never weary of singing her hero Santa Coloma's praises—his dauntless courage and patience in defeat; his strange romantic adventures; the innumerable disguises and stratagems he had resorted to when going about in his own country, where a price was set on his head; ever labouring to infuse fresh valour into his beaten, disheartened followers. That the governing party had any right to be in power, or possessed any virtue of any kind, or were, in fact, anything but an incubus and a curse to the Banda Orientál, she would not for one moment admit. To her mind her country always appeared like Andromeda bound on her rock and left weeping and desolate to be a prey to the abhorred Colorado monster; while ever to the deliverance of this lovely being came her glorious Perseus, swift as the winds of heaven, the lightnings of terrible vengeance flashing from his eyes, the might of the immortals in his strong right arm. Often she tried to persuade me to join this romantic adventurer, and it was hard, very hard, to resist her eloquent appeals, and perhaps it grew harder every day as the influence of her passionate beauty strengthened itself upon my heart. Invariably I took refuge in the argument that I was a foreigner, that I loved my country with an ardour equal to hers, and that by taking arms in the Banda Orientál I should at once divest myself of all an Englishman's rights and privileges. She scarcely had patience to listen to this argument, it seemed so trivial to her, and when she demanded other better reasons I had none to offer. I dared not quote to her the words of sulky Achilles—

> The distant Trojans never injured me,

for that argument would have sounded even weaker to her than the former one. She had never read Homer in any language, of course, but she would have quickly made me tell her about Achilles, and when the end came with miserable Hector dragged thrice round the walls of besieged Troy—Montevideo was called Modern Troy, she knew—then she would have turned my argument against me and bidden me go and serve the Uruguayan President as Achilles served Hector. Seeing me silent she would turn indignantly away; only for a moment, however; the bright smile would quickly return and she would exclaim, "No, no, Richard, I shall not forget my promise, though I sometimes think you try to make me do so."

It was noon: the house was quiet, for Doña Mercedes had retired after breakfast to take her unfailing siesta, leaving us to our conversation. In that spacious, cool room where I had first reposed in the house, I was lying on the sofa smoking a cigarette. Dolores, seating herself near me with her guitar, said, "Now let me play and sing you to sleep with something very soft." But the more she played and sang the further was I from unneeded slumber.

"What, not sleeping yet, Richard!" she would say with a little laugh after each song.

"Not yet, Dolores," I would reply, pretending to get drowsy. "But my eyes are getting heavy now. One more song will send me to the region of dreams. Sing me that sweet favourite—

Desde aquel doloroso momento.

At length, finding that my sleepiness was all pretence, she refused to sing any more, and presently we drifted once more into the old subject.

"Ah yes," she replied to that argument about my nationality, which was my only shield, "I have always been taught to believe foreigners a cold, practical, calculating kind of people—so different from us. You never seemed to me like a foreigner; ah, Richard, why will you make me remember that you are not one of us! Tell me, dear friend, if a beautiful woman cried out to you to deliver her from some great misfortune or danger, would you stop to ask her nationality before going to her rescue?"

"No, Dolores; you know that if you, for instance, were in distress or danger I would fly to your side and risk my life to save you."

"I believe you, Richard. But tell me, is it less noble to help a suffering people cruelly oppressed by wicked men who have succeeded by crimes and treachery and foreign aid in climbing into power? Will you tell me that no Englishman has drawn a sword in a cause like that? Oh, friend, is not my mother-country more beautiful and worthy to be helped than any woman? Has not God given her spiritual eyes that shed tears and look for comfort; lips, sweeter than any woman's lips, that cry bitterly every day for deliverance? Can you look on the blue skies above you and walk on the green grass where the white and purple flowers smile up at you and be deaf and blind to her beauty and to her great need? Oh, no, no, it is impossible!"

"Ah, if you were a man, Dolores, what a flame you would kindle in the hearts of your countrymen!"

"Yes, if I were a man!" she exclaimed, starting to her feet; "then I should serve my country not with words only; then I would strike and bleed for her—how willingly! Being only a weak woman, I would give my heart's blood to win one arm to aid in the sacred cause."

She stood before me with flashing eyes, her face glowing with enthusiasm; then I also rose to my feet and took her hands in mine, for I was intoxicated with her loveliness and almost ready to throw all restraints to the winds.

"Dolores," I said, "are not your words extravagant? Shall I test their sincerity? Tell me, would you give even as much as one kiss with your sweet lips to win a strong arm for your country?"

She turned crimson and cast her eyes down; then, quickly recovering herself, answered—

"What do your words mean? Speak plainly, Richard."

"I cannot speak plainer, Dolores. Forgive me if I have offended once more. Your beauty and grace and eloquence have made me forget myself."

Her hands were moist and trembling in mine, still she did not withdraw them. "No, I am not offended," she returned in a strangely low tone. "Put me to the test, Richard. Do you wish me to understand clearly that for such a favour as that you would join us?"

"I cannot say," I replied, still endeavouring to be prudent, though my heart was on fire and my words when I spoke seemed to choke me. "But, Dolores, if you would shed your blood to win one strong arm, will you think it too much to bestow the favour I spoke of in the hope of winning an arm?"

She was silent. Then drawing her closer I touched her lips with mine. But who was ever satisfied with that one touch on the lips for which the heart has craved? It was like contact with a strange celestial fire that instantly kindled my love to madness. Again and yet again I kissed her; I pressed her lips till they were dry and burned like fire, then kissed cheek, forehead, hair, and casting my arms about her strained her to my breast in a long passionate embrace; then the violence of the paroxysm was over, and with a pang I released her. She trembled: her face was whiter than alabaster, and covering it with her hands she sank down on the sofa. I sat down beside her and drew her head down on my breast, but we remained silent, only our hearts were beating very fast. Presently she disengaged herself, and without bestowing one glance on me rose and left the room.

Before long I began to blame myself bitterly for this imprudent outburst. I dared not hope to continue longer on the old familiar footing. So high-spirited and sensitive a woman as Dolores would not easily be brought to forget or forgive my conduct. She had not repelled me, she had even tacitly consented to that one first kiss, and was therefore partly to blame herself; but her extreme pallor, her silence and cold manner had plainly shown me that I had wounded her. My passion had overcome me, and I felt that I had compromised myself. For that one first kiss I had all but promised to do a certain thing, and not to do it now seemed very dishonourable, much as I shrank from joining the Blanco rebels. I had proposed the thing myself; she had silently consented to the stipulation. I had taken my kiss and much more, and having now had my delirious evanescent joy, I could not endure the thought of meanly skulking off without paying the price.

I went out full of trouble and paced up and down in the orchard for two or three hours, hoping that Dolores might come to me there, but I saw no more of her that day. At dinner Doña Mercedes was excessively affable, showing clearly that she was not in her daughter's confidence. She informed me, simple soul! that Dolores was suffering from a grievous headache caused by taking a glass of claret at breakfast after eating a slice of water-melon, an imprudence against which she did not omit to caution me.

Lying awake that night—for the thought that I had pained and offended Dolores made it impossible for me to sleep—I resolved to join Santa Coloma immediately. That act alone would salve my conscience, and I only hoped that it would serve to win back the friendship and esteem of the woman I had learned to love too well. I had no sooner determined on taking this step than I began to see so many advantages in it that it seemed strange I had not taken it before; but we lose half our opportunities in life through too much caution. A few more days of adventure, all the pleasanter for being spiced with danger, and I would be once more in Montevideo with a host of great and grateful friends to start me in some career in the country. Yes, I said to myself, becoming enthusiastic, once this oppressive, scandalous, and besotted Colorado party is swept with bullet and steel out of the country, as of course it will be, I shall go to Santa Coloma to lay down my sword, resuming by that act my own nationality, and as sole reward of my chivalrous conduct in aiding the rebellion, ask for his interest in getting me placed, say, at the head of some large estancia in the interior. There, possibly on one of his own establishments, I shall be in my element and happy, hunting ostriches, eating *carne con cuero*, possessing a *tropilla* of twenty cream-coloured horses for my private use, and building up a modest fortune out of hides, horns, tallow, and other native products. At break of day I rose and saddled my horse; then finding the dignified Nepomucino, who was the early bird (blackbird) of the establishment, told him to inform his mistress that I was going to spend the day with General Santa Coloma. After taking a maté from the old fellow I mounted and galloped out of the village of Molino.

Arrived at the camp, which had been moved to a distance of four or five miles from El Molino, I found Santa Coloma just ready to mount his horse to start on an expedition to a small town eight or nine leagues distant. He at once asked me to go with him, and remarked that he was very much pleased, though not surprised, at my having changed my mind about joining him. We did not return till late in the evening, and the whole of the following day was spent in monotonous cavalry exercises. I then went to the General and requested permission to visit the Casa Blanca to bid adieu to my friends there. He informed me that he intended going to El Molino the next morning himself and would take me with him. The first thing he did on our arrival at the village was to send me to the principal storekeeper in the place, a man who had faith in the Blanco leader, and was rapidly disposing of a large stock of goods at a splendid profit, receiving in payment sundry slips of paper signed by Santa Coloma. This good fellow, who mixed politics with business, provided me with a complete and much-needed outfit, which included a broadcloth suit of clothes, soft brown hat rather broad in the brim, long riding-boots, and poncho. Going back to the official building or headquarters in the plaza I received my sword, which did not harmonise very well with the civilian costume I wore; but I was no worse off in this respect than forty-nine out of every fifty men in our little army.

In the afternoon we went together to see the ladies, and the General had a very hearty welcome from both of them, as I also had from Doña Mercedes, while Dolores received me with the utmost indifference, expressing no pleasure or surprise at seeing me wearing a sword in the cause which she had professed to have so much at heart. This was a sore disappointment, and I was also nettled at her treatment of me. After dinner, over which we sat talking some time, the General left us, telling me before doing so to join him in the plaza at five o'clock next morning. I then tried to get an opportunity of speaking to Dolores alone, but she studiously avoided me, and in the evening there were several visitors, ladies from the town with three or four officers from the camp, and dancing and singing were kept up till towards midnight. Finding that I could not speak to her, and anxious about my appointment at five in the morning, I at length retired sorrowful and baffled to my apartment. Without undressing I threw myself on my bed, and being very much fatigued with so much riding about I soon fell asleep. When I woke the brilliant light of the moon, shining in at open window and door, made me fancy it was already daylight, and I quickly sprang up. I had no means of telling the time, except by going into the large living-room, where there was an old eight-day clock. Making my way thither, I was amazed to see, on entering it, Dolores in her white dress sitting beside the open window in a dejected attitude. She started and rose up when I entered, the extreme pallor of her face heightened by contrast with her long raven-black hair hanging unbound on her shoulders.

"Dolores, do I find you here at this hour?" I exclaimed.

"Yes," she returned coldly, sitting down again. "Do you think it very strange, Richard?"

"Pardon me for disturbing you," I said; "I came here to find out the time from your clock."

"It is two o'clock. Is that all you came for? Did you imagine I could retire to sleep without first knowing what your motive was in returning to this house? Have you then forgotten everything?"

I came to her and sat down by the window before speaking. "No, Dolores," I said; "had I forgotten, you would not have seen me here enlisted in a cause which I looked on only as your cause."

"Ah, then you have honoured the Casa Blanca with this visit not to speak to me—that you considered unnecessary — but merely to exhibit yourself wearing a sword!"

I was stung by the extreme bitterness of her tone. "You are unjust to me," I said. "Since that fatal moment when my passion overcame me I have not ceased thinking of you, grieving that I had offended you. No, I did not come to exhibit my sword, which is not worn for ornament; I came only to speak to you, Dolores, and you purposely avoided me."

"Not without reason," she retorted quickly. "Did I not sit quietly by you after you had acted in that way towards me, waiting for you to speak—to explain, and you were silent? Well, señor, I am here now, waiting again."

"This then is what I have to say," I replied. "After what passed I considered myself bound in honour to join your cause, Dolores. What more can I say except to implore your forgiveness? Believe me, dear friend, in that moment of passion I forgot everything—forgot that I—forgot that your hand was already given to another."

"Given to another? What do you mean, Richard? Who told you that?"

"General Santa Coloma."

"The General? What right has he to occupy himself

with my affairs? This is a matter that concerns myself only, and it is presumption on his part to interfere in it."

"Do you speak in that tone of your hero, Dolores? Remember that he only warned me of my danger out of pure friendship. But his warning was thrown away; my unhappy passion, the sight of your loveliness, your own incautious words, were too much for my heart."

She dropped her face on her hands and remained silent.

"I have suffered for my fault, and must suffer more. Will you not say you forgive me, Dolores?" I said, offering my hand.

She took it, but continued silent.

"Say, dearest friend, that you forgive me, that we part friends."

"Oh, Richard, must we part then?" she murmured.

"Yes—now, Dolores; for, before you are up, I must be on horseback and on my way to join the troops. The march to Montevideo will probably commence almost immediately."

"Oh, I cannot bear it!" she suddenly exclaimed, taking my hand in both hers. "Let me open my heart to you now. Forgive me, Richard, for being so angry with you, but I did not know the General had said such a thing. Believe me, he imagines more than he knows. When you took me in your arms and held me against your breast it was a revelation to me. I cannot love or give my hand to any other man. You are everything in the world to me now, Richard; must you leave me to mingle in this cruel civil strife in which all my dearest friends and relations have perished?"

She had had her revelation; I now had mine, and it was an exceedingly bitter one. I trembled at the thought of confessing my secret to her, now when she had so unmistakably responded to the passion I had insanely revealed.

Suddenly she raised her dark, luminous eyes to mine, anger and shame struggling for mastery on her pale face.

"Speak, Richard!" she exclaimed. "Your silence at this moment is an insult to me."

"For God's sake, have mercy on me, Dolores," I said. "I am not free—I have a wife."

For some moments she sat staring fixedly at me, then flinging my hand from her, covered her face. Presently she uncovered it again, for shame was overcome and cast out by anger. She rose and stood up before me, her face very white.

"You have a wife—a wife whose existence you concealed from me till this moment!" she said. "Now you ask for mercy when your secret has been wrung from you! Married, and you have dared to take me in your arms, to excuse yourself afterwards with the plea of passion! Passion—do you know what it means, traitor? Ah no; a breast like yours cannot know any great or generous emotion. Would you have dared show your face to me again had you been capable of shame even? And you judged my heart as shallow as your own, and after treating me in that way thought to win my forgiveness and admiration even by parading before me with a sword! Leave me. I can feel nothing but contempt for you. Go; you are a disgrace to the cause you have espoused!"

I had sat utterly crushed and humiliated, not daring even to raise my sight to her face, for I felt that my own unspeakable weakness and folly had brought this tempest upon me. But there is a limit to patience, even in the most submissive mood; and when that was overpassed, then my anger blazed out all the more hotly for the penitential meekness I had preserved during the whole interview. Her words from the first had fallen like whip-cuts, making me writhe with the pain they inflicted; but that last taunt stung me beyond endurance. I, an Englishman, to be told that I was a disgrace to the Blanco cause, which I had joined in spite of my better judgment purely out of my romantic devotion to this very woman! I too was now upon my feet, and there face to face we stood for some moments, silent and trembling. At length I found my speech.

"This," I cried, "from the woman who was ready yesterday to shed her heart's blood to win one strong arm for her country? I have renounced everything, allied myself with abhorred robbers and cut-throats, only to learn that her one desire is everything to her, her divine, beautiful country nothing. I wish that a man had spoken those words to me, Dolores, so that I might have put this sword you speak of to one good use before breaking it and flinging it from me like the vile thing it is! Would to God the earth would open and swallow up this land for ever, though I sank down into hell with it for the detestable crime of taking part in its pirate wars!"

She stood perfectly still, gazing at me with widely dilated eyes, a new expression coming into her face; then when I paused for her to speak, expecting only a fresh outburst of scorn and bitterness, a strange, sorrowful smile flitted over her lips, and coming close to me she placed her hand on my shoulder.

"Oh," she said, "what a strength of passion you are capable of! Forgive me, Richard, for I have forgiven you. Ah, we were made for each other, and it can never, never be."

She dropped her head dejectedly on my shoulder. My anger vanished at those sad words; love only remained —love mingled with profoundest compassion and remorse for the pain I had inflicted. Supporting her with my arm, I tenderly stroked her dark hair, and stooping pressed my lips against it.

"Do you love me so much, Dolores," I said, "enough even to forgive the cruel, bitter words I have just spoken? Oh, I was mad—mad to say such things to you, and shall repent it all my life long! How cruelly have I wounded you with my love and my anger! Tell me, dearest Dolores, can you forgive me?"

"Yes, Richard; everything. Is there any word you can speak, any deed you can do, and I not forgive it? Does your wife love you like that—can you love her as you love me? How cruel destiny is to us! Ah, my beloved country, I was ready to shed my blood for you—just to win one strong arm to fight for you, but I did not dream that this would be the sacrifice required of me. Look, it will soon be time for you to go—we cannot sleep now, Richard. Sit down here with me, and let us spend this last hour together with my hand in yours, for we shall never, never, never meet again."

And so sitting there hand in hand we waited for the dawn, speaking many sad and tender words to one another; and at last when we parted I held her once more unresisting to my breast, thinking, as she did, that our separation would be an eternal one.

CHAPTER XVIII

REST ON THY ROCK, ANDROMEDA!

ABOUT the stirring events of the succeeding days I have little to relate, and no reader who has suffered the malady of love in its acutest form will wonder at it. During those days I mixed with a crowd of adventurers, returned exiles, criminals, and malcontents, every one of them worth studying; the daylight hours were passed in cavalry exercises or in long expeditions about the country, while every evening beside the camp fire romantic tales enough to fill a volume were told in my hearing. But the image of Dolores was ever before my mind, so that all this crowded period, lasting nine or ten days, passed before me like a phantasmagoria, or an uneasy dream, leaving only a very confused impression on my brain. I not only grieved for the sorrow I had occasioned her, but mourned also that my own heart had so terribly betrayed me, so that for the moment the beautiful girl I had persuaded to fly from home and parents, promising her my undying affection, had ceased to be what she had been, so great was this new inconvenient passion. The General had offered me a commission in his tatterdemalion gathering, but as I had no knowledge of military matters, I had prudently declined it, only requesting, as a special favour, that I might be employed constantly on the expeditions he sent out over the surrounding country to beat up recruits, seize arms, cattle, and horses, and to depose the little local authorities in the villages, putting creatures of his own in their places. This request had been granted, so that morning, noon, and night I was generally in the saddle.

One evening I was in the camp seated beside a large fire and gloomily staring into the flames, when the other men, who were occupied playing cards or sipping maté, hastily rose to their feet, making the salute. Then I saw the General standing near gazing fixedly at me. Motioning to the men to resume their cards, he sat down by my side.

"What is the matter with you?" he said. "I have noticed that you are like a different person since you joined us. Do you regret that step?"

"No," I answered, and then was silent, not knowing what more to say.

He looked searchingly at me. Doubtless some suspicion of the truth was in his mind; for he had gone to the Casa Blanca with me, and it was scarcely likely that his keen eyes had failed to notice the cold reception Dolores gave me on that occasion. He did not, however, touch on that matter.

"Tell me," he said at length, "what can I do for you?"

I laughed. "What can you do except to take me to Montevideo?" I replied.

"Why do you say that?" he returned quickly.

"We are not merely friends now as we were before I joined you," I said. "You are my General; I am simply one of your men."

"The friendship remains just the same, Richard. Let me know frankly what you think of this campaign, since you have now suddenly turned the current of the conversation in that direction?"

There was a slight sting in the concluding words, but I had, perhaps, deserved it. "Since you bid me speak," I said, "I, for one, feel very much disappointed at the little progress we are making. It seems to me that before you are in a position to strike, the enthusiasm and courage of your people will have vanished. You cannot get anything like a decent army together, and the few men you have are badly armed and undisciplined. Is it not plain that a march to Montevideo in these circumstances is impossible, that you will be obliged to retire into the remote and difficult places to carry on a guerilla war?"

"No," he returned; "there is to be no guerilla war. The Colorados made the Orientals sick of it, when that arch-traitor and chief of cut-throats, General Rivera, desolated the Banda for ten years. We must ride on to Montevideo soon. As for the character of my force, that is a matter it would perhaps be useless to discuss, my young friend. If I could import a well-equipped and disciplined army from Europe to do my fighting, I should do so. The Oriental farmer, unable to send to England for a threshing-machine, is obliged to go out and gather his wild mares from the plain to tread out his wheat, and

I, in like manner, having only a few scattered ranchos to draw my soldiers from, must be satisfied to do what I can with them. And now tell me, are you anxious to see something done at once—a fight, for instance, in which we might possibly be the losers?"

"Yes, that would be better than standing still. If you are strong, the best thing you can do is to show your strength."

He laughed. "Richard, you were made for an Orientál," he said, "only nature at your birth dropped you down in the wrong country. You are brave to rashness, abhor restraint, love women, and have a light heart; the Castilian gravity you have recently assumed is, I fancy, only a passing mood."

"Your words are highly complimentary and fill me with pride," I answered, "but I scarcely see their connection with the subject of our conversation."

"There is a connection, nevertheless," he returned pleasantly. "Though you refuse a commission from me. I am so convinced that you are in heart one of us that I will take you into my confidence and tell you something known to only half a dozen trusted individuals here. You rightly say that if we have strength we must show it to the country. That is what we are now about to do. A cavalry force has been sent against us and we shall engage it before two days are over. As far as I know, the forces will be pretty evenly balanced, though our enemies will, of course, be better armed. We shall choose our own ground; and should they attack us tired with a long march, or if there should be any disaffection amongst them, the victory will be ours, and after that every Blanco sword in the Banda will be unsheathed in our cause. I need not repeat to you that in the hour of my triumph, if it ever comes, I shall not forget my debt to you; my wish is to bind you, body and heart, to this Oriental country. It is, however, possible that I may suffer defeat, and if in two days' time we are all scattered to the winds, let me advise you what to do. Do not attempt to return immediately to Montevideo, as that might be dangerous. Make your way by Minas to the southern coast; and when you reach the department of Rocha, inquire for the little settlement of Lomas de Rocha, a village three leagues west of the lake. You will find there a storekeeper, one Florentino Blanco—a Blanco in heart as well. Tell him I sent you to him, and ask him to procure you an English passport from the capital; after which it will be safe for you to travel to Montevideo. Should you ever be identified as a follower of mine, you can invent some story to account for your presence in my force. When I remember that botanical lecture you once delivered, also some other matters, I am convinced that you are not devoid of imagination."

After giving some further kind advice, he bade me good night, leaving me with a strangely unpleasant conviction in my mind that we had changed characters for the nonce, and that I had bungled as much in my new part as I had formerly done in my old. He had been sincerity itself, while I, picking up the discarded mask, had tied it on, probably upside down, for it made me feel excessively uncomfortable during our interview. To make matters worse, I was also sure that it had quite failed to hide my countenance, and that he knew as well as I knew myself the real cause of the change he had noticed in me.

These disagreeable reflections did not trouble me long, and then I began to feel considerable excitement at the prospect of a brush with the government troops. My thoughts kept me awake most of the night; still, next morning, when the trumpet sounded its shrill reveillé close at hand, I rose quickly and in a much more cheerful mood than I had known of late. I began to feel that I was getting the better of that insane passion for Dolores which had made us both so unhappy, and when we were once more in the saddle the "Castilian gravity," to which the General had satirically alluded, had pretty well vanished.

No expeditions were sent out that day; after we had marched about twelve or thirteen miles eastward and nearer to the immense range of the Cuchilla Grande we encamped, and after the midday meal spent the afternoon in cavalry exercises.

On the next day happened the great event for which we had been preparing, and I am positive that with the wretched material he commanded, no man could have done more than Santa Coloma, though, alas! all his efforts ended in disaster. Alas, I say, not because I took, even then, any very serious interest in Oriental politics, but because it would have been greatly to my advantage if things had turned out differently. Besides, a great many poor devils who had been an unconscionable time out in the cold would have come into power, and the rascally Colorados sent away in their turn to eat the "bitter bread" of proscription. The fable of the fox and the flies might here possibly occur to the reader: I, however, preferred to remember Lucero's fable of the tree called Montevideo, with the chattering colony in its branches, and to look upon myself as one in the majestic bovine army about to besiege the monkeys and punish them for their naughty behaviour.

Quite early in the morning we had breakfast, then every man was ordered to saddle his best horse; for every one of us was the owner of three or four steeds. I, of course, saddled the horse the General had given me, which had been reserved for important work. We mounted and proceeded at a gentle pace through a very wild and broken country still in the direction of the Cuchilla. About midday scouts came riding in and reported that the enemy were close upon us. After halting for half an hour, we again proceeded at the same gentle pace till about two o'clock, when we crossed the Cañada de San Paulo, a deep valley beyond which the plain rose to a height of about one hundred and fifty feet. In the cañada we stopped to water our horses, and there heard that the enemy were advancing along it at a rapid pace, evidently hoping to cut off our supposed retreat towards the Cuchilla. Crossing the little stream of San Paulo, we began slowly ascending the sloping plain on the further side till the highest point was gained; then turning we saw the enemy, numbering about seven hundred men, beneath us spread out in a line of extraordinary length.

Up from the valley they came towards us at a brisk trot. We were then rapidly disposed in three columns, the centre one numbering about two hundred and fifty men, the others about two hundred men each. I was in one of the outside columns, within about four men from the front. My fellow-soldiers, who had hitherto been very light-hearted and chatty, had suddenly become grave and quiet, some of them even looking pale and scared. On one side of me was an irrepressible scamp of a boy about eighteen years old, a dark little fellow, with a monkey face and a feeble falsetto voice like a very old woman. I watched him take out a small sharp knife and without looking down draw it across the upper part of his surcingle three or four times; but this he did evidently only for practice, as he did not cut into the hide. Seeing me watching, he grinned mysteriously and made a sign with head and shoulders thrust forward in imitation of a person riding away at full speed, after which he restored his knife to its sheath.

"You intend cutting your surcingle and running away, little coward?" I said.

"And what are you going to do?" he returned.

"Fight," I said.

"It is the best thing you can do, Sir Frenchman," said he, with a grin.

"Listen," I said, "when the fight is over, I will look you up to thrash you for your impertinence in calling me a Frenchman."

"After the fight!" he exclaimed, with a funny grimace. "Do you mean next year? Before that distant time arrives some Colorado will fall in love with you, and—and—and——"

Here he explained himself without words by drawing the edge of his hand briskly across his throat, then closing his eyes and making gurgling sounds, supposed to be uttered by a person undergoing the painful operation of having his throat cut.

Our colloquy was carried on in whispers, but his pantomimic performance drew on us the attention of our neighbours, and now he looked round to inform them with a grin and a nod that his Oriental wit was getting the victory. I was determined not to be put down by him, however, and tapped my revolver with my hand to call his attention to it.

"Look at this, you young miscreant," I said. "Do you not know that I and many others in this column have received orders from the General to shoot down every man who attempts to run away?"

This speech effectually silenced him. He turned as pale as his dark skin would let him and looked round like a hunted animal in search of a hole to hide in.

On my other hand a grizzly-bearded old gaucho, in somewhat tattered garments, lit a cigarette and, oblivious of everything except the stimulating fragrance of the strongest black tobacco, expanded his lungs with long inspirations to send forth thereafter clouds of blue smoke into his neighbours' faces, scattering the soothing perfume over a third portion of the army.

Santa Coloma rose equal to the occasion; swiftly riding from column to column he addressed each in turn, and using the quaint expressive phraseology of the gauchos, which he knew so well, poured forth his denunciations of the Colorados with a fury and eloquence that brought the blood with a rush to many of his followers' pale cheeks. They were traitors, plunderers, assassins, he cried; they had committed a million crimes, but all these things were nothing, nothing compared with that one black crime which no other political party had been guilty of. By the aid of Brazilian gold and Brazilian bayonets they had risen to power; they were the infamous pensioners of the empire of slaves. He compared them to the man who marries a beautiful wife and sells her to some rich person so as to live luxuriously on the wages of his own dishonour. The foul stain which they had brought on the honour of the Banda Orientál could only be washed away with their blood. Pointing to the advancing troops, he said that when those miserable hirelings were scattered like thistle-down before the wind, the entire country would be with him, and the Banda Orientál, after half a century of degradation, free at last and for ever from the Brazilian curse.

Waving his sword, he galloped back to the front of his column greeted by a storm of *vivas*.

Then a great silence fell upon our ranks; while up the slope, their trumpets sounding merrily, trotted the enemy, till they had covered about three hundred yards of the ascending ground, threatening to close us round in an immense circle, when suddenly the order was given to charge, and led by Santa Coloma we thundered down the incline upon them.

Soldiers reading this plain unvarnished account of an Oriental battle might feel inclined to criticise Santa Coloma's tactics; for his men were, like the Arabs, horsemen and little else; they were, moreover, armed with lance and broadsword, weapons requiring a great deal of space to be used effectively. Yet, considering all the circumstances, I am sure that he did the right thing. He knew that he was too weak to meet the enemy in the usual way, pitting man against man; also that if he failed to fight, his temporary prestige would vanish like smoke and the rebellion collapse. Having decided to hazard all, and knowing that in a stand-up fight he would infallibly be beaten, his only plan was to show a bold front, mass his feeble followers together in columns and hurl them upon the enemy, hoping by this means to introduce a panic amongst his opponents and so snatch the victory.

A discharge of carbines with which we were received did us no damage. I, at any rate, saw no saddles emptied near me, and in a few moments we were dashing through the advancing lines. A shout of trumph went up from our men, for our cowardly foes were flying before us in all directions. On we rode in triumph till we reached the bottom of the hill, then we reined up, for before us was the stream of San Paulo, and the few scattered men who had crossed it and were scuttling away like hunted ostriches scarcely seemed worth chasing. Suddenly with a great shout a large body of Colorados came thundering down the hill on our rear and flank, and dismay seized upon us. The feeble efforts made by some of our officers to bring us round to face them proved unavailing. I am utterly unable to give any clear account of what followed immediately after that, for we were all, friends and foes, mixed up for some minutes in the wildest confusion, and how I ever got out of it all without a scratch is a mystery to me. More than once I was in violent collision with Colorado men, distinguished from ours by their uniform, and several furious blows with sword and lance were aimed at me, but somehow I escaped them all. I emptied the six chambers of my Colt's revolver, but whether my bullets did any execution or not I cannot pretend to say. In the end I found myself surrounded by four of our men who were furiously spurring their horses out of the fight.

"Whip up, Captain, come with us this way," shouted one of them who knew me, and who always insisted on giving me a title to which I had no right.

As we rode away, skirting the hill towards the south, he assured me that all was lost, in proof of which he pointed to scattered bodies of our men flying from the field in all directions. Yes, we were defeated; that was plain to see, and I needed little encouragement from my fellow-runaways to spur my horse to its utmost speed. Had the falcon eye of Santa Coloma rested on me at that moment he might have added to the list of Oriental traits he had given me the un-English faculty of knowing when I was beaten. I was quite as anxious, I believe, to save my skin—*throat*, we say in the Banda Orientál—as any horseman there, not even excepting the monkey-faced boy with the squeaky voice.

If the curious reader, thirsting for knowledge, will consult the Uruguayan histories, I daresay he will find a more scientific description of the battle of San Paulo than I have been able to give. My excuse must be, that it was the only battle—pitched or other—at which I have ever assisted, also that my position in the Blanco forces was a very humble one. Altogether I am not overproud of my soldiering performances; still, as I did no worse than Frederick the Great of Prussia, who ran away from his first battle, I do not consider that I need blush furiously. My companions took our defeat with the usual Oriental resignation. "You see," said one in explanation of his mental attitude, "there must always be one side defeated in every fight, for had we gained the day then the Colorados would have lost." There was in this remark a sound practical philosophy; it could not be controverted, it burdened our brains with no new thing, and it made us all very cheerful. For myself, I did not care very much, but could not help thinking a great deal of Dolores, who would now have a fresh grief to increase her pain.

For a distance of three or four miles we rode at a fast gallop, then on the slopes of the Cuchilla paused to breathe our horses, and, dismounting, stood for some time gazing back over the wide landscape spread out before us. At our backs rose the giant green and brown walls of the sierras, the range stretching away on either hand in violet and deep blue masses. At our feet lay the billowy green and yellow plain, vast as ocean, and channelled by innumerable streams, while one black patch on a slope far away showed us that our foes were camping on the very spot where they had overcome us. Not a cloud appeared in the immense heavens, only low down in the west purple and rose-coloured vapours were beginning to form, staining the clear intense whity-blue sky about the sinking sun. Over all reigned deep silence; until, suddenly, a flock of orange and flame-coloured orioles with black wings swept down on a clump of bushes hard by and poured forth a torrent of wild joyous music. A strange performance! screaming notes that seemed to scream jubilant gladness to listening heaven, and notes abrupt and guttural mingling with others more clear and soul-piercing than ever human lips drew from reed or metal. It soon ended; up sprang the vocalists like a fountain of fire and fled away to their roost among the hills, then silence reigned once more. What brilliant hues, what gay fantastic music! were they indeed birds, or the glad winged inhabitants of a mystic region, resembling earth, but sweeter than earth and never entered by death, upon whose threshold I had stumbled by chance? Then, while the last rich flood of sunshine came over the earth from that red everlasting urn resting on the far horizon, I could, had I been alone, have cast myself upon the ground to adore the great God of Nature, who had given me this precious moment of life. For here the religion that languishes in crowded cities or steals shame-faced to hide itself in dim churches flourishes greatly, filling the soul with a solemn joy. Face to face with nature on the vast hills at eventide, who does not feel himself near to the Unseen?

Out of his heart God shall not pass:
His image stampèd is on every grass.

My comrades, anxious to get through the Cuchilla, were already on horseback shouting to me to mount. One more lingering glance over that wide prospect—wide, yet how small a portion of the Banda's twenty thousand miles of everlasting verdure, watered by innumerable beautiful streams? Again the thought of Dolores swept like a moaning wind over my heart. For this rich prize, her beautiful country, how weakly and with what feeble hands had we striven! Where now was her hero, the glorious deliverer Perseus? Lying, perhaps, stark and stained with blood on yon darkening moor. Not yet was the Colorado monster overcome. "Rest on thy rock, Andromeda!" I sadly murmured, then leaping into the saddle galloped away after my retreating comrades, already half a mile away down in the shadowy mountain pass.

CHAPTER XIX

TALES OF THE PURPLE LAND

BEFORE it had been long dark, we had crossed the range and into the department of Minas. Nothing happened till towards midnight, when our horses began to be greatly distressed. My companions hoped to reach before morning an estancia, still many leagues distant, where they were known and would be allowed to lie in concealment for a few days till the storm blew over; for usually shortly after an outbreak has been put down an *indulto*, or proclamation of pardon, is issued, after which it is safe for all those who have taken arms against the constituted government to return to their homes. For the time we were, of course, outlaws, and liable to have our throats cut at any moment. Our poor horses at last became incapable even of a trot, and, dismounting, we walked on, leading them by the bridles.

About midnight we approached a watercourse, the upper part of the Rio Barriga Negra—Black Belly River —and on coming near it the tinkling of a bell attracted our attention. It is the usual thing for every man in the Banda Orientál to have one mare, called *madrina*, in his *tropilla*, or herd of geldings; the *madrina* always carries a bell attached to her neck, and at night her fore feet are usually hobbled to prevent her wandering far from home; for the horses are always very much attached to her and will not leave her.

After listening for a few moments, we concluded that the sound came from the bell of a *madrina*, and that her fore feet were bound, for the tinkle came in violent jerks as from an animal laboriously hopping along. Proceeding to the spot, we found a *tropilla* of eleven or twelve dun-coloured horses feeding near the river. Driving them very gently towards the bank, where a sharp bend in the stream enabled us to corner them, we set to work catching fresh horses. Fortunately they were not very shy of strangers, and after we had caught and secured the *madrina*, they gathered whinnying round her, and we were not very long in selecting the five best-looking duns in the herd.

"My friends, I call this stealing," I said, though at that very moment I was engaged in hastily transferring my saddle to the animal I had secured.

"That is very interesting information," said one of my comrades.

"A stolen horse will always carry you well," said another.

"If you cannot steal a horse without compunction, you have not been properly brought up," cried the third.

"In the Banda Orientál," said the fourth, "you are not looked upon as an honest man unless you steal."

We then crossed the river and broke into a swift gallop, which we kept up till morning, reaching our destination a little while before sunrise. There was here a fine plantation of trees not far from the house, surrounded by a deep ditch and a cactus hedge, and after we had taken maté and then breakfast at the house, where the people received us very kindly, we proceeded to conceal our horses and ourselves in the plantation. We found a comfortable little grassy hollow, partly shaded with the surrounding trees, and here we spread our rugs, and fatigued with our exertions soon dropped into a deep sleep which lasted pretty well all day. It was a pleasant day for me, for I had waking intervals during which I experienced that sensation of absolute rest of mind and body which is so exceedingly sweet after a long period of toil and anxiety. During my waking intervals I smoked cigarettes and listened to the querulous pipings of a flock of young black-headed siskins flying about from tree to tree after their parents and asking to be fed.

Occasionally the long clear cry of the venteveo, a lemon-coloured bird with black head and long beak like a kingfisher, rung through the foliage; or a flock of pecho amarillos, olive-brown birds with bright yellow vests, would visit the trees and utter their confused chorus of gay notes.

I did not think very much about Santa Coloma. Probably he had escaped, and was once more a wanderer disguised in the humble garments of a peasant; but that would be no new experience to him. The bitter bread of expatriation had apparently been his usual food, and his periodical descents upon the country had so far always ended in disaster: he had still an object to live for. But when I remembered Dolores lamenting her lost cause and vanished peace of mind, then, in spite of the bright sunshine flecking the grass, the soft, warm wind fanning my face and whispering in the foliage overhead, and the merry-throated birds that came to visit me, a pang was in my heart, and tears came to my eyes.

When evening came we were all wide awake and sat till a very late hour round the fire we had made in the hollow, sipping maté and conversing. We were all in a talkative mood that evening, and after the ordinary subjects of Banda Orientál conversation had been exhausted, we drifted into matters extraordinary—wild creatures of strange appearance and habits, apparitions, and marvellous adventures.

"The manner in which the lampalagua captures its prey is very curious," said one of the company, named Rivarola, a stout man with an immense fierce-looking black beard and moustache, but who was very mild-eyed and had a gentle, cooing voice.

We had all heard of the lampalagua, a species of boa found in these countries, with a very thick body and extremely sluggish in its motions. It preys on the larger rodents, and captures them, I believe, by following them into their burrows, where they cannot escape from its jaws by running.

"I will tell you what I once witnessed, for I have never seen a stranger thing," continued Rivarola. "Riding one day through a forest I saw some distance before me a fox sitting on the grass watching my approach. Suddenly I saw it spring high up into the air, uttering a great scream of terror, then fall back upon the earth, where it lay for some time growling, struggling, and biting as if engaged in deadly conflict with some invisible enemy. Presently it began to move away through the wood, but very slowly and still frantically struggling. It seemed to be getting exhausted, its tail dragged, the mouth foamed, and the tongue hung out, while it still moved on as if drawn by an unseen cord. I followed, going very close to it, but it took no notice of me. Sometimes it dug its claws into the ground or seized a twig or stalk with its teeth, and it would then remain resting for a few moments till the twig gave away, when it would roll over many times on the ground, loudly yelping, but still dragged onwards. Presently I saw in the direction we were going a huge serpent, thick as a man's thigh, its head lifted high above the grass, and motionless as a serpent of stone. Its cavernous, blood-red mouth was gaping wide, and its eyes were fixed on the struggling fox. When about twenty yards from the serpent, the fox began moving very rapidly over the ground, its struggles growing feebler every moment, until it seemed to fly through the air, and in an instant was in the serpent's mouth. Then the reptile dropped its head and began slowly swallowing its prey."

"And you actually witnessed this yourself?" said I.

"With these eyes," he returned, indicating the orbs in question by pointing at them with the tube of the maté-cup he held in his hand. "This was the only occasion on which I have actually seen the lampalagua take its prey, but its manner of doing it is well known to everyone from hearsay. You see, it draws an animal towards it by means of its power of suction. Sometimes, when the animal attacked is very strong or very far off—say two thousand yards—the serpent becomes so inflated with the quantity of air inhaled while drawing the victim towards it——"

"That it bursts?" I suggested.

"That it is obliged to stop drawing to blow the wind out. When this happens, the animal, finding itself released from the drawing force, instantly sets off at full speed. Vain effort! The serpent has no sooner discharged the accumulated wind with a report like a cannon——"

"No, no, like a musket! I have heard it myself," interrupted Blas Aria, one of the listeners.

"Like a musket, than it once more brings its power of suction to bear; and in this manner the contest continues until the victim is finally drawn into the monster's jaws. It is well known that the lampalagua is the strongest of all God's creatures, and that if a man, stripped to the skin, engages one, and conquers it by sheer muscular strength, the serpent's power goes into him, after which he is invincible."

I laughed at this fable, and was severely rebuked for my levity.

"I will tell you the strangest thing that ever befell me," said Blas Aria. "I happened to be travelling alone—for reasons—on the northern frontier. I crossed the river Yaguaron into Brazilian territory, and for a whole day rode through a great marshy plain, where the reeds were dead and yellow, and the water shrunk into muddy pools. It was a place to make a man grow weary of life. When the sun was going down, and I began to despair of getting to the end of this desolation, I discovered a low hovel made of mud and thatched with rushes. It was about fifteen yards long, with only one small door, and seemed to be uninhabited, for no person answered me when I rode round it shouting aloud. I heard a grunting and squealing within, and by-and-by a sow, followed by a litter of young pigs, came out, looked at me, then went in again. I would have ridden on, but my horses were tired; besides, a great storm with thunder and lightning was coming up, and no other shelter appeared in sight. I therefore unsaddled, loosed my horses to feed, and took my gear into the hovel. The room I entered was so small that the sow and her young occupied all the floor; there was, however, another room, and opening the door, which was closed, I went into it and found that it was very much larger than the first; also, that it contained a dirty bed made of skins in one corner, while on the floor was a heap of ashes and a black pot. There was nothing else except old bones, sticks, and other rubbish littering the floor. Afraid of being caught unawares by the owner of this foul den, and finding nothing to eat in it, I returned to the first room, turned the pigs out of doors, and sat down on my saddle to wait. It was beginning to get dark when a woman, bringing in a bundle of sticks, suddenly appeared at the door. Never, sirs, have I beheld a fouler, more hideous object than this person. Her face was hard, dark, and rough like the bark of the ñandubuy tree, while her hair, which covered her head and shoulders in a tangled mass, was of a dry earthy colour. Her body was thick and long, yet she looked like a dwarf, for she scarcely had any legs, only enormous knees and feet; and her garments were old ragged horse-rugs tied round her body with thongs of hide. She stared at me out of a pair of small black rat eyes, then, setting down her bundle, asked me what I wanted. I told her I was a tired traveller, and wanted food and shelter. 'Shelter you can have: food there is none,' she said; then, taking up her sticks, she passed to the inner room and secured it with a bolt on the inside. She had not inspired me with love, and there was little danger of my attempting to intrude on her there. It was a black, stormy night, and very soon the rain began to fall in torrents. Several times the sow, with her young pigs loudly squealing, came in for shelter, and I was forced to get up and beat them out with my whip. At length, through the mud partition separating the two rooms, I heard the crackling of a fire which the vile woman was lighting; and, before long, through the chinks came the savoury smell of roast meat. That surprised me greatly, for I had searched the room and failed to find anything to eat in it. I concluded that she had brought in the meat under her garments, but where she had got it was a mystery. At length I began to doze. There were many sounds in my ear as of thunder and wind, the pigs grunting at the door, and the crackling of the fire in the hag's room. But by-and-by other sounds seemed to mingle with these—voices of several persons talking, laughing, and singing. At length I became wide awake, and found that these voices proceeded from the next room. Some person was playing a guitar and singing, then others were loudly talking and laughing. I tried to peep through the cracks in the door and partition, but could not see through them. High up in the middle of the wall there was one large crack through which I was sure the interior could be seen, so much red firelight streamed through it. I placed my saddle against the partition, and all my rugs folded small, one above the other, until I had heaped them as high as my knees. Standing on my toes on this pile, and carefully clinging to the wall with my finger-nails, I managed to bring my eyes to a level with the crack, and peeped through it. The room inside was brightly lighted by a big wood fire burning at one end, while on the floor a large crimson cloak was spread, on which the people I had heard were sitting with some fruit and bottles of wine before them. There was the foul hag looking almost as tall sitting as she had appeared when standing; she was playing on a guitar and singing a ballad in Portuguese. Before her on the cloak lay a tall well-formed negro woman, wearing only a narrow white cloth round her loins, and broad silver armlets on her round black arms. She was eating a banana, and against her knees, which were drawn up, sat a beautiful girl about fifteen years old, with a dark pale face. She was dressed in white, her arms were bare, and round her head she wore a gold band keeping back her black hair, which fell unbound on her back. Before her, on his knees on the cloak, was an old man with a face brown and wrinkled as a walnut, and beard white as thistle-down. With one of his hands he was holding the girl's arm, and with the other offering her a glass of wine. All this I saw at one glance, and then all of them together turned their eyes up at the crack as if they knew that someone was watching them. I started back in alarm, and fell with a crash to the ground. Then I heard loud screams of laughter, but I dared not attempt to look in on them again. I took my rugs to the further side of the room, and sat down to wait for morning. The talking and laughter continued for about two hours, then it gradually died away, the light faded from the chinks, and all was dark and silent. No person came out; and at last, overcome with drowsiness, I fell asleep. It was day when I woke. I rose and walked round the hovel, and finding a crack in the wall, I peered into the hag's room. It looked just as I had seen it the day before; there was the pot and pile of ashes, and in the corner the brutish woman lying asleep in her skins. After that I got on to my horse and rode away. May I never again have such an experience as I had that night."

Something was then said about witchcraft by the others, all looking very solemn.

"You were very hungry and tired that night," I ventured to remark, "and perhaps after the woman locked her door you went to sleep and dreamed all that about people eating fruit and playing on the guitar."

"Our horses were tired and we were flying for our lives yesterday," returned Blas contemptuously. "Perhaps it made us dream that we caught five dun horses to carry us."

"When a person is incredulous, it is useless arguing with him," said Mariano, a small dark grey-haired man. "I will now tell you a strange adventure I had when I was a young man; but remember I do not put a blunderbuss to any man's breast to compel him to believe me. For what is, is; and let him that disbelieves shake his head till he shakes it off, and it falls to the ground like a cocoanut from the tree.

"After I got married I sold my horses, and taking all my money purchased two ox-carts, intending to make my living by carrying freight. One cart I drove myself, and to drive the other I hired a boy whom I called Mula, though that was not the name his godfathers gave him, but because he was stubborn and sullen as a mule. His mother was a poor widow, living near me, and when she heard about the ox-carts she came to me with her son and said, 'Neighbour Mariano, for your mother's sake, take my son and teach him to earn his bread, for he is a boy that loves not to do anything.' So I took Mula and paid the widow for his services after each journey. When there was no freight to be had I sometimes went to the lagoons to cut rushes, and loading the carts with them we would go about the country to sell the rushes to those who required them to thatch their houses. Mula loved not this work. Often when we were all day wading up to our thighs in the water, cutting the rushes down close to their roots, then carrying them in large bundles on our shoulders to land, he would cry, complaining bitterly of his hard lot. Sometimes I thrashed him, for it angered me to see a poor boy so fastidious: then he would curse me and say that some day he would have his revenge. 'When I am dead,' he often told me, 'my ghost will come to haunt and terrify you for all the blows you have given me.' This always made me laugh.

"At last, one day, while crossing a deep stream, swollen with rains, my poor Mula fell down from his perch on the shaft and was swept away by the current into deep water and drowned. Well, sirs, about a year after that event I was out in search of a couple of strayed oxen when night overtook me a long distance from home. Between me and my house there was a range of hills running down to a deep river, so close that there was only a narrow passage to get through, and for a long distance there was no other opening. When I reached the pass I fell into a narrow path with bushes and trees growing on either side; here, suddenly, the figure of a young man stepped out from the trees and stood before me. It was all in white—poncho, *chiripà*, drawers, even its boots, and wore a broad-brimmed straw hat on its head. My horse stood still trembling; nor was I less frightened, for my hair rose up on my head like bristles on a pig's back; and the sweat broke out on my face like raindrops. Not a word said the figure; only it remained standing still with arms folded on its breast, preventing me from passing. Then I cried out, 'In Heaven's name, who are you, and what do you want with Mariano Montes de Oca, that you bar his path?' At this speech it laughed; then it said, 'What, does my old master not know me? I am Mula; did I not often tell you that some day I should return to pay you out for all the thrashings you gave me? Ah, Master Mariano, you see I have kept my word!' Then it began to laugh again. 'May ten thousand curses light on your head!' I shouted. 'If you wish for my life, Mula, take it and be for ever damned; or else let me pass, and go back to Satan, your master, and tell him from me to keep a stricter watch on your movements; for why should the stench of purgatory be brought to my nostrils before my time! And now, hateful ghost, what more have you got to say to me?' At this speech the ghost shouted with laughter, slapping its thighs, and doubling itself up with mirth. At last, when it was able to speak, it said, 'Enough of this fooling, Mariano. I did not intend frightening you so much; and it is no great matter if I have laughed a little at you now, for you have often made me cry. I stopped you because I had something important to say. Go to my mother and tell her you have seen and spoken with me; tell her to pay for another mass for my soul's repose, for after that I shall be out of purgatory. If she has no money lend her a few dollars for the mass, and I will repay you, old man, in another world.'

"This it said and vanished. I lifted my whip but needed not to strike my horse, for not a bird that has wings could fly faster than he now flew with me on his back. No path was before me, nor did I know where we were going. Through rushes and through thickets, over burrows of wild animals, stones, rivers, marshes, we flew as if all the devils that are on the earth and under it were at our heels; and when the horse stopped it was at my own door. I stayed not to unsaddle him, but cutting the surcingle with my knife left him to shake the saddle off; then with the bridle I hammered on the door shouting to my wife to open. I heard her fumbling for the tinder-box. 'For the love of Heaven, woman, strike no light,' I cried. '*Santa Barbara bendita!* have you seen a ghost?' she exclaimed, opening to me. 'Yes,' I replied, rushing in and bolting the door, 'and had you struck a light you would now have been a widow.'

"For thus it is, sirs, the man who after seeing a ghost is confronted with a light immediately drops down dead."

I made no sceptical remarks, and did not even shake my head. The circumstances of the encounter were described by Mariano with such graphic power and minuteness that it was impossible not to believe his story. Yet some things in it afterwards struck me as somewhat absurd; that straw hat, for instance, and it also seemed strange that a person of Mula's disposition should have been so much improved in temper by his sojourn in a warmer place.

"Talking of ghosts," said Laralde, the other man—but proceeded no further, for I interrupted him. Laralde was a short, broad-chested man, with bow legs and bushy grey whiskers; he was called by his familiars Lechuza (owl) on account of his immense round tawny-coloured eyes, which had a tremendous staring power in them.

I thought we had had enough of the supernatural by this time.

"My friend," I said, "pardon me for interrupting you; but there will be no sleep for us to-night if we have any more stories about spirits from the other world."

"Talking of ghosts," resumed Lechuza, without noticing my remark, and this nettled me; so I cut in once more—

"I protest that we have heard quite enough about them," I said. "This conversation was only to be about rare and curious things. Now, visitors from the other world are very common. I put it to you, my friends—have you not all seen more ghosts than lampalaguas drawing foxes with their breath?"

"I have seen that once only," said Rivarola gravely. "I have often seen ghosts."

The others also confessed to having seen more than one ghost apiece.

Lechuza sat inattentive, smoking his cigarette, and when we had all done speaking began again—

"Talking of ghosts——"

Nobody interrupted him this time, though he seemed to expect it, for he made a long, deliberate pause.

"Talking of ghosts," he repeated, staring around him triumphantly, "I once had an encounter with a strange being that was *not* a ghost. I was a young man then—young and full of the fire, strength and courage of youth—for what I am now going to relate happened over twenty years ago. I had been playing cards at a friend's house, and left it at midnight to ride to my father's house, a distance of five leagues. I had quarrelled that evening and left a loser, burning with anger against the man who had cheated and insulted me, and with whom I was not allowed to fight. Vowing vengeance on him, I rode away at a fast gallop; the night being serene, and almost as light as day, for the moon was at its full. Suddenly I saw before me a huge man sitting on a white horse, which stood perfectly motionless directly in my path. I dashed on till I came near him, then shouted aloud, 'Out of my path, friend, lest I ride over you'; for I was still raging in my heart.

"Seeing that he took no notice of my words, I dug my spurs into my horse and hurled myself against him; then at the very moment my horse struck his with a tremendous shock, I brought down my iron whip-handle with all the force that was in me upon his head. The blow rang as if I had struck upon an anvil, while at the same moment he, without swerving, clutched my cloak with both hands. I could feel that they were bony, hard hands, armed with long, crooked, sharp talons like an eagle's, which pierced through my cloak into my flesh. Dropping my whip, I seized him by the throat, which seemed scaly and hard, between my hands, and thus, locked together in a desperate struggle, we swayed this way and that, each trying to drag the other from his seat till we came down together with a crash upon the earth. In a moment we were disengaged and on our feet. Quick as lightning flashed out his long, sharp weapon, and finding I was too late to draw mine I hurled myself against him, seizing his armed hand in both mine before he could strike. For a few moments he stood still, glaring at me out of a pair of eyes that shone like burning coals; then mad with rage, he flung me off my feet and whirled me round and round like a ball in a sling, and finally cast me from him to a distance of a hundred yards, so great was his strength.

I was launched with tremendous force into the middle of some thorny bushes, but had no sooner recovered from the shock than out I burst with a yell of rage and charged him again. For, you will hardly believe it, sirs, by some strange chance I had carried away his weapon, firmly grasped in my hands. It was a heavy two-edged dagger, sharp as a needle, and while I grasped the hilt I felt the strength and fury of a thousand fighting-men in me. As I advanced he retreated before me, until, seizing the topmost boughs of a great thorny bush he swung his body to one side and wrenched it out of the earth by the roots. Swinging the bush with the rapidity of a whirlwind round his head, he advanced against me and dealt a blow that would have crushed me had it descended on me; but it fell too far, for I had dodged under it to close with him and delivered a stab with such power that the long weapon was buried to its hilt in his bosom. He uttered a deafening yell, and at the same moment a torrent of blood spouted forth, scalding my face like boiling water, and drenching my clothes through to the skin. For a moment I was blinded; but when I had dashed the blood from my eyes and looked round he had vanished, horse and all.

"Then mounting my horse I rode home and told everyone what had happened, showing the knife, which I still carried in my hand. Next day all the neighbours gathered at my house, and we rode in company to the spot where the fight had taken place. There we found the bush torn up by the roots, and all the earth about it ploughed up where we had fought. The ground was also dyed with blood for several yards round, and where it had fallen the grass was withered up to the roots, as if scorched with fire. We also picked up a cluster of hairs—long, wiry, crooked hairs, barbed at the ends like fish-hooks; also three or four scales like fish-scales, only rougher, and as large as doubloons. The spot where the fight took place is now called *La Cañada del Diablo*, and I have heard that since that day the devil has never appeared corporeally to fight any man in the Banda Orientál."

Lechuza's narrative gave great satisfaction. I said nothing, feeling half stupid with amazement, for the man apparently told it in the full conviction that it was true, while the other listeners appeared to accept every word of it with the most implicit faith. I began to feel very melancholy, for evidently they expected something from me now, and what to tell them I knew not. It went against my conscience to be the only liar amongst these exceedingly veracious Orientals, and so I could not think of inventing anything.

"My friends," I began at length, "I am only a young man; also a native of a country where marvellous things do not often happen, so that I can tell you nothing to equal in interest the stories I have heard. I can only relate a little incident which happened to me in my own country before I left it. It is trivial, perhaps, but will lead me to tell you something about London—that great city you have all heard of."

"Yes, we have heard of London; it is in England, I believe. Tell us your story about London," said Blas encouragingly.

"I was very young—only fourteen years old," I continued, flattering myself that my modest introduction had not been ineffective, "when one evening I came to London from my home. It was in January, in the middle of winter, and the whole country was white with snow."

"Pardon me, Captain," said Blas, "but you have got the cucumber by the wrong end. We say that January is in summer."

"Not in my country, where the seasons are reversed," I said. "When I rose next morning it was dark as night, for a black fog had fallen upon the city."

"A black fog!" exclaimed Lechuza.

"Yes, a black fog that would last all day and make it darker than night, for though the lamps were lighted in the streets they gave no light."

"Demons!" exclaimed Rivarola; "there is no water in the bucket. I must go to the well for some or we shall have none to drink in the night."

"You might wait till I finish," I said.

"No, no, Captain," he returned. "Go on with your story; we must not be without water." And taking up the bucket he trudged off.

"Finding it was going to be dark all day," I continued, "I determined to go a little distance away, not out of London, you will understand, but about three leagues from my hotel to a great hill, where I thought the fog would not be so dark, and where there is a palace of glass."

"A palace of glass!" repeated Lechuza, with his immense round eyes fixed sternly on me.

"Yes, a palace of glass—is there anything so wonderful in that?"

"Have you any tobacco in your pouch, Mariano?" said Blas. "Pardon, Captain, for speaking, but the things you are telling require a cigarette, and my pouch is empty."

"Very well, sirs, perhaps you will now allow me to proceed," I said, beginning to feel rather vexed at these constant interruptions. "A palace of glass large enough to hold all the people in this country."

"The Saints assist us! Your tobacco is dry as ashes, Mariano," exclaimed Blas.

"That is not strange," said the other, "for I have had it three days in my pocket. Proceed, Captain. A palace of glass large enough to hold all the people in the world. And then?"

"No, I shall not proceed," I returned, losing my temper. "It is plain to see that you do not wish to hear my story. Still, sirs, from motives of courtesy you might have disguised your want of interest in what I was about to relate; for I have heard it said that the Orientals are a polite people."

"There you are saying too much, my friend," broke in Lechuza. "Remember that we were speaking of actual experiences, not inventing tales of black fogs and glass palaces and men walking on their heads, and I know not what other marvels."

"Do you know that what I am telling you is untrue?" I indignantly asked.

"Surely, friend, you do not consider us such simple

persons in the Banda Orientál as not to know truth from fable?"

And this from the fellow who had just told us of his tragical encounter with Apollyon, a yarn which quite put Bunyan's narrative in the shade! It was useless talking; my irritation gave place to mirth, and stretching myself out on the grass I roared with laughter. The more I thought of Lechuza's stern rebuke the louder I laughed, until I yelled with laughter, slapping my thighs and doubling myself up after the manner of Mariano's hilarious visitor from purgatory. My companions never smiled. Rivarola came back with the bucket of water and after staring at me for some time said, "If the tears, which they say always follow laughter, come in the same measure then we shall have to sleep in the wet."

This increased my mirth.

"If the whole country is to be informed of our hiding-place," said Blas the timid, "we were putting ourselves to an unnecessary trouble by running away from San Paulo."

Fresh screams of laughter greeted this protest.

"I once knew a man," said Mariano, "who had a most extraordinary laugh; you could hear it a league away, it was so loud. His name was Aniceto, but we called him El Burro on account of his laugh, which sounded like the braying of an ass. Well, sirs, he one day burst out laughing, like the Captain here, at nothing at all, and fell down dead. You see, the poor man had aneurism of the heart."

At this I fairly yelled, then, feeling quite exhausted, I

looked apprehensively at Lechuza, for this important member of the quartet had not yet spoken.

With his immense unspeakably serious eyes fixed on me he remarked quietly. "And this. my friends, is the man who says it is wrong to steal horses!"

But I was past shrieking now. Even this rich specimen of topsy-turvey Banda Orientál morality only evoked a faint gurgling as I rolled about on the grass, my sides aching, as if I had received a good bruising.

CHAPTER XX

A GHASTLY GIFT

DAY had just dawned when I rose to join Mariano at the fire he had already kindled to heat the water for his early maté. I did not like the idea of lying there concealed amongst the trees like some hunted animal for an indefinite time; moreover, I had been advised by Santa Coloma to proceed directly to the Lomas de Rocha, on the south coast, in the event of a defeat, and this now seemed to me the best thing to do. It had been very pleasant lying there "under the greenwood tree," while those veracious stories of hags, lampalaguas, and apparitions had proved highly entertaining; but a long spell, a whole month perhaps, of that kind of life was not to be thought of; and if I did not get to Rocha now, before the rural police were set to catch runaway rebels, it would perhaps be impossible to do so later on. I determined, therefore, to go my own way, and after drinking bitter maté, I caught and saddled the dun horse. I really had not deserved the severe censure Lechuza had passed on me the previous evening in reference to horse-stealing, for I had taken the dun with very little more compunction than one is accustomed to feel in England when "borrowing" an umbrella on a rainy day. To all people in all parts of the world, a time comes when to appropriate their neighbour's goods is held not only justifiable, but even meritorious: to Israelites in Egypt, Englishmen under a cloud in their own moist island, and to Orientals running away after a fight. By keeping the dun over thirty hours in my possession I had acquired a kind of prescriptive right to it, and now began to look on it as my very own; subsequent experience of his endurance and other good qualities enables me to endorse the Oriental saying that a "stolen horse carries you well."

Bidding farewell to my companions in defeat, who had certainly not been frightened out of their imaginations, I rode forth just when it was beginning to grow light. Roads and houses I studiously avoided, travelling on at an easy gallop, which took me about ten miles an hour, till noon; then I rested at a small rancho, where I fed and watered my horse and recruited my own energies with roast beef and bitter maté. On again till dark; by that time I had covered about forty miles and began to feel both hungry and tired. I had passed several ranchos and estancia-houses, but was shy of seeking entertainment at any of them, and so went further only to fare worse. When the brief twilight was darkening to night I came upon a broad cart-track, leading, I suppose, to Montevideo from the eastern part of the country, and seeing a long, low rancho near it, which I recognised as a *pulpería*, or store, by the flagstaff planted before it, I resolved to purchase some refreshment for myself, then to ride on a mile or two and spend the night under the stars—a safe roof if an airy one. Tying my horse to the gate, I went into the porch-like projection at the end of the rancho, which I found divided from the interior by the counter, with its usual grating of thick iron bars to protect the treasures of gin, rum, and comestibles from drunken or quarrelsome customers. As soon as I came into the porch I began to regret having alighted at the place, for there, standing at the counter, smoking and drinking, were about a dozen very rough-looking men. Unfortunately for me, they had tied their horses under the shadow of a clump of trees some distance from the gate, so that I had missed seeing them on my arrival. Once amongst them, however, my only plan was to disguise my uneasiness, be very polite, get my refreshments, then make my escape as speedily as possible. They stared rather hard at me, but returned my salutation courteously; then going to a disengaged corner of the counter I rested my left elbow on it and called for bread, a box of sardines, and a tumbler of wine.

"If you will join me, señores, the table is spread," said I; but they all declined my invitation with thanks, and I began to eat my bread and sardines.

They appeared to be all persons living in the immediate neighbourhood, for they addressed each other familiarly and were conversing about love matters. One of them, however, soon dropped out of the conversation, and edging away from the others stood a little space apart leaning against the wall on the side of the porch furthest from me. I began to notice this man very particularly, for it was plain to see that I had excited his interest in an extraordinary manner, and I did not like his scrutiny. He was, without exception, the most murderous-looking villain I have ever had the misfortune to meet: that was the deliberate opinion I came to before I formed a closer acquaintance with him. He was a broad-chested, powerful-looking man of medium height; his hands he kept concealed under the large cloth poncho he wore, and he had on a slouch hat that just allowed his eyes to be seen under the rim. They were truculent, yellowish-green eyes, that seemed to grow fiery and dim and fiery again by turns, yet never for a single instant were they averted from my face. His black hair hung to his shoulders, and he also had a bristly moustache, which did not conceal his brutal mouth, nor was there any beard to hide his broad, swarthy jowl. His jaws were the only part of him that had any motion, while he stood there, still as a bronze statue, watching me. At intervals he ground his teeth, after which he would slap his lips together two or three times, while a slimy froth, most sickening to see, gathered at the corners of his mouth.

"Gandara, you are not drinking," said one of the gauchos, turning to him. He shook his head slightly without speaking or taking his eyes off my face; whereupon the man who had spoken smiled and resumed his conversation with the others.

The long, intense, soul-trying scrutiny this brutal wretch had subjected me to came to a very sudden end. Quick as lightning a long, broad knife flashed out from its concealment under his poncho, and with one cat-like bound he was before me, the point of his horrid weapon touching my poncho just over the pit of my stomach.

"Do not move. rebel," he said in a husky voice. "If you move one hair's-breadth, that moment you die."

The other men all ceased talking and looked on with some interest, but did not offer to interfere or make any remark.

For one moment I felt as if an electric shock had gone through me, and then instantly I was calm—never, in fact, have I felt more calm and collected than at that terrible moment. 'Tis a blessed instinct of self-preservation which nature has provided us with; feeble, timid men possess it in common with the strong and brave, just as weak, persecuted wild animals have it as well as those that are fierce and bloodthirsty. It is the calm which comes without call when death suddenly and unexpectedly rises up to stare us in the face; it tells us that there is one faint chance which a premature attempt to escape or even a slight agitation will destroy.

"I have no wish to move, friend," I said, "but I am curious to know why you attack me?"

"Because you are a rebel. I have seen you before, you are one of Santa Coloma's officers. Here you shall stand with this knife touching you till you are arrested, or else with this knife in you here you shall die."

"You are making a mistake," I said.

"Neighbours," said he, speaking to the others, but without taking his eyes from my face, "will you tie this man hand and foot while I stand before him to prevent him from drawing any weapon he may have concealed under his poncho?"

"We have not come here to arrest travellers," returned one of the men. "If he is a rebel it is no concern of ours. Perhaps you are mistaken, Gandara."

"No, no, I am not mistaken," he returned. "He shall not escape. I saw him at San Paulo with these eyes—when did they ever deceive me? If you refuse to assist me, then go one of you to the Alcalde's house and tell him to come without delay, while I keep guard here."

After a little discussion one of the men offered to go and inform the Alcalde. When he had left, I said, "My friend, may I finish my meal? I am hungry and had just begun to eat when you drew your knife against me."

"Yes; eat," he said; "only keep your hands well up so that I can see them. Perhaps you have a weapon at your waist."

"I have not," I said, "for I am an inoffensive person and do not require weapons."

"Tongues were made to lie," he returned, truly enough. "If I see you drop your hand lower than the counter I shall rip you up. We shall then be able to see whether you digest your food or not."

I began to eat and sip my wine, still with those brutal eyes on my face and the keen knife-point touching my poncho. There was now a ghastly look of horrible excitement on his face, while his teeth-grinding performances became more frequent and the slimy froth dropped continually from the corners of his mouth on to his bosom. I dared not look at the knife, because a terrible impulse to wrest it out of his hands kept rising in me. It was almost too strong to be overcome, yet I knew that even the slightest attempt at escape would be fatal to me; for the fellow was evidently thirsty for my blood and only wanted an excuse to run me through. But what, I thought, if he were to grow tired of waiting, and, carried away by his murderous instincts, to plunge his weapon into me? In that case I should die like a dog without having availed myself of my one chance of escape through over-caution. These thoughts were maddening, still through it all I laboured to observe an outwardly calm demeanour.

My supper was done. I began to feel strangely weak and nervous. My lips grew dry; I was intensely thirsty and longed for more wine, yet dared not take it for fear that in my excited state even a very moderate amount of alcohol might cloud my brain.

"How long will it take your friend to return with the Alcalde?" I asked at length.

Gandara made no reply. "A long time," said one of the other men. "I, for one, cannot wait till he comes," and after that he took his departure. One by one they now began to drop away till only two men besides Gandara remained in the porch. Still that murderous wretch kept before me like a tiger watching its prey, or rather like a wild boar, gnashing and foaming, and ready to rip up its adversary with horrid tusk.

At length I made an appeal to him, for I began to despair of the Alcalde coming to deliver me. "Friend," I said, "if you will allow me to speak, I can convince you that you are mistaken. I am a foreigner, and know nothing about Santa Coloma."

"No, no," he interrupted, pressing the knife-point warningly against my stomach, then suddenly withdrawing it as if about to plunge it into me. "I know you are a rebel. If I thought the Alcalde were not coming I would run you through at once and cut your throat afterwards. It is a virtue to kill a Blanco traitor, and if you do not go bound hand and foot from here then here you must die. What, do you dare to say that I did not see you at San Paulo—that you are not an officer of Santa Coloma? Look, rebel, I will swear on this cross that I saw you there."

Suiting the action to the word, he raised the hilt of the weapon to his lips to kiss the guard, which with the handle formed a cross. That pious action was the first slip he had made, and gave the first opportunity that had come to me during all that terrible interview. Before he had ceased speaking the conviction that my time had come flashed like lightning through my brain. Just as his slimy lips kissed the hilt, my right hand dropped to my side and grasped the handle of my revolver under my poncho. He saw the movement and very quickly recovered the handle of his knife. In another second of time he would have driven the blade through me; but that second was all I now required. Straight from my waist, and from under my poncho, I fired. His knife fell ringing on to the floor; he swerved, then fell back, coming to the ground with a heavy thud. Over his falling body I leaped, and almost before he had touched the ground was several yards away, then wheeling round, I found the other two men rushing out after me.

"Back!" I shouted, covering the foremost of the two with my revolver.

They instantly stood still.

"We are not following you, friend," said one, "but only wish to get out of the place."

"Back, or I fire!" I repeated, and then they retreated into the porch. They had stood by unconcerned while their cut-throat comrade Gandara was threatening my life, so that I naturally felt angry with them.

I sprang upon my horse, but instead of riding away at once stood for some minutes by the gate watching the two men. They were kneeling by Gandara, one opening his clothes to look for the wound, the other holding a flaring candle over his ashen corpse-like face.

"Is he dead?" I asked.

One of the men looked up and answered, "It appears so."

"Then," I returned, "I make you a present of his carcass."

After that, digging my spurs into my horse, I galloped away.

Some readers might imagine, after what I have related, that my sojourn in the Purple Land had quite brutalised me; I am happy to inform them that it was not so. Whatever a man's individual character may happen to be, he has always a strong inclination in him to reply to an attack in the spirit in which it is made. He does not call the person who playfully ridicules his foibles a whitened sepulchre or an unspeakable scoundrel, and the same principle holds good when it comes to actual physical fighting. If a French gentleman were to call me out, I daresay I should go to the encounter twirling my moustache, bowing down to the ground, all smiles and compliments; and that I should select my rapier with a pleasant kind of feeling, like that experienced by the satirist about to write a brilliant article while picking out a pen with a suitable nib. On the other hand, if a murderous brute with truculent eyes and gnashing teeth attempts to disembowel me with a butcher's knife, the instinct of self-preservation comes out in all its old original ferocity, inspiring the heart with such implacable fury that after spilling his blood I could spurn his loathsome carcass with my foot. I do not wonder at myself for speaking those savage words. That he was past recall seemed certain, yet not a shade of regret did I feel at his death. Joy at the terrible retribution I had been able to inflict on the murderous wretch was the only emotion I experienced when galloping away into the darkness—such joy that I could have sung and shouted aloud had it not seemed imprudent to indulge in such expressions of feeling.

CHAPTER XXI

LIBERTY AND DIRT

AFTER my terrible adventure I did not rest badly that night, albeit I slept on an empty stomach (the sardines counting as nothing), and under the vast, void sky, powdered with innumerable stars. And when I proceeded next day on my journey, *God's light*, as the pious Orientals call the first wave of glory with which the rising sun floods the world, had never seemed so pleasant to my eyes, nor had earth ever looked fresher or lovelier, with the grass and bushes everywhere hung with starry lace, sparkling with countless dewy gems, which the epeiras had woven overnight. Life seemed very sweet to me on that morning, so softening my heart that when I remembered the murderous wretch who had endangered it I almost regretted that he was now probably blind and deaf to nature's sweet ministrations.

Before noon I came to a large thatched house, with clumps of shady trees growing near it, also surrounded with brushwood fences and sheep and cattle enclosures.

The blue smoke curling peacefully up from the chimney and the white gleam of the walls through the shady trees —for this rancho actually boasted a chimney and whitewashed walls—looked exceedingly inviting to my tired eyes. How pleasant a good breakfast with a long siesta in the shade after it would be, thought I; but, alas! was I not pursued by the awful phantoms of political vengeance? Uncertain whether to call or not, my horse jogged straight on towards the house, for a horse always knows when his rider is in doubt and never fails at such times to give his advice. It was lucky for me that on this occasion I condescended to take it. "I will, at all events, call for a drink of water and see what the people are like," I thought, and in a few minutes I was standing at the gate, apparently an object of great interest to half a dozen children ranging from two to thirteen years old, all staring at me with wide-open eyes. They had dirty faces, the smallest one dirty legs also, for he or she wore nothing but a small shirt. The next in size had a shirt supplemented with a trousers-like garment reaching to the knees; and so on, progressively, up to the biggest boy, who wore the cast-off parental toggery, and so instead of having too little on, was, in a sense, overdressed. I asked this youngster for a can of water to quench my thirst and a stick of fire to light my cigar. He ran into the kitchen, or living-room, and by-and-by came out again without either water or fire. "Papita wishes you to come in to drink maté," said he.

Then I dismounted, and with the careless air of a blameless non-political person, strode into the spacious kitchen, where an immense cauldron of fat was boiling over a big fire on the hearth; while beside it, ladle in hand, sat a perspiring, greasy-looking woman of about thirty. She was engaged in skimming the fat and throwing the scum on the fire, which made it blaze with a furious joy and loudly cry out in a crackling voice for more; and from head to feet she was literally bathed in grease—certainly the most greasy individual I had ever seen. It was not easy under the circumstances to tell the colour of her skin, but she had fine large Juno eyes, and her mouth was unmistakably good-humoured, as she smiled when returning my salutation. Her husband sat on the clay floor against the wall, his bare feet stretched straight out before him, while across his lap lay an immense surcingle, twenty inches broad at least, of a pure white, untanned hide; and on it he was laboriously working a design representing an ostrich hunt, with threads of black skin. He was a short, broad-shouldered man with reddish-grey hair, stiff bristly whiskers and moustache of the same hue, sharp blue eyes and a nose decidedly upturned.

He wore a red cotton handkerchief tied on his head, a blue check shirt, and a shawl wound round his body in place of the *chiripà* usually worn by native peasants. He jerked out his "Buen dia" to me in a short, quick, barking voice, and invited me to sit down.

"Cold water is bad for the constitution at this hour," he said. "We will drink maté."

There was such a rough burr-like sound in his speech that I at once concluded he was a foreigner, or hailed from some Oriental district corresponding to our Durham or Northumberland.

"Thank you," I said, "a maté is always welcome. I am an Oriental in that respect if in nothing else." For I wished everyone I met to know that I was not a native.

"Right, my friend," he exclaimed. "Maté is the best thing in this country. As for the people, they are not worth cursing."

"How can you say such a thing," I returned. "You are a foreigner, I suppose, but your wife is surely an Oriental."

The Juno of the grease-pot smiled and threw a ladleful of tallow on the fire to make it roar; possibly this was meant for applause.

He waved his hand deprecatingly, the bradawl used for his work in it.

"True, friend, she is," he replied. "Women, like horned cattle, are much the same all the world over. They have their value wherever you find them—America, Europe, Asia. We know it. I spoke of men."

"You scarcely do women justice—

La mujer es un angel del cielo,"

I returned, quoting the old Spanish song.

He barked out a short little laugh.

"That does very well to sing to a guitar," he said.

"Talking of guitars," spoke the woman, addressing me for the first time; "while we are waiting for the maté, perhaps you will sing us a ballad. The guitar is lying just behind you."

"Señora, I do not play on it," I answered. "An Englishman goes forth into the world without that desire common to people of other nations of making himself agreeable to those he may encounter on his way; this is why he does not learn to perform on musical instruments."

The little man stared at me; then deliberately disencumbering himself of surcingle, threads, and implements, he got up, advanced to me, and held out his hand.

His grave manner almost made me laugh. Taking his hand in mine, I said—

"What am I to do with this, my friend?"

"Shake it," he replied. "We are countrymen."

We then shook hands very vigorously for some time in silence, while his wife looked on with a smile and stirred the fat.

"Woman," he said, turning to her, "leave your grease till to-morrow. Breakfast must be thought of. Is there any mutton in the house?"

"Half a sheep—only," she replied.

"That will do for one meal," said he. "Here, Teofilo, run and tell Anselmo to catch two pullets—fat ones, mind. To be plucked at once. You may look for half a dozen fresh eggs for your mother to put in the stew. And, Felipe, go find Cosme and tell him to saddle the roan pony to go to the store at once. Now, wife, what is wanted—rice, sugar, vinegar, oil, raisins, pepper, saffron, salt, cloves, cummin seed, wine, brandy——"

"Stop one moment," I cried. "If you think it necessary to get provisions enough for an army to give me breakfast, I must tell you that I draw the line at brandy. I never touch it—in this country."

He shook hands with me again.

"You are right," he said. "Always stick to the native drink, wherever you are, even if it is black draught.

Whisky in Scotland, in the Banda Orientál rum—that's my rule."

The place was now in a great commotion, the children saddling ponies, shouting in pursuit of fugitive chickens, and my energetic host ordering his wife about.

After the boy was despatched for the things and my horse taken care of, we sat for half an hour in the kitchen sipping maté and conversing very agreeably. Then my host took me out into his garden behind the house to be out of his wife's way while she was engaged cooking breakfast, and there he began talking in English.

"Twenty-five years I have been on this continent," said he, telling me his history, "eighteen of them in the Banda Orientál."

"Well, you have not forgotten your language," I said. "I suppose you read?"

"Read! What! I would as soon think of wearing trousers. No, no, my friend, never read. Leave politics alone. When people molest you, shoot 'em—those are my rules. Edinburgh was my home. Had enough reading when I was a boy; heard enough psalm-singing, saw enough scrubbing and scouring to last me my lifetime. My father was a bookseller in the High Street, near the Cowgate—you know! Mother, she was pious—they were all pious. Uncle, a minister, lived with us. That was all worse than purgatory to me. I was educated at the High School—intended for the ministry, ha, ha! My only pleasure was to get a book of travels in some savage country, skulk into my room, throw off my boots, light a pipe, and lie on the floor reading—locked up from everyone. Sundays just the same. They called me a sinner, said I was going to the devil—fast. It was my nature. They didn't understand—kept on ding-donging in my ears. Always scrubbing, scouring—you might have eaten your dinner off the floor; always singing psalms—praying—scolding. Couldn't bear it; ran away at fifteen, and have never heard a word from home since. What happened? I came here, worked, saved, bought land, cattle; married a wife, lived as I liked to live—am happy. There's my wife—mother of six children—you have seen her yourself, a woman for a man to be proud of. No ding-donging, black looks, scouring from Monday to Saturday—you couldn't eat your dinner off *my* kitchen floor. There are my children, six of 'em, all told, boys and girls, healthy, dirty as they like to be, happy as the day's long; and here am I, John Carrickfergus—Don Juan all the country over, my surname no native can pronounce—respected, feared, loved; a man his neighbour can rely on to do him a good turn; one who never hesitates about putting a bullet in any vulture, wild cat, or assassin that crosses his path. Now you know all."

"An extraordinary history," I said, "but I suppose you teach your children something?"

"Teach 'em nothing," he returned with emphasis. 'All we think about in the old country are books, cleanliness, clothes; what's good for soul, brain, stomach, and we make 'em miserable. Liberty for everyone—that's my rule. Dirty children are healthy, happy children. If a bee stings you in England, you clap on fresh dirt to cure the pain. Here we cure all kinds of pains with dirt.

If my child is ill I dig up a spadeful of fresh mould and rub it well—best remedy out. I'm not religious, but I remember *one* miracle. The Saviour spat on the ground and made mud with the spittle to anoint the eyes of the blind man. Made him see directly. What does that mean? Common remedy of the country, of course. *He* didn't need the clay, but followed the custom, same as in the other miracles. In Scotland dirt's wickedness—how'd they reconcile that with Scripture? I don't say *Nature*, mind, I say *Scripture*, because the Bible's the book they swear by, though they didn't write it."

"I shall think over what you say about children, and the best way to rear them," I returned. "I needn't decide in a hurry, as I haven't any yet."

He barked his short laugh and led me back to the house, where the arrangements for breakfast were now completed. The children took their meal in the kitchen, we had ours in a large cool room adjoining it. There was a small table laid with a spotless white cloth, and real crockery plates and real knives and forks. There were also real glass tumblers, bottles of Spanish wine, and snow-white *pan creollo.* Evidently my hostess had made good use of her time. She came in immediately after we were seated, and I scarcely recognised her; for she was not only clean now, but good-looking as well, with that rich olive colour on her oval face, her black hair well arranged, and her dark eyes full of tender loving light. She was now wearing a white merino dress with a quaint maroon-coloured pattern on it, and a white silk kerchief fastened with a gold brooch at her neck. It was pleasant to look at her, and noticing my admiring glances, she blushed when she sat down, then laughed. The breakfast was excellent. Roast mutton to begin, then a dish of chickens stewed with rice, nicely flavoured and coloured with red Spanish *pimenton.* A fowl roasted or boiled, as we eat them in England, is wasted, compared with this delicious *guiso de pollo* which one gets in any rancho in the Banda Orientál. After the meats we sat for an hour cracking walnuts, sipping wine, smoking cigarettes, and telling amusing stories; and I doubt whether there were three happier people in all Uruguay that morning than the un-Scotched Scotchman, John Carrickfergus, his un-ding-donging native wife, and their guest, who had shot his man on the previous evening.

After breakfast I spread my poncho on the dry grass under a tree to sleep the siesta. My slumbers lasted a long time, and on waking I was surprised to find my host and hostess seated on the grass near me, he busy ornamenting his surcingle, she with the maté-cup in her hand and a kettle of hot water beside her. She was drying her eyes, I fancied, when I opened mine.

"Awake at last!" cried Don Juan pleasantly. "Come and drink maté. Wife just been crying, you see."

She made a sign for him to hold his peace.

"Why not speak of it, Candelaria?" he said. "Where is the harm? You see my wife thinks you have been in the wars—a Santa Coloma man running away to save his throat."

"How does she make that out?" I asked in some confusion and very much surprised.

"How! Don't you know women? You said nothing about where you had been—prudence. That was one thing. Looked confused when we talked of the revolution—not a word to say about it. More evidence. Your poncho, lying there, shows two big cuts in it. 'Torn by thorns,' said I. 'Sword cuts,' said she. We were arguing about it when you woke."

"She guessed rightly," I said, "and I am ashamed of myself for not telling you before. But why should your wife cry?"

"Woman like—woman like," he answered, waving his hand. "Always ready to cry over the beaten one—that is the only politics they know."

"Did I not say that woman is an angel from heaven," I returned; then taking her hand, I kissed it. "This is the first time I have kissed a married woman's hand, but the husband of such a wife will know better than to be jealous."

"Jealous—ha, ha!" he laughed. "It would have made me prouder if you had kissed her cheek."

"Juan—a nice thing to say!" exclaimed his wife, slapping his hand tenderly.

Then while we sipped maté I told them the history of my campaign, finding it necessary, when explaining my motives for joining the rebels, to make some slight deviations from the strictest form of truth. He agreed that my best plan was to go on to Rocha to wait there for a passport before proceeding to Montevideo. But I was not allowed to leave them that day; and while we talked over our maté, Candelaria deftly repaired the tell-tale cuts in my poncho.

I spent the afternoon making friends with the children, who proved to be very intelligent and amusing little beggars, telling them some nonsensical stories I invented, and listening to their bird's-nesting, armadillo-chasing, and other adventures. Then came a late dinner, after which the children said their prayers and retired, then we smoked and sang songs without an accompaniment, and I finished a happy day by sinking to sleep in a soft, clean bed.

I had announced my intention of leaving at daybreak next morning; and when I woke, finding it already light, I dressed hastily, and, going out, found my horse already saddled standing, with three other saddled horses, at the gate. In the kitchen I found Don Juan, his wife, and the two biggest boys having their early maté. My host told me that he had been up an hour, and was only waiting to wish me a prosperous journey before going out to gather up his cattle. He at once wished me good-bye, and with his two boys went off, leaving me to partake of poached eggs and coffee—quite an English breakfast.

I then rose and thanked the good señora for her hospitality.

"One moment," she said, when I held out my hand, and drawing a small silk bag from her bosom, she offered it to me. "My husband has given me permission to present you with this at parting. It is only a small gift, but while you are in this trouble and away from all your friends it perhaps might be of use to you."

I did not wish to take money from her after all the kind treatment I had received, and so allowed the purse to lie on my open hand where she had placed it.

"And if I cannot accept it——" I began.

"Then you will hurt me very much," she replied. "Could you do that after the kind words you spoke yesterday?"

I could not resist, but after putting the purse away, took her hand and kissed it.

"Good-bye, Candelaria," I said, "you have made me love your country and repent every harsh word I have ever spoken against it."

Her hand remained in mine; she stood smiling, and did not seem to think the last word had been spoken yet. Then seeing her there looking so sweet and loving, and remembering the words her husband had spoken the day before, I stooped and kissed her cheek and lips.

"Adieu, my friend, and God be with you," she said.

I think there were tears in her eyes when I left her, but I could not see clearly, for mine also had suddenly grown dim.

And only the day before I had felt amused at the sight of this woman sitting hot and greasy over her work, and had called her Juno of the grease-pot! Now, after an acquaintance of about eighteen hours I had actually kissed her—a wife and the mother of six children, bidding her adieu with trembling voice and moist eyes! I know that I shall never forget those eyes, full of sweet, pure affection and tender sympathy, looking into mine; all my life long shall I think of Candelaria, loving her like a sister. Could any woman in my own ultra-civilised and excessively proper country inspire me with a feeling like that in so short a time? I fancy not. O civilisation, with your million conventions, soul and body withering prudishnesses, vain education for the little ones, going to church in best black clothes, unnatural craving for cleanliness, feverish striving after comforts that bring no comfort to the heart, are you a mistake altogether? Candelaria and that genial runaway John Carrickfergus make me think so. Ah yes, we are all vainly seeking after happiness in the wrong way. It was with us once and ours, but we despised it, for it was only the old common happiness which Nature gives to all her children, and we went away from it in search of another grander kind of happiness which some dreamer—Bacon or another—assured us we should find. We had only to conquer Nature, find out her secrets, make her our obedient slave, then the earth would be Eden, and every man Adam and every woman Eve. We are still marching bravely on, conquering Nature, but how weary and sad we are getting! The old joy in life and gaiety of heart have vanished, though we do sometimes pause for a few moments in our long forced march to watch the labours of some pale mechanician seeking after perpetual motion and indulge in a little, dry, cackling laugh at his expense.

CHAPTER XXII

A CROWN OF NETTLES

AFTER leaving John and Candelaria's home of liberty and love, nothing further worth recording happened till I had nearly reached the desired haven of the Lomas de Rocha, a place which I was, after all, never destined to see except from a great distance. A day unusually brilliant even for this bright climate was drawing to a close, it being within about two hours of sunset, when I turned out of my way to ascend a hill with a very long ridge-like summit, falling away at one end, appearing like the last sierra of a range just where it dies down into the level plain; only in this instance the range itself did not exist. The solitary hill was covered with short tussocks of yellow, wiry grass, with occasional bushes, while near the summit large slabs of sandstone appeared just above the surface, looking like gravestones in some old village churchyard, with all their inscriptions obliterated by time and weather. From this elevation, which was about a hundred feet above the plain, I wished to survey the country before me, for I was tired and hungry, so was my horse, and I was anxious to find a resting-place before night. Before me the country stretched away in vast undulations towards the ocean, which was not, however, in sight. Not the faintest stain of vapour appeared on the immense crystalline dome of heaven, while the stillness and transparency of the atmosphere seemed almost preternatural. A blue gleam of water, south-east of where I stood and many leagues distant, I took to be the lake of Rocha; on the western horizon were faint blue cloud-like masses with pearly peaks. They were not clouds, however, but the sierras of the range weirdly named *Cuchilla de las Animas*—Ghost-haunted mountains. At length, like a person who puts his binocular into his pocket and begins to look about him, I recalled my vision from its wanderings over illimitable space to examine the objects close at hand. On the slope of the hill, sixty yards from my standpoint, were some deep green, dwarf bushes, each bush looking in that still brilliant sunshine as if it had been hewn out of a block of malachite; and on the pale purple solanaceous flowers covering them some humble-bees were feeding. It was the humming of the bees coming distinctly to my ears that first attracted my attention to the bushes; for so still was the atmosphere that at that distance apart—sixty yards—two persons might have conversed easily without raising their voices. Much further down, about two hundred yards from the bushes, a harrier hawk stood on the ground, tearing at something it had captured, feeding in that savage, suspicious manner usual with hawks, with long pauses between the bites. Over the harrier hovered a brown milvago hawk, a vulture-like bird in its habits, that lives by picking up unconsidered trifles. Envious at the other's good fortune, or fearing, perhaps, that not even the crumbs or feathers of the feast were going to be left, it was persecuting the harrier by darting down at intervals with an angry cry and aiming a blow with its wing. The harrier methodically ducked its head each time its tormentor rushed down at it, after which it would tear its prey again in its uncomfortable manner. Further away, in the depression running along at the foot of the hill, meandered a small stream so filled with aquatic grasses and plants that the water was quite concealed, its course appearing like a vivid green snake, miles long, lying there basking in the sunshine. At the point of the stream nearest to me an old man was seated on the ground, apparently washing himself, for he was stooping over a little pool of water, while behind him stood his horse with patient, drooping head, occasionally switching off the flies with its tail. A mile further on stood a dwelling, which looked to me like an old estancia-house, surrounded by large shade trees growing singly or in irregular clumps. It was the only house near, but after gazing at it for some time I concluded that it was uninhabited. For even at that distance I could see plainly that there were no human beings moving about it, no horse or other domestic animal near, and there were certainly no hedges or enclosures of any description.

Slowly I went down the hill, and to the old man sitting beside the stream. I found him engaged in the seemingly difficult operation of disentangling a luxuriant crop of very long hair, which had somehow—possibly from long neglect—got itself into great confusion. He had dipped his head into the water, and with an old comb, boasting about seven or eight teeth, was laboriously and with infinite patience drawing out the long hairs, a very few at a time. After saluting him, I lit a cigarette, and leaning on the neck of my horse, watched his efforts for some time with profound interest. He toiled away in silence for five or six minutes, then dipped his head in the water again, and while carefully wringing the wet out he remarked that my horse looked tired.

"Yes," I replied; "so is his rider. Can you tell me who lives in that estancia?"

"My master," he returned laconically.

"Is he a good-hearted man—one who will give shelter to a stranger?" I asked.

He took a very long time to answer me, then said—

"He has nothing to say about such matters."

"An invalid?" I remarked.

Another long pause; then he shook his head and tapped his forehead significantly; after which he resumed his mermaid task.

"Demented?" said I.

He elevated an eyebrow and shrugged his shoulders, but said nothing.

After a long silence, for I was anxious not to irritate him with too much questioning, I ventured to remark—

"Well, they will not set the dogs on me, will they?"

He grinned and said that it was an establishment without dogs.

I paid him for his information with a cigarette, which he took very readily, and seemed to think smoking a pleasant relief after his disentangling labours.

"An estancia without dogs, and where the master has nothing to say—that sounds strange," I remarked tentatively, but he puffed on in silence.

"What is the name of the house?" I said, after remounting my horse.

"It is a house without a name," he replied; and after this rather unsatisfactory interview I left him and slowly went on to the estancia.

On approaching the house I saw that there had formerly been a large plantation behind it, of which only a few dead stumps now remained, the ditches that had enclosed them being now nearly obliterated. The place was ruinous and overgrown with weeds. Dismounting, I led my horse along a narrow path through a perfect wilderness of wild sunflowers, horehound, red-weed, and thorn-apple, up to some poplar trees where there had once been a gate, of which only two or three broken posts remained standing in the ground. From the old gate the path ran on, still through weeds, to the door of the house, which was partly of stone and partly of red brick, with a very steep, sloping, tiled roof. Beside the ruined gate, leaning against a post, with the hot afternoon sun shining on her uncovered head, stood a woman in a rusty-black dress. She was about twenty-six or twenty-seven years old, and had an unutterably weary, desponding expression on her face, which was colourless as marble, except for the purple stains under her large dark eyes. She did not move when I approached her, but raised her sorrowful eyes to my face, apparently feeling little interest in my arrival.

I took off my hat to salute her, and said—

"Señora, my horse is tired, and I am seeking for a resting-place; can I have shelter under your roof?"

"Yes, caballero; why not?" she returned in a voice even more significant of sorrow than her countenance.

I thanked her, and waited for her to lead the way; but she still remained standing before me with eyes cast down, and a hesitating, troubled look on her face.

"Señora," I began, "if a stranger's presence in the house would be inconvenient——"

"No, no, señor, it is not that," she interrupted quickly. Then, sinking her voice almost to a whisper, she said—"Tell me, señor, have you come from the department of Florida? Have you—have you been at San Paulo?"

I hesitated a little, then answered that I had.

"On which side?" she asked quickly, with a strange eagerness in her voice.

"Ah, señora," I returned, "why do you ask me, only a poor traveller who comes for a night's shelter, such a question——"

"Why? Perhaps for your good, señor. Remember, women are not like men—implacable. A shelter you shall have, señor; but it is best that I should know."

"You are right," I returned, "forgive me for not answering you at once. I was with Santa Coloma—the rebel."

She held out her hand to me, but, before I could take it, withdrew it and, covering her face, began to cry. Presently recovering herself and turning towards the house, she asked me to follow.

Her gestures and tears had told me eloquently enough that she too belonged to the unhappy Blanco party.

"Have you then lost some relation in this fight, señora?" I asked.

"No, señor," she replied; "but if our party had triumphed perhaps deliverance would have come to me. Ah no; I lost my relations long ago—all except my father. You shall know presently, when you see him, why our cruel enemies have refrained from shedding *his* blood."

By that time we had reached the house. There had once been a verandah to it, but this had long fallen away, leaving the walls, doors, and windows exposed to sun and rain. Lichen covered the stone walls, while in the crevices and over the tiled roof weeds and grass had flourished; but this vegetation had died with the summer heats and was now parched and yellow. She led me into a spacious room, so dimly lighted from the low door and one small window that it seemed quite dark to me coming from the bright sunlight. I stood for a few moments trying to accustom my eyes to the gloom, while she, advancing to the middle of the apartment, bent down and spoke to an aged man seated in a leather-bound easy-chair.

"Papa," she said, "I have brought in a young man—a stranger who has asked for shelter under our roof. Welcome him, papa."

Then she straightened herself, and passing behind the chair stood leaning on it, facing me.

"I wish you good day, señor," I said, advancing with a little hesitation.

There before me sat a tall, bent old man, wasted almost to a skeleton, with a grey, desolate face and long hair and beard of a silver whiteness. He was wrapped in a light-coloured poncho, and wore a black skull-cap on his head. When I spoke he leant back in his seat and began scanning my face with strangely fierce eager eyes, all the time twisting his long, thin fingers together in a nervous, excited manner.

"What, Calixto," he exclaimed at length, "is this the way you come into my presence? Ha, you thought I would not recognise you! Down—down, boy, on your knees!"

I glanced at his daughter standing behind him; she was watching my face anxiously, and made a slight inclination with her head.

Taking this as an intimation to obey the old man's commands, I went down on my knees, and touched my lips to the hand he extended.

"May God give you grace, my son," he said with tremulous voice. Then he continued: "What, did you expect to find your old father blind then? I would know you amongst a thousand, Calixto. Ah, my son, my son, why have you kept away so long? Stand, my son, and let me embrace you."

He rose up tottering from his chair and threw his arm about me; then, after gazing into my face for some moments, deliberately kissed me on both cheeks.

"Ha, Calixto," he continued, putting his trembling hands upon my shoulders and gazing into my face out of his wild, sunken eyes, "do I need ask where you have been? Where should a Peralta be but in the smoke of the battle, in the midst of carnage, fighting for the

Banda Orientál? I did not complain of your absence, Calixto — Demetria will tell you that I was patient through all these years, for I knew you would come back to me at last wearing the laurel wreath of victory. And I, Calixto, what have I worn, sitting here? A crown of nettles! Yes, for a hundred years I have worn it—you are my witness, Demetria, my daughter, that I have worn this crown of stinging-nettles for a hundred years."

He sank back, apparently exhausted, in his chair, and I uttered a sigh of relief, thinking the interview was now over. But I was mistaken. His daughter placed a chair for me at his side. "Sit here, señor, and talk to my father, while I have your horse taken care of," she whispered, and then quickly glided from the room. This was rather hard on me, I thought; but while whispering those few words she touched my hand lightly and turned her wistful eyes with a grateful look on mine, and I was glad for her sake that I had not blundered.

Presently the old man roused himself again and began talking eagerly, asking me a hundred wild questions, to which I was compelled to reply, still trying to keep up the character of the long-lost son just returned victorious from the wars.

"Tell me where you have fought and overcome the enemy," he exclaimed, raising his voice almost to a scream. "Where have they flown from you like chaff before the wind?—where have you trodden them down under your horses' hoofs?—name—name the places and the battles to me, Calixto?"

I felt strongly inclined just then to jump up and rush

out of the room, so trying was this mad conversation to my nerves; but I thought of his daughter Demetria's white, pathetic face, and restrained the impulse. Then in sheer desperation I began to talk madly as himself. I thought I would make him sick of warlike subjects. Everywhere, I cried, we had defeated, slaughtered, scattered to the four winds of heaven, the infamous Colorados. From the sea to the Brazilian frontier we have been victorious. With sword, lance, and bayonet we have stormed and taken every town from Tacuarembó to Montevideo. Every river from the Yaguaron to the Uruguay had run red with Colorado blood. In forests and sierras we had hunted them, flying like wild beasts from us; we had captured them in thousands, only to cut their throats, crucify them, blow them from guns, and tear them limb by limb to pieces with wild horses.

I was only pouring oil on the blazing fire of his insanity.

"Aha!" he shouted, his eyes sparkling while he wildly clutched my arm with his skinny, claw-like hands, "did I not know—have I not said it? Did I not fight for a hundred years, wading through blood every day, and then at last send you forth to finish the battle? And every day our enemies came and shouted in my ears, 'Victory—victory!' They told me you were dead, Calixto—that their weapons had pierced you, that they had given your flesh to be devoured of wild dogs. And I shouted with laughter to hear them. I laughed in their faces and clapped my hands and cried out, 'Prepare your throats for the sword, traitors, slaves, assassins. for a Peralta—

even Calixto, devoured of wild dogs—is coming to execute vengeance! What, will God not leave one strong arm to strike at the tyrant's breast—one Peralta in all this land! Fly, miscreants! Die, wretches! He has risen from the grave—he has come back from hell, armed with hell-fire to burn your towns to ashes—to extirpate you utterly from the earth!'"

His thin, tremulous voice had risen towards the close of this mad speech to a reedy shriek that rang through the quiet, darkening house like the long, shrill cry of some water-fowl heard at night in the desolate marshes.

Then he loosened his hold on my arm and dropped back moaning and shivering into his seat. His eyes closed, his whole frame trembled, and he looked like a person just recovering from an epileptic fit; then he seemed to sink to sleep. It was now getting quite dark, for the sun had been down some time, and it was with the greatest relief that I saw Doña Demetria gliding like a ghost into the room. She touched me on the arm and whispered, "Come, señor, he is asleep now."

I followed her out into the fresh air, which had never seemed so fresh before; then, turning to me, she hurriedly whispered, "Remember, señor, that what you have told me is a secret. Say not one word of it to any other person here."

CHAPTER XXIII

THE RED FLAG OF VICTORY

SHE then led me to the kitchen at the end of the house. It was one of those roomy, old-fashioned kitchens still to be found in a few estancia-houses built in colonial times, in which the fireplace, raised a foot or two above the floor, extends the whole width of the room. It was large and dimly lighted, the walls and rafters black with a century's smoke and abundantly festooned with sooty cobwebs; but a large, cheerful fire blazed on the hearth, while before it stood a tall, gaunt woman engaged in cooking the supper and serving maté. This was Ramona, an old servant on the estancia. There also sat my friend of the tangled tresses, which he had evidently succeeded in combing well out, for they now hung down quite smooth on his back and as long as a woman's hair. Another person was also seated near the fire, whose age might have been anything from twenty-five to forty-five, for he had, I think, a mixture of Indian blood in his veins, and one of those smooth, dry, dark faces that change but little with age. He was an undersized, wiry-looking man with a small, intensely black moustache, but no whiskers or beard. He seemed to be a person of some consequence in the house, and when my conductress introduced him to me as "Don Hilario," he rose to his feet and received me with a profound bow. In spite of his excessive politeness I conceived a feeling of distrust towards him from the moment I saw him; and this was because his small, watchful eyes were perpetually glancing at my face in a furtive manner, only to glance swiftly away again whenever I looked at him; for he seemed quite incapable of meeting the gaze of another. We drank maté and talked a little, but were not a lively party. Doña Demetria, though she sat with us, scarcely contributed a word to the conversation; while the long-haired man—Santos by name, and the only peon on the establishment—smoked his cigarette and sipped his maté in absolute silence.

Bony old Ramona at length dished up the supper and carried it out of the kitchen; we followed to the large living-room where I had been before and gathered round a small table; for these people, though apparently poverty-stricken, ate their meals after the manner of civilised beings. At the head of the table sat the fierce, old, white-haired man staring at us out of his sunken eyes as we entered. Half rising from his seat he motioned to me to take a chair near him, then addressing Don Hilario, who sat opposite, he said, "This is my son Calixto just returned from the wars, where, as you know, he has greatly distinguished himself."

Don Hilario rose and bowed gravely. Demetria took the other end of the table, while Santos and Ramona occupied the two remaining seats.

I was greatly relieved to find that the old man's mood

had changed; there were no more wild outbursts like the one I had witnessed earlier in the evening; only occasionally he would fix his strange, burning eyes on me in a way that made me exceedingly uncomfortable. We began the meal with broth, which we finished in silence; and while we ate, Don Hilario's swift glances incessantly flew from face to face; Demetria, pale and evidently ill at ease, keeping her eyes cast down all the time.

"Is there no wine this evening, Ramona?" asked the old man in querulous tones when the old woman rose to remove the broth basins.

"The *master* has not ordered me to put any on the table," she replied with asperity and strongly emphasising the obnoxious word.

"What does this mean, Don Hilario?" said the old man, turning to his neighbour. "My son has just returned after a long absence; are we to have no wine for an occasion like this?"

Don Hilario with a faint smile on his lips drew a key from his pocket and passed it silently to Ramona. She rose, muttering, from the table and proceeded to unlock a cupboard, from which she took a bottle of wine. Then going round the table she poured out half a tumblerful for each person, excepting herself and Santos, who, to judge from his stolid countenance, did not expect any.

"No, no," said old Peralta, "give Santos wine, and pour yourself out a glass also, Ramona. You have both been good, faithful friends to me, and have nursed Calixto in his infancy. It is right that you should drink his health and rejoice with us at his return."

She obeyed with alacrity, and old Santos' wooden face almost relaxed into a grin when he received his share of the purple fluid (I can scarcely call it juice) which maketh glad the heart of man.

Presently old Peralta raised his glass and fixed his fierce, insane eyes on me. "Calixto, my son, we will drink your health," he said, "and may the curse of the Almighty fall on our enemies; may their bodies lie where they fall, till the hawks have consumed their flesh, and their bones have been trodden into dust by the cattle; and may their souls be tormented with everlasting fire."

Silently they all raised their glasses to their lips, but when they set them down again, the points of Don Hilario's black moustache were raised as if by a smile, while Santos smacked his lips in token of enjoyment.

After this ghastly toast nothing more was spoken by anyone at the table. In oppressive silence we consumed the roast and boiled meat set before us; for I dared not hazard even the most commonplace remark for fear of rousing my volcanic host into a mad eruption. When we had finished eating, Demetria rose and brought her father a cigarette. It was the signal that supper was over; and immediately afterwards she left the room, followed by the two servants. Don Hilario politely offered me a cigarette and lit one for himself. For some minutes we smoked in silence, until the old man gradually dropped to sleep in his chair, after which we rose and went back to the kitchen. Even that sombre retreat now seemed cheerful after the silence and gloom of the dining-room. Presently

Don Hilario got up, and with many apologies for leaving me, explaining that he had been invited to assist at a dance at a neighbouring estancia, took himself off. Soon afterwards, though it was only about nine o'clock, I was shown to a room where a bed had been prepared for me. It was a large, musty-smelling apartment, almost empty, there being only my bed and a few tall, upright chairs bound with leather and black with age. The floor was tiled, and the ceiling was covered with a dusty canopy of cobwebs, on which flourished a numerous colony of long-legged house-spiders. I had no disposition to sleep at that early hour, and even envied Don Hilario away enjoying himself with the Rocha beauties. My door, looking out to the front, was standing wide open; the full moon had just risen and was filling the night with its mystic splendour. Putting out my candle, for the house was now all dark and silent, I softly went out for a stroll. Under a clump of trees not far off I found an old rustic bench, and sat down on it; for the place was all such a tangled wilderness of great weeds that walking was scarcely practicable and very unpleasant.

The old half-ruined house in the midst of the dusky desolation began to assume in the moonlight a singularly weird and ghost-like appearance. Near me on one side was an irregular row of poplar trees, and the long, dark lines cast from them by the moon fell across a wide, open space where the rank-growing thorn-apples predominated. In the spaces between the broad bands made by the poplar-tree shadows, the foliage appeared of a dim, hoary blue, starred over with the white blossoms of this night flowering weed. About these flowers several big, grey moths were hovering, suddenly appearing out of the black shadows, and when looked for, noiselessly vanishing again in their mysterious ghost-like manner. Not a sound disturbed the silence except the faint melancholy trill of one small night-singing cicada from somewhere near—a faint, aerial voice that seemed to be wandering lost in infinite space, rising and floating away in its loneliness, while earth listened, hushed into preternatural stillness. Presently a large owl came noiselessly flying by, and perching on the topmost boughs of a neighbouring tree, began hooting a succession of monotonous notes, sounding like the baying of a bloodhound at a vast distance. Another owl by-and-by responded from some far-off quarter, and the dreary duet was kept up for half an hour. Whenever one bird ceased his solemn *boo-boo-boo-boo-boo*, I found myself with stilled breath straining my sense to catch the answering notes, fearing to stir lest I should lose them. A phosphorescent gleam swept by close to my face, making me start at its sudden appearance, then passed away, trailing a line of faint light over the dusky weeds. The passing firefly served to remind me that I was not smoking, and the thought then occurred to me that a cigar might possibly have the effect of relieving me from the strange, indefinable feeling of depression that had come over me. I put my hand into my pocket and drew out a cigar, and bit the end off; but when about to strike a vesta on my matchbox, I shuddered and dropped my hand.

The very thought of striking a loud exploding match

was unendurable to me, so strangely nervous did I feel. Or, possibly it was a superstitious mood I had fallen into. It seemed to me at that moment that I had somehow drifted into a region of mystery, peopled only by unearthly, fantastic beings. The people I had supped with did not seem like creatures of flesh and blood. The small, dark countenance of Don Hilario with its shifty glances and Mephistophelian smile; Demetria's pale, sorrowful face, and the sunken, insane eyes of her old, white-haired father, were all about me in the moonlight and amongst the tangled greenery. I dared not move; I scarcely breathed; the very weeds with their pale, dusky leaves were like things that had a ghostly life. And while I was in this morbid condition of mind, with that irrational fear momentarily increasing on me, I saw at a distance of about thirty yards a dark object, which seemed to move, fluttering in an uncertain way towards me. I gazed intently on it, but it was motionless now, and appeared like a black, formless shadow within the shade of the trees. Presently it came again towards me, and passing into the clear moonlight, revealed a human figure. It flitted across the bright space and was lost in the shade of other trees; but it still approached, a waving, fluttering figure, advancing and receding, but always coming nearer. My blood turned cold in my veins; I could feel my hair standing up on my head, until, unable to endure the terrible suspense longer, I jumped up from my seat. A loud exclamation of terror came from the figure, and then I saw that it was Demetria. I stammered out an apology for frightening her by jumping up, and finding that I had recognised her, she advanced to me.

"Ah, you are not asleep, señor," said she quietly. "I saw you from my window come out here more than an hour ago. Finding you did not return I began to grow anxious, and thought that, tired with your journey, you had fallen asleep out here. I came to wake you and to warn you that it is very dangerous to lie sleeping with your face exposed to the full moon."

I explained that I had felt restless and disinclined to sleep, regretted that I had caused her anxiety, and thanked her for her thoughtful kindness.

Instead of leaving me then she sat quietly down on the bench. "Señor," she said, "if it is your intention to continue your journey to-morrow, let me advise you not to do so. You can safely remain here for a few days, for in this sad house we have no visitors."

I told her that acting on Santa Coloma's advice, given to me before the fight, I was going on to the Lomas de Rocha to see a person named Florentino Blanco in that place, who would probably be able to procure me a passport from Montevideo.

"How fortunate it is that you have told me this!" she replied. "Every stranger now entering the Lomas is rigorously examined, and you could not possibly escape arrest if you went there. Remain with us, señor; it is a poor house, but we are well disposed towards you. To-morrow Santos shall go with a letter from you to Don Florentino, who is always ready to serve us, and he will do what you wish without seeing you."

I thanked her warmly and accepted the offer of a refuge in her house. Somewhat to my surprise she still remained seated on the bench. Presently she said—

"It is natural, señor, that you should not be glad to remain in a house so *triste*. But there will be no repetition of all you were obliged to endure on first entering it. Whenever my father sees a young man, a stranger to him, he receives him as he received you to-day, mistaking him for his son. After the first day, however, he loses all interest in the new face, becoming indifferent, and forgetting all he has said or imagined."

This information relieved me, and I remarked that I supposed the loss of his son had been the cause of his malady.

"You are right; let me tell you how it happened," she replied. "For this estancia must seem to you a place unlike all others in the world, and it is only natural that a stranger should wish to know the reason of its sad condition. I know that I can speak without fear of these things to one who is a friend to Santa Coloma."

"And to you, I hope, señorita," I said.

"Thank you, señor. All my life has been spent here. When I was a child my brother went into the army, then my mother died, and I was left here alone, for the siege of Montevideo had begun and I could not go there. At length my father received a terrible wound in action and was brought here to die, as we thought. For months he lay on his bed, his life trembling in the balance. Our enemies triumphed at last; the siege was over, the Blanco leaders dead or driven into exile. My father had been one of the bravest officers in the Blanco forces, and could not hope to escape the general persecution. They only waited for his recovery to arrest him and convey him to the capital, where, doubtless, he would have been shot. While he lay in this precarious condition every wrong and indignity was heaped upon us. Our horses were seized by the commander of the department, our cattle slaughtered or driven off and sold, while our house was searched for arms and visited every week by an officer who came to report on my father's health. One reason for this animosity was that Calixto, my brother, had escaped and maintained a guerilla war against the government on the Brazilian frontier. At length my father recovered so far from his wounds as to be able to creep out for an hour every day leaning on someone for support; then two armed men were sent to keep guard here to prevent his escape. We were thus living in continual dread when one day an officer came and produced a written order from the Commandante. He did not read it to me, but said it was an order for every person in the Rocha department to display a red flag on his house in token of rejoicing at a victory won by the government troops. I told him that we did not wish to disobey the Commandante's orders, but had no red flag in the house to hang out. He answered that he had brought one for that purpose with him. He unrolled it and fastened it to a pole; then climbing to the roof of the house he raised and made it fast there. Not satisfied with these insults, he ordered me to wake my father, who was sleeping, so that he also might see the flag over his house. My father came out leaning on my shoulder, and when he had cast up his eyes and seen the red flag he turned and cursed the officer. 'Go back,' he cried, 'to the dog, your master, and tell him that Colonel Peralta is still a Blanco in spite of your dishonourable flag. Tell that insolent slave of Brazil that when I was disabled I passed my sword on to my son Calixto, who knows how to use it, fighting for his country's independence.' The officer, who had mounted his horse by this time, laughed, and tossing the order from the commandancia at our feet, bowed derisively and galloped away. My father picked up the paper and read these words: 'Let there be displayed on every house in this department a red flag, in token of joy at the happy tidings of a victory won by the government troops, in which that recreant son of the Republic, the infamous assassin and traitor, Calixto Peralta, was slain!' Alas, señor, loving his son above all things, hoping so much from him, and enfeebled by long suffering, my poor father could not resist this last blow. From that cruel moment he was deprived of reason; and to that calamity we owe it that he was not put to death and that our enemies ceased to persecute us."

Demetria shed some tears when telling me this tragical story. Poor woman, she had said little or nothing about herself, yet how great and enduring must have been her grief. I was deeply moved, and taking her hand told her how deeply her sad story had pained me. Then she rose and bade me good night with a sad smile—sad, but the first smile that had visited her grief-clouded countenance since I had seen her. I could well imagine that even the sympathy of a stranger must have seemed sweet to her in that dreary isolation.

After she left me I lit my cigar. The night had lost its ghostly character and my fantastic superstitions had vanished. I was back once more in the world of men and women, and could only think of the inhumanity of man to man, and of the infinite pain silently endured by many hearts in that Purple Land. The only mystery still unsolved in that ruinous estancia was Don Hilario, who locked up the wine and was called *master* with bitter irony by Ramona, and who had thought it necessary to apologise to me for depriving me of his precious company that evening.

CHAPTER XXIV

MYSTERY OF THE GREEN BUTTERFLY

I SPENT several days with the Peraltas at their desolate, *kineless* cattle-farm, which was known in the country round simply as *Estancia* or *Campos de Peralta.* Such wearisome days they proved to me, and so anxious was I getting about Paquíta away in Montevideo, that I was more than once on the point of giving up waiting for the passport, which Don Florentino had promised to get for me, and boldly venture forth without even that fig-leaf into the open. Demetria's prudent counsels, however, prevailed, so that my departure was put off from day to day. The only pleasure I experienced in the house arose from the belief I entertained that my visit had made an agreeable break in the sad, monotonous life of my gentle hostess. Her tragical story had stirred my heart to a very deep pity, and as I grew every day to know her better I began to appreciate and esteem her for her own pure, gentle, self-sacrificing character. Notwithstanding the dreary seclusion in which she had lived, seeing no society, and with only those old servants, so primitive in their ways, for company, there was not the slightest trace of rusticity in her manner. That, however, is not saying much for Demetria, since in most ladies—most women I might almost say—of Spanish origin there is a natural grace and dignity of manner one only expects to find in women socially well placed in our own country. When we were all together at meals, or in the kitchen sipping maté, she was invariably silent, always with that shadow of some concealed anxiety on her face; but when alone with me, or when only old Santos and Ramona were present, the cloud would be gone, her eyes would lighten up and the rare smile come more frequently to her lips. Then, at times, she would become almost animated in conversation, listening with lively interest to all I told her about the great world of which she was so ignorant, and laughing, too, at her own ignorance of things known to every town-bred child. When these pleasant conversations took place in the kitchen the two old servants would sit gazing at the face of their mistress apparently absorbed in admiration. They evidently regarded her as the most perfect being that had ever been created; and though there was a ludicrous side to their simple idolatry, I ceased to wonder at it when I began to know her better. They reminded me of two faithful dogs always watching a beloved master's face, and showing in their eyes, glad or pathetic, how they sympathise with all his moods. As for old Colonel Peralta, he did nothing to make me uneasy; after the first day he never talked to me, scarcely even noticing my presence except to salute me in a ceremonious manner when we met at table. He would spend his day between his easy-chair in the house and the rustic bench under the trees, where he would sit for hours at a time leaning forward on his stick, his preternaturally brilliant eyes watching everything seemingly with a keen, intelligent interest. But he would not speak. He was waiting for his son, thinking his fierce thoughts to himself. Like a bird blown far out over a tumultuous sea and wandering lost, his spirit was ranging over that wild and troubled past—that half a century of fierce passions and bloody warfare in which he had acted a conspicuous part. And perhaps it was sometimes even more in the future than the past—that glorious future when Calixto, lying far off in some mountain pass, or on some swampy plain with the trailing creepers covering his bones, should come back victorious from the wars.

My conversations with Demetria were not frequent, and before long they ceased altogether; for Don Hilario, who was not in harmony with us, was always there, polite subdued, watchful, but not a man that one could take into his heart. The more I saw of him the less I liked him; and though I am not prejudiced about snakes, as the reader already knows, believing as I do that ancient tradition has made us very unjust towards these interesting children of our universal mother, I can think of no epithet except *snaky* to describe this man. Wherever I happened to be about the place he had a way of coming upon me, stealing through the weeds on his belly as it were, then suddenly appearing unawares before me; while something in his manner suggested a subtle, cold-blooded, venomous nature. Those swift glances of his, which perpetually came and went with such bewildering rapidity, reminded me not of the immovable, stony gaze of the serpent's lidless eyes, but of the flickering little forked tongue, that flickers, flickers, vanishes and flickers again, and is never for one moment at rest. Who was this man, and what did he there? Why was he, though manifestly not loved by anyone, absolute master of the estancia? He never asked me a question about myself, for it was not in his nature to ask questions, but he had evidently formed some disagreeable suspicions about me that made him look on me as a possible enemy. After I had been a few days in the house he ceased going out, and wherever I went he was always ready to accompany me, or when I met Demetria and began conversing with her, there he would be to take part in our conversation.

At length the piece of paper so long waited for came from the Lomas de Rocha, and with that sacred document, testifying that I was a subject of her Britannic Majesty, Queen Victoria, all fears and hesitation were dismissed from my mind and I prepared to depart for Montevideo.

The instant Don Hilario heard that I was about to leave the estancia his manner toward me changed; he became, in a moment, excessively friendly, pressing me to prolong my visit, also to accept a horse from him as a gift, and saying many kind things about the agreeable moments he had spent in my company. He completely reversed the old saying about welcome the coming, speed the parting guest; but I knew very well that he was anxious enough to see the last of me.

After supper on the eve of my departure he saddled his horse and rode off to attend a dance or gathering of some kind at a neighbouring estancia, for now that he had recovered from his suspicions he was very eager to resume the social pleasures my presence had interfered with.

I went out to smoke a cigar amongst the trees, it being a very lovely autumnal evening, with the light of an unclouded new moon to temper the darkness. I was walking up and down in a narrow path amongst the weeds, thinking of my approaching meeting with Paquíta, when old Santos came out to me and mysteriously informed me that Doña Demetria wished to see me. He led me through the large room where we always had our meals, then through a narrow dimly lighted passage into another room I had not entered before. Though the rest of the house was now in darkness, the old colonel having already retired to bed, it was very light here, there being about half a dozen candles placed about the room. In the centre of the floor, with her old face beaming with delighted admiration, stood Ramona gazing on another person seated on the sofa. And on this individual I also gazed silently for some time; for though I recognised Demetria in her, she was so changed that astonishment prevented me from speaking. The rusty grub had come forth as a splendid green and gold butterfly. She had on a grass-green silk dress, made in a fashion I had never seen before; extremely high in the waist, puffed out on the shoulders, and with enormous bell-shaped sleeves reaching to the elbows, the whole garment being plentifully trimmed with very fine cream-coloured lace. Her long, thick hair, which had hitherto always been worn in heavy plaits on her back, was now piled up in great coils on her head and surmounted by a tortoise-shell comb a foot high at least, and about fifteen inches broad at the top, looking like an immense crest on her head. In her ears were curious gold filigree pendants reaching to her bare shoulders; she also wore a necklet of half-doubloons linked together in a chain, and heavy gold bracelets on her arms. It was extremely quaint. Possibly this finery had belonged to her grandmother a hundred years ago; and I daresay that bright green was not the proper tint for Demetria's pallid complexion; still I must confess, at the risk of being set down as a barbarian in matters of taste, that it gave me a shock of pleasure to see her. She saw that I was very much surprised, and a blush of confusion overspread her face; then recovering her usual quiet, self-possessed manner she invited me to sit on the sofa by her. I took her hand and complimented her on her appearance. She laughed a little shy laugh, then said that as I was going to leave her next day she did not wish me to remember her only as a woman in rusty black. I replied that I would always remember her not for the colour and fashion of her garments, but for her great unmerited misfortunes, her virtuous heart, and for the kindness she had shown to me. My words evidently pleased her, and while we sat together conversing pleasantly, before us were Ramona and Santos, one standing, the other seated, both feasting their eyes on their mistress in her brilliant attire. Their delight was quite open and childlike, and gave an additional zest to the pleasure I felt. Demetria seemed pleased to think she looked well, and was more light-hearted than I had seen her before. That antique finery, which would have been laughable on another woman, somehow or other seemed appropriate to her; possibly because the strange simplicity and ignorance of the world displayed in her conversation and that gentle dignity of manner natural to her would have prevented her from appearing ridiculous in any costume.

At length, after we had partaken of maté served by Ramona, the old servants retired from the room, not without many longing, lingering glances at their metamorphosed mistress. Then somehow or other our conversation began to languish, Demetria becoming constrained in manner, while that anxious shadow I had grown so familiar with came again like a cloud over her face. Thinking that it was time to leave her, I rose to go, and thanked her for the pleasant evening I had spent, and expressed a wish that her future would be brighter than her past had been.

"Thank you, Richard," she returned, her eyes cast down, and allowing her hand to rest in mine. "But must you leave me so soon?—there is so much I wish to say to you."

"I will gladly remain and hear it," I said, sitting down again by her side.

"My past has been very sad, as you say, Richard, but you do not know all," and here she put her handkerchief to her eyes. There were, I noticed, several beautiful rings on her fingers, and the handkerchief she held to her eyes was a dainty little embroidered thing with a lace border; for everything in her make-up was complete and in keeping that evening. Even the quaint little shoes she wore were embroidered with silver thread and had large rosettes on them. After removing the handkerchief from her face, she continued silent and with eyes cast down, looking very pale and troubled.

"Demetria," I said, "tell me how I can serve you? I cannot guess the nature of the trouble you speak of, but if it is one I can help you out of, speak to me without reserve."

"Perhaps you can help me, Richard. It was of this matter I wished to speak this evening. But now—how can I speak of it?"

"Not to one who is your friend, Demetria? I wish you could think that the spirit of your lost brother Calixto was here in me, for I am as ready to help you as he would have been; and I know, Demetria, that you were very dear to him."

Her face flushed, and for a moment her eyes met mine; then, casting them down again, she replied sadly, "It is impossible! I can say no more to you now. My heart oppresses me so that my lips refuse to speak. To-morrow, perhaps."

"To-morrow morning I leave you, and there will be no opportunity of speaking," I said. "Don Hilario will be here watching you, and though he is so much in the house, I cannot believe that you trust him."

She started at the name of Don Hilario, and cried a little in silence; then suddenly she rose and gave me her hand to bid good night. "You shall know everything to-morrow, Richard," she said. "Then you will know how much I trust you and how little I trust him. I cannot speak myself, but I can trust Santos, who knows everything, and he shall tell you all."

There was a sad, wistful look in her eyes when we parted that haunted me for hours afterwards. Coming into the kitchen I disturbed Ramona and Santos deep in a whispered consultation. They started up, looking somewhat confused; then, when I had lit a cigar and turned to go out, they got up and went back to their mistress.

While I smoked I pondered over the strange evening I had passed, wondering very much what Demetria's secret trouble could be. "The mystery of the green butterfly," I called it; but it was really all too sad even for a mental joke, though a little timely laughter is often the best weapon to meet trouble with, sometimes having an effect like that of a gay sunshade suddenly opened in the face of an angry bull. Unable to solve the riddle, I retired to my room to sleep my last sleep under Peralta's dreary roof.

CHAPTER XXV

DELIVER ME FROM MINE ENEMY!

ABOUT eight o'clock next morning I bade the Peraltas good-bye, and set out on my long-delayed journey, still mounted on that dishonestly acquired steed that had served me so well, for I had declined the good Hilario's offer of a horse. Though all my toils, wanderings, and many services to the cause of liberty (or whatever people fight for in the Banda) had not earned me one copper coin, it was some comfort to think that Candelaria's never-to-be-forgotten generosity had saved me from being penniless; I was, in fact, returning to Paquíta well dressed, on a splendid horse, and with dollars enough in my pocket to take us comfortably out of the country. Santos rode out with me, ostensibly to put me on the right road to Montevideo; only I knew, of course, that he was the bearer of an important communication from Demetria. When we had ridden about half a league without any approach to the subject on his part, in spite of sundry hints I threw out, I asked him plainly if he had a message for me.

After pondering over the question for as long a time as would be necessary to work out a rather difficult mathematical problem, he answered that he had.

"Then," said I, "let me hear it."

He grinned. "Do you think," he said, "that it is a thing to be spoken in half a dozen words? I have not come all this distance merely to say that the moon came in dry, or that yesterday, being Friday, Doña Demetria tasted no meat. It is a long story, señor."

"How many leagues long? Do you intend it to last all the way to Montevideo? The longer it is the sooner you ought to begin it."

"There are things easy to say, and there are other things not so easy," returned Santos. "But as to saying anything on horseback, who could do that?"

"Why not?"

"The question!" said he. "Have you not observed that when liquor is drawn from a cask—wine, or bitter orange juice to make orangeade, or even rum, which is by nature white and clear—that it runs thick when the cask is shaken? It is the same with us, señor; our brain is the cask out of which we draw all the things we say."

"And the spigot——"

"That is so," he struck in, pleased with my ready intelligence; "the mouth is the spigot."

"I should have thought the nose more like the spigot," I replied.

"No," he gravely returned. "You can make a loud noise with the nose when you snore or blow it in a handkerchief; but it has no door of communication with the brain. The things that are in the brain flow out by the mouth."

"Very well," said I, getting impatient, "call the mouth

spigot, bung-hole, or what you like, and the nose merely an ornament on the cask. The thing is this. Doña Demetria has entrusted you with some liquor to pass on to me; now pass it, thick or clear."

"Not thick," he answered stubbornly.

"Very well; clear then," I shouted.

"To give it to you clear I must give it off and not on my horse, sitting still and not moving."

Anxious to have it over without more beating about the bush, I reined up my horse, jumped off and sat down on the grass without another word. He followed my example, and after seating himself in a comfortable position, deliberately drew out his tobacco-pouch and began making a cigarette. I could not quarrel with him for this further delay, for without the soothing, stimulating cigarette an Oriental finds it difficult to collect his thoughts. Leaving him to carry out his instructions in his own laborious fashion, I vented my irritation on the grass, plucking it up by handfuls.

"Why do you do that?" he asked, with a grin.

"Pluck grass? What a question! When a person sits down on the grass, what is the first thing he does?"

"Makes a cigarette," he returned.

"In my country he begins plucking up the grass," I said.

"In the Banda Orientál we leave the grass for the cattle to eat," said he.

I at once gave up pulling the grass, for it evidently distracted his mind, and lighting a cigarette, began smoking as placidly as I could.

At length he began: "There is not in all the Banda Orientál a worse person to express things than myself."

"You are speaking the truth," I said.

"But what is to be done?" he continued, staring straight before him and giving as little heed to my interruption as a hunter riding at a stiff fence would pay to a remark about the weather. "When a man cannot get a knife, he breaks in two an old pair of sheep-shears and with one of the blades makes himself an implement which has to serve him for a knife. This is how it is with Doña Demetria; she has no one but her poor Santos to speak for her. If she had asked me to expose my life in her service, that I could easily have done; but to speak for her to a man who can read the almanac and knows the names of all the stars in the sky, that kills me, señor. And who knows this better than my mistress, who has been intimate with me from her infancy, when I often carried her in my arms? I can only say this, señor; when I speak, remember my poverty and that my mistress has no instrument except my poor tongue to convey her wishes. Words has she told me to say to you, but my devil of a memory has lost them all. What am I to do in this case? If I wished to buy my neighbour's horse and went to him and said, 'Sell me your horse, neighbour, for I have fallen in love with it and my heart is sick with desire, so that I must have it at any price,' would that not be madness, señor? Yet I must be like that imprudent person. I come to you for something, and all her expressions, which were like rare flowers culled from a garden, have been lost by the way. Therefore I can only say this thing which my mistress desires, putting it in my own brute words, which are like wild flowers I have myself gathered on the plain, that have neither fragrance nor beauty to recommend them."

This quaint exordium did not advance matters much, but it had the effect of rousing my attention and convincing me that the message entrusted to Santos was one of very grave import. He had finished his first cigarette and now began slowly making himself a second one; but I waited patiently for him to speak, my irritation had quite vanished, those "wild flowers" of his were not without beauty, and his love and devotion for his unhappy mistress made them smell very sweet.

Presently he resumed: "Señor, you have told my mistress that you are a poor man; that you look upon this country life as a free and happy one; that above all things you would like to possess an estancia where you could breed cattle and race-horses and hunt ostriches. All this she has revolved in her mind, and because it is in her power to offer you the things you desire does she now ask you to aid her in her trouble. And now, señor, let me tell you this. The Peralta property extends all the way to the Rocha waters; five leagues of land, and there is none better in this department. It was formerly well stocked. There were thousands of cattle and mares; for my master's party then ruled in the country; the Colorados were shut up in Montevideo, and that cut-throat Frutos Rivera never came into this part. Of the cattle only a remnant remains, but the land is a fortune for any man, and when my old master dies Doña Demetria inherits all. Even now it is hers, since her father has lost his calabash as you have seen. Now let me tell you what happened many years ago. Don Hilario was at first a peon—a poor boy the Colonel befriended. When he grew up he was made capatas, then mayordomo. Don Calixto was killed and the Colonel lost his reason, then Don Hilario made himself all-powerful, doing what he liked with his master, and setting Doña Demetria's authority aside. Did he protect the interests of the estancia? On the contrary, he was one with our enemies, and when they came like dogs for our cattle and horses he was behind them. This he did to make friends of the reigning party, when the Blancos had lost everything. Now he wishes to marry Doña Demetria to make himself owner of the land. Don Calixto is dead, and who is there to bell the cat? Even now he acts like the only owner; he buys and sells and the money is his. My mistress is scarcely allowed clothes to wear; she has no horse to ride on and is a prisoner in her own house. He watches her like a cat watching a bird shut in a room; if he suspected her of an intention to make her escape he would murder her. He has sworn to her that unless she marries him he will kill her. Is not this sad? Señor, she asks you to deliver her from this man. Her words I have forgotten, but imagine that you see her before you a suppliant on her knees, and that you know what the thing is she asks, and see her lips move, though you do not hear her words."

"Tell me how I can deliver her?" I said. feeling very much moved at what I had heard

"How! By carrying her off forcibly—do you understand? Is it not in your power to return in a few days' time with two or three friends to do this thing? You must come disguised and armed. If I am in the way I will do what I can to protect her, but you will easily knock me down and stun me—do you understand? Don Hilario must not know that we are in the plot. From him fear nothing, for though he is brave enough to threaten a woman with death, before armed men he is like a dog that hears thunder. You can then take her to Montevideo and conceal her there. The rest will be easy. Don Hilario will fail to find her; Ramona and I will take care of the Colonel, and when his daughter is out of his sight perhaps he will forget her. Then, señor, there will be no trouble about the property; for who can resist a legal claim?"

"I do not understand you, Santos," said I. "If Demetria wishes me to do what you say, and there is no other way to save her from Don Hilario's persecutions, I will do it. I will do anything to serve her, and I have no fear of that dog Hilario. But when I have placed her in concealment, who in Montevideo, where she is without a friend, will take up her cause and see that she is not defrauded of her rights? I can give her liberty, but that will be all."

"The property will be the same as yours when you marry her," said he.

I had never suspected that this was coming, and was amazed to hear it.

"Will you tell me, Santos," said I, "that Demetria sent you to say this to me? Does she think that only by marrying her I can deliver her from this robber and save her property?"

"There is, of course, no other way," said he. "If it could be done by other means would she not have spoken last night and explained everything to you? Consider, señor, all this large property will be yours. If you do not like this department then she will sell everything for you to buy an estancia elsewhere, or to do whatever you wish. And I ask you this, señor, could any man marry a better woman?"

"No," said I; "but, Santos, I cannot marry your mistress."

I remembered then, sadly enough, that I had told her next to nothing about myself. Seeing me so young, wandering homeless about the country, she had naturally taken me for a single man; and, perhaps thinking that I had conceived an affection for her, had been driven in her despair to make this proposal. Poor Demetria, was there to be no deliverance for her after all!

"Friend," said Santos, dropping the ceremonious señor in his anxiety to serve his mistress, "never speak without first considering all things. There is no woman like her. If you do not love her now you will love her when you know her better; no good man could help feeling affection for her. You saw her last evening in a green silk dress, also wearing a tortoise-shell comb and gold ornaments—was she not elegant, señor? Did she not then appear to your eyes a woman suitable for a wife? You have been everywhere, and have seen many women, and perhaps in some distant place you have met one more beautiful than my mistress. But consider the life she has led! Grief has made her pale and thin, staining her face with purple under the eyes. Can laughter and song come out of a heart where fear is? Another life would change all; she would be a flower amongst women."

Poor old simple-minded Santos, he had done himself great injustice; his love for his mistress had inspired him with an eloquence that went to my heart. And poor Demetria, driven by her weary desolate life and torturing fears to make in vain this unwomanly proposal to a stranger! And after all it was not unwomanly; for in all countries where they are not abject slaves it is permissible for women in some circumstances to propose marriage. Even in England it is so, where society is like a huge Clapham Junction, with human creatures moving like trucks and carriages on cast-iron conventional rails, which they can only leave at the risk of a destructive collision. And a proposal of the kind was never more justifiable than in this case. Shut away from the sight of men in her dreary seclusion, haunted by nameless fears, her offer was to bestow her hand along with a large property on a penniless adventurer. Nor had she done this before she had learnt to love me, and to think, perhaps, that the feeling was returned. She had waited, too, till the very last moment, only making her offer when she had despaired of its coming from me. This explained the reception of the previous evening; the ancient splendid attire which she had worn to win favour in my sight; the shy, wistful expression of her eyes, the hesitation she could not overcome. When I had recovered from the first shock of surprise I could only feel the greatest respect and compassion for her, bitterly regretting that I had not told her all my past history, so that she might have been spared the shame and grief she would now be compelled to endure. These sad thoughts passed through my mind while Santos expatiated on the advantages of the proposed alliance until I stopped him.

"Say no more," I said; "for I swear to you, Santos, that were it possible I would gladly take Demetria for a wife, so greatly do I admire and esteem her. But I am married. Look at this; it is my wife's portrait"; and taking from my bosom the miniature which I always wore round my neck, I handed it to him.

He stared at me in silent astonishment for a few moments, then took the portrait into his hand; and while he gazed admiringly at it I pondered over what I had heard. I could not now think of leaving this poor woman who had offered herself with all her inheritance to me without some attempt to rescue her from her sad position. She had given me a refuge when I was in trouble and danger, and the appeal she had just made to me, accompanied by so convincing a proof of her trust and affection, would have gone to the heart of the most cold-blooded man in existence, to make him, in spite of his nature, her devoted champion.

At length Santos handed back the miniature with a sigh. "Such a face as that my eyes have never seen," he remarked. "There is nothing more to be said."

"There is a great deal more to be said," I returned. "I have thought of an easy plan to help your mistress. When you have reported this conversation, tell her to remember the offer of assistance made to her last night. I said I would be a brother to her, and I shall keep my promise. You three cannot think of any better scheme to save Demetria than this one you have told me, but it is after all a very poor scheme, full of difficulty and danger to her. My plan is a simpler and safer one. Tell her to come out to-night at midnight, after the moon has set, to meet me under the trees behind the house. I shall be there waiting with a horse for her, and will take her away to some safe place of concealment where Don Hilario will never find her. When she is once out of his power it will be time enough to think of some way to turn him out of the estancia and to arrange matters. See that she does not fail to meet me, and let her take a few clothes and some money if she has any; also her jewels, for it would not be safe to leave them in the house with Don Hilario."

Santos was delighted with my scheme, which was so much more practical though less romantic than the one hatched by those three simple-minded conspirators. With heart full of hope he was about to leave me when he suddenly exclaimed, "But, señor, how will you get a horse and side-saddle for Doña Demetria?"

"Leave it all to me," I said; then we separated, he to return to his mistress, who was no doubt anxiously waiting to know the result of our conversation, I to get through the next fifteen hours in the best way I could.

CHAPTER XXVI

LOCK AND KEY AND SINNERS THREE

AFTER leaving Santos I rode on to a belt of wood about two miles east of the road, and passing through it surveyed the country lying beyond. The only habitation near it was a shepherd's lonely rancho, standing on an open plain of yellow grass, over which a scattered flock of sheep and a few horses were grazing. I determined to remain in the wood till near noon, then proceed to the rancho to get breakfast, and commence my search for a horse and side-saddle in the neighbourhood. After unsaddling my horse and tying him to a tree, where there were some pickings of grass and herbage about the roots, I lit a cigar and made myself comfortable on my rugs in the shade. Presently I had some visitors in a flock of *urracas*, or magpies, as they are called in the vernacular, or Guira cuckoos; a graceful, loquacious bird resembling a magpie, only with a longer tail and a bold, red beak. These ill-mannered birds skulked about in the branches over me all the time I remained in the wood, scolding me so incessantly in their intolerably loud, angry, rattling notes, varied occasionally with shrill whistlings and groans, that I could scarcely even hear myself think. They soon succeeded in bringing all the other birds within hearing-distance to the spot to take part in the demonstration. It was unreasonable of the cuckoos, to say the least of it, for it was now long past their breeding season, so that parental solicitude could not be pleaded as an excuse for their churlish behaviour. The others—tanagers, finches, tyrant-birds; red, white, blue, grey, yellow, and mixed—were, I must own, less troublesome, for, after hopping about for a while, screaming, chirping, and twittering, they very sensibly flew away, no doubt thinking their friends the cuckoos were making a great deal too much fuss. My sole mammalian visitor was an armadillo, that came hurrying towards me, looking curiously like a little old bent-backed gentleman in a rusty black coat trotting briskly about on some very important business. It came to within three yards of my feet, then stopped, and seemed astonished beyond measure at my presence, staring at me with its little, bleary, blinking eyes, and looking more like the shabby old gentleman than ever. Then it trotted away through the trees, but presently returned for a second inspection; and after that it kept coming and going till I inadvertently burst out laughing, whereupon it scuttled away in great alarm, and returned no more. I was sorry I had frightened the amusing little beggar, for I felt in that exceedingly light-hearted mood when one's merriment is ready to brim over at the slightest provocation. Yet that very morning poor Demetria's appeal had deeply stirred my heart, and I was now embarked on a most Quixotic and perhaps perilous adventure! Possibly the very fact of that adventure being before me had produced an exhilarating effect on my mind, and made it impossible for me to be sad or even decently composed.

After spending a couple of hours in the pleasant shade, the blue smoke ascending from the rancho before me gave notice of the approaching breakfast hour; so, saddling my horse, I went to make my morning call, the cuckoos hailing my departure with loud, mocking shouts and whistling calls, meant to inform all their feathered friends that they had at last succeeded in making their haunt too hot for me.

At the rancho I was received by a somewhat surly-looking young man, with long, intensely black hair and moustache, and who wore in place of a hat a purple cotton handkerchief tied about his head. He did not seem to be over-pleased at my visit, and invited me rather ungraciously to alight if I thought proper. I followed him into the kitchen, where his little brown-skinned wife was preparing breakfast, and I fancied after seeing her that her prettiness was the cause of his inhospitable manner towards a stranger. She was singularly pretty, with a seductive soft brown skin, ripe pouting lips of a rich purple-red, and when she laughed, which happened very frequently, her teeth glistened like pearls. Her crisp black hair hung down unbound and disordered, for she looked like a very careless little beauty; but when she saw me enter, she blushed and tossed her tresses away from her shoulders, then carefully felt the pendants dropping from her ears to assure herself that they were safe, or possibly to attract my attention to them. The frequent glances her laughing dark eyes shot at me soon convinced me that she was one of those charming little wives—charming, that is, when they are the wives of other people—who are not satisfied with a husband's admiration.

I had timed my arrival well, for the roast lamb over the coals was just assuming a deep golden brown colour, and sending out a most delicious fragrance. During the repast which followed I amused my auditors, and myself, by telling a few innocent lies, and began by saying that I was on my return to Rocha from Montevideo.

The shepherd remarked suspiciously that I was not on the right road.

I answered that I knew it; then proceeded to say that I had met with a misfortune on the previous evening, which in the end had led me out of the right road. I had only been married a few days, I continued, and at this declaration my host looked relieved, while little gipsy suddenly seemed to lose all interest in me.

"My wife," I said, "set her heart on having a side-saddle, as she is very fond of riding; so, having business which took me to town, I there purchased one for her, and was returning with it on a led horse—my wife's horse, unfortunately—when I stopped last evening to get some refreshment at a *pulpería* on the road. While eating some bread and sausage a tipsy person, who happened to be there, imprudently began to explode some fire-crackers, which so terrified the horses tied at the gate that several of them broke loose and escaped. My wife's horse with the side-saddle on him escaped with them; then mounting my own horse I started in pursuit, but failed to overtake the runaway. Finally it joined a herd of mares, and these becoming terrified, fled from me, leading me a chase of several leagues, till I lost sight of them in the darkness."

"If your wife resembles mine in disposition, friend,' said he, with a somewhat sorrowful smile, "you would have continued following that runaway animal with the side-saddle to the end of the world."

"I can say this," I returned gravely, "without a side-saddle, good or bad, I am not going to present myself before her. I intend inquiring at every house on my way to the Lomas de Rocha till I can hear of one for sale."

"What will you give for one?" said he, becoming interested.

"That will depend on its condition. If it is as good as new I will give the amount it cost and two dollars profit besides."

"I know of a side-saddle that cost ten dollars a year ago, but it has never been used. It belongs to a neighbour three leagues from here, and she would sell it, I believe."

"Show me the house," I said, "and I will go directly and offer twelve dollars for it."

"You speak of Doña Petrona's side-saddle, Antonio?" said the little wife. "She would sell it for what it cost—perhaps for eight dollars. Ah, pumpkin-head, why did you not think to make all that profit? Then I could have bought slippers and a thousand things."

"You are never satisfied, Cleta," he returned. "Have you not got slippers to your feet?"

She tossed up a pretty foot and displayed it cased in

rather a shabby little slipper. Then with a laugh she kicked it off towards him. "There," she exclaimed, "put it in your bosom and keep it—something precious! And some day when you go to Montevideo, and wish to appear very grand before all the town, wear it on your great toe."

"Who expects reason from a woman?" said Antonio, shrugging his shoulders.

"Reason! you have no more brains than a Muscovy duck, Antonio. You might have made this profit, but you never can make money like other men, and therefore you will always be poorer than the spiders. I have said this before very often and only hope you will not forget it, for in future I intend to speak of other things."

"Where would I have got the ten dollars to pay Petrona for the saddle?" he retorted, losing his temper.

"My friend," I said, "if the saddle can be had it is only just that you should have the profit. Take ten dollars, and if you buy it for me I will pay you two more."

This proposal pleased him greatly, while Cleta, the volatile, clapped her hands with delight. While Antonio prepared to go to his neighbour's after the saddle I went out to a solitary thorn tree about fifty yards from the rancho, and spreading my poncho in the shade lay down to sleep the siesta.

Before the shepherd had been long gone I heard a great noise in the house, like banging on doors and on copper vessels, but took no notice, supposing it to proceed from Cleta engaged in some unusually noisy domestic operation. At length I heard a voice calling to me, "Señor! Señor!"

Getting up I went to the kitchen, but no person was

there. Suddenly a loud knock was given on the door communicating with the second room. "Oh, my friend," cried Cleta's voice behind it, "my ruffian of a husband has locked me in—can you let me out, do you think?"

"Why has he locked you in?" I asked.

"The question! Because he is a brute, of course. He always does it when he goes out. Is it not horrible?"

"It only shows how fond he is of you," I returned.

"Are you so atrocious as to defend him? And I thought you had a heart—so handsome, too! When I saw you I said, Ah, had I married this man what a happy life"

"Thank you for your good opinion," I said. "I am very sorry you are locked in because it prevents me from seeing your pretty face."

"Oh, you think it pretty? Then you *must* let me out. I have put up my hair now, and look prettier than when you saw me."

"You look prettier with it down," I answered.

"Ah, down it goes again then!" she exclaimed—"Yes, you are right, it does look best that way. Is it not like silk? You shall feel it when you liberate me."

"That I cannot do, Cletita mine. Your Antonio has taken away the key."

"Oh, cruel man! He left me no water and I am perishing with thirst. What shall I do? Look, I will put my hand under the door for you to feel how hot it is; I am consumed with fever and thirst in this oven."

Presently her little brown hand came out at my feet, there being sufficient space between the floor and wood to pass it through. I stooped and took it in mine, and found it a hot, moist little hand, with a pulse beating very fast.

"Poor child!" I said, "I will pour some water in a plate and pass it to you under the door."

"Oh, you are bad to insult me!" she cried. "What. am I a cat to drink water from a plate? I could cry my eyes out"; here followed sob-like sounds. "Besides," she suddenly resumed, "it is fresh air, not water, I require. I am suffocated, I cannot breathe. Oh, dear friend, save me from fainting. Force back the door till the bolt slips out."

"No, no, Cleta, it cannot be done."

"What, with your strength! I could almost do it myself with my poor little hands. Open, open, open, before I faint."

She had evidently sunk down on the floor sobbing, after making that practical suggestion; and casting about for burglarious implements to aid me, I found the spit and a wedge-shaped piece of hard wood. These I inserted just above and below the lock, and forcing back the door on its frame, I soon had the satisfaction of seeing the bolt slip from the catch.

Out sprang Cleta, flushed, tearful, her hair all in disorder, but laughing gleefully at having regained her liberty.

"Oh, dear friend, I thought you were going to leave me!" she cried. "How agitated I am—feel how my heart beats. Never mind, I can now pay that wretch out. Is not revenge sweet, sweet, sweet?"

"Now, Cleta," I said, "take three mouthfuls of fresh air and a drink of water, then let me lock you in again."

She laughed mockingly, and shook her hair like a wild young colt.

"Ah, you are not serious—do you not think I know?" she cried. "Your eyes tell me everything. Besides, you could not shut me up again if you tried." Here she made a sudden dash at the door, but I caught her and held her a close prisoner.

"Let me go, monster—oh no, not monster, dear, sweet friend, beautiful as the—moon, sun, stars. I am dying for fresh air. I will come back to the oven before he returns. If he caught me out, what blows! Come, let us sit under the tree together."

"That would be disobeying your husband," I said, trying to look stern.

"Never mind, I will confess it all to the priest some day, then it will be as if it had never happened. Such a husband—poof! If you were not a married man—*are* you married? What a pity! Say again, am I pretty?"

"Say first, Cleta, have you a horse a woman can ride on, and if you have one, will you sell it to me?"

"Oh yes, the best horse in the Banda Orientál. They say it is worth six dollars—will you buy it for six dollars? No, I shall not sell it—I shall not tell you that I have a horse till you answer me. Am I pretty, sir stranger?"

"Tell me first about the horse, then ask me what you like."

"Nothing more will I tell you—not a word. Yes, everything. Listen. When Antonio comes back ask him to sell you a horse for your wife to ride. He will try to sell you one of his own, a demon full of faults like his master; false-footed, lame in the shoulder, a roarer, old as the south wind. A black piebald—remember. Offer to buy a roan with a cream nose. That is my horse. Offer him six dollars. Now say, am I pretty?"

"Oh, beautiful, Cleta; your eyes are stars, your mouth is a rosebud, sweeter than honey a thousand times."

"Now you talk like a wise man," she laughed; then holding my hand, she led me to the tree and sat down by my side on the poncho.

"And how old are you, little one?" I asked.

"Fourteen—is that very old? Ah, fool, to tell my age truly—no woman does that. Why did I not say thirteen? And I have been married six months, such a long time! I am sure I have green, blue, yellow, grey hairs coming out all over my head by this time. And what about my hair, sir, you never spoke of that? Did I not let it down for you? Is it not soft and beautiful? Tell me, sir, what about my hair?"

"In truth it is soft and beautiful, Cleta, and covers you like a dark cloud."

"Does it not! Look, I will cover my face with it. Now I am hidden like the moon in a cloud, and now, look, out comes the moon again! I have a great respect for the moon. Say, holy friar, am I like the moon?"

"Say, little sweet lips, why do you call me holy friar?"

"Say first, holy friar, am I like the moon?"

"No, Cleta, you are not like the moon, though you are both married women; you are married to Antonio——"

"Poor me!"

"And the moon is married to the sun."

"Happy moon, to be so far from him!"

"The moon is a quiet wife, but you chatter like a paroquet."

"And am I not able to be quiet also, monk? Look, I will be quiet as the moon—not a word, not a breath." Then she threw herself back on the poncho, feigning sleep, her arms above her head, her hair scattered everywhere, only a tress or two half shading her flushed face and round heaving bosom that would not be quiet. There was just a little mocking smile on her lips, just a little gleam of laughing eyes under her drooping lashes, for she could not help watching my face for admiration. In such an attitude the tempting little witch might have made the tepid blood of an ascetic boil.

Two or three hours thus flew swiftly by while I listened to her lively prattle, which, like the lark's singing, had scarcely a pause in it, her attempt at being still and moonlike having ended in a perfect fiasco. At length, pouting her pretty lips and complaining of her hard lot, she said it was time to go back to her prison; but all the time I was engaged in forcing back the bolt into its place she chattered without ceasing. "Adieu, Sun, husband of the moon," she said. "Adieu, sweet, sweet friend, buyer of side-saddles! They were all lies you told—I know, I know. You want a horse and side-saddle to carry off some girl to-night. Happy she! Now I must sit in the dark alone, alone, alone, till Antonio, the atrocious comes to liberate me with his old iron key—ah fool!"

Before I had been long back under my tree, Antonio appeared, bringing the side-saddle in triumph on his horse before him. After going in to release his wife he came out and invited me to take maté. I then mentioned my wish to buy a good horse; he was only too willing to sell, and in a few minutes his horses were driven up for inspection. The black piebald was first offered, a very handsome, quiet-looking animal, apparently quite sound. The cream-nose, I noticed, was a bony, long-bodied brute, with sleepy eyes and a ewe neck. Could it be that the little double-dealing witch had intended to deceive me? But in a moment I dismissed such a suspicion with the scorn it merited. Let a woman be as false as she can, and able to fool her husband to the top of her bent, she is, compared with the man who wishes to sell you a horse, openness and truth itself. I examined the piebald critically, walking and trotting him round; looked into his mouth, then at hoofs and fetlocks, beloved of windgalls; gazed with fixed attention into his eyes, and dealt him a sudden brisk blow on the shoulder.

"No weak spot will you find, señor," said Antonio the mendacious, who was certainly the greatest of the three sinners met together in that place. "He is my best horse, only four years old, gentle as a lamb, sound as a bell. Sure-footed, señor, like no other horse; and with such an easy pace you can ride him at a gallop with a tumbler of water in your hand and not spill a drop. I will give him away to you for ten dollars, because you have been generous about the side-saddle, and I am anxious to serve you well."

"Thank you, my friend," I said. "Your piebald is fifteen years old, lame in the shoulders, broken in his wind, and has more vices than any seven horses in the Banda Orientál. I would not allow my wife to ride such a dangerous brute, for, as I told you, I have not been long married."

Antonio framed his face to express astonishment and virtue indignant; then with the point of his knife he scratched the figure of a cross on the ground, and was about to swear solemnly on it that I was egregiously mistaken, that his beast was a kind of equine angel, or a Pegasus, at least, when I interfered to stop him. "Tell as many lies as you like," I said, "and I will listen to them with the greatest interest; but do not swear on the figure of the cross to what is false, for then the four or five or six dollars profit you have made on the side-saddle will scarcely be sufficient to buy you absolution for such a sin."

He shrugged his shoulders and restored the sacrilegious knife to its sheath. "There are my horses," he said in an injured tone. "They are a kind of animal you seem to know a great deal about; select one and deceive yourself. I have endeavoured to serve you; but there are some people who do not know a friend when they see one."

I then minutely examined all the other horses, and finally finished the farce by leading out the roan creamnose, and was pleased to notice the crestfallen expression of my good shepherd.

"Your horses do not suit me," I said, "so I cannot buy one. I will, however, purchase this old cow; for it is the only animal here I could trust my wife on. You can have seven dollars for it—not one copper more, for like the Emperor of China, I speak once only."

He plucked off his purple headgear and scratched his raven head, then led me back to the kitchen to consult his wife, "For, señor," he said, "you have, by some fatality, selected her horse." When Cleta heard that seven dollars had been offered for the roan, she laughed with joy. "Oh, Antonio, he is only worth six dollars! Yes, señor, you shall have him, and pay the seven dollars to me. Not to my husband. Who will say now that I cannot make money? And now, Antonio, I have no horse to ride on, you can give me the bay with white fore-feet."

"Do not imagine such a thing!" exclaimed her husband.

After taking maté I left them to settle their affairs, not doubting which would come out best from a trial of skill. When I arrived in sight of Peralta's trees I unsaddled and picketed my horses, then stretched myself out on my rugs. After the excitements and pleasures of that day, which had robbed me of my siesta, I quickly fell into a very sound sleep.

CHAPTER XXVII

NIGHT AND FLIGHT

WHEN I woke I did not remember for some moments where I was. Feeling about me, my hand came in contact with the grass wet with dew. It was very dark, only low down in the sky a pale gleam of light gave promise, as I imagined, of coming day. Then recollection flashed upon me, and I sprang up alarmed to my feet, only to discover with inexpressible relief that the light I had remarked was in the west, not the east, and proceeded from the young moon just sinking beneath the horizon. Saddling my two animals expeditiously I rode to Peralta's estancia, and on arriving there carefully drew the horses into the shadow of a clump of trees growing on the borders of the ancient well-nigh obliterated foss or ditch. I then dropped on to the ground so as to listen better for approaching footsteps. and began waiting for Demetria. It was past midnight: not a sound reached me except at intervals the mournful far-away reedy note of the little nocturnal cicada that always seemed to be there lamenting the lost fortunes of the house of Peralta. For upwards of half an hour I remained lying on the ground, growing more anxious every moment and fearing that Demetria was going to fail me, when I caught a sound like a human whisper. Listening intently, I found that it pronounced my name and proceeded from a clump of tall thorn-apples some yards from me.

"Who speaks?" I replied.

The tall, gaunt form of Ramona drew itself up out of the weeds and cautiously approached me. She was shaking with nervous excitement, and had not ventured to come near without speaking for fear of being mistaken for an enemy and fired at.

"Mother of Heaven!" she exclaimed as well as her chattering teeth would allow her to speak. "I have been so agitated all the evening! Oh, señor, what are we to do now? Your plan was such a good one; when I heard it I knew an angel had flown down and whispered it in your ear. And now my mistress will not stir! All her things are ready—clothes, money, jewels; and for the last hour we have been urging her to come out, but nothing will serve. She will not see you, señor."

"Is Don Hilario in the house?"

"No, he is out—could anything have been better? But it is useless, she has lost heart and will not come. She only sits crying in her room, saying that she cannot look on your face again."

"Go and tell her that I am here with the horses waiting for her," I said.

"Señor, she knows you are here. Santos watched for you and hastened in to inform her of your arrival. Now she has sent me out only to say that she cannot meet you, that she thanks you for all you have done, and begs you to go away and leave her."

I was not greatly surprised at Demetria's reluctance to meet me at the last moment, but was determined not to leave without first seeing her and trying to change her mind. Securing the horses to a tree, I went with Ramona to the house. Stealing in on tiptoe, we found Demetria in that room where she had received me the evening before in her quaint finery, lying on the sofa, while old Santos stood by her the picture of distress. The moment she saw me enter she covered her face with her hands and turned from me. Yet a glance was sufficient to show that with or without her consent everything had been got ready for her flight. On a chair near her lay a pair of saddle-bags in which her few belongings had been stowed; a mantilla was drawn half over her head, and by her side was a large woollen shawl, evidently intended to protect her against the night air.

"Santos," I said, "go out to the horses under the trees and wait there for us: and you, Ramona, say good-bye now to your mistress, then leave us together; for by-and-by she will recover courage and go with me."

Santos, looking immensely relieved and grateful, though a little surprised at my confident tone, was hurrying out when I pointed to the saddle-bags. He nodded, grinned, and snatching them up left the room. Poor old Ramona threw herself on to her knees, sobbing and pouring out farewell blessings on her mistress, kissing her hands and hair with sorrowful devotion.

When she left us I sat down by Demetria's side, but she would not take her hands from her face or speak to me, and only wept hysterically when I addressed her. I succeeded at last in getting one of her hands in mine, and then drew her head gently down till it rested on my shoulder. When her sobs began to subside I said—

"Tell me, dear Demetria, have you lost faith in me that you fear to trust yourself with me now?"

"No, no, Richard, it is not that," she faltered. "But I can never look into your face again. If you have any compassion for me you will leave me now."

"What, leave you, Demetria, my sister, to that man—how can you imagine such a thing? Tell me, where is Don Hilario—is he coming back to-night?"

"I know nothing. He may come back at any moment. Leave me, Richard; every minute you remain here increases your danger." Then she attempted to draw away from me, but I would not release her.

"If you fear his returning to-night then it is time for you to come with me," I answered.

"No, no, no, I cannot. All is changed now. It would kill me with shame to look on your face again."

"You shall look on it again many times, Demetria. Do you think that after coming here to rescue you out of the coils of that serpent I am going to leave you because you are a little timid? Listen, Demetria, I shall save you from that devil to-night, even if I have to carry you out in my arms. Afterwards we can consider all there is to be done about your father and your property. Perhaps when the poor Colonel is taken out of this sad atmosphere his health, his reason even, may improve."

"Oh, Richard, are you deceiving me?" she exclaimed, suddenly dropping her hands and gazing full into my face.

"No, I am not deceiving you. And now, you will lose all fear, Demetria, for you have looked into my face again and have not been changed to stone."

She turned crimson in a moment; but did not attempt to cover her face again, for just then a clatter of hoofs was heard approaching the house.

"Mother of Heaven, save us!" she exclaimed in terror. "It is Don Hilario."

I quickly blew out the one candle burning dimly in the room. "Fear nothing," I said. "When all is quiet after he has gone to his room we will make our escape."

She was trembling with apprehension and nestled close to me; while we both listened intently and heard Don Hilario unsaddle his horse, then going softly, whistling to himself, to his room.

"Now he has shut himself up," I said, "and in a few minutes will be asleep. When you think of that man whose persecutions have made your life a burden, so that you tremble when he approaches you, do you not feel glad that I have come to take you away?"

"Richard, I could go willingly with you to-night but for one thing. Do you think after what has passed that I could ever face your wife?"

"She will know nothing of what has passed, Demetria.

It would be dishonourable in me and a cruel injustice to you to speak to her of it. She will welcome you as a dear sister and love you as much as I love you. All these doubts and fears troubling you are very unsubstantial and can be blown away like thistle-down. And now that you have confessed so much to me, Demetria, I wish to confess also the one thing that troubles my heart."

"What is it, Richard, tell me?" she said very gently.

"Believe me, Demetria, I never had a suspicion that you loved me. Your manner did not show it, otherwise I should have told you long ago all about my past. I only knew you regarded me as a friend and one you could trust. If I have been mistaken all along, Demetria, if you have really felt a passion in your heart, then I shall have to lament bitterly that I have been the cause of a lasting sorrow to you. Will you not open your heart more to me and tell me frankly how it is with you?"

She caressed my hand in silence for a little while and then answered, "I think you were right, Richard. Perhaps I am not capable of passion like some women. I felt—I knew that you were my friend. To be near you was like sitting in the shade of a green tree in some hot, desolate place. I thought it would be pleasant to sit there always and forget the bitter years. But, Richard, if you will always be my friend—my brother, I shall be more than content, and my life will seem different."

"Demetria, how happy you have made me! Come, the serpent is sleeping now, let us steal away and leave him to his evil dreams. God grant that I may return some day to bruise his head with my heel."

Then, wrapping the shawl about her, I led her out treading softly, and in a few moments we were with Santos, patiently keeping watch beside the horses.

I gladly let him assist Demetria to her seat on the side-saddle, for that was perhaps the last personal service he would be able to render her. The poor old fellow was crying, I believe, his utterance was so husky. Before leaving I gave him on a scrap of paper my address in Montevideo, and bade him take it to Don Florentino Blanco with a request to write me a letter in the course of the next two or three days to inform me of Don Hilario's movements. We then trotted softly away over the sward, and in about half an hour struck the road leading from Rocha to Montevideo. This we followed till daylight, scarcely pausing once from our swift gallop, and a hundred times during that dark ride over a country utterly unknown to me I blessed the little witch Cleta; for never was there a more steady, sure-footed beast than the ugly roan that carried my companion, and when we drew rein in the pale morning light he seemed fresh as when we started. We then left the highway and rode across country in a north-westerly direction for a distance of eight or nine miles, for I was anxious to be far away from public roads and from the prying, prating people that use them. About eleven o'clock that morning we had breakfast at a rancho, then rode on again till we came to a forest of scattered thorn trees growing on the slopes of a range of hills. It was a wild, secluded spot, with water and good pasturage for the horses and pleasant shade for ourselves; so after unsaddling and turning loose our horses to feed we sat down to rest under a large tree with our backs against its portly trunk. From our shady retreat we commanded a splendid view of the country over which we had been riding all the morning extending for many leagues behind us, and while I smoked my cigar I talked to my companion, calling her attention to the beauty of that wide, sunlit prospect.

"Do you know, Demetria," I said, "when the long winter evenings come, and I have plenty of leisure, I intend writing a history of my wanderings in the Banda Orientál, and I will call my book *The Purple Land;* for what more suitable name can one find for a country so stained with the blood of her children? You will never read it, of course, for I shall write it in English and only for the pleasure it will give to my own children—if I ever have any—at some distant date, when their little moral and intellectual stomachs are prepared for other food than milk. But you will have a very important place in my narrative, Demetria, for during these last days we have been very much to each other. And perhaps the very last chapter will recount this wild ride of ours together, flying from that evil genius Hilario to some blessed refuge far away beyond the hills and woods and the blue line of the horizon. For when we reach the capital I believe—I think—I know, in fact——"

I hesitated to tell her that it would probably be necessary for me to leave the country immediately, but she did not encourage me to go on, and glancing round I discovered that she was fast asleep.

Poor Demetria, she had been dreadfully nervous all night and almost afraid to stop to rest anywhere, but now her fatigue had quite overcome her. Her position against the tree was uncomfortable and insecure, so drawing her head very gently down until it rested on my shoulder, and shading her eyes with her mantilla, I let her sleep on. Her face looked strangely worn and pallid in that keen noonday light, and gazing on it while she slumbered, and remembering all the dark years of grief and anxiety she had endured down to that last pain of which I had been the innocent cause, I felt my eyes grow dim with compassion.

After sleeping for about two hours she woke with a start and was greatly distressed to learn that I had been supporting her all that time. But after that refreshing slumber a change seemed to come over her. Not only her great fatigue, but the tormenting apprehensions had very nearly vanished. Out of the nettle Danger she had plucked the flower Safety, and now she could rejoice in its possession and was filled with new life and spirits. The unaccustomed freedom and exercise with constant change of scene also had an exhilarating effect on mind and body. A new colour came into her pale cheeks; the purple stains telling of anxious days and sleepless nights faded away; she smiled brightly and was full of animation, so that on that long journey, whether resting in the noonday shade or swiftly cantering over the green turf, I could not have had a more agreeable companion than

Demetria. This change in her often made me remember Santos' pathetic words when he told of the ravages of grief, and said that another life would make his mistress a "flower amongst women." It was a comfort that her affection for me had been, indeed, nothing but affection. But what was I to do with her in the end? for I knew that my wife was most anxious to return without further delay to her own country; and yet it seemed to me that it would be a hard thing to leave poor Demetria behind amongst strangers. Finding her so improved in spirits, I at length ventured to speak to her on the subject. At first she was depressed, but presently, recovering courage, she begged to be allowed to go with us to Buenos Ayres. The prospect of being left alone was unendurable to her, for in Montevideo she had no personal friends, while the political friends of her family were all out of the country or living in very close retirement. Across the water she would be with friends and safe for a season from her dreaded enemy. This proposal seemed a very sensible one and relieved my mind very much, although it only served to remove my difficulty for a time.

In the department of Camelones, about six leagues from Montevideo, I found the house of a fellow-countryman named Barker, who had lived for many years in the country and had a wife and children. We arrived in the afternoon at his estancia, and seeing that Demetria was very much knocked up with our long journey, I asked Mr. Barker to give us shelter for the night. Our host was very kind and pleasant with us, asking no disagreeable questions, and after a few hours' acquaintance, which made us quite intimate, I took him aside and told him Demetria's history, whereupon, like the good-hearted fellow he was, he at once offered to shelter her in his house until matters could be arranged in Montevideo, an offer which was joyfully accepted.

CHAPTER XXVIII

GOOD-BYE TO THE PURPLE LAND

I WAS soon back in Montevideo after that. When I bade Demetria good-bye she appeared reluctant to part with me, retaining my hand in hers for an unusual time. For the first time in her life, probably, she was about to be left in the company of entire strangers, and for many days past we had been much to each other, so that it was only natural she should cling to me a little at parting. Once more I pressed her hand and exhorted her to be of good courage, reminding her that in a very few days all trouble and danger would be over; still, however, she did not release my hand. This tender reluctance to lose me was affecting and also flattering, but slightly inopportune, for I was anxious to be in the saddle and away. Presently she said, glancing down at her rusty habiliments, "Richard, if I am to remain concealed here till I go to join you on board, then I must meet your wife in these poor garments."

"Oh, *that* is what you are thinking about, Demetria!" I exclaimed.

At once I called in our kind hostess, and when this serious matter was explained to her she immediately offered to go to Montevideo to procure the necessary outfit, a thing I had thought nothing about, but which had evidently been preying on Demetria's mind.

When I at length reached the little suburban retreat of my aunt (by marriage), Paquíta and I acted for some time like two demented persons, so overjoyed were we at meeting after our long separation. I had received no letters from her, and only two or three of the score I had written had reached their destination, so that we had ten thousand questions to ask and answers to make. She could never gaze enough at me or finish admiring my bronzed skin and the respectable moustache I had grown; while she, poor darling! looked unusually pale, yet withal so beautiful that I marvelled at myself for having, after possessing her, considered any other woman even passably good-looking. I gave her a circumstantial account of my adventures, omitting only a few matters I was in honour bound not to disclose.

Thus, when I told her the story of my sojourn at the estancia Peralta, I said nothing to betray Demetria's confidence; nor did I think it necessary to mention the episode of that wicked little sprite, Cleta; with the result that she was pleased at the chivalrous conduct I had displayed throughout the whole of that affair, and was ready to take Demetria to her heart.

I had not been back twenty-four hours in Montevideo before a letter from the Lomas de Rocha storekeeper came to justify my caution in having left Demetria at some distance from the town. The letter informed me that Don Hilario had quickly guessed that I had carried off his unhappy master's daughter, and that no doubt was left in his mind when he discovered that on the day I left the estancia a person answering to my description in every particular had purchased a horse and side-saddle and had ridden off towards the estancia in the evening. My correspondent warned me that Don Hilario would be in Montevideo even before his letter, also that he had discovered something about my connection with the late rebellion, and would be sure to place the matter in the hands of the government, so as to have me arrested, after which he would have little difficulty in compelling Demetria to return to the estancia.

For a moment this intelligence dismayed me. Luckily, Paquíta was out of the house when it came, and fearing that she might return and surprise me while I was in that troubled state, I rushed out; then, skulking through back streets and narrow lanes, peering cautiously about in fear of encountering the minions of the law, I made my escape out of the town. My only desire just then was to get away into some place of safety where I would be able to think over the position quietly, and if possible devise some plan to defeat Don Hilario, who had been a little too quick for me. Of many schemes that suggested themselves to my mind, while I sat in the shade of a cactus hedge about a mile from town, I finally determined, in accordance with my old and well-tried rule, to adopt the boldest one, which was to go straight back to Montevideo and claim the protection of my country. The only trouble was that on my way thither I might be caught, and then Paquíta would be in terrible distress about me, and perhaps Demetria's escape would be prevented. While I was occupied with these thoughts I saw a closed carriage pass by driven towards the town by a tipsy-looking coachman. Coming out of my hiding-place I managed to stop him and offered him two dollars to drive me to the British Consulate. The carriage was a private one, but the two dollars tempted the man, so after securing the fare in advance he allowed me to get in,. and then I closed the windows, leant back on the cushion, and was driven rapidly and comfortably to the house of refuge. I introduced myself to the Consul, and told him a story concocted for the occasion, a judicious mixture of truth and lies, to the effect that I had been unlawfully and forcibly seized and compelled to serve in the Blanco army, and that having escaped from the rebels and made my way to Montevideo, I was amazed to hear that the government proposed arresting me. He asked me a few questions, looked at the passport which he had sent me a few days before, then laughing good-humouredly put on his hat and invited me to accompany him to the War Office close by. The secretary, Colonel Arocena, he informed me, was a personal friend of his, and if we could see him it would be all right. Walking by his side I felt quite safe and bold again, for I was, in a sense, walking with my hand resting on the superb mane of the British Lion, whose roar was not to be provoked with impunity. At the War Office I was introduced by the Consul to his friend, Colonel Arocena, a genial old gentleman with a bald head and a cigarette between his lips. He listened with some interest and a smile, slightly incredulous I thought, to the sad story of the ill-treatment I had been subjected to at the hands of Santa Coloma's rebellious rascals. When I had finished he pushed over a sheet of paper on which he had scrawled a few words to me with the remark, "Here, my young friend, take this, and you will be safe in Montevideo. We have heard about your doings in Florida, also in Rocha, but we do not propose going to war with England on your account."

At this speech we all laughed; then when I had pocketed the paper, which bore the sacred seal of the War Office on the margin and requested all persons to refrain from molesting the bearer in his lawful outgoings and incomings, we thanked the pleasant old Colonel and retired. I spent half an hour strolling about with the Consul, then we separated. I had noticed two men in military uniform at some distance from us when we were together, and now returning homewards I found that they were following me. By-and-by they overtook me and politely intimated their intention of making me their prisoner. I smiled, and drawing forth my protection from the War Office, handed it to them. They looked surprised, and gave it back, with an apology for having molested me, then left me to pursue my way in peace.

I had, of course, been very lucky throughout all this adventure; still I did not wish to attribute my easy escape entirely to luck, for I had, I thought, contributed a good deal towards it by my promptness in acting and in inventing a plausible story on the spur of the moment.

Feeling very much elated, I strolled along the sunny streets, gaily swinging my cane, when turning a corner near Doña Isidora's house I suddenly came face to face with Don Hilario. This unexpected encounter threw us both off our guard, he recoiling two or three paces backward and turning as pale as the nature of his complexion would allow. I recovered first from the shock. So far I had been able to baffle him, and knew, moreover, many things of which he was ignorant; still, he was there in the town with me and had to be reckoned with, and I quickly resolved to meet him as a friend, affecting entire ignorance of his object in coming to Montevideo.

"Don Hilario—you here! Happy the eyes that behold you," I exclaimed, seizing and shaking his hand, pretending to be overjoyed at the meeting.

In a moment he recovered his usual self-possessed manner, and when I asked after Doña Demetria he answered after a moment's hesitation that she was in very good health.

"Come, Don Hilario," I said, "we are close to my aunt Isidora's house where I am staying, and it will give me great pleasure to present you to my wife, who will be glad to thank you for your kindness to me at the estancia."

"Your wife, Don Ricardo! Do you tell me that you are married?" he exclaimed in amazement, thinking probably that I was already the husband of Demetria.

"What, did I not tell you before!" I said. "Ah, I remember speaking to Doña Demetria about it. Strange that she has not mentioned it to you. Yes, I was married before coming to this country—my wife is an Argentine. Come with me and you shall see a beautiful woman, if that is an inducement."

He was without doubt astonished and mystified, but he had recovered his mask, and was now polite, col lected, watchful.

When we entered the house I presented him to Doña Isidora, who happened to be in the way, and left her to entertain him. I was very glad to do so, knowing that he would seize the opportunity to try and discover something from the garrulous old lady, and that he would discover nothing since she had not been let into our secrets.

I found Paquíta lying down in her room having a siesta; and while she arrayed herself at my express desire in her best dress — a black velvet which set off her matchless beauty better than anything else, I told her how I wished her to treat Don Hilario. She knew all about him, of course, and hated him with all her heart, looking on him as a kind of evil genius from whose castle I had carried off the unhappy Demetria; but I made her understand that our wisest plan was to treat him graciously. She readily consented, for Argentine women can be more charmingly gracious than any other women on the globe, and what people do well they like to be called on to do.

The subtle caution of our snaky guest did not serve to hide from my watchful eyes that he was very much surprised when he beheld her. She placed herself near him and spoke in her sweetest artless manner of the pleasure my return had given her, and of the gratitude she had felt towards him and all the people at the estancia Peralta for the hospitable treatment I had received there.

He was, as I had foreseen, completely carried away by her exquisite beauty and the charm of her manner towards him. He was flattered, and exerted himself to be agreeable, but at the same time he was very much puzzled. The baffled expression was more apparent on his face every moment, while his restless glances darted here and there about the room, yet ever returned, like the doomed moth to the candle, to those lustrous violet eyes overflowing with hypocritical kindness. Paquíta's acting delighted me, and I only hoped that he would long suffer from the effect of the subtle poison she was introducing into his system. When he rose to go I was sure that Demetria's disappearance was a greater mystery to him than ever; and as a parting shot I warmly invited him to come and see us frequently while he remained in the capital, even offering him a bed in the house; while Paquíta, not to be behindhand, for she had thoroughly entered into the fun of the thing, entrusted him with a prettily worded affectionate message to Demetria, a person whom she already loved and hoped some day to meet.

Two days after this adventure I heard that Don Hilario had left Montevideo. That he had discovered nothing I was positive; it was possible, however, that he had left some person to watch the house, and as Paquíta was now anxious to get back to her own country I determined to delay our departure no longer.

Going down to the harbour, I found the captain of a small schooner trading between Montevideo and Buenos Ayres, and learning that he intended leaving for the last port in three days' time, I bargained with him to take us, and got him also to consent to receive Demetria on board at once. I then sent a message to Mr. Barker, asking him to bring his guest up to town and put her on board the schooner without coming near me. Two days later, early in the morning, I heard that she was safe on board; and having thus baffled the scoundrel Hilario, on whose ophidian skull I should have been very pleased to set my heel, and having still an idle day before me, I went once more to visit the mountain, to take from its summit my last view of the Purple Land where I had spent so many eventful days.

When I approached the crest of the great, solitary hill I did not gaze admiringly on the magnificent view that opened before me, nor did the wind, blowing fresh from the beloved Atlantic, seem to exhilarate me. My eyes were cast down and I dragged my feet like one that was weary. Yet I was not weary, but now I began to remember that on a former occasion I had on this mountain spoken many vain and foolish things concerning a people about whose character and history I was then ignorant. I also remembered with exceeding bitterness that my visit to this land had been the cause of great and perhaps lasting sorrow to one noble heart.

How often, said I to myself, have I repented of those cruel, scornful words I addressed to Dolores at our last interview, and now once more "I come to pluck the berries harsh and crude" of repentance and of expiation, to humble my insular pride in the dust and unsay all the unjust things I formerly spoke in my haste.

It is not an exclusively British characteristic to regard the people of other nationalities with a certain amount of contempt, but with us, perhaps, the feeling is stronger than with others, or else expressed with less reserve. Let me now at last rid myself of this error, which is harmless and perhaps even commendable in those who stay at home, and also very natural, since it is a part of our unreasonable nature to distrust and dislike the things that are far removed and unfamiliar. Let me at last divest myself of these old English spectacles, framed in oak and with lenses of horn, to bury them for ever in this mountain, which for half a century and upwards has looked down on the struggles of a young and feeble people against foreign aggression and domestic foes, and where a few months ago I sang the praises of British civilisation, lamenting that it had been planted here and abundantly watered with blood, only to be plucked up again and cast into the sea. After my rambles in the interior, where I carried about in me only a fading remnant of that old time-honoured superstition to prevent the most perfect sympathy between me and the natives I mixed with, I cannot say that I am of that opinion now. I cannot believe that if this country had been conquered and recolonised by England, and all that is crooked in it made straight according to our notions, my intercourse with the people would have had the wild, delightful flavour I have found in it. And if that distinctive flavour cannot be had along with the material prosperity resulting from Anglo-Saxon energy, I must breathe the wish that this land may never know such prosperity. I do not wish to be murdered; no man does; yet rather than see the ostrich and deer chased beyond the horizon, the flamingo and black-necked swan slain on the blue lakes, and the herdsman sent to twang his romantic guitar in Hades as a preliminary to security of person, I would prefer to go about prepared at any moment to defend my life against the sudden assaults of the assassin.

We do not live by bread alone, and British occupation does not give to the heart all the things for which it craves. Blessings may even become curses when the gigantic power that bestows them on us scares from our midst the shy spirits of Beauty and of Poesy. Nor is it solely because it appeals to the poetic feelings in us that this country endears itself to my heart. It is the perfect republic: the sense of emancipation experienced in it by the wanderer from the Old World is indescribably sweet and novel. Even in our ultra-civilised condition at home we do periodically escape back to nature; and, breathing the fresh mountain air and gazing over vast expanses of ocean or land, we find that she is still very much to us. It is something more than these bodily sensations we experience when first mingling with our fellow-creatures, where all men are absolutely free and equal as here. I fancy I hear some wise person exclaiming, "No, no, no! In name only is your Purple Land a republic; its constitution is a piece of waste paper, its government an oligarchy tempered by assassination and revolution." True; but the knot of ambitious rulers all striving to pluck each other down have no power to make the people miserable. The unwritten constitution, mightier than the written one, is in the heart of every man to make him still a republican and free with a freedom it would be hard to match anywhere else on the globe. The Bedouin himself is not so free, since he accords an almost superstitious reverence and implicit obedience to his sheikh. Here the lord of many leagues of land and of herds unnumbered sits down to talk with the hired shepherd, a poor, bare-footed fellow in his smoky rancho, and no class or caste difference divides them, no consciousness of their widely different positions chills the warm current of sympathy between two human hearts. How refreshing it is to meet with this perfect freedom of intercourse, tempered only by that innate courtesy and native grace of manner peculiar to Spanish Americans! What a change to a person coming from lands with higher and lower classes, each with its innumerable hateful subdivisions—to one who aspires not to mingle with the class above him, yet who shudders at the slouching carriage and abject demeanour of the class beneath him! If this absolute equality is inconsistent with perfect political order, I for one should grieve to see such order established. Moreover, it is by no means true that the communities which oftenest startle us with crimes of disorder and violence are morally worse than others. A community in which there are not many crimes cannot be morally healthy. There were practically *no* crimes in Peru under the Inca dynasty; it was a marvellous thing for a person to commit an offence in that empire. And the reason for this most unnatural state of things was this—the Inca system of government was founded on that most iniquitous and disastrous doctrine that the individual bears the same relation to the state as a child to its parent, that its life from the cradle to the grave must be regulated for it by a power it is taught to regard as omniscient—a power practically omnipresent and almighty. In such a state there could be no individual will, no healthy play of passions, and consequently no crime. What wonder that a system so unspeakably repugnant to a being who feels that his will is a divinity working within him fell to pieces at the first touch of foreign invasion, or that it left no vestige of its pernicious existence on the continent it had ruled! For the whole state was, so to speak, putrid even before dissolution, and when it fell it mingled with the dust and was forgotten. Poland, before its conquest by Russia, a country ill-governed and disorderly as the Banda Orientál, did not mingle with the dust like that when it fell—the implacable despotism of the Czar was unable to crush its fierce spirit; its *Will* still survived to gild dreary oppression with hallowed dreams, to make it clutch with a fearful joy the dagger concealed in its bosom. But I had no need to go away from this Green Continent to illustrate the truth of what I have said. People who talk and write about the disorderly South American republics are fond of pointing to Brazil, that great, peaceful, progressive empire, as setting an example to be followed. An orderly country, yes, and the people in it steeped to their lips in every abominable vice! Compared with these emasculated children of the equator, the Orientals are nature's noblemen.

I can very well imagine some over-righteous perso

saying, "Alas, poor deluded soul, how little importance can we attach to your specious apologies of a people's lawlessness, when your own personal narrative shows that the moral atmosphere you have been breathing has quite corrupted you! Go back over your own record, and you will find that you have, according to *our* notions, offended in various ways and on divers occasions, and that you are even without the grace to repent of all the evil things you have thought, said, and done."

I have not read many books of philosophy, because when I tried to be a philosopher "happiness was always breaking in," as someone says; also because I have loved to study men rather than books; but in the little I have read there occurs a passage I remember well, and this I shall quote as my answer to anyone who may call me an immoral person because my passions have not always remained in a quiescent state, like hounds—to quote the simile of a South American poet—slumbering at the feet of the huntsman resting against a rock at noon. "We should regard the perturbations of the mind," says Spinoza, "not in the light of vices of human nature, but as properties just as pertinent to it as are heat, storms, thunder, and the like to the nature of the atmosphere, which phenomena, though inconvenient, are yet necessary, and have fixed causes by means of which we endeavour to understand their nature, and the mind has just as much pleasure in seeing them aright as in knowing such things as flatter the senses." Let me have the phenomena which are inconvenient as well as the things which flatter the senses, and the chances are that my life will be a healthier and happier one than that of the person who spends his time on a cloud blushing at nature's naughtiness.

It is often said that an ideal state—an Utopia where there is no folly, crime, or sorrow—has a singular fascination for the mind. Now, when I meet with a falsehood, I care not who the great persons who proclaim it may be, I do not try to like it or believe it or mimic the fashionable prattle of the world about it. I hate all dreams of perpetual peace, all wonderful cities of the sun, where people consume their joyless monotonous years in mystic contemplations, or find their delight like Buddhist monks in gazing on the ashes of dead generations of devotees. The state is one unnatural, unspeakably repugnant: the dreamless sleep of the grave is more tolerable to the active, healthy mind than such an existence. If Signor Gaudentio di Lucca, still keeping himself alive by means of his marvellous knowledge of the secrets of nature, were to appear before me now on this mountain to inform me that the sacred community he resided with in Central Africa was no mere dream, and should offer to conduct me to it, I should decline to go with him. I should prefer to remain in the Banda Orientál, even though by so doing I should grow at last to be as bad as any person in it, and ready to "wade through slaughter" to the Presidential Chair. For even in my own country of England, which is not so perfect as old Peru or the Pophar's country in Central Africa, I have been long divided from nature, and now in this Oriental country, whose political misdeeds are a scandal alike to pure England and impure Brazil, I have been reunited to her. For this reason I love her with all her faults. Here. like Santa Coloma, I will kneel down and kiss this stone as an infant might kiss the breast that feeds it; here, fearless of dirt like John Carrickfergus, I will thrust my hands into the loose brown soil to clasp the hands, as it were, of dear mother Nature after our long separation.

Farewell, beautiful land of sunshine and storm, of virtue and of crime; may the invaders of the future fare on your soil like those of the past and leave you in the end to your own devices; may the chivalrous instinct of Santa Coloma, the passion of Dolores, the loving-kindness of Candelaria still live in your children to brighten their lives with romance and beauty; may the blight of our superior civilisation never fall on your wild flowers, or the yoke of our progress be laid on your herdsman—careless, graceful, music-loving as the birds—to make him like the sullen abject peasant of the Old World!

CHAPTER XXIX

BACK TO BUENOS AYRES

THE meeting of my fellow-travellers took place next day on board the ship, where we three were the only cabin passengers. On going down into the little saloon I found Demetria waiting for us, considerably improved in appearance by her new dress, but looking pale and anxious, for she probably found this meeting a trying one. The two women looked earnestly at each other, but Demetria, to hide her nervousness, I suppose, had framed her face in the old, impassive, almost cold expression it had worn when I first knew her, and Paquíta was repelled by it; so after a somewhat lukewarm greeting they sat down and made commonplace remarks. Two women more unlike each other in appearance, character, education, and disposition it would have been difficult to find; still I had hoped they might be friends, and felt keenly disappointed at the result of their first meeting. After an uncomfortable interval we all rose. I was about to proceed to the deck, they to their respective cabins, when Paquíta, without any warning of what was coming suddenly burst into tears and threw her arms about Demetria's neck.

"Oh, dear Demetria, what a sad life yours has been!" she exclaimed.

That was like her, so impulsive and with such a true instinct to make her do the right thing always! The other gladly responded to the embrace, and I hastily retreated, leaving them kissing and mingling their tears.

When I got out on deck I found that we were already on our way, sails up, and a fresh wind sending us swiftly through the dull green water. There were five steerage passengers, disreputable-looking fellows in ponchos and slouch hats, lounging about the deck smoking; but when we got outside the harbour and the ship began to toss a little, they very soon dropped their cigars and began ignominiously creeping away out of sight of the grinning sailors. Only one remained, a grizzly-bearded, rough-looking old gaucho, who firmly kept his seat at the stern, as if determined to see the last of "The Mount," as the pretty city near the foot of Magellan's Hill is called by the English people in this region.

To satisfy myself that none of these fellows were sent in pursuit of Demetria, I asked our Italian captain who they were and how long they had been on board, and was much relieved to hear that they were fugitives—rebels probably—and had all been concealed for the past three or four days in the ship, waiting to get away from Montevideo.

Towards evening it came on very rough, the wind veering round to the south and blowing half a gale, a very favourable wind, as it happened, to take us across this unlovely "Silver Sea," as the poets of the Plata insist on calling it, with its villainous, brick-red, chopping waves, so disagreeable to bad sailors. Paquíta and

Demetria suffered agonies, so that I was obliged to keep with them a good deal. I very imprudently told them not to be alarmed, that it was nothing—*only sea-sickness*—and I verily believe they both hated me with all their hearts for a little while in consequence. Fortunately I had anticipated these harrowing scenes, and had provided a bottle of champagne for the occasion; and after I had consumed two or three glassfuls to encourage them, showing how easy this kind of medicine is to take, I prevailed on them to drink the remainder. At length, about ten o'clock in the evening, they began to suspect that their malady was not going to prove fatal, and seeing them so much better, I went up to get some fresh air. There at the stern still sat the stoical old gaucho looking extremely miserable.

"Good evening, old comrade," said I, "will you smoke a cigar?"

"Young master, you seem to have a good heart," he returned, shaking his head at the proffered cigar, "do, for God's sake, get me a little rum. I am dying for something to warm my inside and stop my head from going round like a top, but nothing can I get from these jabbering foreign brutes on board."

"Yes, why not, my old friend," said I, and going to the master of the boat, I succeeded in getting a pint of rum in a bottle.

The old fellow clutched it with eager delight and took a long draught. "Ah!" he said, patting first the bottle, then his stomach, "this puts new life into a man! Will this voyage never end, master? When I am on horseback I can forget that I am old, but these cursed waves remind me that I have lived many years."

I lit my cigar and sat down to have a talk with him.

"Ah, with you foreigners it is just the same—land or water," he continued. "You can even smoke—what a calm head and quiet stomach you must have! But what puzzles me is this, señor; how you, a foreigner, come to be travelling with native women. Now there is that beautiful young señora with the violet eyes, who can she be?"

"She is my wife, old man," said I, laughing, a little amused at his curiosity.

"Ah, you are married then—so young? She is beautiful, graceful, well educated, the daughter of wealthy parents, no doubt, but frail, frail, señor; and some day, not a very distant day—but why should I predict sorrow to a gay heart? Only her face, señor, is strange to me; it does not recall the features of any Oriental family I know."

"That is easily explained," I said, surprised at his shrewdness, "she is an Argentine, not an Oriental."

"Ah, that explains it," he said, taking another long pull at the bottle. "As for the other señora with you, I need not ask you who *she* is."

"Why, who is she?" I returned.

"A Peralta, if there ever was one," he returned confidently.

His reply disturbed me not a little, for after all my precautions this old man had perhaps been sent to follow Demetria.

"Yes," he continued, with an evident pride in his

knowledge of families and faces which tended to allay my suspicions; "a Peralta and not a Madariaga, nor a Sanchez, nor a Zelaya, nor an Ibarra. Do I not know a Peralta when I see one?" And here he laughed scornfully at the absurdity of such an idea.

"Tell me," I said, "how do you know a Peralta?"

"The question!" he exclaimed. "You are a Frenchman or a German from over the sea, and do not understand these things. Have I borne arms forty years in my country's service not to know a Peralta! On earth they are with me; if I go to heaven I meet them there, and in hell I see them; for when have I charged into the hottest of the fight and have not found a Peralta there before me? But I am speaking of the past, señor; for now I am also like one that has been left on the field forgotten—left for the vultures and foxes. You will no longer find them walking on the earth; only where men have rushed together sword in hand you will find their bones. Ah, friend!" And here, overcome with sad memories, the ancient warrior took another drink from his bottle.

"They cannot all be dead," said I, "if, as you imagine, the señora travelling with me is a Peralta."

"As I imagine!" he repeated scornfully. "Do I not know what I am talking about, young sir? They are dead, I tell you—dead as the past, dead as Oriental independence and honour. Did I not ride into the fight at Gil de los Medanos with the last of the Peraltas, Calixto, when he received his baptism of blood? Fifteen years old, señor, only fifteen, when he galloped into the fight, for he had the light heart, the brave spirit, and the hand swift to strike of a Peralta. And after the fight our colonel, Santa Coloma, who was killed the other day at San Paulo, embraced the boy before all the troops. He is dead, señor, and with Calixto died the house of Peralta."

"You knew Santa Coloma, then?" I said. "But you are mistaken, he was not killed at San Paulo, he made his escape."

"So they say—the ignorant ones," he returned. "But he is dead, for he loved his country, and all who are of that mind are slain. How should he escape?"

"I tell you he is not dead," I repeated, vexed at his stubborn persistence. "I also knew him, old man, and was with him at San Paulo."

He looked at me for a long time, and then took another swig from his bottle.

"Señor, this is not a thing I love joking about," said he. "Let us talk of other things. What I want to know is, what is Calixto's sister doing here? Why has she left her country?"

Receiving no reply to this question he went on: "Has she not got property? Yes, a large estancia, impoverished, ruined, if you like, but still a very large tract of land. When your enemies do not fear you then they cease to persecute. A broken old man, bereft of reason—surely they would not trouble him! No, no, she is leaving her country for other reasons. Yes, there is some private plot against her; some design, perhaps, to carry her off, or even to destroy her and get possession of her property. Naturally in such a case she would fly for protection to

Buenos Ayres, where there is one with some of her blood in his veins able to protect her person and her property."

I was astonished to hear him, but his last words were a mystery to me.

"There is no one in Buenos Ayres to protect her," I said; "I only will be there as I am here to shield her, and if, as you think, she has an enemy, he must reckon with me—one who, like that Calixto you speak of, has a hand quick to strike."

"There spoke the heart of a Blanco!" he exclaimed, clutching my arm, and then, the boat giving a lurch at that moment, almost dragging me down in his efforts to steady himself. After another sip of rum he went on: "But who are you, young sir, if that is not an impertinent question? Do you possess money, influence, powerful friends, that you take upon yourself the care of this woman? Is it in your power to baffle and crush her enemy or enemies, to protect not only her person, but her property, which, in her absence, will become the prey of robbers?"

"And who are you, old man?" I returned, unable to give a satisfactory answer to one of his searching questions, "and why do you ask me these things? And who is this powerful person you speak of in Buenos Ayres with some of her blood in his veins, but of whose existence she is ignorant?"

He shook his head silently, then deliberately proceeded to take out and light a cigarette. He smoked with a placid enjoyment which made me think that his refusal of my cigar and his bitter complaints about the effects of the ship's tossing on him had merely been to get the bottle of rum out of me. He was evidently a veteran in more senses than one, and now finding that I would tell him no more secrets he refused to answer any questions. Fearing that I had imprudently told him too much already, I finally left him and retired to my bunk.

Next morning we arrived at Buenos Ayres, and cast anchor about two miles from shore, for that was as near the land as we could get. Presently we were boarded by a Custom House officer, and for some time longer I was engaged in getting out our luggage and in bargaining with the captain to put us on shore. When I had completed these arrangements I was very much surprised to see the cunning old soldier I had talked with the evening before sitting in the Custom House boat which was just putting off from the side. Demetria had been looking on when the old fellow had left the ship, and she now came to me looking very excited.

"Richard," she said, "did you notice that man who was a passenger with us and who has just gone off in the boat? It is Santa Coloma."

"Oh, absurd!" I exclaimed. "I talked with that old man last night for an hour—an old grey-bearded gaucho, and no more like Santa Coloma than that sailor."

"I know I am right," she returned. "The General has visited my father at the estancia and I know him well. He is disguised now and has made himself look like a peasant, but when he went over the side into the boat he looked full into my face; I knew him and started, then he smiled, for he saw that I had recognised him."

The very fact that this common-looking old man had gone on shore in the Custom House boat proved that he was a person of consequence in disguise, and I could not doubt that Demetria was right. I felt excessively annoyed at myself for having failed to penetrate his disguise; for something of the old Marcos Marcó style of speaking might very well have revealed his identity if I had only had my wits about me. I was also very much concerned on Demetria's account, for it seemed that I had missed finding out something for her which would have been to her advantage to know. I was ashamed to tell her of that conversation about a relation in Buenos Ayres, but secretly determined to try and find Santa Coloma to get him to tell me what he knew.

After landing we put our small luggage into a fly and were driven to an hotel in Calle Lima, an out-of-the-way place kept by a German; but I knew the house to be a quiet, respectable one and very moderate in its charges.

About five o'clock in the afternoon we were together in the sitting-room on the first floor looking down on the street from the window, when a well-appointed carriage with a gentleman and two young ladies in it drew up before the door.

"Oh, Richard," exclaimed Paquíta in the greatest excitement, "it is Don Pantaleon Villaverde with his daughters, and they are getting out!"

"Who is Villaverde?" I asked.

"What, do you not know? He is a Judge of First Instance and his daughters are my dearest friends. Is it not strange to meet them like this? Oh, I must see them to ask for papa and mamita!" and here she began to cry.

The waiter came up with a card from the Señor Villaverde requesting an interview with the Señorita Peralta.

Demetria, who had been trying to soothe Paquíta's intense excitement and infuse a little courage into her, was too much amazed to speak; and in another moment our visitors were in the room. Paquíta started up tearful and trembling; then her two young friends, after staring at her for a few moments, delivered a screech of astonishment and rushed into her arms, and all three were locked together for some time in a triangular embrace.

When the excitement of this tempestuous meeting had spent itself, Señor Villaverde, who stood looking on with grave, impassive face, spoke to Demetria, telling her that his old friend, General Santa Coloma, had just informed him of her arrival in Buenos Ayres and of the hotel where she was staying. Probably she did not even know who he was, he said; he was her relation; his mother was a Peralta, a first cousin of her unhappy father, Colonel Peralta. He had come to see her with his daughters to invite her to make his house her home during her stay in Buenos Ayres. He also wished to help her with her affairs, which, his friend the General had informed him, were in some confusion. He had, he concluded, many influential friends in the sister city, who would be ready to assist him in arranging matters for her.

Demetria, recovering from the nervousness she had experienced on finding that Paquíta's great friends were her visitors, thanked him warmly and accepted his offer of a home and assistance; then, with a quiet dignity and self-possession one would hardly expect from a girl coming amongst fashionable people for the first time in her life, she greeted her new-found relations and thanked them for their visit.

As they insisted on taking Demetria away with them at once she left us to make her preparations, while Paquíta remained conversing with her friends, having many questions to ask them. She was consumed with anxiety to know how her family, and especially her father, who made the domestic laws, now, after so many months, regarded her elopement and marriage with me. Her friends, however, either knew nothing or would not tell her what they knew.

Poor Demetria! she had, with no time given her for reflection, taken the wise course of at once accepting the offer of her influential and extremely dignified kinsman; but it was hard for her to leave her friends at such short notice, and when she came back prepared for her departure the separation tried her severely. With tears in her eyes she bade Paquíta farewell, but when she took my hand in hers, for some time her trembling lips refused to speak. Overcoming her emotions by a great effort, she at length said, addressing her visitors, "For my escape from a sad and perilous position and for the pleasure of finding myself here amongst relations, I am indebted to this young friend who has been a brother to me."

Señor Villaverde listened and bowed towards me, but

with no softening in his stern, calm face, while his cold grey eyes seemed to look straight through me at something beyond. His manner towards me made me feel a kind of despair, for how strong must have been his disapproval of my conduct in running off with his friend's daughter—how great his indignation against me, when it prevented him from bestowing one smile or one kind word on me to thank me for all I had done for his kinswoman! Yet this was only the reflected indignation of my father-in-law.

We went down to the carriage to see them off, and then finding myself for a moment by the side of one of the young ladies I tried to find out something for myself. "Pray tell me, señorita," I said, "what you know about my father-in-law. If it is very bad, I promise you my wife shall not hear a word of it; but it is best that I should know the truth before meeting him."

A cloud came over her bright, expressive face while she glanced anxiously at Paquíta; then bending towards me she whispered, "Ah, my friend, he is implacable! I am so sorry for Paquíta's sake." And then with a smile of irrepressible coquetry she added, "And for yours."

The carriage drove away, and Demetria's eyes looking back at me were filled with tears, but in Señor Villaverde's eyes, also glancing back, there was an expression that boded ill for my future. His feeling was natural, perhaps, for he was the father of two very pretty girls.

Implacable, and I was now divided from him by no silver or brick-coloured sea! By returning I had made myself amenable to the laws I had broken by marrying a girl under age without her father's consent. The person in England who runs away with a ward in Chancery is not a greater offender against the law than I was. It was now in his power to have me punished, to cast me into prison for an indefinite time, and if not to crush my spirit, he would at least be able to break the heart of his unhappy daughter. Those wild, troubled days in the Purple Land now seemed to my mind peaceful, happy days, and the bitter days with no pleasure in them were only now about to begin. Implacable!

Suddenly looking up, I found Paquíta's violet eyes full of sad questioning fixed on my face.

"Tell me truly, Richard, what have you heard?" she asked.

I forced a smile, and taking her hand assured her that I had heard nothing to cause her any uneasiness. "Come," I said, "let us go in and prepare to leave town to-morrow. We will go back to the point we started from—your father's estancia, for the sooner this meeting you are thinking about so anxiously is over the better will it be for all of us."

APPENDIX

HISTORY OF THE BANDA ORIENTÁL

THE country, called in this work the Purple Land, was discovered by Magellan in the year 1500, and he called the hill, or mountain, which gives its name to the capital, Monte Vidi. He described it as a hat-shaped mountain; and it is probable that, four centuries ago, the tall conical hat, which is worn to this day by women in South Wales, was a common form in Spain and Portugal.

In due time settlements were made; but the colonists of those days loved gold and adventure above everything, and finding neither in the Banda, they little esteemed it. For two centuries it was neglected by its white possessors, while the cattle they had imported continued to multiply, and returning to a feral life, overran the country in amazing numbers.

The heroic period in South American history then passed away. El Dorado, the Spaniard's New Jerusalem, has changed into a bank of malarious mist and a cloud of mosquitoes. Amazons, giants, pigmies,

> "The Anthropophagi, and men whose heads
> Do grow beneath their shoulders,"

when closely looked for, turned out to be Red Indians of a type which varied but little throughout the entire vast continent. Wanderers from the Old World grew weary of seeking the tropics only to sink into flowery graves. They turned away sick at heart from the great desolation where the splendid empire of the Children of the Sun had so lately flourished. The accumulated treasures had been squandered. The cruel crusades of the Paulists against the Jesuit missions had ceased, for the inhuman slave-hunters had utterly destroyed the smiling gardens in the wilderness. A remnant of the escaped converts had gone back to a wild life in the woods, and the Fathers, who had done their Master's work so well, drifted away to mingle in other scenes or die of broken hearts. Then, in the sober eighteenth century, when the disillusion was complete, Spain woke up to the fact that in the temperate part of the continent, shared by her with Portugal, she possessed a new bright little Spain worth cultivating. About the same time Portugal discovered that the acquisition of this pretty country, with its lovely Lusitanian climate, would nicely round off her vast possessions on the south side. Forthwith these two great colonising powers fell to fighting over the Banda, where there were no temples of beaten gold, or mythical races of men, or fountains of everlasting youth. The quarrel might have continued to the end of time, so languidly was it conducted by both parties, had not great events come to swallow up the little ones.

At the beginning of the nineteenth century the English invasion burst like a sudden terrible thunderstorm on the country. Montevideo on the east and Buenos Ayres on the west side of the sea-like river were captured and lost again. The storm was soon over, but it had the effect of precipitating the revolution of 1810, which presently ended in the loss to Spain of all her American possessions. These changes brought only fresh wars and calamities to the long-suffering Banda. The ancient feud between Spain and Portugal descended to the new Brazilian Empire and the new Argentine Confederation, and these claimants contended for the country until 1828, when they finally agreed to let it govern itself in its own fashion. After thus acquiring its independence the little Belgium of the New World cast off its pretty but hated appellation of Cisplatina and resumed its old joyous name of Banda Oriental. With light hearts the people then proceeded to divide themselves into two political parties—Whites and Reds. Endless struggles for mastery ensued, in which the Argentines and Brazilians, forgetting their solemn compact, were for ever taking sides. But of these wars of crows and pies it would be idle to say more, since after going on for three-quarters of a century they are not wholly ended yet. The rambles and adventures described in the book take us back to the late sixties or early seventies of the last century, when the country was still in the condition in which it had remained since the colonial days, when the ten years' siege of Montevideo was not yet a remote event, and many of the people one met had had a part in it.

GREEN MANSIONS

A Romance of The Tropical Forest

PROLOGUE

IT is a cause of very great regret to me that this task has taken so much longer a time than I had expected for its completion. It is now many months—over a year, in fact—since I wrote to Georgetown announcing my intention of publishing, *in a very few months*, the whole truth about Mr. Abel. Hardly less could have been looked for from his nearest friend, and I had hoped that the discussion in the newspapers would have ceased, at all events, until the appearance of the promised book. It has not been so; and at this distance from Guiana I was not aware of how much conjectural matter was being printed week by week in the local press, some of which must have been painful reading to Mr. Abel's friends. A darkened chamber, the existence of which had never been suspected in that familiar house in Main Street, furnished only with an ebony stand on which stood a cinerary urn, its surface ornamented with flower and leaf and thorn, and winding through it all the figure of a serpent; an inscription, too, of seven short words which no one could understand or rightly interpret; and finally, the disposal of the mysterious ashes—that was all there was relating to an untold chapter in a man's life for imagination to work on. Let us hope that now, at last, the romance-weaving will come to an end. It was, however, but natural that the keenest curiosity should have been excited; not only because of that peculiar and indescribable charm of the man, which all recognised and which won all hearts, but also because of that hidden chapter—that sojourn in the desert, about which he preserved silence. It was felt in a vague way by his intimates that he had met with unusual experiences which had profoundly affected him and changed the course of his life. To me alone was the truth known, and I must now tell, briefly as possible, how my great friendship and close intimacy with him came about.

When, in 1887, I arrived in Georgetown to take up an appointment in a public office, I found Mr. Abel an old resident there, a man of means and a favourite in society. Yet he was an alien, a Venezuelan, one of that turbulent people on our border whom the colonists have always looked on as their natural enemies. The story told to me was that about twelve years before that time he had arrived at Georgetown from some remote district in the interior; that he had journeyed alone on foot across half the continent to the coast, and had first appeared among them, a young stranger, penniless, in rags, wasted almost to a skeleton by fever and misery of all kinds, his face blackened by long exposure to sun and wind. Friendless, with but little English, it was a hard struggle for him to live; but he managed somehow, and eventually letters from Caracas informed him that a considerable property of which he had been deprived was once more his own, and he was also invited to return to his country to take his part in the government of the republic. But Mr. Abel, though young, had already outlived political passions and aspirations, and, apparently, even the love of his country; at all events, he elected to stay where he was—his enemies, he would say smilingly, were his best friends—and one of the first uses he made of his fortune was to buy that house in Main Street which was afterwards like a home to me.

I must state here that my friend's full name was Abel Guevez de Argensola, but in his early days in Georgetown he was called by his christian name only, and later he wished to be known simply as "Mr. Abel."

I had no sooner made his acquaintance than I ceased to wonder at the esteem and even affection with which he, a Venezuelan, was regarded in this British colony. All knew and liked him, and the reason of it was the personal charm of the man, his kindly disposition, his manner with women, which pleased them and excited no man's jealousy—not even the old hot-tempered planter's, with a very young and pretty and light-headed wife—his love of little children, of all wild creatures, of nature, and of whatsoever was furthest removed from the common material interests and concerns of a purely commercial community. The things which excited other men—politics, sport, and the price of crystals—were outside of his thoughts; and when men had done with them for a season, when like the tempest they had "blown their fill" in office and club-room and house and wanted a change, it was a relief to turn to Mr. Abel and get him to discourse of *his* world—the world of nature and of the spirit.

It was, all felt, a good thing to have a Mr. Abel in Georgetown. That it was indeed good for me I quickly discovered. I had certainly not expected to meet in such a place with any person to share my tastes—that love of poetry which has been the chief passion and delight of my life; but such an one I had found in Mr. Abel. It surprised me that he, suckled on the literature of Spain, and a reader of only ten or twelve years of English literature, possessed a knowledge of our modern poetry as intimate as my own, and a love of it equally great. This feeling brought us together, and made us two—the nervous olive-skinned Hispano-American of the tropics and the phlegmatic blue-eyed Saxon of the cold north—one in spirit and more than brothers. Many were the daylight hours we spent together and "tired the sun with talking"; many, past counting, the precious evenings in that restful house of his where I was an almost daily guest. I had not looked for such happiness; nor, he often said, had he. A result of this intimacy was that the vague idea concerning his hidden past, that some unusual experience had profoundly affected him and perhaps changed the whole course of his life, did not diminish, but, on the contrary, became accentuated, and was often in my mind. The change in him was almost painful to witness whenever our wandering talk touched on the subject of the aborigines, and of the knowledge he had acquired of their character and languages when living or travelling among them; all that made his conversation most engaging—the lively, curious mind, the wit, the gaiety of spirit tinged with a tender melancholy—appeared to fade out of it; even the expression of his face would change, becoming hard and set, and he would deal you out facts in a dry mechanical way as if reading them in a book. It grieved me to note this, but I dropped no hint of such a feeling, and would never have spoken about it but for a quarrel which came at last to make the one brief solitary break in that close friendship of years. I got into a bad state of health, and Abel was not only much concerned about it, but annoyed, as if I had not treated him well by being ill, and he would even say that I could get well if I wished to. I did not take this seriously, but one morning, when calling to see me at the office, he attacked me in a way that made me downright angry with him. He told me that indolence and the use of stimulants was the cause of my bad health. He spoke in a mocking way, with a pretence of not quite meaning it, but the feeling could not be wholly disguised. Stung by his reproaches, I blurted out that he had no right to talk to me, even in fun, in such a way. Yes, he said, getting serious, he had the best right—that of our friendship. He would be no true friend if he kept his peace about such a matter. Then, in my haste, I retorted that to me the friendship between us did not seem so perfect and complete as it did to him. One condition of friendship is that the partners in it should be known to each other. He had had my whole life and mind open to him, to read it as in a book. *His* life was a closed and clasped volume to me.

His face darkened, and after a few moments' silent reflection he got up and left me with a cold good-bye, and without that hand-grasp which had been customary between us.

After his departure I had the feeling that a great loss, a great calamity, had befallen me, but I was still smarting at his too candid criticism, all the more because in my heart I acknowledged its truth. And that night, lying awake, I repented of the cruel retort I had made, and resolved to ask his forgiveness and leave it to him to determine the question of our future relations. But he was beforehand with me, and with the morning came a letter begging my forgiveness and asking me to go that evening to dine with him.

We were alone, and during dinner and afterwards, when we sat smoking and sipping black coffee in the verandah, we were unusually quiet, even to gravity, which caused the two white-clad servants that waited on us—the brown-faced subtle-eyed old Hindoo butler and an almost blue-black young Guiana negro—to direct many furtive glances at their master's face. They were accustomed to see him in a more genial mood when he had a friend to dine. To me the change in his manner was not surprising: from the moment of seeing him I had divined that he had determined to open the shut and clasped volume of which I had spoken—that the time had now come for him to speak.

CHAPTER I

NOW that we are cool, he said, and regret that we hurt each other, I am not sorry that it happened. I deserved your reproach: a hundred times I have wished to tell you the whole story of my travels and adventures among the savages, and one of the reasons which prevented me was the fear that it would have an unfortunate effect on our friendship. That was precious, and I desired above everything to keep it. But I must think no more about that now. I must think only of how I am to tell you my story. I will begin at a time when I was twenty-three. It was early in life to be in the thick of politics, and in trouble to the extent of having to fly my country to save my liberty, perhaps my life.

Every nation, someone remarks, has the government it deserves, and Venezuela certainly has the one it deserves and that suits it best. We call it a republic, not only because it is not one, but also because a thing must have a name; and to have a good name, or a fine name, is very convenient—especially when you want to borrow money. If the Venezuelans, thinly distributed over an area of half a million square miles, mostly illiterate peasants, half-breeds, and indigenes, were educated, intelligent men, zealous only for the public weal, it would be possible for them to have a real republic. They have instead a government by cliques, tempered by revolution; and a very good government it is, in harmony with the physical conditions of the country and the national temperament. Now it happens that the educated men, representing your higher classes, are so few that there are not many persons unconnected by ties of blood or marriage with prominent members of the political groups to which they belong. By this you will see how easy and almost inevitable it is that we should become accustomed to look on conspiracy and revolt against the regnant party—the men of another clique—as only in the natural order of things. In the event of failure such outbreaks are punished, but they are not regarded as immoral. On the contrary, men of the highest intelligence and virtue among us are seen taking a leading part in these adventures. Whether such a condition of things is intrinsically wrong or not, or would be wrong in some circumstances and is not wrong, because inevitable, in others, I cannot pretend to decide; and all this tiresome prolusion is only to enable you to understand how I—a young man of unblemished character, not a soldier by profession, not ambitious of political distinction, wealthy for that country, popular in society, a lover of social pleasures, of books, of nature—actuated, as I believed, by the highest motives, allowed myself to be drawn very readily by friends and relations into a conspiracy to overthrow the government of the moment, with the object of replacing it by more worthy men—ourselves, to wit.

Our adventure failed because the authorities got wind

of the affair and matters were precipitated. Our leaders at the moment happened to be scattered over the country —some were abroad; and a few hot-headed men of the party, who were in Caracas just then, and probably feared arrest, struck a rash blow: the President was attacked in the street and wounded. But the attackers were seized, and some of them shot on the following day. When the news reached me I was at a distance from the capital, staying with a friend on an estate he owned on the River Quebrada Honda, in the State of Guarico, some fifteen to twenty miles from the town of Zaraza. My friend, an officer in the army, was a leader in the conspiracy; and as I was the only son of a man who had been greatly hated by the Minister of War, it became necessary for us both to fly for our lives. In the circumstances we could not look to be pardoned, even on the score of youth.

Our first decision was to escape to the sea-coast; but as the risk of a journey to La Guayra, or any other port of embarkation on the north side of the country, seemed too great, we made our way in a contrary direction to the Orinoco, and downstream to Angostura. Now, when we had reached this comparatively safe breathing-place—safe, at all events, for the moment—I changed my mind about leaving or attempting to leave the country. Since boyhood I had taken a very peculiar interest in that vast and almost unexplored territory we possess south of the Orinoco, with its countless unmapped rivers and trackless forests; and in its savage inhabitants, with their ancient customs and character, unadulterated by contact with Europeans. To visit this primitive wilderness had been a cherished dream; and I had to some extent even prepared myself for such an adventure by mastering more than one of the Indian dialects of the northern states of Venezuela. And now, finding myself on the south side of our great river, with unlimited time at my disposal, I determined to gratify this wish. My companion took his departure towards the coast, while I set about making preparations and hunting up information from those who had travelled in the interior to trade with the savages. I decided eventually to go back upstream, and penetrate to the interior in the western part of Guayana, and the Amazonian territory bordering on Colombia and Brazil, and to return to Angostura in about six months' time. I had no fear of being arrested in the semi-independent, and in most part savage region, as the Guayana authorities concerned themselves little enough about the political upheavals at Caracas.

The first five or six months I spent in Guayana, after leaving the city of refuge, were eventful enough to satisfy a moderately adventurous spirit. A complaisant Government employé at Angostura had provided me with a passport, in which it was set down (for few to read) that my object in visiting the interior was to collect information concerning the native tribes, the vegetable products of the country, and other knowledge which would be of advantage to the Republic; and the authorities were requested to afford me protection and assist me in my pursuits.

I ascended the Orinoco, making occasional expeditions to the small Christian settlements in the neighbourhood of the right bank, also to the Indian villages; and travelling in this way, seeing and learning much, in about three months I reached the River Meta. During this period I amused myself by keeping a journal, a record of personal adventures, impressions of the country and people, both semi-civilised and savage; and as my journal grew, I began to think that on my return at some future time to Caracas, it might prove useful and interesting to the public, and also procure me fame; which thought proved pleasurable and a great incentive, so that I began to observe things more narrowly and to study expression. But the book was not to be.

From the mouth of the Meta I journeyed on, intending to visit the settlement of Atahapo, where the great River Guaviare, with other rivers, empty themselves into the Orinoco. But I was not destined to reach it, for at the small settlement of Manapuri I fell ill of a low fever; and here ended the first half-year of my wanderings, about which no more need be told.

A more miserable place than Manapuri for a man to be ill of a low fever in could not well be imagined. The settlement, composed of mean hovels, with a few large structures of mud, or plastered wattle, thatched with palm leaves, was surrounded by water, marsh, and forest, the breeding-place of myriads of croaking frogs and of clouds of mosquitoes; even to one in perfect health existence in such a place would have been a burden. The inhabitants mustered about eighty or ninety, mostly Indians of that degenerate class frequently to be met with in small trading outposts. The savages of Guayana are great drinkers, but not drunkards in our sense, since their fermented liquors contain so little alcohol that inordinate quantities must be swallowed to produce intoxication; in the settlements they prefer the white man's more potent poisons, with the result that in a small place like Manapuri one can see enacted, as on a stage, the last act in the great American tragedy. To be succeeded, doubtless, by other and possibly greater tragedies. My thoughts at that period of suffering were pessimistic in the extreme. Sometimes, when the almost continuous rain held up for half a day, I would manage to creep out a short distance; but I was almost past making any exertion, scarcely caring to live, and taking absolutely no interest in the news from Caracas, which reached me at long intervals. At the end of two months, feeling a slight improvement in my health, and with it a returning interest in life and its affairs, it occurred to me to get out my diary and write a brief account of my sojourn at Manapuri. I had placed it for safety in a small deal box, lent to me for the purpose by a Venezuelan trader, an old resident at the settlement, by name Pantaleon—called by all Don Panta—one who openly kept half a dozen Indian wives in his house, and was noted for his dishonesty and greed, but who had proved himself a good friend to me. The box was in a corner of the wretched palm-thatched hovel I inhabited; but on taking it out I discovered that for several weeks the rain had been dripping on it, and that the manuscript was reduced to a sodden pulp. I flung it upon the floor with a curse, and threw myself back on my bed with a groan.

In that desponding state I was found by my friend

Panta, who was constant in his visits at all hours; and, when in answer to his anxious inquiries I pointed to the pulpy mass on the mud floor, he turned it over with his foot, and then, bursting into a loud laugh, kicked it out, remarking that he had mistaken the object for some unknown reptile that had crawled in out of the rain. He affected to be astonished that I should regret its loss. It was all a true narrative, he exclaimed; if I wished to write a book for the stay-at-homes to read, I could easily invent a thousand lies far more entertaining than any real experiences. He had come to me, he said, to propose something. He had lived twenty years at that place, and had got accustomed to the climate, but it would not do for me to remain any longer if I wished to live. I must go away at once to a different country—to the mountains, where it was open and dry. "And if you want quinine when you are there," he concluded, "smell the wind when it blows from the south-west, and you will inhale it into your system, fresh from the forest." When I remarked despondingly that in my condition it would be impossible to quit Manapuri, he went on to say that a small party of Indians was now in the settlement; that they had come, not only to trade, but to visit one of their own tribe, who was his wife, purchased some years ago from her father. "And the money she cost me I have never regretted to this day," said he, "for she is a good wife—not jealous," he added, with a curse on all the others. These Indians came all the way from the Queneveta mountains, and were of the Maquiritari tribe. He, Panta, and, better still, his good wife, would interest them on my behalf, and for a suitable reward they would take me by slow, easy stages to their own country, where I would be treated well and recover my health.

This proposal, after I had considered it well, produced so good an effect on me, that I not only gave a glad consent, but, on the following day, I was able to get about and begin the preparations for my journey with some spirit.

In about eight days I bade good-bye to my generous friend Panta, whom I regarded, after having seen much of him, as a kind of savage beast that had sprung on me, not to rend, but to rescue from death; for we know that even cruel savage brutes and evil men have at times sweet, beneficent impulses, during which they act in a way contrary to their natures, like passive agents of some higher power. It was a continual pain to travel in my weak condition, and the patience of my Indians was severely taxed; but they did not forsake me; and, at last, the entire distance, which I conjectured to be about sixty-five leagues. was accomplished; and at the end I was actually stronger and better in every way than at the start. From this time my progress towards complete recovery was rapid. The air, with or without any medicinal virtue blown from the cinchona trees in the far-off Andean forest, was tonic; and when I took my walks on the hill-side above the Indian village, or later, when able to climb to the summits, the world as seen from those wild Queneveta mountains had a largeness and varied glory of scenery peculiarly refreshing and delightful to the soul.

With the Maquiritari tribe I passed some weeks, and

the sweet sensations of returning health made me happy for a time; but such sensations seldom outlast convalescence. I was no sooner well again than I began to feel a restless spirit stirring in me. The monotony of savage life in this place became intolerable. After my long listless period the reaction had come, and I wished only for action, adventure—no matter how dangerous; and for new scenes, new faces, new dialects. In the end I conceived the idea of going on to the Casiquiare river, where I would find a few small settlements, and perhaps obtain help from the authorities there which would enable me to reach the Rio Negro. For it was now in my mind to follow that river to the Amazons, and so down to Para and the Atlantic coast.

Leaving the Queneveta range, I started with two of the Indians as guides and travelling companions; but their journey ended only half-way to the river I wished to reach; and they left me with some friendly savages living on the Chunapay, a tributary of the Cunucumana, which flows to the Orinoco. Here I had no choice but to wait until an opportunity of attaching myself to some party of travelling Indians, going south-west, should arrive; for by this time I had expended the whole of my small capital in ornaments and calico brought from Manapuri, so that I could no longer purchase any man's service. And perhaps it will be as well to state at this point just what I possessed. For some time I had worn nothing but sandals to protect my feet; my garments consisted of a single suit, and one flannel shirt, which I washed frequently, going shirtless while it was drying. Fortunately I had an excellent blue cloth cloak, durable and handsome, given to me by a friend at Angostura, whose prophecy on presenting it, that it would outlast *me*, very nearly came true. It served as a covering by night, and to keep a man warm and comfortable when travelling in cold and wet weather no better garment was ever made. I had a revolver and metal cartridge box in my broad leather belt, also a good hunting-knife with strong buckhorn handle and a heavy blade about nine inches long. In the pocket of my cloak I had a pretty silver tinder-box, and a match-box—to be mentioned again in this narrative—and one or two other trifling objects: these I was determined to keep until they could be kept no longer.

During the tedious interval of waiting on the Chunapay I was told a flattering tale by the village Indians, which eventually caused me to abandon the proposed journey to the Rio Negro. These Indians wore necklets, like nearly all the Guayana savages; but one, I observed, possessed a necklet unlike that of the others, which greatly aroused my curiosity. It was made of thirteen gold plates, irregular in form, about as broad as a man's thumb-nail, and linked together with fibres. I was allowed to examine it, and had no doubt that the pieces were of pure gold, beaten flat by the savages. When questioned about it they said that it was originally obtained from the Indians of Parahuari, and Parahuari, they further said, was a mountainous country west of the Orinoco. Every man and woman in that place, they assured me, had such a necklet. This report inflamed my mind to such a degree that I could not rest by night or day for dreaming golden dreams, and considering how to get to that rich district, unknown to civilised men. The Indians gravely shook their heads when I tried to persuade them to take me. They were far enough from the Orinoco, and Parahuari was ten, perhaps fifteen, days' journey further on—a country unknown to them, where they had no relations.

In spite of difficulties and delays, however, and not without pain and some perilous adventures, I succeeded at last in reaching the upper Orinoco, and, eventually, in crossing to the other side. With my life in my hand I struggled on westward through an unknown difficult country, from Indian village to village, where at any moment I might have been murdered with impunity for the sake of my few belongings. It is hard for me to speak a good word for the Guayana savages; but I must now say this of them, that they not only did me no harm when I was at their mercy during this long journey, but they gave me shelter in their villages, and fed me when I was hungry, and helped me on my way when I could make no return. You must not, however, run away with the idea that there is any sweetness in their disposition, any humane or benevolent instincts such as are found among the civilised nations: far from it. I regard them now, and, fortunately for me, I regarded them then, when, as I have said, I was at their mercy, as beasts of prey, plus a cunning or low kind of intelligence vastly greater than that of the brute; and, for only morality, that respect for the rights of other members of the same family, or tribe, without which even the rudest communities cannot hold together. How, then, could I do this thing, and dwell and travel freely, without receiving harm, among tribes that have no peace with and no kindly feelings towards the stranger, in a district where the white man is rarely or never seen? Because I knew them so well. Without that knowledge, always available, and an extreme facility in acquiring new dialects, which had increased by practice until it was almost like intuition, I should have fared badly after leaving the Maquiritari tribe. As it was, I had two or three very narrow escapes.

To return from this digression. I looked at last on the famous Parahuari mountains, which, I was greatly surprised to find, were after all nothing but hills, and not very high ones. This, however, did not depress me. The very fact that Parahuari possessed no imposing feature in its scenery seemed rather to prove that it must be rich in gold: how else could its name and the fame of its treasures be familiar to people dwelling so far away as the Cunucumana?

But there was no gold. I searched through the whole range, which was about seven leagues long, and visited the villages, where I talked much with the Indians, interrogating them, and they had no necklets of gold, nor gold in any form; nor had they ever heard of its presence in Parahuari, nor in any other place known to them.

The very last village where I spoke on the subject of my quest, albeit now without hope, was about a league from the western extremity of the range, in the midst of a high broken country of forest and savannah and many swift streams; near one of these, called the Curicay, the village stood, among low scattered trees—a large building, in which all the people, numbering eighteen, passed most of their time when not hunting, with two smaller buildings attached to it. The head, or chief, Runi by name, was about fifty years old, a taciturn, finely formed, and somewhat dignified savage, who was either of a sullen disposition or not well pleased at the intrusion of a white man. And for a time I made no attempt to conciliate him. What profit was there in it at all? Even that light mask, which I had worn so long and with such good effect, incommoded me now: I would cast it aside and be myself—silent and sullen as my barbarous host. If any malignant purpose was taking form in his mind, let it, and let him do his worst; for when failure first stares a man in the face it has so dark and repellent a look that not anything that can be added can make him more miserable; nor has he any apprehension. For weeks I had been searching with eager, feverish eyes in every village, in every rocky crevice, in every noisy mountain streamlet, for the glittering yellow dust I had travelled so far to find. And now all my beautiful dreams—all the pleasure and power to be—had vanished like a mere mirage on the savannah at noon.

It was a day of despair which I spent in this place, sitting all day indoors, for it was raining hard, immersed in my own gloomy thoughts, pretending to doze in my seat, and out of the narrow slits of my half-closed eyes seeing the others, also sitting or moving about, like shadows or people in a dream; and I cared nothing about them, and wished not to seem friendly, even for the sake of the food they might offer me by-and-by.

Towards evening the rain ceased; and rising up I went out a short distance to the neighbouring stream, where I sat on a stone, and casting off my sandals, laved my bruised feet in the cool running water. The western half of the sky was blue again with that tender lucid blue seen after rain, but the leaves still glittered with water, and the wet trunks looked almost black under the green foliage. The rare loveliness of the scene touched and lightened my heart. Away back in the east the hills of Parahuari, with the level sun full on them, loomed with a strange glory against the grey rainy clouds drawing off on that side, and their new mystic beauty almost made me forget how these same hills had wearied, and hurt, and mocked me. On that side, also to the north and south, there was open forest, but to the west a different prospect met the eye. Beyond the stream and the strip of verdure that fringed it, and the few scattered dwarf trees growing near its banks, spread a brown savannah sloping upwards to a long, low, rocky ridge, beyond which rose a great solitary hill, or rather mountain, conical in form, and clothed in forest almost to the summit. This was the mountain Ytaioa, the chief landmark in that district. As the sun went down over the ridge, beyond the savannah, the whole western sky changed to a delicate rose-colour that had the appearance of rose-coloured smoke blown there by some far off-wind, and left suspended—a thin, brilliant veil showing through it the distant sky beyond, blue and ethereal. Flocks of birds, a kind of troupial, were flying past me overhead, flock succeeding flock, on their way to their roosting-place, uttering as they flew a clear, bell-like chirp; and there was something ethereal too in those drops of melodious sound, which fell into my heart like raindrops falling into a pool to mix their fresh heavenly water with the water of earth.

Doubtless into the turbid tarn of my heart some sacred drops had fallen—from the passing birds, from that crimson disc which had now dropped below the horizon, the darkening hills, the rose and blue of infinite heaven, from the whole visible circle; and I felt purified and had a strange sense and apprehension of a secret innocence and spirituality in nature—a prescience of some bourn, incalculably distant perhaps, to which we are all moving; of a time when the heavenly rain shall have washed us clean from all spot and blemish. This unexpected peace which I had found now seemed to me of infinitely greater value than that yellow metal I had missed finding, with all its possibilities. My wish now was to rest for a season at this spot, so remote and lovely and peaceful, where I had experienced such unusual feelings, and such a blessed disillusionment.

This was the end of my second period in Guayana; the first had been filled with that dream of a book to win me fame in my country, perhaps even in Europe: the second, from the time of leaving the Queneveta mountains, with the dream of boundless wealth—the old dream of gold in this region that has drawn so many minds since the days of Alonzo Pizarro. But to remain I must propitiate Runi, sitting silent with gloomy brows over there indoors; and he did not appear to me like one that might be won with words, however flattering. It was clear to me that the time had come to part with my one remaining valuable trinket—the tinder-box of chased silver.

I returned to the house, and going in seated myself on a log by the fire, just opposite to my grim host, who was smoking and appeared not to have moved since I left him. I made myself a cigarette, then drew out the tinder-box, with its flint and steel attached to it by means of two small silver chains. His eyes brightened a little as they curiously watched my movements, and he pointed without speaking to the glowing coals of fire at my feet. I shook my head, and striking the steel, sent out a brilliant spray of sparks, then blew on the tinder and lit my cigarette. This done, instead of returning the box to my pocket I passed the chain through the buttonhole of my cloak and let it dangle on my breast as an ornament. When the cigarette was smoked I cleared my throat in the orthodox manner, and fixed my eyes on Runi, who, on his part, made a slight movement to indicate that he was ready to listen to what I had to say.

My speech was long, lasting at least half an hour, delivered in a profound silence; it was chiefly occupied with an account of my wanderings in Guayana; and being little more than a catalogue of names of all the places I had visited, and the tribes and chief or head men with whom I had come in contact, I was able to speak continuously, and so to hide my ignorance of a dialect which was still new to me. The Guayana savage judges a man for his staying powers. To stand as motionless as a bronze statue for one or two hours watching for a bird; to sit or lie still for half a day; to endure pain, not seldom self-inflicted, without wincing; and when delivering a speech to pour it out in a copious stream, without pausing to take breath or hesitating over a word—to be able to do all this is to prove yourself a man, an equal, one to be respected and even made a friend of. What I really wished to say to him was put in a few words at the conclusion of my well-nigh meaningless oration. Everywhere, I said, I had been the Indian's friend, and I wished to be his friend, to live with him at Parahuari, even as I had lived with other chiefs and heads of villages and families; to be looked on by him, as these others had looked on me, not as a stranger or a white man, but as a friend, a brother, an Indian.

I ceased speaking, and there was a slight murmurous sound in the room, as of wind long pent up in many lungs suddenly exhaled; while Runi, still unmoved, emitted a low grunt. Then I rose, and detaching the silver ornament from my cloak presented it to him. He accepted it; not very graciously, as a stranger to these people might have imagined; but I was satisfied, feeling sure that I had made a favourable impression. After a little he handed the box to the person sitting next to him, who examined it and passed it on to a third, and in this way it went round and came back once more to Runi. Then he called for a drink. There happened to be a store of casserie in the house; probably the women had been busy for some days past in making it, little thinking that it was destined to be prematurely consumed. A large jarful was produced; Runi politely quaffed the first cup; I followed; then the others; and the women drank also, a woman taking about one cupful to a man's three. Runi and I, however, drank the most, for we had our positions as the two principal personages there to maintain. Tongues were loosened now; for the alcohol, small as the quantity contained in this mild liquor is, had begun to tell on our brains. I had not their pottle-shaped stomach, made to hold unlimited quantities of meat and drink; but I was determined on this most important occasion not to deserve my host's contempt—to be compared, perhaps, to the small bird that delicately picks up six drops of water in its bill and is satisfied. I would measure my strength against his, and if necessary drink myself into a state of insensibility. At last I was scarcely able to stand on my legs. But even the seasoned old savage was affected by this time. *In vino veritas*, said the ancients; and the principle holds good where there is no vinum, but only mild casserie. Runi now informed me that he had once known a white man, that he was a bad man, which had caused him to say that all white men were bad; even as David, still more sweepingly, had proclaimed that all men were liars. Now he found that it was not so, that I was a good man. His friendliness increased with intoxication. He presented me with a curious little tinder-box, made from the conical tail of an armadillo, hollowed out, and provided with a wooden stopper;—this to be used in place of the box I had deprived myself of. He also furnished me with a grass hammock, and had it hung up there and then, so that I could lie down when inclined. There was nothing he would not do for me. And at last, when many more cups had been emptied, and a third or fourth jar brought out, he began to unburthen his heart of its dark and dangerous secrets. He shed tears—for the "man without a tear" dwells not in the woods of Guayana: tears for those who had been treacherously slain long years ago; for his father, who had been killed by Tripica, the father of Managa, who was still above ground. But let him and all his people beware of Runi. He had spilt their blood before, he had fed the fox and vulture with their flesh, and would never rest while Managa lived with his people at Uritay—the five hills of Uritay, which were two days' journey from Parahuari. While thus talking of his old enemy he lashed himself into a kind of frenzy, smiting his chest and gnashing his teeth; and finally seizing a spear, he buried its point deep into the clay floor, only to wrench it out and strike it into the earth again and again, to show how he would serve Managa, and any one of Managa's people he might meet with — man, woman, or child. Then he staggered out from the door to flourish his spear; and looking to the north-west, he shouted aloud to Managa to come and slay his people and burn down his house, as he had so often threatened to do.

"Let him come! Let Managa come!" I cried, staggering out after him. "I am your friend, your brother; I have no spear and no arrows, but I have this—this!" And here I drew out and flourished my revolver. "Where is Managa?" I continued. "Where are the hills of Uritay?" He pointed to a star low down in the south-west. "Then," I shouted, "let this bullet find Managa, sitting by the fire among his people, and let him fall and pour out his blood on the ground!" And with that I discharged my pistol in the direction he had pointed to.

A scream of terror burst out from the women and children, while Runi at my side, in an access of fierce delight and admiration, turned and embraced me. It was the first and last embrace I ever suffered from a naked male savage, and although this did not seem a time for fastidious feelings, to be hugged to his sweltering body was an unpleasant experience.

More cups of casserie followed this outburst; and at last, unable to keep it up any longer, I staggered to my hammock; but being unable to get into it, Runi, overflowing with kindness, came to my assistance, whereupon we fell and rolled together on the floor. Finally, I was raised by the others and tumbled into my swinging bed, and fell at once into a deep, dreamless sleep, from which I did not awake until after sunrise on the following morning.

CHAPTER II

IT is fortunate that casserie is manufactured by an extremely slow, laborious process, since the women, who are the drink-makers, in the first place have to reduce the material (cassava bread) to a pulp by means of their own molars, after which it is watered down and put away in troughs to ferment. Great is the diligence of these willing slaves; but, work how they will, they can only satisfy their lords' love of a big drink at long intervals. Such a function as that at which I had assisted is therefore the result of much patient mastication and silent fermentation—the delicate flower of a plant that has been a long time growing.

Having now established myself as one of the family, at the cost of some disagreeable sensations and a pang or two of self-disgust, I resolved to let nothing further trouble me at Parahuari, but to live the easy, careless life of the idle man, joining in hunting and fishing expeditions when in the mood; at other times enjoying existence in my own way, apart from my fellows, conversing with wild nature in that solitary place.

Besides Runi, there were, in our little community, two oldish men, his cousins I believe, who had wives and grown-up children. Another family consisted of Piaké, Runi's nephew, his brother Kua-kó—about whom there will be much to say—and a sister Oalava. Piaké had a wife and two children; Kua-kó was unmarried and about nineteen or twenty years old; Oalava was the youngest of the three. Last of all, who should perhaps have been first, was Runi's mother, called Cla-cla, probably in imitation of the cry of some bird, for in these latitudes a person is rarely, perhaps never, called by his or her real name, which is a secret jealously preserved, even from near relations. I believe that Cla-cla herself was the only living being who knew the name her parents had bestowed on her at birth. She was a very old woman, spare in figure, brown as old sun-baked leather, her face written over with innumerable wrinkles, and her long coarse hair perfectly white; yet she was exceedingly active, and seemed to do more work than any other woman in the community; more than that, when the day's toil was over and nothing remained for the others to do, then Cla-cla's night work would begin; and this was to talk all the others, or at all events all the men, to sleep. She was like a self-regulating machine, and punctually every evening, when the door was closed, and the night-fire made up, and every man in his hammock, she would set herself going, telling the most interminable stories, until the last listener was fast asleep: later in the night, if any man woke with a snort or grunt, off she would go again, taking up the thread of the tale where she had dropped it.

Old Cla-cla amused me very much, by night and day, and I seldom tired of watching her owlish countenance as she sat by the fire, never allowing it to sink low for want of fuel; always studying the pot when it was on to simmer, and at the same time attending to the movements of the others about her, ready at a moment's notice to give assistance or to dart out on a stray chicken or refractory child.

So much did she amuse me, although without intending it, that I thought it would be only fair, in my turn, to do something for her entertainment. I was engaged one day in shaping a wooden foil with my knife, whistling and singing snatches of old melodies at my work, when all at once I caught sight of the ancient dame looking greatly delighted, chuckling internally, nodding her head, and keeping time with her hands. Evidently she was able to appreciate a style of music superior to that of the aboriginals, and forthwith I abandoned my foils for the time and set about the manufacture of a guitar, which cost me much labour, and brought out more ingenuity than I had ever thought myself capable of. To reduce the wood to the right thinness, then to bend and fasten it with wooden pegs and with gums, to add the arm, frets, keys, and finally the catgut strings—those of another kind being out of the question—kept me busy for some days. When completed it was a rude instrument, scarcely tunable; nevertheless when I smote the strings, playing lively music, or accompanied myself in singing, I found that it was a great success, and so was as much pleased with my own performance as if I had had the most perfect guitar ever made in old Spain. I also skipped about the floor, strum-strumming at the same time, instructing them in the most lively dances of the whites, in which the feet must be as nimble as the player's fingers. It is true that these exhibitions were always witnessed by the adults with a profound gravity, which would have disheartened a stranger to their ways. They were a set of hollow bronze statues that looked at me, but I knew that the living animals inside of them were tickled at my singing, strumming, and pirouetting. Cla-cla was, however, an exception, and encouraged me not infrequently by emitting a sound, half cackle and half screech, by way of laughter; for she had come to her second childhood, or, at all events, had dropped the stolid mask which the young Guayana savage, in imitation of his elders, adjusts to his face at about the age of twelve, to wear it thereafter all his life long, or only to drop it occasionally when very drunk. The youngsters also openly manifested their pleasure, although, as a rule, they try to restrain their feelings in the presence of grown-up people, and with them I became a great favourite.

By-and-by I returned to my foil-making, and gave them fencing lessons, and sometimes invited two or three of the biggest boys to attack me simultaneously, just to show how easily I could disarm and kill them. This practice excited some interest in Kua-kó, who had a little more of curiosity and geniality and less of the put-on dignity of the others, and with him I became most intimate. Fencing with Kua-kó was highly amusing: no sooner was he in position, foil in hand, than all my instructions were thrown to the winds, and he would charge and attack me in his own barbarous manner, with the result that I would send his foil spinning a dozen yards away, while he, struck motionless, would gaze after it in open-mouthed astonishment.

Three weeks had passed by not unpleasantly when, one morning, I took it into my head to walk by myself across that somewhat sterile savannah west of the village and stream, which ended, as I have said, in a long, low, stony ridge. From the village there was nothing to attract the eye in that direction; but I wished to get a better view of that great solitary hill or mountain of Ytaioa, and of the cloud-like summits beyond it in the distance. From the stream the ground rose in a gradual slope, and the highest part of the ridge for which I made was about two miles from the starting-point—a parched brown plain, with nothing growing on it but scattered tussocks of sere hair-like grass.

When I reached the top and could see the country beyond, I was agreeably disappointed at the discovery that the sterile ground extended only about a mile and a quarter on the further side, and was succeeded by a forest—a very inviting patch of woodland covering five or six square miles, occupying a kind of oblong basin, extending from the foot of Ytaioa on the north to a low range of rocky hills on the south. From the wooded basin long narrow strips of forest ran out in various directions like the arms of an octopus, one pair embracing the slopes of Ytaioa, another much broader belt extending along a valley which cut through the ridge of hills on the south side at right angles, and was lost to sight beyond; far away in the west and south and north distant mountains appeared, not in regular ranges, but in groups or singly, or looking like blue banked-up clouds on the horizon.

Glad at having discovered the existence of this forest so near home, and wondering why my Indian friends had never taken me to it, or ever went out on that side, I set forth with a light heart to explore it for myself, regretting only that I was without a proper weapon for procuring game. The walk from the ridge over the savannah was easy, as the barren, stony ground sloped downward the whole way. The outer part of the wood on my side was very open, composed in most part of dwarf trees that grow on stony soil, and scattered thorny bushes bearing a yellow pea-shaped blossom. Presently I came to thicker wood, where the trees were much taller and in greater variety; and after this came another sterile strip, like that on the edge of the wood, where stone cropped out from the ground and nothing grew except the yellow-flowered thorn bushes. Passing this sterile ribbon, which seemed to extend to a considerable distance north and south, and was fifty to a hundred yards wide, the forest again became dense and the trees large, with much undergrowth in places obstructing the view and making progress difficult.

I spent several hours in this wild paradise, which was so much more delightful than the extensive gloomier forests I had so often penetrated in Guayana: for here, if the trees did not attain to such majestic proportions, the variety of vegetable forms was even greater; as far as I went it was nowhere dark under the trees, and the number of lovely parasites everywhere illustrated the kindly influence of light and air. Even where the trees were largest the sunshine penetrated, subdued by the foliage to exquisite greenish-golden tints, filling the wide lower spaces with tender half-lights, and faint blue-and-grey shadows. Lying on my back and gazing up, I felt reluctant to rise and renew my ramble. For what a roof was that above my head! Roof I call it, just as the poets in their poverty sometimes describe the infinite ethereal sky by that word; but it was no more roof-like and hindering to the soaring spirit than the higher clouds that float in changing forms and tints, and like the foliage chasten the intolerable noonday beams. How far above me seemed that leafy cloudland into which I gazed! Nature, we know, first taught the architect to produce by long colonnades the illusion of distance; but the light-excluding roof prevents him from getting the same effect above. Here Nature is unapproachable with her green, airy canopy, a sun-impregnated cloud—cloud above cloud; and though the highest may be unreached by the eye, the beams yet filter through, illuming the wide spaces beneath—chamber succeeded by chamber, each with its own special lights and shadows. Far above me, but not nearly so far as it seemed, the tender gloom of one such chamber or space is traversed now by a golden shaft of light falling through some break in the upper foliage, giving a strange glory to everything it touches—projecting leaves, and beard-like tuft of moss, and snaky bush-rope. And in the most open part of that most open space, suspended on nothing to the eye, the shaft reveals a tangle of shining silver threads—the web of some large tree spider. These seemingly distant, yet distinctly visible threads, serve to remind me that the human artist is only able to get his horizontal distance by a monotonous reduplication of pillar and arch, placed at regular intervals, and that the least departure from this order would destroy the effect. But Nature produces her effects at random, and seems only to increase the beautiful illusion by that infinite variety of decoration in which she revels, binding tree to tree in a tangle of anaconda-like lianas, and dwindling down from these huge cables to airy webs and hair-like fibres that vibrate to the wind of the passing insect's wing.

Thus in idleness, with such thoughts for company, I spent my time, glad that no human being, savage or civilised, was with me. It was better to be alone to listen to the monkeys that chattered without offending; to watch them occupied with the unserious business of their lives. With that luxuriant tropical nature, its green clouds and illusive aerial spaces, full of mystery, they harmonised well in language, appearance, and motions;—mountebank angels, living their fantastic lives far above earth in a half-way heaven of their own.

I saw more monkeys on that morning than I usually saw in the course of a week's rambling. And other animals were seen; I particularly remember two accouries I startled, that after rushing away a few yards stopped and stood peering back at me as if not knowing whether to regard me as friend or enemy. Birds, too, were strangely abundant; and altogether this struck me as being the richest hunting-ground I had seen, and it astonished me to think that the Indians of the village did not appear to visit it.

On my return in the afternoon I gave an enthusiastic account of my day's ramble, speaking not of the things that had moved my soul, but only of those which move the Guayana Indian's soul—the animal food he craves, and which, one would imagine, Nature would prefer him to do without, so hard he finds it to wrest a sufficiency from her. To my surprise they shook their heads and looked troubled at what I said; and finally, my host informed me that the wood I had been in was a dangerous place; that if they went there to hunt a great injury would be done to them; and he finished by advising me not to visit it again.

I began to understand from their looks and the old man's vague words that their fear of the wood was superstitious. If dangerous creatures had existed there—tigers, or camoodis, or solitary murderous savages—they would have said so; but when I pressed them with questions they could only repeat that "something bad" existed in the place, that animals were abundant there because no Indian who valued his life dared venture into it. I replied that unless they gave me some more definite information I should certainly go again, and put myself in the way of the danger they feared.

My reckless courage, as they considered it, surprised them; but they had already begun to find out that their superstitions had no effect on me, that I listened to them as to stories invented to amuse a child, and for the moment they made no further attempt to dissuade me.

Next day I returned to the forest of evil report, which had now a new and even greater charm—the fascination of the unknown and the mysterious; still, the warning I had received made me distrustful and cautious at first, for I could not help thinking about it. When we consider how much of their life is passed in the woods, which become as familiar to them as the streets of our native town to us, it seems almost incredible that these savages have a superstitious fear of all forests, fearing them as much, even in the bright light of day, as a nervous child with memory filled with ghost-stories fears a dark room. But, like the child in the dark room, they fear the forest only when alone in it, and for this reason always hunt in couples or parties. What, then, prevented them from visiting this particular wood, which offered so tempting a harvest? The question troubled me not a little; at the same time I was ashamed of the feeling, and fought against it; and in the end I made my way to the same sequestered spot where I had rested so long on my previous visit.

In this place I witnessed a new thing, and had a strange experience. Sitting on the ground in the shade of a large tree, I began to hear a confused noise as of a coming tempest of wind mixed with shrill calls and cries. Nearer and nearer it came, and at last a multitude of birds of many kinds, but mostly small, appeared in sight swarming through the trees, some running on the trunks and larger branches, others flitting through the foliage, and many keeping on the wing, now hovering and now darting this way or that. They were all busily searching for and pursuing the insects, moving on at the same time, and in a very few minutes they had finished examining the trees near me, and were gone; but not satisfied with what I had witnessed, I jumped up and rushed after the flock to keep it in sight. All my caution and all recollection of what the Indians had said was now forgot, so great was my interest in this bird-army; but as they moved on without pause they quickly left me behind, and presently my career was stopped by an impenetrable tangle of bushes, vines, and roots of large trees extending like huge cables along the ground. In the midst of this leafy labyrinth I sat down on a projecting root to cool my blood before attempting to make my way back to my former position. After that tempest of motion and confused noises the silence of the forest seemed very profound; but before I had been resting many moments it was broken by a low strain of exquisite bird-melody, wonderfully pure and expressive, unlike any musical sound I had ever heard before. It seemed to issue from a thick cluster of broad leaves of a creeper only a few yards from where I sat. With my eyes fixed on this green hiding-place I waited with suspended breath for its repetition, wondering whether any civilised being had ever listened to such a strain before. Surely not, I thought, else the fame of so divine a melody would long ago have been noised abroad. I thought of the rialejo, the celebrated organ-bird or flute-bird, and of the various ways in which hearers are affected by it. To some its warbling is like the sound of a beautiful mysterious instrument, while to others it seems like the singing of a blithe-hearted child with a highly melodious voice. I had often heard and listened with delight to the singing of the rialejo in the Guayana forests, but this song, or musical phrase, was utterly unlike it in character. It was purer, more expressive, softer—so low that at a distance of forty yards I could hardly have heard it. But its greatest charm was its resemblance to the human voice—a voice purified and brightened to something almost angelic. Imagine, then, my impatience as I sat there straining my sense, my deep disappointment when it was not repeated! I rose at length very reluctantly and slowly began making my way back; but when I had progressed about thirty yards, again the sweet voice sounded just behind me, and turning quickly I stood still and waited. The same voice, but not the same song—not the same phrase; the notes were different, more varied and rapidly enunciated, as if the singer had been more excited. The blood rushed to my heart as I listened; my nerves tingled with a strange new delight, the rapture produced by such music heightened by a sense of mystery. Before many moments I heard it again, not rapid now, but a soft warbling, lower than at first, infinitely sweet and tender, sinking to lisping sounds that soon ceased to be audible; the whole having lasted as long as it would take me to repeat a sentence of a dozen words. This seemed the singer's farewell to me, for I waited and listened in vain to hear it repeated; and after getting back to the starting-point I sat for upwards of an hour, still hoping to hear it once more!

The westering sun at length compelled me to quit the wood, but not before I had resolved to return the next morning and seek for the spot where I had met with so enchanting an experience. After crossing the sterile belt I have mentioned within the wood, and just before I came to the open outer edge where the stunted trees and bushes die away on the border of the savannah, what was my delight and astonishment at hearing the mysterious melody once more! It seemed to issue from a clump of bushes close by; but by this time I had come to the conclusion that there was a ventriloquism in this woodland voice which made it impossible for me to determine its exact direction. Of one thing I was, however, now quite convinced, and that was that the singer had been following me all the time. Again and again as I stood there listening it sounded, now so faint and apparently far off as to be scarcely audible; then all at once it would ring out bright and clear within a few yards of me, as if the shy little thing had suddenly grown bold; but, far or near, the vocalist remained invisible, and at length the tantalising melody ceased altogether.

CHAPTER III

I WAS not disappointed on my next visit to the forest, nor on several succeeding visits; and this seemed to show that if I was right in believing that these strange, melodious utterances proceeded from one individual, then the bird or being, although still refusing to show itself, was always on the watch for my appearance, and followed me wherever I went. This thought only served to increase my curiosity; I was constantly pondering over the subject, and at last concluded that it would be best to induce one of the Indians to go with me to the wood on the chance of his being able to explain the mystery.

One of the treasures I had managed to preserve in my sojourn with these children of nature, who were always anxious to become possessors of my belongings, was a small prettily fashioned metal match-box, opening with a spring. Remembering that Kua-kó, among others, had looked at this trifle with covetous eyes—the covetous way in which they all looked at it had given it a fictitious value in my own—I tried to bribe him with the offer of it to accompany me to my favourite haunt. The brave young hunter refused again and again; but on each occasion he offered to perform some other service or to give me something in exchange for the box. At last I told him that I would give it to the first person who should accompany me, and fearing that someone would be found valiant enough to win the prize, he at length plucked up a spirit, and on the next day, seeing me going out for a walk, he all at once offered to go with me. He cunningly tried to get the box before starting—his cunning, poor youth! was not very deep. I told him that the forest we were about to visit abounded with plants and birds unlike any I had seen elsewhere, that I wished to learn their names, and everything about them, and that when I had got the required information the box would be his—not sooner. Finally we started, he, as usual, armed with his zabatana, with which, I imagined, he would procure more game than usually fell to his little poisoned arrows. When we reached the wood I could see that he was ill at ease: nothing would persuade him to go into the deeper parts; and even where it was very open and light he was constantly gazing into bushes and shadowy places, as if expecting to see some frightful creature lying in wait for him. This behaviour might have had a disquieting effect on me had I not been thoroughly convinced that his fears were purely superstitious, and that there could be no dangerous animal in a spot I was accustomed to walk in every day. My plan was to ramble about with an unconcerned air, occasionally pointing out an uncommon tree or shrub or vine, or calling his attention to a distant bird cry and asking the bird's name, in the hope that the mysterious voice would make itself heard, and that he would be able to give me some explanation of it. But for upwards of two hours we moved about, hearing nothing except the usual bird voices, and during all that time he never stirred a yard from my side nor made an attempt to capture anything. At length we sat down under a tree, in an open spot close to the border of the wood. He sat down very reluctantly, and seemed more troubled in his mind than ever, keeping his eyes continually roving about, while he listened intently to every sound. The sounds were not few, owing to the abundance of animal and especially of bird life in this favoured spot. I began to question my companion as to some of the cries we heard. There were notes and cries familiar to me as the crowing of the cock—parrot screams and yelping of toucans, the distant wailing calls of maam and duraquara; and shrill laughter-like notes of the large tree-climber as it passed from tree to tree; the quick whistle of cotingas; and strange throbbing and thrilling sounds, as of pigmies beating on metallic drums, of the skulking pitta-thrushes; and with these mingled other notes less well known. One came from the treetops, where it was perpetually wandering amid the foliage—a low note, repeated at intervals of a few seconds, so thin and mournful and full of mystery, that I half expected to hear that it proceeded from the restless ghost of some dead bird. But no; he only said that it was uttered by a "little bird"—too little presumably to have a name. From the foliage of a neighbouring tree came a few tinkling chirps, as of a small mandolin, two or three strings of which had been carelessly struck by the player. He said that it came from a small green frog that lived in trees; and in this way my rude Indian—vexed perhaps at being asked such trivial questions—brushed away the pretty fantasies my mind had woven in the woodland solitude. For I often listened to this tinkling music, and it had suggested the idea that the place was frequented by a tribe of fairy-like troubadour monkeys, and that if I could only be quick-sighted enough I might one day be able to detect the minstrel sitting, in a green tunic perhaps, cross-legged on some high, swaying bough, carelessly touching his mandolin suspended from his neck by a yellow ribbon.

By-and-by a bird came with low, swift flight, its great tail spread open fan-wise, and perched itself on an exposed bough not thirty yards from us. It was all of a chestnut-red colour, long-bodied, in size like a big pigeon: its actions showed that its curiosity had been greatly excited, for it jerked from side to side, eyeing us first with one eye, then the other, while its long tail rose and fell in a measured way.

"Look, Kua-kó," I said in a whisper, "there is a bird for you to kill."

But he only shook his head, still watchful.

"Give me the blow-pipe, then," I said, with a laugh, putting out my hand to take it. But he refused to let me take it, knowing that it would only be an arrow wasted if I attempted to shoot anything.

As I persisted in telling him to kill the bird, he at last bent his lips near me and said in a half-whisper, as if fearful of being overheard, "I can kill nothing here. If I shot at the bird the daughter of the Didi would catch the dart in her hand and throw it back and hit me here," touching his breast just over his heart.

I laughed again, saying to myself, with some amusement, that Kua-kó was not such a bad companion after all—that he was not without imagination. But in spite of my laughter his words roused my interest, and suggested the idea that the voice I was curious about had been heard by the Indians, and was as great a mystery to them as to me; since not being like that of any creature known to them, it would be attributed by their superstitious minds to one of the numerous demons or semi-human monsters inhabiting every forest, stream, and mountain; and fear of it would drive them from the wood. In this case, judging from my companion's words, they had varied the form of the superstition somewhat, inventing a daughter of a water-spirit to be afraid of. My thought was that if their keen, practised eyes had never been able to see this flitting woodland creature with a musical soul, it was not likely that I would succeed in my quest.

I began to question him, but he now appeared less inclined to talk and more frightened than ever, and each time I attempted to speak he imposed silence, with a quick gesture of alarm, while he continued to stare about him with dilated eyes. All at once he sprang to his feet as if overcome with terror, and started running at full speed. His fear infected me, and, springing up, I followed as fast as I could, but he was far ahead of me, running for dear life; and before I had gone forty yards my feet were caught in a creeper trailing along the surface, and I measured my length on the ground. The sudden, violent shock almost took away my senses for a moment, but when I jumped up and stared round to see no unspeakable monster—Curupitá or other—rushing on to slay and devour me there and then, I began to feel ashamed of my cowardice; and in the end I turned and walked back to the spot I had just quitted and sat down once more. I even tried to hum a tune, just to prove to myself that I had completely recovered from the panic caught from the miserable Indian; but it is never possible in such cases to get back one's serenity immediately, and a vague suspicion continued to trouble me for a time. After sitting there for half an hour or so, listening to distant bird sounds, I began to recover my old confidence, and even to feel inclined to penetrate further into the wood. All at once, making me almost jump, so sudden it was, so much nearer and louder than I had ever heard it before, the mysterious melody began. Unmistakably it was uttered by the same being heard on former occasions; but to-day it was different in character. The utterance was far more rapid, with fewer silent intervals, and it had none of the usual tenderness in it, nor ever once sunk to that low, whisper-like talking, which had seemed to me as if the spirit of the wind had breathed its low sighs in syllables and speech. Now it was not only loud, rapid, and continuous, but, while still musical, there was an incisiveness in it, a sharp ring as of resentment, which made it strike painfully on the sense.

The impression of an intelligent unhuman being addressing me in anger took so firm a hold on my mind that the old fear returned, and, rising, I began to walk rapidly away, intending to escape from the wood. The voice continued violently rating me, as it seemed to my mind, moving with me, which caused me to accelerate my steps; and very soon I would have broken into a run, when its character began to change again. There were pauses now, intervals of silence, long or short, and after each one the voice came to my ear with a more subdued and dulcet sound—more of that melting, flute-like quality it had possessed at other times; and this softness of tone, coupled with the talking-like form of utterance, gave me the idea of a being no longer incensed, addressing me now in a peaceable spirit, reasoning away my unworthy tremors, and imploring me to remain with it in the wood. Strange as this voice without a body was, and always productive of a slightly uncomfortable feeling on account of its mystery, it seemed impossible to doubt that it came to me now in a spirit of pure friendliness; and when I had recovered my composure I found a new delight in listening to it—all the greater because of the fear so lately experienced, and of its seeming intelligence. For the third time I reseated myself on the same spot, and at intervals the voice talked to me there for some time, and to my fancy expressed satisfaction and pleasure at my presence. But later, without losing its friendly tone, it changed again. It seemed to move away and to be thrown back from a considerable distance; and, at long intervals, it would approach me again with a new sound, which I began to interpret as of command, or entreaty. Was it, I asked myself, inviting me to follow? And if I obeyed, to what delightful discoveries or frightful dangers might it lead? My curiosity, together with the belief that the being—I called it being, not bird, now—

was friendly to me, overcame all timidity, and I rose and walked at random towards the interior of the wood. Very soon I had no doubt left that the being had desired me to follow; for there was now a new note of gladness in its voice, and it continued near me as I walked, at intervals approaching me so closely as to set me staring into the surrounding shadowy places like poor scared Kua-kó.

On this occasion, too, I began to have a new fancy, for fancy or illusion I was determined to regard it, that some swift-footed being was treading the ground near me; that I occasionally caught the faint rustle of a light footstep, and detected a motion in leaves and fronds and thread-like stems of creepers hanging near the surface, as if some passing body had touched and made them tremble; and once or twice that I even had a glimpse of a grey, misty object moving at no great distance in the deeper shadows.

Led by this wandering tricksy being, I came to a spot where the trees were very large and the damp dark ground almost free from undergrowth; and here the voice ceased to be heard. After patiently waiting and listening for some time I began to look about me with a slight feeling of apprehension. It was still about two hours before sunset; only in this place the shade of the vast trees made a perpetual twilight: moreover, it was strangely silent here, the few bird cries that reached me coming from a long distance. I had flattered myself that the voice had become to some extent intelligible to me; its outburst of anger caused no doubt by my cowardly flight after the Indian; then its recovered friendliness which had induced me to return; and, finally, its desire to be followed. Now that it had led me to this place of shadow and profound silence, and had ceased to speak and to lead, I could not help thinking that this was my goal, that I had been brought to this spot with a purpose, that in this wild and solitary retreat some tremendous adventure was about to befall me.

As the silence continued unbroken there was time to dwell on this thought. I gazed before me and listened intently, scarcely breathing, until the suspense became painful—too painful at last, and I turned and took a step with the idea of going back to the border of the wood, when close by, clear as a silver bell, sounded the voice once more, but only for a moment—two or three syllables in response to my movement, then it was silent again.

Once more I was standing still, as if in obedience to a command, in the same state of suspense; and whether the change was real or only imagined I know not, but the silence every minute grew more profound and the gloom deeper. Imaginary terrors began to assail me. Ancient fables of men allured by beautiful forms and melodious voices to destruction all at once acquired a fearful significance. I recalled some of the Indian beliefs, especially that of the misshapen, man-devouring monster who is said to beguile his victims into the dark forest by mimicking the human voice—the voice sometimes of a woman in distress—or by singing some strange and beautiful melody. I grew almost afraid to look round lest I should catch sight of him stealing towards me on his huge feet with toes pointing backwards, his mouth snarling horribly to display his great green fangs. It was distressing to have such fancies in this wild, solitary spot—hateful to feel their power over me when I knew that they were nothing but fancies and creations of the savage mind. But if these supernatural beings had no existence, there were other monsters, only too real, in these woods which it would be dreadful to encounter alone and unarmed, since against such adversaries a revolver would be as ineffectual as a popgun. Some huge camoodi, able to crush my bones like brittle twigs in its constricting coils, might lurk in these shadows, and approach me stealthily, unseen in its dark colour on the dark ground. Or some jaguar or black tiger might steal towards me, masked by a bush or tree-trunk, to spring upon me unawares. Or worse still, this way might suddenly come a pack of those swift-footed, unspeakably terrible hunting-leopards, from which every living thing in the forest flies with shrieks of consternation or else falls paralysed in their path to be instantly torn to pieces and devoured.

A slight rustling sound in the foliage above me made me start and cast up my eyes. High up, where a pale gleam of tempered sunlight fell through the leaves, a grotesque human-like face, black as ebony and adorned with a great red beard, appeared staring down upon me. In another moment it was gone. It was only a large araguato, or howling monkey, but I was so unnerved that I could not get rid of the idea that it was something more than a monkey. Once more I moved, and again, the instant I moved my foot, clear, and keen, and imperative, sounded the voice! It was no longer possible to doubt its meaning. It commanded me to stand still—to wait—to watch—to listen! Had it cried "Listen! Do not move!" I could not have understood it better. Trying as the suspense was, I now felt powerless to escape. Something very terrible, I felt convinced, was about to happen, either to destroy or to release me from the spell that held me.

And while I stood thus rooted to the ground, the sweat standing in large drops on my forehead, all at once close to me sounded a cry, fine and clear at first, and rising at the end to a shriek so loud, piercing, and unearthly in character that the blood seemed to freeze in my veins, and a despairing cry to heaven escaped my lips; then, before that long shriek expired, a mighty chorus of thunderous voices burst forth around me; and in this awful tempest of sound I trembled like a leaf; and the leaves on the trees were agitated as if by a high wind, and the earth itself seemed to shake beneath my feet. Indescribably horrible were my sensations at that moment; I was deafened, and would possibly have been maddened had I not, as by a miracle, chanced to see a large araguato on a branch overhead, roaring with open mouth and inflated throat and chest.

It was simply a concert of howling monkeys which had so terrified me! But my extreme fear was not strange in the circumstances; since everything that had led up to the display, the gloom and silence, the period of suspense and my heated imagination, had raised my mind to the highest degree of excitement and expectancy. I had rightly conjectured, no doubt, that my unseen guide had led me to that spot for a purpose; and the purpose had been to set me in the midst of a congregation of araguatos to enable me for the first time fully to appreciate their unparalleled vocal powers. I had always heard them at a distance: here they were gathered in scores, possibly hundreds—the whole araguato population of the forest, I should think—close to me; and it may give some faint conception of the tremendous power and awful character of the sound thus produced by their combined voices when I say that this animal—miscalled "howler" in English—would outroar the mightiest lion that ever woke the echoes of an African wilderness.

This roaring concert, which lasted three or four minutes, having ended, I lingered a few minutes longer on the spot, and not hearing the voice again, went back to the edge of the wood, and then started on my way back to the village.

CHAPTER IV

PERHAPS I was not capable of thinking quite coherently on what had just happened until I was once more fairly outside of the forest shadows—out in that clear open daylight, where things seem what they are, and imagination, like a juggler detected and laughed at, hastily takes itself out of the way. As I walked homewards I paused midway on the barren ridge to gaze back on the scene I had left, and then the recent adventure began to take a semi-ludicrous aspect in my mind. All that circumstance of preparation, that mysterious prelude to something unheard of, unimaginable, surpassing all fables ancient and modern, and all tragedies—to end at last in a concert of howling monkeys! Certainly the concert was very grand, indeed one of the most astounding in nature, but still—I sat down on a stone and laughed freely.

The sun was sinking behind the forest, its broad red disc still showing through the topmost leaves, and the higher part of the foliage was of a luminous green, like green flame, throwing off flakes of quivering, fiery light, but lower down the trees were in profound shadow.

I felt very light-hearted while I gazed on this scene; for how pleasant it was just now to think of the strange experience I had passed through—to think that I had come safely out of it, that no human eye had witnessed my weakness, and that the mystery existed still to fascinate me! For, ludicrous as the dénouement now looked, the cause of all, the voice itself, was a thing to marvel at more than ever. That it proceeded from an intelligent being I was firmly convinced; and although too materialistic in my way of thinking to admit for a moment that it was a supernatural being, I still felt that there was something more than I had at first imagined in Kua-kó's speech about a daughter of the Didi. That the Indians knew a great deal about the mysterious voice, and had held it in great fear, seemed evident. But they were savages, with ways that were not mine; and however friendly they might be towards one of a superior race, there was always in their relations with him a low cunning, prompted partly by suspicion, underlying their words and actions. For the white man to put himself mentally on their level is not more impossible than for these aborigines to be perfectly open, as children are, towards the white. Whatever subject the stranger within their gates exhibits an interest in, that they will be reticent about; and their reticence, which conceals itself under easily invented lies or an affected stupidity, invariably increases with his desire for information. It was plain to them that some very unusual interest took me to the wood, consequently I could not expect that they would tell me anything they might know to enlighten me about the matter; and I concluded that Kua-kó's words about the daughter of the Didi, and what she would do if he blew an arrow at a bird, had accidentally escaped him in a moment of excitement. Nothing, therefore, was to be gained by questioning them, or, at all events, by telling them how much the subject attracted me. And I had nothing to fear; my independent investigations had made this much clear to me; the voice might proceed from a very frolicsome and tricksy creature, full of wild fantastic humours, but nothing worse. It was friendly to me, I felt sure; at the same time it might not be friendly towards the Indians; for, on that day, it had made itself heard only after my companion had taken flight; and it had then seemed incensed against me, possibly because the savage had been in my company.

That was the result of my reflections on the day's events, when I returned to my entertainer's roof, and sat down among my friends to refresh myself with stewed fowl and fish from the household pot, into which a hospitable woman invited me with a gesture to dip my fingers.

Kua-kó was lying in his hammock, smoking, I think—certainly not reading. When I entered he lifted his head and stared at me, probably surprised to see me alive, unharmed, and in a placid temper. I laughed at the look, and somewhat disconcerted, he dropped his head down again. After a minute or two I took the metal match-box and tossed it on to his breast. He clutched it, and starting up, stared at me in the utmost astonishment. He could scarcely believe his good fortune; for he had failed to carry out his part of the compact and had resigned himself to the loss of the coveted prize. Jumping down to the floor, he held up the box triumphantly, his joy overcoming the habitual stolid look; while all the others gathered about him, each trying to get the box into his own hands to admire it again, notwithstanding that they had all seen it a dozen times before. But it was Kua-kó's now and not the stranger's, and therefore more nearly their own than formerly, and must look different, more beautiful, with a brighter polish on the metal. And that wonderful enamelled cock on the lid—figured in Paris probably, but just like a cock in Guayana, the pet bird which they no more think of killing and eating than we do our purring pussies and lemon-coloured canaries — must now look more strikingly valiant and cock-like than ever, with its crimson comb and wattles, burnished red hackles, and dark green arching tail-plumes. But Kua-kó, while willing enough to have it admired and praised, would not let it out of his hands, and told them pompously that it was not theirs for them to handle, but his—Kua-ko's—for all time; that he had won it by accompanying me—valorous man that he was!—to that evil wood into which they—timid, inferior creatures that they were!—would never have ventured to set foot. I am not translating his words, but that was what he gave them to understand pretty plainly, to my great amusement.

After the excitement was over, Runi, who had maintained a dignified calm, made some roundabout remarks, apparently with the object of eliciting an account of what I had seen and heard in the forest of evil fame. I replied carelessly that I had seen a great many birds and monkeys

—monkeys so tame that I might have procured one if I had had a blow-pipe, in spite of my never having practised shooting with that weapon.

It interested them to hear about the abundance and tameness of the monkeys, although it was scarcely news: but how tame they must have been when I, the stranger not to the manner born—not naked, brown-skinned, lynx-eyed, and noiseless as an owl in his movements—had yet been able to look closely at them! Runi only remarked, apropos of what I had told him, that they could not go there to hunt; then he asked me if I feared nothing.

"Nothing," I replied carelessly. "The things you fear hurt not the white man, and are no more than this to me," saying which I took up a little white wood-ash in my hand and blew it away with my breath. "And against other enemies I have this," I added, touching my revolver. A brave speech, just after that araguato episode; but I did not make it without blushing—mentally.

He shook his head, and said it was a poor weapon against some enemies; also—truly enough—that it would procure no birds and monkeys for the stew-pot.

Next morning my friend Kua-kó, taking his zabatana, invited me to go out with him, and I consented with some misgivings, thinking he had overcome his superstitious fears, and, inflamed by my account of the abundance of game in the forest, intended going there with me. The previous day's experience had made me think that it would be better in the future to go there alone. But I was giving the poor youth more credit than he deserved: it was far from his intention to face the terrible unknown again. We went in a different direction, and tramped for hours through woods where birds were scarce and only of the smaller kinds. Then my guide surprised me a second time by offering to teach me to use the zabatana. This, then, was to be my reward for giving him the box! I readily consented, and with the long weapon, awkward to carry, in my hand, and imitating the noiseless movements and cautious, watchful manner of my companion, I tried to imagine myself a simple Guayana savage, with no knowledge of that artificial social state to which I had been born, dependent on my skill and little roll of poison-darts for a livelihood. By an effort of the will I emptied myself of my life experience and knowledge—or as much of it as possible—and thought only of the generations of my dead imaginary progenitors, who had ranged these woods back to the dim forgotten years before Columbus; and if the pleasure I had in the fancy was childish, it made the day pass quickly enough. Kua-kó was constantly at my elbow to assist and give advice; and many an arrow I blew from the long tube, and hit no bird. Heaven knows what I hit, for the arrows flew away on their wide and wild career to be seen no more, except a few which my keen-eyed comrade marked to their destination and managed to recover. The result of our day's hunting was a couple of birds, which Kua-kó, not I, shot, and a small opossum his sharp eyes detected high up a tree lying coiled up on an old nest, over the side of which the animal had incautiously allowed his snaky tail to dangle. The number of darts I wasted must have been a rather serious loss to him, but he did not seem troubled at it, and made no remark.

Next day, to my surprise, he volunteered to give me a second lesson, and we went out again. On this occasion he had provided himself with a large bundle of darts, but—wise man!—they were not poisoned, and it therefore mattered little whether they were wasted or not. I believe that on this day I made some little progress; at all events, my teacher remarked that before long I would be able to hit a bird. This made me smile and answer that if he could place me within twenty yards of a bird not smaller than a small man I might manage to touch it with an arrow.

This speech had a very unexpected and remarkable effect. He stopped short in his walk, stared at me wildly, then grinned, and finally burst into a roar of laughter, which was no bad imitation of the howling monkey's performance, and smote his naked thighs with tremendous energy. At length recovering himself, he asked whether a small woman was not the same as a small man, and being answered in the affirmative, went off into a second extravagant roar of laughter.

Thinking it was easy to tickle him while he continued in this mood, I began making any number of feeble jokes —feeble, but quite as good as the one which had provoked such outrageous merriment—for it amused me to see him acting in this unusual way. But they all failed of their effect—there was no hitting the bull's-eye a second time; he would only stare vacantly at me, then grunt like a peccary—not appreciatively—and walk on.

Still, at intervals he would go back to what I said about hitting a very big bird, and roar again, as if this wonderful joke was not easily exhausted.

Again on the third day we were out together practising at the birds—frightening, if not killing them; but before noon, finding that it was his intention to go to a distant spot where he expected to meet with larger game, I left him and returned to the village. The blow-pipe practice had lost its novelty, and I did not care to go on all day and every day with it; more than that, I was anxious after so long an interval to pay a visit to *my* wood, as I began to call it, in the hope of hearing that mysterious melody, which I had grown to love and to miss when even a single day passed without it.

CHAPTER V

AFTER making a hasty meal at the house, I started, full of pleasing anticipations, for the wood; for how pleasant a place it was to be in! What a wild beauty and fragrance and melodiousness it possessed above all forests, because of that mystery that drew me to it! And it was mine, truly and absolutely—as much mine as any portion of earth's surface could belong to any man—mine with all its products; the precious woods and fruits and fragrant gums that would never be trafficked away; its wild animals that man would never persecute; nor would any jealous savage dispute my ownership or pretend that it was part of his hunting-ground. As I crossed the savannah I played with this fancy; but when I reached the ridgy eminence, to look down once more on my new domain, the fancy changed to a feeling so keen that it pierced to my heart, and was like pain in its intensity, causing tears to rush to my eyes. And caring not in that solitude to disguise my feelings from myself, and from the wide heaven that looked down and saw me—for this is the sweetest thing that solitude has for us, that we are free in it, and no convention holds us—I dropped on my knees and kissed the stony ground, then casting up my eyes, thanked the

Author of my being for the gift of that wild forest, those green mansions where I had found so great a happiness!

Elated with this strain of feeling, I reached the wood not long after noon; but no melodious voice gave me familiar and expected welcome; nor did my invisible companion make itself heard at all on that day, or, at all events, not in its usual bird-like warbling language. But on this day I met with a curious little adventure, and heard something very extraordinary, very mysterious, which I could not avoid connecting in my mind with the unseen warbler that so often followed me in my rambles.

It was an exceedingly bright day, without cloud, but windy, and finding myself in a rather open part of the wood, near its border, where the breeze could be felt, I sat down to rest on the lower part of a large branch, which was half broken, but still remained attached to the trunk of the tree, while resting its terminal twigs on the ground. Just before me, where I sat, grew a low, wide-spreading plant, covered with broad, round, polished leaves; and the roundness, stiffness, and perfectly horizontal position of the upper leaves made them look like a collection of small platforms or round table-tops placed nearly on a level. Through the leaves, to the height of a foot or more above them, a slender dead stem protruded, and from a twig at its summit depended a broken spider's web. A minute dead leaf had become attached to one of the loose threads, and threw its small but distinct shadow on the platform leaves below: and as it trembled and swayed in the current of air the black spot trembled with it or flew swiftly over the bright green surfaces, and was seldom at rest. Now, as I sat looking down on the leaves and the small dancing shadow, scarcely thinking of what I was looking at, I noticed a small spider, with a flat body and short legs, creep cautiously out on to the upper surface of a leaf. Its pale red colour barred with velvet black first drew my attention to it, for it was beautiful to the eye; and presently I discovered that this was no web-spinning, sedentary spider, but a wandering hunter, that captured its prey, like a cat, by stealing on it concealed and making a rush or spring at the last. The moving shadow had attracted it, and, as the sequel showed, was mistaken for a fly running about over the leaves, and flitting from leaf to leaf. Now began a series of wonderful manœuvres on the spider's part, with the object of circumventing the imaginary fly, which seemed specially designed to meet this special case; for certainly no insect had ever before behaved in quite so erratic a manner. Each time the shadow flew past, the spider ran swiftly in the same direction, hiding itself under the leaves, always trying to get near without alarming its prey; and then the shadow would go round and round in a small circle, and some new strategic move on the part of the hunter would be called forth. I became deeply interested in this curious scene; I began to wish that the shadow would remain quiet for a moment or two, so as to give the hunter a chance. And at last I had my wish: the shadow was almost motionless, and the spider moving towards it, yet seeming not to move, and as it crept closer I fancied that I could almost see the little striped body quivering with excitement. Then came the final scene: swift and straight as an arrow the hunter shot himself on to the fly-like shadow, then wriggled round and round, evidently trying to take hold of his prey with fangs and claws; and finding nothing under him, he raised the fore part of his body vertically, as if to stare about him in search of the delusive fly; but the action may have simply expressed astonishment. At this moment I was just on the point of giving free and loud vent to the laughter which I had been holding in, when, just behind me, as if from some person who had been watching the scene over my shoulder and was as much amused as myself at its termination, sounded a clear trill of merry laughter. I started up and looked hastily around, but no living creature was there. The mass of loose foliage I stared into was agitated, as if from a body having just pushed through it. In a moment the leaves and fronds were motionless again; still, I could not be sure that a slight gust of wind had not shaken them. But I was so convinced that I had heard close to me a real human laugh, or sound of some living creature that exactly simulated a laugh, that I carefully searched the ground about me, expecting to find a being of some kind. But I found nothing, and going back to my seat on the hanging branch, I remained seated for a considerable time, at first only listening, then pondering on the mystery of that sweet trill of laughter; and finally I began to wonder whether I, like the spider that chased the shadow, had been deluded, and had seemed to hear a sound that was not a sound.

On the following day I was in the wood again, and after a two or three hours' ramble, during which I heard nothing, thinking it useless to haunt the known spots any longer, I turned southwards and penetrated into a denser part of the forest, where the undergrowth made progress difficult. I was not afraid of losing myself; the sun above and my sense of direction, which was always good, would enable me to return to the starting-point.

In this direction I had been pushing resolutely on for over half an hour, finding it no easy matter to make my way without constantly deviating to this side or that from the course I wished to keep, when I came to a much more open spot. The trees were smaller and scantier here, owing to the rocky nature of the ground, which sloped rather rapidly down; but it was moist and overgrown with mosses, ferns, creepers, and low shrubs, all of the liveliest green. I could not see many yards ahead owing to the bushes and tall fern fronds; but presently I began to hear a low, continuous sound, which, when I had advanced twenty or thirty yards further, I made out to be the gurgling of running water; and at the same moment I made the discovery that my throat was parched and my palms tingling with heat. I hurried on, promising myself a cool draught, when all at once, above the soft dashing and gurgling of the water, I caught yet another sound—a low, warbling note, or succession of notes, which might have been emitted by a bird. But it startled me nevertheless—bird-like warbling sounds had come to mean so much to me—and pausing, I listened intently. It was not repeated, and finally, treading with the utmost caution so as not to alarm the mysterious vocalist, I crept on until, coming to a greenheart with a quantity of feathery foliage of a shrub growing about its roots, I saw that just beyond the tree the ground was more open still, letting in the sunlight from above, and that the channel of the stream I sought was in this open space, about twenty yards from me, although the water was still hidden from sight. Something else was there, which I did see; instantly my cautious advance was arrested. I stood gazing with concentrated vision, scarcely daring to breathe lest I should scare it away.

It was a human being—a girl form, reclining on the moss among the ferns and herbage, near the roots of a small tree. One arm was doubled behind her neck for her head to rest upon, while the other arm was held extended before her, the hand raised towards a small brown bird perched on a pendulous twig just beyond its reach. She appeared to be playing with the bird, possibly amusing herself by trying to entice it on to her hand; and the hand appeared to tempt it greatly, for it persistently hopped up and down, turning rapidly about this way and that, flirting its wings and tail, and always appearing just on the point of dropping on to her finger. From my position it was impossible to see her distinctly, yet I dared not move. I could make out that she was small, not above four feet six or seven inches in height, in figure slim, with delicately shaped little hands and feet. Her feet were bare, and her only garment was a slight chemise-shaped dress reaching below her knees, of a whitish-grey colour, with a faint lustre as of a silky material. Her hair was very wonderful; it was loose and abundant, and seemed wavy or curly, falling in a cloud on her shoulders and arms. Dark it appeared, but the precise tint was indeterminable, as was that of her skin, which looked neither brown nor white. Altogether, near to me as she actually was, there was a kind of mistiness in the figure which made it appear somewhat vague and distant, and a greenish grey seemed the prevailing colour. This tint I presently attributed to the effect of the sunlight falling on her through the green foliage; for once, for a moment, she raised herself to reach her finger nearer to the bird, and then a gleam of unsubdued sunlight fell on her hair and arm, and the arm at that moment appeared of a pearly whiteness, and the hair, just where the light touched it, had a strange lustre and play of iridescent colour.

I had not been watching her more than three seconds before the bird, with a sharp, creaking little chirp, flew up and away in sudden alarm; at the same moment she turned and saw me through the light leafy screen. But although catching sight of me thus suddenly, she did not exhibit alarm like the bird; only her eyes, wide open, with a surprised look in them, remained immovably fixed on my face. And then slowly, imperceptibly—for I did not notice the actual movement, so gradual and smooth it was, like the motion of a cloud of mist which changes its form and place, yet to the eye seems not to have moved—she rose to her knees, to her feet, retired, and with face still towards me, and eyes fixed on mine, finally disappeared, going as if she had melted away into the verdure. The leafage was there occupying the precise spot where she had been a moment before—the feathery foliage of an acacia shrub, and stems and broad, arrow-shaped leaves of an aquatic plant, and slim, drooping fern fronds, and they were motionless, and seemed not to have been touched by something passing through them. She had gone, yet I continued still, bent almost double, gazing fixedly at the spot where I had last seen her, my mind in a strange condition, possessed by sensations which were keenly felt and yet contradictory. So vivid was the image left on my brain that she still seemed to be actually before my eyes; and she was not there, nor had been, for it was a dream, an illusion, and no such being existed, or could exist, in this gross world: and at the same time I knew that she had been there—that imagination was powerless to conjure up a form so exquisite.

With the mental image I had to be satisfied, for although I remained for some hours at that spot I saw her no more, nor did I hear any familiar melodious sound. For I was now convinced that in this wild solitary girl I had at length discovered the mysterious warbler that so often followed me in the wood. At length, seeing that it was growing late, I took a drink from the stream and slowly and reluctantly made my way out of the forest, and went home.

Early next day I was back in the wood full of delightful anticipations, and had no sooner got well among the trees than a soft, warbling sound reached my ears; it was like that heard on the previous day just before catching sight of the girl among the ferns. So soon! thought I, elated, and with cautious steps I proceeded to explore the ground, hoping again to catch her unawares. But I saw nothing; and only after beginning to doubt that I had heard anything unusual, and had sat down to rest on a rock, the sound was repeated, soft and low as before, very near and distinct. Nothing more was heard at this spot, but an hour later, in another place, the same mysterious note sounded near me. During my remaining time in the forest I was served many times in the same way, and still nothing was seen, nor was there any change in the voice.

Only when the day was near its end did I give up my quest, feeling very keenly disappointed. It then struck me that the cause of the elusive creature's behaviour was that she had been piqued at my discovery of her in one of her most secret hiding-places in the heart of the wood, and that it had pleased her to pay me out in this manner.

On the next day there was no change; she was there again, evidently following me, but always invisible, and varied not from that one mocking note of yesterday, which seemed to challenge me to find her a second time. In the end I was vexed, and resolved to be even with her by not visiting the wood for some time. A display of indifference on my part would, I hoped, result in making her less coy in the future.

Next day, firm in my new resolution, I accompanied Kua-kó and two others to a distant spot where they expected that the ripening fruit on a cashew tree would attract a large number of birds. The fruit, however, proved still green, so that we gathered none and killed few birds. Returning together, Kua-kó kept at my side, and by-and-by, falling behind our companions, he complimented me on my good shooting, although, as usual. I had only wasted the arrows I had blown.

"Soon you will be able to hit," he said; "hit a bird as big as a small woman"; and he laughed once more immoderately at the old joke. At last, growing confidential, he said that I would soon possess a zabatana of my own, with arrows in plenty. He was going to make the arrows himself, and his uncle Otawinki, who had a straight eye, would make the tube. I treated it all as a joke, but he solemnly assured me that he meant it.

Next morning he asked me if I was going to the forest of evil fame, and when I replied in the negative seemed surprised and, very much to *my* surprise, evidently disappointed. He even tried to persuade me to go, where before I had been earnestly recommended not to go, until, finding that I would not, he took me with him to hunt in the woods. By-and-by he returned to the same subject: he could not understand why I would not go to that wood, and asked me if I had begun to grow afraid.

"No, not afraid," I replied; "but I know the place well, and am getting tired of it." I had seen everything in it—birds and beasts—and had heard all its strange noises.

"Yes, heard," he said, nodding his head knowingly;

"but you have *seen* nothing strange; your eyes are not good enough yet."

I laughed contemptuously, and answered that I had seen everything strange the wood contained, including a strange young girl; and I went on to describe her appearance, and finished by asking if he thought a white man was frightened at the sight of a young girl.

What I said astonished him; then he seemed greatly pleased, and, growing still more confidential and generous than on the previous day, he said that I would soon be a most important personage among them, and greatly distinguish myself. He did not like it when I laughed at all this, and went on with great seriousness to speak of the unmade blow-pipe that would be mine—speaking of it as if it had been something very great, equal to the gift of a large tract of land, or the governorship of a province, north of the Orinoco. And by-and-by he spoke of something else more wonderful even than the promise of a blow-pipe, with arrows galore, and this was that young sister of his, whose name was Oolava, a maid of about sixteen, shy and silent and mild-eyed, rather lean and dirty; not ugly, nor yet prepossessing. And this copper-coloured little drab of the wilderness he proposed to bestow in marriage on me! Anxious to pump him, I managed to control my muscles, and asked him what authority he—a young nobody, who had not yet risen to the dignity of buying a wife for himself—could have to dispose of a sister in this off-hand way? He replied that there would be no difficulty: that Runi would give his consent, as would also Otawinki, Piaké, and other relations; and last, *and* least, according to the matrimonial customs of these latitudes, Oolava herself would be ready to bestow her person—queyou, worn fig-leaf-wise, necklace of accouri teeth, and all—on so worthy a suitor as myself. Finally, to make the prospect still more inviting, he added that it would not be necessary for me to subject myself to any voluntary tortures to prove myself a man and fitted to enter into the purgatorial state of matrimony. He was a great deal too considerate, I said, and, with all the gravity I could command, asked him what kind of torture he would recommend. For me—so valorous a person—"no torture," he answered magnanimously. But he—Kua-kó—had made up his mind as to the form of torture he meant to inflict some day on his own person. He would prepare a large sack and into it put fire-ants—"As many as that!" he exclaimed triumphantly, stooping and filling his two hands with loose sand. He would put them in the sack, and then get into it himself naked, and tie it tightly round his neck, so as to show to all spectators that the hellish pain of innumerable venomous stings in his flesh could be endured without a groan, and with an unmoved countenance. The poor youth had not an original mind, since this was one of the commonest forms of self-torture among the Guayana tribes. But the sudden wonderful animation with which he spoke of it, the fiendish joy that illumined his usually stolid countenance, sent a sudden disgust and horror through me. But what a strange inverted kind of fiendishness is this, which delights at the anticipation of torture inflicted on oneself and not on an enemy! And towards others these savages are mild and peaceable! No, I could not believe in their mildness; that was only on the surface, when nothing occurred to rouse their savage, cruel instincts. I could have laughed at the whole matter, but the exulting look on my companion's face had made me sick of the subject, and I wished not to talk any more about it.

But he would talk still—this fellow whose words, as a rule, I had to take out of his mouth with a fork, as we say; and still on the same subject, he said that not one person in the village would expect to see me torture myself; that after what I would do for them all—after delivering them from a great evil—nothing further would be expected of me.

I asked him to explain his meaning; for it now began to appear plain that in everything he had said he had been leading up to some very important matter. It would, of course, have been a great mistake to suppose that my savage was offering me a blow-pipe and a marketable virgin sister from purely disinterested motives.

In reply he went back to that still unforgotten joke about my being able eventually to hit a bird as big as a small woman with an arrow. Out it all came, when he went on to ask me if that mysterious girl I had seen in the wood was not of a size to suit me as a target when I had got my hand in with a little more practice. That was the great work I was asked to do for them—that shy, mysterious girl with the melodious wild-bird voice was the evil being I was asked to slay with poisoned arrows! This was why he now wished me to go often to the wood, to become more and more familiar with her haunts and habits, to overcome all shyness and suspicion in her; and at the proper moment, when it would be impossible to miss my mark, to plant the fatal arrow! The disgust he had inspired in me before, when gloating over anticipated tortures, was a weak and transient feeling to what I now experienced. I turned on him in a sudden transport of rage, and in a moment would have shattered the blow-pipe I was carrying in my hand on his head, but his astonished look as he turned to face me made me pause, and prevented me from committing so fatal an indiscretion. I could only grind my teeth and struggle to overcome an almost overpowering hatred and wrath. Finally, I flung the tube down and bade him take it, telling him that I would not touch it again if he offered me all the sisters of all the savages in Guayana for wives.

He continued gazing at me mute with astonishment, and prudence suggested that it would be best to conceal as far as possible the violent animosity I had conceived against him. I asked him somewhat scornfully if he believed that I should ever be able to hit anything—bird or human being—with an arrow. "No," I almost shouted, so as to give vent to my feelings in some way, and drawing my revolver, "this is the white man's weapon; but he kills men with it—men who attempt to kill or injure him—but neither with this nor any other weapon does he murder innocent young girls treacherously."

After that we went on in silence for some time; at length he said that the being I had seen in the wood and was not afraid of was no innocent young girl, but a daughter of the Didi, an evil being; and that so long as she continued to inhabit the wood they could not go there to hunt, and even in other woods they constantly went in fear of meeting her. Too much disgusted to talk with him, I went on in silence; and when we reached the stream near the village I threw off my clothes and plunged into the water to cool my anger before going in to the others.

CHAPTER VI

THINKING about the forest girl while lying awake that night, I came to the conclusion that I had made it sufficiently plain to her how little her capricious behaviour had been relished, and had therefore no need to punish myself more by keeping any longer out of my beloved green mansions. Accordingly, next day, after the heavy rain that fell during the morning hours had ceased, I set forth about noon to visit the wood. Overhead the sky was clear again ; but there was no motion in the heavy sultry atmosphere, while dark blue masses of banked-up clouds on the western horizon threatened a fresh downpour later in the day. My mind was, however, now too greatly excited at the prospect of a possible encounter with the forest nymph to allow me to pay any heed to these ominous signs.

I had passed through the first strip of wood, and was in the succeeding stony sterile space, when a gleam of brilliant colour close by on the ground caught my sight. It was a snake lying on the bare earth ; had I kept on without noticing it, I should most probably have trodden upon or dangerously near it. Viewing it closely, I found that it was a coral snake, famed as much for its beauty and singularity as for its deadly character. It was about three feet long, and very slim; its ground colour a brilliant vermilion, with broad jet-black rings at equal distances round its body, each black ring or band divided by a narrow yellow strip in the middle. The symmetrical pattern and vividly contrasted colours would have given it the appearance of an artificial snake made by some fanciful artist, but for the gleam of life in its bright coils. Its fixed eyes, too, were living gems, and from the point of its dangerous arrowy head the glistening tongue flickered ceaselessly as I stood a few yards away regarding it.

"I admire you greatly, Sir Serpent," I said, or thought, "but it is dangerous, say the military authorities, to leave an enemy or possible enemy in the rear; the person who does such a thing must be either a bad strategist or a genius, and I am neither."

Retreating a few paces, I found and picked up a stone about as big as a man's hand, and hurled it at the dangerous-looking head with the intention of crushing it; but the stone hit upon the rocky ground a little on one side of the mark, and being soft flew into a hundred small fragments. This roused the creature's anger, and in a moment with raised head he was gliding swiftly towards me. Again I retreated, not so slowly on this occasion: and finding another stone, I raised and was about to launch it when a sharp, ringing cry issued from the bushes growing near, and, quickly following the sound, forth stepped the forest girl; no longer elusive and shy, vaguely seen in the shadowy wood, but boldly challenging attention, exposed to the full power of the meridian sun, which made her appear luminous and rich in colour beyond example. Seeing her thus, all those emotions of fear and abhorrence invariably excited in us by the sight of an active venomous serpent in our path vanished instantly from my mind: I could now only feel astonishment and admiration at the brilliant being as she advanced with swift, easy, undulating motion towards me; or rather towards the serpent, which was now between us, moving more and more slowly as she came nearer. The cause of this sudden wonderful boldness, so unlike her former habit, was unmistakable. She had been watching my approach from some hiding-place among the bushes, ready no doubt to lead me a dance through the wood with her mocking voice, as on previous occasions, when my attack on the serpent caused that outburst of wrath. The torrent of ringing and to me inarticulate sounds in that unknown tongue, her rapid gestures, and above all her wide-open sparkling eyes and face aflame with colour, made it impossible to mistake the nature of her feeling.

In casting about for some term or figure of speech in which to describe the impression produced on me at that moment, I think of *waspish*, and, better still, *avispada*—literally the same word in Spanish, not having precisely the same meaning nor ever applied contemptuously—only to reject both after a moment's reflection. Yet I go back to the image of an irritated wasp as perhaps offering the best illustration; of some large tropical wasp advancing angrily towards me, as I have witnessed a hundred times, not exactly flying, but moving rapidly, half running and half flying, over the ground, with loud and angry buzz, the glistening wings open and agitated; beautiful beyond most animated creatures in its sharp but graceful lines, polished surface, and varied brilliant colouring, and that wrathfulness that fits it so well and seems to give it additional lustre.

Wonder-struck at the sight of her strange beauty and passion, I forgot the advancing snake until she came to a stop at about five yards from me; then to my horror I saw that it was beside her naked feet. Although no longer advancing, the head was still raised high as if to strike; but presently the spirit of anger appeared to die out of it; the lifted head, oscillating a little from side to side, sunk down lower and lower to rest finally on the girl's bare instep; and lying there motionless, the deadly thing had the appearance of a gaily coloured silken garter just dropped from her leg. It was plain to see that she had no fear of it, that she was one of those exceptional persons to be found, it is said, in all countries, who possess some magnetic quality which has a soothing effect on even the most venomous and irritable reptiles.

Following the direction of my eyes, she too glanced down, but did not move her foot; then she made her voice heard again, still loud and sharp, but the anger was not now so pronounced.

"Do not fear, I shall not harm it," I said in the Indian tongue.

She took no notice of my speech, and continued speaking with increasing resentment.

I shook my head, replying that her language was unknown to me. Then by means of signs I tried to make her understand that the creature was safe from further molestation. She pointed indignantly at the stone in my hand, which I had forgotten all about. At once I threw it from me, and instantly there was a change; the resentment had vanished, and a tender radiance lit her face like a smile.

I advanced a little nearer, addressing her once more in the Indian tongue; but my speech was evidently unintelligible to her, as she stood now glancing at the snake lying at her feet, now at me. Again I had recourse to signs and gestures; pointing to the snake, then to the stone I had cast away, I endeavoured to convey to her that in the future I would for her sake be a friend to all venomous reptiles, and that I wished her to have the same kindly feelings towards me as towards these creatures. Whether or not she understood me, she showed no disposition to go into hiding again, and continued silently regarding me with a look that seemed to express pleasure at finding herself at last thus suddenly brought face to face with me. Flattered at this, I gradually drew nearer until at the last I was standing at her side, gazing down with the utmost delight into that face which so greatly surpassed in loveliness all human faces I had ever seen or imagined.

And yet to you, my friend, it probably will not seem that she was so beautiful, since I have, alas! only the words we all use to paint commoner, coarser things, and no means to represent all the exquisite details, all the delicate lights, and shades, and swift changes of colour and expression. Moreover, is it not a fact that the strange or unheard of can never appear beautiful in a mere description, because that which is most novel in it attracts too much attention and is given undue prominence in the picture, and we miss that which would have taken away the effect of strangeness—the perfect balance of the parts and harmony of the whole? For instance, the blue eyes of the northerner would, when first described to the black-eyed inhabitants of warm regions, seem unbeautiful and a monstrosity, because they would vividly see with the mental vision that unheard-of blueness, but not in the same vivid way the accompanying flesh and hair tints with which it harmonises.

Think, then, less of the picture as I have to paint it in words than of the feeling its original inspired in me, when looking closely for the first time on that rare loveliness, trembling with delight I mentally cried: "Oh, why has Nature, maker of so many types and of innumerable individuals of each, given to the world but one being like this?"

Scarcely had the thought formed itself in my mind before I dismissed it as utterly incredible. No, this exquisite being was without doubt one of a distinct race which had existed in this little-known corner of the continent for thousands of generations, albeit now perhaps reduced to a small and dwindling remnant.

Her figure and features were singularly delicate, but it was her colour that struck me most, which indeed made her differ from all other human beings. The colour of the skin would be almost impossible to describe, so greatly did it vary with every change of mood—and the moods were many and transient—and with the angle on which the sunlight touched it, and the degree of light.

Beneath the trees, at a distance, it had seemed a somewhat dim white or pale grey; near in the strong sunshine it was not white, but alabastrian, semi-pellucid, showing an underlying rose-colour; and at any point where the rays fell direct this colour was bright and luminous, as we see in our fingers when held before a strong firelight. But that part of her skin that remained in shadow appeared of a dimmer white, and the underlying colour varied from dim, rosy purple to dim blue. With the skin the colour of the eyes harmonised perfectly. At first, when lit with anger, they had appeared flame-like; now the iris was of a peculiar soft or dim and tender red, a shade sometimes seen in flowers. But only when looked closely at could this delicate hue be discerned, the pupils being large, as in some grey eyes, and the long, dark, shading lashes at a short distance made the whole eye appear dark. Think not, then, of the red flower, exposed to the light and sun in conjunction with the vivid green of the foliage; think only of such a hue in the half-hidden iris, brilliant and moist with the eye's moisture, deep with the eye's depth, glorified by the outward look of a bright, beautiful soul. Most variable of all in colour was the hair, this being due to its extreme fineness and glossiness, and to its elasticity, which made it lie fleecy and loose on head, shoulders, and back; a cloud with a brightness on its surface made by the freer outer hairs, a fit setting and crown for a countenance of such rare, changeful loveliness. In the shade, viewed closely, the general colour appeared a slate, deepening in places to purple; but even in the shade the nimbus of free flossy hairs half veiled the darker tints with a downy pallor; and at a distance of a few yards it gave the whole hair a vague, misty appearance. In the sunlight the colour varied more, looking now dark, sometimes intensely black, now of a light uncertain hue, with a play of iridescent colour on the loose surface, as we see on the glossed plumage of some birds; and at a short distance, with the sun shining full on her head, it sometimes looked white as a noonday cloud. So changeful was it and ethereal in appearance with its cloud colours, that all other human hair, even of the most beautiful golden shades, pale or red, seemed heavy and dull and dead-looking by comparison.

But more than form and colour and that enchanting variability was the look of intelligence, which at the same time seemed complementary to and one with the all-seeing, all-hearing alertness appearing in her face; the alertness one remarks in a wild creature, even when in repose and fearing nothing; but seldom in man, never perhaps in intellectual or studious man. She was a wild, solitary girl of the woods, and did not understand the language of the country in which I had addressed her. What inner or mind life could such a one have more than that of any wild animal existing in the same conditions? Yet looking at her face it was not possible to doubt its intelligence. This union in her of two opposite qualities which, with us, cannot or do not exist together, although so novel, yet struck me as the girl's principal charm. Why had Nature not done this before—why in all others does the brightness of the mind dim that beautiful physical brightness which the wild animals have? But enough for me that that which no man had ever looked for or hoped to find existed here; that through that unfamiliar lustre of the wild life shone the spiritualising light of mind that made us kin.

These thoughts passed swiftly through my brain as I stood feasting my sight on her bright, piquant face; while she on her part gazed back into my eyes, not only with fearless curiosity, but with a look of recognition and pleasure at the encounter so unmistakably friendly that, encouraged by it, I took her arm in my hand, moving at the same time a little nearer to her. At that moment a swift, startled expression came into her eyes; she glanced down and up again into my face; her lips trembled and slightly parted as she murmured some sorrowful sounds in a tone so low as to be only just audible.

Thinking she had become alarmed and was on the point of escaping out of my hands, and fearing, above all things, to lose sight of her again so soon, I slipped my arm round her slender body to detain her, moving one foot at the same time to balance myself; and at that moment I felt a slight blow and a sharp burning sensation shoot into my leg, so sudden and intense that I dropped my arm, at the same time uttering a cry of pain, and recoiled one or two paces from her. But she stirred not when I released her; her eyes followed my movements; then she glanced down at her feet. I followed her look, and figure to yourself my horror when I saw there the serpent I had so completely forgotten, and which even that sting of sharp pain had not brought back to remembrance! There it lay, a coil of its own tail thrown round one of her ankles, and its head, raised nearly a foot high, swaying slowly from side to side, while the swift forked tongue flickered continuously. Then—only then—I knew what had happened, and at the same time I understood the reason of that sudden look of alarm in her face, the murmuring sounds she had uttered, and the downward startled glance. Her fears had been solely for my safety, and she had warned me! Too late! too late! In moving I had trodden on or touched the serpent with my foot, and it had bitten me just above the ankle. In a few moments I began to realise the horror of my position. "Must I die! must I die! Oh, my God, is there nothing that can save me?" I cried in my heart.

She was still standing motionless in the same place: her eyes wandered back from me to the snake; gradually its swaying head was lowered again, and the coil unwound from her ankle; then it began to move away, slowly at first, and with the head a little raised, then faster, and in the end it glided out of sight. Gone!—but it had left its venom in my blood—O cursed reptile!

Back from watching its retreat, my eyes returned to her face, now strangely clouded with trouble; her eyes dropped before mine, while the palms of her hands were pressed together, and the fingers clasped and unclasped alternately. How different she seemed now; the brilliant face grown so pallid and vague-looking! But not only because this tragic end to our meeting had pierced her with pain: that cloud in the west had grown up and now covered half the sky with vast lurid masses of vapour, blotting out the sun, and a great gloom had fallen on the earth.

That sudden twilight and a long roll of approaching thunder, reverberating from the hills, increased my anguish and desperation. Death at that moment looked unutterably terrible. The remembrance of all that made life dear pierced me to the core—all that nature was to me, all the pleasures of sense and intellect, the hopes I had cherished—all was revealed to me as by a flash of lightning. Bitterest of all was the thought that I must now bid everlasting farewell to this beautiful being I had found in the solitude—this lustrous daughter of the Didi—just when I had won her from her shyness—that I must go away into the cursed blackness of death, and never know the mystery of her life! It was that which utterly unnerved me, and made my legs tremble under me, and brought great drops of sweat to my forehead, until I thought that the venom was already doing its swift, fatal work in my veins.

With uncertain steps I moved to a stone a yard or two away and sat down upon it. As I did so the hope came to me that this girl, so intimate with nature, might know of some antidote to save me. Touching my leg, and using other signs, I addressed her again in the Indian language.

"The snake has bitten me," I said. "What shall I do? Is there no leaf, no root you know that would save me from death? Help me! help me!" I cried in despair.

My signs she probably understood if not my words, but she made no reply; and still she remained standing motionless, twisting and untwisting her fingers, and regarding me with a look of ineffable grief and compassion.

Alas! It was vain to appeal to her: she knew what had happened, and what the result would most likely be, and pitied, but was powerless to help me. Then it occurred to me that if I could reach the Indian village before the venom overpowered me something might be done to save me. Oh, why had I tarried so long, losing so many precious minutes! Large drops of rain were falling now, and the gloom was deeper, and the thunder almost continuous. With a cry of anguish I started to my feet, and was about to rush away towards the village when a dazzling flash of lightning made me pause for a moment. When it vanished I turned a last look on the girl, and her face was deathly pale, and her hair looked blacker than night; and as she looked she stretched out her arms towards me and uttered a low, wailing cry. "Good-bye for ever!" I murmured, and turning once more from her, rushed away like one crazed into the wood. But in my confusion I had probably taken the wrong direction, for instead of coming out in a few minutes into the open border of the forest, and on to the savannah, I found myself every moment getting deeper among the trees. I stood still, perplexed, but could not shake off the conviction that I had started in the right direction Eventually I resolved to keep on for a hundred yards or so, and then, if no opening appeared, to turn back and retrace my steps. But this was no easy matter. I soon became entangled in a dense undergrowth, which so confused me that at last I confessed despairingly to myself that for the first time in this wood I was hopelessly lost. And in what terrible circumstances! At intervals a flash of lightning would throw a vivid blue glare down into the interior of the wood and only serve to show that I had lost myself in a place where even at noon in cloudless weather progress would be most difficult; and now the light would only last a moment, to be followed by thick gloom; and I could only tear blindly on, bruising and lacerating my flesh at every step, falling again and again only to struggle up and on again, now high above the surface climbing over prostrate trees and branches, now plunged to my middle in a pool or torrent of water.

Hopeless—utterly hopeless seemed all my mad efforts; and at each pause, when I would stand exhausted, gasping for breath, my throbbing heart almost suffocating me, a dull, continuous, teasing pain in my bitten leg served to remind me that I had but a little time left to exist—that by delaying at first I had allowed my only chance of salvation to slip by.

How long a time I spent fighting my way through this dense black wood I know not; perhaps two or three hours, only to me the hours seemed like years of prolonged agony. At last, all at once, I found that I was free of the close undergrowth, and walking on level ground: but it was darker here—darker than the darkest night; and at length when the lightning came and flared down through the dense roof of foliage overhead, I discovered that I was in a spot that had a strange look, where the trees were very large and grew wide apart, and with no undergrowth to impede progress beneath them. Here, recovering breath, I began to run, and after a while found that I had left the large trees behind me, and was now in a more open place, with small trees and bushes: and this made me hope for a while that I had at last reached the border of the forest. But the hope proved vain; once more I had to force my way through dense undergrowth, and finally emerged on to a slope where it was open, and I could once more see for some distance around me by such light as came through the thick pall of clouds. Trudging on to the summit of the slope, I saw that there was open savannah country beyond, and for a moment rejoiced that I had got free from the forest. A few steps more, and I was standing on the very edge of a bank, a precipice not less than fifty feet deep. I had never seen that bank before, and therefore knew that I could not be on the right side of the forest. But now my only hope was to get completely away from the trees and then to look for the village, and I began following the bank in search of a descent. No break occurred, and presently I was stopped by a dense thicket of bushes. I was about to retrace my steps when I noticed that a tall slender tree growing at the foot of the precipice, its green top not more than a couple of yards below my feet, seemed to offer a means of escape. Nerving myself with the thought that if I got crushed by the fall I should probably escape a lingering and far more painful death, I dropped into the cloud of foliage beneath me and clutched desperately at the twigs as I fell. For a moment I felt myself sustained; but branch after branch gave way beneath my weight, and then I only remember, very dimly, a swift flight through the air before losing consciousness.

CHAPTER VII

WITH the return of consciousness, I at first had a vague impression that I was lying somewhere, injured, and incapable of motion; that it was night, and necessary for me to keep my eyes fast shut to prevent them from being blinded by almost continuous vivid flashes of lightning. Injured, and sore all over, but warm and dry—surely dry: nor was it lightning that dazzled, but firelight. I began to notice things little by little. The fire was burning on a clay floor a few feet from where I was lying. Before it, on a log of wood, sat or crouched a human figure. An old man, with chin on breast and hands clasped before his drawn-up knees; only a small portion of his forehead and nose visible to me. An Indian I took him to be, from his coarse, lank, grey hair and dark brown skin. I was in a large hut, falling at the sides to within two feet of the floor: but there were no hammocks in it, nor bows and spears, and no skins, not even under me, for I was lying on straw mats I could hear the storm still raging outside; the rush and splash of rain, and, at intervals, the distant growl of thunder. There was wind, too; I listened to it sobbing in the trees, and occasionally a puff found its way in, and blew up the white ashes at the old man's feet. and shook the yellow flames like a flag. I remembered now how the storm began, the wild girl, the snake-bite, my violent efforts to find a way out of the wood, and, finally, that leap from the bank where recollection ended. That I had not been killed by the venomous tooth, nor the subsequent fearful fall, seemed like a miracle to me. And in that wild, solitary place, lying insensible, in that awful storm and darkness, I had been found by a fellow-creature —a savage, doubtless, but a good Samaritan all the same —who had rescued me from death! I was bruised all over and did not attempt to move, fearing the pain it would give me; and I had a racking headache; but these seemed trifling discomforts after such adventures and such perils. I felt that I had recovered or was recovering from that venomous bite; that I would live and not die—live to return to my country; and the thought filled my heart to overflowing, and tears of gratitude and happiness rose to my eyes.

At such times a man experiences benevolent feelings, and would willingly bestow some of that overplus of happiness on his fellows to lighten other hearts; and this old man before me, who was probably the instrument of my salvation, began greatly to excite my interest and compassion. For he seemed so poor in his old age and rags, so solitary and dejected as he sat there with knees drawn up, his great, brown, bare feet looking almost black by contrast with the white wood-ashes about them! What could I do for him? What could I say to cheer his spirits in that Indian language, which has few or no words to express kindly feelings? Unable to think of anything better to say, I at length suddenly cried aloud, "Smoke, old man! Why do you not smoke? It is good to smoke."

He gave a mighty start, and, turning, fixed his eyes on me. Then I saw that he was not a pure Indian, for although as brown as old leather, he wore a beard and moustache. A curious face had this old man, which looked as if youth and age had made it a battling ground. His forehead was smooth, except for two parallel lines in the middle running its entire length, dividing it in zones; his arched eyebrows were black as ink, and his small black eyes were bright and cunning, like the eyes of some wild carnivorous animal. In this part of his face youth had held its own, especially in the eyes, which looked young and lively. But lower down age had conquered, scribbling his skin all over with wrinkles, while moustache and beard were white as thistledown.

"Aha, the dead man is alive again!" he exclaimed, with a chuckling laugh. This in the Indian tongue; then in Spanish he added, "But speak to me in the language you know best, señor; for if you are not a Venezuelan call me an owl."

"And you, old man?" said I.

"Ah, I was right! Why, sir, what I am is plainly written on my face. Surely you do not take me for a pagan! I might be a black man from Africa, or an Englishman, but an Indian—that, no! But a minute ago you had the goodness to invite me to smoke. How, sir, can a poor man smoke who is without tobacco?"

"Without tobacco—in Guayana!"

"Can you believe it? But, sir, do not blame me; if the beast that came one night and destroyed my plants when ripe for cutting had taken pumpkins and sweet potatoes instead, it would have been better for him, if curses have any effect. And the plant grows slowly, sir—it is not an evil weed to come to maturity in a single day. And as for other leaves in the forest, I smoke them, yes; but there is no comfort to the lungs in such smoke."

"My tobacco-pouch was full," I said. "You will find it in my coat, if I did not lose it."

"The saints forbid!" he exclaimed. "Grandchild—Rima, have you got a tobacco-pouch with the other things? Give it to me."

Then I first noticed that another person was in the hut, a slim young girl, who had been seated against the wall on the other side of the fire, partially hid by the shadows. She had my leather belt, with the revolver in its case, and my hunting-knife attached, and the few articles I had had in my pockets, on her lap. Taking up the pouch, she handed it to him, and he clutched it with a strange eagerness.

"I will give it back presently, Rima," he said. "Let me first smoke a cigarette—and then another."

It seemed probable from this that the good old man had already been casting covetous eyes on my property, and that his granddaughter had taken care of it for me. But how the silent, demure girl had kept it from him was a puzzle, so intensely did he seem now to enjoy it, drawing the smoke vigorously into his lungs, and after keeping it ten or fifteen seconds there, letting it fly out again from mouth and nose in blue jets and clouds. His face softened visibly, he became more and more genial and loquacious, and asked me how I came to be in that solitary place. I told him that I was staying with the Indian Runi, his neighbour.

"But, señor," he said, "if it is not an impertinence, how is it that a young man of so distinguished an appearance as yourself, a Venezuelan, should be residing with these children of the devil?"

"You love not your neighbours, then?"

"I know them, sir—how should I love them?" He was rolling up his second or third cigarette by this time, and I could not help noticing that he took a great deal more tobacco than he required in his fingers, and that the surplus on each occasion was conveyed to some secret receptacle among his rags. "Love them, sir! They are infidels, and therefore the good Christian must only hate them. They are thieves—they will steal from you before your very face, so devoid are they of all shame. And also murderers; gladly would they burn this poor thatch above my head, and kill me and my poor grandchild, who shares this solitary life with me, if they had the courage. But they are all arrant cowards, and fear to approach me—fear even to come into this wood. You would laugh to hear what they are afraid of—a child would laugh to hear it!"

"What do they fear?" I said, for his words had excited my interest in a great degree.

"Why, sir, would you believe it? They fear this child—my granddaughter, seated there before you. A poor innocent girl of seventeen summers, a Christian who knows her Catechism, and would not harm the smallest thing that God has made—no, not a fly, which is not regarded on account of its smallness. Why, sir, it is due to her tender heart that you are safely sheltered here, instead of being left out of doors in this tempestuous night."

"To her—to this girl?" I returned in astonishment. "Explain, old man, for I do not know how I was saved."

"To-day, señor, through your own heedlessness you were bitten by a venomous snake."

"Yes, that is true, although I do not know how it came to your knowledge. But why am I not a dead man, then—have you done something to save me from the effects of the poison?"

"Nothing. What could I do so long after you were bitten? When a man is bitten by a snake in a solitary place he is in God's hands. He will live or die as God wills. There is nothing to be done. But surely, sir, you remember that my poor grandchild was with you in the wood when the snake bit you?"

"A girl was there—a strange girl I have seen and heard before when I have walked in the forest. But not this girl—surely not this girl!"

"No other," said he, carefully rolling up another cigarette.

"It is not possible!" I returned.

"Ill would you have fared, sir, had she not been there. For after being bitten, you rushed away into the thickest part of the wood, and went about in a circle like a demented person for Heaven knows how long. But she never left you; she was always close to you—you might have touched her with your hand. And at last some good angel who was watching you, in order to stop your career, made you mad altogether and caused you to jump over a precipice and lose your senses. And you were no sooner on the ground than she was with you—ask me not how *she* got down! And when she had propped you up against the bank she came for me. Fortunately the spot where you had fallen is near—not five hundred yards from the door. And I, on my part, was willing to assist her in saving you; for I knew it was no Indian that had fallen, since she loves not that breed, and they come not here. It was not an easy task, for you weigh, señor; but between us we brought you in."

While he spoke the girl continued sitting in the same listless attitude as when I first observed her, with eyes cast down and hands folded in her lap. Recalling that brilliant being in the wood that had protected the serpent from me, and calmed its rage, I found it hard to believe his words, and still felt a little incredulous.

"Rima—that is your name, is it not?" I said. "Will you come here and stand before me, and let me look closely at you?"

"Si, señor," she meekly answered; and removing the things from her lap she stood up; then, passing behind the old man, came and stood before me, her eyes still bent on the ground—a picture of humility.

She had the figure of the forest girl, but wore now a scanty faded cotton garment, while the loose cloud of hair was confined in two plaits and hung down her back. The face also showed the same delicate lines, but of the brilliant animation and variable colour and expression there appeared no trace. Gazing at her countenance, as she stood there silent, shy, and spiritless before me, the image of her brighter self came vividly to my mind, and I could not recover from the astonishment I felt at such a contrast.

Have you ever observed a humming-bird moving about in an aërial dance among the flowers—a living prismatic gem that changes its colour with every change of position—how in turning it catches the sunshine on its burnished neck and gorget plumes—green and gold and flame-coloured, the beams changing to visible flakes as they fall, dissolving into nothing, to be succeeded by others and yet others? In its exquisite form, its changeful splendour, its swift motions and intervals of aërial suspension, it is a creature of such fairly-like loveliness as to mock all description. And have you seen this same fairy-like creature suddenly perch itself on a twig, in the shade, its misty wings and fanlike tail folded, the iridescent glory vanished, looking like some common dull-plumaged little bird sitting listless in a cage? Just so great was the difference in the girl, as I had seen her in the forest and as she now appeared under the smoky roof in the firelight.

After watching her for some moments I spoke: "Rima, there must be a good deal of strength in that frame of yours, which looks so delicate; will you raise me up a little?"

She went down on one knee, and placing her arms round me assisted me to a sitting posture.

"Thank you, Rima—O misery!" I groaned. "Is there a bone left unbroken in my poor body?"

"Nothing broken," cried the old man, clouds of smoke flying out with his words. "I have examined you well—legs, arms, ribs. For this is how it was, señor. A thorny bush into which you fell saved you from being flattened on the stony ground. But you are bruised, sir, black with bruises; and there are more scratches of thorns on your skin than letters on a written page."

"A long thorn might have entered my brain," I said, "from the way it pains. Feel my forehead, Rima; is it very hot and dry?"

She did as I asked, touching me lightly with her little cool hand. "No, señor, not hot, but warm and moist," she said.

"Thank Heaven for that!" I said. "Poor girl! And you followed me through the wood in all that terrible storm! Ah, if I could lift my bruised arm I would take your hand to kiss it in gratitude for so great a service. I owe you my life, sweet Rima—what shall I do to repay so great a debt?"

The old man chuckled as if amused, but the girl lifted not her eyes nor spoke.

"Tell me, sweet child," I said, "for I cannot realise it yet; was it really you that saved the serpent's life when I would have killed it—did you stand by me in the wood with the serpent lying at your feet?"

"Yes, señor," came her gentle answer.

"And it was you I saw in the wood one day, lying on the ground playing with a small bird?"

"Yes, señor."

"And it was you that followed me so often among the trees, calling to me, yet always hiding so that I could never see you?"

"Yes, señor."

"Oh, this is wonderful!" I exclaimed; whereat the old man chuckled again.

"But tell me this, my sweet girl," I continued. "You never addressed me in Spanish; what strange musical language was it you spoke to me in?"

She shot a timid glance at my face and looked troubled at the question, but made no reply.

"Señor," said the old man, "that is a question which you must excuse my child from answering. Not, sir, from want of will, for she is docile and obedient, though I say it, but there is no answer beyond what I can tell you. And this is, sir, that all creatures, whether man or bird, have the voice that God has given them; and in some the voice is musical and in others not so."

"Very well, old man," said I to myself; "there let the matter rest for the present. But, if I am destined to live and not die, I shall not long remain satisfied with your too simple explanation."

"Rima," I said, "you must be fatigued; it is thoughtless of me to keep you standing here so long."

Her face brightened a little, and bending down she replied in a low voice, "I am not fatigued, sir. Let me get you something to eat now."

She moved quickly away to the fire, and presently returned with an earthenware dish of roasted pumpkin and sweet potatoes, and kneeling at my side fed me deftly with a small wooden spoon. I did not feel grieved at the absence of meat and the stinging condiments the Indians love, nor did I even remark that there was no salt in the vegetables, so much was I taken up with watching her beautiful delicate face while she ministered to me. The exquisite fragrance of her breath was more to me than the most delicious viands could have been; and it was a delight each time she raised the spoon to my mouth to catch a momentary glimpse of her eyes, which now looked dark as wine when we lift the glass to see the ruby gleam of light within the purple. But she never for a moment laid aside the silent, meek, constrained manner; and when I remembered her bursting out in her brilliant wrath on me, pouring forth that torrent of stinging invective in her mysterious language, I was lost in wonder and admiration at the change in her, and at her double personality. Having satisfied my wants she moved quietly away, and raising a straw mat disappeared behind it into her own sleeping-apartment, which was divided off by a partition from the room I was in.

The old man's sleeping-place was a wooden cot or stand on the opposite side of the room, but he was in no hurry to sleep, and after Rima had left us put a fresh log on the blaze, and lit another cigarette. Heaven knows how many he had smoked by this time. He became very talkative and called to his side his two dogs, which I had not noticed in the room before, for me to see. It amused me to hear their names—Susio and Goloso: Dirty and Greedy. They were surly-looking brutes, with rough yellow hair, and did not win my heart, but according to his account they possessed all the usual canine virtues; and he was still holding forth on the subject when I fell asleep.

CHAPTER VIII

WHEN morning came I was too stiff and sore to move, and not until the following day was I able to creep out to sit in the shade of the trees. My old host, whose name was Nuflo, went off with his dogs, leaving the girl to attend to my wants. Two or three times during the day she appeared to serve me with food and drink, but she continued silent and constrained in manner as on the first evening of seeing her in the hut.

Late in the afternoon old Nuflo returned, but did not say where he had been; and shortly afterwards Rima reappeared, demure as usual, in her faded cotton dress, her cloud of hair confined in two long plaits. My curiosity was more excited than ever, and I resolved to get to the bottom of the mystery of her life. The girl had not shown herself responsive, but now that Nuflo was back I was treated to as much talk as I cared to hear. He talked of many things, only omitting those which I desired to hear about; but his pet subject appeared to be the divine government of the world —"God's politics" —and its manifest imperfections, or in other words, the manifold abuses which from time to time had been allowed to creep into it. The old man was pious, but like many of his class in my country, he permitted himself to indulge in very free criticisms of the powers above, from the King of Heaven down to the smallest saint whose name figures in the calendar.

"These things, señor," he said, "are not properly managed. Consider my position. Here am I compelled for my sins to inhabit this wilderness with my poor granddaughter——"

"She is not your granddaughter!" I suddenly interrupted, thinking to surprise him into an admission.

But he took his time to answer. "Señor, we are never sure of anything in this world. Not absolutely sure. Thus, it may come to pass that you will one day marry, and that your wife will in due time present you with a son—one that will inherit your fortune and transmit your name to posterity. And yet, sir, in this world, you will never know to a certainty that he is your son."

"Proceed with what you were saying," I returned, with some dignity.

"Here we are," he continued, "compelled to inhabit this land and do not meet with proper protection from the infidel. Now, sir, this is a crying evil, and it is only becoming in one who has the true faith, and is a loyal subject of the All-Powerful, to point out with due humility that He is growing very remiss in His affairs, and is losing a good deal of His prestige. And what, señor, is at the bottom of it? Favoritism. We know that the Supreme cannot Himself be everywhere, attending to each little trike-traka that arises in the world—matters altogether beneath His notice; and that He must, like the

President of Venezuela or the Emperor of Brazil, appoint men—angels if you like—to conduct His affairs and watch over each district. And it is manifest that for this country of Guayana the proper person has not been appointed. Every evil is done and there is no remedy, and the Christian has no more consideration shown him than the infidel. Now, señor, in a town near the Orinoco I once saw on a church the archangel Michael, made of stone, and twice as tall as a man, with one foot on a monster shaped like a cayman, but with bat's wings, and a head and neck like a serpent. Into this monster he was thrusting his spear. That is the kind of person that should be sent to rule these latitudes—a person of firmness and resolution, with strength in his wrist. And yet it is probable that this very man—this St. Michael—is hanging about the palace, twirling his thumbs, waiting for an appointment, while other weaker men, and—Heaven forgive me for saying it, not above a bribe, perhaps—are sent out to rule over this province."

On this string he would harp by the hour; it was a lofty subject on which he had pondered much in his solitary life, and he was glad of an opportunity of ventilating his grievance and expounding his views. At first it was a pure pleasure to hear Spanish again, and the old man, albeit ignorant of letters, spoke well; but this, I may say, is a common thing in our country, where the peasant's quickness of intelligence and poetic feeling often compensate for want of instruction. His views also amused me, although they were not novel. But after a while I grew tired of listening, yet I listened still, agreeing with him, and leading him on to let him have his fill of talk, always hoping that he would come at last to speak of personal matters and give me an account of his history and of Rima's origin. But the hope proved vain; not a word to enlighten me would he drop, however cunningly I tempted him.

"So be it," thought I; "but if you are cunning. old man, I shall be cunning too—and patient; for all things come to him who waits."

He was in no hurry to get rid of me. On the contrary, he more than hinted that I would be safer under his roof than with the Indians, at the same time apologising for not giving me meat to eat.

"But why do you not have meat? Never have I seen animals so abundant and tame as in this wood."

Before he could reply Rima, with a jug of water from the spring in her hand, came in: glancing at me he lifted his finger to signify that such a subject must not be discussed in her presence; but as soon as she quitted the room he returned to it.

"Señor," he said, "have you forgotten your adventure with the snake? Know, then, that my grandchild would not live with me for one day longer if I were to lift my hand against any living creature. For us, señor, every day is fast-day—only without the fish. We have maize, pumpkin, cassava, potatoes, and these suffice. And even of these cultivated fruits of the earth she eats but little in the house, preferring certain wild berries and gums, which are more to her taste, and which she picks here and there in her rambles in the wood. And I, sir, loving her as I do, whatever my inclination may be, shed no blood and eat no flesh."

I looked at him with an incredulous smile.

"And your dogs, old man?"

"My dogs? Sir, they would not pause or turn aside if a coatimundi crossed their path—an animal with a strong odour. As a man is, so is his dog. Have you not seen dogs eating grass, sir, even in Venezuela, where these sentiments do not prevail? And when there is no meat—when meat is forbidden—these sagacious animals accustom themselves to a vegetable diet."

I could not very well tell the old man that he was lying to me—that would have been bad policy—and so I passed it off. "I have no doubt that you are right," I said. "I have heard that there are dogs in China that eat no meat, but are themselves eaten by their owners after being fattened on rice. I should not care to dine on one of your animals, old man."

He looked at them critically and replied, "Certainly they are lean."

"I was thinking less of their leanness than of their smell," I returned. "Their odour when they approach me is not flowery, but resembles that of other dogs which feed on flesh, and have offended my too sensitive nostrils even in the drawing-rooms of Caracas. It is not like the fragrance of cattle when they return from the pasture."

"Every animal," he replied, "gives out that odour which is peculiar to its kind"; an incontrovertible fact which left me nothing to say.

When I had sufficiently recovered the suppleness of my limbs to walk with ease I went for a ramble in the wood, in the hope that Rima would accompany me, and that out among the trees she would cast aside that artificial constraint and shyness which was her manner in the house.

It fell out just as I had expected: she accompanied me in the sense of being always near me, or within earshot, and her manner was now free and unconstrained as I could wish; but little or nothing was gained by the change. She was once more the tantalising, elusive, mysterious creature I had first known through her wandering, melodious voice. The only difference was that the musical, inarticulate sounds were now less often heard, and that she was no longer afraid to show herself to me. This for a short time was enough to make me happy, since no lovelier being was ever looked upon, nor one whose loveliness was less likely to lose its charm through being often seen.

But to keep her near me or always in sight was, I found, impossible: she would be free as the wind, free as the butterfly, going and coming at her wayward will, and losing herself from sight a dozen times every hour. To induce her to walk soberly at my side or sit down and enter into conversation with me seemed about as impracticable as to tame the fiery-hearted little humming-bird that flashes into sight, remains suspended motionless for a few seconds before your face, then, quick as lightning, vanishes again.

At length, feeling convinced that she was most happy

when she had me out following her in the wood, that in spite of her bird-like wildness she had a tender, human heart, which was easily moved, I determined to try to draw her closer by means of a little innocent stratagem. Going out in the morning, after calling her several times to no purpose, I began to assume a downcast manner, as if suffering pain or depressed with grief; and at last, finding a convenient exposed root under a tree, on a spot where the ground was dry and strewn with loose yellow sand, I sat down and refused to go any further. For she always wanted to lead me on and on, and whenever I paused she would return to show herself, or to chide or encourage me in her mysterious language. All her pretty little arts were now practised in vain: with cheek resting on my hand I still sat, my eyes fixed on that patch of yellow sand at my feet, watching how the small particles glinted like diamond dust when the sunlight touched them. A full hour passed in this way, during which I encouraged myself by saying mentally: "This is a contest between us, and the most patient and the strongest of will, which should be the man, must conquer. And if I win on this occasion it will be easier for me in the future—easier to discover those things which I am resolved to know, and the girl must reveal to me, since the old man has proved impracticable."

Meanwhile she came and went and came again; and at last, finding that I was not to be moved, she approached and stood near me. Her face, when I glanced at it, had a somewhat troubled look—both troubled and curious.

"Come here, Rima," I said, "and stay with me for a little while—I cannot follow you now."

She took one or two hesitating steps, then stood still again; and at length, slowly and reluctantly, advanced to within a yard of me. Then I rose from my seat on the root, so as to catch her face better, and placed my hand against the rough bark of the tree.

"Rima," I said, speaking in a low, caressing tone, "will you stay with me here a little while and talk to me, not in your language, but in mine, so that I may understand? Will you listen when I speak to you, and answer me?"

Her lips moved, but made no sound. She seemed strangely disquieted, and shook back her loose hair, and with her small toes moved the sparkling sand at her feet, and once or twice her eyes glanced shyly at my face.

"Rima, you have not answered me," I persisted. "Will you not say 'yes'?"

"Yes."

"Where does your grandfather spend his day when he goes out with his dogs?"

She shook her head slightly, but would not speak.

"Have you no mother, Rima? Do you remember your mother?"

"My mother! My mother!" she exclaimed in a low voice, but with a sudden, wonderful animation. Bending a little nearer she continued: "Oh, she is dead! Her body is in the earth and turned to dust. Like that," and she moved the loose sand with her foot. "Her soul is up there, where the stars and the angels are, grandfather says. But what is that to me? I am here—am I not? I talk to her just the same. Everything I see I point out, and tell her everything. In the daytime—in the woods, when we are together. And at night when I lie down I cross my arms on my breast—so, and say, 'Mother, mother, now you are in my arms; let us go to sleep together.' Sometimes I say, 'Oh, why will you never answer me when I speak and speak?' Mother—mother—mother!"

At the end her voice suddenly rose to a mournful cry, then sunk, and at the last repetition of the word died to a low whisper.

"Ah, poor Rima! she is dead and cannot speak to you—cannot hear you! Talk to me, Rima; I am living and can answer."

But now the cloud, which had suddenly lifted from her heart, letting me see for a moment into its mysterious depths—its fancies so childlike and feelings so intense—had fallen again; and my words brought no response, except a return of that troubled look to her face.

"Silent still?" I said. "Talk to me, then, of your mother, Rima. Do you know that you will see her again some day?"

"Yes, when I die. That is what the priest said."

"The priest?"

"Yes, at Voa—do you know? Mother died there when I was small—it is so far away! And there are thirteen houses by the side of the river—just here; and on this other side—trees, trees."

This was important, I thought, and would lead to the

very knowledge I wished for; so I pressed her to tell me more about the settlement she had named, and of which I had never heard.

"Everything have I told you," she returned, surprised that I did not know that she had exhausted the subject in those half-dozen words she had spoken.

Obliged to shift my ground, I said at a venture: "Tell me, what do you ask of the Virgin Mother when you kneel before her picture? Your grandfather told me that you had a picture in your little room."

"You know!" flashed out her answer, with something like resentment. "It is all there—in there," waving her hand towards the hut. "Out here in the wood it is all gone—like this," and stooping quickly she raised a little yellow sand on her palm, then let it run away through her fingers.

Thus she illustrated how all the matters she had been taught slipped from her mind when she was out-of-doors, out of sight of the picture. After an interval she added, "Only mother is here—always with me."

"Ah, poor Rima!" I said; "alone without a mother, and only your old grandfather! He is old—what will you do when he dies and flies away to the starry country where your mother is?"

She looked inquiringly at me, then made answer in a low voice, "You are here."

"But when I go away?"

She was silent; and not wishing to dwell on a subject that seemed to pain her, I continued: "Yes, I am here now, but you will not stay with me and talk freely.

Will it always be the same if I remain with you? Why are you always so silent in the house, so cold with your old grandfather? So different—so full of life, like a bird, when you are alone in the woods? Rima, speak to me! Am I no more to you than your old grandfather? Do you not like me to talk to you?"

She appeared strangely disturbed at my words. "Oh, you are not like him," she suddenly replied. "Sitting all day on a log by the fire—all day, all day; Goloso and Susio lying beside him—sleep, sleep. Oh, when I saw you in the wood I followed you, and talked and talked; still no answer. Why will you not come when I call? To me!" Then, mocking my voice, "Rima, Rima! Come here! Do this! Say that! Rima! Rima! It is nothing, nothing—it is not you," pointing to my mouth; and then, as if fearing that her meaning had not been made clear, suddenly touching my lips with her finger. "Why do you not answer me?—speak to me—speak to me, like this!" And turning a little more towards me, and glancing at me with eyes that had all at once changed, losing their clouded expression for one of exquisite tenderness, from her lips came a succession of those mysterious sounds which had first attracted me to her, swift and low and bird-like, yet with something so much higher and more soul-penetrating than any bird music. Ah, what feeling and fancies, what quaint turns of expression, unfamiliar to my mind, were contained in those sweet, wasted symbols! I could never know—never come to her when she called, or respond to her spirit. To me they would always be inarticulate sounds, affecting me like a tender spiritual music—a language without words, suggesting more than words to the soul.

The mysterious speech died down to a lisping sound, like the faint note of some small bird falling from a cloud of foliage on the topmost bough of a tree; and at the same time that new light passed from her eyes, and she half averted her face in a disappointed way.

"Rima," I said at length, a new thought coming to my aid, "it is true that I am not here," touching my lips as she had done, "and that my words are nothing. But look into my eyes, and you will see me there—all, all that is in my heart."

"Oh, I know what I should see there!" she returned quickly.

"What would you see—tell me?"

"There is a little black ball in the middle of your eye; I should see myself in it no bigger than that," and she marked off about an eighth of her little finger-nail. "There is a pool in the wood, and I look down and see myself there. That is better. Just as large as I am—not small and black like a small, small fly." And after saying this a little disdainfully she moved away from my side and out into the sunshine; and then, half turning towards me, and glancing first at my face and then upwards, she raised her hand to call my attention to something there.

Far up, high as the tops of the tallest trees, a great blue-winged butterfly was passing across the open space with loitering flight. In a few moments it was gone over the trees; then she turned once more to me with a little rippling sound of laughter—the first I had heard from her, and called, "Come, come!"

I was glad enough to go with her then; and for the next two hours we rambled together in the wood; that is, together in her way, for though always near she contrived to keep out of my sight most of the time. She was evidently now in a gay, frolicsome temper; again and again, when I looked closely into some wide-spreading bush, or peered behind a tree, when her calling voice had sounded, her rippling laughter would come to me from some other spot. At length, somewhere about the centre of the wood, she led me to an immense mora tree, growing almost isolated, covering with its shade a large space of ground entirely free from undergrowth. At this spot she all at once vanished from my side; and after listening and watching some time in vain I sat down beside the giant trunk to wait for her. Very soon I heard a low, warbling sound which seemed quite near.

"Rima! Rima!" I called, and instantly my call was repeated like an echo. Again and again I called, and still the words flew back to me, and I could not decide whether it was an echo or not. Then I gave up calling; and presently the low, warbling sound was repeated, and I knew that Rima was somewhere near me.

"Rima, where are you?" I called.

"Rima, where are you?" came the answer.

"You are behind the tree."

"You are behind the tree."

"I shall catch you, Rima." And this time, instead of repeating my words, she answered, "Oh no."

I jumped up and ran round the tree, feeling sure that I should find her. It was about thirty-five or forty feet in circumference; and after going round two or three times I turned and ran the other way, but failing to catch a glimpse of her I at last sat down again.

"Rima, Rima!" sounded the mocking voice as soon as I had sat down. "Where are you, Rima? I shall catch you, Rima! Have you caught Rima?"

"No, I have not caught her. There is no Rima now. She has faded away like a rainbow—like a drop of dew in the sun. I have lost her; I shall go to sleep." And stretching myself out at full length under the tree, I remained quiet for two or three minutes. Then a slight rustling sound was heard, and I looked eagerly round for her. But the sound was overhead and caused by a great avalanche of leaves which began to descend on to me from that vast leafy canopy above.

"Ah, little spider-monkey—little green tree-snake—you are there!" But there was no seeing her in that immense aerial palace hung with dim drapery of green and copper-coloured leaves. But how had she got there? Up the stupendous trunk even a monkey could not have climbed, and there were no lianas dropping to earth from the wide horizontal branches that I could see; but by-and-by, looking further away, I perceived that on one side the longest lower branches reached and mingled with the shorter boughs of the neighbouring trees. While gazing up I heard her low, rippling laugh, and then caught sight of her as she ran along an exposed horizontal branch, erect on her feet; and my heart stood still with terror, for she was fifty to sixty feet above the ground. In another moment she vanished from sight in a cloud of foliage, and I saw no more of her for about ten minutes, when all at once she appeared at my side once more, having come round the trunk of the mora. Her face had a bright, pleased expression, and showed no trace of fatigue or agitation.

I caught her hand in mine. It was a delicate, shapely little hand, soft as velvet, and warm—a real human hand: only now when I held it did she seem altogether like a human being, and not a mocking spirit of the wood, a daughter of the Didi.

"Do you like me to hold your hand, Rima?"

"Yes," she replied, with indifference.

"Is it I?"

"Yes." This time as if it was small satisfaction to make acquaintance with this purely physical part of me.

Having her so close gave me an opportunity of examining that light sheeny garment she wore always in the woods. It felt soft and satiny to the touch, and there was no seam nor hem in it that I could see, but it was all in one piece, like the cocoon of the caterpillar. While I was feeling it on her shoulder and looking narrowly at it, she glanced at me with a mocking laugh in her eyes.

"Is it silk?" I asked. Then, as she remained silent, I continued, "Where did you get this dress, Rima? Did you make it yourself? Tell me."

She answered not in words, but in response to my question a new look came into her face; no longer restless and full of change in her expression, she was now as immovable as an alabaster statue; not a siken hair on her head trembled; her eyes were wide open, gazing fixedly before her; and when I looked into them they seemed to see and yet not to see me. They were like the clear, brilliant eyes of a bird, which reflect as in a miraculous mirror all the visible world but do not return our look, and seem to see us merely as one of the thousand small details that make up the whole picture. Suddenly she darted out her hand like a flash, making me start at the unexpected motion, and quickly withdrawing it, held up a finger before me. From its tip a minute gossamer spider, about twice the bigness of a pin's head, appeared suspended from a fine, scarcely visible line three or four inches long.

"Look!" she exclaimed, with a bright glance at my face.

The small spider she had captured, anxious to be free, was falling, falling earthward, but could not reach the surface. Leaning her shoulder a little forward, she placed the finger-tip against it, but lightly, scarcely touching, and moving continuously, with a motion rapid as that of a fluttering moth's wing; while the spider, still paying out his line, remained suspended, rising and falling slightly at nearly the same distance from the ground. After a few moments she cried, "Drop down, little spider." Her finger's motion ceased, and the minute captive fell, to lose itself on the shaded ground.

"Do you not see?" she said to me, pointing to he shoulder. Just where the finger-tip had touched the garment a round shining spot appeared, looking like a silver coin on the cloth; but on touching it with my finger it seemed part of the original fabric, only whiter and more shiny on the grey ground, on account of the freshness of the web of which it had just been made.

And so all this curious and pretty performance, which seemed instinctive in its spontaneous quickness and dexterity, was merely intended to show me how she made her garments out of the fine floating lines of small gossamer spiders!

Before I could express my surprise and admiration she cried again, with startling suddenness, "Look!"

A minute shadowy form darted by, appearing like a dim line traced across the deep glossy mora foliage, then on the lighter green foliage further away. She waved her hand in imitation of its swift, curving flight, then dropping it exclaimed, "Gone—oh, little thing!"

"What was it?" I asked, for it might have been a bird, a bird-like moth, or a bee.

"Did you not see? And you asked me to look into your eyes!"

"Ah, little squirrel Sakawinki, you remind me of that!" I said, passing my arm round her waist and drawing her a little closer. "Look into my eyes now and see if I am blind, and if there is nothing in them except an image of Rima like a small, small fly."

She shook her head and laughed a little mockingly, but made no effort to escape from my arm.

"Would you like me always to do what you wish, Rima—to follow you in the woods when you say 'Come' —to chase you round the tree to catch you, and lie down for you to throw leaves on me, and to be glad when you are glad?"

"Oh yes."

"Then let us make a compact. I shall do everything to please you, and you must promise to do everything to please me."

"Tell me."

"Little things, Rima—none so hard as chasing you round a tree. Only to have you stand or sit by me and talk will make me happy. And to begin you must call me by my name—Abel."

"Is that your name? Oh, not your real name! Abel, Abel—what is that? It says nothing. I have called you by so many names—twenty, thirty—and no answer."

"Have you? But, dearest girl, every person has a name—one name he is called by. Your name, for instance, is Rima, is it not?"

"Rima! only Rima—to you? In the morning, in the evening . . . now in this place and in a little while where know I? . . . in the night when you wake and it is dark, dark, and you see me all the same. Only Rima—oh, how strange!"

"What else, sweet girl? Your grandfather Nuflo calls you Rima."

"Nuflo?" She spoke as if putting a question to herself. "Is that an old man with two dogs that lives somewhere in the wood?" And then, with sudden petulance, "And you ask me to talk to you!"

"Oh, Rima, what can I say to you? Listen——"

"No, no," she exclaimed, quickly turning and putting

her fingers on my mouth to stop my speech, while a sudden merry look shone in her eyes. "You shall listen when I speak, and do all I say. And tell me what to do to please you with your eyes—let me look in your eyes that are not blind."

She turned her face more towards me, and with head a little thrown back and inclined to one side, gazing now full into my eyes as I had wished her to do. After a few moments she glanced away to the distant trees. But I could see into those divine orbs, and knew that she was not looking at any particular object. All the ever-varying expressions—inquisitive, petulant, troubled, shy, frolicsome—had now vanished from the still face, and the look was inward and full of a strange, exquisite light, as if some new happiness or hope had touched her spirit.

Sinking my voice to a whisper I said, "Tell me what you have seen in my eyes, Rima?"

She murmured in reply something melodious and inarticulate, then glanced at my face in a questioning way; but only for a moment, then her sweet eyes were again veiled under those drooping lashes.

"Listen, Rima," I said. "Was that a humming-bird we saw a little while ago? You are like that, now dark, a shadow in the shadow, seen for an instant, and then—gone, oh, little thing! And now in the sunshine standing still, how beautiful!—a thousand times more beautiful than the humming-bird. Listen, Rima, you are like all beautiful things in the wood—flower, and bird, and butterfly, and green leaf, and frond, and little silky-haired monkey high up in the trees. When I look at you I see them all—all and more, a thousand times, for I see Rima herself. And when I listen to Rima's voice, talking in a language I cannot understand, I hear the wind whispering in the leaves, the gurgling running water, the bee among the flowers, the organ-bird singing far, far away in the shadows of the trees. I hear them all, and more, for I hear Rima. Do you understand me now? Is it I speaking to you—have I answered you—have I come to you?"

She glanced at me again, her lips trembling, her eyes now clouded with some secret trouble. "Yes," she replied in a whisper, and then, "No, it is not you," and after a moment, doubtfully, "Is it you?"

But she did not wait to be answered: in a moment she was gone round the mora; nor would she return again for all my calling.

CHAPTER IX

THAT afternoon with Rima in the forest under the mora tree had proved so delightful that I was eager for more rambles and talks with her, but the variable little witch had a great surprise in store for me. All her wild natural gaiety had unaccountably gone out of her: when I walked in the shade she was there, but no longer as the blithe, fantastic being, bright as an angel, innocent and affectionate as a child, tricksy as a monkey, that had played at hide-and-seek with me. She was now my shy, silent attendant, only occasionally visible, and appearing then like the mysterious maid I had found reclining among the ferns who had melted away mist-like from sight as I gazed. When I called she would not now answer as formerly, but in response would appear in sight as if to assure me that I had not been forsaken; and after a few moments her grey shadowy form would once more vanish among the trees. The hope that as her confidence increased and she grew accustomed to talk with me she would be brought to reveal the story of her life had to be abandoned, at all events for the present. I must, after all, get my information from Nuflo, or rest in ignorance. The old man was out for the greater part of each day with his dogs, and from these expeditions he brought back nothing that I could see but a few nuts and fruits, some thin bark for his cigarettes, and an occasional handful of haima gum to perfume the hut of an evening. After I had wasted three days in vainly trying to overcome the girl's now inexplicable shyness, I resolved to give for a while my undivided attention to her grandfather to discover, if possible, where he went and how he spent his time.

My new game of hide-and-seek with Nuflo instead of with Rima began on the following morning. He was cunning: so was I. Going out and concealing myself among the bushes, I began to watch the hut. That I could elude Rima's keener eyes I doubted; but that did not trouble me. She was not in harmony with the old man, and would do nothing to defeat my plan. I had not been long in my hiding-place before he came out, followed by his two dogs, and going to some distance from the door he sat down on a log. For some minutes he smoked, then rose, and after looking cautiously round slipped away among the trees. I saw that he was going off in the direction of the low range of rocky hills south of the forest. I knew that the forest did not extend far in that direction, and thinking that I should be able to catch a sight of him on its borders, I left the bushes and ran through the trees as fast as I could to get ahead of him. Coming to where the wood was very open, I found that a barren plain beyond it, a quarter of a mile wide, separated it from the range of hills; thinking that the old man might cross this open space I climbed into a tree to watch. After some time he appeared, walking rapidly among the trees, the dogs at his heels, but not going towards the open plain; he had, it seemed, after arriving at the edge of the wood, changed his direction, and was going west, still keeping in the shelter of the trees. When he had been gone about five minutes I dropped to the ground and started in pursuit; once more I caught sight of him through the trees, and I kept him in sight for about twenty minutes longer; then he came to a broad strip of dense wood which extended into and through the range of hills, and here I quickly lost him. Hoping still to overtake him, I pushed on, but after struggling through the underwood for some distance, and finding the forest growing more difficult as I progressed, I at last gave him up. Turning eastward I got out of the wood to find myself at the foot of a steep rough hill, one of the range which the wooded valley cut through at right angles. It struck me that it would be a good plan to climb the hill to get a view of the forest belt in which I had lost the old man; and after walking a short distance I found a spot which allowed of an ascent. The summit of the hill was about three hundred feet above the surrounding level, and did not take me long to reach; it commanded a fair view, and I now saw that the belt of wood beneath me extended right through the range, and on the south side opened out into an extensive forest. "If that is your destination," thought I, "old fox, your secrets are safe from me."

It was still early in the day, and a slight breeze tempered the air and made it cool and pleasant on the hilltop after my exertions. My scramble through the wood had fatigued me somewhat, and resolving to spend some hours on that spot, I looked round for a comfortable resting-place. I soon found a shady spot on the west side of an upright block of stone where I could recline at ease on a bed of lichen. Here, with shoulders resting against the rock, I sat thinking of Rima, alone in her wood to-day, with just a tinge of bitterness in my thoughts which made me hope that she would miss me as much as I missed her; and in the end I fell asleep.

When I woke it was past noon, and the sun was shining directly on me. Standing up to gaze once more on the prospect, I noticed a small wreath of white smoke issuing from a spot about the middle of the forest belt beneath me, and I instantly divined that Nuflo had made a fire at that place, and I resolved to surprise him in his retreat. When I got down to the base of the hill the smoke could no longer be seen, but I had studied the spot well from above, and had singled out a large clump of trees on the edge of the belt as a starting-point; and after a search of half an hour I succeeded in finding the old man's hiding-place. First I saw smoke again through an opening in the trees, then a small rude hut of sticks and palm-leaves. Approaching cautiously, I peered through a crack and discovered old Nuflo engaged in smoking some meat over a fire, and at the same time grilling some bones on the coals. He had captured a coatimundi, an animal somewhat larger than a tame tom cat, with a long snout and long ringed tail: one of the dogs was gnawing at the animal's head, and the tail and the feet were also lying on the floor, among the old bones and rubbish that littered it. Stealing round I suddenly presented myself at the opening to his den, when the dogs rose up with a growl and Nuflo instantly leaped to his feet, knife in hand.

"Aha, old man," I cried, with a laugh, "I have found you at one of your vegetarian repasts; and your grass-eating dogs as well!"

He was disconcerted and suspicious, but when I explained that I had seen a smoke while on the hills, where I had gone to search for a curious blue flower which grew in such places, and had made my way to it to discover the cause, he recovered confidence and invited me to join him at his dinner of roast meat.

I was hungry by this time and not sorry to get animal food once more; nevertheless, I ate this meat with some disgust, as it had a rank taste and smell, and it was also unpleasant to have those evil-looking dogs savagely gnawing at the animal's head and feet at the same time.

"You see," said the old hypocrite, wiping the grease from his moustache, "this is what I am compelled to do in order to avoid giving offence. My granddaughter is a strange being, sir, as you have perhaps observed——"

"That reminds me," I interrupted, "that I wish you to relate her history to me. She is, as you say, strange, and has speech and faculties unlike ours, which shows that she comes of a different race."

"No, no, her faculties are not different from ours. They are sharper, that is all. It pleases the All-Powerful to give more to some than to others. Not all the fingers on the hand are alike. You will find a man who will take up a guitar and make it speak, while I——"

"All that I understand," I broke in again. "But her origin, her history—that is what I wish to hear."

"And that, sir, is precisely what I am about to relate. Poor child, she was left on my hands by her sainted mother—my daughter, sir—who perished young. Now her birthplace, where she was taught letters and the Catechism by the priest, was in an unhealthy situation. It was hot and wet—always wet—a place suited to frogs rather than to human beings. At length, thinking that it would suit the child better—for she was pale and weakly—to live in a drier atmosphere among mountains, I brought her to this district. For this, señor, and for all I have done for her, I look for no reward here, but to that place where my daughter has got her foot; not, sir, on the threshold, as you might think, but well inside. For, after all, it is to the authorities above, in spite of some blots which we see in their administration, that we must look for justice. Frankly, sir, this is the whole story of my granddaughter's origin."

"Ah, yes," I returned, "your story explains why she can call a wild bird to her hand, and touch a venomous serpent with her bare foot and receive no harm."

"Doubtless you are right," said the old dissembler. "Living alone in the wood she had only God's creatures to play and make friends with; and wild animals, I have heard it said, know those who are friendly towards them."

"You treat her friends badly," said I, kicking the long tail of the coatimundi away with my foot, and regretting that I had joined him in his repast.

"Señor, you must consider that we are only what Heaven made us. When all this was formed," he continued, opening his arms wide to indicate the entire creation, "the Person who concerned himself with this matter gave seeds and fruitlets and nectar of flowers for the sustentation of His small birds. But we have not their delicate appetites. The more robust stomach which he gave to man cries out for meat. Do you understand? But of all this, friend, not one word to Rima!"

I laughed scornfully. "Do you think me such a child, old man, as to believe that Rima, that little sprite, does not know that you are an eater of flesh? Rima, who is everywhere in the wood, seeing all things, even if I lift my hand against a serpent, she herself unseen."

"But, sir, if you will pardon my presumption, you are saying too much. She does not come here, and therefore cannot see that I eat meat. In all that wood where she flourishes and sings, where she is in her house and garden, and mistress of the creatures, even of the small butterfly with painted wings, there, sir, I hunt no animal. Nor will my dogs chase any animal there. That is what I meant when I said that if an animal should stumble against their legs, they would lift up their noses and pass on without seeing it. For in that wood there is one law, the law that Rima imposes, and outside of it a different law."

"I am glad that you have told me this," I replied. "The thought that Rima might be near, and, unseen herself, look in upon us feeding with the dogs and, like dogs, on flesh, was one which greatly troubled my mind."

He glanced at me in his usual quick, cunning way.

"Ah, señor, you have that feeling too—after so short a time with us! Consider, then, what it must be for me, unable to nourish myself on gums and fruitlets, and that little sweetness made by wasps out of flowers, when I am compelled to go far away and eat secretly to avoid giving offence."

It was hard, no doubt, but I did not pity him; secretly I could only feel anger against him for refusing to enlighten me, while making such a pretence of openness; and I also felt disgusted with myself for having joined him in his rank repast. But dissimulation was necessary, and so, after conversing a little more on indifferent topics, and thanking him for his hospitality, I left him alone to go on with his smoky task.

On my way back to the lodge, fearing that some taint of Nuflo's evil-smelling den and dinner might still cling to me, I turned aside to where a streamlet in the wood widened and formed a deep pool, to take a plunge in the water. After drying myself in the air, and thoroughly ventilating my garments by shaking and beating them, I found an open, shady spot in the wood and threw myself on the grass to wait for evening before returning to the house. By that time the sweet, warm air would have purified me. Besides, I did not consider that I had sufficiently punished Rima for her treatment of me. She would be anxious for my safety, perhaps even looking for me everywhere in the wood. It was not much to make her suffer one day after she had made me miserable for three; and perhaps when she discovered that I could exist without her society she would begin to treat me less capriciously.

So ran my thoughts as I rested on the warm ground, gazing up into the foliage, green as young grass in the lower, shady parts, and above luminous with the bright sunlight, and full of the murmuring sounds of insect life. My every action, word, thought, had my feeling for Rima as a motive. Why, I began to ask myself, was Rima so much to me? It was easy to answer that question: Because nothing so exquisite had ever been created. All the separate and fragmentary beauty and melody and graceful motion found scattered throughout nature were concentrated and harmoniously combined in her. How various, how luminous, how divine she was! A being for the mind to marvel at, to admire continually, finding some new grace and charm every hour, every moment, to add to the old. And there was, besides, the fascinating mystery surrounding her origin to arouse and keep my interest in her continually active.

That was the easy answer I returned to the question I had asked myself. But I knew that there was another answer—a reason more powerful than the first. And I could no longer thrust it back, or hide its shining face with the dull, leaden mask of mere intellectual curiosity. *Because I loved her;* loved her as I had never loved before, never could love any other being, with a passion which had caught something of her own brilliance and intensity, making a former passion look dim and commonplace in comparison—a feeling known to everyone, something old and worn out, a weariness even to think of.

From these reflections I was roused by the plaintive

three-syllabled call of an evening bird—a nightjar common in these woods; and was surprised to find that the sun had set, and the woods already shadowed with the twilight. I started up and began hurriedly walking homewards, thinking of Rima, and was consumed with impatience to see her; and as I drew near to the house, walking along a narrow path which I knew, I suddenly met her face to face. Doubtless she had heard my approach, and instead of shrinking out of the path and allowing me to pass on without seeing her, as she would have done on the previous day, she had sprung forward to meet me. I was struck with wonder at the change in her as she came with a swift, easy motion, like a flying bird, her hands outstretched as if to clasp mine, her lips parted in a radiant, welcoming smile, her eyes sparkling with joy.

I started forward to meet her, but had no sooner touched her hands than her countenance changed, and she shrunk back trembling, as if the touch had chilled her warm blood; and moving some feet away, she stood with downcast eyes, pale and sorrowful as she had seemed yesterday. In vain I implored her to tell me the cause of this change and of the trouble she evidently felt; her lips trembled as if with speech, but she made no reply, and only shrunk further away when I attempted to approach her; and at length, moving aside from the path, she was lost to sight in the dusky leafage.

I went on alone, and sat outside for some time, until old Nuflo returned from his hunting; and only after he had gone in and had made the fire burn up did Rima make her appearance, silent and constrained as ever

CHAPTER X

ON the following day Rima continued in the same inexplicable humour; and feeling my defeat keenly, I determined once more to try the effect of absence on her, and to remain away on this occasion for a longer period. Like old Nuflo, I was secret in going forth next morning, waiting until the girl was out of the way, then slipping off among the bushes into the deeper wood; and finally quitting its shelter I set out across the savannah towards my old quarters. Great was my surprise on arriving at the village to find no person there. At first I imagined that my disappearance in the forest of evil fame had caused them to abandon their home in a panic; but on looking round I concluded that my friends had only gone on one of their periodical visits to some neighbouring village. For when these Indians visit their neighbours they do it in a very thorough manner; they all go, taking with them their entire stock of provisions, their cooking utensils, weapons, hammocks, and even their pet animals. Fortunately in this case they had not taken quite everything; my hammock was there, also one small pot, some cassava bread, purple potatoes, and a few ears of maize. I concluded that these had been left for me in the event of my return; also that they had not been gone very many hours, since a log of wood buried under the ashes of the hearth was still alight. Now as their absences from home usually last many days, it was plain that I would have the big naked barn-like house to myself for as long as I thought proper to remain, with little food to eat; but the prospect did not disturb me, and I resolved to amuse myself with music. In vain I hunted for my guitar; the Indians had taken it to delight their friends by twanging its strings. At odd moments during the last day or two I had been composing a simple melody in my brain, fitting it to ancient words; and now, without an instrument to assist me, I began softly singing to myself:—

Muy mas clara que la luna
Sola una
en el mundo vos nacistes.

After music I made up the fire and parched an ear of maize for my dinner, and while laboriously crunching the dry hard grain I thanked Heaven for having bestowed on me such good molars. Finally, I slung my hammock in its old corner, and placing myself in it in my favourite oblique position, my hands clasped behind my head, one knee cocked up, the other leg dangling down, I resigned myself to idle thought. I felt very happy. How strange, thought I, with a little self-flattery, that I, accustomed to the agreeable society of intelligent men and charming women, and of books, should find such perfect contentment here! But I congratulated myself too soon. The profound silence began at length to oppress me. It was not like the forest, where one has wild birds for company, where their cries, albeit inarticulate, have a meaning and give a charm to solitude. Even the sight and whispered sounds of green leaves and rushes trembling in the wind have for us something of intelligence and sympathy; but I could not commune with mud walls and an earthen pot. Feeling my loneliness too acutely, I began to regret that I had left Rima, then to feel remorse at the secrecy I had practised. Even now, while I reclined idly in my hammock, she would be roaming the forest in search of me, listening for my footsteps, fearing perhaps that I had met with some accident where there was no person to succour me. It was painful to think of her in this way, of the pain I had doubtless given her by stealing off without a word of warning. Springing to the floor, I flung out of the house and went down to the stream. It was better there, for now the greatest heat of the day was over, and the westering sun began to look large, and red, and rayless through the afternoon haze.

I seated myself on a stone within a yard or two of the limpid water: and now the sight of nature and the warm, vital air and sunshine infected my spirit, and made it possible for me to face the position calmly, even hopefully. The position was this: for some days the idea had been present in my mind, and was now fixed there, that this desert was to be my permanent home. The thought of going back to Caracas, that little Paris in America, with its old-world vices, its idle political passions, its empty round of gaieties, was unendurable. I was changed, and this change—so great, so complete—was proof that the old artificial life had not been and could not be the real one, in harmony with my deeper and truer nature. I deceived myself, you will say, as I have often myself said. I had and I had not. It is too long a question to discuss here, but just then I felt that I had quitted the hot, tainted atmosphere of the ballroom, that the morning air of heaven refreshed and elevated me, and was sweet to breathe. Friends and relations I had who were dear to me; but I could forget them, even as I could forget the splendid dreams which had been mine. And the woman I had loved, and who had perhaps loved me in return—I could forget her too. A daughter of civilisation and of that artificial life, she could never experience such feelings as these and return to nature as I was doing. For women, though within narrow limits more plastic than men, are yet without that larger adaptiveness which can take us back to the sources of life, which they have left eternally behind. Better, far better for both of us that she should wait through the long, slow months, growing sick at heart with hope deferred; that, seeing me no more, she should weep my loss, and be healed at last by time, and find love and happiness again in the old way, in the old place.

And while I thus sat thinking, sadly enough, but not despondingly, of past and present and future, all at once on the warm, still air came the resonant, far-reaching *kling-klang* of the campanero from some leafy summit half a league away. *Kling-klang* fell the sound again, and often again, at intervals, affecting me strangely at that moment, so bell-like, so like the great wide-travelling sounds associated in our minds with Christian worship. And yet so unlike. A bell, yet not made of gross metal dug out of earth, but of an ethereal, sublimer material that floats impalpable and invisible in space—a vital bell suspended on nothing, giving out sounds in harmony with the vastness of blue heaven, the unsullied purity of nature, the glory of the sun, and conveying a mystic, a higher message to the soul than the sounds that surge from tower and belfry.

O mystic bell-bird of the heavenly race of the swallow and dove, the quetzal and the nightingale! When the brutish savage and the brutish white man that slay thee, one for food, the other for the benefit of science, shall have passed away, live still, live to tell thy message to the blameless spiritualised race that shall come after us to possess the earth, not for a thousand years, but for ever; for how much shall thy voice be to our clarified successors when even to my dull, unpurged soul, thou canst speak such high things, and bring it a sense of an impersonal, all-comprising One who is in me and I in him, flesh of his flesh and soul of his soul.

The sounds ceased, but I was still in that exalted mood, and, like a person in a trance, staring fixedly before me into the open wood of scattered dwarf trees on the other side of the stream, when suddenly on the field of vision appeared a grotesque human figure moving towards me. I started violently, astonished and a little alarmed, but in a very few moments I recognised the ancient Cla-cla, coming home with a large bundle of dry sticks on her shoulders, bent almost double under the burden, and still ignorant of my presence. Slowly she came down to the stream, then cautiously made her way over the line of stepping-stones by which it was crossed; and only when within ten yards did the old creature catch sight of me sitting silent and motionless in her path. With a sharp cry of amazement and terror she straightened herself up, the bundle of sticks dropping to the ground, and turned to run from me. That, at all events, seemed her intention, for her body was thrown forward, and her head and arms working like those of a person going at full speed, but her legs seemed paralysed and her feet remained planted on the same spot. I burst out laughing; whereat she twisted her neck until her wrinkled, brown old face appeared over her shoulder staring at me. This made me laugh again, whereupon she straightened herself up once more and turned round to have a good look at me.

"Come, Cla-cla," I cried; "can you not see that I am a living man and no spirit? I thought no one had remained behind to keep me company and give me food. Why are you not with the others?"

"Ah, why!" she returned tragically. And then deliberately turning from me and assuming a most unladylike attitude, she slapped herself vigorously on the small of the back, exclaiming, "Because of my pain here!"

As she continued in that position with her back towards me for some time, I laughed once more and begged her to explain.

Slowly she turned round and advanced cautiously towards me, staring at me all the time. Finally, still eyeing me suspiciously, she related that the others had all gone on a visit to a distant village, she starting with them: that after going some distance a pain had attacked her in her hind quarters, so sudden and acute that it had instantly brought her to a full stop; and to illustrate how full the stop was she allowed herself to go down, very unnecessarily, with a flop to the ground. But she no sooner touched the ground than up she started to her feet again, with an alarmed look on her owlish face, as if she had sat down on a stinging-nettle.

"We thought you were dead," she remarked, still thinking that I might be a ghost after all.

"No, still alive," I said. "And so because you came to the ground with your pain they left you behind! Well, never mind, Cla-cla, we are two now and must try to be happy together."

By this time she had recovered from her fear and began to feel highly pleased at my return, only lamenting that she had no meat to give me. She was anxious to hear my adventures, and the reason of my long absence. I had no wish to gratify her curiosity, with the truth at all events, knowing very well that with regard to the daughter of the Didi her feelings were as purely savage and malignant as those of Kua-kò. But it was necessary to say something, and, fortifying myself with the good old Spanish notion that lies told to the heathen are not recorded, I related that a venomous serpent had bitten me; after which a terrible thunderstorm had surprised me in the forest, and night coming on prevented my escape from it; then, next day, remembering that he who is bitten by a serpent dies, and not wishing to distress my friends with the sight of my dissolution, I elected to remain, sitting there in the wood, amusing myself by singing songs and smoking cigarettes; and after several days and nights had gone by, finding that I was not going to die after all, and beginning to feel hungry, I got up and came back.

Old Cla-cla looked very serious, shaking and nodding her head a great deal, muttering to herself; finally, she gave it as her opinion that nothing ever would or could kill me; but whether my story had been believed or not she only knew.

I spent an amusing evening with my old savage hostess. She had thrown off her ailments, and pleased at having a companion in her dreary solitude, she was good-tempered and talkative, and much more inclined to laugh than when the others were present, when she was on her dignity.

We sat by the fire, cooking such food as we had, and talked and smoked; then I sang her songs in Spanish with that melody of my own—

Muy mas clara que la luna;

and she rewarded me by emitting a barbarous chant in a shrill, screechy voice; and, finally, starting up, I danced for her benefit polka, mazurka, and valse, whistling and singing to my motions.

More than once during the evening she tried to introduce serious subjects, telling me that I must always live with them, learn to shoot the birds and catch the fishes, and have a wife; and then she would speak of her granddaughter Oolava, whose virtues it was proper to mention.

but whose physical charms needed no description since they had never been concealed. Each time she got on this topic I cut her short, vowing that if I ever married she only should be my wife. She informed me that she was old and past her fruitful period; that not much longer would she make cassava-bread, and blow the fire to a flame with her wheezy old bellows, and talk the men to sleep at night. But I stuck to it that she was young and beautiful, that our descendants would be more numerous than the birds in the forest. I went out to some bushes close by, where I had noticed a passion plant in bloom, and gathering a few splendid scarlet blossoms with their stems and leaves, I brought them in and wove them into a garland for the old dame's head; then I pulled her up, in spite of screams and struggles, and waltzed her wildly to the other end of the room and back again to her seat beside the fire. And as she sat there, panting and grinning with laughter, I knelt before her, and with suitable passionate gestures, declaimed again the old delicate lines sung by Mena before Columbus sailed the seas:—

Muy mas clara que la luna
Sola una
en el mundo vos nacistes
tan gentil, que no vecistes
ni tuvistes
competedora ninguna
Desdi niñez en la cuna
cobrastes fama, beldad,
con tanta graciosidad,
que vos dotó la fortuna.

Thinking of another all the time! O poor old Cla-cla, knowing not what the jingle meant nor the secret of my wild happiness, now when I recall you sitting there, your old grey owlish head crowned with scarlet passion flowers, flushed with firelight, against the background of smoke-blackened walls and rafters, how the old undying sorrow comes back to me!

Thus our evening was spent, merrily enough; then we made up the fire with hard wood that would last all night, and went to our hammocks, but wakeful still. The old dame, glad and proud to be on duty once more, religiously went to work to talk me to sleep; but although I called out at intervals to encourage her to go on, I did not attempt to follow the ancient tales she told, which she had imbibed in childhood from other white-headed grandmothers long, long turned to dust. My own brain was busy thinking, thinking, thinking now of the woman I had once loved, far away in Venezuela, waiting and weeping and sick with hope deferred; now of Rima, wakeful and listening to the mysterious night-sounds of the forest—listening, listening for my returning footsteps.

Next morning I began to waver in my resolution to remain absent from Rima for some days: and before evening my passion, which I had now ceased to struggle against, coupled with the thought that I had acted unkindly in leaving her, that she would be a prey to anxiety, overcame me, and I was ready to return. The old woman, who had been suspiciously watching my movements, rushed out after me as I left the house, crying out that a storm was brewing, that it was too late to go far, and night would be full of danger. I waved my hand in good-bye, laughingly reminding her that I was proof against all perils. Little she cared what evil might befall me, I thought; but she loved not to be alone; even for her, low down as she was intellectually, the solitary earthen pot had no "mind stuff" in it, and could not be sent to sleep at night with the legends of long ago.

By the time I reached the ridge I had discovered that she had prophesied truly, for now an ominous change had come over nature. A dull grey vapour had overspread the entire western half of the heavens; down, beyond the forest, the sky looked black as ink, and behind this blackness the sun had vanished. It was too late to go back now; I had been too long absent from Rima, and could only hope to reach Nuflo's lodge, wet or dry, before night closed round me in the forest.

For some moments I stood still on the ridge, struck by the somewhat weird aspect of the shadowed scene before me—the long strip of dull uniform green, with here and there a slender palm lifting its feathery crown above the other trees, standing motionless, in strange relief against the advancing blackness. Then I set out once more at a run, taking advantage of the downward slope to get well on my way before the tempest should burst. As I approached the wood there came a flash of lightning, pale, but covering the whole visible sky, followed after a long interval by a distant roll of thunder, which lasted several seconds, and ended with a succession of deep throbs. It was as if Nature herself, in supreme anguish and abandonment, had cast herself prone on the earth, and her great heart had throbbed audibly, shaking the world with its beats. No more thunder followed, but the rain was coming down heavily now in huge drops that fell straight through the gloomy, windless air. In half a minute I was drenched to the skin; but for a short time the rain seemed an advantage, as the brightness of the falling water lessened the gloom, turning the air from dark to lighter grey. This subdued rain-light did not last long: I had not been twenty minutes in the wood before a second and greater darkness fell on the earth, accompanied by an even more copious downpour of water. The sun had evidently gone down, and the whole sky was now covered with one thick cloud. Becoming more nervous as the gloom increased, I bent my steps more to the south, so as to keep near the border and more open part of the wood. Probably I had already grown confused before deviating and turned the wrong way, for instead of finding the forest easier, it grew closer and more difficult as I advanced. Before many minutes the darkness so increased that I could no longer distinguish objects more than five feet from my eyes. Groping blindly along, I became entangled in a dense undergrowth, and after struggling and stumbling along for some distance in vain endeavours to get through it, I came to a stand at last in sheer despair. All sense of direction was now lost: I was entombed in thick blackness—blackness of night and cloud and rain and of dripping foliage and network of branches bound with bush-ropes and creepers in a wild tangle. I had struggled into a hollow, or hole, as it were, in the midst of that mass of vegetation, where I could stand upright and turn round and round without touching anything; but when I put out my hands they came into contact with vines and bushes. To move from that spot seemed folly; yet how dreadful to remain there standing on the sodden earth, chilled with rain, in that awful blackness in which the only luminous thing one could look to see would be the eyes, shining with their own internal light, of some savage beast of prey. Yet the danger, the intense physical discomfort, and the anguish of looking forward to a whole night spent in that situation, stung my heart less than the thought of Rima's anxiety and of the pain I had carelessly given by secretly leaving her.

It was then, with that pang in my heart, that I was startled by hearing, close by, one of her own low, warbled expressions. There could be no mistake; if the forest had been full of the sounds of animal life and songs of melodious birds, her voice would have been instantly distinguished from all others. How mysterious, how infinitely tender it sounded in that awful blackness!—so musical and exquisitely modulated, so sorrowful, yet piercing my heart with a sudden, unutterable joy.

"Rima! Rima!" I cried. "Speak again. Is it you? Come to me here."

Again that low, warbling sound, or series of sounds, seemingly from a distance of a few yards. I was not disturbed at her not replying in Spanish: she had always spoken it somewhat reluctantly, and only when at my side; but when calling to me from some distance she would return instinctively to her own mysterious language, and call to me as bird calls to bird. I knew that she was inviting me to follow her, but I refused to move.

"Rima," I cried again, "come to me here, for I know not where to step, and cannot move until you are at my side, and I can feel your hand."

There came no response, and after some moments, becoming alarmed, I called to her again.

Then close by me, in a low, trembling voice, she returned, "I am here."

I put out my hand and touched something soft and wet; it was her breast, and moving my hand higher up, I felt her hair, hanging now and streaming with water. She was trembling, and I thought the rain had chilled her.

"Rima—poor child! How wet you are! How strange to meet you in such a place! Tell me, dear Rima, how did you find me?"

"I was waiting—watching—all day. I saw you coming across the savannah, and followed at a distance through the wood."

"And I had treated you so unkindly! Ah, my guardian angel, my light in the darkness, how I hate myself for giving you pain! Tell me, sweet, did you wish me to come back and live with you again?"

She made no reply. Then, running my fingers down her arm, I took her hand in mine. It was hot, like the hand of one in a fever. I raised it to my lips, and then attempted to draw her to me, but she slipped down and out of my arms to my feet. I felt her there, on her knees, with head bowed low. Stooping and putting my arm round her body, I drew her up and held her against my breast, and felt her heart throbbing wildly. With many endearing words I begged her to speak to me; but her only reply was, "Come—come," as she slipped again out of my arms, and holding my hand in hers, guided me through the bushes.

Before long we came to an open path or glade, where the darkness was not so profound; and releasing my hand she began walking rapidly before me, always keeping at such a distance as just enabled me to distinguish her grey, shadowy figure, and with frequent doublings to follow the natural paths and openings which she knew so well. In this way we kept on nearly to the end, without exchanging a word, and hearing no sound except the continuous rush of rain, which to our accustomed ears had ceased to have the effect of sound, and the various gurgling noises of innumerable runnels. All at once, as we came to a more open place, a strip of bright firelight appeared before us, shining from the half-open door of Nuflo's lodge. She turned round as much as to say, "Now you know where you are," then hurried on, leaving me to follow as best I could.

CHAPTER XI

THERE was a welcome change in the weather when I rose early next morning; the sky was now without cloud, and had that purity in its colour and look of infinite distance seen only when the atmosphere is free from vapour. The sun had not yet risen, but old Nuflo was already among the ashes, on his hands and knees, blowing the embers he had uncovered to a flame. Then Rima appeared only to pass through the room with quick light tread to go out of the door without a word or even a glance at my face. The old man, after watching at the door for a few minutes, turned and began eagerly questioning me about my adventures on the previous evening. In reply I related to him how the girl had found me in the forest lost and unable to extricate myself from the tangled undergrowth.

He rubbed his hands on his knees and chuckled. "Happy for you, señor," he said, "that my granddaughter regards you with such friendly eyes, otherwise you might have perished before morning. Once she was at your side, no light, whether of sun or moon or lantern, was needed, nor that small instrument which is said to guide a man aright in the desert, even in the darkest night—let him that can believe such a thing!"

"Yes, happy for me," I returned. "I am filled with remorse that it was all through my fault that the poor child was exposed to such weather."

"O señor," he cried airily, "let not that distress you! Rain and wind and hot suns, from which we seek shelter, do not harm her. She takes no cold, and no fever, with or without ague."

After some further conversation I left him to steal away unobserved on his own account, and set out for a ramble in the hope of encountering Rima and winning her to talk to me.

My quest did not succeed: not a glimpse of her delicate shadowy form did I catch among the trees; and not one note from her melodious lips came to gladden me. At noon I returned to the house, where I found food placed ready for me, and knew that she had come there during my absence and had not been forgetful of my wants. "Shall I thank you for this?" I said. "I ask you for heavenly nectar for the sustentation of the higher winged nature in me, and you give me a boiled sweet potato, toasted strips of sun-dried pumpkins, and a handful of parched maize! Rima! Rima! my woodland fairy, my sweet saviour, why do you yet fear me? Is it that love struggles in you with repugnance? Can you discern with clear spiritual eyes the grosser elements in me, and hate them; or has some false imagination made me appear all dark and evil, but too late for your peace, after the sweet sickness of love has infected you?"

But she was not there to answer me, and so after a time I went forth again and seated myself listlessly on the root of an old tree not far from the house. I had sat there a full hour, when all at once Rima appeared at my side. Bending forward she touched my hand, but without glancing at my face; "Come with me," she said, and turning, moved swiftly towards the northern extremity of the forest. She seemed to take it for granted that I would follow, never casting a look behind, nor pausing in her rapid walk; but I was only too glad to obey, and starting up, was quickly after her. She led me by easy ways, familiar to her, with many doublings to escape the undergrowth, never speaking or pausing until we came out from the thick forest, and I found myself for the first time at the foot of the great hill or mountain Ytaioa. Glancing back for a few moments, she waved a hand towards the summit, and then at once began the ascent. Here too it seemed all familiar ground to her. From below the sides had presented an exceedingly rugged appearance—a wild confusion of huge jagged rocks, mixed with a tangled vegetation of trees, bushes, and vines; but following her in all her doublings it became easy enough, although it fatigued me greatly owing to our rapid pace. The hill was conical, but I found that it had a flat top; an oblong or pear-shaped area, almost level, of a soft, crumbly sandstone, with a few blocks and boulders of a harder stone scattered about; and no vegetation, except the grey mountain lichen and a few sere-looking dwarf shrubs.

Here Rima, at a distance of a few yards from me, remained standing still for some minutes, as if to give me time to recover my breath; and I was right glad to sit down on a stone to rest. Finally she walked slowly to the centre of the level area, which was about two acres in extent; rising I followed her, and climbing on to a huge block of stone, began gazing at the wide prospect spread out before me. The day was windless and bright, with only a few white clouds floating at a great height above and casting travelling shadows over that wild, broken country, where forest, marsh, and savannah were only distinguishable by their different colours, like the greys and greens and yellows on a map. At a great distance the circle of the horizon was broken here and there by mountains, but the hills in our neighbourhood were all beneath our feet.

After gazing all round for some minutes, I jumped down from my stand, and leaning against the stone, stood watching the girl, waiting for her to speak. I felt convinced that she had something of the very highest importance (to herself) to communicate, and that only the pressing need of a confidant, not Nuflo, had overcome her shyness of me; and I determined to let her take her own time to say it in her own way. For a while she continued silent, her face averted, but her little movements and the way she clasped and unclasped her fingers showed that she was anxious and her mind working. Suddenly, half turning to me, she began speaking eagerly and rapidly.

"Do you see," she said, waving her hand to indicate the whole circuit of earth, "how large it is? Look!" pointing now to mountains in the west. "Those are the Vahanas—one, two, three—the highest—I can tell you their names—Vahana-Chara, Chumi, Aranoa. Do you see that water? It is a river, called Guaypero. From the hills it comes down, Inaruna is their name, and you can see them over there in the south—far, far." And in this way she went on pointing out and naming all the mountains and rivers within sight. Then she suddenly dropped her hands to her sides, and continued, "That is all. Because we can see no further. But the world is larger than that! Other mountains, other rivers. Have I not told you of Voa, on the River Voa, where I was born, where mother died, where the priest taught me, years, years ago? All that you cannot see, it is so far away—so far."

I did not laugh at her simplicity, nor did I smile or feel any inclination to smile. On the contrary, I only experienced a sympathy so keen that it was like pain, while watching her clouded face, so changeful in its expression, yet in all changes so wistful. I could not yet form any idea as to what she wished to communicate or to discover, but seeing that she paused for a reply I answered, "The world is so large, Rima, that we can only see a very small portion of it from any one spot. Look at this," and with a stick I had used to aid me in my ascent I traced a circle six or seven inches in circumference on the soft stone and in its centre placed a small pebble. "This represents the mountain we are standing on," I continued, touching the pebble; "and this line encircling it encloses all of the earth we can see from the mountain-top. Do you understand?—the line I have traced is the blue line of the horizon beyond which we cannot see. And outside of this little circle is all the flat top of Ytaioa representing the world. Consider, then, how small a portion of the world we can see from this spot!"

"And do you know it all?" she returned excitedly. "All the world?" waving her hand to indicate the little stone plain. "All the mountains, and rivers, and forests, —all the people in the world?"

"That would be impossible, Rima; consider how large it is."

"That does not matter. Come, let us go together—we two and grandfather, and see all the world; all the mountains and forests, and know all the people."

"You do not know what you are saying, Rima. You might as well say, 'Come, let us go to the sun and find out everything in it.'"

"It is you who do not know what you are saying," she retorted, with brightening eyes which for a moment glanced full into mine. "We have no wings like birds to fly to the sun. Am I not able to walk on the earth, and run? Can I not swim? Can I not climb every mountain?"

"No, you cannot. You imagine that all the earth is like this little portion you see. But it is not all the same. There are great rivers which you cannot cross by swimming; mountains you cannot climb; forests you cannot penetrate—dark, and inhabited by dangerous beasts, and so vast that all this space your eyes look on is a mere speck of earth in comparison."

She listened excitedly. "Oh, do you know all that?" she cried, with a strangelv brightening look; and then half turning from me, she added, with sudden petulance, 'Yet only a minute ago you knew nothing of the world —because it is so large! Is anything to be gained by speaking to one who says such contrary things?"

I explained that I had not contradicted myself, that she had not rightly interpreted my words. I knew, I said, something about the principal features of the different countries of the world, as, for instance, the largest mountain ranges, and rivers, and the cities. Also something, but very little, about the tribes of savage men. She heard me with impatience, which made me speak rapidly, in very general terms; and to simplify the matter I made the world stand for the continent we were in. It seemed idle to go beyond that, and her eagerness would not have allowed it.

"Tell me all you know," she said the moment I ceased speaking. "What is there—and there—and there?" pointing in various directions. "Rivers and forests—they are nothing to me. The villages, the tribes, the people everywhere; tell me, for I must know it all."

"It would take long to tell, Rima."

"Because you are so slow. Look how high the sun is! Speak, speak! What is there?" pointing to the north.

"All that country," I said, waving my hands from east to west, "is Guayana; and so large is it that you could go in this direction, or in this, travelling for months, without seeing the end of Guayana. Still it would be Guayana; rivers, rivers, rivers, with forests between, and other forests and rivers beyond. And savage people, nations and tribes—Guahibo, Aguaricoto, Ayano, Maco, Piaroa, Quiriquiripo, Tuparito—shall I name a hundred more? It would be useless, Rima; they are all savages, and live widely scattered in the forests, hunting with bow and arrow and the zabatana. Consider, then, how large Guayana is!"

"Guayana—Guayana! Do I not know all this is Guayana? But beyond, and beyond, and beyond? Is there no end to Guayana?"

"Yes; there northwards it ends at the Orinoco, a mighty river, coming from mighty mountains, compared with which Ytaioa is like a stone on the ground on which we have sat down to rest. You must know that Guayana is only a portion, a half, of our country, Venezuela. Look," I continued, putting my hand round my shoulder to touch the middle of my back, "there is a groove running down my spine dividing my body into equal parts. Thus does the great Orinoco divide Venezuela, and on one side of it is all Guayana; and on the other side the countries or provinces of Cumana, Maturin, Barcelona, Bolivar, Guarico, Apure, and many others." I then gave a rapid description of the northern half of the country, with its vast llanos covered with herds in one part, its plantations of coffee, rice, and sugar-cane in another, and its chief towns; last of all Caracas, the gay and opulent little Paris in America.

This seemed to weary her; but the moment I ceased speaking, and before I could well moisten my dry lips, she demanded to know what came after Caracas—after all Venezuela.

"The ocean—water, water, water," I replied.

"There are no people there—in the water; only fishes," she remarked; then suddenly continued, "Why are you silent—is Venezuela, then, all the world?"

The task I had set myself to perform seemed only at its commencement yet. Thinking how to proceed with it my eyes roved over the level area we were standing on, and it struck me that this little irregular plain, broad at one end, and almost pointed at the other, roughly resembled the South American continent in its form.

"Look, Rima," I began, "here we are on this small pebble—Ytaioa; and this line round it shuts us in—we cannot see beyond. Now let us imagine that we can see beyond—that we can see the whole flat mountain-top; and that, you know, is the whole world. Now listen while I tell you of all the countries, and principal mountains, and rivers, and cities of the world."

The plan I had now fixed on involved a great deal of walking about and some hard work in moving and setting up stones and tracing boundary and other lines; but it gave me pleasure, for Rima was close by all the time, following me from place to place, listening to all I said in silence but with keen interest. At the broad end of the level summit I marked out Venezuela, showing by means of a long line how the Orinoco divided it, and also marking several of the greater streams flowing into it. I also marked the sites of Caracas and other large towns with stones; and rejoiced that we are not like the Europeans, great city builders, for the stones proved heavy to lift. Then followed Colombia and Ecuador on the west; and, successively, Bolivia, Peru, Chili, ending at last in the south with Patagonia, a cold arid land, bleak and desolate. I marked the littoral cities as we progressed on that side, where earth ends and the Pacific Ocean begins, and infinitude.

Then, in a sudden burst of inspiration, I described the Cordilleras to her—that world-long, stupendous chain; its sea of Titicaca, and wintry, desolate Paramo, where lie the ruins of Tiahuanaco, older than Thebes. I mentioned its principal cities—those small inflamed or festering pimples that attract much attention from appearing on such a body. Quito, called—not in irony, but by its own people—the Splendid and the Magnificent; so high above the earth as to appear but a little way removed from heaven—"de Quito al cielo," as the saying is. But of its sublime history, its kings and conquerors, Haymar Capac the Mighty, and Huascar, and Atahualpa the Unhappy, not one word. Many words—how inadequate!—of the summits, white with everlasting snows, above it—above this navel of the world, above the earth, the ocean, the darkening tempest, the condor's flight. Flame-breathing Cotopaxi, whose wrathful mutterings are audible two hundred leagues away, and Chimborazo, Antisana, Sarata, Illimani, Aconcagua—names of mountains that affect us like the names of gods, implacable Pachacamac and Viracocha, whose everlasting granite thrones they are. At the last I showed her Cuzco, the city of the sun, and the highest dwelling-place of men on earth.

I was carried away by so sublime a theme; and remembering that I had no critical hearer, I gave free reins to fancy, forgetting for the moment that some undiscovered thought or feeling had prompted her questions. And while I spoke of the mountains she hung on my words, following me closely in my walk, her countenance brilliant, her frame quivering with excitement.

There yet remained to be described all that unimaginable space east of the Andes; the rivers—what rivers!—the green plains that are like the sea—the illimitable waste of water where there is no land—and the forest region. The very thought of the Amazonian forest made my spirit droop. If I could have snatched her up and placed her on the dome of Chimborazo she would have looked on an area of ten thousand square miles of earth, so vast is the horizon at that elevation. And possibly her imagination would have been able to clothe it all with an unbroken forest. Yet how small a portion this would be of the stupendous whole—of a forest region equal in extent to the whole of Europe! All loveliness, all grace, all majesty are there; but we cannot see, cannot conceive—come away! From this vast stage, to be occupied in the distant future by millions and myriads of beings, like us of upright form, the nations that will be born when all the existing dominant races on the globe and the civilisations they represent have perished as utterly as those who sculptured the stones of old Tiahuanaco—from this theatre of palms prepared for a drama unlike any which the Immortals have yet witnessed—I hurried away; and then slowly conducted her along the Atlantic coast, listening to the thunder of its great waves, and pausing at intervals to survey some maritime city.

Never probably since old Father Noah divided the earth among his sons had so grand a geographical discourse been delivered; and having finished, I sat down, exhausted with my efforts, and mopped my brow, but glad that my huge task was over, and satisfied that I had convinced her of the futility of her wish to see the world for herself.

Her excitement had passed away by now. She was standing a little apart from me, her eyes cast down and thoughtful. At length she approached me and said, waving her hand all round, "What is beyond the mountains over there, beyond the cities on that side—beyond the world?"

"Water, only water. Did I not tell you?" I returned stoutly; for I had, of course, sunk the Isthmus of Panama beneath the sea.

"Water! All round?" she persisted.

"Yes."

"Water, and no beyond? Only water—always water?"

I could no longer adhere to so gross a lie. She was too intelligent, and I loved her too much. Standing up, I pointed to distant mountains and isolated peaks.

"Look at those peaks," I said. "It is like that with the world—this world we are standing on. Beyond that great water that flows all round the world, but far away, so far that it would take months in a big boat to reach them, there are islands, some small, others as large as this world. But, Rima, they are so far away, so impossible to reach, that it is useless to speak or to think of them. They are to us like the sun and moon and stars, to which we cannot fly. And now sit down and rest by my side, for you know everything."

She glanced at me with troubled eyes.

"Nothing do I know—nothing have you told me. Did I not say that mountains and rivers and forests are nothing? Tell me about all the people in the world. Look! there is Cuzco over there, a city like no other in the world—did you not tell me so? Of the people nothing. Are they also different from all others in the world?"

"I will tell you that if you will first answer me one question, Rima."

She drew a little nearer, curious to hear, but was silent.

"Promise that you will answer me," I persisted, and as she continued silent I added, "Shall I not ask you, then?"

"Say," she murmured.

"Why do you wish to know about the people of Cuzco?"

She flashed a look at me, then averted her face. For some moments she stood hesitating, then coming closer, touched me on the shoulder, and said softly, "Turn away, do not look at me."

I obeyed, and bending so close that I felt her warm breath on my neck, she whispered, "Are the people in Cuzco like me? Would they understand me—the things you cannot understand? Do you know?"

Her tremulous voice betrayed her agitation, and her words, I imagined, revealed the motive of her action in bringing me to the summit of Ytaioa, and of her desire to visit and know all the various peoples inhabiting the world. She had begun to realise, after knowing me, her isolation and unlikeness to others, and at the same time to dream that all human beings might not be unlike her and unable to understand her mysterious speech and to enter into her thoughts and feelings.

"I can answer that question, Rima," I said. "Ah no, poor child, there are none there like you—not one, not one. Of all there—priests, soldiers, merchants, workmen, white, black, red, and mixed; men and women, old and young, rich and poor, ugly and beautiful—not one would understand the sweet language you speak."

She said nothing, and glancing round, I discovered that she was walking away, her fingers clasped before her, her eyes cast down, and looking profoundly dejected. Jumping up, I hurried after her. "Listen!" I said, coming to her side. "Do you know that there are others in the world like you who would understand your speech?"

"Oh, do I not! Yes—mother told me. I was young when you died, but, O mother, why did you not tell me more?"

"But where?"

"Oh, do you not think that I would go to them if I knew—that I would ask?"

"Does Nuflo know?"

She shook her head, walking dejectedly along.

"But have you asked him?" I persisted.

"Have I not! Not once—not a hundred times."

Suddenly she paused. "Look," she said, "now we are standing in Guayana again. And over there in Brazil, and up there towards the Cordilleras it is unknown. And there are people there. Come, let us go and seek for my mother's people in that place. With grandfather, but not the dogs; they would frighten the animals and betray us by barking to cruel men who would slay us with poisoned arrows."

"O Rima, can you not understand? It is too far. And your grandfather, poor old man, would die of weariness and hunger and old age in some strange forest."

"Would he die—old grandfather? Then we could cover him up with palm leaves in the forest and leave him. It would not be grandfather; only his body that must turn to dust. He would be away—away where the stars are. *We* should not die, but go on, and on, and on."

To continue the discussion seemed hopeless. I was silent, thinking of what I had heard—that there were others like her somewhere in that vast green world, so much of it imperfectly known, so many districts never yet explored by white men. True, it was strange that no report of such a race had reached the ears of any traveller; yet here was Rima herself at my side, a living proof that such a race did exist. Nuflo probably knew more than he would say; I had failed, as we have seen, to win the secret from him by fair means, and could not have recourse to foul—the rack and thumbscrew—to wring it from him. To the Indians she was only an object of superstitious fear—a daughter of the Didi—

and to them nothing of her origin was known. And she, poor girl, had only a vague remembrance of a few words heard in childhood from her mother, and probably not rightly understood.

While these thoughts had been passing through my mind Rima had been standing silent by, waiting, perhaps, for an answer to her last words. Then stooping, she picked up a small pebble and tossed it three or four yards away.

"Do you see where it fell?" she cried, turning towards me. "That is on the border of Guayana—is it not? Let us go there first."

"Rima, how you distress me! We cannot go there. It is all a savage wilderness, almost unknown to men—a blank on the map——"

"The map?—speak no word that I do not understand."

In a very few words I explained my meaning; even fewer would have sufficed, so quick was her apprehension.

"If it is a blank," she returned quickly, "then you know of nothing to stop us—no river we cannot swim, and no great mountains like those where Quito is."

"But I happen to know, Rima, for it has been related to me by old Indians, that of all places that is the most difficult of access. There is a river there, and although it is not on the map, it would prove more impassable to us than the mighty Orinoco and Amazon. It has vast malarious swamps on its borders, overgrown with dense forest, teeming with savage and venomous animals, so that even the Indians dare not venture near it. And even before the river is reached there is a range of precipitous mountains called by the same name—just there where your pebble fell—the mountains of Riolama——"

Hardly had the name fallen from my lips before a change swift as lightning came over her countenance; all doubt, anxiety, petulance, hope, and despondence, and these in ever-varying degrees, chasing each other like shadows, had vanished, and she was instinct and burning with some new powerful emotion which had flashed into her soul.

"Riolama! Riolama!" she repeated so rapidly and in a tone so sharp that it tingled in the brain. "That is the place I am seeking! There was my mother found—there are her people and mine! Therefore was I called Riolama—that is my name!"

"Rima!" I returned, astonished at her words.

"No, no, no—Riolama. When I was a child, and the priest baptised me, he named me Riolama—the place where my mother was found. But it was long to say, and they called me Rima."

Suddenly she became still, and then cried in a ringing voice—

"And he knew it all along—that old man—he knew that Riolama was near—only there where the pebble fell—that we could go there!"

While speaking she turned towards her home, pointing with raised hand. Her whole appearance now reminded me of that first meeting with her when the serpent bit me; the soft red of her irides shone like fire, her delicate skin seemed to glow with an intense rose-colour. and her frame trembled with her agitation, so that her loose cloud of hair was in motion as if blown through by the wind.

"Traitor! Traitor!" she cried, still looking homewards and using quick, passionate gestures. "It was all known to you, and you deceived me all these years; even to me, Rima, you lied with your lips! Oh, horrible! Was there ever such a scandal known in Guayana? Come, follow me, let us go at once to Riolama." And without so much as casting a glance behind to see whether I followed or no, she hurried away, and in a couple of minutes disappeared from sight over the edge of the flat summit.

"Rima! Rima! Come back and listen to me! Oh, you are mad! Come back! Come back!"

But she would not return or pause and listen; and looking after her I saw her bounding down the rocky slope like some wild, agile creature possessed of padded hoofs and an infallible instinct; and before many minutes she vanished from sight among crags and trees lower down.

"Nuflo, old man," said I, looking out towards his lodge, "are there no shooting pains in those old bones of yours to warn you in time of the tempest about to burst on your head?"

Then I sat down to think.

CHAPTER XII

TO follow impetuous, bird-like Rima in her descent of the hill would have been impossible, nor had I any desire to be a witness of old Nuflo's discomfiture at the finish. It was better to leave them to settle their quarrel themselves, while I occupied myself in turning over these fresh facts in my mind to find out how they fitted into the speculative structure I had been building during the last two or three weeks. But it soon struck me that it was getting late, that the sun would be gone in a couple of hours; and at once I began the descent. It was not accomplished without some bruises and a good many scratches. After a cold draught, obtained by putting my lips to a black rock from which the water was trickling, I set out on my walk home, keeping near the western border of the forest for fear of losing myself. I had covered about half the distance from the foot of the hill to Nuflo's lodge when the sun went down. Away on my left the evening uproar of the howling monkeys burst out, and after three or four minutes ceased; the after silence was pierced at intervals by screams of birds going to roost among the trees in the distance, and by many minor sounds close at hand, of small bird, frog, and insect. The western sky was now like amber-coloured flame, and against that immeasurably distant luminous background the near branches and clustered foliage looked black; but on my left hand the vegetation still appeared of a uniform dusky green. In a little while night would drown all colour, and there would be no light but that of the wandering lantern-fly, always unwelcome to the belated walker in a lonely place, since, like the ignis fatuus, it is confusing to the sight and sense of direction.

With increasing anxiety I hastened on, when all at once a low growl issuing from the bushes some yards ahead of me brought me to a stop. In a moment the dogs, Susio and Goloso, rushed out from some hiding-place furiously barking; but they quickly recognised me and slunk back again. Relieved from fear, I walked on for a short distance; then it struck me that the old man must be about somewhere, as the dogs scarcely ever stirred from his side. Turning back I went to the spot where they had appeared to me; and there, after a while, I caught sight of a dim, yellow form, as one of the brutes rose up to look at me. He had been lying on the ground by the side of a wide-spreading bush, dead and dry, but overgrown by a creeping plant which had completely covered its broad, flat top like a piece of tapestry thrown over a table, its slender terminal stems and leaves hanging over the edge like a deep fringe. But the fringe did not reach to the ground, and under the bush, in its dark interior, I caught sight of the other dog; and after gazing in for some time I also discovered a black, recumbent form, which I took to be Nuflo.

"What are you doing there, old man?" I cried. "Where is Rima—have you not seen her? Come out."

Then he stirred himself, slowly creeping out on all fours; and, finally, getting free of the dead twigs and leaves, he stood up and faced me. He had a strange, wild look, his white beard all disordered, moss and dead leaves clinging to it, his eyes staring like an owl's, while his mouth opened and shut, the teeth striking together audibly, like an angry peccary's. After silently glaring at me in this mad way for some moments he burst out: "Cursed be the day when I first saw you, man of Caracas! Cursed be the serpent that bit you and had not sufficient power in its venom to kill! Ha! you come from Ytaioa, where you talked with Rima? And you have now returned to the tiger's den to mock that dangerous animal with the loss of its whelp. Fool, if you did not wish the dogs to feed on your flesh it would have been better if you had taken your evening walk in some other direction."

These raging words did not have the effect of alarming me in the least, nor even of astonishing me very much, albeit up till now the old man had always shown himself suave and respectful. His attack did not seem quite spontaneous. In spite of the wildness of his manner and the violence of his speech, he appeared to be acting a part which he had rehearsed beforehand. I was only angry, and stepping forward I dealt him a very sharp rap with my knuckles on his chest. "Moderate your language, old man," I said; "remember that you are addressing a superior."

"What do you say to me?" he screamed in a shrill,

broken voice, accompanying his words with emphatic gestures. "Do you think you are on the pavement of Caracas? Here are no police to protect you—here we are alone in the desert, where names and titles are nothing, standing man to man."

"An old man to a young one," I returned. "And in virtue of my youth I am your superior. Do you wish me to take you by the throat and shake your insolence out of you?"

"What, do you threaten me with violence?" he exclaimed, throwing himself into a hostile attitude. "You, the man I saved, and sheltered, and fed, and treated like a son! Destroyer of my peace, have you not injured me enough? You have stolen my grandchild's heart from me; with a thousand inventions you have driven her mad! My child, my angel, Rima, my saviour! With your lying tongue you have changed her into a demon to persecute me! And you are not satisfied, but must finish your evil work by inflicting blows on my worn body! All, all is lost to me! Take my life if you wish it, for now it is worth nothing, and I desire not to keep it!" And here he threw himself on his knees, and tearing open his old, ragged mantle, presented his naked breast to me. "Shoot! Shoot!" he screeched. "And if you have no weapon take my knife and plunge it into this sad heart, and let me die!" And drawing his knife from its sheath, he flung it down at my feet.

All this performance only served to increase my anger and contempt; but before I could make any reply I caught sight of a shadowy object at some distance moving towards us—something grey and formless, gliding swift and noiseless, like some great low-flying owl among the trees. It was Rima, and hardly had I seen her before she was with us, facing old Nuflo, her whole frame quivering with passion, her wide-open eyes appearing luminous in that dim light.

"You are here!" she cried in that quick, ringing tone that was almost painful to the sense. "You thought to escape me! To hide yourself from my eyes in the wood! Miserable! Do you not know that I have need of you—that I have not finished with you yet? Do you then wish to be scourged to Riolama with thorny twigs—to be dragged thither by the beard?"

He had been staring open-mouthed at her, still on his knees, and holding his mantle open with his skinny hands. "Rima! Rima! have mercy on me!" he cried out piteously. "Oh, my child, I cannot go to Riolama, it is so far—so far. And I am old and should meet my death. Oh, Rima, child of the woman I saved from death, have you no compassion? I shall die, I shall die!"

"Shall you die? Not until you have shown me the way to Riolama. And when I have seen Riolama with my eyes then you may die, and I shall be glad at your death; and the children and the grandchildren and cousins and friends of all the animals you have slain and fed on shall know that you are dead and be glad at your death. For you have deceived me with lies all these years—even me—and are not fit to live! Come now to Riolama; rise instantly, I command you!"

Instead of rising he suddenly put out his hand and

snatched up the knife from the ground. "Do you then wish me to die?" he cried. "Shall you be glad at my death? Behold, then I shall slay myself before your eyes. By my own hand, Rima, I am now about to perish, striking this knife into my heart!"

While speaking he waved the knife in a tragic manner over his head, but I made no movement; I was convinced that he had no intention of taking his own life—that he was still acting. Rima, incapable of understanding such a thing, took it differently.

"Oh, you are going to kill yourself!" she cried. "Oh, wicked man, wait until you know what will happen to you after death. All shall now be told to my mother. Hear my words, then kill yourself."

She also now dropped on to her knees, and lifting her clasped hands and fixing her resentful sparkling eyes on the dim blue patch of heaven visible beyond the tree-tops, began to speak rapidly in clear, vibrating tones. She was praying to her mother in heaven; and while Nuflo listened absorbed, his mouth open, his eyes fixed on her, the hand that clutched the knife dropped to his side. I also heard with the greatest wonder and admiration. For she had been shy and reticent with me, and now, as if oblivious of my presence, she was telling aloud the secrets of her inmost heart.

"O mother, mother, listen to me, to Rima, your beloved child!" she began. "All these years I have been wickedly deceived by grandfather—Nuflo—the old man that found you. Often have I spoken to him of Riolama, where you once were, and your people are, and he denied all knowledge of such a place. Sometimes he said that it was at an immense distance, in a great wilderness full of serpents larger than the trunks of great trees, and of evil spirits and savage men, slayers of all strangers. At other times he affirmed that no such place existed; that it was a tale told by the Indians; such false things did he say to me — to Rima, your child. O mother, can you believe such wickedness?

"Then a stranger, a white man from Venezuela, came into our woods: this is the man that was bitten by a serpent, and his name is Abel: only I do not call him by that name, but by other names which I have told you. But perhaps you did not listen, or did not hear, for I spoke softly and not as now, on my knees, solemnly. For I must tell you, O mother, that after you died the priest at Voa told me repeatedly that when I prayed, whether to you or to any of the saints, or to the Mother of Heaven, I must speak as he had taught me, if I wished to be heard and understood. And that was most strange, since you had taught me differently; but you were living then, at Voa, and now that you are in Heaven perhaps you know better. Therefore listen to me now, O mother, and let nothing I say escape you.

"When this white man had been for some days with us a strange thing happened to me, which made me different, so that I was no longer Rima, although Rima still—so strange was this thing; and I often went to the pool to look at myself and see the change in me, but nothing different could I see. In the first place it came from his eyes passing into mine, and filling me just as the lightning fills a cloud at sunset: afterwards it was no longer from his eyes only, but it came into me whenever I saw him, even at a distance, when I heard his voice, and most of all when he touched me with his hand. When he is out of my sight I cannot rest until I see him again; and when I see him then I am glad, yet in such fear and trouble that I hide myself from him. O mother, it could not be told; for once when he caught me in his arms and compelled me to speak of it he did not understand; yet there was need to tell it; then it came to me that only to our people could it be told, for they would understand, and reply to me, and tell me what to do in such a case.

"And now, O mother, this is what happened next. I went to grandfather and first begged and then commanded him to take me to Riolama; but he would not obey, nor give attention to what I said, but whenever I spoke to him of it he rose up and hurried from me; and when I followed he flung back a confused and angry reply, saying in the same breath that it was so long since he had been to Riolama that he had forgotten where it was, and that no such place existed. And which of his words were true and which false I knew not: so that it would have been better if he had returned no answer at all; and there was no help to be got from him. And having thus failed, and there being no other person to speak to except this stranger, I determined to go to him, and in his company seek through the whole world for my people. This will surprise you, O mother, because of that fear which came on me in his presence, causing me to hide from his sight; but my wish was so great that for a time it overcame my fear; so that I went to him as he sat alone in the wood, sad because he could not see me, and spoke to him, and led him to the summit of Ytaioa to show me all the countries of the world from the summit. And you must also know that I tremble in his presence, not because I fear him as I fear Indians and cruel men; for he has no evil in him, and is beautiful to look at, and his words are gentle, and his desire is to be always with me, so that he differs from all other men I have seen, just as I differ from all women, except from you only, O sweet mother.

"On the mountain-top he marked out and named all the countries of the world, the great mountains, the rivers, the plains, the forests, the cities; and told me also of the peoples, whites and savages, but of our people nothing. And beyond where the world ends there is water, water, water. And when he spoke of that unknown part on the borders of Guayana, on the side of the Cordilleras, he named the mountains of Riolama, and in that way I first found out where my people are. I then left him on Ytaioa, he refusing to follow me, and ran to grandfather and taxed him with his falsehoods; and he, finding I knew all, escaped from me into the woods, where I have now found him once more, talking with the stranger. And now, O mother, seeing himself caught and unable to escape a second time, he has taken up a knife to kill himself, so as not to take me to Riolama; and he is only waiting until I finish speaking to you, for I wish him to know what will happen to him after death. Therefore, O mother, listen well and do what I tell you. When he has killed himself and has come into that place where you are, see that he does not escape the punishment he merits. Watch well for his coming, for he is full of cunning and deceit, and will endeavour to hide himself from your eyes. When you have recognised him—an old man, brown as an Indian, with a white beard—point him out to the angels, and say, 'This is Nuflo, the bad man that lied to Rima.' Let them take him and singe his wings with fire, so that he may not escape by flying; and afterwards thrust him into some dark cavern under a mountain, and place a great stone that a hundred men could not remove over its mouth, and leave him there alone and in the dark for ever!"

Having ended, she rose quickly from her knees, and at the same moment Nuflo, dropping the knife, cast himself prostrate at her feet.

"Rima—my child, my child, not that!" he cried out in a voice that was broken with terror. He tried to take hold of her feet with his hands, but she shrank from him with aversion; still he kept on crawling after her like a disabled lizard, abjectly imploring her to forgive him, reminding her that he had saved from death the woman whose enmity had now been enlisted against him, and declaring that he would do anything she commanded him, and gladly perish in her service.

It was a pitiable sight, and moving quickly to her side I touched her on the shoulder and asked her to forgive him.

The response came quickly enough. Turning to him once more she said: "I forgive you, grandfather. And now get up and take me to Riolama."

He rose, but only to his knees. "But you have not told *her!*" he said, recovering his natural voice, although still anxious, and jerking a thumb over his shoulder. "Consider, my child, that I am old and shall doubtless perish on the way. What would become of my soul in such a case? For now you have told her everything, and it will not be forgotten."

She regarded him in silence for a few moments, then moving a little way apart, dropped on to her knees again, and with raised hands and eyes fixed on the blue space above, already sprinkled with stars, prayed again.

"O mother, listen to me, for I have something fresh to say to you. Grandfather has not killed himself, but has asked my forgiveness and has promised to obey me. O mother, I have forgiven him, and he will now take me to Riolama, to our people. Therefore, O mother, if he dies on the way to Riolama let nothing be done against him, but remember only that I forgave him at the last; and when he comes into that place where you are, let him be well received, for that is the wish of Rima, your child."

As soon as this second petition was ended she was up again and engaged in an animated discussion with him, urging him to take her without further delay to Riolama; while he, now recovered from his fear, urged that so important an undertaking required a great deal of thought and preparation; that the journey would occupy about twenty days, and unless he set out well provided with food he would starve before accomplishing half the distance; and his death would leave her worse off than before: he concluded by affirming that he could not start in less time than seven or eight days.

For a while I listened with keen interest to this dispute, and at length interposed once more on the old man's side. The poor girl in her petition had unwittingly revealed to me the power I possessed, and it was a pleasing experience to exercise it. Touching her shoulder again, I assured her that seven or eight days was only a reasonable time in which to prepare for so long a journey: she instantly yielded, and after one glance at my face she moved swiftly away into the darker shadows, leaving me alone with the old man.

As we returned together through the now profoundly dark wood I explained to him how the subject of Riolama had first come up during my conversation with Rima, and he then apologised for the violent language he had used to me. This personal question disposed of, he spoke of the pilgrimage before him, and informed me in confidence that he intended preparing a quantity of smoke-dried meat and packing it in a bag, with a layer of cassava bread, dried pumpkin slips, and such innocent trifles to conceal it from Rima's keen sight and delicate nostrils. Finally, he made a long rambling statement, which, I vainly imagined, was intended to lead up to an account of Rima's origin, with something about her people at Riolama; but it led to nothing except an expression of opinion that the girl was afflicted with a maggot in the brain, but that as she had interest with the powers above, especially with her mother, who was now a very important person among the celestials, it was good policy to submit to her wishes. Turning to me, doubtless to wink (only I missed the sign owing to the darkness), he added that it was a fine thing to have a friend at court. With a little gratulatory chuckle he went on to say that for others it was necessary to obey all the ordinances of the Church, to contribute to its support, hear mass, confess from time to time, and receive absolution: consequently those who went out into the wilderness, where there were no churches and no priests to absolve them, did so at the risk of losing their souls. But with him it was different: he expected in the end to escape the fires of purgatory, and go directly in all his uncleanness to heaven—a thing, he remarked, which happened to very few; and he, Nuflo, was no saint, and had first become a dweller in the desert, as a very young man, in order to escape the penalty of his misdeeds.

I could not resist the temptation of remarking here that to an unregenerate man the celestial country might turn out a somewhat uncongenial place for a residence. He replied airily that he had considered the point and had no fear about the future; that he was old, and from all he had observed of the methods of government followed by those who ruled over earthly affairs from the sky, he had formed a clear idea of that place, and believed that even among so many glorified beings he would be able to meet with those who would prove companionable enough, and would think no worse of him on account of his little blemishes.

How he had first got this idea into his brain about Rima's ability to make things smooth for him after death

I cannot say; probably it was the effect of the girl's powerful personality and vivid faith acting on an ignorant and extremely superstitious mind. While she was making that petition to her mother in heaven it did not seem in the least ridiculous to me: I had felt no inclination to smile, even when hearing all that about the old man's wings being singed to prevent his escape by flying. Her rapt look; the intense conviction that vibrated in her ringing, passionate tones; the brilliant scorn with which she, a hater of bloodshed, one so tender towards all living things, even the meanest, bade him kill himself, and only hear first how her vengeance would pursue his deceitful soul into other worlds; the clearness with which she had related the facts of the case, disclosing the inmost secrets of her heart—all this had had a strange, convincing effect on me. Listening to her I was no longer the enlightened, the creedless man. She herself was so near to the supernatural that it seemed brought near me; indefinable feelings, which had been latent in me, stirred into life, and following the direction of her divine, lustrous eyes, fixed on the blue sky above, I seemed to see there another being like herself, a Rima glorified, leaning her pale, spiritual face to catch the winged words uttered by her child on earth. And even now, while hearing the old man's talk, showing as it did a mind darkened with such gross delusions, I was not yet altogether free from the strange effect of that prayer. Doubtless it was a delusion; her mother was not really there above listening to the girl's voice. Still, in some mysterious way, Rima had become to me, even as to superstitious old Nuflo, a being apart and sacred, and this feeling seemed to mix with my passion, to purify and exalt it and make it infinitely sweet and precious.

After we had been silent for some time I said, "Old man, the result of the grand discussion you have had with Rima is that you have agreed to take her to Riolama, but about my accompanying you not one word has been spoken by either of you."

He stopped short to stare at me, and although it was too dark to see his face, I felt his astonishment. "Señor!" he exclaimed, "we cannot go without you. Have you not heard my granddaughter's words—that it is only because of you that she is about to undertake this crazy journey? If you are not with us in this thing, then, señor, here we must remain. But what will Rima say to that?"

"Very well, I will go, but only on one condition."

"What is it?" he asked, with a sudden change of tone, which warned me that he was becoming cautious again.

"That you tell me the whole story of Rima's origin, and how you came to be now living with her in this solitary place, and who these people are she wishes to visit at Riolama."

"Ah, señor, it is a long story, and sad. But you shall hear it all. You must hear it, señor, since you are now one of us; and when I am no longer here to protect her then she will be yours. And although you will never be able to do more than old Nuflo for her, perhaps she will be better pleased; and you, señor, better able to exist innocently by her side, without eating flesh, since you will always have that rare flower to delight you.

But the story would take long to tell. You shall hear it all as we journey to Riolama. What else will there be to talk about when we are walking that long distance, and when we sit at night by the fire?"

"No, no, old man, I am not to be put off in that way. *I* must hear it before I start."

But he was determined to reserve the narrative until the journey, and after some further argument I yielded the point.

CHAPTER XIII

THAT evening by the fire old Nuflo, lately so miserable, now happy in his delusions, was more than usually gay and loquacious. He was like a child, who by timely submission has escaped a threatened severe punishment. But his lightness of heart was exceeded by mine; and, with the exception of one other yet to come, that evening now shines in memory as the happiest my life has known. For Rima's sweet secret was known to me; and her very ignorance of the meaning of the feeling she experienced, which caused her to fly from me as from an enemy, only served to make the thought of it more purely delightful.

On this occasion she did not steal away like a timid mouse to her own apartment, as her custom was, but remained to give that one evening a special grace, seated well away from the fire in that same shadowy corner where I had first seen her indoors, when I had marvelled at her altered appearance.

From that corner she could see my face, with the firelight full upon it, she herself in shadow, her eyes veiled by their drooping lashes. Sitting there the vivid consciousness of my happiness was like draughts of strong, delicious wine, and its effect was like wine, imparting such freedom to fancy, such fluency, that again and again old Nuflo applauded, crying out that I was a poet, and begging me to put it all into rhyme. I could not do that to please him, never having acquired the art of improvisation—that idle trick of making words jingle which men of Nuflo's class in my country so greatly admire: yet it seemed to me on that evening that my feelings could be adequately expressed only in that sublimated language used by the finest minds in their inspired moments; and, accordingly, I fell to reciting. But not from any modern, nor from the poets of the last century, nor even from the greater seventeenth century. I kept to the more ancient romances and ballads, the sweet old verse that, whether glad or sorrowful, seems always natural and spontaneous as the song of a bird, and so simple that even a child can understand it.

It was late that night before all the romances I remembered or cared to recite were exhausted, and not until then did Rima come out of her shaded corner and steal silently away to her sleeping-place.

Although I had resolved to go with them, and had set Nuflo's mind at rest on the point, I was bent on getting the request from Rima's own lips; and the next morning the opportunity of seeing her alone presented itself, after old Nuflo had sneaked off with his dogs. From the moment of his departure I kept a close watch on the house, as one watches a bush in which a bird he wishes to see has concealed itself, and out of which it may dart at any moment and escape unseen.

At length she came forth, and seeing me in the way, would have slipped back into hiding; for, in spite of her boldness on the previous day, she now seemed shyer than ever when I spoke to her.

"Rima," I said, "do you remember where we first talked together under a tree one morning, when you spoke of your mother, telling me that she was dead?"

"Yes."

"I am going now to that spot to wait for you. I must speak to you again in that place about this journey to Riolama." As she kept silent, I added, "Will you promise to come to me there?"

She shook her head, turning half away.

"Have you forgotten our compact, Rima?"

"No," she returned; and then, suddenly coming near, spoke in a low tone, "I will go there to please you, and you must also do as I tell you."

"What do you wish, Rima?"

She came nearer still. "Listen! You must not look into my eyes, you must not touch me with your hands."

"Sweet Rima, I must hold your hand when I speak with you."

"No, no, no," she murmured, shrinking from me; and finding that it must be as she wished, I reluctantly agreed.

Before I had waited long she appeared at the trysting-place, and stood before me, as on a former occasion, on that same spot of clean yellow sand, clasping and unclasping her fingers, troubled in mind even then. Only now her trouble was different and greater, making her shyer and more reticent.

"Rima, your grandfather is going to take you to Riolama. Do you wish me to go with you?"

"Oh, do you not know that?" she returned, with a swift glance at my face.

"How should I know?"

Her eyes wandered away restlessly. "On Ytaioa you told me a hundred things which I did not know," she replied in a vague way, wishing, perhaps, to imply that with so great a knowledge of geography it was strange I did not know everything, even her most secret thoughts.

"Tell me, why must you go to Riolama?"

"You have heard. To speak to my people."

"What will you say to them? Tell me."

"What you do not understand. How tell you?"

"I understand you when you speak in Spanish."

"Oh, that is not speaking."

"Last night you spoke to your mother in Spanish. Did you not tell her everything?"

"Oh no—not then. When I tell her everything I speak in another way, in a low voice—not on my knees and praying. At night, and in the woods, and when I am alone I tell her. But perhaps she does not hear me; she is not here, but up there—so far! She never answers, but when I speak to my people they will answer me."

Then she turned away as if there was nothing more to be said.

"Is this all I am to hear from you, Rima—these few words?" I exclaimed. "So much did you say to your grandfather, so much to your dead mother, but to me you say so little!"

She turned again, and with eyes cast down replied—

"He deceived me—I had to tell him that, and then to pray to mother. But to you that do not understand, what can I say? Only that you are not like him and all those that I knew at Voa. It is so different—and the same. You are you, and I am I; why is it—do you know?"

"No; yes—I know, but cannot tell you. And if you find your people what will you do—leave me to go to them? Must I go all the way to Riolama only to lose you?"

"Where I am there you must be."

"Why?"

"Do I not see it there?" she returned, with a quick gesture to indicate that it appeared in my face.

"Your sight is keen, Rima—keen as a bird's. Mine is not so keen. Let me look once more into those beautiful wild eyes, then perhaps I shall see in them as much as you see in mine."

"Oh no, no, not that!" she murmured in distress, drawing away from me; then with a sudden flash of brilliant colour cried—

"Have you forgotten the compact—the promise you made me?"

Her words made me ashamed, and I could not reply. But the shame was as nothing in strength compared to the impulse I felt to clasp her beautiful body in my arms and cover her face with kisses. Sick with desire, I turned away, and sitting on a root of the tree, covered my face with my hands.

She came nearer: I could see her shadow through my fingers; then her face and wistful, compassionate eyes.

"Forgive me, dear Rima," I said, dropping my hands again. "I have tried so hard to please you in everything. Touch my face with your hand—only that, and I will go to Riolama with you, and obey you in all things."

For a while she hesitated, then stepped quickly aside so that I could not see her; but I knew that she had not left me, that she was standing just behind me. And after waiting a moment longer I felt her fingers touching my skin, softly, trembling over my cheek as if a soft-winged moth had fluttered against it; then the slight aerial touch was gone, and she, too, moth-like, had vanished from my side.

Left alone in the wood I was not happy. That fluttering, flattering touch of her finger-tips had been to me like spoken language, and more eloquent than language, yet the sweet assurance it conveyed had not given perfect satisfaction; and when I asked myself why the gladness of the previous evening had forsaken me—why I was infected with this new sadness when everything promised well for me, I found that it was because my passion had greatly increased during the last few hours; even during sleep it had been growing, and could no longer be fed by merely dwelling in thought on the charms, moral and physical, of its object, and by dreams of future fruition.

I concluded that it would be best for Rima's sake as well as my own to spend a few of the days, before setting out on our journey, with my Indian friends, who would be troubled at my long absence; and, accordingly, next morning I bade good-bye to the old man, promising to return in three or four days, and then started without seeing Rima, who had quitted the house before her usual time. After getting free of the woods, on casting back my eyes I caught sight of the girl standing under an isolated tree watching me with that vague, misty, greenish appearance she so frequently had when seen in the light shade at a short distance.

"Rima!" I cried, hurrying back to speak to her, but when I reached the spot she had vanished; and after waiting some time, seeing and hearing nothing to indicate that she was near me, I resumed my walk, half thinking that my imagination had deceived me.

I found my Indian friends home again, and was not surprised to observe a distinct change in their manner towards me. I had expected as much; and considering that they must have known very well where and in whose company I had been spending my time, it was not strange. Coming across the savannah that morning I had first begun to think seriously of the risk I was running. But this thought only served to prepare me for a new condition of things; for now to go back and appear before Rima, and thus prove myself to be a person not only capable of forgetting a promise occasionally, but also of a weak, vacillating mind, was not to be thought of for a moment.

I was received—not welcomed—quietly enough: not a question, not a word, concerning my long absence fell from anyone; it was as if a stranger had appeared among them, one about whom they knew nothing, and consequently regarded with suspicion, if not actual hostility. I affected not to notice the change, and dipped my hand uninvited in the pot to satisfy my hunger, and smoked and dozed away the sultry hours in my hammock. Then I got my guitar and spent the rest of the day over it, tuning it, touching the strings so softly with my finger-tips that to a person four yards off the sound must have seemed like the murmur or buzz of an insect's wings; and to this scarcely audible accompaniment I murmured in an equally low tone a new song.

In the evening, when all were gathered under the roof and I had eaten again, I took up the instrument once more, furtively watched by all those half-closed animal eyes, and swept the strings loudly, and sang aloud. I sang an old simple Spanish melody, to which I had put words in their own language—a language with no words not in everyday use, in which it is so difficult to express feelings out of and above the common. What I had been constructing and practising all the afternoon *sotto voce* was a kind of ballad, an extremely simple tale of a poor Indian living alone with his young family in a season of dearth: how day after day he ranged the voiceless woods to return each evening with nothing but a few withered sour berries in his hand, to find his lean, large-eyed wife still nursing the fire that cooked nothing, and his children crying for food, showing their bones more plainly through their skins every day; and how, without anything miraculous, anything wonderful, happening, that barrenness passed from earth, and the garden once more yielded them pumpkin and maize and manioc, the wild fruits ripened, and the birds returned, filling the forest with their cries; and so their long hunger was satisfied, and the children grew sleek, and played and laughed in the sunshine; and the wife, no longer brooding over the empty pot, wove a hammock of silk grass, decorated with blue-and-scarlet feathers of the macaw; and in that new hammock the Indian rested long from his labours, smoking endless cigars.

When I at last concluded with a loud note of joy, a long, involuntary suspiration in the darkening room told me that I had been listened to with profound interest; and, although no word was spoken, though I was still a stranger and under a cloud, it was plain that the experiment had succeeded, and that for the present the danger was averted.

I went to my hammock and slept, but without undressing. Next morning I missed my revolver and found that the holster containing it had been detached from the belt. My knife had not been taken, possibly because it was under me in the hammock while I slept. In answer to my inquiries I was informed that Runi had *borrowed* my weapon to take it with him to the forest, where he had gone to hunt, and that he would return it to me in the evening. I affected to take it in good part, although feeling secretly ill at ease. Later in the day I came to the conclusion that Runi had had it in his mind to murder me, that I had softened him by singing that Indian story, and that by taking possession of the revolver he showed that he now only meant to keep me a prisoner. Subsequent events confirmed me in this suspicion. On his return he explained that he had gone out to seek for game in the woods; and, going without a companion, he had taken my revolver to preserve him from dangers—meaning those of a supernatural kind; and that he had had the misfortune to drop it among the bushes while in pursuit of some animal. I answered hotly that he had not treated me like a friend; that if he had asked me for the weapon it would have been lent to him; that as he had taken it without permission he must pay me for it. After some pondering, he said that when he took it I was sleeping soundly; also, that it would not be lost; he would take me to the place where he had dropped it, when we could search together for it.

He was in appearance more friendly towards me now, even asking me to repeat my last evening's song, and so we had that performance all over again to everybody's satisfaction. But when morning came he was not inclined to go to the woods: there was food enough in the house, and the pistol would not be hurt by lying where it had fallen a day longer. Next day the same excuse; still I disguised my impatience and suspicion of him and waited, singing the ballad for the third time that evening. Then I was conducted to a wood about a league and half away, and we hunted for the lost pistol among the bushes, I with little hope of finding it, while he attended to the bird voices and frequently asked me to stand or lie still when a chance of something offered.

The result of that wasted day was a determination on my part to escape from Runi as soon as possible, although at the risk of making a deadly enemy of him and of being compelled to go on that long journey to Riolama with no better weapon than a hunting-knife. I had noticed, while appearing not to do so, that outside of the house I was followed or watched by one or other of the Indians, so that great circumspection was needed. On the following day I attacked my host once more about the revolver, telling him with well-acted indignation that if not found it must be paid for. I went so far as to give a list of the articles I should require, including a bow and arrows, zabatana, two spears, and other things which I need not specify, to set me up for life as a wild man in the woods of Guayana. I was going to add a wife, but as I had already been offered one it did not appear to be necessary. He seemed a little taken aback at the value I set upon my weapon, and promised to go and look for it again. Then I begged that Kua-kó, in whose sharpness of sight I had great faith, might accompany us. He consented, and named the next day but one for the expedition. Very well, thought I, to-morrow their suspicion will be less, and my opportunity will come; then taking up my rude instrument, I gave them an old Spanish song—

Desde aquel doloroso momento :

but this kind of music had lost its charm for them, and I was asked to give them the ballad they understood so well, in which their interest seemed to increase with every repetition. In spite of anxiety it amused me to see old Cla-cla regarding me fixedly with owlish eyes and lips moving. My tale had no wonderful things in it, like hers of the olden time, which she told only to send her hearers to sleep. Perhaps she had discovered by now that it was the strange honey of melody which made the coarse, common cassava-bread of everyday life in my story so pleasant to the palate. I was quite prepared to receive a proposal to give her music and singing lessons, and to bequeath a guitar to her in my last will and testament. For, in spite of her hoary hair and million wrinkles, she, more than any other savage I had met with, seemed to have taken a draught from Ponce de Leon's undiscovered fountain of eternal youth. Poor old witch!

The following day was the sixth of my absence from Rima, and one of intense anxiety to me, a feeling which I endeavoured to hide by playing with the children, fighting our old comic stick fights, and by strumming noisily on the guitar. In the afternoon, when it was hottest, and all the men who happened to be indoors were lying in their hammocks, I asked Kua-kó to go with me to the stream to bathe. He refused—I had counted on that—and earnestly advised me not to bathe in the pool I was accustomed to, as some little caribe fishes had made their appearance there and would be sure to attack me. I laughed at his idle tale, and taking up my cloak swung out of the door, whistling a lively air. He knew that I always threw my cloak over my head and shoulders as a protection from the sun and stinging flies when coming out of the water, and so his suspicion was not aroused, and I was not followed.

The pool was about ten minutes' walk from the house; I arrived at it with palpitating heart, and going round to its end, where the stream was shallow, sat down to rest for a few moments and take a few sips of cool water dipped up in my palm. Presently I rose, crossed the stream, and began running, keeping among the low trees near the bank until a dry gully, which extended for some distance across the savannah, was reached. By following its course the distance to be covered would be considerably increased, but the shorter way would have exposed me to sight and made it more dangerous. I had put forth too much speed at first, and in a short time my exertions, and the hot sun, together with my intense excitement, overcame me. I dared not hope that my flight had not been observed; I imagined that the Indians, unencumbered by any heavy weight, were already close behind me, and ready to launch their deadly spears at my back. With a sob of rage and despair I fell prostrate on my face in the dry bed of the stream, and for two or three minutes remained thus exhausted and unmanned, my heart throbbing so violently that my whole frame was shaken. If my enemies had come on me then disposed to kill me, I could not have lifted a hand in defence of my life. But minutes passed, and they came not. I rose and went on, at a fast walk now, and when the sheltering stream-bed ended, I stooped among the sere dwarfed shrubs scattered about here and there on its southern side; and now creeping and now running, with an occasional pause to rest and look back, I at last reached the dividing ridge at its southern extremity. The rest of the way was over comparatively easy ground, inclining downwards; and with that glad green forest now full in sight, and hope growing stronger every minute in my breast, my knees ceased to tremble, and I ran on again, scarcely pausing until I had touched and lost myself in the welcome shadows.

CHAPTER XIV

AH that return to the forest where Rima dwelt, after so anxious a day, when the declining sun shone hotly still, and the green woodland shadows were so grateful! The coolness, the sense of security, allayed the fever and excitement I had suffered on the open savannah; I walked leisurely, pausing often to listen to some bird voice or to admire some rare insect or parasitic flower shining star-like in the shade. There was a strangely delightful sensation in me. I likened myself to a child that, startled at something it had seen while out playing in the sun, flies to its mother to feel her caressing hand on its cheek and forget its tremors. And describing what I felt in that way, I was a little ashamed and laughed at myself; nevertheless the feeling was very sweet. At that moment Mother and Nature seemed one and the same thing. As I kept to the more open part of the wood, on its southernmost border, the red flame of the sinking sun was seen at intervals through the deep humid green of the higher foliage. How every object it touched took from it a new wonderful glory! At one spot, high up where the foliage was scanty, and slender bush ropes and moss depended like broken cordage from a dead limb—just there, bathing itself in that glory-giving light, I noticed a fluttering bird, and stood still to watch its antics. Now it would cling, head downwards, to the slender twigs, wings and tail open; then, righting itself, it would flit from waving line to line, dropping lower and lower; and anon soar upwards a distance of twenty feet and alight to recommence the flitting and swaying and dropping towards the earth. It was one of those birds that have a polished plumage, and as it moved this way and that, flirting its feathers, they caught the beams and shone at moments like glass or burnished metal. Suddenly another bird of the same kind dropped down to it as if from the sky, straight and swift as a falling stone; and the first bird sprang up to meet the comer, and after rapidly wheeling round each other for a moment they fled away in company, screaming shrilly through the wood, and were instantly lost to sight, while their jubilant cries came back fainter and fainter at each repetition.

I envied them not their wings: at that moment earth did not seem fixed and solid beneath me, nor I bound by gravity to it. The faint, floating clouds, the blue infinite heaven itself, seemed not more ethereal and free than I, or the ground I walked on. The low, stony hills on my right hand, of which I caught occasional glimpses through the trees, looking now blue and delicate in the level rays, were no more than the billowy projections on the moving cloud of earth: the trees of unnumbered kinds—great mora, cecropia, and greenheart, bush and fern and suspended lianas, and tall palms balancing their feathery foliage on slender stems—all was but a fantastic mist embroidery covering the surface of that floating cloud on which my feet were set, and which floated with me near the sun.

The red evening flame had vanished from the summits of the trees, the sun was setting, the woods in shadow, when I got to the end of my walk. I did not approach the house on the side of the door, yet by some means those within became aware of my presence, for out they came in a great hurry, Rima leading the way, Nuflo behind her, waving his arms and shouting. But as I drew near the girl dropped behind and stood motionless regarding me, her face pallid and showing strong excitement. I could scarcely remove my eyes from her eloquent countenance: I seemed to read in it relief and gladness mingled with surprise and something like vexation. She was piqued perhaps that I had taken her by surprise, that after much watching for me in the wood I had come through it undetected when she was indoors.

"Happy the eyes that see you!" shouted the old man, laughing boisterously.

"Happy are mine that look on Rima again," I answered. "I have been long absent."

"Long—you may say so," returned Nuflo. "We had given you up. We said that, alarmed at the thought of the journey to Riolama, you had abandoned us."

"*We* said!" exclaimed Rima, her pallid face suddenly flushing. "I spoke differently."

"Yes, I know—I know!" he said airily, waving his hand. "You said that he was in danger, that he was kept against his will from coming. He is present now—let him speak,"

"She was right," I said. "Ah, Nuflo, old man, you have lived long, and got much experience, but not insight—not that inner vision that sees further than the eyes."

"No, not that—I know what you mean," he answered. Then, tossing his hand towards the sky, he added, "The knowledge you speak of comes from there."

The girl had been listening with keen interest, glancing from one to the other. "What!" she spoke suddenly, as if unable to keep silence, "do you think, grandfather, that *she* tells me—when there is danger—when the rain will cease—when the wind will blow—everything? Do I not ask and listen, lying awake at night? She is always silent, like the stars."

Then, pointing to me with her finger, she finished—

"*He* knows so many things! Who tells them to *him*?"

"But distinguish, Rima. You do not distinguish the great from the little," he answered loftily. "*We* know a thousand things, but they are things that any man with a forehead can learn. The knowledge that comes from the blue is not like that—it is more important and miraculous. Is it not so, señor?" he ended, appealing to me.

"Is it, then, left for me to decide?" said I, addressing the girl.

But though her face was towards me she refused to meet my look and was silent. Silent, but not satisfied: she doubted still, and had perhaps caught something in my tone that strengthened her doubt.

Old Nuflo understood the expression. "Look at me,

Rima," he said, drawing himself up. "I am old, and he is young—do I not know best? I have spoken and have decided it."

Still that unconvinced expression, and the face turned expectant to me.

"Am I to decide?" I repeated.

"Who, then?" she said at last, her voice scarcely more than a murmur; yet there was reproach in the tone, as if she had made a long speech and I had tyrannously driven her to it.

"Thus, then, I decide," said I. "To each one of us, as to every kind of animal, even to small birds and insects, and to every kind of plant, there is given something peculiar—a fragrance, a melody, a special instinct, an art, a knowledge, which no other has. And to Rima has been given this quickness of mind and power to divine distant things; it is hers, just as swiftness and grace and changeful, brilliant colour are the humming-bird's; therefore she need not that anyone dwelling in the blue should instruct her."

The old man frowned and shook his head; while she, after one swift, shy glance at my face, and with something like a smile flitting over her delicate lips, turned and re-entered the house.

I felt convinced from that parting look that she had understood me, that my words had in some sort given her relief; for, strong as was her faith in the supernatural, she appeared as ready to escape from it, when a way of escape offered, as from the limp cotton gown and constrained manner worn in the house. The religion and cotton dress were evidently remains of her early training at the settlement of Voa.

Old Nuflo, strange to say, had proved better than his word. Instead of inventing new causes for delay, as I had imagined would be the case, he now informed me that his preparations for the journey were all but complete, that he had only waited for my return to set out.

Rima soon left us in her customary way, and then, talking by the fire, I gave an account of my detention by the Indians and of the loss of my revolver, which I thought very serious.

"You seem to think little of it," I said, observing that he took it very coolly. "Yet I know not how I shall defend myself in case of an attack."

"I have no fear of an attack," he answered. "It seems to me the same thing whether you have a revolver or many revolvers and carbines and swords, or no revolver—no weapon at all. And for a very simple reason. While Rima is with us, so long as we are on her business, we are protected from above. The angels, señor, will watch over us by day and night. What need of weapons, then, except to procure food?"

"Why should not the angels provide us with food also?" said I.

"No, no, that is a different thing," he returned. "That is a small and low thing, a necessity common to all creatures, which all know how to meet. You would not expect an angel to drive away a cloud of mosquitoes, or to remove a bush-tick from your person. No, sir, you may talk of natural gifts, and try to make Rima believe that she is what she is, and knows what she knows, because, like a humming-bird or some plants with a peculiar fragrance, she has been made so. It is wrong, señor, and pardon me for saying it, it ill becomes you to put such fables into her head."

I answered, with a smile, "She herself seems to doubt what you believe."

"But, señor, what can you expect from an ignorant girl like Rima? She knows nothing, or very little, and will not listen to reason. If she would only remain quietly indoors, with her hair braided, and pray and read her Catechism, instead of running about after flowers and birds and butterflies and such unsubstantial things, it would be better for both of us."

"In what way, old man?"

"Why, it is plain that if she would cultivate the acquaintance of the people that surround her—I mean those that come to her from her sainted mother—and are ready to do her bidding in everything, she could make it more safe for us in this place. For example, there is Runi and his people, why should they remain living so near us as to be a constant danger when a pestilence of small-pox or some other fever might easily be sent to kill them off?"

"And have you ever suggested such a thing to your grandchild?"

He looked surprised and grieved at the question. "Yes, many times, señor," he said. "I should have been a poor Christian had I not mentioned it. But when I speak of it she gives me a look and is gone, and I see no more of her all day, and when I see her she refuses even to answer me;—so perverse, so foolish is she in her ignorance; for, as you can see for yourself, she has no more sense or concern about what is most important than some little painted fly that flits about all day long without any object."

CHAPTER XV

THE next day we were early at work. Nuflo had already gathered, dried, and conveyed to a place of concealment the greater portion of his garden produce. He was determined to leave nothing to be taken by any wandering party of savages that might call at the house during our absence. He had no fear of a visit from his neighbours; they would not know, he said, that he and Rima were out of the wood. A few large earthen pots, filled with shelled maize, beans, and sun-dried strips of pumpkin, still remained to be disposed of. Taking up one of these vessels and asking me to follow with another, he started off through the wood. We went a distance of five or six hundred yards; then made our way down a very steep incline, close to the border of the forest on the western side; arrived at the bottom, we followed the bank a little further, and I then found myself once more at the foot of the precipice over which I had desperately thrown myself on the stormy evening after the snake had bitten me. Nuflo, stealing silently and softly before me through the bushes, had observed a caution and secrecy in approaching this spot resembling that of a wise old hen when she visits her hidden nest to lay an egg. And here was his nest, his most secret treasure-house, which he had probably not revealed even to me without a sharp inward conflict, notwithstanding that our fates were now linked together. The lower portion of the bank was of rock; and in it, about ten or twelve feet above the ground, but easily reached from below, there was a natural cavity large enough to contain all his portable property. Here, besides the food-stuff, he had already stored a quantity of dried tobacco leaf, his rude weapons, cooking utensils, ropes, mats, and other objects. Two or three more journeys were made for the remaining pots, after which we adjusted a slab of sandstone to the opening, which was fortunately narrow, plastered up the crevices with clay, and covered them over with moss to hide all traces of our work.

Towards evening, after we had refreshed ourselves with a long siesta, Nuflo brought out from some other hiding-place two sacks; one weighing about twenty pounds and containing smoke-dried meat, also grease and gum for lighting purposes, and a few other small objects. This was his load; the other sack, which was smaller and contained parched corn and raw beans, was for me to carry.

The old man, cautious in all his movements, always acting as if surrounded by invisible spies, delayed setting out until an hour after dark. Then, skirting the forest on its west side, we left Ytaioa on our right hand, and after travelling over rough, difficult ground, with only the stars to light us, we saw the waning moon rise not long before dawn. Our course had been a north-easterly one at first; now it was due east, with broad, dry savannahs and patches of open forest as far as we could see before us. It was weary walking on that first night, and weary waiting on the first day when we sat in the shade during the long, hot hours, persecuted by small stinging flies; but the days and nights that succeeded were far worse, when the weather became bad with intense heat and frequent heavy falls of rain. The one compensation I had looked for, which would have outweighed all the extreme discomforts we suffered, was denied me. Rima was no more to me or with me now than she had been during those wild days in her native woods, when every bush and bole and tangled creeper or fern-frond had joined in a conspiracy to keep her out of my sight. It is true that at intervals in the daytime she was visible, sometimes within speaking distance, so that I could address a few words to her, but there was no companionship, and we were fellow-travellers only like birds flying independently in the same direction, not so widely separated but that they can occasionally hear and see each other. The pilgrim in the desert is sometimes attended by a bird, and the bird, with its freer motions, will often leave him a league behind and seem lost to him, but only to return and show its form again; for it has never lost sight nor recollection of the traveller toiling slowly over the surface. Rima kept us company in some such wild erratic way as that. A word, a sign from Nuflo was enough for her to know the direction to take; the distant forest or still more distant mountain near which we should have to pass. She would hasten on and be lost to our sight, and when there was a forest in the way she would explore it, resting in the shade and finding her own food; but invariably she was before us at each resting or camping place.

Indian villages were seen during the journey, but only to be avoided: and in like manner, if we caught sight of Indians travelling or camping at a distance, we would alter our course, or conceal ourselves to escape observation. Only on one occasion, two days after setting out, were we compelled to speak with strangers. We were going round a hill, and all at once came face to face with three persons travelling in an opposite direction—two men and a woman, and, by a strange fatality, Rima at that moment happened to be with us. We stood for some time talking to these people, who were evidently surprised at our appearance, and wished to learn who we were; but Nuflo, who spoke their language like one of themselves, was too cunning to give any true answer. They, on their side, told us that they had been to visit a relation at Chani, the name of a river three days ahead of us, and were now returning to their own village at Baila-baila, two days beyond Parahuari. After parting from them Nuflo was much troubled in his mind for the rest of that day. These people, he said, would probably rest at some Parahuari village, where they would be sure to give a description of us, and so it might eventually come to the knowledge of our unneighbourly neighbour Runi that we had left Ytaioa.

Other incidents of our long and wearisome journey need not be related. Sitting under some shady tree during the sultry hours, with Rima only too far out of earshot, or by the nightly fire, the old man told me little by little and with much digression, chiefly on sacred subjects, the strange story of the girl's origin.

About seventeen years back—Nuflo had no sure method to compute time by—when he was already verging on old age, he was one of a company of nine men, living a kind of roving life in the very part of Guayana through which we were now travelling; the others, much younger than himself, were all equally offenders against the laws of Venezuela, and fugitives from justice. Nuflo was the leader of this gang, for it happened that he had passed a great portion of his life outside the pale of civilisation, and could talk the Indian languages, and knew this part of Guayana intimately. But according to his own account he was not in harmony with them. They were bold, desperate men, whose evil appetites had so far only been whetted by the crimes they had committed; while he, with passions worn out, recalling his many bad acts, and with a vivid conviction of the truth of all he had been taught in early life—for Nuflo was nothing if not religious—was now grown timid and desirous only of making his peace with Heaven. This difference of disposition made him morose and quarrelsome with his companions; and they would, he said, have murdered him without remorse if he had not been so useful to them. Their favourite plan was to hang about the neighbourhood of some small isolated settlement, keeping a watch on it, and, when most of the male inhabitants were absent, to swoop down on it and work their will. Now shortly after one of these raids it happened that a woman they had carried off, becoming a burden to them, was flung into a river to the alligators; but when being dragged down to the waterside she cast up her eyes, and in a loud voice cried to God to execute vengeance on her murderers. Nuflo affirmed that he took no part in this black deed nevertheless, the woman's dying appeal to Heaven preyed on his mind; he feared that it might have won a hearing, and the "person" eventually commissioned to execute vengeance—after the usual delays, of course—might act on the principle of the old proverb—*Tell me whom you are with, and I will tell you what you are*—and punish the innocent (himself to wit) along with the guilty. But while thus anxious about his spiritual interests he was not yet prepared to break with his companions. He thought it best to temporise, and succeeded in persuading them that it would be unsafe to attack another Christian settlement for some time to come; that in the interval they might find some pleasure, if no great profit, by turning their attention to the Indians. The infidels, he said, were God's natural enemies and fair game to the Christian. To make a long story short, Nuflo's Christian band, after some successful adventures, met with a reverse which reduced their number from nine to five. Flying from their enemies they sought safety at Riolama, an uninhabited place, where they found it possible to exist for some weeks on game, which was abundant, and wild fruits.

One day at noon, while ascending a mountain at the southern extremity of the Riolama range, in order to get a view of the country beyond from the summit, Nuflo and his companions discovered a cave; and finding it dry, without animal occupants, and with a level floor, they at once determined to make it their dwelling-place for a season. Wood for firing and water were to be had close by; they were also well provided with smoked flesh of a tapir they had slaughtered a day or two before, so that they could afford to rest for a time in so comfortable a shelter. At a short distance from the cave they made a fire on the rock to toast some slices of meat for their dinner; and while thus engaged all at once one of the men uttered a cry of astonishment, and casting up his eyes Nuflo beheld, standing near and regarding them with surprise and fear in her wide-open eyes, a woman of a most wonderful appearance. The one slight garment she had on was silky and white as the snow on the summit of some great mountain, but of the snow when the sinking sun touches and gives it some delicate changing colour which is like fire. Her dark hair was like a cloud from which her face looked out, and her head was surrounded by an aureole like that of a saint in a picture, only more beautiful. For, said Nuflo, a picture is a picture, and the other was a reality, which is finer. Seeing her he fell on his knees and crossed himself; and all the time her eyes, full of amazement and shining with such a strange splendour that he could not meet them, were fixed on him and not on the others; and he felt that she had come to save his soul, in danger of perdition owing to his companionship with men who were at war with God and wholly bad.

But at this moment his comrades, recovering from their astonishment, sprang to their feet, and the heavenly woman vanished. Just behind where she had stood, and not twelve yards from them, there was a huge chasm in the mountain, its jagged precipitous sides clothed with thorny bushes; the men now cried out that she had made her escape that way, and down after her they rushed, pell-mell.

Nuflo cried out after them that they had seen a saint and that some horrible thing would befall them if they allowed any evil thought to enter their hearts; but they scoffed at his words, and were soon far down out of hearing, while he, trembling with fear, remained praying to the woman that had appeared to them, and had looked with such strange eyes at him, not to punish him for the sins of the others.

Before long the men returned, disappointed and sullen, for they had failed in their search for the woman; and perhaps Nuflo's warning words had made them give up the chase too soon. At all events, they seemed ill at ease, and made up their minds to abandon the cave: in a short time they left the place to camp that night at a considerable distance from the mountain. But they were not satisfied: they had now recovered from their fear, but not from the excitement of an evil passion; and finally, after comparing notes, they came to the conclusion that they had missed a great prize through Nuflo's cowardice; and when he reproved them they blasphemed all the saints in the calendar and even threatened him with violence. Fearing to remain longer in the company of such godless men, he only waited until they slept, then rose up cautiously, helped himself to most of the provisions, and made his escape, devoutly hoping that after losing their guide they would all speedily perish.

Finding himself alone now and master of his own actions, Nuflo was in terrible distress, for while his heart was in the utmost fear, it yet urged him imperiously to go back to the mountain, to seek again for that sacred being who had appeared to him, and had been driven away by his brutal companions. If he obeyed that inner voice, he would be saved; if he resisted it then there would be no hope for him, and along with those who had cast the woman to the alligators he would be lost eternally. Finally, on the following day, he went back, although not without fear and trembling, and sat down on a stone just where he had sat toasting his tapir meat on the previous day. But he waited in vain, and at length that voice within him, which he had so far obeyed, began urging him to descend into the valley-like chasm down which the woman had escaped from his comrades, and to seek for her there. Accordingly he rose and began cautiously and slowly climbing down over the broken jagged rocks and through a dense mass of thorny bushes and creepers. At the bottom of the chasm a clear, swift stream of water rushed with foam and noise along its rocky bed; but before reaching it, and when it was still twenty yards lower down, he was startled by hearing a low moan among the bushes, and looking about for the cause, he found the wonderful woman—his saviour, as he expressed it. She was not now standing nor able to stand, but half reclining among the rough stones, one foot, which she had sprained in that headlong flight down the ragged slope, wedged immovably between the rocks; and in this painful position she had remained a prisoner since noon on the previous day. She now gazed on her visitor in silent consternation; while he, casting himself prostrate on the ground, implored her forgiveness and begged to know her will. But she made no reply; and at length, finding that she was powerless to move, he concluded that, though a saint and one of the beings that men worship, she was also flesh and liable to accidents while sojourning on earth; and perhaps, he thought, that accident which had befallen her had been specially designed by the powers above to prove him. With great labour, and not without causing her much pain, he succeeded in extricating her from her position; and then finding that the injured foot was half crushed and blue and swollen, he took her up in his arms and carried her to the stream. There, making a cup of a broad green leaf, he offered her water, which she drank eagerly; and he also laved her injured foot in the cold stream and bandaged it with fresh aquatic leaves; finally he made her a soft bed of moss and dry grass and placed her on it. That night he spent keeping watch over her, at intervals applying fresh wet leaves to her foot as the old ones became dry and wilted from the heat of the inflammation.

The effect of all he did was that the terror with which she regarded him gradually wore off; and next day, when she seemed to be recovering her strength, he proposed by signs to remove her to the cave higher up, where she would be sheltered in case of rain. She appeared to understand him, and allowed herself to be taken up in his arms, and carried with much labour to the top of the chasm. In the cave he made her a second couch, and tended her assiduously. He made a fire on the floor and kept it burning night and day, and supplied her with water to drink and fresh leaves for her foot. There was little more that he could do. From the choicest and fattest bits of toasted tapir flesh he offered her she turned away with disgust. A little cassava-bread soaked in water she would take, but seemed not to like it. After a time, fearing that she would starve, he took to hunting after wild fruits, edible bulbs and gums, and on these small things she subsisted during the whole time of their sojourn together in the desert.

The woman, although lamed for life, was now so far recovered as to be able to limp about without assistance, and she spent a portion of each day out among the rocks and trees on the mountains. Nuflo at first feared that she would now leave him, but before long he became convinced that she had no such intentions. And yet she was profoundly unhappy. He was accustomed to see her seated on a rock, as if brooding over some secret grief, her head bowed, and great tears falling from half-closed eyes.

From the first he had conceived the idea that she was in the way of becoming a mother at no distant date—an idea which seemed to accord badly with the suppositions as to the nature of this heavenly being he was privileged to minister to and so win salvation; but he was now convinced of its truth, and he imagined that in her condition he had discovered the cause of that sorrow and anxiety which preyed continually on her. By means of that dumb language of signs which enabled them to converse together a little, he made it known to her that at a great distance from the mountains there existed a place where there were beings like herself, women, and mothers of children, who would comfort and tenderly care for her. When she had understood, she seemed pleased and willing to accompany him to that distant place; and so it came to pass that they left their rocky shelter and the mountains of Riolama far behind. But for several days, as they slowly journeyed over the plain, she would pause at intervals in her limping walk to gaze back on those blue summits, shedding abundant tears.

Fortunately the village of Voa, on the river of the same name, which was the nearest Christian settlement to Riolama, whither his course was directed, was well known to him; he had lived there in former years, and what was of great advantage, the inhabitants were ignorant of his worst crimes, or, to put it in his own subtle way, of the crimes committed by the men he had acted with. Great was the astonishment and curiosity of the people of Voa when, after many weeks' travelling, Nuflo arrived at last with his companion. But he was not going to tell the truth, nor even the least particle of the truth, to a gaping crowd of inferior persons. For these, ingenious lies: only to the priest he told the whole story, dwelling minutely on all he had done to rescue and protect her; all of which was approved by the holy man, whose first act was to baptise the woman for fear that she was not a Christian. Let it be said to Nuflo's credit that he objected to this ceremony, arguing that she could not be a saint, with an aureole in token of her sainthood, yet stand in need of being baptised by a priest. A priest—he added, with a little chuckle of malicious pleasure—who was often seen drunk, who cheated at cards, and was sometimes suspected of putting poison on his fighting-cock's spur to make sure of the victory! Doubtless the priest had his faults; but he was not without humanity, and for the whole seven years of that unhappy stranger's sojourn at Voa he did everything in his power to make her existence tolerable. Some weeks after arriving she gave birth to a female child, and then the priest insisted on naming it Riolama, in order, he said, to keep in remembrance the strange story of the mother's discovery at that place.

Rima's mother could not be taught to speak either Spanish or Indian; and when she found that the mysterious and melodious sounds that fell from her own lips were understood by none she ceased to utter them, and thereafter preserved an unbroken silence among the people she lived with. But from the presence of others she shrank, as if in disgust or fear, excepting only Nuflo and the priest, whose kindly intentions she appeared to understand and appreciate. So far her life in the village was silent and sorrowful. With her child it was different; and every day that was not wet, taking the little thing by the hand, she would limp painfully out into the forest, and there, sitting on the ground, the two would commune with each other by the hour in their wonderful language.

At length she began to grow perceptibly paler and feebler week by week. day by day, until she could no longer go out into the wood, but sat or reclined, panting for breath in the dull hot room, waiting for death to release her. At the same time little Rima, who had always appeared frail, as if from sympathy now began to fade and look more shadowy, so that it was expected she would not long survive her parent. To the mother death came slowly, but at last it seemed so near that Nuflo and the priest were together at her side waiting to see the end. It was then that little Rima, who had learnt from infancy to speak in Spanish, rose from the couch where her mother had been whispering to her, and began with some difficulty to express what was in the dying woman's mind. Her child, she had said, could not continue alive in that hot wet place, but if taken away to a distance where there were mountains and a cooler air she would revive and grow strong again.

Hearing this, old Nuflo declared that the child should not perish; that he himself would take her away to Parahuari, a distant place where there were mountains and dry plains and open woods; that he would watch over her and care for her there as he had cared for her mother at Riolama.

When the substance of this speech had been made known by Rima to the dying woman, she suddenly rose up from the couch, which she had not risen from for many days, and stood erect on the floor, her wasted face shining with joy. Then Nuflo knew that God's angels had come for her, and put out his arms to save her from falling; and even while he held her that sudden glory went out from her face, now of a dead white like burnt-out ashes;

and murmuring something soft and melodious, her spirit passed away.

Once more Nuflo became a wanderer, now with the fragile-looking little Rima for companion, the sacred child who had inherited the position of his intercessor from a sacred mother. The priest, who had probably become infected with Nuflo's superstitions, did not allow them to leave Voa empty-handed, but gave the old man as much calico as would serve to buy hospitality and whatsoever he might require from the Indians for many a day to come.

At Parahuari, where they arrived safely at last, they lived for some little time at one of the villages. But the child had an instinctive aversion to all savages, or possibly the feeling was derived from her mother, for it had shown itself early at Voa, where she had refused to learn their language; and this eventually led Nuflo to go away and live apart from them, in the forest by Ytaioa, where he made himself a house and garden. The Indians, however, continued friendly with him and visited him with frequency. But when Rima grew up, developing into that mysterious woodland girl I found her, they became suspicious, and in the end regarded her with dangerously hostile feeling. She, poor child, detested them because they were incessantly at war with the wild animals she loved, her companions; and having no fear of them, for she did not know that they had it in their minds to turn their little poisonous arrows against herself, she was constantly in the woods frustrating them; and the animals, in league with her, seemed to understand her note of warning and hid themselves or took to flight at the approach of danger. At length their hatred and fear grew to such a degree that they determined to make away with her, and one day, having matured a plan, they went to the wood and spread themselves two and two about it. The couples did not keep together, but moved about or remained concealed at a distance of forty or fifty yards apart, lest she should be missed. Two of the savages, armed with blow-pipes, were near the border of the forest on the side nearest to the village, and one of them, observing a motion in the foliage of a tree, ran swiftly and cautiously towards it to try and catch a glimpse of the enemy. And he did see her no doubt, as she was there watching both him and his companions, and blew an arrow at her, but even while in the act of blowing it he was himself struck by a dart that buried itself deep in his flesh just over the heart. He ran some distance with the fatal barbed point in his flesh and met his comrade, who had mistaken him for the girl and shot him. The wounded man threw himself down to die, and dying related that he had fired at the girl sitting up in a tree and that she had caught the arrow in her hand only to hurl it instantly back with such force and precision that it pierced his flesh just over the heart. He had seen it all with his own eyes, and his friend who had accidentally slain him believed his story and repeated it to the others. Rima had seen one Indian shoot the other, and when she told her grandfather he explained to her that it was an accident, but he guessed why the arrow had been fired.

From that day the Indians hunted no more in the wood; and at length one day Nuflo, meeting an Indian who did not know him and with whom he had some talk, heard the strange story of the arrow, and that the mysterious girl who could not be shot was the offspring of an old man and a Didi who had become enamoured of him ; that, growing tired of her consort, the Didi had returned to her river, leaving her half-human child to play her malicious pranks in the wood.

This, then, was Nuflo's story, told not in Nuflo's manner, which was infinitely prolix ; and think not that it failed to move me—that I failed to bless him for what he had done, in spite of his selfish motives.

CHAPTER XVI

WE were eighteen days travelling to Riolama, on the last two making little progress, on account of continuous rain, which made us miserable beyond description. Fortunately the dogs had found, and Nuflo had succeeded in killing, a great ant-eater, so that we were well supplied with excellent, strength-giving flesh. We were among the Riolama mountains at last, and Rima kept with us, apparently expecting great things. I expected nothing, for reasons to be stated by-and-by. My belief was that the only important thing that could happen to us would be starvation.

The afternoon of the last day was spent in skirting the foot of a very long mountain, crowned at its southern extremity with a huge, rocky mass resembling the head of a stone sphinx above its long, couchant body, and at its highest part about a thousand feet above the surrounding level. It was late in the day, raining fast again, yet the old man still toiled on, contrary to his usual practice, which was to spend the last daylight hours in gathering firewood and in constructing a shelter. At length, when we were nearly under the peak, he began to ascend. The rise in this place was gentle, and the vegetation, chiefly composed of dwarf thorn trees rooted in the clefts of the rock, scarcely impeded our progress; yet Nuflo moved obliquely, as if he found the ascent difficult, pausing frequently to take breath and look round him. Then we came to a deep, ravine-like cleft in the side of the mountain, which became deeper and narrower above us, but below it broadened out to a valley; its steep sides as we looked down were clothed with dense, thorny vegetation, and from the bottom rose to our ears the dull sound of a hidden torrent. Along the border of this ravine Nuflo began toiling upwards, and finally brought us out upon a stony plateau on the mountain-side. Here he paused, and turning and regarding us with a look as of satisfied malice in his eyes, remarked that we were at our journey's end, and he trusted the sight of that barren mountainside would compensate us for all the discomforts we had suffered during the last eighteen days.

I heard him with indifference. I had already recognised the place from his own exact description of it, and I now saw all that I had looked to see—a big, barren hill. But Rima, what had she expected that her face wore that blank look of surprise and pain? "Is this the place where mother appeared to you?" she suddenly cried. "The very place—this! this!" Then she added, "The cave where you tended her—where is it?"

"Over there," he said, pointing across the plateau, which was partially overgrown with dwarf trees and bushes, and ended at a wall of rock, almost vertical and about forty feet high.

Going to this precipice, we saw no cave until Nuflo

had cut away two or three tangled bushes, revealing an opening behind, about half as high and twice as wide as the door of an ordinary dwelling-house.

The next thing was to make a torch, and aided by its light we groped our way in and explored the interior. The cave, we found, was about fifty feet long, narrowing to a mere hole at the extremity; but the anterior portion formed an oblong chamber, very lofty, with a dry floor. Leaving our torch burning, we set to work cutting bushes to supply ourselves with wood enough to last us all night. Nuflo, poor old man, loved a big fire dearly; a big fire and fat meat to eat (the ranker its flavour the better he liked it) were to him the greatest blessings that man could wish for: in me also the prospect of a cheerful blaze put a new heart, and I worked with a will in the rain, which increased in the end to a blinding downpour. By the time I dragged my last load in, Nuflo had got his fire well alight, and was heaping on wood in a most lavish way. "No fear of burning our house down to-night," he remarked, with a chuckle—the first sound of that description he had emitted for a long time.

After we had satisfied our hunger, and had smoked one or two cigarettes, the unaccustomed warmth, and dryness, and the firelight affected us with drowsiness, and I had probably been nodding for some time; but starting at last and opening my eyes, I missed Rima. The old man appeared to be asleep, although still in a sitting posture close to the fire. I rose and hurried out, drawing my cloak close around me to protect me from the rain; but what was my surprise on emerging from the cave to feel a dry, bracing wind in my face and to see the desert spread out for leagues before me in the brilliant white light of a full moon! The rain had apparently long ceased, and only a few thin white clouds appeared moving swiftly over the wide blue expanse of heaven. It was a welcome change, but the shock of surprise and pleasure was instantly succeeded by the maddening fear that Rima was lost to me. She was nowhere in sight beneath, and running to the end of the little plateau to get free of the thorn trees, I turned my eyes towards the summit, and there, at some distance above me, caught sight of her standing motionless and gazing upwards. I quickly made my way to her side, calling to her as I approached; but she only half turned to cast a look at me and did not reply.

"Rima," I said, "why have you come here? Are you actually thinking of climbing the mountain at this hour of the night?"

"Yes—why not?" she returned, moving one or two steps from me.

"Rima—sweet Rima, will you listen to me?"

"Now? Oh, no—why do you ask that? Did I not listen to you in the wood before we started, and you also promised to do what I wished? See, the rain is over and the moon shines brightly. Why should I wait? Perhaps from the summit I shall see my people's country. Are we not near it now?"

"Oh, Rima, what do you expect to see? Listen—you must listen, for I know best. From that summit you would see nothing but a vast dim desert, mountain and forest, mountain and forest, where you might wander for years, or until you perished of hunger, or fever, or were slain by some beast of prey or by savage men; but oh, Rima, never, never, never would you find your people, for they exist not. You have seen the false water of the mirage on the savannah, when the sun shines bright and hot; and if one were to follow it he would at last fall down and perish, with never a cool drop to moisten his parched lips. And your hope, Rima—this hope to find your people which has brought you all the way to Riolama—is a mirage, a delusion, which will lead to destruction if you will not abandon it."

She turned to face me with flashing eyes. "You know best!" she exclaimed. "You know best, and tell me that! Never until this moment have you spoken falsely. Oh, why have you said such things to me—named after this place, Riolama? Am I also like that false water you speak of—no divine Rima, no sweet Rima? My mother, had she no mother, no mother's mother? I remember her, at Voa, before she died, and this hand seems real—like yours; you have asked to hold it. But it is not he that speaks to me—not one that showed me the whole world on Ytaioa. Ah, you have wrapped yourself in a stolen cloak, only you have left your old grey beard behind! Go back to the cave and look for it, and leave me to seek my people alone!"

Once more, as on that day in the forest when she prevented me from killing the serpent, and as on the occasion of her meeting with Nuflo after we had been together on Ytaioa, she appeared transformed and instinct with intense resentment—a beautiful human wasp, and every word a sting.

"Rima," I cried, "you are cruelly unjust to say such words to me. If you know that I have never deceived you before, give me a little credit now. You are no delusion—no mirage, but Rima, like no other being on earth. So perfectly truthful and pure I cannot be, but rather than mislead you with falsehoods I would drop down and die on this rock, and lose you and the sweet light that shines on us for ever."

As she listened to my words, spoken with passion, she grew pale and clasped her hands: "What have I said? What have I said?" She spoke in a low voice charged with pain, and all at once she came nearer, and with a low, sobbing cry sank down at my feet, uttering, as on the occasion of finding me lost at night in the forest near her home, tender, sorrowful expressions in her own mysterious language. But before I could take her in my arms she rose again quickly to her feet and moved away a little space from me.

"Oh no, no, it cannot be that you know best!" she began again. "But I know that you have never sought to deceive me. And now, because I falsely accused you, I cannot go there without you"—pointing to the summit—"but must stand still and listen to all you have to say."

"You know, Rima, that your grandfather has now told me your history—how he found your mother at this place, and took her to Voa, where you were born; but of your mother's people he knows nothing, and therefore he can now take you no further."

"Ah, you think that! He says that now; but he deceived me all these years, and if he lied to me in the past, can he not still lie, affirming that he knows nothing of my people, even as he affirmed that he knew not Riolama?"

"He tells lies and he tells truth, Rima, and one can be distinguished from the other. He spoke truthfully at last, and brought us to this place, beyond which he cannot lead you."

"You are right; I must go alone."

"Not so, Rima, for where you go there we must go; only you will lead and we follow, believing only that our quest will end in disappointment, if not in death."

"Believe that and yet follow! Oh no! Why did he consent to lead me so far for nothing?"

"Do you forget that you compelled him? You know what he believes; and he is old and looks with fear at death, remembering his evil deeds, and is convinced that only through your intercession and your mother's he can escape from perdition. Consider, Rima, he could not refuse, to make you more angry and so deprive himself of his only hope."

My words seemed to trouble her, but very soon she spoke again with renewed animation. "If my people exist, why must it be disappointment and perhaps death? He does not know; but she came to him here—did she not? The others are not here, but perhaps not far off. Come, let us go to the summit together to see from it the desert beneath us—mountain and forest, mountain and forest. Somewhere there! You said that

I had knowledge of distant things. And shall I not know which mountain—which forest?"

"Alas! no, Rima; there is a limit to your far-seeing; and even if that faculty were as great as you imagine it would avail you nothing, for there is no mountain, no forest, in whose shadow your people dwell."

For a while she was silent, but her eyes and clasping fingers were restless and showed her agitation. She seemed to be searching in the depths of her mind for some argument to oppose to my assertions. Then in a low, almost despondent voice, with something of reproach in it, she said, "Have we come so far to go back again? You were not Nuflo to need my intercession, yet you came too."

"Where you are there I must be—you have said it yourself. Besides, when we started I had some hope of finding your people. Now I know better, having heard Nuflo's story. Now I know that your hope is a vain one."

"Why? Why? Was she not found here—mother? Where, then, are the others?"

"Yes, she was found here, alone. You must remember all the things she spoke to you before she died. Did she ever speak to you of her people—speak of them as if they existed, and would be glad to receive you among them some day?"

"No. Why did she not speak of that? Do you know—can you tell me?"

"I can guess the reason, Rima. It is very sad—so sad that it is hard to tell it. When Nuflo tended her in the cave and was ready to worship her and do everything she wished, and conversed with her by signs, she showed no wish to return to her people. And when he offered her, in a way she understood, to take her to a distant place, where she would be among strange beings, among others like Nuflo, she readily consented, and painfully performed that long journey to Voa. Would you, Rima, have acted thus—would you have gone so far away from your beloved people, never to return, never to hear of them or speak to them again? Oh no, you could not; nor would she, if her people had been in existence. But she knew that she had survived them, that some great calamity had fallen upon and destroyed them. They were few in number, perhaps, and surrounded on every side by hostile tribes, and had no weapons, and made no war. They had been preserved because they inhabited a place apart, some deep valley perhaps, guarded on all sides by lofty mountains and impenetrable forests and marshes; but at last the cruel savages broke into this retreat and hunted them down, destroying all except a few fugitives, who escaped singly like your mother, and fled away to hide in some distant solitude."

The anxious expression on her face deepened as she listened to one of anguish and despair; and then, almost before I concluded, she suddenly lifted her hands to her head, uttering a low, sobbing cry, and would have fallen on the rock had I not caught her quickly in my arms. Once more in my arms—against my breast, her proper place! But now all that bright life seemed gone out of her; her head fell on my shoulder, and there was no motion in her except at intervals a slight shudder in her frame accompanied by a low, gasping sob. In a little while the sobs ceased, the eyes were closed, the face still and deathly white, and with a terrible anxiety in my heart I carried her down to the cave.

CHAPTER XVII

AS I re-entered the cave with my burden Nuflo sat up and stared at me with a frightened look in his eyes. Throwing my cloak down I placed the girl on it and briefly related what had happened.

He drew near to examine her; then placed his hand on her heart. "Dead!—she is dead!" he exclaimed.

My own anxiety changed to an irrational anger at his words. "Old fool! She has only fainted," I returned. "Get me some water, quick!"

But the water failed to restore her, and my anxiety deepened as I gazed on that white, still face. Oh, why had I told her that sad tragedy I had imagined with so little preparation? Alas! I had succeeded too well in my purpose, killing her vain hope and her at the same moment.

The old man, still bending over her, spoke again. "No, I will not believe that she is dead yet; but, sir, if not dead, then she is dying."

I could have struck him down for his words. "She will die in my arms, then," I exclaimed, thrusting him roughly aside, and lifting her up with the cloak beneath her.

And while I held her thus, her head resting on my

arm, and gazed with unutterable anguish into her strangely white face, insanely praying to Heaven to restore her to me, Nuflo fell on his knees before her, and with bowed head, and hands clasped in supplication, began to speak.

"Rima! Grandchild!" he prayed, his quivering voice betraying his agitation. "Do not die just yet: you must not die—not wholly die—until you have heard what I have to say to you. I do not ask you to answer in words—you are past that, and I am not unreasonable. Only, when I finish, make some sign—a sigh, a movement of the eyelid, a twitch of the lips, even in the small corners of the mouth; nothing more than that, just to show that you have heard, and I shall be satisfied. Remember all the years that I have been your protector, and this long journey that I have taken on your account; also all that I did for your sainted mother before she died at Voa, to become one of the most important of those who surround the Queen of Heaven, and who, when they wish for any favour, have only to say half a word to get it. And do not cast in oblivion that at the last I obeyed your wish and brought you safely to Riolama. It is true that in some small things I deceived you; but that must not weigh with you, because it is a small matter and not worthy of mention when you consider the claims I have on you. In your hands, Rima, I leave everything, relying on the promise you made me, and on my services. Only one word of caution remains to be added. Do not let the magnificence of the place you are now about to enter, the new sights and colours, and the noise of shouting, and musical instruments and blowing of trumpets, put these things out of your head. Nor must you begin to think meanly of yourself and be abashed when you find yourself surrounded by saints and angels; for you are not less than they, although it may not seem so at first when you see them in their bright clothes, which, they say, shine like the sun. I cannot ask you to tie a string round your finger: I can only trust to your memory, which was always good, even about the smallest things; and when you are asked, as no doubt you will be, to express a wish, remember before everything to speak of your grandfather, and his claims on you, also on your angelic mother, to whom you will present my humble remembrances."

During this petition, which in other circumstances would have moved me to laughter but now only irritated me, a subtle change seemed to come to the apparently lifeless girl to make me hope. The small hand in mine felt not so icy cold, and though no faintest colour had come to the face, its pallor had lost something of its deathly waxen appearance; and now the compressed lips had relaxed a little and seemed ready to part. I laid my finger-tips on her heart and felt, or imagined that I felt, a faint fluttering; and at last I became convinced that her heart was really beating.

I turned my eyes on the old man, still bending forward, intently watching for the sign he had asked her to make. My anger and disgust at his gross, earthy egoism had vanished. "Let us thank God, old man," I said, the tears of joy half choking my utterance. "She lives—she is recovering from her fit."

He drew back, and on his knees, with bowed head, murmured a prayer of thanks to Heaven.

Together we continued watching her face for half an hour longer, I still holding her in my arms, which could never grow weary of that sweet burden, waiting for other, surer signs of returning life; and she seemed now like one that had fallen into a profound, deathlike sleep which must end in death. Yet when I remembered her face as it had looked an hour ago, I was confirmed in the belief that the progress to recovery, so strangely slow, was yet sure. So slow, so gradual was this passing from death to life that we had hardly ceased to fear when we noticed that the lips were parted, or almost parted, that they were no longer white, and that under her pale, transparent skin a faint, bluish-rosy colour was now visible. And at length, seeing that all danger was past and recovery so slow, old Nuflo withdrew once more to the fireside, and stretching himself out on the sandy floor, soon fell into a deep sleep.

If he had not been lying there before me in the strong light of the glowing embers and dancing flames, I could not have felt more alone with Rima—alone amid those remote mountains, in that secret cavern, with lights and shadows dancing on its grey vault. In that profound silence and solitude the mysterious loveliness of the still face I continued to gaze on, its appearance of life without consciousness, produced a strange feeling in me, hard, perhaps impossible, to describe.

Once, when clambering among the rough rocks, overgrown with forest, among the Queneveta mountains,

I came on a single white flower which was new to me, which I have never seen since. After I had looked long at it, and passed on, the image of that perfect flower remained so persistently in my mind that on the following day I went again, in the hope of seeing it still untouched by decay. There was no change; and on this occasion I spent a much longer time looking at it, admiring the marvellous beauty of its form, which seemed so greatly to exceed that of all other flowers. It had thick petals, and at first gave me the idea of an artificial flower, cut by a divinely inspired artist from some unknown precious stone, of the size of a large orange and whiter than milk, and yet, in spite of its opacity, with a crystalline lustre on the surface. Next day I went again, scarcely hoping to find it still unwithered; it was fresh as if only just opened; and after that I went often, sometimes at intervals of several days, and still no faintest sign of any change, the clear, exquisite lines still undimmed, the purity and lustre as I had first seen it. Why, I often asked, does not this mystic forest flower fade and perish like others? That first impression of its artificial appearance had soon left me; it was, indeed, a flower, and, like other flowers, had life and growth, only with that transcendent beauty it had a different kind of life. Unconscious, but higher; perhaps immortal. Thus it would continue to bloom when I had looked my last on it; wind and rain and sunlight would never stain, never tinge, its sacred purity; the savage Indian, though he sees little to admire in a flower, yet seeing this one would veil his face and turn back; even the browsing beast crashing his way through the forest, struck with its strange glory, would swerve aside and pass on without harming it. Afterwards I heard from some Indians, to whom I described it, that the flower I had discovered was called Hata; also that they had a superstition concerning it—a strange belief. They said that only one Hata flower existed in the world; that it bloomed in one spot for the space of a moon; that on the disappearance of the moon in the sky the Hata disappeared from its place, only to reappear blooming in some other spot, sometimes in some distant forest. And they also said that whosoever discovered the Hata flower in the forest would overcome all his enemies and obtain all his desires, and finally outlive other men by many years. But, as I have said, all this I heard afterwards, and my half-superstitious feeling for the flower had grown up independently in my own mind. A feeling like that was in me while I gazed on the face that had no motion, no consciousness in it, and yet had life, a life of so high a kind as to match with its pure, surpassing loveliness. I could almost believe that, like the forest flower, in this state and aspect it would endure for ever; endure and perhaps give of its own immortality to everything around it—to me, holding her in my arms and gazing fixedly on the pale face framed in its cloud of dark, silken hair; to the leaping flames that threw changing lights on the dim stony wall of rock; to old Nuflo and his two yellow dogs stretched out on the floor in eternal, unawakening sleep.

This feeling took such firm possession of my mind that

it kept me for a time as motionless as the form I held in my arms. I was only released from its power by noting still further changes in the face I watched, a more distinct advance towards conscious life. The faint colour, which had scarcely been more than a suspicion of colour, had deepened perceptibly; the lids were lifted so as to show a gleam of the crystal orbs beneath; the lips, too, were slightly parted.

And, at last, bending lower down to feel her breath, the beauty and sweetness of those lips could no longer be resisted, and I touched them with mine. Having once tasted their sweetness and fragrance, it was impossible to keep from touching them again and again. She was not conscious—how could she be and not shrink from my caress? Yet there was a suspicion in my mind, and drawing back I gazed into her face once more. A strange new radiance had overspread it. Or was this only an illusive colour thrown on her skin by the red firelight? I shaded her face with my open hand, and saw that her pallor had really gone, that the rosy flame on her cheeks was part of her life. Her lustrous eyes, half open, were gazing into mine. Oh, surely consciousness had returned to her! Had she been sensible of those stolen kisses? Would she now shrink from another caress? Trembling I bent down and touched her lips again, lightly, but lingeringly, and then again, and when I drew back and looked at her face the rosy flame was brighter, and the eyes, more open still, were looking into mine. And gazing with those open, conscious eyes, it seemed to me that at last, at last, the shadow that had rested between us had vanished, that we were united in perfect love and confidence, and that speech was superfluous. And when I spoke it was not without doubt and hesitation: our bliss in those silent moments had been so complete, what could speaking do but make it less!

"My love, my life, my sweet Rima, I know that you will understand me now as you did not before, on that dark night—do you remember it, Rima?—when I held you clasped to my breast in the wood. How it pierced my heart with pain to speak plainly to you as I did on the mountain to-night—to kill the hope that had sustained and brought you so far from home! But now that anguish is over; the shadow has gone out of those beautiful eyes that are looking at me. Is it because loving me, knowing now what love is, knowing, too, how much I love you, that you no longer need to speak to any other living being of such things? To tell it, to show it, to me is now enough—is it not so, Rima? How strange it seemed, at first, when you shrank in fear from me! But, afterwards, when you prayed aloud to your mother, opening all the secrets of your heart, I understood it. In that lonely, isolated life in the wood you had heard nothing of love, of its power over the heart, its infinite sweetness; when it came to you at last it was a new, inexplicable thing, and filled you with misgivings and tumultuous thoughts, so that you feared it and hid yourself from its cause. Such tremors would be felt if it had always been night, with no light except that of the stars and the pale moon, as we saw it a little while ago on the mountain; and, at last, day dawned, and a strange, unheard-of rose and purple flame kindled in the eastern sky, foretelling the coming sun. It would seem beautiful beyond anything that night had shown to you, yet you would tremble, and your heart beat fast at that strange sight; you would wish to fly to those who might be able to tell you its meaning, and whether the sweet things it prophesied would ever really come. That is why you wished to find your people, and came to Riolama to seek them: and when you knew—when I cruelly told you—that they would never be found, then you imagined that that strange feeling in your heart must remain a secret for ever, and you could not endure the thought of your loneliness. If you had not fainted so quickly, then I should have told you what I must tell you now. They are lost, Rima—your people—but I am with you, and know what you feel, even if you have no words to tell it. But what need of words? It shines in your eyes, it burns like a flame in your face; I can feel it in your hands. Do you not also see it in my face—all that I feel for you, the love that makes me happy? For this is love, Rima, the flower and the melody of life, the sweetest thing, the sweet miracle that makes our two souls one."

Still resting in my arms, as if glad to rest there, still gazing into my face, it was clear to me that she understood my every word. And then, with no trace of doubt or fear left, I stooped again, until my lips were on hers; and when I drew back once more, hardly knowing which bliss was greatest—kissing her delicate mouth or gazing into her face—she all at once put her arms about my neck and drew herself up until she sat on my knee.

"Abel—shall I call you Abel now—and always?" she spoke, still with her arms round my neck. "Ah, why did you let me come to Riolama? I would come! I made him come—old grandfather, sleeping there: he does not count, but you—you! After you had heard my story, and knew that it was all for nothing! And all I wished to know was there—in you. Oh, how sweet it is! But a little while ago, what pain! When I stood on the mountain when you talked to me, and I knew that you knew best, and tried and tried not to know. At last I could try no more; they were all dead like mother; I had chased the false water on the savannah. 'Oh, let me die too,' I said, for I could not bear the pain. And afterwards, here in the cave, I was like one asleep, and when I woke I did not really wake. It was like morning with the light teasing me to open my eyes and look at it. Not yet, dear light; a little while longer, it is so sweet to lie still. But it would not leave me, and stayed teasing me still, like a small shining green fly; until, because it teased me so, I opened my lids just a little. It was not morning, but the firelight, and I was in your arms, not in my little bed. Your eyes looking, looking into mine. But I could see yours better. I remembered everything then, how you once asked me to look into your eyes. I remembered so many things—oh, so many!"

"How many things did you remember, Rima?"

"Listen, Abel, do you ever lie on the dry moss and look straight up into a tree and count a thousand leaves?"

"No, sweetest, that could not be done, it is so many to count. Do you know how many a thousand are?"

"Oh, do I not! When a humming-bird flies close to my face and stops still in the air, humming like a bee, and then is gone, in that short time I can count a hundred small round bright feathers on its throat. That is only a hundred; a thousand are more, ten times. Looking up I count a thousand leaves; then stop counting, because there are thousands more behind the first, and thousands more, crowded together so that I cannot count them. Lying in your arms, looking up into your face, it was like that; I could not count the things I remembered. In the wood, when you were there, and before; and long, long ago at Voa, when I was a child with mother."

"Tell me some of the things you remembered, Rima."

"Yes, one—only one now. When I was a child at Voa mother was very lame—you know that. Whenever we went out, away from the houses, into the forest, walking slowly, slowly, she would sit under a tree while I ran about playing. And every time I came back to her I would find her so pale, so sad, crying—crying. That was when I would hide and come softly back so that she would not hear me coming. 'Oh, mother, why are you crying? Does your lame foot hurt you?' And one day she took me in her arms and told me truly why she cried."

She ceased speaking, but looked at me with a strange new light coming into her eyes.

"Why did she cry, my love?"

"Oh, Abel, can you understand—now—at last!" And putting her lips close to my ear, she began to murmur soft, melodious sounds that told me nothing. Then drawing back her head, she looked again at me, her eyes glistening with tears, her lips half parted with a smile, tender and wistful.

Ah, poor child! in spite of all that had been said, all that had happened, she had returned to the old delusion that I must understand her speech. I could only return her look, sorrowfully and in silence.

Her face became clouded with disappointment, then she spoke again with something of pleading in her tone. "Look, we are not now apart, I hiding in the wood, you seeking, but together, saying the same things. In your language—yours and now mine. But before you came I knew nothing, nothing, for there was only grandfather to talk to. A few words each day, the same words. If yours is mine, mine must be yours. Oh, do you not know that mine is better?"

"Yes, better; but alas! Rima, I can never hope to understand your sweet speech, much less to speak it. The bird that only chirps and twitters can never sing like the organ-bird."

Crying, she hid her face against my neck, murmuring sadly between her sobs, "Never—never!"

How strange it seemed, in that moment of joy, such a passion of tears, such despondent words!

For some minutes I preserved a sorrowful silence, realising for the first time, so far as it was possible to realise such a thing, what my inability to understand her secret language meant to her—that finer language in which alone her swift thoughts and vivid emotions could be expressed. Easily and well as she seemed able to declare herself in my tongue, I could well imagine that to her it would seem like the merest stammering. As she had said to me once when I asked her to speak in Spanish, "That is not speaking." And so long as she could not commune with me in that better language, which reflected her mind, there would not be that perfect union of soul she so passionately desired.

By-and-by, as she grew calmer, I sought to say something that would be consoling to both of us. "Sweetest Rima," I spoke, "it is so sad that I can never hope to talk with you in your way; but a greater love than this that is ours we could never feel, and love will make us happy, unutterably happy, in spite of that one sadness. And perhaps, after a while, you will be able to say all you wish in my language, which is also yours, as you said some time ago. When we are back again in the beloved wood, and talk once more under that tree where we first talked, and under the old mora, where you hid yourself and threw down leaves on me, and where you caught the little spider to show me how you made yourself a dress, you shall speak to me in your own sweet tongue, and then try to say the same things in mine. . . . And in the end, perhaps, you will find that it is not so impossible as you think."

She looked at me, smiling again through her tears, and shook her head a little.

"Remember what I have heard, that before your mother

died you were able to tell Nuflo and the priest what her wish was. Can you not, in the same way, tell me why she cried?"

"I can tell you, but it will not be telling you."

"I understand. You can tell the bare facts. I can imagine something more, and the rest I must lose. Tell me, Rima."

Her face became troubled; she glanced away and let her eyes wander round the dim, firelit cavern; then they returned to mine once more.

"Look," she said, "grandfather lying asleep by the fire. So far away from us—oh, so far! But if we were to go out from the cave, and on and on to the great mountains where the city of the sun is, and stood there at last in the midst of great crowds of people, all looking at us, talking to us, it would be just the same. They would be like the trees and rocks and animals—so far! Not with us nor we with them. But we are everywhere alone together, apart—we two. It is love; I know it now, but I did not know it before because I had forgotten what she told me. Do you think I can tell you what she said when I asked her why she cried? Oh no! Only this, she and another were like one, always, apart from the others. Then something came—something came! O Abel, was that the something you told me about on the mountain? And the other was lost for ever, and she was alone in the forests and mountains of the world. Oh, why do we cry for what is lost? Why do we not quickly forget it and feel glad again? Now only do I know what you felt, O sweet mother, when you sat still and cried. while I ran about and played and laughed! O poor mother! Oh, what pain!" And hiding her face against my neck, she sobbed once more.

To my eyes also love and sympathy brought the tears; but in a little while the fond, comforting words I spoke and my caresses recalled her from that sad past to the present: then, lying back as at first, her head resting on my folded cloak, her body partly supported by my encircling arm and partly by the rock we were leaning against, her half-closed eyes turned to mine expressed a tender assured happiness—the chastened gladness of sunshine after rain; a soft delicious languor that was partly passionate with the passion etherealised.

"Tell me, Rima," I said, bending down to her, "in all those troubled days with me in the woods had you no happy moments? Did not something in your heart tell you that it was sweet to love, even before you knew what love meant?"

"Yes; and once—O Abel, do you remember that night, after returning from Ytaioa, when you sat so late talking by the fire—I in the shadow, never stirring, listening, listening; you by the fire with the light on your face, saying so many strange things? I was happy then—oh, how happy! It was black night and raining, and I a plant growing in the dark, feeling the sweet rain-drops falling, falling on my leaves. Oh, it will be morning by-and-by and the sun will shine on my wet leaves; and that made me glad till I trembled with happiness. Then suddenly the lightning would come, so bright, and I would tremble with fear, and wish that it would be dark again. That was when you looked at me sitting in the shadow, and I could not take my eyes away quickly and could not meet yours, so that I trembled with fear."

"And now there is no fear—no shadow; now you are perfectly happy?"

"Oh, so happy! If the way back to the wood was longer, ten times, and if the great mountains, white with snow on their tops, were between, and the great dark forest, and rivers wider than Orinoco, still I would go alone without fear, because you would come after me, to join me in the wood, to be with me at last and always."

"But I should not let you go alone, Rima—your lonely days are over now."

She opened her eyes wider, and looked earnestly into my face. "I must go back alone, Abel," she said. "Before day comes I must leave you. Rest here, with grandfather, for a few days and nights, then follow me."

I heard her with astonishment. "It must not be, Rima," I cried. "What, let you leave me—now you are mine—to go all that distance, through all that wild country where you might lose yourself and perish alone? Oh, do not think of it!"

She listened, regarding me with some slight trouble in her eyes, but smiling a little at the same time. Her small hand moved up my arm and caressed my cheek; then she drew my face down to hers until our lips met. But when I looked at her eyes again I saw that she had not consented to my wish. "Do I not know all the way now," she spoke, "all the mountains, rivers, forests—how should I lose myself? And I must return quickly, not step by step, walking—resting, resting—walking, stopping to cook and eat, stopping to gather firewood, to make a shelter—so many things! Oh, I shall be back in half the time; and I have so much to do."

"What can you have to do, love?—everything can be done when we are in the wood together."

A bright smile with a touch of mockery in it flitted over her face as she replied, "Oh, must I tell you that there are things you cannot do? Look, Abel," and she touched the slight garment she wore, thinner now than at first, and dulled by long exposure to sun and wind and rain.

I could not command her, and seemed powerless to persuade her; but I had not done yet, and proceeded to use every argument I could find to bring her round to my view; and when I finished she put her arms round my neck and drew herself up once more. "O Abel, how happy I shall be!" she said, taking no notice of all I had said. "Think of me alone, days and days, in the wood, waiting for you, working all the time; saying, 'Come quickly, Abel; come slow, Abel. O Abel, how long you are! Oh, do not come until my work is finished!' And when it is finished and you arrive you shall find me, but not at once. First you will seek for me in the house, then in the wood, calling, 'Rima! Rima!' And she will be there, listening, hid in the trees, wishing to be in your arms, wishing for your lips—oh, so glad, yet fearing to show herself. Do you know why? He told you—did he not?—that when he first saw her she was standing before him, all in white—a dress that was like snow on the mountain-tops, when the sun is setting and gives it rose and purple colour. I shall be like that, hidden among the trees, saying, 'Am I different—not like Rima? Will he know me—will he love me just the same?' Oh, do I not know that you will be glad, and love me, and call me beautiful? Listen! Listen!" she suddenly exclaimed, lifting her face.

Among the bushes not far from the cave's mouth a small bird had broken out in song, a clear, tender melody soon taken up by other birds further away.

"It will soon be morning," she said, and then clasped her arms about me once more and held me in a long, passionate embrace; then slipping away from my arms and with one swift glance at the sleeping old man, passed out of the cave.

For a few moments I remained sitting, not yet realising that she had left me, so suddenly and swiftly had she passed from my arms and my sight; then, recovering my faculties, I started up and rushed out in hopes of overtaking her.

It was not yet dawn, but there was still some light from the full moon, now somewhere behind the mountains. Running to the verge of the bush-grown plateau, I explored the rocky slope beneath without seeing her form, and then called, "Rima! Rima!"

A soft, warbling sound, uttered by no bird, came up from the shadowy bushes far below; and in that direction I ran on; then pausing called again. The sweet sound was repeated once more, but much lower down now, and so faintly that I scarcely heard it. And when I went on further, and called again and again, there was no reply, and I knew that she had indeed gone on that long journey alone.

CHAPTER XVIII

WHEN Nuflo at length opened his eyes he found me sitting alone and despondent by the fire, just returned from my vain chase. I had been caught in a heavy mist on the mountain-side, and was wet through as well as weighed down by fatigue and drowsiness, consequent upon the previous day's laborious march and my night-long vigil; yet I dared not think of rest. *She* had gone from me, and I could not have prevented it; yet the thought that I had allowed her to slip out of my arms, to go away alone on that long, perilous journey, was as intolerable as if I had consented to it.

Nuflo was at first startled to hear of her sudden departure; but he laughed at my fears, affirming that after having once been over the ground she could not lose herself; that she would be in no danger from the Indians, as she would invariably see them at a distance and avoid them, and that wild beasts, serpents, and other evil creatures would do her no harm. The small amount of food she required to sustain life could be found anywhere; furthermore, her journey would not be interrupted by bad weather, since rain and heat had no effect on her. In the end he seemed pleased that she had left us, saying that with Rima in the wood the house and cultivated patch and hidden provisions and implements would be safe, for no Indian would venture to come where she was. His confidence reassured me, and casting myself down on the sandy floor of the cave, I fell into a deep slumber, which lasted until evening; then I only woke to share a meal with the old man, and sleep again until the following day.

Nuflo was not ready to start yet; he was enamoured of the unaccustomed comforts of a dry sleeping-place and a fire blown about by no wind and into which fell no hissing rain-drops. Not for two days more would he consent to set out on the return journey, and if he could have persuaded me our stay at Riolama would have lasted a week.

We had fine weather at starting; but before long it clouded, and then for upwards of a fortnight we had it wet and stormy, which so hindered us that it took us twenty-three days to accomplish the return journey, whereas the journey out had only taken eighteen. The adventures we met with and the pains we suffered during this long march need not be related. The rain made us miserable, but we suffered more from hunger than from any other cause, and on more than one occasion were reduced to the verge of starvation. Twice we were driven to beg for food at Indian villages, and as we had nothing to give in exchange for it, we got very little. It is possible to buy hospitality from the savage without fish-hooks, nails, and calico; but on this occasion I found myself without that impalpable medium of exchange, which had been so great a help to me on my first journey to

Parahuari. Now I was weak and miserable and without cunning. It is true that we could have exchanged the two dogs for cassava-bread and corn, but we should then have been worse off than ever. And in the end the dogs saved us by an occasional capture—an armadillo surprised in the open and seized before it could bury itself in the soil, or an iguana, opossum, or labba, traced by means of their keen sense of smell to its hiding-place. Then Nuflo would rejoice and feast, rewarding them with the skin, bones, and entrails. But at length one of the dogs fell lame, and Nuflo, who was very hungry, made its lameness an excuse for despatching it, which he did apparently without compunction, notwithstanding that the poor brute had served him well in its way. He cut up and smoke-dried the flesh, and the intolerable pangs of hunger compelled me to share the loathsome food with him. We were not only indecent, it seemed to me, but cannibals to feed on the faithful servant that had been our butcher. "But what does it matter?" I argued with myself. "All flesh, clean and unclean, should be, and is, equally abhorrent to me, and killing animals a kind of murder. But now I find myself constrained to do this evil thing that good may come. Only to live I take it now—this hateful strength-giver that will enable me to reach Rima, and the purer, better life that is to be."

During all that time, when we toiled onwards league after league in silence, or sat silent by the nightly fire, I thought of many things; but the past, with which I had definitely broken, was little in my mind. Rima was still the source and centre of all my thoughts; from her they rose, and to her returned. Thinking, hoping, dreaming, sustained me in those dark days and nights of pain and privation. Imagination was the bread that gave me strength, the wine that exhilarated. What sustained old Nuflo's mind I know not. Probably it was like a chrysalis, dormant, independent of sustenance; the bright-winged image to be called at some future time to life by a great shouting of angelic hosts and noises of musical instruments slept secure, coffined in that dull, gross nature.

The old beloved wood once more! Never did his native village in some mountain valley seem more beautiful to the Switzer, returning, war-worn, from long voluntary exile, than did that blue cloud on the horizon—the forest where Rima dwelt, my bride, my beautiful—and towering over it the dark cone of Ytaioa, now seem to my hungry eyes! How near at last—how near! And yet the two or three intervening leagues to be traversed so slowly, step by step—how vast the distance seemed! Even at far Riolama, when I set out on my return, I scarcely seemed so far from my love. This maddening impatience told on my strength, which was small, and hindered me. I could not run nor even walk fast; old Nuflo, slow, and sober, with no flame consuming his heart, was more than my equal in the end, and to keep up with him was all I could do.

At the finish he became silent and cautious, first entering the belt of trees leading away through the low range of hills at the southern extremity of the wood. For a mile or upwards we trudged on in the shade; then I began to recognise familiar ground, the old trees under which I had walked or sat, and knew that a hundred yards further on there would be a first glimpse of the palm-leaf thatch. Then all weakness forsook me; with a low cry of passionate longing and joy I rushed on ahead; but I strained my eyes in vain for a sight of that sweet shelter: no patch of pale yellow colour appeared amidst the universal verdure of bushes, creepers, and trees—trees beyond trees, trees towering above trees.

For some moments I could not realise it. No, I had surely made a mistake, the house had not stood on that spot; it would appear in sight a little further on. I took a few uncertain steps onwards, and then again stood still, my brain reeling, my heart swelling nigh to bursting with anguish. I was still standing motionless, with hand pressed to my breast, when Nuflo overtook me. "Where is it—the house?" I stammered, pointing with my hand. All his stolidity seemed gone now; he was trembling too, his lips silently moving. At length he spoke: "They have come—the children of hell have been here, and have destroyed everything!"

"Rima! What has become of Rima?" I cried; but without replying he walked on, and I followed.

The house, we soon found, had been burnt down. Not a stick remained. Where it had stood a heap of black ashes covered the ground—nothing more. But on looking round we could discover no sign of human beings having recently visited the spot. A rank growth of grass and herbage now covered the once clear space surrounding the site of the dwelling, and the ash heap looked as if it had been lying there for a month at least. As to what had become of Rima the old man could say no word. He sat down on the ground overwhelmed at the calamity: Runi's people had been there, he could not doubt it, and they would come again, and he could only look for death at their hands. The thought that Rima had perished, that she was lost, was unendurable. It could not be! No doubt the Indians had come and destroyed the house during our absence; but she had returned, and they had gone away again to come no more. She would be somewhere in the forest, perhaps not far off, impatiently waiting our return. The old man stared at me while I spoke; he appeared to be in a kind of stupor, and made no reply: and at last, leaving him still sitting on the ground, I went into the wood to look for Rima.

As I walked there, occasionally stopping to peer into some shadowy glade or opening, and to listen, I was tempted again and again to call the name of her I sought aloud; and still the fear that by so doing I might bring some hidden danger on myself, perhaps on her, made me silent. A strange melancholy rested on the forest, a quietude seldom broken by a distant bird's cry. How, I asked myself, should I ever find her in that wide forest while I moved about in that silent, cautious way? My only hope was that she would find me. It occurred to me that the most likely place to seek her would be some of the old haunts known to us both, where we had talked together. I thought first of the mora tree, where she had hidden herself from me, and thither I directed my steps.

About this tree, and within its shade, I lingered for upwards of an hour; and, finally, casting my eyes up into the great dim cloud of green and purple leaves, I softly called, "Rima, Rima, if you have seen me, and have concealed yourself from me in your hiding-place, in mercy answer me—in mercy come down to me now!" But Rima answered not, nor threw down any red glowing leaves to mock me: only the wind, high up, whispered something low and sorrowful in the foliage; and turning I wandered away at random into the deeper shadows.

By-and-by I was startled by the long, piercing cry of a wild fowl, sounding strangely loud in the silence; and no sooner was the air still again than it struck me that no bird had uttered that cry. The Indian is a good mimic of animal voices, but practice had made me able to distinguish the true from the false bird note. For a minute or so I stood still, at a loss what to do, then moved on again with greater caution, scarcely breathing, straining my sight to pierce the shadowy depths. All at once I gave a great start, for directly before me, on the projecting root in the deeper shade of a tree, sat a dark, motionless human form. I stood still, watching it for some time, not yet knowing that it had seen me, when all doubts were put to flight by the form rising and deliberately advancing—a naked Indian with a zabatana in his hand. As he came up out of the deeper shade I recognised Piaké, the surly elder brother of my friend Kua-kó.

It was a great shock to meet him in the wood, but I had no time to reflect just then. I only remembered that

I had deeply offended him and his people, that they probably looked on me as an enemy, and would think little of taking my life. It was too late to attempt to escape by flight; I was spent with my long journey and the many privations I had suffered, while he stood there in his full strength with a deadly weapon in his hand.

Nothing was left but to put a bold face on, greet him in a friendly way, and invent some plausible story to account for my action in secretly leaving the village.

He was now standing still, silently regarding me, and glancing round I saw that he was not alone: at a distance of about forty yards on my right hand two other dusky forms appeared watching me from the deep shade.

"Piaké!" I cried, advancing three or four steps.

"You have returned," he answered, but without moving. "Where from?"

"Riolama."

He shook his head, then asked where it was.

"Twenty days towards the setting sun," I said. As he remained silent I added, "I heard that I could find gold in the mountains there. An old man told me, and we went to look for gold."

"What did you find?"

"Nothing."

"Ah!"

And so our conversation appeared to be at an end. But after a few moments my intense desire to discover whether the savages knew aught of Rima or not made me hazard a question.

"Do you live here in the forest now?" I asked.

He shook his head, and after a while said, "We come to kill animals."

"You are like me now," I returned quickly; "you fear nothing."

He looked distrustfully at me, then came a little nearer and said—

"You are very brave. I should not have gone twenty days' journey with no weapons and only an old man for companion. What weapons did you have?"

I saw that he feared me, and wished to make sure that I had it not in my power to do him some injury. "No weapon except my knife," I replied, with assumed carelessness. With that I raised my cloak so as to let him see for himself, turning my body round before him. "Have you found my pistol?" I added.

He shook his head; but he appeared less suspicious now and came close up to me. "How do you get food? Where are you going?" he asked.

I answered boldly, "Food! I am nearly starving. I am going to the village to see if the women have got any meat in the pot, and to tell Runi all I have done since I left him."

He looked at me keenly, a little surprised at my confidence perhaps, then said that he was also going back and would accompany me. One of the other men now advanced, blow-pipe in hand, to join us, and, leaving the wood, we started to walk across the savannah.

It was hateful to have to recross that savannah again, to leave the woodland shadows where I had hoped to find Rima; but I was powerless: I was a prisoner once more, the lost captive recovered and not yet pardoned, probably never to be pardoned. Only by means of my own cunning could I be saved, and Nuflo, poor old man, must take his chance.

Again and again as we tramped over the barren ground, and when we climbed the ridge, I was compelled to stand still to recover breath, explaining to Piaké that I had been travelling day and night, with no meat during the last three days, so that I was exhausted. This was an exaggeratíon, but it was necessary to account in some way for the faintness I experienced during our walk, caused less by fatigue and want of food than by anguish of mind.

At intervals I talked to him, asking after all the other members of the community by name. At last, thinking only of Rima, I asked him if any other person or persons besides his people came to the wood now or lived there.

He said no.

"Once," I said, "there was a daughter of the Didi, a girl you all feared: is she there now?"

He looked at me with suspicion and then shook his head. I dared not press him with more questions; but after an interval he said plainly, "She is not there now."

And I was forced to believe him; for had Rima been in the wood *they* would not have been there. She was not there, this much I had discovered. Had she, then, lost her way, or perished on that long journey from Riolama? Or had she returned only to fall into the hands of her cruel enemies? My heart was heavy in me; but if these devils in human shape knew more than they had told me, I must, I said, hide my anxiety and wait patiently to find it out, should they spare my life. And if they spared me and had not spared that other sacred life interwoven with mine, the time would come when they would find, too late, that they had taken to their bosom a worse devil than themselves.

CHAPTER XIX

MY arrival at the village created some excitement; but I was plainly no longer regarded as a friend or one of the family. Runi was absent, and I looked forward to his return with no little apprehension; he would doubtless decide my fate. Kua-kó was also away. The others sat or stood about the great room, staring at me in silence. I took no notice, but merely asked for food, then for my hammock, which I hung up in the old place, and lying down I fell into a doze. Runi made his appearance at dusk. I rose and greeted him, but he spoke no word, and, until he went to his hammock, sat in sullen silence, ignoring my presence.

On the following day the crisis came. We were once more gathered in the room all but Kua-kó and another of the men, who had not yet returned from some expedition—and for the space of half an hour not a word was spoken by anyone. Something was expected; even the children were strangely still, and whenever one of the pet birds strayed in at the open door, uttering a little plaintive note, it was chased out again, but without a sound. At length Runi straightened himself on his seat and fixed his eyes on me; then cleared his throat and began a long harangue, delivered in the loud, monotonous sing-song which I knew so well and which meant that the occasion was an important one. And as is usual in such efforts, the same thought and expressions were used again and again, and yet again, with dull, angry insistence. The orator of Guayana to be impressive must be long, however little he may have to say. Strange as it may seem, I listened critically to him, not without a feeling of scorn at his lower intelligence. But I was easier in my mind now. From the very fact of his addressing such a speech to me I was convinced that he wished not to take my life, and would not do so if I could clear myself of the suspicion of treachery.

I was a white man, he said, they were Indians; nevertheless they had treated me well. They had fed and sheltered me. They had done a great deal for me: they had taught me the use of the zabatana, and had promised to make one for me, asking for nothing in return. They had also promised me a wife. How had I treated them? I had deserted them, going away secretly to a distance, leaving them in doubt as to my intentions. How could they tell why I had gone, and where? They had an enemy. Managa was his name; he and his people hated them; I knew that he wished them evil; I knew where to find him, for they had told me. That was what they thought when I suddenly left them. Now I returned to them, saying that I had been to Riolama. He knew where Riolama was, although he had never been there: it was so far. Why did I go to Riolama? It was a bad place. There were Indians there, a few; but they were not good

Indians like those of Parahuari, and would kill a white man. *Had* I gone there? Why had I gone there?

He finished at last, and it was my turn to speak, but he had given me plenty of time, and my reply was ready. "I have heard you," I said. "Your words are good words They are the words of a friend. I am the white man's friend, you say: is he my friend? He went away secretly, saying no word: why did he go without speaking to his friend who had treated him well? Has he been to my enemy Managa? Perhaps he is a friend of my enemy? Where has he been? I must now answer these things, saying true words to my friend. You are an Indian, I am a white man. You do not know all the white man's thoughts. These are the things I wish to tell you. In the white man's country are two kinds of men. There are the rich men, who have all that a man can desire—houses made of stone, full of fine things, fine clothes, fine weapons, fine ornaments; and they have horses, cattle, sheep, dogs—everything they desire. Because they have gold, for with gold the white man buys everything. The other kind of white men are the poor, who have no gold and cannot buy or have anything: they must work hard for the rich man for the little food he gives them, and a rag to cover their nakedness; and if he gives them shelter they have it; if not they must lie down in the rain out of doors. In my own country, a hundred days from here, I was the son of a great chief, who had much gold, and when he died it was all mine, and I was rich. But I had an enemy, one worse than Managa, for he was rich and had many people. And in a war his people overcame mine, and he took my gold, and all I possessed, making me poor. The Indian kills his enemy, but the white man takes his gold, and that is worse than death. Then I said: I have been a rich man and now I am poor, and must work like a dog for some rich man, for the sake of the little food he will throw me at the end of each day. No, I cannot do it! I will go away and live with the Indians, so that those who have seen me a rich man shall never see me working like a dog for a master, and cry out and mock at me. For the Indians are not like white men: they have no gold; they are not rich and poor; all are alike. One roof covers them from the rain and sun. All have weapons which they make; all kill birds in the forest and catch fish in the rivers; and the women cook the meat and all eat from one pot. And with the Indians, I will be an Indian, and hunt in the forest and eat with them and drink with them. Then I left my country and came here, and lived with you, Runi, and was well treated. And now, why did I go away? This I have now to tell you. After I had been here a certain time I went over there to the forest. You wished me not to go, because of an evil thing, a daughter of the Didi, that lived there; but I feared nothing and went. There I met an old man, who talked to me in the white man's language. He had travelled and seen much, and told me one strange thing. On a mountain at Riolama he told me that he had seen a great lump of gold, as much as a man could carry. And when I heard this I said, 'With the gold I could return to my country, and buy weapons for myself and all my people and go to war with my enemy and deprive him of all his possessions and serve him as he served me.' I asked the old man to take me to Riolama; and when he had consented I went away from here without saying a word, so as not to be prevented. It is far to Riolama, and I had no weapons; but I feared nothing. I said, 'If I must fight I must fight, and if I must be killed I must be killed.' But when I got to Riolama I found no gold. There was only a yellow stone which the old man had mistaken for gold. It was yellow, like gold, but it would buy nothing. Therefore I came back to Parahuari again, to my friend; and if he is angry with me still because I went away without informing him, let him say, 'Go and seek elsewhere for a new friend, for I am your friend no longer.'"

I concluded thus boldly, because I did not wish him to know that I had suspected him of harbouring any sinister designs, or that I looked on our quarrel as a very serious one. When I had finished speaking he emitted a sound which expressed neither approval nor disapproval, but only the fact that he had heard me. But I was satisfied. His expression had undergone a favourable change; it was less grim. After a while he remarked, with a peculiar twitching of the mouth which might have developed into a smile, "The white man will do much to get gold. You walked twenty days to see a yellow stone that would buy nothing." It was fortunate that he took this view of the case, which was flattering to his Indian nature, and perhaps touched his sense of the ludicrous. At all events, he said nothing to discredit my story, to which they had all listened with profound interest.

From that time it seemed to be tacitly agreed to let

bygones be bygones; and I could see that as the dangerous feeling that had threatened my life diminished the old pleasure they had once found in my company returned. But my feelings towards them did not change, nor could they while that black and terrible suspicion concerning Rima was in my heart. I talked again freely with them, as if there had been no break in the old friendly relations. If they watched me furtively whenever I went out of doors I affected not to see it. I set to work to repair my rude guitar, which had been broken in my absence, and studied to show them a cheerful countenance. But when alone, or in my hammock, hidden from their eyes, free to look into my own heart, then I was conscious that something new and strange had come into my life; that a new nature, black and implacable, had taken the place of the old. And sometimes it was hard to conceal this fury that burnt in me; sometimes I felt an impulse to spring like a tiger on one of the Indians, to hold him fast by the throat until the secret I wished to learn was forced from his lips, then to dash his brains out against the stone. But they were many, and there was no choice but to be cautious and patient if I wished to outwit them with a cunning superior to their own.

Three days after my arrival at the village, Kua-kó returned with his companion. I greeted him with affected warmth, but was really pleased that he was back, believing that if the Indians knew anything of Rima he among them all would be most likely to tell it.

Kua-kó appeared to have brought some important news, which he discussed with Runi and the others; and on the following day I noticed that preparations for an expedition were in progress. Spears and bows and arrows were got ready, but not blow-pipes, and I knew by this that the expedition would not be a hunting one. Having discovered so much, also that only four men were going out, I called Kua-kó aside and begged him to let me go with them. He seemed pleased at the proposal, and at once repeated it to Runi, who considered for a little and then consented.

By-and-by he said, touching his bow, "You cannot fight with our weapons; what will you do if we meet an enemy?"

I smiled and returned that I would not run away. All I wished to show him was that his enemies were my enemies, that I was ready to fight for my friend.

He was pleased at my words, and said no more and gave me no weapons. Next morning, however, when we set out before daylight, I made the discovery that he was carrying my revolver fastened to his waist. He had concealed it carefully under the one simple garment he wore, but it bulged slightly, and so the secret was betrayed. I had never believed that he had lost it, and I was convinced that he took it now with the object of putting it into my hands at the last moment in case of meeting with an enemy.

From the village we travelled in a north-westerly direction, and before noon camped in a grove of dwarf trees, where we remained until the sun was low, then continued our walk through a rather barren country. At night we camped again beside a small stream, only a few inches deep, and after a meal of smoked meat and parched maize prepared to sleep till dawn on the next day.

Sitting by the fire I resolved to make a first attempt to discover from Kua-kó anything concerning Rima which might be known to him. Instead of lying down when the others did I remained seated, my guardian also sitting —no doubt waiting for me to lie down first. Presently I moved nearer to him and began a conversation in a low voice, anxious not to rouse the attention of the other men.

"Once you said that Oolava would be given to me for a wife," I began. "Some day I shall want a wife."

He nodded approval, and remarked sententiously that the desire to possess a wife was common to all men.

"What has been left to me?" I said despondingly and spreading out my hands. "My pistol gone, and did I not give Runi the tinder-box, and the little box with a cock painted on it to you? I had no return—not even the blow-pipe. How, then, can I get me a wife?"

He, like the others—dull-witted savage that he was—had come to the belief that I was incapable of the cunning and duplicity they practised. I could not see a green parrot sitting silent and motionless amidst the green foliage as they could; I had not their preternatural keenness of sight; and, in like manner, to deceive with lies and false seeming was their faculty and not mine. He fell readily into the trap. My return to practical subjects pleased him. He bade me hope that Oolava might yet be mine in spite of my poverty. It was not always necessary to have things to get a wife: to be able to maintain her was enough; some day I would be like one of themselves, able to kill animals and catch fish. Besides, did not Runi wish to keep me with them for other reasons? But he could not keep me wifeless. I could do much: I could sing and make music; I was brave and feared nothing; I could teach the children to fight.

He did not say, however, that I could teach anything to one of his years and attainments.

I protested that he gave me too much praise, that they were just as brave. Did they not show a courage equal to mine by going every day to hunt in that wood which was inhabited by the daughter of the Didi?

I came to this subject with fear and trembling, but he took it quietly. He shook his head, and then all at once began to tell me how they first came to go there to hunt. He said that a few days after I had secretly disappeared, two men and a woman, returning home from a distant place where they had been on a visit to a relation, stopped at the village. These travellers related that two days' journey from Ytaioa they had met three persons travelling in an opposite direction: an old man with a white beard, followed by two yellow dogs, a young man in a big cloak, and a strange-looking girl. Thus it came to be known that I had left the wood with the old man and the daughter of the Didi. It was great news to them, for they did not believe that we had any intention of returning, and at once they began to hunt in the wood, and went there every day, killing birds, monkeys, and other animals in numbers.

His words had begun to excite me greatly, but I

studied to appear calm, and only slightly interested, so as to draw him on to say more.

"Then we returned," I said at last. "But only two of us, and not together. I left the old man on the road, and *she* left us in Riolama. She went away from us into the mountains—who knows whither!"

"But she came back!" he returned, with a gleam of devilish satisfaction in his eyes that made the blood run cold in my veins.

It was hard to dissemble still, to tempt him to say something that would madden me! "No, no," I answered, after considering his words. "She feared to return; she went away to hide herself in the great mountains beyond Riolama. She could not come back."

"But she came back!" he persisted, with that triumphant gleam in his eyes once more. Under my cloak my hand had clutched my knife-handle, but I strove hard against the fierce, almost maddening impulse to pluck it out and bury it, quick as lightning, in his accursed throat.

He continued: "Seven days before you returned we saw her in the wood. We were always expecting, watching, always afraid; and when hunting we were three and four together. On that day I and three others saw her. It was in an open place, where the trees are big and wide apart. We started up and chased her when she ran from us, but feared to shoot. And in one moment she climbed up into a small tree, then, like a monkey, passed from its highest branches into a big tree. We could not see her there, but she was there in the big tree, for there was no other tree near—no way of escape. Three of us sat down to watch, and the other went back to the village. He was long gone; we were just going to leave the tree, fearing that she would do us some injury, when he came back, and with him all the others, men, women, and children. They brought axes and knives. Then Runi said, 'Let no one shoot an arrow into the tree thinking to hit her, for the arrow would be caught in her hand and thrown back at him. We must burn her in the tree; there is no way to kill her except by fire.' Then we went round and round looking up, but could see nothing; and someone said, She has escaped, flying like a bird from the tree; but Runi answered that fire would show. So we cut down the small tree, and lopped the branches off and heaped them round the big trunk. Then, at a distance, we cut down ten more small trees, and afterwards, further away, ten more, and then others, and piled them all round, tree after tree, until the pile reached as far from the trunk as that," and here he pointed to a bush forty to fifty yards from where we sat.

The feeling with which I had listened to this recital had become intolerable. The sweat ran from me in streams; I shivered like a person in a fit of ague, and clenched my teeth together to prevent them from rattling. "I must drink," I said, cutting him short and rising to my feet. He also rose, but did not follow me, when, with uncertain steps, I made my way to the waterside, which was ten or twelve yards away. Lying prostrate on my chest, I took a long draught of clear cold water, and held my face for a few moments in the current. It sent a chill through me, drying my wet skin, and bracing me for the concluding part of the hideous narrative. Slowly I stepped back to the fireside and sat down again, while he resumed his old place at my side.

"You burnt the tree down," I said. "Finish telling me now and let me sleep—my eyes are heavy."

"Yes. While the men cut and brought trees, the women and children gathered dry stuff in the forest and brought it in their arms and piled it round. Then they set fire to it on all sides, laughing and shouting, 'Burn, burn, daughter of the Didi!' At length all the lower branches of the big tree were on fire, and the trunk was on fire, but above it was still green, and we could see nothing. But the flames went up higher and higher with a great noise; and at last from the top of the tree, out of the green leaves, came a great cry, like the cry of a bird, 'Abel! Abel!' and then looking we saw something fall; through leaves and smoke and flame it fell like a great white bird killed with an arrow and falling to the earth, and fell into the flames beneath. And it was the daughter of the Didi, and she was burnt to ashes like a moth in the flames of a fire, and no one has ever heard or seen her since."

It was well for me that he spoke rapidly, and finished quickly. Even before he had quite concluded I drew my cloak round my face and stretched myself out. And I suppose that he at once followed my example, but I had grown blind and deaf to outward things just then. My heart no longer throbbed violently; it fluttered and seemed to grow feebler and feebler in its action: I remember that there was a dull, rushing sound in my ears, that I gasped for breath, that my life seemed ebbing away. After these horrible sensations had passed, I remained quiet for about half an hour; and during this time the picture of that last act in the hateful tragedy grew more and more distinct and vivid in my mind, until I seemed to be actually gazing on it, that my ears were filled with the hissing and crackling of the fire, the exultant shouts of the savages, and above all the last piercing cry of "Abel! Abel!" from the cloud of burning foliage. I could not endure it longer, and rose at last to my feet. I glanced at Kua-kó lying two or three yards away, and he, like the others, was, or appeared to be, in a deep sleep; he was lying on his back, and his dark firelit face looked as still and unconscious as a face of stone. Now was my chance to escape—if to escape was my wish. Yes; for I now possessed the coveted knowledge, and nothing more was to be gained by keeping with my deadly enemies. And now, most fortunately for me, they had brought me far on the road to that place of the five hills where Managa lived—Managa, whose name had been often in my mind since my return to Parahuari. Glancing away from Kua-kó's still stone-like face, I caught sight of that pale solitary star which Runi had pointed out to me low down in the north-western sky when I had asked him where his enemy lived. In that direction we had been travelling since leaving the village; surely if I walked all night by to-morrow I could reach Managa's hunting-ground, and be safe and think over what I had heard and on what I had to do.

I moved softly away a few steps, then thinking that it would be well to take a spear in my hand, I turned back. and was surprised and startled to notice that Kua-kó had moved in the interval. He had turned over on his side, and his face was now towards me. His eyes appeared closed, but he might be only feigning sleep, and I dared not go back to pick up the spear. After a moment's hesitation I moved on again, and after a second glance back and seeing that he did not stir, I waded cautiously across the stream, walked softly twenty or thirty yards, and then began to run. At intervals I paused to listen for a moment; and presently I heard a pattering sound as of footsteps coming swiftly after me. I instantly concluded that Kua-kó had been awake all the time watching my movements, and that he was now following me. I now put forth my whole speed, and while thus running could distinguish no sound. That he would miss me, for it was very dark, although with a starry sky above, was my only hope; for with no weapon except my knife my chances would be small indeed should he overtake me. Besides, he had no doubt roused the others before starting, and they would be close behind. There were no bushes in that place to hide myself in and let them pass me; and presently, to make matters worse, the character of the soil changed, and I was running over level clayey ground, so white with a salt efflorescence that a dark object moving on it would show conspicuously at a distance. Here I paused to look back and listen, when distinctly came the sound of footsteps, and the next moment I made out the vague form of an Indian advancing at a rapid rate of speed and with his uplifted spear in his hand. In the brief pause I had made he had advanced almost to within hurling distance of me, and turning, I sped on again, throwing off my cloak to ease my flight. The next time I looked back he was still in sight, but not so near; he had stopped to pick up my cloak, which would be his now, and this had given me a slight advantage. I fled on, and had continued running for a distance perhaps of fifty yards when an object rushed past me, tearing through the flesh of my left arm close to the shoulder on its way; and not knowing that I was not badly wounded nor how near my pursuer might be, I turned in desperation to meet him, and saw him not above twenty-five yards away, running towards me with something bright in his hand. It was Kua-kó, and after wounding me with his spear he was about to finish me with his knife. O fortunate young savage, after such a victory, and with that noble blue cloth cloak for trophy and covering, what fame and happiness will be yours! A change swift as lightning had come over me, a sudden exultation. I was wounded, but my right hand was sound and clutched a knife as good as his, and we were on an equality. I waited for him calmly. All weakness, grief, despair had vanished, all feelings except a terrible raging desire to spill his accursed blood; and my brain was clear and my nerves like steel, and I remembered with something like laughter our old amusing encounters with rapiers of wood. Ah, that was only making believe and childish play; this was reality. Could any white man, deprived of his treacherous, far-killing weapon, meet the resolute savage, face to face and foot to foot and equal him with the old primitive weapons? Poor youth, this delusion will cost you dear! It was scarcely an equal contest when he hurled himself against me, with only his savage strength and courage to match my skill; in a few moments he was lying at my feet, pouring out his life blood on that white thirsty plain. From his prostrate form I turned, the wet, red knife in my hand, to meet the others, still thinking that they were on the track and close at hand. Why had he stooped to pick up the cloak if they were not following—if he had not been afraid of losing it? I turned only to receive their spears, to die with my face to them; nor was the thought of death terrible to me; I could die calmly now after killing my first assailant. But had I indeed killed him? I asked, hearing a sound like a groan escape from his lips. Quickly stooping I once more drove my weapon to the hilt in his prostrate form, and when he exhaled a deep sigh, and his frame quivered, and the blood spurted afresh, I experienced a feeling of savage joy. And still no sound of hurrying footsteps came to my listening ears and no vague forms appeared in the darkness. I concluded that he had either left them sleeping or that they had not followed in the right direction. Taking up the cloak, I was about to walk on, when I noticed the spear he had thrown at me lying where it had fallen some yards away, and picking that up also, I went on once more, still keeping the guiding star before me.

CHAPTER XX

THAT good fight had been to me like a draught of wine, and made me for a while oblivious of my loss and of the pain from my wound. But the glow and feeling of exultation did not last: the lacerated flesh smarted; I was weak from loss of blood, and oppressed with sensations of fatigue. If my foes had appeared on the scene they would have made an easy conquest of me; but they came not, and I continued to walk on, slowly and painfully, pausing often to rest.

At last, recovering somewhat from my faint condition, and losing all fear of being overtaken, my sorrow revived in full force, and thought returned to madden me.

Alas! this bright being, like no other in its divine brightness, so long in the making, now no more than a dead leaf, a little dust, lost and forgotten for ever—O pitiless! O cruel!

But I knew it all before—this law of nature and of necessity, against which all revolt is idle: often had the remembrance of it filled me with ineffable melancholy; only now it seemed cruel beyond all cruelty.

Not nature the instrument, not the keen sword that cuts into the bleeding tissues, but the hand that wields it

—the unseen unknown something, or person, that manifests itself in the horrible workings of nature.

"Did you know, beloved, at the last, in that intolerable heat, in that moment of supreme anguish, that *he* is unlistening, unhelpful as the stars, that you cried not to him? To me was your cry: but your poor, frail fellow-creature was not there to save, or, failing that, to cast himself into the flames and perish with you, hating God."

Thus, in my insufferable pain, I spoke aloud; alone in that solitary place, a bleeding fugitive in the dark night, looking up at the stars I cursed the Author of my being and called on Him to take back the abhorred gift of life.

Yet, according to my philosophy, how vain it was! All my bitterness and hatred and defiance were as empty, as ineffectual, as utterly futile, as are the supplications of the meek worshipper, and no more than the whisper of a leaf, the light whirr of an insect's wing. Whether I loved Him who was over all, as when I thanked Him on my knees for guiding me to where I had heard so sweet and mysterious a melody, or hated and defied Him as now, it all came from Him—love and hate, good and evil.

But I know—I knew then—that in one thing my philosophy was false, that it was not the whole truth; that though my cries did not touch nor come near Him they would yet hurt me; and, just as a prisoner maddened at his unjust fate beats against the stone walls of his cell until he falls back bruised and bleeding to the floor, so did I wilfully bruise my own soul, and knew that those wounds I gave myself would not heal.

Of that night, the beginning of the blackest period of my life, I shall say no more; and over subsequent events I shall pass quickly.

Morning found me at a distance of many miles from the scene of my duel with the Indian, in a broken, hilly country, varied with savannah and open forest. I was well-nigh spent with my long march, and felt that unless food was obtained before many hours my situation would be indeed desperate. With labour I managed to climb to the summit of a hill about three hundred feet high, in order to survey the surrounding country, and found that it was one of a group of five, and conjectured that these were the five hills of Uritay, and that I was in the neighbourhood of Managa's village. Coming down I proceeded to the next hill, which was higher; and before reaching it came to a stream in a narrow valley dividing the hills, and proceeding along its banks in search of a crossing-place, I came full in sight of the settlement sought for. As I approached people were seen moving hurriedly about: and by the time I arrived, walking slowly and painfully, seven or eight men were standing before the village, some with spears in their hands, the women and children behind them, all staring curiously at me. Drawing near I cried out in a somewhat feeble voice that I was seeking for Managa; whereupon a grey-haired man stepped forth, spear in hand, and replied that he was Managa, and demanded to know why I sought him. I told him a part of my story, enough to show that I had a deadly feud with Runi, that I had escaped from him after killing one of his people.

I was taken in and supplied with food; my wound was examined and dressed; and then I was permitted to lie down and sleep, while Managa, with half a dozen of his people, hurriedly started to visit the scene of my fight with Kua-kó, not only to verify my story, but partly also with the hope of meeting Runi. I did not see him again until the next morning, when he informed me that he had found the spot where I had been overtaken, that the dead man had been discovered by the others and carried back towards Parahuari. He had followed the trace for some distance, and he was satisfied that Runi had come thus far in the first place only with the intention of spying on him.

My arrival, and the strange tidings I had brought, had thrown the village into a great commotion; it was evident that from that time Managa lived in constant apprehension of a sudden attack from his old enemy. This gave me great satisfaction; it was my study to keep the feeling alive, and, more than that, to drop continual hints of his enemy's secret murderous purpose, until he was wrought up to a kind of frenzy of mingled fear and rage. And being of a suspicious and somewhat truculent temper, he one day all at once turned on me as the immediate cause of his miserable state, suspecting perhaps that I only wished to make an instrument of him. But I was strangely bold and careless of danger then, and only mocked at his rage, telling him proudly that I feared him not; that Runi, his mortal enemy and mine, feared not him but me; that Runi knew perfectly well where I had taken refuge and would not venture to make his meditated attack while I remained in his village, but would wait for my departure. "Kill me, Managa," I cried, smiting my chest as I stood facing him. "Kill me, and the result will be that he will come upon you unawares and murder you all, as he has resolved to do sooner or later."

After that speech he glared at me in silence, then flung down the spear he had snatched up in his sudden rage and stalked out of the house and into the wood. but before long he was back again seated in his old place, brooding on my words with a face black as night.

It is painful to recall that secret dark chapter of my life—that period of moral insanity. But I wish not to be a hypocrite, conscious or unconscious, to delude myself or another with this plea of insanity. My mind was very clear just then; past and present were clear to me; the future clearest of all: I could measure the extent of my action and speculate on its future effect, and my sense of right or wrong—of individual responsibility—was more vivid than at any other period of my life. Can I even say that I was blinded by passion? Driven, perhaps, but certainly not blinded. For no reaction, or submission, had followed on that furious revolt against the unknown being, personal or not, that is behind nature, in whose existence I believed. I was still in revolt: I would hate Him, and show my hatred by being like Him, as He appears to us reflected in that mirror of Nature. Had He given me good gifts—the sense of right and wrong and sweet humanity? The beautiful sacred flower He had caused to grow in me I would crush ruthlessly; its beauty and fragrance and grace would be dead for ever; there was nothing evil, nothing cruel and contrary to my nature, that I would not be guilty of, glorying in my guilt. This was not the temper of a few days: I remained for close upon two months at Managa's village, never repenting nor desisting in my efforts to induce the Indians to join me in that most barbarous adventure on which my heart was set.

I succeeded in the end: it would have been strange if I had not. The horrible details need not be given. Managa did not wait for his enemy, but fell on him unexpectedly, an hour after nightfall in his own village. If I had really been insane during those two months, if some cloud had been on me, some demoniacal force dragging me on, the cloud and insanity vanished and the constraint was over in one moment, when that hellish enterprise was completed. It was the sight of an old woman, lying where she had been struck down, the fire of the blazing house lighting her wide-open glassy eyes and white hair dabbled in blood, which suddenly, as by a miracle, wrought this change in my brain. For they were all dead at last, old and young, all who had lighted the fire round that great green tree in which Rima had taken refuge, who had danced round the blaze, shouting, "Burn! burn!"

At the moment my glance fell on that prostrate form, I paused and stood still, trembling like a person struck with a sudden pang in the heart, who thinks that his last moment has come to him unawares. After a while I slunk away out of the great circle of firelight into the thick darkness beyond. Instinctively I turned towards the forest across the savannah—my forest again; and fled away from the noise and the sight of flames, never pausing until I found myself within the black shadow of the trees. Into the deeper blackness of the interior I dared not venture: on the border I paused to ask myself what I did there alone in the night time. Sitting down I covered my face with my hands as if to hide it more effectually than it could be hidden by night and the forest shadows. What horrible thing—what calamity that frightened my soul to think of, had fallen on me? The revulsion of feeling, the unspeakable horror, the remorse, was more than I could bear. I started up with a cry of anguish, and would have slain myself to escape at that moment; but Nature is not always and utterly cruel, and on this occasion she came to my aid. Consciousness forsook me, and I lived not again until the light of early morning was in the east; then found myself lying on the wet herbage—wet with rain that had lately fallen. My physical misery was now so great that it prevented me from dwelling on the scenes witnessed on the previous evening. Nature was again merciful in this. I only remembered that it was necessary to hide myself, in case the Indians should be still in the neighbourhood and pay the wood a visit. Slowly and painfully I crept away into the forest, and there sat for several hours, scarcely thinking at all, in a half-stupefied condition. At noon the sun shone out and dried the wood. I felt no hunger, only a vague sense of bodily misery, and with it the fear that if I left my hiding-place I might meet some human creature face to face. This fear prevented me from stirring until the twilight came, when I crept forth and made my way to the border of the forest, to spend the night there. Whether sleep visited me during the dark hours or not I cannot say: day and night my condition seemed the same; I experienced only a dull sensation of utter misery which seemed in spirit and flesh alike, an inability to think clearly, or for more than a few moments consecutively, about anything. Scenes in which I had been principal actor came and went, as in a dream when the will slumbers: now with devilish ingenuity and persistence I was working on Managa's mind; now standing motionless in the forest listening for that sweet, mysterious melody; now staring aghast at old Cla-cla's wide-open glassy eyes and white hair dabbled in blood; then suddenly, in the cave at Riolama, I was fondly watching the slow return of life and colour to Rima's still face.

When morning came again I felt so weak that a vague fear of sinking down and dying of hunger at last roused me and sent me forth in quest of food. I moved slowly and my eyes were dim to see, but I knew so well where to seek for small morsels—small edible roots and leaf-stalks, berries, and drops of congealed gum—that it would have been strange in that rich forest if I had not been able to discover something to stay my famine. It was little, but it sufficed for the day. Once more Nature was merciful to me; for that diligent seeking among the concealing leaves left no interval for thought; every chance morsel gave a momentary pleasure, and as I prolonged my search my steps grew firmer, the dimness passed from my eyes. I was more forgetful of self, more eager, and like a wild animal with no thought or feeling beyond its immediate wants. Fatigued at the end, I fell asleep as soon as darkness brought my busy rambles to a close, and did not wake until another morning dawned.

My hunger was extreme now. The wailing notes of a pair of small birds, persistently flitting round me, or perched with gaping bills and wings trembling with agitation, served to remind me that it was now breeding-time; also that Rima had taught me to find a small bird's-nest. She found them only to delight her eyes with the sight; but they would be food for me; the crystal and yellow fluid in the gem-like, white or blue or red-speckled shells would help to keep me alive. All day I hunted, listening to every note and cry, watching the motions of every winged thing, and found, besides gums and fruits, over a score of nests containing eggs, mostly of small birds, and although the labour was great and the scratches many, I was well satisfied with the result.

A few days later I found a supply of Haima gum, and eagerly began picking it from the tree; not that it could be used, but the thought of the brilliant light it gave was so strong in my mind that mechanically I gathered it all. The possession of this gum, when night closed round me again, produced in me an intense longing for artificial light and warmth. The darkness was harder than ever to endure. I envied the fireflies their natural lights, and ran about in the dusk to capture a few and hold them in the hollow of my two hands, for the sake of their cold, fitful flashes. On the following day I wasted two or three hours trying to get fire in the primitive method with dry wood, but failed, and lost much time, and suffered more than ever from hunger in consequence. Yet there was fire in everything; even when I struck at hard wood with my knife sparks were emitted. If I could only arrest those wonderful heat and light-giving sparks! And all at once, as if I had just lighted upon some new, wonderful truth, it occurred to me that with my steel hunting-knife and a piece of flint fire could be obtained. Immediately I set about preparing tinder with dry moss, rotten wood, and wild cotton; and in a short time I had the wished fire, and heaped wood dry and green on it to make it large. I nursed it well, and spent the night beside it; and it also served to roast some huge white grubs which I had found in the rotten wood of a prostrate trunk. The sight of these great grubs had formerly disgusted me; but they tasted good to me now, and stayed my hunger, and that was all I looked for in my wild forest food.

For a long time an undefined feeling prevented me from going near the site of Nuflo's burnt lodge. I went there at last; and the first thing I did was to go all round the fatal spot, cautiously peering into the rank herbage, as if I feared a lurking serpent; and at length, at some distance from the blackened heap, I discovered a human skeleton, and knew it to be Nuflo's. In his day he had been a great armadillo hunter, and these quaint carrion eaters had no doubt revenged themselves by devouring his flesh when they found him dead—killed by the savages.

Having once returned to this spot of many memories, I could not quit it again; while my wild woodland life lasted here must I have my lair, and being here I could not leave that mournful skeleton above ground. With labour I excavated a pit to bury it, careful not to cut or injure a broad-leafed creeper that had begun to spread itself over the spot; and after refilling the hole I drew the long, trailing stems over the mound.

"Sleep well, old man," said I, when my work was done; and these few words, implying neither censure nor praise, was all the burial service that old Nuflo had from me.

I then visited the spot where the old man, assisted by me, had concealed his provisions before starting for Riolama, and was pleased to find that it had not been discovered by the Indians. Besides the store of tobacco-leaf, maize, pumpkin, potatoes, and cassava-bread, and the cooking utensils, I found among other things a chopper—a great acquisition, since with it I would be able to cut down small palms and bamboos to make myself a hut.

The possession of a supply of food left me time for many things: time in the first place to make my own conditions; doubtless after them there would be further progression on the old lines—luxuries added to necessaries; a healthful, fruitful life of thought and action combined; and at the last a peaceful, contemplative old age.

I cleared away ashes and rubbish, and marked out the very spot where Rima's separate bower had been for my habitation, which I intended to make small. In five days it was finished; then after lighting a fire, I stretched myself out in my dry bed of moss and leaves with a feeling that was almost triumphant. Let the rain now fall in torrents, putting out the firefly's lamp; let the wind and thunder roar their loudest, and the lightnings smite the earth with intolerable light, frightening the poor monkeys in their wet, leafy habitations, little would I heed it all on my dry bed, under my dry, palm-leaf thatch, with glorious fire to keep me company and protect me from my ancient enemy, Darkness.

From that first sleep under shelter I woke refreshed, and was not driven by the cruel spur of hunger into the wet forest. The wished time had come of rest from labour, of leisure for thought. Resting here, just where she had rested, night by night clasping a visionary mother in her arms, whispering tenderest words in a visionary ear, I too now clasped her in my arms—a visionary Rima. How different the nights had seemed when I was without shelter, before I had rediscovered fire! How had I endured it? That strange ghostly gloom of the woods at night-time full of innumerable strange shapes; still and dark, yet with something seen at times moving amidst them, dark and vague and strange also—an owl perhaps, or bat, or great winged moth, or nightjar. Nor had I any choice then but to listen to the night-sounds of the forest; and they were various as the day-sounds, and for every day-sound, from the faintest lisping and softest trill to the deep boomings and piercing cries, there was an analogue; always with something mysterious, unreal, in its tone, something proper to the night. They were ghostly sounds, uttered by the ghosts of dead animals; they were a hundred different things by turns, but always with a meaning in them, which I vainly strove to catch—something to be interpreted only by a sleeping faculty in us, lightly sleeping, and now, now on the very point of awaking!

Now the gloom and the mystery was shut out; now I had that which stood in the place of pleasure to me, and was more than pleasure. It was a mournful rapture to lie awake now, wishing not for sleep and oblivion, hating the thought of daylight that would come at last to drown and scare away my vision. To be with Rima again—my lost Rima recovered—mine, mine at last! No longer the old vexing doubt now—"You are you and I am I—why is it?"—the question asked when our souls were near together, like two raindrops side by side, drawing irresistibly nearer, ever nearer: for now they had touched and were not two, but one inseparable drop, crystallised beyond change, not to be disintegrated by time, nor shattered by death's blow, nor resolved by any alchemy.

I had other company besides this unfailing vision, and the bright dancing fire that talked to me in its fantastic fire language. It was my custom to secure the door well on retiring: grief had perhaps chilled my blood, for I suffered less from heat than from cold at this period, and the fire seemed grateful all night long; I was also anxious to exclude all small winged and creeping night-wanderers. But to exclude them entirely proved impossible: through a dozen invisible chinks they would find their way to me; also some entered by day to lie concealed until after nightfall. A monstrous hairy hermit spider found an asylum in a dusky corner of the hut, under the thatch, and day after day he was there, all day long, sitting close and motionless; but at dark he invariably disappeared—who knows on what murderous errand! His hue was a deep dead-leaf yellow, with a black and grey pattern, borrowed from some wild cat; and so large was he that his great outspread hairy legs, radiating from the flat disc of his body, would have covered a man's open hand. It was easy to see him in my small interior; often in the night-time my eyes would stray to his corner, never to encounter that strange hairy figure; but daylight failed not to bring him. He troubled me; but now, for Rima's sake, I could slay no living thing except from motives of hunger. I had it in my mind to injure him—to strike off one of his legs, which would not be missed much, as they were many—so as to make him go away and return no more to so inhospitable a place. But courage failed me. He might come stealthily back at night to plunge his long, crooked falces into my throat, poisoning my blood with fever and delirium and black death. So I left him alone, and glanced furtively and fearfully at him, hoping that he had not divined any thoughts; thus we lived on unsocially together. More companionable, but still in an uncomfortable way, were the large crawling, running insects—crickets, beetles, and others. They were shapely and black and polished, and ran about here and there on the floor, just like intelligent little horseless carriages; then they would pause with their immovable eyes fixed on me, seeing, or in some mysterious way divining my presence; their pliant horns waving up and down, like delicate instruments used to test the air. Centipedes and millipedes in dozens came too, and were not welcome. I feared not their venom, but it was a weariness to see them; for they seemed no living things, but the vertebræ of snakes and eels and long slim fishes, dead and desiccated, made to move mechanically over walls and floor by means of some jugglery of nature. I grew skilful at picking them up with a pair of pliant green twigs, to thrust them forth into the outer darkness.

One night a moth fluttered in and alighted on my hand as I sat by the fire, causing me to hold my breath as I gazed on it. Its fore wings were pale grey, with shadings dark and light written all over in finest characters with some twilight mystery or legend; but the round underwings were clear amber-yellow, veined like a leaf with red and purple veins; a thing of such exquisite chaste beauty that the sight of it gave me a sudden shock of pleasure. Very soon it flew up circling about, and finally lighted on the palm-leaf thatch directly over the fire. The heat, I thought, would soon drive it from the spot; and, rising, I opened the door, so that it might find its way out again into its own cool, dark, flowery world. And standing by the open door I turned and addressed it: "O night-wanderer of the pale, beautiful wings, go forth, and should you by chance meet her somewhere in the shadowy depths, revisiting her old haunts, be my messenger——" Thus much had I spoken, when the frail thing loosened its hold to fall without a flutter, straight and swift, into the white blaze beneath. I sprang forward with a shriek, and stood staring into the fire, my whole frame trembling with a sudden, terrible emotion. Even thus had Rima fallen—fallen from the great height—into the flames that instantly consumed her beautiful flesh and bright spirit! O cruel Nature!

A moth that perished in the flame; an indistinct faint sound; a dream in the night; the semblance of a shadowy form moving mist-like in the twilight gloom of the forest, would suddenly bring back a vivid memory, the old anguish, to break for a while the calm of that period. It was calm then after the storm. Nevertheless, my health deteriorated. I ate little and slept little and grew thin and weak. When I looked down on the dark, glassy forest pool, where Rima would look no more to see herself so much better than in the small mirror of her lover's pupil, it showed me a gaunt, ragged man with a tangled mass of black hair falling over his shoulders, the bones of his face showing through the dead-looking, sun-parched skin, the sunken eyes with a gleam in them that was like insanity.

To see this reflection had a strangely disturbing effect on me. A torturing voice would whisper in my ear: "Yes, you are evidently going mad. By-and-by you will rush howling through the forest, only to drop down at last and die: and no person will ever find and bury *your* bones. Old Nuflo was more fortunate in that he perished first."

"A lying voice!" I retorted in sudden anger. "My faculties were never keener than now. Not a fruit can ripen but I find it. If a small bird darts by with a feather or straw in its bill I mark its flight, and it will be a lucky bird if I do not find its nest in the end.

Could a savage born in the forest do more? He would starve where I find food!"

"Ah, yes, there is nothing wonderful in that," answered the voice. "The stranger from a cold country suffers less from the heat, when days are hottest, than the Indian who knows no other climate. But mark the result! The stranger dies, while the Indian, sweating and gasping for breath, survives. In like manner the low-minded savage, cut off from all human fellowship, keeps his faculties to the end, while your finer brain proves your ruin."

I cut from a tree a score of long, blunt thorns, tough and black as whalebone, and drove them through a strip of wood in which I had burnt a row of holes to receive them, and made myself a comb, and combed out my long, tangled hair to improve my appearance.

"It is not the tangled condition of your hair," persisted the voice, "but your eyes, so wild and strange in their expression, that show the approach of madness. Make your locks as smooth as you like, and add a garland of those scarlet, star-shaped blossoms hanging from the bush behind you—crown yourself as you crowned old Cla-cla—but the crazed look will remain just the same."

And being no longer able to reply, rage and desperation drove me to an act which only seemed to prove that the hateful voice had prophesied truly. Taking up a stone I hurled it down on the water to shatter the image I saw there, as if it had been no faithful reflection of myself, but a travesty, cunningly made of enamelled clay or some other material, and put there by some malicious enemy to mock me

CHAPTER XXI

MANY days had passed since the hut was made—how many may not be known, since I notched no stick and knotted no cord—yet never in my rambles in the wood had I seen that desolate ash-heap where the fire had done its work. Nor had I looked for it. On the contrary, my wish was never to see it, and the fear of coming accidentally upon it made me keep to the old familiar paths. But at length, one night, while thinking of Rima's fearful end, it all at once occurred to me that the hated savage, whose blood I had shed on the white savannah, might have only been practising his natural deceit when he told me that most pitiful story. If that were so—if he had been prepared with a fictitious account of her death to meet my questions—then Rima might still exist: lost, perhaps, wandering in some distant place, exposed to perils day and night, and unable to find her way back, but living still! Living! her heart on fire with the hope of reunion with me, cautiously threading her way through the undergrowth of immeasurable forests; spying out the distant villages and hiding herself from the sight of all men, as she knew so well how to hide; studying the outlines of distant mountains, to recognise some familiar landmark at last, and so find her way back to the old wood once more! Even now, while I sat there idly musing, she might be somewhere in the wood—somewhere near me; but after so long an absence full of apprehension, waiting in concealment for what to-morrow's light might show.

I started up and replenished the fire with trembling hands, then set the door open to let the welcoming radiance stream out into the wood. But Rima had done more; going out into the black forest in the pitiless storm, she had found and led me home. Could I do less! I was quickly out in the shadows of the wood. Surely it was more than a mere hope that made my heart beat so wildly! How could a sensation so strangely sudden, so irresistible in its power, possess me unless she were living and near? Can it be, can it be that we shall meet again? To look again into your divine eyes—to hold you again in my arms at last! I so changed—so different! But the old love remains; and of all that has happened in your absence I shall tell you nothing—not one word; all shall be forgotten now—sufferings, madness, crime, remorse! Nothing shall ever vex you again—not Nuflo, who vexed you every day; for he is dead now—murdered, only I shall not say that—and I have decently buried his poor old sinful bones. We alone together in the wood—*our* wood now! The sweet old days again; for I know that you would not have it different, nor would I.

Thus I talked to myself, mad with the thoughts of the joy that would soon be mine; and at intervals I stood still and made the forest echo with my calls. "Rima! Rima!" I called again and again, and waited for some response; and heard only the familiar night-sounds—voices of insect and bird and tinkling tree-frog, and a low murmur in the topmost foliage, moved by some light breath of wind unfelt below. I was drenched with dew, bruised and bleeding from falls in the dark, and from rocks and thorns and rough branches, but had felt nothing: gradually the excitement burnt itself out; I was hoarse with shouting and ready to drop down with fatigue, and hope was dead: and at length I crept back to my hut, to cast myself on my grass bed and sink into a dull, miserable, desponding stupor.

But on the following morning I was out once more, determined to search the forest well; since, if no evidence of the great fire Kua-kó had described to me existed, it would still be possible to believe that he had lied to me, and that Rima lived. I searched all day and found nothing; but the area was large, and to search it thoroughly would require several days.

On the third day I discovered the fatal spot, and knew that never again would I behold Rima in the flesh, that my last hope had indeed been a vain one. There could be no mistake: just such an open place as the Indian had pictured to me was here, with giant trees standing apart; while one tree stood killed and blackened by fire, surrounded by a huge heap, sixty or seventy yards across, of prostrate charred tree-trunks and ashes. Here and there slender plants had sprung up through the ashes, and the omnipresent small-leaved creepers were beginning to throw their pale green embroidery over the blackened trunks. I looked long at the vast funeral tree that had a buttressed girth of not less than fifty feet, and rose straight as a ship's mast, with its top about a hundred and fifty feet from the earth. What a distance to fall, through burning leaves and smoke, like a white bird shot dead with a poisoned arrow, swift and straight into that sea of flame below! How cruel imagination was to turn that desolate ash-heap, in spite of feathery foliage and embroidery of creepers, into roaring leaping flames again —to bring those dead savages back, men, women, and children—even the little ones I had played with—to set them yelling around me, "Burn! burn!" Oh, no, this damnable spot must not be her last resting-place! If the fire had not utterly consumed her, bones as well as sweet tender flesh, shrivelling her like a frail white-winged moth into the finest white ashes, mixed inseparably with the ashes of stems and leaves innumerable, then whatever remained of her must be conveyed elsewhere to be with me, to mingle with my ashes at last.

Having resolved to sift and examine the entire heap, I at once set about my task. If she had climbed into the central highest branch, and had fallen straight, then she would have dropped into the flames not far from the roots; and so to begin I made a path to the trunk, and when darkness overtook me I had worked all round the tree, in a width of three to four yards, without discovering any remains. At noon on the following day I found the skeleton, or, at all events, the larger bones, rendered so fragile by the fierce heat they had been subjected to, that they fell to pieces when handled. But I was careful—how careful!—to save these last sacred relics, all that was now left of Rima!—kissing each white fragment as I lifted it, and gathering them all in my old frayed cloak, spread out to receive them. And when I had recovered them all, even to the smallest, I took my treasure home.

Another storm had shaken my soul, and had been succeeded by a second calm, which was more complete and promised to be more enduring than the first. But it was no lethargic calm; my brain was more active than ever; and by-and-by it found a work for my hands to do, of such a character as to distinguish me from all other forest hermits, fugitives from their fellows, in that savage land. The calcined bones I had rescued were kept in one of the big, rudely shaped, half-burnt earthen jars, which Nuflo had used for storing grain and other food-stuff. It was of a wood-ash colour; and after I had given up my search for the peculiar fine clay he had used in its manufacture—for it had been in my mind to make a more shapely funeral urn myself—I set to work to ornament its surface. A portion of each day was given to this artistic labour; and when the surface was covered with a pattern of thorny stems, and a trailing creeper with curving leaf and twining tendril, and pendent bud and blossom, I gave it colour. Purples and black only were used, obtained from the juices of some deeply coloured berries; and when a tint, or shade, or line failed to satisfy me I erased it, to do it again; and this so often that I never completed my work. I might, in the proudly modest spirit of the old sculptors, have inscribed on the vase the words, *Abel was doing this.* For was not my ideal beautiful like theirs, and the best that my art could do only an imperfect copy—a rude sketch? A serpent was represented wound round the lower portion of the jar, dull-hued, with a chain of irregular black spots or blotches extending along its body: and if any person had curiously examined these spots he would have discovered that every other one was a rudely shaped letter, and that the letters, by being properly divided, made the following words:—

Sin vos y siu dios y mi.

Words that to some might seem wild, even insane in their extravagance, sung by some ancient forgotten poet; or possibly the motto of some love-sick knight-errant, whose passion was consumed to ashes long centuries ago. But not wild nor insane to me, dwelling alone on a vast stony plain in everlasting twilight, where there was no motion, nor any sound; but all things, even trees, ferns, and grasses, were stone. And in that place I had sat for many a thousand years, drawn up and motionless, with stony fingers clasped round my legs, and forehead resting on my knees; and there would I sit, unmoving, immovable, for many a thousand years to come—I, no longer I, in a universe where *she* was not, and God was not.

The days went by, and to others grouped themselves into weeks and months; to me they were only days—not Saturday, Sunday, Monday, but nameless. They were so many and their sum so great, that all my previous life, all the years I had existed before this solitary time, now looked like a small island immeasurably far away, scarcely discernible, in the midst of that endless desolate waste of nameless days.

My stock of provisions had been so long consumed that had forgotten the flavour of pulse and maize and pumpkins and purple and sweet potatoes. For Nuflo's cultivated patch had been destroyed by the savages—not a stem, not a root had they left: and I, like the sorrowful man that broods on his sorrow and the artist who thinks only of his art, had been improvident, and had consumed the seed without putting a portion into the ground. Only wild food, and too little of that, found with much seeking and got with many hurts. Birds screamed at and scolded me; branches bruised and thorns scratched me; and still worse were the angry clouds of waspish things no bigger than flies. Buzz—buzz! Sting—sting! A serpent's tooth has failed to kill me; little do I care for your small drops of fiery venom so that I get at the spoil—grubs and honey. My white bread and purple wine! Once my soul hungered after knowledge; I took delight in fine thoughts finely expressed; I sought them carefully in printed books: now only this vile bodily hunger, this eager seeking for grubs and honey, and ignoble war with little things!

A bad hunter I proved after larger game. Bird and beast despised my snares, which took me so many waking hours at night to invent, so many daylight hours to make. Once, seeing a troop of monkeys high up in the tall trees, I followed and watched them for a long time, thinking how royally I should feast if by some strange unheard-of accident one were to fall disabled to the ground and be at my mercy. But nothing impossible happened, and I had no meat. What meat did I ever have except an occasional fledgling, killed in its cradle.

or a lizard, or small tree-frog detected, in spite of its green colour, among the foliage? I would roast the little green minstrel on the coals. Why not? Why should he live to tinkle on his mandolin and clash his airy cymbals with no appreciative ear to listen? Once I had a different and strange kind of meat; but the starved stomach is not squeamish. I found a serpent coiled up in my way in a small glade, and arming myself with a long stick, I roused him from his siesta, and slew him without mercy. Rima was not there to pluck the rage from my heart and save his evil life. No coral snake this, with slim, tapering body, ringed like a wasp with brilliant colour; but thick and blunt, with lurid scales, blotched with black; also a broad, flat, murderous head, with stony, ice-like, whity-blue eyes, cold enough to freeze a victim's blood in its veins and make it sit still, like some wide-eyed creature carved in stone, waiting for the sharp, inevitable stroke—so swift at last, so long in coming. "O abominable flat head, with icy-cold, human-like, fiend-like eyes, I shall cut you off and throw you away!" And away I flung it, far enough in all conscience; yet I walked home troubled with a fancy that somewhere, somewhere down on the black, wet soil where it had fallen, through all that dense, thorny tangle and millions of screening leaves, the white, lidless, living eyes were following me still, and would always be following me in all my goings and comings and windings about in the forest. And what wonder? For were we not alone together in this dreadful solitude, I and the serpent, eaters of the dust, singled out and cursed above all cattle? *He* would not have bitten me, and I—faithless cannibal!—had murdered him. That cursed fancy would live on, worming itself into every crevice of my mind; the severed head would grow and grow in the night-time to something monstrous at last, the hellish white lidless eyes increasing to the size of two full moons. "Murderer! murderer!" they would say; "first a murderer of your own fellow-creatures—that was a small crime; but God, our enemy, had made them in His image, and he cursed you; and we two were together, alone and apart—you and I, murderer! you and I, murderer!"

I tried to escape the tyrannous fancy by thinking of other things and by making light of it. "The starved, bloodless brain," I said, "has strange thoughts." I fell to studying the dark, thick, blunt body in my hands; I noticed that the livid, rudely blotched, scaly surface showed in some lights a lovely play of prismatic colours. And growing poetical, I said, "When the wild west wind broke up the rainbow on the flying grey cloud and scattered it over the earth, a fragment doubtless fell on this reptile to give it that tender celestial tint. For thus it is Nature loves all her children, and gives to each some beauty, little or much; only to me, her hated stepchild, she gives no beauty, no grace. But stay, am I not wronging her? Did not Rima, beautiful above all things, love me well? said she not that I was beautiful?"

"Ah, yes, that was long ago," spoke the voice that mocked me by the pool when I combed out my tangled hair. "Long ago, when the soul that looked from your eyes was not the accursed thing it is now. *Now* Rima would start at the sight of them; now she would fly in terror from their insane expression."

O spiteful voice, must you spoil even such appetite as I have for this fork-tongued spotty food? You by day and Rima by night — what shall I do — what shall I do?"

For it had now come to this, that the end of each day brought not sleep and dreams, but waking visions. Night by night, from my dry grass bed I beheld Nuflo sitting in his old doubled-up posture, his big brown feet close to the white ashes—sitting silent and miserable. I pitied him; I owed him hospitality; but it seemed intolerable that he should be there. It was better to shut my eyes; for then Rima's arms would be round my neck; the silky mist of her hair against my face, her flowery breath mixing with my breath. What a luminous face was hers! Even with close-shut eyes I could see it vividly, the translucent skin showing the radiant rose beneath, the lustrous eyes, spiritual and passionate, dark as purple wine under their dark lashes. Then my eyes would open wide. No Rima in my arms! But over there, a little way back from the fire, just beyond where old Nuflo had sat brooding a few minutes ago, Rima would be standing, still and pale and unspeakably sad. Why does she come to me from the outside darkness to stand there talking to me, yet never once lifting her mournful eyes to mine? "Do not believe it, Abel; no, that was only a phantom of your brain, the What-I-was that you remember so well. For do you not see that when I come she fades away and is nothing? Not that—do not ask it. I know that I once refused to look into your eyes, and afterwards, in the cave at Riolama, I looked long and was happy—unspeakably happy! But now—oh, you do not know what you ask; you do not know the sorrow that has come into mine; that if you once beheld it for very sorrow you would die. And you must live. But I will wait patiently, and we shall be together in the end, and see each other without disguise. Nothing shall divide us. Only wish not for it soon; think not that death will ease your pain, and seek it not. Austerities? Good works? Prayers? They are not seen; they are not heard, they are less than nothing, and there is no intercession. I did not know it then, but you knew it. Your life was your own; you are not saved nor judged; acquit yourself—undo that which you have done, which Heaven cannot undo—and Heaven will say no word nor will I. You cannot, Abel, you cannot. That which you have done is done, and yours must be the penalty and the sorrow—yours and mine—yours and mine—yours and mine."

This, too, was a phantom, a Rima of the mind, one of the shapes the ever-changing black vapours of remorse and insanity would take; and all her mournful sentences were woven out of my own brain. I was not so crazed as not to know it; only a phantom, an illusion, yet more real than reality—real as my crime and vain remorse and death to come. It was, indeed, Rima returned to tell me that I that loved her had been more cruel to her than her cruellest enemies; for they had but tortured and destroyed her body with fire, while I had cast this shadow on her soul—this sorrow transcending all sorrows, darker than death, immitigable, eternal.

If I could only have faded gradually, painlessly, growing feebler in body and dimmer in my senses each day, to sink at last into sleep! But it could not be. Still the fever in my brain, the mocking voice by day, the phantoms by night; and at last I became convinced that unless I quitted the forest before long, death would come to me in some terrible shape. But in the feeble condition I was now in, and without any provisions, to escape from the neighbourhood of Parahuari was impossible, seeing that it was necessary at starting to avoid the villages where the Indians were of the same tribe as Runi, who would recognise me as the white man who was once his guest and afterwards his implacable enemy. I must wait, and in spite of a weakened body and a mind diseased, struggle still to wrest a scanty subsistence from wild nature.

One day I discovered an old prostrate tree, buried under a thick growth of creeper and fern, the wood of which was nearly or quite rotten, as I proved by thrusting my knife to the haft in it. No doubt it would contain grubs—those huge, white wood-borers which now formed an important item in my diet. On the following day I returned to the spot with a chopper and a bundle of wedges to split the trunk up, but had scarcely commenced operations when an animal, startled at my blows, rushed or rather wriggled from its hiding-place under the dead wood at a distance of a few yards from me. It was a robust, round-headed, short-legged creature, about as big as a good-sized cat, and clothed in a thick, greenish-brown fur. The ground all about was covered with creepers, binding the ferns, bushes, and old dead branches together; and in this confused tangle the animal scrambled and tore with a great show of energy, but really made very little progress; and all at once it flashed into my mind that it was a sloth—a common animal, but rarely seen on the ground—with no tree near to take refuge in. The shock of joy this discovery produced was great enough to unnerve me, and for some moments I stood trembling, hardly able to breathe; then recovering I hastened after it, and stunned it with a blow from my chopper on its round head.

"Poor sloth!" I said as I stood over it. "Poor old lazy-bones! Did Rima ever find you fast asleep in a tree, hugging a branch as if you loved it, and with her little hand pat your round, human-like head; and laugh mockingly at the astonishment in your drowsy, waking eyes; and scold you tenderly for wearing your nails so long, and for being so ugly? Lazy-bones, your death is revenged! O to be out of this wood—away from this sacred place—to be anywhere where killing is not murder!"

Then it came into my mind that I was now in possession of the supply of food which would enable me to quit the wood. A noble capture! As much to me as if a stray, migratory mule had rambled into the wood and found me, and I him. Now I would be my own mule, patient, and long-suffering, and far-going, with naked feet hardened to hoofs, and a pack of provender on my back to make me independent of the dry, bitter grass on the sunburnt savannahs.

Part of that night and the next morning was spent in curing the flesh over a smoky fire of green wood and in manufacturing a rough sack to store it in, for I had resolved to set out on my journey. How safely to convey Rima's treasured ashes was a subject of much thought and anxiety. The clay vessel on which I had expended so much loving, sorrowful labour had to be left, being too large and heavy to carry; eventually I put the fragments into a light sack; and in order to avert suspicion from the people I would meet on the way, above the ashes I packed a layer of roots and bulbs. These I would say contained medicinal properties, known to the white doctors, to whom I would sell them on my arrival at a Christian settlement, and with the money buy myself clothes to start life afresh.

On the morrow I would bid a last farewell to that forest of many memories. And my journey would be eastwards, over a wild savage land of mountains, rivers, and forests, where every dozen miles would be like a hundred of Europe; but a land inhabited by tribes not unfriendly to the stranger. And perhaps it would be my good fortune to meet with Indians travelling east, who would know the easiest routes; and from time to time some compassionate voyager would let me share his wood-skin, and many leagues would be got over without weariness, until some great river, flowing through British or Dutch Guiana, would be reached; and so on, and on, by slow or swift stages, with little to eat perhaps, with much labour and pain, in hot sun and in storm, to the Atlantic at last, and towns inhabited by Christian men.

In the evening of that day, after completing my preparations, I supped on the remaining portions of the sloth, not suitable for preservation, roasting bits of fat on the coals and boiling the head and bones into a broth; and after swallowing the liquid I crunched the bones and sucked the marrow, feeding like some hungry carnivorous animal.

Glancing at the fragments scattered on the floor, I remembered old Nuflo, and how I had surprised him at his feast of rank coatimundi in his secret retreat. "Nuflo, old neighbour," said I, "how quiet you are under your green coverlet, spangled just now with yellow flowers! It is no sham sleep, old man, I know. If any suspicion of these curious doings, this feast of flesh on a spot once sacred, could flit like a small moth into your mouldy hollow skull, you would soon thrust out your old nose to sniff the savour of roasting fat once more."

There was in me at that moment an inclination to laughter: it came to nothing, but affected me strangely, like an impulse I had not experienced since boyhood—familiar, yet novel. After the good-night to my neighbour, I tumbled into my straw and slept soundly, animal-like. No fancies and phantoms that night: the lidless, white, implacable eyes of the serpent's severed head were turned to dust at last: no sudden dream-glare lighted up old Cla-cla's wrinkled dead face and white, blood-dabbled locks: old Nuflo stayed beneath his green coverlet; nor did my mournful spirit-bride come to me to make my heart faint at the thought of immortality.

But when morning dawned again it was bitter to rise

up and go away for ever from that spot where I had often talked with Rima—the true and the visionary. The sky was cloudless and the forest wet as if rain had fallen; it was only a heavy dew, and it made the foliage look pale and hoary in the early light. And the light grew, and a whispering wind sprung as I walked through the wood; and the fast-evaporating moisture was like a bloom on the feathery fronds and grass and rank herbage; but on the higher foliage it was like a faint iridescent mist—a glory above the trees. The everlasting beauty and freshness of nature was over all again, as I had so often seen it with joy and adoration before grief and dreadful passions had dimmed my vision. And now as I walked, murmuring my last farewell, my eyes grew dim again with the tears that gathered to them.

CHAPTER XXII

BEFORE that well-nigh hopeless journey to the coast was half over I became ill—so ill that anyone who had looked on me might well have imagined that I had come to the end of my pilgrimage. That was what I feared. For days I remained sunk in the deepest despondence; then, in a happy moment, I remembered how, after being bitten by the serpent, when death had seemed near and inevitable, I had madly rushed away through the forest in search of help, and wandered lost for hours in the storm and darkness, and in the end escaped death, probably by means of these frantic exertions. The recollection served to inspire me with a new desperate courage. Bidding good-bye to the Indian village where the fever had smitten me, I set out once more on that apparently hopeless adventure. Hopeless, indeed, it seemed to one in my weak condition. My legs trembled under me when I walked, while hot sun and pelting rain were like flame and stinging ice to my morbidly sensitive skin.

For many days my sufferings were excessive, so that I often wished myself back in that milder purgatory of the forest, from which I had been so anxious to escape. When I try to retrace my route on the map there occurs a break here—a space on the chart where names of rivers and mountains call up no image to my mind, although, in a few cases, they were names I seem to have heard in a troubled dream. The impressions of nature received during that sick period are blurred, or else so coloured and exaggerated by perpetual torturing anxiety, mixed with half-delirious night-fancies, that I can only think of that country as an earthly inferno, where I fought against every imaginable obstacle, alternately sweating and freezing, toiling as no man ever toiled before. Hot and cold, cold and hot, and no medium. Crystal waters; green shadows under coverture of broad, moist leaves; and night with dewy fanning winds—these chilled but did not refresh me; a region in which there was no sweet and pleasant thing; where even the Ita palm and mountain glory and airy epiphyte starring the woodland twilight with pendent blossoms had lost all grace and beauty; where all brilliant colours in earth and heaven were like the unmitigated sun that blinded my sight and burnt my brain. Doubtless I met with help from the natives, otherwise I do not see how I could have continued my journey: yet, in my dim mental picture of that period I see myself incessantly dogged by hostile savages. They flit like ghosts through the dark forest; they surround me and cut off all retreat, until I burst through them, escaping out of their very hands, to fly over some wide, naked savannah, hearing their shrill, pursuing yells behind me, and feeling the sting of their poisoned arrows in my flesh.

This I set down to the workings of remorse in a disordered mind and to clouds of venomous insects perpetually shrilling in my ears and stabbing me with their small, fiery needles.

Not only was I pursued by phantom savages and pierced by phantom arrows, but the creations of the Indian imagination had now become as real to me as anything in nature. I was persecuted by that superhuman man-eating monster supposed to be the guardian of the forest. In dark, silent places he is lying in wait for me: hearing my slow, uncertain footsteps he starts up suddenly in my path, out-yelling the bearded aguaratos in the trees; and I stand paralysed, my blood curdled in my veins. His huge, hairy arms are round me; his foul, hot breath is on my skin; he will tear my liver out with his great green teeth to satisfy his raging hunger. Ah, no, he cannot harm me! For every ravening beast, every cold-blooded, venomous thing, and even the frightful Curupitá, half brute and half devil, that shared the forest with her, loved and worshipped Rima, and that mournful burden I carried, her ashes, was a talisman to save me. He has left me, the semi-human monster, uttering such wild, lamentable cries as he hurries away into the deeper, darker woods, that horror changes to grief, and I, too, lament Rima for the first time: a memory of all the mystic, unimaginable grace and loveliness and joy that had vanished smites on my heart with such sudden, intense pain that I cast myself prone on the earth and weep tears that are like drops of blood.

Where, in the rude savage heart of Guiana was this region where the natural obstacles and pain and hunger and thirst and everlasting weariness were terrible enough without the imaginary monsters and legions of phantoms that peopled it, I cannot say. Nor can I conjecture how far I strayed north or south from my course. I only know that marshes that were like Sloughs of Despond, and barren and wet savannahs, were crossed; and forests that seemed infinite in extent and never to be got through; and scores of rivers that boiled round the sharp rocks, threatening to submerge or dash in pieces the frail bark canoe—black and frightful to look on as rivers in hell; and nameless mountain after mountain to be toiled round or toiled over. I may have seen Roraima during that mentally clouded period. I vaguely remember a far-extending gigantic wall of stone that seemed to bar all further progress—a rocky precipice rising to a stupendous height, seen by moonlight, with a huge sinuous rope of white mist suspended from its summit; as if the guardian camoodi of the mountain had been a league-long spectral serpent which was now dropping its coils from the mighty stone table to frighten away the rash intruder.

That spectral moonlight camoodi was one of many serpent fancies that troubled me. There was another, surpassing them all, which attended me many days. When the sun grew hot overhead and the way was over open savannah country I would see something moving on the ground at my side and always keeping abreast of me. A small snake, one or two feet long. No, not a small snake, but a sinuous mark in the pattern on a huge serpent's head, five or six yards long, always moving deliberately at my side. If a cloud came over the sun, or a fresh breeze sprang up, gradually the outline of that awful head would fade and the well-defined pattern would resolve itself into the motlings on the earth. But if the sun grew more and more hot and dazzling as the day progressed, then the tremendous ophidian head would become increasingly real to my sight, with glistening scales and symmetrical markings; and I would walk carefully not to stumble against or touch it; and when I cast my eyes behind me I could see no end to its great coils extending across the savannah. Even looking back from the summit of a high hill I could see it stretching leagues and leagues away through forests and rivers, across wide plains, valleys and mountains, to lose itself at last in the infinite blue distance.

How or when this monster left me—washed away by cold rains perhaps—I do not know. Probably it only transformed itself into some new shape, its long coils perhaps changing into those endless processions and multitudes of pale-faced people I seem to remember having encountered. In my devious wanderings I must have reached the shores of the undiscovered great White Lake, and passed through the long shining streets of Manoa, the mysterious city in the wilderness. I see myself there, the wide thoroughfare filled from end to end with people, gaily dressed as if for some high festival, all drawing aside to let the wretched pilgrim pass, staring at his fever and famine-wasted figure, in its strange rags, with its strange burden.

A new Ahasuerus, cursed by inexpiable crime, yet sustained by a great purpose.

But Ahasuerus prayed ever for death to come to him and ran to meet it, while I fought against it with all my little strength. Only at intervals, when the shadows seemed to lift and give me relief, would I pray to Death to spare me yet a little longer; but when the shadows darkened again and hope seemed almost quenched in utter gloom, then I would curse it and defy its power.

Through it all I clung to the belief that my will would conquer, that it would enable me to keep off the great enemy from my worn and suffering body until the wished goal was reached; then only would I cease to fight and let death have its way. There would have been comfort in this belief had it not been for that fevered imagination which corrupted everything that touched me and gave it some new hateful character. For soon enough this conviction that the will would triumph grew to something monstrous, a parent of monstrous fancies. Worst of all, when I felt no actual pain, but only unutterable weariness of body and soul, when feet and legs were numb so that I knew not whether I trod on dry hot rock or in slime, was the fancy that I was already dead, so far as the body was concerned—had perhaps been dead for days that only the unconquerable will survived to compel the dead flesh to do its work.

Whether it really was will—more potent than the bark of barks and wiser than the physicians—or merely the *vis medicatrix* with which nature helps our weakness even when the will is suspended, that saved me I cannot say; but it is certain that I gradually recovered health, physical and mental, and finally reached the coast comparatively well, although my mind was still in a gloomy, desponding state when I first walked the streets of Georgetown, in rags, half-starved and penniless.

But even when well, long after the discovery that my flesh was not only alive, but that it was of an exceedingly tough quality, the idea born during the darkest period of my pilgrimage, that die I must, persisted in my mind. I had lived through that which would have killed most men—lived only to accomplish the one remaining purpose of my life. Now it was accomplished ; the sacred ashes brought so far, with such infinite labour, through so many and such great perils, were safe and would mix with mine at last. There was nothing more in life to make me love it or keep me prisoner in its weary chains. This prospect of near death faded in time; love of life returned, and the earth had recovered its everlasting freshness and beauty: only that feeling about Rima's ashes did not fade or change, and is as strong now as it was then. Say that it is morbid—call it superstition if you like; but there it is, the most powerful motive I have known, always in all things to be taken into account—a philosophy of life to be made to fit it. Or take it as a symbol, since that may come to be one with the thing symbolised. In those darkest days in the forest I had her as a visitor—a Rima of the mind, whose words when she spoke reflected my despair. Yet even then I was not entirely without hope. Heaven itself, she said, could not undo that which I had done; and she also said that if I forgave myself Heaven would say no word, nor would she. That is my philosophy still: prayers, austerities, good works—they avail nothing, and there is no intercession, and outside of the soul there is no forgiveness in heaven or earth for sin. Nevertheless there is a way, which every soul can find out for itself—

even the most rebellious, the most darkened with crime and tormented by remorse. In that way I have walked; and, self-forgiven and self-absolved, I know that if she were to return once more and appear to me—even here where her ashes are—I know that her divine eyes would no longer refuse to look into mine, since the sorrow which seemed eternal and would have slain me to see would not now be in them.

EL OMBÚ

TO MY FRIEND

R. B. CUNNINGHAME GRAHAM

(" *Singularisimo escritor ingles* ")

Who has lived with and knows (even to the marrow, as they would themselves say) the horsemen of the Pampas, and who alone of European writers has rendered something of the vanishing colour of that remote life.

EL OMBÚ

This history of a house that had been was told in the shade, one summer's day, by Nicandro, that old man to whom we all loved to listen, since he could remember and properly narrate the life of every person he had known in his native place, near to the lake of Chascomus, on the southern pampas of Buenos Ayres.

CHAPTER I

IN all this district, though you should go twenty leagues to this way and that, you will not find a tree as big as this ombú, standing solitary, where there is no house; therefore it is known to all as "the ombú," as if but one existed; and the name of all this estate, which is now ownerless and ruined, is El Ombú. From one of the higher branches, if you can climb, you will see the lake of Chascomus, two thirds of a league away, from shore to shore, and the village on its banks. Even smaller things will you see on a clear day; perhaps a red line moving across the water—a flock of flamingos flying in their usual way. A great tree standing alone, with no house near it; only the old brick foundations of a house, so overgrown with grass and weeds that you have to look closely to find them. When I am out with my flock in the summer time, I often come here to sit in the shade. It is near the main road; travellers, droves of cattle, the diligence, and bullock-carts pass in sight. Sometimes, at noon, I find a traveller resting in the shade, and if he is not sleeping we talk and he tells me the news of that great world my eyes have never seen. They say that sorrow and at last ruin comes upon the house on whose roof the shadow of the ombú tree falls; and on that house which now is not, the shadow of this tree came every summer day when the sun was low. They say, too, that those who sit much in the ombú shade become crazed. Perhaps, sir, the bone of my skull is thicker than in most men, since I have been accustomed to sit here all my life, and though now an old man I have not yet lost my reason. It is truc that evil fortune came to the old house in the end; but into every door sorrow must enter—sorrow and death that comes to all men; and every house must fall at last.

Do you hear the mangangá, the carpenter bee, in the foliage over our heads? Look at him, like a ball of shining gold among the green leaves, suspended in one place, humming loudly! Ah, señor, the years that are gone, the people that have lived and died, speak to me thus audibly when I am sitting here by myself. These are memories; but there are other things that come back to us from the past; I mean ghosts. Sometimes, at midnight, the whole tree, from its great roots to its topmost leaves, is seen from a distance shining like white fire. What is that fire, seen of so many, which does not scorch the leaves? And, sometimes, when a traveller lies down here to sleep the siesta, he hears sounds of footsteps coming and going, and noises of dogs and fowls, and of children shouting and laughing, and voices of people talking; but when he starts up and listens, the sounds grow faint, and seem at last to pass away into the tree with a low murmur as of wind among the leaves.

As a small boy, from the time when I was able, at the age of about six years, to climb on to a pony and ride, I knew this tree. It was then what it is now; five men with their arms stretched to their utmost length could hardly encircle it. And the house stood there, where you see a bed of nettles—a long, low house, built of bricks, when there were few brick houses in this district, with a thatched roof.

The last owner was just touching on old age. Not that he looked aged; on the contrary, he looked what he was, a man among men, a head taller than most, with the strength of an ox; but the wind had blown a little sprinkling of white ashes into his great beard and his hair, which grew to his shoulders like the mane of a black horse. That was Don Santos Ugarte, known to all men in this district as the White Horse, on account of the whiteness of his skin where most men look dark; also because of that proud temper and air of authority which he had. And for still another reason—the number of children in this neighbourhood of which he was said to be the father. In all houses, for many leagues around, the children were taught to reverence him, calling him "uncle," and when he appeared they would run and, dropping on their knees before him, cry out "*Bendicion mi tio.*" He would give them his blessing; then, after tweaking a nose and pinching an ear or two, he would flourish his whip over their heads to signify that he had done with them, and that they must quickly get out of his way.

These were children of the wind, as the saying is, and the desire of his heart was for a legitimate son, an Ugarte by name, who would come after him at El Ombú, as he had come after his father. But though he had married thrice, there was no son born, and no child. Some thought it a mystery that one with so many sons should yet be without a son. The mystery, friend, was only for those who fail to remember that such things are not determined by ourselves. We often say, that He who is above us is too great to concern Himself with our small affairs. There are so many of us; and how shall He, seated on his throne at so great a distance, know all that passes in his dominions! But Santos was no ordinary person, and He who was greater than Santos had doubtless had his attention drawn to this man; and had considered the matter, and had said, "You shall not have your desire; for though you are a devout man, one who gives freely of his goods to the church and my poor, I am not wholly satisfied with you." And so it came to pass that he had no son and heir.

His first two wives had died, so it was said, because of his bitterness against them. I only knew the third—Doña Mericie, a silent, sad woman, who was of less account than any servant, or any slave in the house. And I, a simple boy, what could I know of the secrets of her heart? Nothing! I only saw her pale and silent and miserable, and because her eyes followed me, I feared her, and tried always to keep out of her way. But one morning, when I came to El Ombú and went into the kitchen, I found her there alone, and before I could escape she caught me in her arms, and lifting me off my feet strained me against her breast, crying, *hijo de mi alma*, and I knew not what beside; and calling God's blessing on me, she covered my face with kisses. Then all at once, hearing Santos' voice without, she dropped me and remained like a woman of stone, staring at the door with scared eyes.

She, too, died in a little while, and her disappearance made no difference in the house, and if Santos wore a black band on his arm, it was because custom demanded it and not because he mourned for her in his heart.

CHAPTER II

THAT silent ghost of a woman being gone, no one could say of him that he was hard; nor could anything be said against him except that he was not a saint, in spite of his name. But, sir, we do not look for saints among strong men, who live in the saddle, and are at the head of big establishments. If there was one who was a father to the poor it was Santos; therefore he was loved by many, and only those who had done him an injury or had crossed him in any way had reason to fear and hate him. But let me now relate what I, a boy of ten, witnessed one day in the year 1808. This will show you what the man's temper was; and his courage, and the strength of his wrists.

It was his custom to pay a visit every two or three months to a monastery at a distance of half-a-day's journey from El Ombú.

He was greatly esteemed by the friars, and whenever he went to see them he had a led horse to carry his presents to the Brothers;—a side of fat beef, a sucking-pig or two, a couple of lambs, when they were in season, a few fat turkeys and ducks, a bunch of big partridges, a brace or two of armadillos, the breast and wings of a fat ostrich; and in summer, a dozen ostriches' eggs, and I know not what besides.

One evening I was at El Ombú, and was just starting for home, when Santos saw me, and cried out, " Get off and let your horse go, Nicandro. I am going to the monastery to-morrow, and you shall ride the laden horse, and save me the trouble of leading it. You will be like a little bird perched on his back and he will not feel your few ounces' weight. You can sleep on a sheepskin in the kitchen, and get up an hour before daybreak."

The stars were still shining when we set out on our journey the next morning, in the month of June, and when we crossed the river Sanboronbón at sunrise the earth was all white with hoar frost. At noon, we arrived at our destination, and were received by the friars, who embraced and kissed Santos on both cheeks, and took charge of our horses. After breakfast in the kitchen, the day being now warm and pleasant, we went and sat out of doors to sip maté and smoke, and for an hour or longer, the conversation between Santos and the Brothers had been going on when, all at once, a youth appeared coming at a fast gallop towards the gate, shouting as he came, " Los Ingleses! Los Ingleses!" We all jumped up and ran to the gate, and climbing up by the posts and bars, saw at a distance of less than half-a-league to the east, a great army of men marching in the direction of Buenos Ayres. We could see that the foremost part of the army had come to a halt on the banks of a stream which flows past the monastery and empties itself into the Plata, two leagues farther east. The army was all composed of infantry, but a great many persons on horseback could be seen following it, and these, the young man said, were neighbours who had come out to look at the English invaders; and he also said that the soldiers, on arriving at the stream, had begun to throw away their blankets, and that the people were picking them up. Santos hearing this, said he would go and join the crowd, and mounting his horse and followed by me, and by two of the Brothers, who said they wished to get a few blankets for the monastery, we set out at a gallop for the stream.

Arrived at the spot, we found that the English, not satisfied with the ford, which had a very muddy bottom, had made a new crossing-place for themselves by cutting down the bank on both sides, and that numbers of blankets had been folded and laid in the bed of the stream where it was about twenty-five yards wide. Hundreds of blankets were also being thrown away, and the people were picking them up and loading their horses with them. Santos at once threw himself into the crowd and gathered about a dozen blankets, the best he could find, for the friars; then he gathered a few for himself and ordered me to fasten them on the back of my horse.

The soldiers, seeing us scrambling for the blankets, were much amused; but when one man among us cried out, "These people must be mad to throw their blankets away in cold weather—perhaps their red jackets will keep them warm when they lie down to-night"—there was one soldier who understood, and could speak Spanish, and he replied, "No, sirs, we have no further need of blankets. When we next sleep it will be in the best beds in the capitol." Then Santos shouted back, "That, sirs, will perhaps be a sleep from which some of you will never awake." That speech attracted their attention to Santos, and the soldier who had spoken before returned, "There are not many men like you in these parts, therefore what you say does not alarm us." Then they looked at the friars fastening the blankets Santos had given them on to their horses, and seeing that they wore heavy iron spurs strapped on their bare feet, they shouted with laughter, and the one who talked with us cried out, "We are sorry, good Brothers, that we have not boots as well as blankets to give you."

But our business was now done, and bidding good-bye to the friars, we set out on our return journey, Santos saying that we should be at home before midnight.

It was past the middle of the afternoon, we having ridden about six leagues, when we spied at a distance ahead a great number of mounted men scattered about over the plain, some standing still, others galloping this way or that.

"El pato! el pato!" cried Santos with excitement, "Come, boy, let us go and watch the battle while it is near, and when it is passed on we will go our way. Urging his horse to a gallop, I following, we came to where the men were struggling for the ball, and stood for a while looking on. But it was not in him to remain a mere spectator for long; never did he see a cattlemarking, or parting, or races, or a dance, or any game, and above all games el Pato, but he must have a part in it. Very soon he dismounted to throw off some of the heaviest parts of his horse-gear, and ordering me to take them up on my horse and follow him, he rode in among the players.

About forty or fifty men had gathered at that spot, and were sitting quietly on their horses in a wide circle, waiting to see the result of a struggle for the Pato between three men who had hold of the ball. They were strong men, well mounted, each resolved to carry off the prize from the others. Sir, when I think of that sight, and remember that the game is no longer played because of the Tyrant who forbade it, I am ready to cry out that there are no longer men on these plains where I first saw the light! How they tugged and strained and sweated, almost dragging each other out of the saddle, their trained horses leaning away, digging their hoofs into the turf, as when they resist the shock of a lassoed animal, when the lasso stiffens and the pull comes! One of the men was a big, powerful mulatto, and the bystanders, thinking the victory would be his, were only waiting to see him wrest the ball from the others to rush upon and try to deprive him of it before he could escape from the crowd.

Santos refused to stand inactive, for was there not a fourth handle to the ball to be grasped by another fighter? Spurring his horse into the group, he very soon succeeded in getting hold of the disengaged handle. A cry of resentment at this action on the part of a stranger went up from some of those who were looking on, mixed with applause at the daring from others, while the three men who had been fighting against each other, each one for himself, now perceived that they had a common enemy. Excited as they were by the struggle, they could not but be startled at the stranger's appearance—that huge man on a big horse, so white-skinned and long-haired, with a black beard, that came down over his breast, and who showed them, when he threw back his poncho, the knife that was like a sword and the big brass-barrelled pistol worn at his waist. Very soon after he joined in the fray all four men came to the earth. But they did not fall together, and the last to go down was Santos, who would not be dragged off his horse, and in the end horse and man came down on the top of the others. In coming down, two of the men had lost their hold of the ball; last of all, the big mulatto, to save himself from being crushed under the falling horse, was forced to let go, and in his rage at being beaten, he whipped out his long knife against the stranger. Santos, too quick for him, dealt him a blow on the forehead with the heavy silver handle of his whip, dropping him stunned to the ground. Of the four, Santos alone had so far escaped injury, and rising and remounting, the ball still in his hand, he rode out from among them, the crowd opening on each side to make room for him.

Now in the crowd there was one tall, imposing-looking man, wearing a white poncho, many silver ornaments, and a long knife in an embossed silver sheath; his horse, too, which was white as milk, was covered with silver trappings. This man alone raised his voice; "Friends and comrades," he cried, "is this to be the finish? If this stranger is permitted to carry the Pato away, it will not be because of his stronger wrist and better horse, but because he carries firearms. Comrades, what do you say?"

But there was no answer. They had seen the power

and resolution of the man, and though they were many they preferred to let him go in peace. Then the man on a white horse, with a scowl of anger and contempt, turned from them and began following us at a distance of about fifty yards. Whenever Santos turned back to come to close quarters with him, he retired, only to turn and follow us again as soon as Santos resumed his course. In this way we rode till sunset. Santos was grave, but calm; I, being so young, was in constant terror. "Oh, uncle," I whispered, "for the love of God fire your pistol at this man and kill him, so that he may not kill us!"

Santos laughed. "Fool of a boy," he replied, "do you know that he wants me to fire at him! He knows that I could not hit him at this distance, and that after discharging my pistol we should be equal, man to man, and knife to knife; and who knows then which would kill the other? God knows best, since He knows everything, and He has put it into my heart not to fire."

When it grew dark we rode slower, and the man then lessened the distance between us. We could hear the chink-chink of his silver trappings, and when I looked back I could see a white misty form following us like a ghost. Then, all at once, there came a noise of hoofs and a whistling sound of something thrown, and Santos' horse plunged and reared and kicked, then stood still trembling with terror. His hind legs were entangled in the bolas which had been thrown. With a curse Santos threw himself off, and, drawing his knife, cut the thong which bound the animal's legs, and remounting we went on as before, the white figure still following us.

At length, about midnight, the Sanborombón was reached, at the ford where we had crossed in the morning, where it was about forty yards wide, and the water only high as the surcingle in the deepest parts.

"Let your heart be glad, Nicandro!" said Santos, as we went down into the water; "for our time is come now, and be careful to do as I bid you."

We crossed slowly, and coming out on the south side, Santos quietly dropped off his horse, and, speaking in a low voice, ordered me to ride slowly on with the two horses and wait for him in the road. He said that the man who followed would not see him crouching under the bank, and thinking it safe would cross over, only to receive the charge fired at a few yards distance.

That was an anxious interval that followed, I waiting alone, scarcely daring to breathe, staring into the darkness in fear of that white figure that was like a ghost, listening for the pistol shot. My prayer to heaven was to direct the bullet in its course, so that it might go to that terrible man's heart, and we be delivered from him. But there was no shot, and no sound except a faint chink of silver and sound of hoof-beats that came to my ears after a time, and soon ceased to be heard. The man, perhaps, had some suspicion of the other's plan and had given up the chase and gone away.

Nothing more do I remember of that journey which ended at El Ombú at cock-crow, except that at one spot Santos fastened a thong round my waist and bound me before and behind to the saddle to prevent my falling from my horse every time I went to sleep.

CHAPTER III

REMEMBER, Señor, that I have spoken of things that passed when I was small. The memories of that time are few and scattered, like the fragments of tiles and bricks and rusty iron which one may find half-buried among the weeds, where the house once stood. Fragments that once formed part of the building. Certain events, some faces, and some voices, I remember, but I cannot say the year. Nor can I say how many years had gone by after Doña Mericie's death, and after my journey to the monastery. Perhaps they were few, perhaps many. Invasions had come, wars with a foreigner and with the savages, and Independence, and many things had happened at a distance. He, Santos Ugarte, was older, I know, greyer, when that great misfortune and calamity came to one whom God had created so strong, so brave, so noble. And all on account of a slave, a youth born at El Ombú, who had been preferred above the others by his master. For, as it is said, we breed crows to pick our eyes out. But I will say nothing against that poor youth, who was the cause of the disaster, for it was not wholly his fault. Part of the fault was in Santos—his indomitable temper and his violence. And perhaps, too, the time was come when He who rules over all men had said, "You have raised your voice and have ridden over others long enough. Look, Santos! I shall set My foot upon you, and you shall be like a wild pumpkin at the end of summer, when it is dryer and more brittle that an empty egg-shell."

Remember that there were slaves in those days, also that there was a law fixing every man's price, old or young, so that if any slave went, money in hand, to his master and offered him the price of his liberty, from that moment he became a free man. It mattered not that his master wished not to sell him. So just was the law.

Of his slaves Santos was accustomed to say, "These are my children, and serve because they love me, not because they are slaves; and if I were to offer his freedom to any one among them, he would refuse to take it." He saw their faces, not their hearts.

His favourite was Meliton, black but well favoured, and though but a youth, he had authority over the others, and dressed well, and rode his master's best horses, and had horses of his own. But it was never said of him that he gained that eminence by means of flattery and a tongue cunning to frame lies. On the contrary, he was loved by all, even by those he was set above, because of his goodness of heart and a sweet and gay disposition. He was one of those who can do almost anything better than others; whatever his master wanted done, whether it was to ride a race, or break a horse, or throw a lasso, or make a bridle, or whip, or surcingle, or play on a guitar, or sing, or dance, it was Meliton, Meliton. There was no one like him.

Now this youth cherished a secret ambition in his heart, and saved, and saved his money; and at length one day he came with a handful of silver and gold to Santos, and said, " Master, here is the price of my freedom, take it and count it, and see that it is right, and let me remain at El Ombú to serve you henceforth without payment. But I shall no longer be a slave."

Santos took the money into his hand, and spoke, " It was for this then that you saved, even the money I gave you to spend and to run with, and the money you made by selling the animals I gave you—you saved it for this! Ingrate, with a heart blacker than your skin! Take back the money, and go from my presence, and never cross my path again if you wish for a long life." And with that he hurled the handful of silver and gold into the young man's face with such force that he was cut and bruised with the coins and well nigh stunned. He went back staggering to his horse, and mounting, rode away, sobbing like a child, the blood running from his face.

He soon left this neighbourhood and went to live at Las Vivoras, on the Vecino river, south of Dolores, and there made good use of his freedom, buying fat animals for the market; and for a space of two years he prospered, and every man, rich or poor, was his friend. Nevertheless he was not happy, for his heart was loyal and he loved his old master, who had been a father to him, and desired above all things to be forgiven. And, at length, hoping that Santos had outlived his resentment and would be pleased to see him again, he one day came to El Ombú and asked to see the master.

The old man came out of the house and greeted him jovially. "Ha, Meliton," he cried with a laugh, "you have returned in spite of my warning. Come down from your horse and let me take your hand once more."

The other, glad to think he was forgiven, alighted, and advancing, put out his hand. Santos took it in his, only to crush it with so powerful a grip, that the young man cried out aloud, and blinded with tears of pain, he did not see that his master had the big brass pistol in his left hand, and did not know that his last moment had come. He fell with a bullet in his heart.

Look, señor, where I am pointing, twenty yards or so from the edge of the shadow of the ombú, do you see a dark green weed with a yellow flower on a tall stem growing on the short, dry grass? It was just there, on the very spot where the yellow flower is, that poor Meliton fell, and was left lying, covered with blood, until noon the next day. For no person dared take up the corpse until the Alcalde had been informed of the matter and had come to inquire into it.

Santos had mounted his horse and gone away without a word, taking the road to Buenos Ayres. He had done that for which he would have to pay dearly; for a life is a life, whether the skin be black or white, and no man can slay another deliberately, in cold blood, and escape the penalty. The law is no respecter of persons, and when he, who commits such a deed, is a man of substance, he must expect that Advocates and Judges, with all those who take up his cause, will bleed him well before they procure him a pardon.

Ugarte cared nothing for that, he had been as good as his word, and the devil in his heart was satisfied. Only he would not wait at his estancia to be taken, nor would he go and give himself up to the authorities, who would then have to place him in confinement, and it would be many months before his liberation. That would be like suffocation to him; to such a man a prison is like a tomb. No, he would go to Buenos Ayres and embark for Montevideo, and from that place he would put the matter in motion, and wait there until it was all settled and he was free to return to El Ombú.

Dead Meliton was taken away and buried in consecrated ground at Chascomus. Rain fell, and washed away the red stains on the ground. In the spring, the swallows returned and built their nests under the eaves; but Ugarte came not back, nor did any certain tidings of him reach us. It was said, I know not whether truly or not, that the Advocate who defended him, and the Judge of First Instance, who had the case before him, had quarrelled about the division of the reward, and both being rich, proud persons, they had allowed themselves to forget the old man waiting there month after month for his pardon, which never came to him.

Better for him if he never heard of the ruin which had fallen on El Ombú during his long exile. There was no one in authority: the slaves, left to themselves, went away, and there was no person to restrain them. As for the cattle and horses, they were blown away like thistledown, and everyone was free to pasture his herds and flocks on the land.

The house for a time was in charge of some person placed there by the authoritics, but little by little it was emptied of its contents; and at last it was abandoned, and for a long time no one could be found to live in it on account of the ghosts.

CHAPTER IV

THERE was living at that time, a few leagues from El Ombú, one Valerio de la Cueva, a poor man, whose all consisted of a small flock of three or four hundred sheep and a few horses. He had been allowed to make a small rancho, a mere hut, to shelter himself and his wife Donata and their one child, a boy named Bruno; and to pay for the grass his few sheep consumed he assisted in the work at the estancia house. This poor man, hearing of El Ombú, where he could have house and ground for nothing, offered himself as occupant, and in time came with wife and child and his small flock, and all the furniture he possessed—a bed, two or three chairs, a pot and kettle, and perhaps a few other things. Such poverty El Ombú had not known, but all others had feared to inhabit such a place on account of its evil name, so that it was left for Valerio, who was a stranger in the district.

Tell me, señor, have you ever in your life met with a man, who was perhaps poor, or even clothed in rags, and who yet when you had looked at and conversed with him, has caused you to say: Here is one who is like no other man in the world? Perhaps on rising and going out, on some clear morning in summer, he looked at the sun when it rose, and perceived an angel sitting in it, and as he gazed, something from that being fell upon and passed into and remained with him. Such a man was Valerio. I have known no other like him.

"Come, friend Nicandro," he would say, "let us sit down in the shade and smoke our cigarettes, and talk of our animals. Here are no politics under this old ombú, no ambitions and intrigues and animosities—no bitterness except in these green leaves. They are our laurels—the leaves of the ombú. Happy Nicandro, who never knew the life of cities! I wish that I, too, had seen the light on these quiet plains, under a thatched roof. Once I wore fine clothes and gold ornaments, and lived in a great house where there were many servants to wait on me. But happy I have never been. Every flower I plucked changed into a nettle to sting my hand. Perhaps that maleficent one, who has pursued me all my days, seeing me now so humbled and one with the poor, has left me and gone away. Yes, I am poor, and this frayed garment that covers me will I press to my lips because it does not shine with silk and gold embroidery. And this poverty which I have found will I cherish, and bequeath it as a precious thing to my child when I die. For with it is peace."

The peace did not last long; for when misfortune has singled out a man for its prey, it will follow him to the end, and he shall not escape from it though he mount up to the clouds like the falcon, or thrust himself deep down into the earth like the armadillo.

Valerio had been two years at El Ombú when there came an Indian invasion on the southern frontier. There was no force to oppose it; the two hundred men stationed at the Guardia del Azul had been besieged by a part of the invaders in the fort, while the larger number of the savages were sweeping away the cattle and horses from the country all round. An urgent order came to the commander at Chascomus to send a contingent of forty men from the department; and I, then a young man of twenty, who had seen no service, was cited to appear at the Commandancia, in readiness to march. There I found that Valerio had also been cited, and from that moment we were together. Two days later we were at the Azul, the Indians having retired with their booty; and when all the contingents from the various departments had come in, the commander, one Colonel Barboza, set out with about six hundred men in pursuit.

It was known that in their retreat the Indians had broken up their force into several parties, and that these had taken different directions, and it was thought that these bodies would reunite after a time, and that the larger number would return to their territory by way of Trinqué Lauquén, about seventy-five leagues west of Azul. Our Colonel's plan was to go quickly to this point and wait the arrival of the Indians. It was impossible that they, burdened with the thousands of cattle they had collected, could move fast, while we were burdened with nothing, the only animals we drove before us being our horses. These numbered about five thousand, but many were unbroken mares, to be used as food. Nothing but mare's flesh did we have to eat.

It was the depth of winter, and worse weather I have never known. In this desert I first beheld that whiteness called snow, when the rain flies like cotton-down before the wind, filling the air and whitening the whole earth. All day and every day our clothes were wet, and there was no shelter from the wind and rain at night, nor could we make fires with the soaked grass and reeds, and wood there was none, so that we were compelled to eat our mare's flesh uncooked.

Three weeks were passed in this misery, waiting for the Indians and seeking for them, with the hills of Gaumini now before us in the south, and now on our left hand; and still no sight and no sign of the enemy. It seemed as if the earth had opened and swallowed him up. Our Colonel was in despair, and we now began to hope that he would lead us back to the Azul.

In these circumstances one of the men, who was thinly clad and had been suffering from a cough, dropped from his horse, and it was then seen that he was likely to die, and that in any case he would have to be left behind. Finding that there was no hope for him, he begged that those who were with him would remember, when they were at home again, that he had perished in the desert and that his soul was suffering in purgatory, and that they would give something to the priests to procure him ease. When asked by his officer to say who his relations were and where they lived, he replied that he had no one belonging to him. He said that he had spent many years in captivity among the Indians at the Salinas Grandes, and that on his return he had failed to find any one of his relations living in the district where he had been born. In answer to further questions, he said that he had been carried away when a small boy, that the Indians on that occasion had invaded the Christian country in the depth of winter, and on their retreat, instead of returning to their own homes, they had gone east, towards the sea coast, and had encamped on a plain by a small stream called Curumamuel, at Los Tres Arroyos, where there was firewood and sweet water, and good grass for the cattle, and where they found many Indians, mostly women and children, who had gone thither to await their coming; and at that spot they had remained until the spring.

The poor man died that night, and we gathered stones and piled them on his body so that the foxes and caranchos should not devour him.

At break of day next morning we were on horseback marching at a gallop toward sunrise, for our Colonel had determined to look for the Indians at that distant spot near the sea where they had hidden themselves from their pursuers so many years before. The distance was about seventy leagues, and the journey took us about nine days. And at last, in a deep valley near the sea, the enemy was discovered by our scouts, and we marched by night until we were within less than a league of their encampment, and could see their fires. We rested there for four hours, eating raw flesh and sleeping. Then every man was ordered to mount his best horse, and we were disposed in a half-moon, so that the free horses could easily be driven before us. The Colonel, sitting on his horse, addressed us. "Boys," he said, "you have suffered much, but now the victory is in our hands, and you shall not lose the reward. All the captives you take, and all the thousands of horses and cattle we succeed in recovering, shall be sold by public auction on our return, and the proceeds divided among you."

He then gave the order, and we moved quietly on for a space of half a league, and coming to the edge of the valley saw it all black with cattle before us, and the Indians sleeping in their camp; and just when the sun rose from the sea and God's light came over the earth, with a great shout we charged upon them. In a moment the multitude of cattle, struck with panic, began rushing away, bellowing, in all directions, shaking the earth beneath their hoofs. Our troop of horses, urged on by our yells, were soon in the encampment, and the savages, rushing hither and thither, trying to save themselves, were shot and speared and cut down by swords. One desire was in all our hearts, one cry on all lips—kill! kill! kill! Such a slaughter had not been known for a long time, and birds and foxes and armadillos must have grown fat on the flesh of the heathen we left for them. But we killed only the men, and few escaped; the women and children we made captive.

Two days we spent in collecting the scattered cattle and horses, numbering about ten thousand; then with our spoil we set out on our return and arrived at the Azul at the end of August. On the following day the force was broken up into the separate contingents of which it was composed, and each in its turn was sent to the Colonel's house to be paid. The Chascomus contingent was the last to go up, and on presenting ourselves, each man received two months' soldiers' pay, after which Colonel

Barboza came out and thanked us for our services, and ordered us to give up our arms at the fort and go back to our district, every man to his own house.

"We have spent some cold nights in the desert together, neighbour Nicandro," said Valerio, laughing, "but we have fared well—on raw horse flesh; and now to make it better we have received money. Why, look, with all this money I shall be able to buy a pair of new shoes for Bruno. Brave little man! I can see him toddling about among the cardoon thistles, searching for hens' eggs for his mother, and getting his poor little feet full of thorns. If there should be any change left he shall certainly have some sugar-plums."

But the others on coming to the fort began to complain loudly of the treatment they had received, when Valerio, rebuking them, told them to act like men and tell the Colonel that they were not satisfied, or else hold their peace.

"Will you, Valerio, be our spokesman?" they cried, and he consenting, they all took up their arms again and followed him back to the Colonel's house.

Barboza listened attentively to what was said and replied that our demands were just. The captives and cattle, he said, had been placed in charge of an officer appointed by the authorities and would be sold publicly in a few days. Let them now return to the fort and give up their arms, and leave Valerio with him to assist in drawing up a formal demand for their share of the spoil.

We then retired once more, giving *vivas* to our Colonel. But no sooner had we given up our arms at the fort than we were sharply ordered to saddle our horses and take our departure. I rode out with the others, but seeing that Valerio did not overtake us I went back to look for him.

This was what had happened. Left alone in his enemy's hands, Barboza had his arms taken from him, then ordered his men to carry him out to the patio and flay him alive. The men hesitated to obey so cruel a command, and this gave Valerio time to speak; "My Colonel," he said, "you put a hard task on these poor men, and my hide when taken will be of no value to you or to them. Bid them lance me or draw a knife across my throat, and I will laud your clemency."

"You shall not lose your hide nor die," returned the Colonel, "for I admire your courage. Take him, boys, and stake him out, and give him two hundred lashes; then throw him into the road so that it may be known that his rebellious conduct has been punished."

This order was obeyed, and out upon the road he was thrown. A compassionate store-keeper belonging to the place saw him lying there insensible, the carrion-hawks attracted by his naked bleeding body hovering about him; and this good man took him and was ministering to him when I found him. He was lying, face down, on a pile of rugs, racked with pains, and all night long his sufferings were terrible; nevertheless, when morning came, he insisted on setting out at once on our journey to Chascomus. When his pain was greatest and caused him to cry out, the cry, when he saw my face, would turn to a laugh. "You are too tender hearted for this world we live in," he would say. "Think nothing of this, Nicandro. I have tasted man's justice and mercy before now. Let us talk of pleasanter things. Do you know that it is the first of September to-day? Spring has come back, though we hardly notice it yet in this cold southern country. It has been winter, winter with us, and no warmth of sun or fire, and no flowers and no birds' song. But our faces are towards the north now; in a few days we shall sit again in the shade of the old ombú, all our toil and suffering over, to listen to the mangangá humming among the leaves and to the call of the yellow ventevéo. And better than all, little Bruno will come to us with his hands full of scarlet verbenas. Perhaps in a few years' time you, too, will be a father, Nicandro, and will know what it is to hear a child's prattle. Come, we have rested long enough, and have many leagues to ride!"

The leagues were sixty by the road, but something was gained by leaving it, and it was easier for Valerio when the horses trod on the turf. To gallop or to trot was impossible, and even walking I had to keep at his side to support him with my arm; for his back was all one ever-bleeding wound, and his hands were powerless, and all his joints swollen and inflamed as a result of his having been stretched out on the stakes. Five days we travelled, and day by day and night by night he grew feebler, but he would not rest; so long as the light lasted he would be on the road; and as we slowly pressed on, I supporting him, he would groan with pain and then laugh and begin to talk of the journey's end and of the joy of seeing wife and child again.

It was afternoon on the fifth day when we arrived. The sight of the ombú which we had had for hours before us, strongly excited him ; he begged me, almost with tears, to urge the horses to a gallop, but it would have killed him, and I would not do it.

No person saw our approach, but the door stood open, and when we had walked our horses to within about twenty yards we heard Bruno's voice prattling to his mother. Then suddenly Valerio slipped from the saddle before I could jump down to assist him, and staggered on for a few paces towards the door. Running to his side I heard his cry—" Donata ! Bruno ! let my eyes see you ! one kiss ! " Only then his wife heard, and running out to us, saw him sink, and with one last gasp expire in my arms.

Strange and terrible scenes have I witnessed but never a sadder one than this ! Tell me, señor, are these things told in books,—does the world know them ?

Valerio was dead. He who was so brave, so generous even in his poverty, of so noble a spirit, yet so gentle ; whose words were sweeter than honey to me ! Of what his loss was to others—to that poor woman who was the mother of his one child, his little Bruno—speak not. There are things about which we must be silent, or say only, turning our eyes up, Has He forgotten us ? Does He know ? But to me the loss was greater than all losses ; for he was my friend, the man I loved above all men, who was more to me than any other, even than Santos Ugarte, whose face I should see no more.

For he, too, was dead.

And now I have once more mentioned the name of that

man, who was once so great in this district, let me, therefore proceeding with the history of El Ombú, tell you his end. I heard of it by chance long after he had been placed under the ground.

It was the old man's custom in that house, on the other side of the Rio de la Plata where he was obliged to live, to go down every day to the water-side. Long hours would be spent there, sitting on the rocks, always with his face towards Buenos Ayres. He was waiting, waiting for the pardon which would, perhaps, in God's good time, come to him from that forgetful place. He was thinking of El Ombú; for what was life to him away from it, in that strange country? And that unsatisfied desire, and perhaps remorse, had, they say, made his face terrible to look at, for it was like the face of a dead man who had died with wide-open eyes.

One day some boatmen on the beach noticed that he was seated on the rocks far out and that when the tide rose he made no movement to escape from the water. They saw him sitting waist-deep in the sea, and when they rescued him from his perilous position and brought him to the shore, he stared at them like a great white owl and talked in a strange way.

"It is very cold and very dark," he said, "and I cannot see your faces, but perhaps you know me. I am Santos Ugarte, of El Ombú. I have had a great misfortune, friends. To-day in my anger I killed a poor youth whom I loved like a son—my poor boy Meliton! Why did he despise my warning and put himself in my way! But I will say no more about that. After killing him I rode away with the intention of going to Buenos Ayres, but on the road I repented of my deed and turned back. I said that with my own hands I would take him up and carry him in, and call my neighbours together to watch with me by his poor body. But, Sirs, the night overtook me and the Sanborombón is swollen with rains, as you no doubt know, and in swimming it I lost my horse. I do not know if he was drowned. Let me have a fresh horse, friends, and show me the way to El Ombú, and God will reward you."

In that delusion he remained till the end, a few days later, when he died. May his soul rest in peace!

CHAPTER V

SEÑOR, when I am here and remember these things, I sometimes say to myself: Why, old man, do you come to this tree to sit for an hour in the shade, since there is not on all these plains a sadder or more bitter place? My answer is: To one who has lived long, there is no house and no spot of ground, overgrown with grass and weeds, where a house once stood and where men have lived, that is not equally sad. For this sadness is in us, in a memory of other days which follows us into all places. But for the child there is no past: he is born into the world light hearted like a bird; for him gladness is everywhere.

That is how it was with little Bruno, too young to feel the loss of a father or to remember him long. It was her great love of this child which enabled Donata to live through so terrible a calamity. She never quitted El Ombú. An embargo had been placed on the estancia so that it could not be sold, and she was not disturbed in her possession of the house. She now shared it with an old married couple, who, being poor and having a few animals, were glad of a place to live in rent free. The man, whose name was Pascual, took care of Donata's flock and the few cows and horses she owned along with his own. He was a simple, good-tempered old man, whose only fault was indolence, and a love of the bottle and of play. But that mattered little, for when he gambled he invariably lost, through not being sober, so that when he had any money it was quickly gone.

Old Pascual first put Bruno on a horse and taught him to ride after the flock, and to do a hundred things. The boy was like his father, of a beautiful countenance, with black curling hair, and eyes as lively as a bird's. It was not strange that Donata loved him as no mother ever loved a son, but as he grew up a perpetual anxiety was in her heart lest he should hear the story of his father's death and the cause of it. For she was wise in this; she knew that the most dangerous of all passions is that of revenge, since when it enters into the heart all others, good or bad, are driven out, and all ties and interests and all the words that can be uttered are powerless to restrain a man; and the end is ruin. Many times she spoke of this to me, begging me with tears never to speak of my dead friend to Bruno, lest he should discover the truth, and that fatal rage should enter into his heart.

It had been Donata's custom, every day since Valerio's death, to take a pitcher of water, fresh from the well, and pour it out on the ground, on the spot where he had sunk down and expired, without that sight of wife and child, that one kiss, for which he had cried. Who can say what caused her to do such a thing? A great grief is like a delirium, and sometimes gives us strange thoughts, and makes us act like demented persons. It may have been because of the appearance of the dead face as she first saw it, dry and white as ashes, the baked black lips, the look of thirst that would give everything for a drink of cold water; and that which she had done in the days of anguish, of delirium, she had continued to do.

The spot where the water was poured each day being but a few yards from the door of the house was of a dryness and hardness of fire-baked bricks, trodden hard by the feet of I know not how many generations of men, and by hoofs of horses ridden every day to the door. But after a long time of watering a little green began to appear in the one spot; and the green was of a creeping plant with small round malva-like leaves, and little white flowers like porcelain shirt buttons. It spread and thickened, and was like a soft green carpet about two yards long placed on that dry ground, and it was of an emerald greenness all the year round, even in the hot weather when the grass was dead and dry and the plains were in colour like a faded yellow rag.

When Bruno was a boy of fourteen I went one day to help him in making a sheepfold, and when our work was finished in the afternoon we went to the house to sip maté. Before going in, on coming to that green patch, Bruno cried out, "Have you ever seen so verdant a spot as this, Nicandro, so soft and cool a spot to lie down on when one is hot and tired?" He then threw himself down full length upon it, and, lying at ease on his back, he looked up at Donata, who had come out to us, and spoke laughingly, "Ah, little mother of my soul! A thousand times have I asked you why you poured water every day on this spot and you would not tell me. Now I have found out. It was all to make me a soft cool spot to lie on when I come back tired and hot from work. Look! is it not like a soft bed with a green and white velvet coverlid; bring water now, mother mine, and pour it on my hot, dusty face."

She laughed, too, poor woman, but I could see the tears in her eyes—the tears which she was always so careful to hide from him.

All this I remember as if it had happened yesterday; I can see and hear it all—Donata's laugh and the tears in her eyes which Bruno could not see. I remember it so well because this was almost the last time I saw her before I was compelled to go away, for my absence was long. But before I speak of that change let me tell you of something that happened about two years before at El Ombú, which brought a new happiness into that poor widow's life.

It happened that among those that had no right to be on the land, but came and settled there because there was no one to forbid them, there was a man named Sanchez, who had built himself a small rancho about half a league from the old house, and kept a flock of sheep. He was a widower with one child, a little girl named Monica. This Sanchez, although poor, was not a good man, and had no tenderness in his heart. He was a gambler, always away from his rancho, leaving the flock to be taken care of by poor little Monica. In winter it was cruel, for then the sheep travel most, and most of all on cold, rough days; and she without a dog to help her, barefooted on the thistle-grown land, often in terror at the sight of cattle, would be compelled to spend the whole day out of doors. More than once on a winter evening in bad weather I have found her trying to drive the sheep home in the face of the rain, crying with misery. It hurt me all the more because she had a pretty face: no person could fail to see its beauty, though she was in rags and her black hair in a tangle, like the mane of a horse that has been feeding among the burrs. At such times I have taken her up on my saddle and driven her flock home for her, and have said to myself: "Poor lamb without a mother, if you were mine I would seat you on the horns of the moon; but, unhappy one! he whom you call father is without compassion."

At length, Sanchez, finding himself without money, just when strangers from all places were coming to Chascomus to witness a great race and anxious not to lose this chance of large winnings, sold his sheep, having nothing of more value to dispose of. But instead of winning he lost, and then leaving Monica in a neighbour's house he went away, promising to return for her in a few days. But he did not return, and it was believed by everybody that he had abandoned the child.

It was then that Donata offered to take her and be a mother to the orphan, and I can say, señor, that the poor child's own mother, who was dead, could not have treated her more tenderly or loved her more. And the pretty one had now been Donata's little daughter and Bruno's playmate two years when I was called away, and I saw them not again and heard no tidings of them for a space of five years—the five longest years of my life.

CHAPTER VI

I WENT away because men were wanted for the army, and I was taken. I was away, I have said, five years, and the five would have been ten, and the ten twenty, supposing that life had lasted, but for a lance wound in my thigh, which made me a lame man for the rest of my life. That was the reason of my discharge and happy escape from that purgatory. Once back in these plains where I first saw heaven's light, I said in my heart: I can no longer spring light as a bird on to the back of an unbroken animal and laugh at his efforts to shake me off; nor can I throw a lasso on a running horse or bull and digging my heel in the ground, pit my strength against his; nor can I ever be what I have been in any work or game on horseback or on foot; nevertheless, this lameness, and all I have lost through it, is a small price to pay for my deliverance.

But this is not the history of my life; let me remember that I speak only of those who have lived at El Ombú in my time, in the old house which no longer exists.

There had been no changes when I returned, except that those five years had made Bruno almost a man, and more than ever like his father, except that he never had that I-know-not-what something to love in the eyes which made Valerio different from all men. Donata was the same, but older. Grey hair had come to her in her affliction; now her hair which should have been black was all white—but she was more at peace, for Bruno was good to her, and as a widow's only son, was exempt from military service. There was something else to make her happy. Those two, who were everything to her, could not grow up under one roof and not love; now she could look with confidence to a union between them, and there would be no separation. But even so, that old fear she had so often spoken of to me in former days was never absent from her heart.

Bruno was now away most of the time, working as a cattle drover, his ambition being, Donata informed me, to make money so as to buy everything needed for the house.

I had been back, living in that poor rancho, half a league from El Ombú, where I first saw the light, for the best part of a year, when Bruno, who had been away with his employer buying cattle in the south, one day appeared at my place. He had not been to El Ombú, and was silent and strange in his manner, and when we were alone together I said to him: "What has happened to you, Bruno, that you have the face of a stranger and speak in an unaccustomed tone to your friend?"

He answered: "Because you, Nicandro, have treated me like a child, concealing from me that which you ought to have told me long ago, instead of leaving me to learn it by accident from a stranger."

"It has come," I said to myself, for I knew what he meant: then I spoke of his mother.

"Ah, yes," he said with bitterness, "I know now why she pours water fresh from the well every day on the spot of ground near the door. Do you, Nicandro, think that water will ever wash away that old stain and memory? A man who is a man, must in such a thing obey, not a mother's wish, nor any woman, but that something which speaks in his heart."

"Let no such thought dwell in you to make you mad," I replied. "Look, Bruno, my friend's son and my friend, leave it to God who is above us, and who considers and remembers all evil deeds that men do, and desires not that anyone should take the sword out of His hand."

"Who is He—this God you talk of?" he answered. "Have you seen or spoken with Him that you tell me what His mind is in this matter? I have only this voice to tell me how a man should act in such a case," and he smote his breast; then overcome with a passion of grief he covered his face with his hands and wept.

Vainly I begged him not to lose himself, telling him what the effect of his attempt, whether he succeeded or failed, would be on Donata and on Monica—it would break those poor women's hearts. I spoke, too, of things I had witnessed in my five years' service; the cruel sentences from which there was no appeal, the torments, the horrible deaths so often inflicted. For these evils there was no remedy on earth: and he, a poor, ignorant boy, what would he do but dash himself to pieces against that tower of brass!

He replied that within that brazen tower there was a heart full of blood; and with that he went away, only asking me as a favour not to tell his mother of this visit to me.

Some ten days later she had a message from him, brought from the capitol by a traveller going to the south. Bruno sent word that he was going to Las Mulitas, a place fifty leagues west of Buenos Ayres, to work on an estancia there, and would be absent some months.

Why had he gone thither? Because he had heard that General Barboza—for that man was now a General—owned a tract of land at that place, which the Government had given him as a reward for his services on the southern frontier; and that he had recently returned from the northern provinces to Buenos Ayres and was now staying at this estancia at Las Mulitas.

Donata knew nothing of his secret motives, but his absence filled her with anxiety; and when at length she fell ill I resolved to go in search of the poor youth and try to persuade him to return to El Ombú. But at Las Mulitas I heard that he was no longer there. All strangers had been taken for the army in the frontier department, and Bruno, in spite of his passport, had been forced to go.

When I returned to El Ombú with this sad news Donata resolved at once to go to the capitol and try to obtain his release. She was ill, and it was a long journey for her to perform on horseback, but she had friends to go with and take care of her. In the end she succeeded in seeing the President, and throwing herself on her knees before him, and with tears in her eyes, implored him to let her have her son back.

He listened to her, and gave her a paper to take to the

War Office. There it was found that Bruno had been sent to El Rosario, and an order was despatched for his immediate release. But when the order reached its destination the unhappy boy had deserted.

That was the last that Donata ever heard of her son. She guessed why he had gone, and knew, as well as if I had told her, that he had found out the secret so long hidden from him. Still, being his mother, she would not abandon hope; she struggled to live. Never did I come into her presence but I saw in her face a question which she dared not put in words. If, it said, you have heard, if you know, when and how his life ended, tell me now before I go. But it also said: If you know, do not tell me so that I and Monica may go on hoping together to the end.

"I know, Nicandro," she would say, "that if Bruno returns he will not be the same—the son I have lost. For in that one thing he is not like his father. Could another be like Valerio? No misfortune and no injustice could change that heart, or turn his sweetness sour. In that freshness and gaiety of temper he was like a child, and Bruno as a child was like him. My son! my son! where are you? God of my soul, grant that he may yet come to me, though his life be now darkened with some terrible passion—though his poor hands be stained with blood, so that my eyes may see him again before I go!"

But he came not, and she died without seeing him.

CHAPTER VII

IF Monica, left alone in the house with old Pascual and his wife, had been disposed to listen to those who were attracted by her face she might have found a protector worthy of her. There were men of substance among those who came for her. But it mattered nothing to her whether they had land and cattle or not, or what their appearance was, and how they were dressed. Hers was a faithful heart. And she looked for Bruno's return, not with that poor half-despairing hope which had been Donata's and had failed to keep her alive, but with a hope that sustained and made her able to support the months and years of waiting. She looked for his coming as the night-watcher for the dawn. On summer afternoons, when the heat of the day was over, she would take her sewing outside the gate and sit there by the hour, where her sight commanded the road to the north. From that side he would certainly come. On dark, rainy nights a lantern would be hung on the wall lest he, coming at a late hour, should miss the house in the dark. Glad she was not, nor lively; she was pale and thin, and those dark eyes that looked too large because of her thinness were the eyes of one who had beheld grief. But with it all, there was a serenity, an air of one whose tears, held back, would all be shed at the proper time, when he returned. And he would, perhaps, come to-day, or, if not to-day, then to-morrow, or perhaps the day after, as God willed.

Nearly three years had passed by since Donata's death when, one afternoon, I rode to El Ombú, and on approaching the house spied a saddled horse, which had got loose, going away at a trot. I went after, and caught, and led it back, and then saw that its owner was a traveller, an old soldier, who with or without the permission of the people of the house, was lying down and asleep in the shade of the ombú.

There had lately been a battle in the northern part of the province, and the defeated force had broken up, and the men carrying their arms had scattered themselves all over the country. This veteran was one of them.

He did not wake when I led the horse up and shouted to him. He was a man about fifty to sixty years old, grey-haired, with many scars of sword and lance wounds on his sun-blackened face and hands. His carbine was leaning against the tree a yard or two away, but he had not unbuckled his sword, and what now attracted my attention as I sat on my horse regarding him, was the way in which he clutched the hilt and shook the weapon until it rattled in its scabbard. His was an agitated sleep; the sweat stood in big drops on his face, he ground his teeth and moaned, and muttered words which I could not catch.

At length, dismounting, I called to him again, then shouted in his ear, and finally shook him by the shoulder. Then he woke with a start, and struggling up to a sitting position, and staring at me like one demented, he exclaimed, "What has happened?"

When I told him about his horse he was silent, and, sitting there with eyes cast down, passed his hand repeatedly across his forehead. Never in any man's face had I seen misery compared to his. "Pardon me, friend," he spoke at last. "My ears were so full of sounds you do not hear that I paid little attention to what you were saying."

"Perhaps the great heat of the day has overcome you," I said. "Or maybe you are suffering from some malady caused by an old wound received in fight."

"Yes, an incurable malady," he returned, gloomily. "Have you, friend, been in the army?"

"Five years had I served when a wound which made me lame for life delivered me from that hell."

"I have served thirty," he returned, "perhaps more. I know that I was very young when I was taken and I remember that a woman I called mother wept to see me go. That any eyes should have shed tears for me! Shall I now in that place in the South where I was born find one who remembers my name? I look not for it! I have no one but this"—and here he touched his sword.

After an interval, he continued, "We say, friend, that in the army we can do no wrong, since all responsibility rests with those who are over us; that our most cruel and sanguinary deeds are no more a sin or crime than is the shedding of the blood of cattle, or of Indians who are not Christians, and are therefore of no more account than cattle in God's sight. We say, too, that once we have become accustomed to kill, not men only, but even those who are powerless to defend themselves—the weak and the innocent—we think nothing of it, and have no compunction nor remorse. If this be so, why does He, the One who is above, torment me before my time? Is it just? Listen: no sooner do I close my eyes than sleep brings to me that most terrible experience a man can have—to be in the midst of a conflict and powerless. The bugles call: there is a movement everywhere of masses of men, foot and horse, and every face has on it the look of one who is doomed. There is a murmur of talking all round me, the officers are shouting and waving their swords; I strive in vain to catch the word of command; I do not know what is happening; it is all confusion, a gloom of smoke and dust, a roar of guns, a great noise and shouting of the enemy charging through us. And I am helpless. I wake, and slowly the noise and terrible scene fade from my mind, only to return when sleep again overcomes me. What repose, what refreshment can I know! Sleep, they say, is a friend to everyone, and makes all equal, the rich and the poor, the guilty and the innocent; they say, too, that this forgetfulness is like a draught of cold water to the thirsty man. But what shall I say of sleep? Often with this blade would I have delivered myself from its torture but for the fear that there may be after death something even worse than this dream."

After an interval of silence, seeing that he had recovered from his agitation, I invited him to go with me to the house. "I see smoke issuing from the kitchen," I said, "let us go in so that you may refresh yourself with maté before resuming your journey."

We went in and found the old people boiling the kettle; and in a little while Monica came in and sat with us. Never did she greet one without that light which was like sunshine in her dark eyes; words were not needed to tell me of the gratitude and friendliness she felt toward me, for she was not one to forget the past. I remember that she looked well that day in her white dress with a red flower. Had not Bruno said that he liked to see her in white, and that a flower on her bosom or in her hair was an ornament that gave her most grace? And Bruno might arrive at any moment. But the sight of that grey-haired veteran in his soiled and frayed uniform, and with his clanking sword and his dark scarred face, greatly disturbed her. I noticed that she grew paler and could scarcely keep her eyes off his face while he talked.

While sipping his maté he told us of fights he had been in, of long marches and sufferings in desert places, and of some of the former men he had served under. Among them he, by chance, named General Barboza.

Monica, I knew, had never heard of that man, and on this account I feared not to speak of him. It had, I said, been reported, I knew not whether truthfully or not, that Barboza was dead.

"On that point I can satisfy you," he returned, "since I was serving with him, when his life came to an end in the province of San Luis about two years ago. He was at the head of nineteen hundred men when it happened, and the whole force was filled with amazement at the event. Not that they regretted his loss; on the contrary, his own followers feared, and were glad to be delivered from him. He exceeded most commanders in ferocity, and was accustomed to say scoffingly to his prisoners that he would not have gunpowder wasted on them. That was not a thing to complain of, but he was capable of treating his own men as he treated a spy or a prisoner of war. Many a one have I seen put to death with a blunted knife, he, Barboza, looking on, smoking a cigarette. It was the manner of his death that startled us, for never had man been seen to perish in such a way.

"It happened on this march, about a month before the end, that a soldier named Bracamonte went one day at noon to deliver a letter from his captain to the General. Barboza was sitting in his shirt-sleeves in his tent when the letter was handed to him, but just when he put out his hand to take it the man made an attempt to stab him. The General throwing himself back escaped the blow, then instantly sprang like a tiger upon his assailant, and seizing him by the wrist, wrenched the weapon out of his hand only to strike it quick as lightning into the poor fool's throat. No sooner was he down than the General bending over him, before drawing out the weapon, called to those who had run to his assistance to get him a tumbler. When, tumbler in hand, he lifted himself up and looked upon them, they say that his face was of the whiteness of iron made white in the furnace, and that his eyes were like two flames. He was mad with rage, and cried out with a loud voice, "Thus, in the presence of the army, do I serve the wretch who thought to shed my blood!"

Then with a furious gesture he threw down and shattered the reddened glass, and bade them take the dead man outside the camp and leave him stripped to the vultures.

"This ended the episode, but from that day it was noticed by those about him that a change had come over the General. If, friend, you have served with, or have even seen him, you know the man he was—tall and well-formed, blue eyes and fair like an Englishman, endowed with a strength, endurance and resolution that was a wonder to everyone: he was like an eagle among birds—that great bird that has no weakness and no mercy, whose cry fills all creatures with dismay, whose pleasure it is to tear his victim's flesh with his crooked talons. But now some secret malady had fallen on him which took away all his mighty strength; the colour of his face changed to sickly paleness, and he bent forward and swayed this way and that in the saddle as he rode like a drunken man, and this strange weakness increased day by day. It was said in the army that the blood of the man he had killed had poisoned him. The doctors who accompanied us in this march could not cure him, and their failure so angered him against them that they began to fear for their own safety. They now said that he could not be properly treated in camp, but must withdraw to some town where a different system could be followed; but this he refused to do.

"Now it happened that we had an old soldier with us who was a curandero. He was a native of Santa Fé, and was famed for his cures in his own department; but having had the misfortune to kill a man, he was arrested and condemned to serve ten years in the army. This person now informed some of the officers that he would undertake to cure the General, and Barboza, hearing of it, sent for and questioned him. The curandero informed him that his malady was one which the doctors could not cure. It was a failure of a natural heat of the blood, and only by means of animal heat, not by drugs, could health be recovered. In such a grave case the usual remedy of putting the feet and legs in the body of some living animal opened for the purpose would not be sufficient. Some very large beast should be procured and the patient placed bodily in it.

"The General agreed to submit himself to this treatment; the doctors dared not interfere, and men were sent out in quest of a large animal. We were then encamped on a wide sandy plain in San Luis, and as we were without tents we were suffering much from the great heat and the dust-laden winds. But at this spot the General had grown worse, so that he could no longer sit on his horse, and here we had to wait for his improvement.

"In due time a very big bull was brought in and fastened to a stake in the middle of the camp. A space, fifty or sixty yards round, was marked out and roped round, and ponchos hung on the rope to form a curtain so that what was being done should not be witnessed by the army. But a great curiosity and anxiety took possession of the entire force, and when the bull was thrown down and his agonising bellowings were heard, from all sides officers and men began to move toward that fatal spot. It had been noised about that the cure would be almost instantaneous, and many were prepared to greet the reappearance of the General with a loud cheer.

"Then very suddenly, almost before the bellowings had ceased, shrieks were heard from the enclosure, and in a moment, while we all stood staring and wondering, out rushed the General, stark naked, reddened with that bath of warm blood he had been in, a sword which he had hastily snatched up in his hand. Leaping over the barrier, he stood still for an instant, then catching sight of the great mass of men before him he flew at them, yelling and whirling his sword round so that it looked like a shining wheel in the sun. The men seeing that he was raving mad fled before him, and for a space of a hundred yards or more he pursued them; then the superhuman energy was ended; the sword flew from his hand, he staggered, and fell prostrate on the earth. For some minutes no one ventured to approach him, but he never stirred, and at length, when examined, was found to be dead."

The soldier had finished his story, and though I had many questions to ask I asked none, for I saw Monica's distress, and that she had gone white even to the lips at the terrible things the man had related. But now he had ended, and would soon depart, for the sun was getting low.

He rolled up and lighted a cigarette, and was about to rise from the bench, when he said, "One thing I forgot to mention about the soldier Bracamonte, who attempted to assassinate the General. After he had been carried out and stripped for the vultures, a paper was found sewn up in the lining of his tunic, which proved to be his passport, for it contained his right description. It said that he was a native of this department of Chascomus, so that you may have heard of him. His name was Bruno de la Cueva."

Would that he had not spoken those last words! Never, though I live to be a hundred, shall I forget that terrible scream that came from Monica's lips before she fell senseless to the floor!

As I raised her in my arms, the soldier turned and said, "She is subject to fits?"

"No," I replied, "that Bruno, of whose death we have now heard for the first time, was of this house."

"It was destiny that led me to this place," he said, "or perhaps that God who is ever against me; but you, friend, are my witness that I crossed not this threshold with a drawn weapon in my hand." And with these words he took his departure, and from that day to this I have never again beheld his face.

She opened her eyes at last, but the wings of my heart drooped when I saw them, since it was easy to see that she had lost her reason; but whether that calamity or the grief she would have known is greatest who can say? Some have died of pure grief—did it not kill Donata in the end?—but the crazed may live many years. We sometimes think it would be better if they were dead; but not in all cases—not, señor, in this.

She lived on here with the old people, for from the first she was quiet and docile as a child. Finally an order came from a person in authority at Chascomus for those who were in the house to quit it. It was going to be pulled down for the sake of the material which was required for a building in the village. Pascual died about that time, and the widow, now old and infirm, went to live with some poor relations at Chascomus and took Monica with her. When the old woman died Monica remained with these people: she lives with them to this day. But she is free to come and go at will, and is known to all in the village as *la loca del Ombú*. They are kind to her, for her story is known to them, and God has put compassion in their hearts.

To see her you would hardly believe that she is the Monica I have told you of, whom I knew as a little one, running bare-footed after her father's flock. For she has grey hairs and wrinkles now. As you ride to Chascomus from this point you will see, on approaching the lake, a very high bank on your left hand, covered with a growth of tall fennel, hoarhound, and cardoon thistle. There on most days you will find her, sitting on the bank in the shade of the tall fennel bushes, looking across the water. She watches for the flamingos. There are many of those great birds on the lake, and they go in flocks, and when they rise and travel across the water, flying low, their scarlet wings may be seen at a great distance. And every time she catches sight of a flock moving like a red line across the lake she cries out with delight. That is her one happiness—her life. And she is the last of all those who have lived in my time at El Ombú.

STORY OF A PIEBALD HORSE

STORY OF A PIEBALD HORSE

THIS is all about a piebald. People there are like birds that come down in flocks, hop about chattering, gobble up their seed, then fly away, forgetting what they have swallowed. I love not to scatter grain for such as these. With you, friend, it is different. Others may laugh if they like at the old man of many stories, who puts all things into his copper memory. I can laugh, too, knowing that all things are ordered by destiny; otherwise I might sit down and cry.

The things I have seen! There was the piebald that died long ago; I could take you to the very spot where his bones used to lie bleaching in the sun. There is a nettle growing on the spot. I saw it yesterday. What important things are these to remember and talk about! Bones of a dead horse and a nettle; a young bird that falls from its nest in the night and is found dead in the morning: puffballs blown about by the wind: a little lamb left behind by the flock bleating at night amongst the thorns and thistles, where only the fox or wild dog can hear it! Small matters are these, and our lives, what are they? And the people we have known, the men and women who have spoken to us and touched us with warm hands—the bright eyes and red lips! Can we cast these things like dead leaves on the fire? Can we lie down full of heaviness because of them, and sleep and rise in the morning without them ? Ah, friend !

Let us to the story of the piebald. There was a cattle-marking at neighbour Sotelo's estancia, and out of a herd of three thousand head we had to part all the yearlings to be branded. After that, dinner and a dance. At sunrise we gathered, about thirty of us, all friends and neighbours, to do the work. Only with us came one person nobody knew. He joined us when we were on our way to the cattle ; a young man, slender, well-formed, of pleasing countenance and dressed as few could dress in those days. His horse also shone with silver trappings. And what an animal ! Many horses have I seen in this life, but never one with such a presence as this young stranger's piebald.

Arrived at the herd, we began to separate the young animals, the men riding in couples through the cattle, so that each calf when singled out could be driven by two horsemen, one on each side, to prevent it from doubling back. I happened to be mounted on a demon with a fiery mouth—there was no making him work, so I had to leave the parters and stand with little to do, watching the yearlings already parted, to keep them from returning to the herd.

Presently neighbour Chapaco rode up to me. He was a good-hearted man, well-spoken, half Indian and half Christian ; but he also had another half, and that was devil.

" What ! neighbour Lucero, are you riding on a donkey or a goat, that you remain here doing boy's work ? "

I began telling him about my horse, but he did not listen; he was looking at the parters.

"Who is that young stranger?" he asked.

"I see him to-day," I replied, "and if I see him again to-morrow then I shall have seen him twice."

"And in what country of which I have never heard did he learn cattle-parting?" said he.

"He rides," I answered, "like one presuming on a good horse. But he is safe, his fellow-worker has all the danger."

"I believe you," said Chapaco. "He charges furiously and hurls the heifer before his comrade, who has all the work to keep it from doubling, and all the danger, for at any moment his horse may go over it and fall. This our young stranger does knowingly, thinking that no one here will resent it. No, Lucero, he is presuming more on his long knife than on his good horse."

Even while we spoke, the two we were watching rode up to us. Chapaco saluted the young man, taking off his hat, and said—"Will you take me for a partner, friend?"

"Yes; why not, friend?" returned the other; and together the two rode back to the herd.

Now I shall watch them, said I to myself, to see what this Indian devil intends doing. Soon they came out of the herd driving a very small animal. Then I knew what was coming. "May your guardian angel be with you to avert a calamity, young stranger!" I exclaimed. Whip and spur those two came towards me like men riding a race and not parting cattle. Chapaco kept close to the calf, so that he had the advantage, for his horse was well trained. At length he got a little ahead, then, quick as lightning, he forced the calf round square before the other. The piebald struck it full in the middle, and fell because it had to fall. But, Saints in Heaven! why did not the rider save himself? Those who were watching saw him throw up his feet to tread his horse's neck and leap away; nevertheless man, horse, and calf, came down together. They ploughed the ground for some distance so great had been their speed, and the man was under. When we picked him up he was senseless, the blood flowing from his mouth. Next morning, when the sun rose and God's light fell on the earth, he expired.

Of course there was no dancing that night. Some of the people, after eating, went away; others remained sitting about all night, talking in low tones, waiting for the end. A few of us were at his bedside watching his white face and closed eyes. He breathed, and that was all. When the sunlight came over the world he opened his eyes, and Sotelo asked him how he did. He took no notice, but presently his lips began to move, though they seemed to utter no sound. Sotelo bent his ear down to listen. "Where does she live?" he asked. He could not answer—he was dead.

"He seemed to be saying many things," Sotelo told us, "but I understood only this—'Tell her to forgive me . . . I was wrong. She loved him from the first . . . I was jealous, and hated him. . . . Tell Elaria not to grieve—Anacleto will be good to her.' Alas! my friends, where shall I find his relations to deliver this dying message to them?"

The Alcalde came that day and made a list of the dead man's possessions, and bade Sotelo take charge of them till the relations could be found. Then, calling all the people together, he bade each person cut on his whip-handle and on the sheath of his knife the mark branded on the flank of the piebald, which was in shape like a horse-shoe with a cross inside, so that it might be shown to all strangers, and made known through the country until the dead man's relations should hear of it.

When a year had gone by, the Alcalde told Sotelo that, all inquiries having failed, he could now take the piebald and the silver trappings for himself. Sotelo would not listen to this, for he was a devout man and coveted no person's property, dead or alive. The horse and things, however, still remained in his charge.

Three years later I was one afternoon sitting with Sotelo, taking maté, when his herd of dun mares were driven up. They came galloping and neighing to the corral and ahead of them, looking like a wild horse, was the piebald, for no person ever mounted him.

" Never do I look on that horse," I remarked, " without remembering the fatal marking, when its master met his death."

" Now you speak of it," said he, " let me inform you that I am about to try a new plan. That noble piebald and all those silver trappings hanging in my room are always reproaching my conscience. Let us not forget the young stranger we put under ground. I have had many masses said for his soul's repose, but that does not quite satisfy me. Somewhere there is a place where he is not forgotten. Hands there are, perhaps, that gather wild flowers to place them with lighted candles before the image of the Blessed Virgin; eyes there are that weep and watch for his coming. You know how many travellers and cattle-drovers going to Buenos Ayres from the south call for refreshment at the *pulperia.* I intend taking the piebald and tying him every day at the gate there. No person calling will fail to notice the horse, and some day perhaps some traveller will recognise the brand on its flank and will be able to tell us what department and what estancia it comes from."

I did not believe anything would result from this, but said nothing, not wishing to discourage him.

Next morning the piebald was tied up at the gate of the *pulperia*, at the road side, only to be released again when night came, and this was repeated every day for a long time. So fine an animal did not fail to attract the attention of all strangers passing that way, still several weeks went by and nothing was discovered. At length, one evening, just when the sun was setting, there appeared a troop of cattle driven by eight men. It had come a great distance, for the troop was a large one—about nine hundred head—and they moved slowly, like cattle that had been many days on the road. Some of the men came in for refreshments; then the store-keeper noticed that one remained outside leaning on the gate.

"What is the capatas doing that he remains outside?" said one of the men.

"Evidently he has fallen in love with that piebald," said another, "for he cannot take his eyes off it."

At length the capatas, a young man of good presence, came in and sat down on a bench. The others were talking and laughing about the strange things they had all been doing the day before; for they had been many days and nights on the road, only nodding a little in their saddles, and at length becoming delirious from want of sleep, they had begun to act like men that are half-crazed.

"Enough of the delusions of yesterday," said the capatas, who had been silently listening to them, "but tell me, boys, am I in the same condition to-day?"

"Surely not!" they replied. "Thanks to those horned devils being so tired and footsore, we all had some sleep last night."

"Very well then," said he, "now you have finished eating and drinking, go back to the troop, but before you leave look well at that piebald tied at the gate. He that is not a cattle-drover may ask, 'How can my eyes deceive me?' but I know that a crazy brain makes us see many strange things when the drowsy eyes can only be held open with the fingers."

The men did as they were told, and when they had looked well at the piebald, they all shouted out, "He has the brand of the estancia de Silva on his flank, and no counter-brand—claim the horse, capatas, for he is yours." And after that they rode away to the herd.

"My friend," said the capatas to the store-keeper, "will you explain how you came possessed of this piebald horse?"

Then the other told him everything, even the dying words of the young stranger, for he knew all.

The capatas bent down his head, and covering his face shed tears. Then he said, " And you died thus, Torcuato, amongst strangers! From my heart I have forgiven you the wrong you did me. Heaven rest your soul, Torcuato; I cannot forget that we were once brothers.' I, friend, am that Anacleto of whom he spoke with his last breath."

Sotelo was then sent for, and when he arrived and the *pulperia* was closed for the night, the capatas told his story, which I will give you in his own words, for I was also present to hear him. This is what he told us :—

I was born on the southern frontier. My parents died when I was very small, but Heaven had compassion on me and raised up one to shelter me in my orphanhood. Don Loreto Silva took me to his estancia on the Sarandi, a stream half a day's journey from Tandil, towards the setting sun. He treated me like one of his own children, and I took the name of Silva. He had two other children, Torcuato, who was about the same age as myself, and his daughter, Elaria, who was younger. He was a widower when he took charge of me, and died when I was still a youth. After his death we moved to Tandil, where we had a house close to the little town; for we were all minors, and the property had been left to be equally divided between us when we should be of age. For four years we lived happily together; then when we were of age we preferred to keep the property undivided. I proposed that we should go and live on the estancia, but Torcuato would not consent, liking the place where we were living best. Finally, not being able to persuade him, I resolved to go and attend to the estancia myself. He said that I could please myself and that he should stay where he was with Elaria. It was only when I told Elaria of these things that I knew how much I loved her. She wept and implored me not to leave her.

"Why do you shed tears, Elaria?" I said; "is it because you love me? Know, then, that I also love you with all my heart, and if you will be mine, nothing can ever make us unhappy. Do not think that my absence at the estancia will deprive me of this feeling which has ever been growing up in me."

"I do love you, Anacleto," she replied, "and I have also known of your love for a long time. But there is something in my heart which I cannot impart to you; only I ask you, for the love you bear me, do not leave me, and do not ask me why I say this to you."

After this appeal I could not leave her, nor did I ask her to tell me her secret. Torcuato and I were friendly, but not as we had been before this difference. I had no evil thoughts of him; I loved him and was with him continually; but from the moment I announced to him that I had changed my mind about going to the estancia, and was silent when he demanded the reason, there was a something in him which made it different between us. I could not open my heart to him about Elaria, and sometimes I thought that he also had a secret which he had no intention of sharing with me. This coldness did not, however, distress me very much, so great was the happiness I now experienced, knowing that I possessed Elaria's love. He was much away from the house, being fond of amusements, and he had also begun to gamble. About three months passed in this way, when one morning Torcuato, who was saddling his horse to go out, said, "Will you come with me, to-day, Anacleto?"

"I do not care to go," I answered.

"Look, Anacleto," said he; "once you were always ready to accompany me to a race or dance, or cattle-marking. Why have you ceased to care for these things? Are you growing devout before your time, or does my company no longer please you?"

"It is best to tell him everything and have done with secrets," said I to myself, and so replied—

"Since you ask me, Torcuato, I will answer you frankly. It is true that I now take less pleasure than formerly in these pastimes; but you have not guessed the reason rightly."

"What then is this reason of which you speak?"

"Since you cannot guess it," I replied, "know that it is love."

"Love for whom?" he asked quickly, and turning very pale.

"Do you need ask? Elaria," I replied.

I had scarcely uttered the name before he turned on me full of rage.

"Elaria!" he exclaimed. "Do you dare tell me of love for Elaria! But you are only a blind fool, and do not know that I am going to marry her myself."

"Are you mad, Torcuato, to talk of marrying your sister?"

"She is no more my sister than you are my brother," he

returned. "I," he continued, striking his breast passionately, "am the only child of my father, Loreto Silva. Elaria, whose mother died in giving her birth, was adopted by my parents. And because she is going to be my wife, I am willing that she should have a share of the property; but you, a miserable foundling, why were you lifted up so high? Was it not enough that you were clothed and fed till you came to man's estate? Not a hand's-breadth of the estancia land should be yours by right, and now you presume to speak of love for Elaria."

My blood was on fire with so many insults, but I remembered all the benefits I had received from his father, and did not raise my hand against him. Without more words he left me. I then hastened to Elaria and told her what had passed.

"This," I said, "is the secret you would not impart to me. Why, when you knew these things, was I kept in ignorance?"

"Have pity on me, Anacleto," she replied, crying. "Did I not see that you two were no longer friends and brothers, and this without knowing of each other's love? I dared not open my lips to you or to him. It is always a woman's part to suffer in silence. God intended us to be poor, Anacleto, for we were both born of poor parents, and had this property never come to us, how happy we might have been!"

"Why do you say such things, Elaria? Since we love each other, we cannot be unhappy, rich or poor."

"Is it a little matter," she replied, "that Torcuato must be our bitter enemy? But you do not know everything.

Before Torcuato's father died, he said he wished his son to marry me when we came of age. When he spoke about it we were sitting together by his bed."

"And what did you say, Elaria?" I asked, full of concern.

"Torcuato promised to marry me. I only covered my face, and was silent, for I loved you best even then, though I was almost a child, and my heart was filled with grief at his words. After we came here, Torcuato reminded me of his father's words. I answered that I did not wish to marry him, that he was only a brother to me. Then he said that we were young and he could wait until I was of another mind. This is all I have to say; but how shall we three live together any longer? I cannot bear to part from you, and every moment I tremble to think what may happen when you two are together."

"Fear nothing," I said. "To-morrow morning you can go to spend a week at some friend's house in the town; then I will speak to Torcuato, and tell him that since we cannot live in peace together we must separate. Even if he answers with insults I shall do nothing to grieve you, and if he refuses to listen to me, I shall send some person we both respect to arrange all things between us."

This satisfied her, but as evening approached she grew paler, and I knew she feared Torcuato's return. He did not, however, come back that night. Early next morning she was ready to leave. It was an easy walk to the town-but the dew was heavy on the grass, and I saddled a horse for her to ride. I had just lifted her to the saddle when Torcuato appeared. He came at great speed, and throwing himself off his horse, advanced to us. Elaria trembled and seemed ready to sink upon the earth to hide herself like a partridge that has seen the hawk. I prepared myself for insults and perhaps violence. He never looked at me; he only spoke to her.

"Elaria," he said, "something has happened—something that obliges me to leave this house and neighbourhood at once. Remember when I am away that my father, who cherished you and enriched you with his bounty, and who also cherished and enriched this ingrate, spoke to us from his dying bed and made me promise to marry you, Think what his love was; do not forget that his last wish is sacred, and that Anacleto has acted a base, treacherous part in trying to steal you from me. He was lifted out of the mire to be my brother and equal in everything except this. He has got a third part of my inheritance—let that satisfy him; your own heart, Elaria, will tell you that a marriage with him would be a crime before God and man. Look not for my return to-morrow nor for many days. But if you two begin to laugh at my father's dying wishes, look for me, for then I shall not delay to come back to you, Elaria, and to you, Anacleto. I have spoken."

He then mounted his horse and rode away. Very soon we learned the cause of his sudden departure. He had quarrelled over his cards and in a struggle that followed had stabbed his adversary to the heart. He had fled to escape the penalty. We did not believe that he would remain long absent; for Torcuato was very young, well off, and much liked, and this was, moreover, his first offence against the law. But time went on and he did not return, nor did any message from him reach us, and we at last concluded that he had left the country. Only now, after four years, have I accidentally discovered his fate through seeing his piebald horse.

After he had been absent over a year, I asked Elaria to become my wife. "We cannot marry till Torcuato returns," she said. "For if we take the property that ought to have been all his, and at the same time disobey his father's dying wish, we shall be doing an evil thing. Let us take care of the property till he returns to receive it all back from us; then, Anacleto, we shall be free to marry."

I consented, for she was more to me than lands and cattle. I put the estancia in order, and leaving a trustworthy person in charge of everything I invested my money in fat bullocks to resell in Buenos Ayres, and in this business I have been employed ever since. From the estancia I have taken nothing, and now it must all come back to us—his inheritance and ours. This is a bitter thing and will give Elaria great grief.

Thus ended Anacleto's story, and when he had finished speaking and still seemed greatly troubled in his mind, Sotelo said to him, "Friend, let me advise you what to do. You will now shortly be married to the woman you love and probably some day a son will be born to you. Let him be named Torcuato, and let Torcuato's inheritance be kept for him. And if God gives you no son, remember what was done for you and for the girl you are going to marry, when you were orphans and friendless, and look out for some unhappy child in the same condition, to protect and enrich him as you were enriched."

"You have spoken well," said Anacleto. "I will report your words to Elaria, and whatever she wishes done that will I do."

So ends my story, friend. The cattle-drover left us that night and we saw no more of him. Only before going he gave the piebald and the silver trappings to Sotelo. Six months after his visit, Sotelo also received a letter from him to say that his marriage with Elaria had taken place; and the letter was accompanied with a present of seven cream-coloured horses with black manes and hoofs.

NIÑO DIABLO

NIÑO DIABLO

THE wide pampa rough with long grass ; a vast level disc now growing dark, the horizon encircling it with a ring as faultless as that made by a pebble dropped into smooth water ; above it the clear sky of June, wintry and pale, still showing in the west the saffron hues of the afterglow tinged with vapoury violet and grey. In the centre of the disc a large, low rancho thatched with yellow rushes, a few stunted trees and cattle enclosures grouped about it ; and dimly seen in the shadows, cattle and sheep reposing. At the gate stands Gregory Gorostiaga, lord of house, lands and ruminating herds, leisurely unsaddling his horse ; for whatsoever Gregory does is done leisurely. Although no person is within earshot he talks much over his task, now rebuking his restive animal, and now cursing his benumbed fingers and the hard knots in his gear. A curse falls readily and not without a certain natural grace from Gregory's lips ; it is the oiled feather with which he touches every difficult knot encountered in life. From time to time he glances towards the open kitchen door, from which issue the far-flaring light of the fire and familiar voices, with savoury smells of cookery that come to his nostrils like pleasant messengers.

The unsaddling over at last the freed horse gallops away, neighing joyfully, to seek his fellows ; but Gregory is not a four-footed thing to hurry himself; and so, stepping slowly and pausing frequently to look about him as if reluctant to quit the cold night air, he turns towards the house.

The spacious kitchen was lighted by two or three wicks in cups of melted fat, and by a great fire in the middle of the clay floor that cast crowds of dancing shadows on the walls and filled the whole room with grateful warmth. On the walls were fastened many deer's heads, and on their convenient prongs were hung bridles and lassos, ropes of onions and garlics, bunches of dried herbs, and various other objects. At the fire a piece of beef was roasting on a spit; and in a large pot suspended by hook and chain from the smoke-blackened central beam, boiled and bubbled an ocean of mutton broth, puffing out white clouds of steam redolent of herbs and cummin-seed. Close to the fire, skimmer in hand, sat Magdalen, Gregory's fat and florid wife, engaged in frying pies in a second smaller pot. There also, on a high, straight-backed chair, sat Ascension, her sister-in-law, a wrinkled spinster; also, in a low rush-bottomed seat, her mother-in-law, an ancient white-headed dame, staring vacantly into the flames. On the other side of the fire were Gregory's two eldest daughters, occupied just now in serving maté to their elders—that harmless bitter decoction the sipping of which fills up all vacant moments from dawn to bed-time—pretty dove-eyed girls of sixteen, both also named Magdalen, but not after their mother nor because confusion was loved by the family for its own sake; they were twins, and born on the day sacred to Santa

Magdalena. Slumbering dogs and cats were disposed about the floor, also four children. The eldest, a boy sitting with legs outstretched before him, was cutting threads from a slip of colt's hide looped over his great toe. The two next, boy and girl, were playing a simple game called nines, once known to English children as nine men's morrice; the lines were rudely scratched on the clay floor, and the men they played with were bits of hardened clay, nine red and as many white. The youngest, a girl of five, sat on the floor nursing a kitten that purred contentedly on her lap and drowsily winked its blue eyes at the fire and as she swayed herself from side to side she lisped out the old lullaby in her baby voice:

A-ro-ró mi niño
A-ro-ró mi sol,
A-ro-ró pedazos
De mi corazon.

Gregory stood on the threshold surveying this domestic scene with manifest pleasure.

" Papa mine, what have you brought me?" cried the child with the kitten.

" Brought you, interested? Stiff whiskers and cold hands to pinch your dirty little cheeks. How is your cold to-night, mother?"

" Yes, son, it is very cold to-night; we knew that before you came in," replied the old dame testily as she drew her chair a little closer to the fire.

" It is useless speaking to her," remarked Ascension. " With her to be out of temper is to be deaf."

" What has happened to put her out ? " he asked.

" I can tell you, papa," cried one of the twins. " She wouldn't let me make your cigars to-day, and sat down out of doors to make them herself. It was after breakfast when the sun was warm."

" And of course she fell asleep," chimed in Ascension.

" Let me tell it, auntie ! " exclaimed the other. " And she fell asleep, and in a moment Rosita's lamb came and ate up the whole of the tobacco-leaf in her lap."

" It didn't ! " cried Rosita, looking up from her game. " I opened its mouth and looked with all my eyes, and there was no tobacco-leaf in it."

" That lamb ! that lamb ! " said Gregory slily. " Is it to be wondered at that we are turning grey before our time—all except Rosita ! Remind me to-morrow, wife, to take it to the flock ; or if it has grown fat on all the tobacco-leaf, aprons and old shoes it has eaten——"

" Oh, no, no, no ! " screamed Rosita, starting up and throwing the game into confusion, just when her little brother had made a row and was in the act of seizing on one of her pieces in triumph.

" Hush, silly child, he will not harm your lamb," said the mother, pausing from her task and raising eyes that were tearful with the smoke of the fire and of the cigarette she held between her good-humoured lips. " And now, if these children have finished speaking of their important affairs, tell me, Gregory, what news do you bring ? "

" They say," he returned, sitting down and taking the maté-cup from his daughter's hand, " that the invading Indians bring seven hundred lances, and that those that first opposed them were all slain. Some say they are now retreating with the cattle they have taken; while others maintain that they are waiting to fight our men."

"Oh, my sons, my sons, what will happen to them!" cried Magdalen, bursting into tears.

"Why do you cry, wife, before God gives you cause?" returned her husband. "Are not all men born to fight the infidel? Our boys are not alone—all their friends and neighbours are with them."

"Say not this to me, Gregory, for I am not a fool nor blind. All their friends indeed! And this very day I have seen the Niño Diablo; he galloped past the house, whistling like a partridge that knows no care. Why must my two sons be called away, while he, a youth without occupation and with no mother to cry for him, remains behind?"

"You talk folly, Magdalen," replied her lord. "Complain that the ostrich and puma are more favoured than your sons, since no man calls on them to serve the state; but mention not the Niño, for he is freer than the wild things which Heaven has made, and fights not on this side nor on that."

"Coward! Miserable!" murmured the incensed mother.

Whereupon one of the twins flushed scarlet, and retorted, "He is not a coward, mother!"

"And if not a coward why does he sit on the hearth among women and old men in times like these? Grieved am I to hear a daughter of mine speak in defence of one who is a vagabond and a stealer of other men's horses!"

The girl's eyes flashed angrily, but she answered not a word.

"Hold your tongue, woman, and accuse no man of crimes," spoke Gregory. "Let every Christian take proper care of his animals; and as for the infidel's horses, he is a virtuous man that steals them. The girl speaks truth; the Niño is no coward, but he fights not with our weapons. The web of the spider is coarse and ill-made compared with the snare he spreads to entangle his prey." Thus fixing his eyes on the face of the girl who had spoken, he added: "therefore be warned in season, my daughter, and fall not into the snare of the Niño Diablo."

Again the girl blushed and hung her head.

At this moment a clatter of hoofs, the jangling of a bell, and shouts of a traveller to the horses driven before him, came in at the open door. The dogs roused themselves, almost overturning the children in their hurry to rush out; and up rose Gregory to find out who was approaching with so much noise.

"I know, *papita*," cried one of the children. "It is Uncle Polycarp."

"You are right, child," said her father. "Cousin Polycarp always arrives at night, shouting to his animals like a troop of Indians." And with that he went out to welcome his boisterous relative.

The traveller soon arrived, spurring his horse, scared at the light and snorting loudly, to within two yards of the door. In a few minutes the saddle was thrown off, the fore feet of the bell-mare fettered, and the horses allowed to wander away in quest of pasturage; then the two men turned into the kitchen.

A short, burly man aged about fifty, wearing a soft hat thrust far back on his head, with truculent greenish eyes beneath arched, bushy eyebrows, and a thick shapeless nose surmounting a bristly moustache—such was Cousin Polycarp. From neck to feet he was covered with a blue cloth poncho, and on his heels he wore enormous silver spurs that clanked and jangled over the floor like the fetters of a convict. After greeting the women and bestowing the avuncular blessing on the children, who had clamoured for it as for some inestimable boon—he sat down, and flinging back his poncho displayed at his waist a huge silver-hilted knife and a heavy brass-barrelled horse-pistol.

"Heaven be praised for its goodness, Cousin Magdalen," he said. "What with pies and spices your kitchen is more fragrant than a garden of flowers. That's as it should be, for nothing but rum have I tasted this bleak day. And the boys are away fighting, Gregory tells me. Good! When the eaglets have found out their wings let them try their talons. What, Cousin Magdalen, crying for the boys! Would you have had them girls?"

"Yes, a thousand times," she replied, drying her wet eyes on her apron.

"Ah, Magdalen, daughters can't be always young and sweet-tempered, like your brace of pretty partridges yonder. They grow old, Cousin Magdalen—old and ugly and spiteful; and are more bitter and worthless than the wild pumpkin. But I speak not of those who are present, for I would say nothing to offend my respected Cousin Ascension, whom may God preserve, though she never married."

"Listen to me, Cousin Polycarp," returned the insulted dame so pointedly alluded to. "Say nothing to me nor of me, and I will also hold my peace concerning you; for you know very well that if I were disposed to open my lips I could say a thousand things."

"Enough, enough, you have already said them a thousand times," he interrupted. "I know all that, cousin; let us say no more."

"That is only what I ask," she retorted, "for I have never loved to bandy words with you; and you know already, therefore I need not recall it to your mind, that if I am single it is not because some men whose names I could mention if I felt disposed—and they are the names not of dead but of living men—would not have been glad to marry me; but because I preferred my liberty and the goods I inherited from my father; and I see not what advantage there is in being the wife of one who is a brawler and a drunkard and spender of other people's money, and I know not what besides."

"There it is!" said Polycarp, appealing to the fire. "I knew that I had thrust my foot into a red ants' nest—careless that I am! But in truth, Ascension, it was fortunate for you in those distant days you mention that you hardened your heart against all lovers. For wives, like cattle that must be branded with their owner's mark, are first of all taught submission to their husbands; and consider, cousin, what tears! what sufferings!" And having ended thus abruptly, he planted his elbows on his knees and busied himself with the cigarette he had been trying to roll up with his cold, drunken fingers for the last five minutes.

Ascension gave a nervous twitch at the red cotton kerchief on her head, and cleared her throat with a sound " sharp and short like the shrill swallow's cry," when——

" *Madre del Cielo*, how you frightened me ! " screamed one of the twins, giving a great start.

The cause of this sudden outcry was discovered in the presence of a young man quietly seated on the bench at the girl's side. He had not been there a minute before, and no person had seen him enter the room—what wonder that the girl was startled ! He was slender in form and had small hands and feet, and oval, olive face, smooth as a girl's except for the incipient moustache on his lip. In place of a hat he wore only a scarlet ribbon bound about his head, to keep back the glossy black hair that fell to his shoulders ; and he was wrapped in a white woollen Indian poncho, while his lower limbs were cased in white colt-skin coverings, shaped like stockings to his feet, with the red tassels of his embroidered garters falling to the ankles.

" The Niño Diablo ! " all cried in a breath, the children manifesting the greatest joy at his appearance. But old Gregory spoke with affected anger. " Why do you always drop on us in this treacherous way, like rain through a leaky thatch ? " he exclaimed. " Keep these strange arts for your visits in the infidel country ; here we are all Christians, and praise God on the threshold when we visit a neighbour's house. And now, Niño Diablo, what news of the Indians ? "

"Nothing do I know and little do I concern myself about specks on the horizon," returned the visitor with a light laugh. And at once all the children gathered round him, for the Niño they considered to belong to them when he came, and not to their elders with their solemn talk about Indian warfare and lost horses. And now, now he would finish that wonderful story, long in the telling, of the little girl alone and lost in the great desert, and surrounded by all the wild animals met to discuss what they should do with her. It was a grand story, even mother Magdalen listened, though she pretended all the time to be thinking only of her pies—and the teller, like the grand old historians of other days, put most eloquent speeches, all made out of his own head, into the lips (and beaks) of the various actors—puma, ostrich, deer, cavy, and the rest.

In the midst of this performance supper was announced, and all gathered willingly round a dish of Magdalen's pies, filled with minced meat, hard-boiled eggs chopped small, raisins, and plenty of spice. After the pies came roast beef; and, finally, great basins of mutton broth fragrant with herbs and cummin-seed. The rage of hunger satisfied, each one said a prayer, the elders murmuring with bowed heads, the children on their knees uplifting shrill voices. Then followed the concluding semi-religious ceremony of the day, when each child in its turn asked a blessing of father, mother, grandmother, uncle, aunt, and not omitting the stranger within the gates, even the Niño Diablo of evil-sounding name.

The men drew forth their pouches, and began making

their cigarettes, when once more the children gathered round the story-teller, their faces glowing with expectation.

" No, no," cried their mother. " No more stories to-night—to bed, to bed ! "

" Oh, mother, mother ! " cried Rosita pleadingly, and struggling to free herself; for the good woman had dashed in among them to enforce obedience. " Oh, let me stay till the story ends ! The reed-cat has said such things ! Oh, what will they do with the poor little girl ? "

" And oh, mother mine ! " drowsily sobbed her little sister ; " the armadillo that said—that said nothing because it had nothing to say, and the partridge that whistled and said—" and here she broke into a prolonged wail. The boys also added their voices until the hubbub was no longer to be borne, and Gregory rose up in his wrath and called on some one to lend him a big whip ; only then they yielded, and still sobbing and casting many a lingering look behind, were led from the kitchen.

During this scene the Niño had been carrying on a whispered conversation with the pretty Magdalen of his choice, heedless of the uproar of which he had been the indirect cause ; deaf also to the bitter remarks of Ascension concerning some people who, having no homes of their own, were fond of coming uninvited into other people's houses, only to repay the hospitality extended to them by stealing their silly daughters' affections, and teaching their children to rebel against their authority.

But the noise and confusion had served to arouse Polycarp from a drowsy fit ; for like a boa constrictor, he had dined largely after his long fast, and dinner had made him dull; bending towards his cousin he whispered earnestly: "Who is this young stranger, Gregory?"

"In what corner of the earth have you been hiding to ask who the Niño Diablo is?" returned the other.

"Must I know the history of every cat and dog?"

"The Niño is not cat nor dog, cousin, but a man among men, like a falcon among birds. When a child of six the Indians killed all his relations and carried him into captivity. After five years he escaped out of their hands, and, guided by sun and stars and signs on the earth, he found his way back to the Christians' country, bringing many beautiful horses stolen from his captors; also the name of Niño Diablo first given to him by the infidel. We know him by no other."

"This is a good story; in truth I like it well—it pleases me mightily," said Polycarp. "And what more, cousin Gregory?"

"More than I can tell, cousin. When he comes the dogs bark not—who knows why? His tread is softer than the cat's; the untamed horse is tame for him. Always in the midst of dangers, yet no harm, no scratch. Why? Because he stoops like the falcon, makes his stroke and is gone—Heaven knows where!"

"What strange things are you telling me? Wonderful! And what more, cousin Gregory?"

"He often goes into the Indian country, and lives freely with the infidel, disguised, for they do not know him who was once their captive. They speak of the Niño Diablo to him, saying that when they catch that thief they will flay him alive. He listens to their strange stories, then leaves them, taking their finest ponchos and silver ornaments, and the flower of their horses."

"A brave youth, one after my own heart, cousin Gregory. Heaven defend and prosper him in all his journeys into the Indian territory! Before we part I shall embrace him and offer him my friendship, which is worth something. More, tell me more, cousin Gregory?"

"These things I tell you to put you on your guard; look well to your horses, cousin."

"What!" shouted the other, lifting himself up from his stooping posture, and staring at his relation with astonish ment and kindling anger in his countenance.

The conversation had been carried on in a low tone, and the sudden loud exclamation startled them all—all except the Niño, who continued smoking and chatting pleasantly to the twins.

"Lightning and pestilence, what is this you say to me, Gregory Gorostiaga!" continued Polycarp, violently slapping his thigh and thrusting his hat farther back on his head.

"Prudence!" whispered Gregory. "Say nothing to offend the Niño; he never forgives an enemy—with horses."

"Talk not to me of prudence!" bawled the other. You hit me on the apple of the eye and counsel me not to cry out. What! have not I, whom men call Polycarp of the South, wrestled with tigers in the desert, and must I hold my peace because of a boy—even a boy devil? Talk of what you like, cousin, and I am a meek man—meek as a sucking babe; but touch not on my horses, for then I am a whirlwind, a conflagration, a river flooded in winter, and all wrath and destruction like an invasion of Indians! Who can stand before me? Ribs of steel are no protection! Look at my knife; do you ask why there are stains on the blade? Listen; because it has gone straight to the robber's heart!" And with that he drew out his great knife and flourished it wildly, and made stabs and slashes at an imaginary foe suspended above the fire.

The pretty girls grew silent and pale and trembled like poplar leaves; the old grandmother rose up, and clutching at her shawl toddled hurriedly away, while Ascension uttered a snort of disdain. But the Niño still talked and smiled, blowing thin smoke-clouds from his lips, careless of the tempest of wrath gathering before him; till, seeing the other so calm, the man of war returned his weapon to its sheath, and glancing round and lowering his voice to a conversational tone, informed his hearers that his name was Polycarp, one known and feared by all men,—especially in the south; that he was disposed to live in peace and amity with the entire human race, and he therefore considered it unreasonable of some men to follow him about the world asking him to kill them. "Perhaps," he concluded, with a touch of irony, "they think I gain something by putting them to death. A mistake, good friends; I gain nothing by it! I am not a vulture, and their dead bodies can be of no use to me."

Just after this sanguinary protest and disclaimer the Niño all at once made a gesture as if to impose silence, and turning his face towards the door, his nostrils dilating, and his eyes appearing to grow large and luminous like those of a cat.

" What do you hear, Niño ? " asked Gregory.

" I hear lapwings screaming," he replied.

" Only at a fox perhaps," said the other. " But go to the door, Niño, and listen."

" No need," he returned, dropping his hand, the light of a sudden excitement passing from his face. " 'Tis only a single horseman riding this way at a fast gallop."

Polycarp got up and went to the door, saying that when a man was among robbers it behoved him to look well after his cattle. Then he came back and sat down again. " Perhaps," he remarked, with a side glance at the Niño, " a better plan would be to watch the thief. A lie, cousin Gregory ; no lapwings are screaming ; no single horseman approaching at a fast gallop. The night is serene, and earth as silent as the sepulchre."

" Prudence ! " whispered Gregory again. " Ah, cousin, always playful like a kitten ; when will you grow old and wise ? Can you not see a sleeping snake without turning aside to stir it up with your naked foot ? "

Strange to say, Polycarp made no reply. A long experience in getting up quarrels had taught him that these impassive men were, in truth, often enough like venomous snakes, quick and deadly when roused. He became secret and watchful in his manner.

All now were intently listening. Then said Gregory, " Tell us, Niño, what voices, fine as the trumpet of the smallest fly, do you hear coming from that great silence ? Has the mother skunk put her little ones to sleep in their kennel and gone out to seek for the pipit's nest ? Have fox and armadillo met to challenge each other to fresh trials of strength and cunning? What is the owl saying this moment to his mistress in praise of her big, green eyes?"

The young man smiled slightly, but answered not; and for full five minutes more all listened, then sounds of approaching hoofs became audible. Dogs began to bark, horses to snort in alarm, and Gregory rose and went forth to receive the late night-wanderer. Soon he appeared, beating the angry barking dogs off with his whip, a white-faced, wild-haired man, furiously spurring his horse like a person demented or flying from robbers.

"*Ave Maria!*" he shouted aloud; and when the answer was given in suitable pious words, the scared-looking stranger drew near and bending down said, "Tell me, good friend, is one whom men call Niño Diablo with you; for to this house I have been directed in my search for him?"

"He is within, friend," answered Gregory. "Follow me and you shall see him with your own eyes. Only first unsaddle, so that your horse may roll before the sweat dries on him."

"How many horses have I ridden their last journey on this quest!" said the stranger, hurriedly pulling off the saddle and rugs. "But tell me one thing more; is he well—no indisposition? Has he met with no accident—a broken bone, a sprained ankle?"

"Friend," said Gregory, "I have heard that once in past times the moon met with an accident, but of the Niño no such thing has been reported to me."

With this assurance the stranger followed his host

into the kitchen, made his salutation, and sat down by the fire. He was about thirty years old, a good-looking man, but his face was haggard, his eyes bloodshot, his manner restless, and he appeared like one half-crazed by some great calamity. The hospitable Magdalen placed food before him and pressed him to eat. He complied, although reluctantly, despatched his supper in a few moments, and murmured a prayer; then, glancing curiously at the two men seated near him, he addressed himself to the burly, well-armed, and dangerous-looking Polycarp. "Friend," he said, his agitation increasing as he spoke, "four days have I been seeking you, taking neither food nor rest, so great was my need of your assistance. You alone, after God, can help me. Help me in this strait, and half of all I possess in land and cattle and gold shall be freely given to you, and the angels above will applaud your deed!"

"Drunk or mad?" was the reply vouchsafed to this appeal.

"Sir," said the stranger with dignity, "I have not tasted wine these many days, nor has my great grief crazed me."

"Then what ails the man?" said Polycarp. "Fear perhaps, for he is white in the face like one who has seen the Indians."

"In truth I have seen them. I was one of those unfortunates who first opposed them, and most of the friends who were with me are now food for wild dogs. Where our houses stood there are only ashes and a stain of blood on the ground. "Oh friend, can you not guess why you alone were in my thought when this trouble came to me—why I have ridden day and night to find you?"

"Demons!" exclaimed Polycarp, "into what quagmires would this man lead me? Once for all I understand you not! Leave me in peace, strange man, or we shall quarrel." And here he tapped his weapon significantly.

At this juncture, Gregory, who took his time about everything, thought proper to interpose. "You are mistaken, friend," said he. "The young man sitting on your right is the Niño Diablo, for whom you inquired a little while ago."

A look of astonishment, followed by one of intense relief, came over the stranger's face. Turning to the young man he said, "My friend, forgive me this mistake. Grief has perhaps dimmed my sight; but sometimes the iron blade and the blade of finest temper are not easily distinguished by the eye. When we try them we know which is the brute metal, and cast it aside to take up the other, and trust our life to it. The words I have spoken were meant for you, and you have heard them."

"What can I do for you, friend?" said the Niño.

"Oh, sir, the greatest service! You can restore my lost wife to me. The savages have taken her away into captivity. What can I do to save her—I who cannot make myself invisible, and fly like the wind, and compass all things!" And here he bowed his head, and covering his face gave way to over-mastering grief.

"Be comforted, friend," said the other, touching him lightly on the arm. "I will restore her to you."

"Oh, friend, how shall I thank you for these words!"

cried the unhappy man, seizing and pressing the Niño's hand.

"Tell me her name—describe her to me."

"Torcuata is her name—Torcuata de la Rosa. She is one finger's width taller than this young woman," indicating one of the twins who was standing. "But not dark; her cheeks are rosy—no, no, I forget, they will be pale now, whiter than the grass plumes, with stains of dark colour under the eyes. Brown hair and blue eyes, but very deep blue. Look well, friend, lest you think them black and leave her to perish."

"Never!" remarked Gregory, shaking his head.

"Enough—you have told me enough, friend," said the Niño, rolling up a cigarette.

"Enough!" repeated the other, surprised. "But you do not know; she is my life; my life is in your hands. How can I persuade you to be with me. Cattle I have. I had gone to pay the herdsmen their wages when the Indians came unexpectedly; and my house at La Chilca on the banks of the Langueyú, was burnt, and my wife taken away during my absence. Eight hundred head of cattle have escaped the savages, and half of them shall be yours; and half of all I possess in money and land."

"Cattle!" returned the Niño, smiling, and holding a lighted stick to his cigarette. "I have enough to eat without molesting myself with the care of cattle."

"But I told you that I had other things," said the stranger, full of distress.

The young man laughed, and rose from his seat.

"Listen to me," he said. "I go now to follow the

Indians—to mix with them, perhaps. They are retreating slowly, burdened with much spoil. In fifteen days go to the little town of Tandil, and wait for me there. As for land, if God has given so much of it to the ostrich it is not a thing for a man to set a great value on." Then he bent down to whisper a few words in the ear of the girl at his side; and immediately afterwards, with a simple "good-night" to the others, stepped lightly from the kitchen. By another door the girl also hurriedly left the room, to hide her tears from the watchful censuring eyes of mother and aunt.

Then the stranger, recovering from his astonishment at the abrupt ending of the conversation, started up, and crying aloud, "Stay! stay one moment—one word more!" rushed out after the young man. At some distance from the house he caught sight of the Niño, sitting motionless on his horse, as if waiting to speak to him.

"This is what I have to say to you," spoke the Niño, bending down to the other. "Go back to Langueyú, and rebuild your house, and expect me there with your wife in about thirty days. When I bade you go to the Tandil in fifteen days, I spoke only to mislead that man Polycarp, who has an evil mind. Can I ride a hundred leagues and back in fifteen days? Say no word of this to any man. And fear not. If I fail to return with your wife at the appointed time take some of that money you have offered me, and bid a priest say a mass for my soul's repose; for eye of man shall never see me again, and the brown hawks will be complaining that there is no more flesh to be picked from my bones."

During this brief colloquy, and afterwards, when Gregory and his women-folk went off to bed, leaving the stranger to sleep in his rugs beside the kitchen fire, Polycarp, who had sworn a mighty oath not to close his eyes that night, busied himself making his horses secure. Driving them home, he tied them to the posts of the gate within twenty-five yards of the kitchen door. Then he sat down by the fire and smoked and dozed, and cursed his dry mouth and drowsy eyes that were so hard to keep open. At intervals of about fifteen minutes he would get up and go out to satisfy himself that his precious horses were still safe. At length in rising, some time after midnight, his foot kicked against some loud-sounding metal object lying beside him on the floor, which on examination proved to be a copper bell of a peculiar shape, and curiously like the one fastened to the neck of his bell-mare. Bell in hand, he stepped to the door and put out his head, and lo! his horses were no longer at the gate! Eight horses: seven iron-grey geldings, every one of them swift and sure-footed, sound as the bell in his hand, and as like each other as seven claret-coloured eggs in the tinamou's nest; and the eighth the gentle piebald mare—the *madrina* his horses loved and would follow to the world's end, now, alas! with a thief on her back! Gone—gone!

He rushed out, uttering a succession of frantic howls and imprecations; and finally, to wind up the performance, dashed the now useless bell with all his energy against the gate, shattering it into a hundred pieces. Oh, that bell, how often and how often in how many a wayside public-house had he boasted, in his cups and when sober, of its mellow, far-reaching tone,—the sweet sound that assured him in the silent watches of the night that his beloved steeds were safe! Now he danced on the broken fragments, digging them into the earth with his heel; now in his frenzy, he could have dug them up again to grind them to powder with his teeth!

The children turned restlessly in bed, dreaming of the lost little girl in the desert; and the stranger half awoke, muttering, "Courage, O Torcuata—let not your heart break. . . . Soul of my life, he gives you back to me—on my bosom, *rosa fresca, rosa fresca!*" Then the hands unclenched themselves again, and the muttering died away. But Gregory woke fully, and instantly divined the cause of the clamour. "Magdalen! Wife!" he said. "Listen to Polycarp; the Niño has paid him out for his insolence! Oh, fool, I warned him, and he would not listen!" But Magdalen refused to wake; and so, hiding his head under the coverlet, he made the bed shake with suppressed laughter, so pleased was he at the clever trick played on his blustering cousin. All at once his laughter ceased, and out popped his head again, showing in the dim light a somewhat long and solemn face. For he had suddenly thought of his pretty daughter asleep in the adjoining room. Asleep! Wide awake, more likely, thinking of her sweet lover, brushing the dew from the hoary pampas grass in his southward flight, speeding away into the heart of the vast mysterious wilderness. Listening also to her uncle, the desperado, apostrophizing the midnight stars; while with his knife he excavates two deep trenches, three yards long and intersecting each other at right angles—a sacred symbol on which he intends, when finished, to swear a most horrible vengeance. "Perhaps," muttered Gregory, "the Niño has still other pranks to play in this house."

When the stranger heard next morning what had happened, he was better able to understand the Niño's motive in giving him that caution overnight; nor was he greatly put out, but thought it better that an evil-minded man should lose his horses than that the Niño should set out badly mounted on such an adventure.

"Let me not forget," said the robbed man, as he rode away on a horse borrowed from his cousin, "to be at the Tandil this day fortnight, with a sharp knife and a blunderbuss charged with a handful of powder and not fewer than twenty-three slugs."

Terribly in earnest was Polycarp of the South! He was there at the appointed time, slugs and all; but the smooth-cheeked, mysterious, child-devil came not; nor, stranger still, did the scared-looking de la Rosa come clattering in to look for his lost Torcuata. At the end of the fifteenth day de la Rosa was at Langueyú, seventy-five miles from the Tandil, alone in his new rancho, which had just been rebuilt with the aid of a few neighbours. Through all that night he sat alone by the fire, pondering many things. If he could only recover his lost wife, then he would bid a long farewell to that wild frontier and take her across the great sea, and to that old tree-shaded stone farm-house in Andalusia, which he had left a boy, and where his aged parents still lived, thinking no more to see their wandering son. His resolution was taken; he would sell all he possessed, all except a portion of land in the Langueyú with the house he had just rebuilt; and to the Niño Diablo, the deliverer, he would say, "Friend, though you despise the things that others value, take this land and poor house for the sake of the girl Magdalen you love; for then perhaps her parents will no longer deny her to you."

He was still thinking of these things, when a dozen or twenty military starlings—that cheerful scarlet-breasted songster of the lonely pampas—alighted on the thatch outside, and warbling their gay, careless winter-music told him that it was day. And all day long, on foot and on horseback, his thoughts were of his lost Torcuata; and when evening once more drew near his heart was sick with suspense and longing; and climbing the ladder placed against the gable of his rancho he stood on the roof gazing westwards into the blue distance. The sun, crimson and large, sunk into the great green sea of grass, and from all the plain rose the tender fluting notes of the tinamou-partridges, bird answering bird. "Oh, that I could pierce the haze with my vision," he murmured, "that I could see across a hundred leagues of level plain, and look this moment on your sweet face, Torcuata!"

And Torcuata was in truth a hundred leagues distant from him at that moment; and if the miraculous sight he wished for had been given, this was what he would have seen. A wide, barren plain scantily clothed with yellow tufts of grass and thorny shrubs, and at its southern extremity, shutting out the view on that side, a low range of dune-like hills. Over this level ground, towards the range, moves a vast herd of cattle and horses—fifteen or twenty thousand head—followed by a scattered horde of savages armed with their long lances. In a small compact body in the centre ride the captives, women and children. Just as the red orb touches the horizon the hills are passed, and lo! a wide, grassy valley beyond, with flocks and herds pasturing, and scattered trees, and the blue gleam of water from a chain of small lakes! There full in sight is the Indian settlement, the smoke rising peacefully up from the clustered huts. At the sight of home the savages burst into loud cries of joy and triumph, answered, as they drew near, with piercing screams of welcome from the village population, chiefly composed of women, children and old men.

It is past midnight; the young moon has set; the last fires are dying down; the shouts and loud noise of excited talk and laughter have ceased, and the weary warriors, after feasting on sweet mare's flesh to repletion, have fallen asleep in their huts, or lying out of doors on the ground. Only the dogs are excited still and keep up an incessant barking. Even the captive women, huddled together in one hut in the middle of the settlement, fatigued with their long rough journey, have cried themselves to sleep at last.

At length one of the sad sleepers wakes, or half wakes, dreaming that someone has called her name. How could such a thing be? Yet her own name still seems ringing in her brain, and at length, fully awake, she finds herself intently listening. Again it sounded—" Torcuata "—a voice fine as the pipe of a mosquito, yet so sharp and distinct that it tingled in her ear. She sat up and listened again, and once more it sounded " Torcuata ! " " Who speaks ? " she returned in a fearful whisper. The voice, still fine and small, replied, " Come out from among the others until you touch the wall." Trembling she obeyed, creeping out from among the sleepers until she came into contact with the side of the hut. Then the voice sounded again, " Creep round the wall until you come to a small crack of light on the other side." Again she obeyed, and when she reached the line of faint light it widened quickly to an aperture, through which a shadowy arm was passed round her waist ; and in a moment she was lifted up, and saw the stars above her, and at her feet dark forms of men wrapped in their ponchos lying asleep. But no one woke, no alarm was given ; and in a very few minutes she was mounted, man-fashion, on a bare-backed horse, speeding swiftly over the dim plains, with the shadowy form of her mysterious deliverer some yards in advance, driving before him a score or so of horses. He had only spoken half-a-dozen words to her since their escape from the hut, but she knew by those words that he was taking her to Langueyú.

MARTA RIQUELME

MARTA RIQUELME
(*From the Sepulvida MSS.*)

CHAPTER I

FAR away from the paths of those who wander to and fro on the earth, sleeps Jujuy in the heart of this continent. It is the remotest of our provinces, and divided from the countries of the Pacific by the giant range of the Cordillera ; a region of mountains and forest, torrid heats and great storms ; and although in itself a country half as large as the Spanish peninsula, it possesses, as its only means of communication with the outside world, a few insignificant roads which are scarcely more than mule-paths.

The people of this region have few wants ; they aspire not after progress, and have never changed their ancient manner of life. The Spanish were long in conquering them ; and now, after three centuries of Christian dominion, they still speak the Quichua, and subsist in a great measure on patay, a sweet paste made from the pod of the wild algarroba tree ; while they still retain as a beast of burden the llama, a gift of their old masters the Peruvian Incas.

This much is common knowledge, but of the peculiar character of the country, or of the nature of the things which happen within its borders, nothing is known to those without; Jujuy being to them only a country lying over against the Andes, far removed from and unaffected by the progress of the world. It has pleased Providence to give me a more intimate knowledge, and this has been a sore affliction and great burden now for many years. But I have not taken up my pen to complain that all the years of my life are consumed in a region where the great spiritual enemy of mankind is still permitted to challenge the supremacy of our Master, waging an equal war against his followers: my sole object is to warn, perhaps also to comfort, others who will be my successors in this place and who will come to the church of Yala ignorant of the means which will be used for the destruction of their souls. And if I set down anything in this narrative which might be injurious to our holy religion, owing to the darkness of our understanding and the little faith that is in us, I pray that the sin I now ignorantly commit may be forgiven me, and that this manuscript may perish miraculously unread by any person.

I was educated for the priesthood in the city of Cordova, that famous seminary of learning and religion; and in 1838, being then in my twenty-seventh year, I was appointed priest to a small settlement in the distant province of which I have spoken. The habit of obedience, early instilled in me by my Jesuit masters, enabled me to accept this command unmurmuringly, and even with an outward show of cheerfulness. Nevertheless it filled me with grief, although I might have suspected that some such hard fate had been designed for me, since I had been made to study the Quichua language, which is now only spoken in the Andean provinces. With secret bitter repinings I tore myself from all that made life pleasant and desirable—the society of innumerable friends, the libraries, the beautiful church where I had worshipped, and that renowned University which has shed on the troubled annals of our unhappy country whatever lustre of learning and poetry they possess.

My first impressions of Jujuy did not serve to raise my spirits. After a trying journey of four weeks' duration—the roads being difficult and the country greatly disturbed at the time—I reached the capital of the province, also called Jujuy, a town of about two thousand inhabitants. Thence I journeyed to my destination, a settlement called Yala, situated on the north-western border of the province, where the river Yala takes its rise, at the foot of that range of mountains which, branching eastwards from the Andes, divides Jujuy from Bolivia. I was wholly unprepared for the character of the place I had come to live in. Yala was a scattered village of about ninety souls—ignorant, apathetic people, chiefly Indians. To my unaccustomed sight the country appeared a rude, desolate chaos of rocks and gigantic mountains, compared with which the famous sierras of Cordova sunk into mere hillocks, and of vast gloomy forests, whose death-like stillness was broken only by the savage screams of some strange fowl, or by the hoarse thunders of a distant waterfall.

As soon as I had made myself known to the people of the village, I set myself to acquire a knowledge of the surrounding country; but before long I began to despair of ever finding the limits of my parish in any direction. The country was wild, being only tenanted by a few widely-separated families, and like all deserts it was distasteful to me in an eminent degree; but as I would frequently be called upon to perform long journeys, I resolved to learn as much as possible of its geography. Always striving to overcome my own inclinations, which made a studious, sedentary life most congenial, I aimed at being very active; and having procured a good mule I began taking long rides every day, without a guide and with only a pocket compass to prevent me from losing myself. I could never altogether overcome my natural aversion to silent deserts, and in my long rides I avoided the thick forest and deep valleys, keeping as much as possible to the open plain.

One day having ridden about twelve or fourteen miles from Yala, I discovered a tree of noble proportions growing by itself in the open, and feeling much oppressed by the heat I alighted from my mule and stretched myself on the ground under the grateful shade. There was a continuous murmur of lecheguanas—a small honey wasp—in the foliage above me, for the tree was in flower, and this soothing sound soon brought that restful feeling to my mind which insensibly leads to slumber. I was, however, still far from sleep, but reclining with eyes half closed, thinking of nothing, when suddenly, from the depths of the dense leafage above me, rang forth a shriek, the most terrible it has ever fallen to the lot of any human being to hear. In sound it was a human cry, yet expressing a degree of agony and despair surpassing the power of any human soul to feel, and my impression was that it could only have been uttered by some tortured spirit allowed to wander for a season on the earth. Shriek after shriek, each more powerful and terrible to hear than the last, succeeded, and I sprang to my feet, the hair standing erect on my head, a profuse sweat of terror breaking out all over me. The cause of all these maddening sounds remained invisible to my eyes; and finally running to my mule, I climbed hastily on to its back and never ceased flogging the poor beast all the way back to Yala.

On reaching my house I sent for one Osuna, a man of substance, able to converse in Spanish, and much respected in the village. In the evening he came to see me, and I then gave an account of the extraordinary experience I had encountered that day.

"Do not distress yourself, Father—you have only heard the Kakué," he replied. I then learnt from him that the Kakué is a fowl frequenting the most gloomy and sequestered forests and known to everyone in the country for its terrible voice. Kakué, he also informed me, was the ancient name of the country, but the word was misspelt Jujuy by the early explorers, and this corrupted name was eventually retained. All this, which I now heard for the first time, is historical; but when he proceeded to inform me that the Kakué is a metamorphosed human being, that women and sometimes men, whose lives have been darkened with great suffering and calamities, are changed by compassionate spirits into the lugubrious birds, I asked him somewhat contemptuously whether he, an enlightened man, believed a thing so absurd.

"There is not in all Jujuy," he replied, "a person who disbelieves it."

"That is a mere assertion," cried I, "but it shows which way your mind inclines. No doubt the superstition concerning the Kakué is very ancient, and has come down to us together with the Quichua language from the aborigines. Transformations of men into animals are common in all the primitive religions of South America. Thus, the Guarines relate that flying from a conflagration caused by the descent of the sun to the earth many people cast themselves into the river Paraguay, and were incontinently changed into capybaras and caymans; while others who took refuge in trees were blackened and scorched by the heat and became monkeys. But to go no further than the traditions of the Incas who once ruled over this region, it is related that after the first creation the entire human family, inhabiting the slopes of the Andes, were changed into crickets by a demon at enmity with man's first creator. Throughout the continent these ancient beliefs are at present either dead or dying out; and if the Kakué legend still maintains its hold on the vulgar here it is owing to the isolated position of the country, hemmed in by vast mountains and having no intercourse with neighbouring states."

Perceiving that my arguments had entirely failed to produce any effect I began to lose my temper, and demanded whether he, a Christian, dared to profess belief in a fable born of the corrupt imagination of the heathen?

He shrugged his shoulders and replied, "I have only stated what we, in Jujuy, know to be a fact. What is, is; and if you talk until to-morrow you cannot make it different, although you may prove yourself a very learned person."

His answer produced a strange effect on me. For the first time in my life I experienced the sensation of anger in all its power. Rising to my feet I paced the floor excitedly, and using many gestures, smiting the table with my hands and shaking my clenched fist close to his face in a threatening manner, and with a violence of language unbecoming to a follower of Christ, I denounced the degrading ignorance and heathenish condition of mind of the people I had come to live with; and more particularly of the person before me, who had some pretensions to education and should have been free from the gross delusions of the vulgar. While addressing him in this tone he sat smoking a cigarette, blowing rings from his lips, and placidly watching them rise towards the ceiling, and with his studied supercilious indifference aggravated my rage to such a degree that I could scarcely restrain myself from flying at his throat or striking him to the earth with one of the cane-bottomed chairs in the room.

As soon as he left me, however, I was overwhelmed with remorse at having behaved in a manner so unseemly. I spent the night in penitent tears and prayer, and resolved in future to keep a strict watch over myself, now that the secret enemy of my soul had revealed itself to me. Nor did I make this resolution a moment too soon. I had hitherto regarded myself as a person of a somewhat mild and placid disposition; the sudden change to new influences, and, perhaps also, the secret disgust I felt at my lot, had quickly developed my true character, which now became impatient to a degree and prone to sudden violent outbursts of passion during which I had little control over my tongue. The perpetual watch over myself and struggle against my evil nature which had now become necessary was the cause of but half my trouble. I discovered that my parishioners, with scarcely an exception, possessed that dull apathetic temper of mind concerning spiritual things, which has so greatly exasperated me in the man Osuna, and which obstructed all my efforts to benefit them. These people, or rather their ancestors centuries ago, had accepted Christianity, but it had never properly filtered down into their hearts. It was on the surface still; and if their half-heathen minds were deeply stirred it was not by the story of the Passion of our Lord, but by some superstitious belief inherited from their progenitors. During all the years I have spent in Yala I never said a Mass, never preached a sermon, never attempted to speak of the consolations of faith, without having the thought thrust on to me that my words were useless, that I was watering the rock where no seed could germinate, and wasting my life in vain efforts to impart religion to souls that were proof against it. Often have I been reminded of our holy and learned Father Guevara's words, when he complains of the difficulties encountered by the earlier Jesuit missionaries. He relates how one endeavoured to impress the Chiriguanos with the danger they incurred by refusing baptism, picturing to them their future condition when they would be condemned to everlasting fire. To which they only replied that they were not disturbed by what he told them, but were, on the contrary, greatly pleased to hear that the flames of the future would be unquenchable, for that would save them infinite trouble, and if they found the fire too hot they would remove themselves to a proper distance from it. So hard it was for their heathen intellects to comprehend the solemn doctrines of our faith!

CHAPTER II

MY knowledge of the Quichua language, acquired solely by the study of the vocabularies, was at first of little advantage to me. I found myself unable to converse on familiar topics with the people of Yala; and this was a great difficulty in my way, and a cause of distress for more reasons than one. I was unprovided with books, or other means of profit and recreation, and therefore eagerly sought out the few people in the place able to converse in Spanish, for I have always been fond of social intercourse. There were only four: one very old man, who died shortly after my arrival; another was Osuna, a man for whom I had conceived an unconquerable aversion; the other two were women, the widow Riquelme and her daughter. About this girl I must speak at some length, since it is with her fortunes that this narrative is chiefly concerned. The widow Riquelme was poor, having only a house in Yala, but with a garden sufficiently large to grow a plentiful provision of fruit and vegetables, and to feed a few goats, so that these women had enough to live on, without ostentation, from their plot of ground. They were of pure Spanish blood; the mother was prematurely old and faded; Marta, who was a little over fifteen when I arrived at Yala, was the loveliest being I had ever beheld; though in this matter my opinion may be biased, for I only saw her side by side with the dark-skinned coarse-haired Indian women, and compared with their faces of ignoble type Marta's was like that of an angel. Her features were regular; her skin white, but with that pale darkness in it seen in some whose families have lived for generations in tropical countries. Her eyes, shaded by long lashes, were of that violet tint seen sometimes in people of Spanish blood—eyes which appear black until looked at closely. Her hair was however the crown of her beauty and chief glory, for it was of great length and a dark shining gold colour—a thing wonderful to see!

The society of these two women, who were full of sympathy and sweetness, promised to be a great boon to me, and I was often with them; but very soon I discovered that, on the contrary, it was only about to add a fresh bitterness to my existence. The Christian affection I felt for this beautiful child insensibly degenerated into a mundane passion of such overmastering strength that all my efforts to pluck it out of my heart proved ineffectual. I cannot describe my unhappy condition during the long months when I vainly wrestled with this sinful emotion, and when I often thought in the bitterness of my heart that my God had forsaken me. The fear that the time would come when my feelings would betray themselves increased on me until at length, to avoid so great an evil, I was compelled to cease visiting the only house in Yala where it was a pleasure for me to enter. What had I done to be thus cruelly persecuted by Satan? was the constant cry of my soul. Now I know that this temptation was only a part of that long and desperate struggle in which the servants of the prince of the power of the air had engaged to overthrow me.

Not for five years did this conflict with myself cease to be a constant danger—a period which seemed to my mind not less than half a century. Nevertheless, knowing that idleness is the parent of evil, I was incessantly occupied; for when there was nothing to call me abroad, I laboured with my pen at home, filling in this way many volumes, which in the end may serve to throw some light on the great historical question of the Incas' Cis-Andine dominion, and its effect on the conquered nations.

When Marta was twenty years old it became known in Yala that she had promised her hand in marriage to one Cosme Luna, and of this person a few words must be said. Like many young men, possessing no property or occupation, and having no disposition to work, he was a confirmed gambler, spending all his time going about from town to town to attend horse-races and cock-fights. I had for a long time regarded him as an abominable pest in Yala, a wretch possessing a hundred vices under a pleasing exterior, and not one redeeming virtue, and it was therefore with the deepest pain that I heard of his success with Marta. The widow, who was naturally disappointed at her daughter's choice, came to me with tears and complaints begging me to assist her in persuading her beloved child to break off an engagement which promised only to make her unhappy for life. But with that secret feeling in my heart, ever-striving to drag me down to my ruin, I dared not help her, albeit, I would gladly have given my right hand to save Marta from the calamity of marrying such a man.

The tempest which these tidings had raised in my heart never abated while the preparations for the marriage were going on. I was forced now to abandon my work, for I was incapable of thought; nor did all my religious exercises avail to banish for one moment the strange, sullen rage which had taken complete possession of me. Night after night I would rise from my bed and pace the floor of my room for hours, vainly trying to shut out the promptings of some fiend perpetually urging me to take some desperate course against this young man. A thousand schemes for his destruction suggested themselves to my mind, and when I had resolutely dismissed them all and prayed that my sinful temper might be forgiven, I would rise from my knees still cursing him a thousand times more than ever.

In the meantime, Marta herself saw nothing wrong in Cosme, for love had blinded her. He was young, good looking, could play on the guitar and sing, and was master of that easy, playful tone in conversation which is always pleasing to women. Moreover, he dressed well and was generous with his money, with which he was apparently well provided.

In due time they were married, and Cosme, having no house of his own, came to live with his mother-in-law in Yala. Then, at length, what I had foreseen also happened. He ran out of money, and his new relations had nothing he could lay his hands on to sell. He was too proud to gamble for coppers, and the poor people of Yala had no silver to risk; he could not or would not work, and the vacant life he was living began to grow wearisome. Once more he took to his old courses, and it soon grew to be a common thing for him to be absent from home for a month or six weeks at a time. Marta looked unhappy, but would not complain or listen to a word against Cosme; for whenever he returned to Yala then his wife's great beauty was like a new thing to him, bringing him to her feet, and making him again for a brief season her devoted lover and slave.

She at length became a mother. For her sake I was glad; for now with her infant boy to occupy her mind, Cosme's neglect would seem more endurable. He was away when the child was born; he had gone, it was reported, into Catamarca, and for three months nothing was heard of him. This was a season of political troubles, and men being required to recruit the forces, all persons found wandering about the country not engaged in any lawful occupation, were taken for military service. And this had happened to Cosme. A letter from him reached Marta at last, informing her that he had been carried away to San Luis, and asking her to send him two hundred pesos, as with that amount he would be able to purchase his release. But it was impossible for her to raise the money: nor could she leave Yala to go to him, for her mother's strength was now rapidly failing, and Marta could not abandon her to the care of strangers. All this she was obliged to tell Cosme in the letter she wrote to him, and which perhaps never reached his hands, for no reply to it ever came.

At length, the widow Riquelme died; then Marta sold the house and garden and all she possessed, and taking her child with her, went out to seek her husband. Travelling first to the town of Jujuy, she there, with other women, attached herself to a convoy about to start on a journey to the southern provinces. Several months went by, and then came the disastrous tidings to Yala that the convoy had been surprised by Indians in a lonely place and all the people slain.

I will not here dwell on the anguish of mind I endured on learning Marta's sad end; for I tried hard to believe that her troubled life was indeed over, although I was often assured by my neighbours that the Indians invariably spare the women and children.

Every blow dealt by a cruel destiny against this most unhappy woman had pierced my heart; and during the years that followed, and when the villagers had long ceased to speak of her, often in the dead of the night I rose and sought the house where she had lived, and walking under the trees in the garden where I had so often held intercourse with her, indulged a grief which time seemed powerless to mitigate.

CHAPTER III

MARTA was not dead; but what happened to her after her departure from Yala was this: When the convoy with which she journeyed was attacked the men only were slain, while the women and children were carried away into captivity. When the victors divided the spoil among themselves, the child, which even in that long painful journey into the desert, with the prospect of a life of cruel slavery before her, had been a comfort to Marta, was taken forcibly from her arms to be conveyed to some distant place, and from that moment she utterly lost sight of it. She was herself bought by an Indian able to pay for a pretty white captive, and who presently made her his wife. She, a Christian, the wife of a man loved only too well, could not endure this horrible fate which had overtaken her. She was also mad with grief at the loss of her child, and stealing out one dark stormy night she fled from the Indian settlement. For several days and nights she wandered about the desert, suffering every hardship and in constant fear of jaguars, and was at length found by the savages in a half-starved condition and unable longer to fly from them. Her owner, when she was restored to him, had no mercy on her: he bound her to a tree growing beside his hovel, and there every day he cruelly scourged her naked flesh to satisfy his barbarous resentment, until she was ready to perish with excessive suffering. He also cut off her hair, and braiding it into a belt wore it always round his waist,—a golden trophy which doubtless won him great honour and distinction amongst his fellow savages. When he had by these means utterly broken her spirit and reduced her to the last condition of weakness, he released her from the tree, but at the same time fastened a log of wood to her ankle, so that only with great labour and drawing herself along with the aid of her hands, could she perform the daily tasks her master imposed on her. Only after a whole year of captivity, and when she had given birth to a child, was the punishment over and her foot released from the log. The natural affection which she felt for this child of a father so cruel was now poor Marta's only comfort. In this hard servitude five years of her miserable existence were consumed; and only those who know the stern, sullen, pitiless character of the Indian can imagine what this period was for Marta, without sympathy from her fellow-creatures, with no hope and no pleasure beyond the pleasure of loving and caressing her own infant savages. Of these she was now the mother of three.

When her youngest was not many months old Marta had one day wandered some distance in search of sticks for firewood, when a woman, one of her fellow-captives from Jujuy, came running to her, for she had been watching for an opportunity of speaking with Marta. It happened that this woman had succeeded in persuading her Indian husband to take her back to her home in the

Christian country, and she had at the same time won his consent to take Marta with them, having conceived a great affection for her. The prospect of escape filled poor Marta's heart with joy, but when she was told that her children could on no account be taken, then a cruel struggle commenced in her breast. Bitterly she pleaded for permission to take her babes, and at last overcome by her importunity her fellow-captive consented to her taking the youngest of the three ; though this concession was made very reluctantly.

In a short time the day appointed for the flight arrived and Marta carrying her infant met her friends in the wood. They were quickly mounted, and the journey began which was to last for many days, and during which they were to suffer much from hunger, thirst and fatigue. One dark night as they journeyed through a hilly and wooded country, Marta being overcome with fatigue so that she could scarcely keep her seat, the Indian, with affected kindness, relieved her of the child she always carried in her arms. An hour passed, and then pressing forward to his side and asking for her child she was told that it had been dropped into a deep, swift stream over which they had swam their horses some time before. Of what happened after that she was unable to give any very clear account. She only dimly remembered that through many days of scorching heat and many nights of weary travel she was always piteously pleading for her lost child—always seeming to hear it crying to her to save it from destruction. The long journey ended at last. She was left by the other at the first Christian settlement they reached, after which, travelling slowly from village to village, she made her way to Yala. Her old neighbours and friends did not know her at first, but when they were at length convinced that it was indeed Marta Riquelme that stood before them she was welcomed like one returned from the grave. I heard of her arrival, and hastening forth to greet her found her seated before a neighbour's house already surrounded by half the people of the village.

Was this woman indeed Marta, once the pride of Yala! It was hard to believe it, so darkened with the burning suns and winds of years was her face, once so fair; so wasted and furrowed with grief and the many hardships she had undergone! Her figure, worn almost to a skeleton, was clothed with ragged garments, while her head, bowed down with sorrow and despair, was divested of that golden crown which had been her chief ornament. Seeing me arrive she cast herself on her knees before me and taking my hands in hers covered it with tears and kisses. The grief I felt at the sight of her forlorn condition mingled with joy for her deliverance from death and captivity overcame me; I was shaken like a reed in the wind, and covering my face with my robe I sobbed aloud in the presence of all the people.

CHAPTER IV

EVERYTHING that charity could dictate was done to alleviate her misery. A merciful woman of Yala received her into her house and provided her with decent garments. But for a time nothing served to raise her desponding spirits; she still grieved for her lost babe, and seemed ever in fancy listening to its piteous cries for help. When assured that Cosme would return in due time, that alone gave her comfort. She believed what they told her, for it agreed with her wish, and by degrees the effects of her terrible experience began to wear off, giving place to a feeling of feverish impatience, with which she looked forward to her husband's return. With this feeling, which I did all I could to encourage, perceiving it to be the only remedy against despair, came also a new anxiety about her personal appearance. She grew careful in her dress, and made the most of her short and sunburnt hair. Beauty she could never recover; but she possessed good features which could not be altered; her eyes also retained their violet colour, and hope brought back to her something of the vanished expression of other years.

At length, when she had been with us over a year, one day there came a report that Cosme had arrived, that he had been seen in Yala, and had alighted at Andrada's door—the store in the main road. She heard it and rose up with a great cry of joy. He had come to her at last—he would comfort her! She could not wait for his arrival: what wonder! Hurrying forth she flew like the wind through the village, and in a few moments stood on Andrada's threshold, panting from her race, her cheeks glowing, all the hope and life and fire of her girlhood rushing back to her heart. There she beheld Cosme, changed but little, surrounded by his old companions, listening in silence and with a dismayed countenance to the story of Marta's sufferings in the great desert, of her escape and return to Yala, where she had been received like one come back from the sepulchre. Presently they caught sight of her standing there. "Here is Marta herself arrived in good time," they cried. "Behold your wife!"

He shook himself from them with a strange laugh. "What, that woman my wife—Marta Riquelme!" he replied. "No, no, my friends, be not deceived; Marta perished long ago in the desert, where I have been to seek for her. Of her death I have no doubt; let me pass."

He pushed by her, left her standing there motionless as a statue, unable to utter a word, and was quickly on his horse riding away from Yala.

Then suddenly she recovered possession of her faculties, and with a cry of anguish hurried after him, imploring him to return to her; but finding that he would not listen to her she was overcome with despair and fell upon the earth insensible. She was taken up by the people who had followed her out and carried back into the house. Unhappily she was not dead, and when she recovered consciousness it was pitiful to hear the excuses she invented for the remorseless wretch who had abandoned her. She was altered, she said, greatly altered—it was not strange that Cosme had refused to believe that she could be the Marta of six years ago! In her heart she knew that nobody was deceived: to all Yala it was patent that she had been deserted. She could not endure it, and when she met people in the street she lowered her eyes and passed on, pretending not to see them. Most of her time was spent indoors, and there she would sit for hours without speaking or stirring, her cheeks resting on her hands, her eyes fixed on vacancy. My heart bled for her; morning and evening I remembered her in my prayers; by every argument I sought to cheer her drooping spirit, even telling her that the beauty and freshness of her youth would return to her in time, and that her husband would repent and come back to her.

These efforts were fruitless. Before many days she disappeared from Yala, and though diligent search was made in the adjacent mountains she could not be found. Knowing how empty and desolate her life had been, deprived of every object of affection, I formed the opinion that she had gone back to the desert to seek the tribe where she had been a captive in the hope of once more seeing her lost children. At length, when all expectation of ever seeing her again had been abandoned, a person named Montero came to me with tidings of her. He was a poor man, a charcoal-burner, and lived with his wife and children in the forest about two hours' journey from Yala, at a distance from any other habitation. Finding Marta wandering lost in the woods he had taken her to his rancho, and she had been pleased to find this shelter, away from the people of Yala who knew her history; and it was at Marta's own request that this good man had ridden to the village to inform me of her safety. I was greatly relieved to hear all this, and thought that Marta had acted wisely in escaping from the villagers, who were always pointing her out and repeating her wonderful history. In that sequestered spot where she had taken refuge, removed from sad associations and gossiping tongues, the wounds in her heart would perhaps gradually heal and peace return to her perturbed spirit.

Before many weeks had elapsed, however, Montero's wife came to me with a very sad account of Marta. She had grown day by day more silent and solitary in her habits, spending most of her time in some secluded spot among the trees, where she would sit motionless, brooding over her memories for hours at a time. Nor was this the worst. Occasionally she would make an effort to assist in the household work, preparing the patay or maize for the supper, or going out with Montero's wife to gather firewood in the forest. But suddenly, in the middle of her task, she would drop her bundle of sticks and, casting herself on the earth, break forth into the most heart-rending cries and lamentations, loudly exclaiming that God had unjustly persecuted her, that He was a being filled with malevolence, and speaking many things against Him very dreadful to hear. Deeply distressed at these things I called for my mule and accompanied the poor woman back to her own house; but when we arrived there Marta could nowhere be found.

Most willingly would I have remained to see her, and try once more to win her back from these desponding moods, but I was compelled to return to Yala. For it happened that a fever epidemic had recently broken out and spread over the country, so that hardly a day passed without its long journey to perform and death-bed to attend. Often during those days, worn out with fatigue and want of sleep I would dismount from my mule and rest for a season against a rock or tree, wishing for death to come and release me from so sad an existence.

When I left Montero's house I charged him to send me news of Marta as soon as they should find her; but for several days I heard nothing. At length word came that they had discovered her hiding-place in the forest, but could not induce her to leave it, or even to speak to them; and they implored me to go to them, for they were greatly troubled at her state, and knew not what to do.

Once more I went out to seek her; and this was the saddest journey of all, for even the elements were charged with unusual gloom, as if to prepare my mind for some unimaginable calamity. Rain, accompanied by terrific thunder and lightning, had been falling in torrents for several days, so that the country was all but impassable: the swollen streams roared between the hills, dragging down rocks and trees, and threatening, whenever we were compelled to ford them, to carry us away to destruction. The rain had ceased, but the whole sky was covered by a dark motionless cloud, unpierced by a single ray of sunshine. The mountains, wrapped in blue vapours, loomed before us, vast and desolate; and the trees, in that still, thick atmosphere, were like figures of trees hewn out of solid ink-black rock and set up in some shadowy subterranean region to mock its inhabitants with an imitation of the upper world.

At length we reached Montero's hut, and, followed by all the family, went to look for Marta. The place where she had concealed herself was in a dense wood half a league from the house, and the ascent to it being steep and difficult Montero was compelled to walk before, leading my mule by the bridle. At length we came to the spot where they had discovered her, and there, in the shadow of the woods, we found Marta still in the same place, seated on the trunk of a fallen tree, which was sodden with the rain and half buried under great creepers and masses of dead and rotting foliage. She was in a crouching attitude, her feet gathered under her garments, which were now torn to rags and fouled with clay; her elbows were planted on her drawn-up knees, and her long, bony fingers thrust into her hair, which fell in tangled disorder over her face. To this pitiable condition had she been brought by great and unmerited sufferings.

Seeing her, a cry of compassion escaped my lips, and casting myself off my mule I advanced towards her. As I approached she raised her eyes to mine, and then I stood still, transfixed with amazement and horror at what I saw; for they were no longer those soft violet orbs which had retained until recently their sweet pathetic expression ; now they were round and wild-looking, open to thrice their ordinary size, and filled with a lurid yellow fire, giving them a resemblance to the eyes of some hunted savage animal.

"Great God, she has lost her reason!" I cried ; then falling on my knees I disengaged the crucifix from my neck with trembling hands, and endeavoured to hold it up before her sight. This movement appeared to infuriate her ; the insane, desolate eyes, from which all human expression had vanished, became like two burning balls, which seemed to shoot out sparks of fire ; her short hair rose up until it stood like an immense crest on her head ; and suddenly bringing down her skeleton-like hands she thrust the crucifix violently from her, uttering at the same time a succession of moans and cries that pierced my heart with pain to hear. And presently flinging up her arms, she burst forth into shrieks so terrible in the depth of agony they expressed that overcome by the sound I sank upon the earth and hid my face. The others, who were close behind me, did likewise, for no human soul could endure those cries, the remembrance of which, even now after many years, causes the blood to run cold in my veins.

"The Kakué! The Kakué!" exclaimed Montero, who was close behind me.

Recalled to myself by these words I raised my eyes only to discover that Marta was no longer before me. For even in that moment, when those terrible cries were ringing through my heart, waking the echoes of the mountain solitudes, the awful change had come, and she had looked her last with human eyes on earth and on man! In another form—that strange form of the Kakué—she had fled out of our sight for ever to hide in those gloomy woods which were henceforth to be her dwelling place. And I—most miserable of men, what had I done that all my prayers and strivings had been thus frustrated, that out of my very hands the spirit of the power of darkness had thus been permitted to wrest this unhappy soul from me!

I rose up trembling from the earth, the tears pouring unchecked down my cheeks, while the members of Montero's family gathered round me and clung to my garments. Night closed on us, black as despair and death, and with the greatest difficulty we made our way back through the woods. But I would not remain at the rancho; at the risk of my life I returned to Yala, and all through that dark solitary ride I was incessantly crying out to God to have mercy on me. Towards midnight I reached the village in safety, but the horror with which that unheard of tragedy infected me, the fears and the doubts which dared not yet shape themselves into words, remained in my breast to torture me. For days I could neither eat nor sleep. I was reduced to a skeleton and my hair began to turn white before its time. Being now incapable of performing my duties, and believing that death was approaching, I yearned once more for the city of my birth. I escaped at length from Yala, and with great difficulty reached the town of Jujuy and from thence by slow stages I journeyed back to Cordova.

CHAPTER V

"ONCE more do I behold thee, O Cordova, beautiful to my eyes as the new Jerusalem coming down from Heaven to those who have witnessed the resurrection! Here, where my life began, may I now be allowed to lie down in peace, like a tired child that falls asleep on its mother's breast."

Thus did I apostrophise my natal city, when, looking from the height above, I at last saw it before me, girdled with purple hills and bright with the sunshine, the white towers of the many churches springing out of the green mist of groves and gardens.

Nevertheless Providence ordained that in Cordova I was to find life and not death. Surrounded by old beloved friends, worshipping in the old church I knew so well, health returned to me, and I was like one who rises after a night of evil dreams and goes forth to feel the sunshine and fresh wind on his face. I told the strange story of Marta to one person only; this was Father Irala, a learned and discreet man of great piety, and one high in authority in the church at Cordova. I was astonished that he was able to listen calmly to the things I related; he spoke some consoling words, but made no attempt then or afterwards to throw any light on the mystery. In Cordova a great cloud seemed to be lifted from my mind which left my faith unimpaired; I was once more cheerful and happy—happier than I had ever been since leaving it. Three months went by; then Irala told me one day that it was time for me to return to Yala, for my health being restored there was nothing to keep me longer from my flock.

Oh that flock, that flock, in which for me there had been only one precious lamb!

I was greatly disquieted; all those nameless doubts and fears which had left me now seemed returning; I begged him to spare me, to send some younger man, ignorant of the matters I had imparted to him, to take my place. He replied that for the very reason that I was acquainted with those matters I was the only fit person to go to Yala. Then in my agitation I unburdened my heart to him. I spoke of that heathenish apathy of the people I had struggled in vain to overcome, of the temptations I had encountered—the passion of anger and earthly love, the impulse to commit some terrible crime. Then had come the tragedy of Marta Riquelme and the spiritual world had seemed to resolve itself into a chaos where Christ was powerless to save; in my misery and despair my reason had almost forsaken me and I had fled from the country. In Cordova hope had revived, my prayers had brought an immediate response, and the Author of salvation seemed to be near to me. Here in Cordova, I said in conclusion, was life, but in the soul-destroying atmosphere of Yala death eternal.

"Brother Sepulvida," he answered, "we know all your sufferings and suffer with you: nevertheless you must return to Yala. Though there in the enemy's country, in the midst of the fight, when hard pressed and wounded, you have perhaps doubted God's omnipotence, He calls you to the front again, where He will be with you and fight at your side. It is for you, not for us, to find the solution of those mysteries which have troubled you; and that you have already come near to the solution your own words seem to show. Remember that we are here not for our own pleasure, but to do our Master's work; that the highest reward will not be for those who sit in the cool shade, book in hand, but for the toilers in the field who are suffering the burden and heat of the day. Return to Yala and be of good heart, and in due time all things will be made clear to your understanding."

These words gave me some comfort, and meditating much on them I took my departure from Cordova, and in due time arrived at my destination.

I had, on quitting Yala, forbidden Montero and his wife to speak of the manner of Marta's disappearance, believing that it would be better for my people to remain in ignorance of such a matter; but now, when going about in the village, on my return I found that it was known to everyone. That "Marta had become a Kakué" was mentioned on all sides; yet it did not affect them with astonishment and dismay that this should be so, it was merely an event for idle women to chatter about, like Quiteria's elopement or Maxima's quarrel with her mother-in-law.

It was now the hottest season of the year, when it was impossible to be very active, or much out of doors. During those days the feeling of despondence began again to weigh heavily on my heart. I pondered on Irala's words, and prayed continually, but the illumination he had prophesied came not. When I preached, my voice was like the buzzing of summer flies to the people : they came and sat or knelt on the floor of the church, and heard me with stolid unmoved countenances, then went forth again unchanged in heart. After the morning Mass I would return to my house, and, sitting alone in my room, pass the sultry hours, immersed in melancholy thoughts, having no inclination to work. At such times the image of Marta, in all the beauty of her girlhood, crowned with her shining golden hair, would rise before me, until the tears gathering in my eyes would trickle through my fingers. Then too I often recalled that terrible scene in the wood—the crouching figure in its sordid rags, the glaring furious eyes —again those piercing shrieks seemed to ring through me, and fill the dark mountain's forest with echoes, and I would start up half maddened with the sensations of horror renewed within me.

And one day, while sitting in my room, with these memories only for company, all at once a voice in my soul told me that the end was approaching, that the crisis was come, and that to whichever side I fell, there I should remain through all eternity. I rose up from my seat staring straight before me, like one who sees an assassin enter his apartment dagger in hand and who nerves himself for the coming struggle. Instantly all my doubts, my fears, my unshapen thoughts found expression, and with a million tongues shrieked out in my soul against my Redeemer. I called aloud on Him to save me, but He came not; and the spirits of darkness, enraged at my long resistance, had violently seized on my soul, and were dragging it down to perdition. I reached forth my hands and took hold of the crucifix standing near me, and clung to it as a drowning mariner does to a floating spar. "Cast it down!" cried out a hundred devils in my ear. "Trample under foot this symbol of a slavery which has darkened your life and made earth a hell! He that died on the Cross is powerless now; miserably do they perish who put their trust in Him! Remember Marta Riquelme, and save yourself from her fate while there is time."

My hands relaxed their hold on the cross, and falling on the stones, I cried aloud to the Lord to slay me and take my soul, for by death only could I escape from that great crime my enemies were urging me to commit.

Scarcely had I pronounced these words before I felt that the fiends had left me, like ravening wolves scared from their quarry. I rose up and washed the blood from my bruised forehead, and praised God; for now there was a great calm in my heart, and I knew that He who died to save the world was with me, and that His grace had enabled me to conquer and deliver my own soul from perdition.

From that time I began to see the meaning of Irala's words, that it was for me and not for him to find the solution of the mysteries which had troubled me, and that I had already come near to finding it. I also saw the reason of that sullen resistance to religion in the minds of the people of Yala; of the temptations which had assailed me—the strange tempests of anger and the carnal passions, never experienced elsewhere, and which had blown upon my heart like hot blighting winds ; and even of all the events of Marta Riquelme's tragic life ; for all these things had been ordered with devilish cunning to drive my soul into rebellion. I no longer dwelt persistently on that isolated event of her transformation, for now the whole action of that tremendous warfare in which the powers of darkness are arrayed against the messengers of the Gospel began to unfold itself before me.

In thought I went back to the time, centuries ago, when as yet not one ray of heavenly light had fallen upon this continent ; when men bowed down in worship to gods, which they called in their several languages Pachacamac, Viracocho, and many others ; names which being translated mean, The All-powerful, Ruler of Men, The Strong Comer, Lord of the Dead, The Avenger. These were not mythical beings ; they were mighty spiritual entities, differing from each other in character, some taking delight in wars and destruction, while others regarded their human worshippers with tolerant and even kindly feelings. And because of this belief in powerful benevolent beings some learned Christian writers have held that the aborigines possessed a knowledge of the true God, albeit obscured by many false notions. This is a manifest error ; for if in the material world light and darkness cannot mingle, much less can the Supreme Ruler stoop to share His sovereignty with Belial and Moloch, or in this continent, with Tupa and Viracocho : but all these demons, great and small, and known by various names, were angels of darkness who had divided amongst themselves this new world and the nations dwelling in it. Nor need we be astonished at finding here resemblance to the true religion—majestic and graceful touches suggesting the Divine Artist; for Satan himself is clothed as an angel of light, and scruples not to borrow the things invented by the Divine Intelligence. These spirits possessed unlimited power and authority; their service was the one great business of all men's lives; individual character and natural feelings were crushed out by an implacable despotism, and no person dreamed of disobedience to their decrees, interpreted by their high priests; but all men were engaged in raising colossal temples, enriched with gold and precious stones, to their honour, and priests and virgins in tens of thousands conducted their worship with a pomp and magnificence surpassing those of ancient Egypt or Babylon. Nor can we doubt that these beings often made use of their power to suspend the order of nature, transforming men into birds and beasts, causing the trembling of the earth which ruins whole cities, and performing many other stupendous miracles to demonstrate their authority or satisfy their malignant natures. The time came when it pleased the Ruler of the world to overthrow this evil empire, using for that end the ancient, feeble instruments despised of men, the missionary priests, and chiefly those of the often persecuted Brotherhood founded by Loyola, whose zeal and holiness have always been an offence to the proud and carnal-minded. Country after country, tribe after tribe, the old gods were deprived of their kingdom, fighting always with all their weapons to keep back the tide of conquest. And at length, defeated at all points, and like an army fighting in defence of its territory, and gradually retiring before the invader to concentrate itself in some apparently inaccessible region and there stubbornly resist to the end; so have all the old gods and demons retired into this secluded country, where, if they cannot keep out the seeds of truth they have at least succeeded in rendering the soil it falls upon barren as stone. Nor does it seem altogether strange that these once potent beings should be satisfied to remain in comparative obscurity and inaction when the entire globe is open to them, offering fields worthy of their evil ambition. For great as their power and intelligence must be they are, nevertheless, infinite beings, possessing, like man, individual characteristics, capabilities and limitations; and after reigning where they have lost a continent, they may possibly be unfit or unwilling to serve elsewhere. For we know that even in the strong places of Christianity there are spirits enough for the evil work of leading men astray; whole nations are given up to damnable heresies, and all religion is trodden under foot by many whose portion will be where the worm dieth not and the fire is not quenched.

From the moment of my last struggle, when this revelation began to dawn upon my mind, I have been safe from their persecutions. No angry passions, no sinful notions, no doubts and despondence disturb the peace of my soul. I was filled with fresh zeal, and in the pulpit felt that it was not my voice, but the voice of some mighty spirit speaking with my lips and preaching to the people with an eloquence of which I was not capable. So far, however, it has been powerless to win their souls. The old gods, although no longer worshipped openly, are their gods still, and could a new Tupac Amaru arise to pluck down the symbols of Christianity, and proclaim once more the Empire of the Sun, men would everywhere bow down to worship his rising beams and joyfully rebuild temples to the Lightning and the Rainbow.

Although the lost spirits cannot harm they are always near me, watching all my movements, ever striving to frustrate my designs. Nor am I unmindful of their presence. Even here, sitting in my study and looking out on the mountains, rising like stupendous stairs towards heaven and losing their summits in the gathering clouds, I seem to discern the awful shadowy form of Pachacamac, supreme among the old gods. Though his temples are in ruins, where the Pharaohs of the Andes and their millions of slaves worshipped him for a thousand years, he is awful still in his majesty and wrath that plays like lightning on his furrowed brows, kindling his stern countenance, and the beard which rolls downward like an immense white cloud to his knees. Around him gather other tremendous forms in their cloudy vestments—The Strong-Comer, the Lord of the Dead, The Avenger, The Ruler of Men, and many others whose names were once mighty throughout the continent. They have met to take counsel together; I hear their voices in the thunder hoarsely rolling from the hills, and in the wind stirring the forest before the coming tempest. Their faces are towards me, they are pointing to me with their cloudy hands, they are speaking of me—even of me, an old, feeble, worn-out man! But I do not quail before them; my soul is firm though my flesh is weak; though my knees tremble while I gaze, I dare look forward even to win another victory over them before I depart.

Day and night I pray for that soul still wandering lost in the great wilderness; and no voice rebukes my hope or tells me that my prayer is unlawful. I strain my eyes gazing out towards the forest; but I know not whether Marta Riquelme will return to me with the tidings of her salvation in a dream of the night, or clothed in the garments of the flesh, in the full light of day. For her salvation I wait, and when I have seen it I shall be ready to depart; for as the traveller, whose lips are baked with hot winds, and who thirsts for a cooling draught and swallows sand, strains his eyeballs to see the end of his journey in some great desert, so do I look forward to the goal of this life, when I shall go to Thee, O my Master, and be at rest!

APPENDIX TO EL OMBÚ

APPENDIX TO EL OMBÚ

THE ENGLISH INVASION AND THE GAME OF EL PATO

I MUST say at once that El Ombú is mostly a true story, although the events did not occur exactly in the order given. The incident relating to the English invasion of June and July, 1807, is told pretty much as I had it from the old gaucho called Nicandro in the narrative. That was in the 'sixties. The undated notes which I made of my talks with the old man, containing numerous anecdotes of Santos Ugarte and the whole history of El Ombú, were written, I think, in 1868—the year of the great dust storm. These ancient notes are now before me, and look very strange, both as to the writing and the quality of the paper; also as to the dirtiness of the same, which makes me think that the old manuscript must have been out in that memorable storm, which, I remember, ended with rain—the rain coming down as liquid mud.

There were other old men living in that part of the country who, as boys, had witnessed the march of an English army on Buenos Ayres, and one of these confirmed the story of the blankets thrown away by the army, and of the chaff between some of the British soldiers and the natives.

I confess I had some doubts as to the truth of this

blanket story when I came to read over my old notes; but in referring to the proceedings of the court-martial on Lieutenant-General Whitelocke, published in London in 1808, I find that the incident is referred to. On page 57 of the first volume occurs the following statement, made by General Gower in his evidence. "The men, particularly of Brigadier-General Lumley's brigade, were very much exhausted, and Lieutenant-General Whitelocke, to give them a chance of getting on with tolerable rapidity, ordered all the blankets of the army to be thrown down."

There is nothing, however, in the evidence about the blankets having been used to make a firmer bottom for the army to cross a river, nor is the name of the river mentioned.

Another point in the old gaucho's story may strike the English reader as very strange and almost incredible; this is, that within a very few miles of the army of the hated foreign invader, during its march on the capital, where the greatest excitement prevailed and every preparation for defence was being made, a large number of men were amusing themselves at the game of El Pato. To those who are acquainted with the character of the gaucho there is nothing incredible in such a fact; for the gaucho is, or was, absolutely devoid of the sentiment of patriotism, and regarded all rulers, all in authority from the highest to the lowest, as his chief enemies, and the worst kind of robbers, since they robbed him not only of his goods but of his liberty.

It mattered not to him whether his country paid tribute

to Spain or to England, whether a man appointed by someone at a distance as Governor or Viceroy had black or blue eyes. It was seen that when the Spanish dominion came to an end his hatred was transferred to the ruling cliques of a so-called Republic. When the gauchos attached themselves to Rosas, and assisted him to climb into power, they were under the delusion that he was one of themselves, and would give them that perfect liberty to live their own lives in their own way, which is their only desire. They found out their mistake when it was too late.

It was Rosas who abolished the game of El Pato, but before saying more on that point it would be best to describe the game. I have never seen an account of it in print, but for a very long period, and down to probably about 1840, it was the most popular outdoor game on the Argentine pampas. Doubtless it originated there; it was certainly admirably suited to the habits and disposition of the horsemen of the plains; and unlike most outdoor games it retained its original simple, rude character to the end.

Pato means duck; and to play the game a duck or fowl, or, as was usually the case, some larger domestic bird—turkey, gosling, or muscovy duck—was killed and sewn up in a piece of stout raw hide, forming a somewhat shapeless ball, twice as big as a football, and provided with four loops or handles of strong twisted raw hide made of a convenient size to be grasped by a man's hand. A great point was to have the ball and handles so strongly made that three or four powerful men could take hold and tug until they dragged each other to the ground without anything giving way.

Whenever it was resolved at any place to have a game, and someone had offered to provide the bird, and the meeting place had been settled, notice would be sent round among the neighbours ; and at the appointed time all the men and youths living within a circle of several leagues would appear on the spot, mounted on their best horses. On the appearance of the man on the ground carrying the duck the others would give chase ; and by-and-by he would be overtaken, and the ball wrested from his hand ; the victor in his turn would be pursued, and when overtaken there would perhaps be a scuffle or scrimmage, as in football, only the strugglers would be first on horseback before dragging each other to the earth. Occasionally when this happened a couple of hot-headed players, angry at being hurt or worsted, would draw their weapons against each other in order to find who was in the right, or to prove which was the better man. But fight or no fight, someone would get the duck and carry it away to be chased again. Leagues of ground would be gone over by the players in this way, and at last some one, luckier or better mounted than his fellows, would get the duck and successfully run the gauntlet of the people scattered about on the plain, and make good his escape. He was the victor, and it was his right to carry the bird home and have it for his dinner. This was, however, a mere fiction ; the man who carried off the duck made for the nearest house, followed by all the others, and there not only the duck was cooked, but a vast amount of meat to feed the whole of the players. While the dinner was in preparation, messengers would be despatched to neighbouring houses to invite the women; and on their arrival dancing would be started and kept up all night.

To the gauchos of the great plains, who took to the back of a horse from childhood, almost as spontaneously as a parasite to the animal on which it feeds, the pato was the game of games, and in their country as much as cricket and football and golf together to the inhabitants of this island. Nor could there have been any better game for men whose existence, or whose success in life, depended so much on their horsemanship; and whose chief glory it was to be able to stick on under difficulties, and, when sticking on was impossible, to fall off gracefully and like a cat, on their feet. To this game the people of the pampa were devoted up to a time when it came into the head of a President of the Republic to have no more of it, and with a stroke of the pen it was abolished for ever.

It would take a strong man in this country to put down any outdoor game to which the people are attached; and he was assuredly a very strong man who did away with El Pato in that land. If any other man who has occupied the position of head of the State at any time during the last ninety years had attempted such a thing, a universal shout of derision would have been the result, and wherever such an absurd decree had appeared pasted up on the walls and doors of churches, shops, and other public places, the gauchos would have been seen filling their mouths with water to squirt it over the despised paper. But this man was more than a president; he was that

Rosas, called by his enemies the "Nero of America." Though by birth a member of a distinguished family, he was by predilection a gaucho, and early in life took to the semi-barbarous life of the plains. Among his fellows Rosas distinguished himself as a dare-devil, one who was not afraid to throw himself from the back of his own horse on to that of a wild horse in the midst of a flying herd into which he had charged. He had all the gaucho's native ferocity, his fierce hates and prejudices; and it was in fact his intimate knowledge of the people he lived with, his oneness in mind with them, that gave him his wonderful influence over them, and enabled him to carry out his ambitious schemes. But why, when he had succeeded in making himself all-powerful by means of their help, when he owed them so much, and the ties uniting him to them were so close, did he deprive them of their beloved pastime? The reason, which will sound almost ridiculous after what I have said of the man's character, was that he considered the game too rough. It is true that it had (for him) its advantages, since it made the men of the plains hardy, daring, resourceful fighters on horseback—the kind of men he most needed for his wars; on the other hand, it caused so much injury to the players, and resulted in so many bloody fights and fierce feuds between neighbours that he considered he lost more than he gained by it.

There were not men enough in the country for his wants; even boys of twelve and fourteen were sometimes torn from the arms of their weeping mothers to be made soldiers of; he could not afford to have full-grown strong men injuring and killing each other for their own amusement. They must, like good citizens, sacrifice their pleasure for their country's sake. And at length, when his twenty years' reign was over, when people were again free to follow their own inclinations without fear of bullet and cold steel—it was generally cold steel in those days—those who had previously played the game had had roughness enough in their lives, and now only wanted rest and ease; while the young men and youths who had not taken part in El Pato nor seen it played, had never come under its fascination, and had no wish to see it revived.

Gardeners' Question Time

plant chooser

Gardeners' Question Time plant chooser

inspired by the popular 'Plant of the Week' feature

Matthew Biggs,
John Cushnie,
Bob Flowerdew
& Bunny Guinness

Kyle Cathie Ltd

Dedication

To Jo, the assistant producer of *GQT*, who somehow manages to keep all of us happy and prevent any duplication of Plant of the Week. Since we don't know the questions in advance, it is nice to have something we can talk about. Thanks, Jo.

First published in Great Britain in 2003 by
Kyle Cathie Limited
122 Arlington Road
London NW1 7HP
general.enquiries@kyle-cathie.com
www.kylecathie.com

by arrangement with the BBC

ISBN 1 85626 515 3

Project editor Caroline Taggart
Design by Geoff Hayes
Picture research by Jess Walton
Text edited by Selina Mumford & Gail Dixon-Smith
Editorial assistant Vicki Murrell
Production by Sha Huxtable

Matthew Biggs, John Cushnie, Bob Flowerdew & Bunny Guinness are hereby identified as the authors of this work in accordance with Section 77 of the Copyright, Designs and Patents Act 1988.

A Cataloguing in Publication record for this title is available from the British Library.

Printed in Singapore through Tien-Wah Press

Half-title page: *Lysichiton americanus;*
Title spread: *Papaver orientalis;*
This page: *Prunus avium*

contents

notes on the text

AGM

The abbreviation AGM, used throughout the text, means the Royal Horticultural Society's Award of Garden Merit, one of the highest accolades the RHS can give a plant. Every AGM plant should have outstanding excellence for garden decoration or use; be available in the trade; be of good constitution; and require neither highly specialist growing conditions nor care.

North American hardiness zones:

The zones quoted in each entry are those established by the US Department of Agriculture, and refer to the maximum and minimum temperatures in which the plants will survive.

1	Below –50°F	Below –45.6°C
2a	–50 to –45°F	–42.8 to –45.5°C
2b	–45 to –40°F	–40.0 to –42.7°C
3a	–40 to –35°F	–37.3 to –39.9°C
3b	–35 to –30°F	–34.5 to –37.2°C
4a	–30 to –25°F	–31.7 to –34.4°C
4b	–25 to –20°F	–28.9 to –31.6°C
5a	–20 to –15°F	–26.2 to –28.8°C
5b	–15 to –10°F	–23.4 to –26.1°C
6a	–10 to –5°F	–20.6 to –23.3°C
6b	–5 to 0°F	–17.8 to –20.5°C
7a	0 to 5°F	–15.0 to –17.7°C
7b	5 to 10°F	–12.3 to –14.9°C
8a	10 to 15°F	–9.5 to –12.2°C
8b	15 to 20°F	–6.7 to –9.4°C
9a	20 to 25°F	–3.9 to –6.6°C
9b	25 to 30°F	–1.2 to –3.8°C
10a	30 to 35°F	1.6 to –1.1°C
10b	35 to 40°F	4.4 to 1.7°C
11	above 40°F	above 4.5°C

acknowledgements

Gardeners' Question Time is a team effort and the production of this book has been the same.

Our thanks go to our editor, Caroline Taggart, who has skilfully steered a safe course through some troubled waters. To our designer, Geoff Hayes, for creating such a good-looking book, and picture researcher Jess Walton, for unearthing some terrific images. To Kyle Cathie for recognizing the potential to transform the weekly radio slot into a book for life.

And finally to our loyal listeners, without whom none of this would be possible.

Matthew Biggs, John Cushnie,
Bob Flowerdew, Bunny Guinness and Trevor Taylor

Right: Taxus baccata

introduction

Gardeners' Question Time was first broadcast in 1947 and it's been on the air every week since. Without a gap. Now it's a foolhardy producer who tinkers with the format of a programme that's one of the world's great broadcasting successes, so it was with some trepidation that I introduced the 'Plant of the Week' feature into the programme in October 2000. The reason I did it was simple: the team was brimming over with great plants they'd like to talk about, but if no one asked the right question they did not have an opportunity to tell us about them.

At production meetings, backstage before a recording and even over a meal after a show I'd hear panel members get really excited as they swapped stories about some new discovery or other. If you could have captured the excitement and enthusiasm, bottled it and sold it, you'd have made a fortune. But without the right questions those plants would remain a green-room secret forever.

Contrary to popular belief, the team don't know the questions in advance. The audience pop their questions in a giant flowerpot when they arrive and I select what is going to be asked on the programme in the half-hour before we record. The first the team knows of a question is when it's asked. We are, therefore, totally dependent upon the topics on the minds of our audience on the day. I may be a gardening producer, but I don't plant questions.

Although this preserved the integrity of the programme it did mean some plants, some really great plants, plants the team were itching to talk about, never got a mention.

'Plant of the Week' changed all that. Here was a slot in the programme where a member of the panel could be totally self-indulgent. Without needing an excuse, except the relevance to the week, our experts could pick a plant, eulogize about it, and commend it to our two million listeners.

The team loved it. Nothing makes a gardener happier than to be able to extol the virtues of his or her favourite plants and persuade others to grow them. Imagine the thrill, therefore, of being able to drop a word in the ear of two million keen gardeners. It was horticultural heaven.

If the team was in heaven then, not surprisingly, the horticultural trade thought they were angels. We'd hear stories of nurseries and garden centres tuning in on a Sunday afternoon; within half an hour signs would be erected pointing customers to that week's '*Gardeners' Question Time* Plant of the Week'. Stocks would vanish and fresh supplies would be hard to find. Retailers would launch searches to locate the current 'Plant of the Week' as customers, our listeners, would be queuing up to buy the team's latest hot tip.

It made us realize just how powerful an influence we had. And with that power came responsibilities. Suppliers would lobby me and panel members seeking to get their plant selected as a 'Plant of the Week'. Inducements were even offered. They were all refused. There were, of course, temptations. When the programme fell on 1st April we mischievously mused about the possibility of inventing a genus with amazing characteristics and letting the horticultural trade sort that one out. We haven't done it...yet.

There are more than a third of a million different plants in the world. Members of the team have met most and are on first-name terms with the majority. In this book they share with you their enthusiasm for the best plants on the planet. Of course there are many more plants here than there are weeks in a year. We've taken the successful 'Plant of the Week' theme and given the team full rein to indulge themselves. From stunning annuals to scrummy fruits, from delicate alpines to perennial thugs, this book contains more than 700 of the team's favourite plants.

You cannot get better advice than from this quartet of Bob Flowerdew, Bunny Guinness, John Cushnie and Matthew Biggs. Read the text and you'll hear their voices. Of course, as on the programme, they do not all agree. Gardening's like that. But one thing they do all agree on, and that is within these two covers you'll find a Plant of the Week for a lifetime of gardening.

Trevor Taylor
Producer
Gardeners' Question Time

Gardeners' Question Time can be heard on BBC Radio 4 (92–95 VHF and 198 LW) on Sundays at 2 p.m. and Wednesdays at 3 p.m.

a note from the authors

John
Choosing my Plant of the Week for *Gardeners' Question Time* is great fun. There is always a plant exactly right for the week the programme is going out. My problem is that I am fickle. I love them all. So many plants, so little space… Seasonally I have favourites that change almost as quickly as new plants come into flower.

My all-time, permanent, 'wouldn't be without them' plants come about because of their colour, texture, shape, fragrance or flavour. Those that bring back childhood memories, such as old-fashioned roses, *Daphne mezereum* and honeysuckle, score well, as do all those associated with relatives and friends. My father loved the 'Peace' rose, Mum liked anemones and sweet William.

Then there are the plants I can't succeed with because of climatic conditions. I keep trying, often winning for a season or two before Jack Frost has his way. That is frustrating, but I appreciate these plants all the more when I see them in their natural habitat. I have grown and love every one of the plants I have recommended and I know that if you have a go you will love them too.

John

Bunny
Plants are the furniture of the garden and as such they should not only thrive in their situation, but must also provide much of its personality.

In my garden I grow nearly all the plants that I have selected for this book. Some I've had for many years, some I've acquired only recently. The remainder are plants that I have been meaning to get for ages and have used fairly extensively in gardens for other people or have observed in different situations.

It is an exacting and challenging job looking for just the right plant for specific spaces and functions. I am extremely lucky in having several members of my close family who have extensive nurseries specializing in different areas and continually sourcing and refining their stock. They are a great pool of knowledge to draw on and I am grateful to them all.

Bunny

Bob
I hope you enjoy reading about my favourite plants. In many ways these are my greatest friends; I'm more interested in them, their history and eccentricities, and I take more effort to care for their needs and well being than anything else in the world. I spend most of my life with them and I can thoroughly recommend their company in your garden or greenhouse. I hope you too will take some, if not all, of them into your lives to love and cherish as much as I have done – and to get as much pleasure in return. And then to lop off their heads and eat their roots or stick them in a vase – they are just plants, after all.

I also hope you enjoy the rest of the book; I'd skip what the others have written but their pictures are quite good!

Bob

Matt
The opportunity to select some of my favourite plants sent a zing of excitement up my spine; it's the request that every plant-lover dreams of. I am in awe of the plant world – they are essential for survival, they clothe and feed us, provide shelter and medicines too, yet also offer something spiritual. Plants create the robes that clothe the earth and gardeners have the privilege of selecting the finest and weaving them into a tapestry that is wrapped around our dwellings to improve our quality of life.

I've chosen plants that quicken the pulse or leave me spellbound by their beauty. It's gratifyingly self-indulgent, but I hope you will be inspired by the selection and enjoy wallowing in pools of pleasure as they grow in your garden. Life would be impossible without them, so don't resist, go out, enjoy and feel the power of plants!

Matthew

our top twelves

Choosing the plants to include in this book wasn't easy. One of the biggest difficulties was limiting ourselves to about 175 each when there are literally thousands to choose from. We compiled our first lists without consulting each other and inevitably there was overlap. All four of us originally put down *Cytisus battandieri*; three of us chose *Crambe maritima* – that's why there is the occasional 'PS', where one of us wanted to add to what another had written. And while we all have our favourite varieties, you'll see that there are lots of roses, lots of salvias, hydrangeas, daphnes and honeysuckles. They are all such great plants.

The 'plants of the week' scattered through the book are our crème de la crème, but then we had to ask ourselves why? Was it because the flowers were followed by attractive fruit and stunning autumn colour; or because an evergreen looked terrific whatever the season? So here are some of our favourite plants for different seasons, different parts of the garden and different purposes.

Spring interest

John

Amelanchier 'Ballerina' A great all-round small tree with spring leaf colour and flower.
Camellia x *williamsii* 'Anticipation' Glossy, dark green foliage with large, double, deep rose-pink flowers in spring.
Ulex europaeus 'Flore Pleno' This variety doesn't produce seedlings. The flowers have a coconut fragrance.
Daphne odora 'Aureomarginata' Fabulous foliage, knock-out scent, long-lasting foliage.

Bunny

Allium hollandicum 'Purple Sensation' Great colour and highly useful form for threading through planting.
Tulipa 'Magier' Exquisite flowers, which are fascinatingly marked
Akebia quinata Beautiful in leaf and best value of all spring flowers

Bob

Smilacina racemosa Better than a hosta and gorgeously scented.
Convallaria Just divine scent and good ground cover in damp places.

Matt

Ribes laurifolium Unusual greenish flowers in early spring are certainly a talking point.
Anemone nemorosa 'Robinsoniana' One of the stars in the firmament of spring; a delicious blue.
Arisarum proboscideum The 'mouse plant', its chocolate flowers have long wispy 'tails'.

Summer interest

John

Fabiana imbricata f. *violacea* Evergreen with mauve-lavender flowers in summer. Ideal for impoverished acid soil.
Philadelphus 'Belle Etoile' Guaranteed to flower every summer with masses of fragrant, white flowers.
Hydrangea sargentiana Clusters of blue fertile flowers surrounded by a ring of pure white sterile flowers.

Bunny

Salvia sclarea var. *turkestanica* Long-lasting, extraordinary flowers with bags of personality.
Salvia patens The intense blue is unbeatable and gives months of colour – a strong favourite.
Rosa 'Ferdinand Pichard' Wonderful stripy roses, with form and good foliage.

Bob

Mathiola bicornis Scent to die for.
Lathyrus odoratus Scent to live for.
Strawberries!!!!!!!!!!!!!!!!!!

Matt

Molinia caerulea 'Transparent' Floating on a late summer breeze, the seedheads and foliage look magnificent.
Dahlia imperialis By late summer, its long leafy stems are starting to create an impact.
Ceratostigma willmottianum The flowers are mid-blue and last from mid-summer to autumn. What more can I say?

Autumn interest

John

Liquidambar styraciflua 'Worplesdon' Autumn leaf colour changes from green through purple to orange-yellow.
Yucca gloriosa Enormous, upright spikes of hundreds of pendant, bell-shaped white flowers.
Gladiolus callianthus Spikes of highly fragrant, tubular, white flowers with a deep crimson centre.

Bunny

Cotinus coggygria Unbeatable tree/shrub for smoky flowers and autumnal foliage.
Anemone x *hybrida* 'Honorine Joubert' Excellent plant all round, but colour is long lasting and very fresh.
Brugmansia arborea 'Aurea' Exotic flowers that knock you out with their size, colour and profusion.

Bob

Grapes (*Vitis* spp.) All of them one after the other, oh I love eating them .
King Edward potatoes (*Solanum tuberosum*) Chips, chips and more chips all winter through.
'Doyenne du Comice' pears (*Pyrus*) Can't live without them.

Matt

Rhus glabra 'Laciniata' Autumn colour with a crackle and a roar!
Cercidiphyllum japonicum You can smell the autumn colour and the fragrance is vanilla!
Aster x *frikartii* 'Monch' A very early starter and one of the best for an autumn display.

Winter interest

John

Betula utilis var. *jacquemontii* Its pure white bark puts this birch in a class of its own.
Taxus baccata 'Fastigiata Aurea' A beautiful, well-behaved, upright conifer with golden-yellow foliage.
Cornus alba 'Sibirica' Bright red bark on new growths to brighten a dull winter day.

Bunny

Taxus baccata I never tire of looking at its many different structural forms, which are outstanding 12 months a year.
Choisya ternata Dependable, well behaved and ever glossy.
Rosmarinus spp. Form, scent, flowers especially in winter and the original Christmas tree.

Bob
Claytonia (*Claytonia perfoliata*) As I would feel starved without its fresh leaves.
Pak-choi (*Brassica rapa chinensis*) As I would starve without its winter long supplies.
Lemons (*Citrus* spp.) For leaf, flower and fruit all winter through.

Matt
Chimonanthus praecox One of the great olfactory pleasures of the plant world.
Edgeworthia chrysantha Fragrant rich yellow flowers cloaked in silvery yellow hairs are my heart's desire.
Acacia dealbata Decked with bright yellow flowers in late winter, at the time when we all need some sunshine.

Fragrance

John
Hyacinthus orientalis 'Lady Derby' A single stem of this pink hyacinth is sufficient to fill a room with perfume.
Sarcococca confusa In winter the small white flowers manufacture unending supplies of incredible fragrance.
Hamamelis mollis 'Coombe Wood' Highly fragrant, bright- yellow flowers in the dead of winter.

Bunny
Mathiola incana Unbeatable fragrance which fills huge spaces for months in summer.
Myrtus communis Rich, spicy fragrance, a plant with romantic associations...the ideal wedding present.
Rosa 'Golden Celebration' You can virtually drink in this scent, a mix of sauterne wine and strawberry.

Bob
Gardenia augusta It is thoroughly decadent.
Cereus grandiflorus The perfume drives me crazy.
Rosa 'Etoile de Hollande' A positively erotic fragrance.

Matt
Zaluizianskia ovata Has an evening and night-time fragrance to make you swoon!
Trachelospermum jasminoides Sensual and exotic; one breath and you're transported to the tropics!
Daphne bolhua 'Jacqueline Postill' A fragrance that every aristocratic perfumier would love to have created, but nature got there first!

Tulipa 'Magier' *and T.* 'Queen of the Night' *with Myosotis* 'Blue Ball'

Dark damp corners

John
Sarcococca confusa It enjoys a shady site protected from cold winds where its perfume will linger.
Gaultheria mucronata Evergreen with masses of beautifully coloured fruit throughout the winter.
Galanthus 'S. Arnott' Flowering in winter and early spring the white flowers of this snowdrop are honey scented.

Bunny
Dicksonia antartica Ideal for adding an unbeatable, lush dimension, but also dramatic.
Dryopteris felix mas The lime-coloured fresh leaves will revive many awkward spaces.
Asplenium scolopendrium An unsophisticated native fern that has a useful and attractive leaf for contrasting with other ferns.

Bob
A shed. Why beat your head against a brick wall?

Matt
Rhodotypos scandens Will survive in the most inhospitable conditions. The flowers are exquisite.
Vinca minor 'Atropurpurea' Deep purple flowers hide among the tangled, scrambling stems.
Dryopteris wallichiana Prefers it not too dark but loves the damp; a remarkably beautiful fern.

Sunny sites

John
Convolvulus cneorum A bushy, silvery shrub plastered with ivory-white flowers in early summer.
Genista lydia Masses of bright yellow pea-like flowers smother the plant in early summer.
Callistemon 'Austraflora Firebrand' Bright crimson 'bottlebrush'-shaped flowers in summer. A real beauty, sport.

Bunny
Buddleia x *Lochinch* Beautiful foliage, good form, superbly coloured blue flowers.
Rosa 'Marie Pavie' Non-stop, beautiful flowers, provides useful low height for action-packed front-of-border positions.
Salvia indica 'Indigo Spires' Unbeatable – reliable but restful, non-stop wands of blue flowers all summer.

Bob
Grapes (*Vitis* spp.) Because I love them so much.
More grapes Because one lot is not enough.
Even more grapes As I never know when to stop.

Matt
Cistus ladanifer A charming plant whose flower and fragrance evoke Mediterranean memories.
Iris 'Brown Lasso' Even among the beautiful iris family, this is outstanding.
Lobelia tupa Wild and wonderful, it illustrates the extraordinary diversity among the relatives of the hanging-basket favourite.

Dry shade

John
Convallaria majalis 'Flore Pleno' For spring fragrance – its common name of lily-of-the-valley says it all. Plant it.
Kniphofia rooperi Strap-like, evergreen leaves and tall 'pokers' of orange-red flowers in autumn.
Tricyrtis formosana Pinkish purple-speckled flowers on a white background with a splash of yellow best describes these late autumn bloomers.

Bunny
Euphorbia amygdaloides 'Purpurea' Great foliage, pungent long-lasting lime flowers, fabulous and easy.
Euonymus fortunei 'Silver Queen' Only boring if you use it predictably; a great performer.
Buxus sempervirens There are limitless possibilities for this plant, but do not let it become a cliché.

Bob
Another shed.

Matt
Fascicularia bicolor Grows in some shade but prefers a little sun; an intriguing spidery specimen.
Helleborus foetidus Wester Flisk Group Unusual, with fascinating red markings.
Buxus sempervirens 'Handsworthiensis' Remarkably tolerant plant with dark green, leathery leaves.

Heavy clay soils

John
Alnus cordata A fast-growing tree with glossy green leaves and attractive male catkins.
Crataegus laevigata 'Paul's Scarlet' As tough as an old boot, this thorn has deep pink, double flowers.
Ilex aquifolium 'J. C. van Tol' Bright red holly berries every Christmas.

Bunny
Salix eleagnos Beautiful silver grey foliage that will star in this situation.
Crataegus monogyna Be it a tree, shrub, hedge, clipped standard, thicket plant or woodland edge specimen, you know it will be a great performer.
Digitalis purpurea A real survivor to add natural charm in spades.

Bob
Cabbages (*Brassica oleracea*) They grow so well in it.
Romanesco (*Brassica oleracea* var. *italica*) As I might then get a big head!
Nothing that needs annual planting or sowing.

Matt
Berberis darwinii Gorgeous orange flowers, attractive holly-like leaves and clay-tolerant. No wonder it's a winner!
Rudbeckia fulgida var. *sullivantii* 'Goldsturm' Many ornamental daisies tolerate clay but this is the best.
Rosa canina Our beautiful native dog rose.

Alkaline soils

John
Dianthus gratianopolitanus Forms a carpet of deep pink, fragrant, single flowers in summer.
Spartium junceum Masses of fragrant, golden yellow flowers throughout summer and autumn.
Syringa vulgaris 'Katherine Havemeyer' Highly fragrant, this lilac has double, lavender-blue flowers.

Bunny
Clematis 'Warsaw Nike' Wonderful, rich purple, bold but beautiful flowers that last.
Clematis heracleifilia 'Wyevale' Late blue flowers with personality; great herbaceous ground cover.
Verbascum bombyciferum 'Polarsommer' Outstanding plant for form, colour and ability to find the most scenic place to set seed.

Bob
Anything other than those miserable ericaceous plants that never give a decent fruit or much perfume – and wouldn't grow on this soil anyway, even if you added an entire peat bog to it.

Matt
Hermodactylus tuberosus Subtle flower colour and fragrance to match. A welcome sight in spring.
Sedum spectabile A jolly autumn plant with fine winter form. Great for butterflies.
Helleborus x *sternii* Unusual pink flowers and bold form make this a striking addition to the garden.

Acid soils

John
Kalmia latifolia 'Olympic Fire' Large clusters of pink flowers from crimped, dark red buds in spring.
Pieris formosa var. *forrestii* 'Wakehurst' Looks magical in spring with red leaves and white flowers.
Rhododendron 'Christmas Cheer' Funnel-shaped, pale pink flowers early in the new year.

Bunny
Amelanchier lamarckii Flowers, form, autumn colour all to die for and in one plant!
Camellia 'Cornish Snow' Fabulous flowers, superb foliage.
Magnolia liliiflora 'Nigra' Long-flowering and flowers early on in life.

Bob
I'd lime it so I could grow some decent vegetables and fruits instead of all those miserable acid lovers!

Crataegus laevigata 'Paul's Scarlet'

Matt
Vaccinium corymbosum 'Blue Crop' Tasty blue berries and good autumn colour for a 'double whammy' of pleasure!
Rhododendron x *praecox* The cerise-pink flowers very early in the year are a welcome reminder that spring is not far away!
Hacquetia epipactis Unusual lime-coloured bracts are a feature on this curious relative of celery.

Sandy soils

John
Tamarix tetandra Ferny foliage follows clouds of light pink flowers in spring.
Fuchsia magellanica 'Riccartonii' It makes a wonderful hedge for coastal gardens with scarlet and purple flowers all summer.
Lavandula angustifolia 'Twickel Purple' The fragrance of lavender in summer brings back childhood memories.

Bunny
Lavandula 'Sawyers' A lavender that actually looks good in winter, and just needs three things: drainage, drainage and drainage.
Galactites tomentosa Superb exotic foliage, beautiful thistly flowers and a controllable self-seeder.
Hebe x *andersonii* Variegated striking foliage to liven awkward spaces.

Bob
Anything I wanted as long as I watered and mulched it well, and especially a lot of asparagus.

Matt
Eryngium bourgatii 'Picos Blue' Beautiful metallic blue flowers and stems await your adoration.
Cytisus battandieri Bright yellow flowers, reflecting the colour of sunshine, and silky leaves and stems ensure that this majestic Moroccan a must for the garden.
Perovskia atriplicifolia A lovely plant in all its forms, with delicate foliage and beautiful blue flowers. Wow!

Exposed sites

John
Arbutus unedo 'Elfin King' The white, urn-shaped flowers and red 'strawberry' fruit appear together in the autumn.
Hippophae rhamnoides Tolerates seaside conditions with bright orange-yellow berries in winter.
Pyracantha atalantioides Evergreen with large clusters of bright orange-red berries throughout the winter.

Bunny
Hebe albicans Well-rounded form with grey-blue foliage that looks neat and prosperous even after a gale – rarely has a bad hair day.
Brachyglottis monroi A wonderful foliage plant with neat but unusual grey/green leaves.
Ligustrum vulgare Far superior to 'hedging privet', this is a useful tough, native plant.

Bob
Anything I wanted as I'd make windbreaks

Matt
Crataegus monogyna 'Biflora' You cannot beat hawthorns for toughness and this one's made more attractive by its quirky flowering habits.
Fuchsia procumbens If it gets too windy, you can always hide, like this pretty, slightly tender New Zealander.
Sorbus cashmiriana The mountain ash and its relatives are bone hardy and beautiful; this is an excellent example.

Urban sites

John
Skimmia japonica subsp. *reevesiana* Evergreen with white flowers in spring and long-lasting, bright red berries.
Laburnum x *watereri* 'Vossii' Long, trailing racemes of bright golden flowers in early summer.
Cotoneaster 'Rothschildianus' Large clusters of golden berries in autumn and winter.

Bunny
Buddleja globosa A great little goer, and I even quite like its orange flowers.
Salix viminalis Extremely fast-growing plant which tolerates many difficult conditions.
Prunus subhirtella 'Autumnalis' Attractive intermittent flowers appearing through the winter are always appreciated.

Matt
Cotonoeaster bullatus Will grow anywhere, in anything; a fine example of horticultural machismo.
Amelanchier 'Ballerina' Beautiful but tough – I've met several ladies like that!
Mespilus germanica A robust tree that's been grown for centuries and has bags of character.

Ground cover

John
Erica carnea 'December Red' This heather is covered from mid- winter until spring with rose-red flower spikes.
Pachysandra terminalis 'Variegata' A low, fast-growing variegated evergreen with white flowers in early summer.
Lithodora diffusa 'Heavenly Blue' Prostrate evergreen covered in azure blue flowers in summer.

Bunny
Geranium renardii Beautiful sheets of velvety foliage, pretty flowers.
Pulmonaria 'Sissinghurst White' Simple, attractive, tolerant and a great performer.
Omphaloides Good foliage but stunning early flowers.

Bob
Hedera spp. So good in shade and good for wildlife.
Limnanthes douglasii Cheap, cheerful and also good for wildlife.
Strawberries (*Fragaria* spp.) Well, why not?

Matt
Gaultheria procumbens One of my favourite plants – it's simple, understated, cheeky and fun.
Daphne blagayana Not your traditional ground cover, but when it's happy it will spread and spread!
Gentiana sino-ornata Perfect if you like deep blue carpets.

Hedging

John
Buxus sempervirens 'Handsworthiensis' Forms a tall, dense, evergreen screen.
x *Cuprocyparis leylandii* There is nothing to beat it for speed of growth. If well maintained it makes a wonderful screen.
Escallonia 'Pride of Donard' Ideal as a hedge with evergreen foliage and pink-red flowers in summer.

Bunny
Carpinus betulus Ideal for many conditions, fastish-growing, tolerant and smart.
Taxus baccata In many cases my first choice for unbeatable structure.
Crataegus monogyna A great native, stockproof, excellent for wildlife and tolerates many situations.

Bob
Crataegus spp. Traditional and the finest formal hedge.
Worcesterberry (*Ribes* hybrid) A brutal statement and good for wildlife and jam.
x *Cuprocyparis leylandii* Much abused, but a fine hedge.

Matt
Colletia hystrix A combination of contemporary sculpture and burglar-proof barrier. How desperately do they want your Rolex?
Ilex aquifolium 'J. C. van Tol' Self-pollination guarantees a regular supply of berries. If only everything in life was that easy!
Escallonia 'Pride of Donard' Glossy leaves and rose-pink flowers; it loves to be by the sea.

Climbers

John
Rosa 'Dublin Bay' A climber with fragrant, crimson, double flowers all summer.
Solanum crispum 'Glasnevin' Clusters of dark blue flowers with golden stamens during summer.
Wisteria sinensis 'Sierra Madre' In late spring and early summer a mass of pendant lavender-blue fragrant flowers flushed white.

Bunny
Trachelospermum jasminoides Brilliant plant, great foliage, superb flowers and good growth rate for an evergreen.
Solanum laxum 'Album' Flowers borne in profusion over a long period.
Rosa 'Mme Alfred Carrière' Outstanding repeat-flowering white rose, with high disease resistance.

Bob
Grapevines (*Vitis* spp.) Surprise, surprise.
Kiwi (*Actinidia chinensis*) Only if there is a sunny spot where it can ramble.
Lonicera etrusca Oh the scent is divine.

Matt
Vitis cognetiae Huge leaves and rich autumn colour; to say it's vigorous is an understatement!
Lonicera periclymenum 'Graham Thomas' Tumbling cascades of flowers with a fragrance that soothes.
Rosa banksiae 'Lutea' Beautiful, elegant and tender. I once saw it growing as a hedge in New Zealand!

For containers

John
Nerine bowdenii Shocking pink flowers on long stems in autumn before the leaves appear.
Gazania Daybreak Series A fantastic range of brightly coloured flowers from summer till autumn.
Helianthus annuus 'Teddy Bear' A dwarf sunflower with big, double, golden yellow flowers ideal for children.

Bunny
Agave americana Sculptural plant that requires minimal watering.
Trachycarpus fortunei Hardy palm that will add a touch of paradise for 12 months of the year.
Buxus sempervirens Well used, but that is not surprising as it looks tip-top all year round.

Bob
Citrus spp. Any of them is amazing value.
Grapevines (*Vitis* spp.) Well of course.
Peaches (*Prunus persica*) Cos this is the only way to get them regularly.

Matt
Astelia chathamica Silvery swords for dappled shade, it's perfect for contemporary style.
Pelargonium 'Lord Bute' A burgundy flower with orange anthers. Now that's class!
Citrus limon 'Garey's Ureka' A regular supply for g & t, and pies submerged in frothy meringue!

Fruits and berries

John
Malus 'John Downie' A charming garden tree with highly ornamental, edible crab apples.
Nicandra physalodes 'Violacea' In autumn the blue flowers are replaced by brown fruit enclosed in papery, purple calyces.
Callicarpa bodinieri var. *giraldii* 'Profusion' Incredible, small, metallic-looking, violet fruit in autumn.

Bunny
Ficus carica 'Brown Turkey' Delicious fruits, stunning foliage and easy to please in dry, hot spaces with next to no soil.
Cydonia oblonga My favourite tree, addictive fruit, superb flowers, beautiful early foliage and just charming for the remaining months.
Fragaria vesca Charming and delicious, neat and unassuming but highly useful.

Bob
My favourite category, so I demanded at least six!
Strawberries (*Fragaria* spp.) For their perfume brought out with cream.
Raspberries (*Rubus idaeus*) For sorbets and jams.
Pineapples (*Ananas comosus*) For the achievement, and perfection of flavour.
Grapes (*Vitis* spp.) For their delight and variety.
Peaches and pears (*Prunus persica* and *Pyrus communis*) For their lusciousness.
Apricots (*Prunus armeniaca*) For their tart melt-in-the-mouth scrumptiousness.

Matt
Callicarpa bodinieri var. *giraldii* 'Profusion' Lilac flowers and funky purple fruits. Flash or what?
Sorbus 'Joseph Rock' Primrose-yellow berries from one of the most gorgeous trees on earth.
Malus 'John Downie' An excellent garden tree with fabulous flowers and cheerful fruits for jellies and wine.

Evergreens

John
Embothrium coccineum Brilliant scarlet flowers in early summer with a backdrop of deep, evergreen leaves.
Juniperus communis 'Compressa' A truly dwarf conifer forming a compact column of needle-like mid-green leaves.
Eleagnus pungens 'Maculata' Dark evergreen leaves splashed with golden yellow.

Bunny
Taxus baccata Love it as a tree, hedge, sculpture – you name it, it will do it.
Astelia chamanica Much hardier than is often supposed (I know one thriving in Yorkshire), and is different but great too.
Cedrus lebani I rarely get to use this, but what a statement when well placed!

Bob
Rosmarinus spp. Useful, edible, scented, easy and pretty
x *Cuprocyparis leylandii* They screen out eyes so well, even upstairs eyes.
Cordyline australis For its head of flowers of gorgeous scent.

Matt
Hoheria sexstylosa 'Stardust' Has elegant leaves, a profusion of starry flowers and is very pretty.
Crinodendron hookerianum Beautiful flowers hang like crimson lanterns against the dark green leaves.

Desfontainia spinosa A Chilean 'wonder plant' with holly-like leaves and brightly coloured flowers.

Bright colours

John
Ceanothus 'Concha' Deep, non-fading, Oxford blue flowers open from deep red buds.
Cotinus 'Flame' Hard to beat when you want brilliant red foliage.
Meconopsis x *sheldonii* 'Slieve Donard' The very best true blue poppy.

Bunny
Canna iridiflora Wonderfully vibrant and exotic.
Cosmos atrosanguineus Freely produced rich velvety maroon red flowers adding a tropical feel
Salvia involucrata 'Bethellii' Amazing bright flowers all summer – they go on and on and on...

Matt
Forsythia x *intermedia* 'Lynwood' Not as bright as some, but you may still need your sunglasses.
Euonymus europeaus 'Red Cascade' Fiery red autumn colour looks great bathed in sunshine.
Schisandra rubriflora Clusters of bright red berries leap into vision during early autumn.

For tiny gardens

John
Cyclamen hederifolium Tiny, perfectly formed and scented flowers in shades of pink in autumn.
Sorbus reducta A miniature rowan tree complete with autumn colour and berries.
Ledum groenlandicum A tough little evergreen with white flowers in late spring/early summer.

Bunny
Thymus minimus Green paving but with scent, dynamic colour and adored by bees.
Galactites tomentosa Magnificent foliage, charming flowers, pops up to surprise you in the best places.
Cynara cardunculus Looks sensational and tastes even better.

Matt
Leucojum autumnale Delicate white flowers in autumn: they don't come much smaller than this!
Carex comans 'Frosted Curls' A swirling leaved sensation for borders or pots.
Clematis x *durandii:* Indigo blue flowers to create an aura of calm.

To attract wildlife

John
Buddleia x *weyeriana* 'Sungold' Unusual variety with orange-yellow flowers that attract butterflies.
Leycesteria formosa Birds love the trailing strings of purple fruit in autumn.
Lonicera periclymenum 'Graham Thomas' White summer flowers and red autumn berries attract birds and bees.

Bunny
Crataegus monogyna Hums with life through much of the year. Aesthetically adaptable – ideal for a chic minimalist city plot or rugged, windswept moors.
Ligustrum vulgare Flowers and fruit but also shelter in winter.
Viburnum opulus A very pretty native with massive appeal to us and them.

Bob
Blackberries (*Ribes* spp.) More use to more creatures than any other garden plant.
Limnanthes douglassii As it is also scented, pretty, easy, good ground cover.
Kniphofia spp. To see the birds taking their nectar.

Matt
Ilex aquifolium 'J. C. van Tol' Food for the birds and holly blue butterflies.
Buddleja 'Lochinch' Please plant buddlejas for butterflies. Thank you.
Foeniculum vulgare 'Purpureum' Flowers are a magnet to a multitude of insects.

For sheltered sites

John
Hebe x *andersonii* 'Variegata' Long, grey-green leaves margined creamy white; spikes of violet flowers in summer.
Clianthus puniceas 'Red Cardinal' Brilliant scarlet 'lobster claw' flowers in summer followed by pea-like seed pods.
Akebia quinata Purple-brown fragrant flowers in early spring followed by odd, sausage-like fruits in autumn.

Bunny
Olea europea Evergreen, beautiful, clippable, evocative, tolerant of dire soil – well, it's just outstanding.
Aloysia triphylla Scented leaves, perfumed flowers – very special.

Pyrus 'Doyenne de Comice'

Pelargonium tomentosum Beautiful form and foliage, with exquisitely scented leaves.

Bob
Banana (*Musa chinensis*) As it's just such a challenge and talking point.
Lemon verbena (*Aloysia triphylla*) For the absolutely gorgeous scent of the leaves.
Loquat (*Eriobotrya japonica*) Should do well and has such big leaves!

Matt
Jeffersonia dubia Dainty and exquisitely beautiful; a plant to savour.
Sanguinaria canadensis A gorgeous yet fleeting flower, it's another to add to your wish list.
Arisaema sikokianum So gorgeous and sumptuously coloured that every garden should have one!

Cornus alba 'Sibirica'

RED-BARKED DOGWOOD

Type: fully hardy, deciduous, spreading shrub
Soil & situation: moist, fertile soil/tolerates heavy, wet ground/full sun
Hardiness zone: 2–8
Height: 2.5m (8ft)
Spread: 2m (6½ft)
Grow for: bright red bark which is one of the joys of midwinter; red autumn leaves; AGM

A clump of leafless, red-stemmed dogwood growing at the edge of a lake and reflected in the surface of the water is a memorable sight. There are *Cornus* with variegated leaves (*C. alba* 'Gouchaultii'), others with yellow (*C. sericea* 'Flaviramea') or purple-black (*C. a* 'Kesselringii') stems, but *C. a.* 'Sibirica' (sometimes listed as *C. a.* 'Westonbirt') is the most accommodating and reliable, medium-sized variety.

The dark green leaves colour to a deep red before they fall, revealing the winter show. Small white flowers in spring and early summer are followed by white fruit, sometimes tinged with blue.

While it is content to grow in marshy and heavy clay sites, it will be more generous in its display if planted in fertile, moist, well-drained soil. It is the young growths that have the brightest bark colour. However, these should be removed close to ground level in spring to encourage new shoots for next winter's display. The bark on older stems fades to a dull, muddy brown-red. Neglected plants can be rejuvenated by a hard pruning in late winter or early spring.

Propagating is simple. A branch will root where it touches the ground and can be removed by taking 30cm (12in) long hardwood cuttings in winter. Insert them 15cm (6in) deep outside, in a trench lined with sand. They will be well rooted within 12 months ready for planting out. **JC**

Abelia x *grandiflora*

Type: hardy, evergreen shrub
Soil & situation: fertile, well-drained soil/full sun/shelter from cold winds
North American hardiness zone: 6–9
Height: 3m (10ft)
Spread: 4m (13ft)
Grow for: arched branches laden with fragrant white flowers in summer and autumn; AGM

An easily managed, evergreen plant that flowers over a long period and, as such, finds its way into lots of my garden designs.

When mature it forms a rounded shrub with arching branches. The glossy, dark green leaves are 5cm (2in) long. It is in flower continuously from mid-summer to the first frosts in autumn. The panicles of funnel-shaped, fragrant, white flowers are tinged pink with deeper pink calyces.

Plant in a sunny site well protected from cold, drying winds, which tend to scorch the new growths. It is a vigorous shrub needing its fair share of the bed. Where close planting causes congestion it loses its leaves and the crowded branches die. The variety *Abelia* x *grandiflora* 'Francis Mason' is less vigorous, growing to 1.5m (5ft) in height with a spread of 2m (6½ft). The leaves are yellow splashed with deep green.

A light pruning immediately after flowering to remove the old flowerheads will keep the plant in shape and encourage next year's flowers. Propagation is easy, either as softwood cuttings in early summer or semi-ripe taken with a heel in early autumn. Remove the tip of the cutting to prevent it flowering. Those rooted in autumn can be potted up in the following spring. **JC**

Abelia x *grandiflora*

Abeliophyllum distichum

Abeliophyllum distichum
WHITE FORSYTHIA

Type: hardy, deciduous shrub
Soil & situation: fertile, free-draining soil/full sun/sheltered site
North American hardiness zone: 5–9
Height & spread: 3m (10ft); 1.5m (5ft) as a border shrub
Grow for: white, pink-tinged, sweetly fragrant flowers in late winter; leaves sometimes turn purple in autumn

It is hard to believe that this elegant, slow-growing shrub, with clusters of dainty white flowers lining its leafless purple-black stems, is a relative of the more familiar yellow-flowered forsythia. Appearing in late winter when little else is in flower, its blooms are deliciously understated. The impact of a single plant is impressive; imagine the delight of a friend of mine who saw thickets of it flowering in the oak forests of South Korea.

Remarkably, in the wild it is scarce; even in 1948 it was noted that 'the distribution was confined to an exceedingly small area, had it not been brought into cultivation, it might easily have become extinct'. Now it is listed as 'critically endangered' – what better incentive to grow one of these treasures in your garden! The cultivar 'Roseum', sometimes called the Roseum Group, has pale pink flowers.

Although hardy, it needs a sunny wall, fence or border to ripen young growths and protect flowers from frost. It should be grown in a well-drained, fertile soil. Prune after flowering. If you are growing it as a wall shrub, cut back flowering shoots to two to three buds; in borders, cut them back to a vigorous branch lower down on the main stem; cut out any weak growth. If the plant is congested remove up to a quarter of the older wood at the base. Propagate by semi-ripe cuttings in mid-summer or by layering. The arching branches layer naturally and can be transplanted a year later. **MB**

Abies koreana

KOREAN FIR

Type: hardy, evergreen conifer
Soil & situation: deep, moist, fertile, well-drained, alkaline soil/full sun
North American hardiness zone: 5–6
Height: 10m (33ft)
Spread: 6m (20ft)
Grow for: a mass of purple-blue cones in winter

I just love to see cones on conifers. With some species they are formed so high up the mature tree you need binoculars, but this plant will oblige by producing cones on plants that are barely 1m (3ft) high.

Small, dark green, upward curving leaves cover the upper part of the stem. On the underside of the leaf there are two broad, silver-white lines.

The insignificant male flowers are deep red and the female purple or pink followed by upright, cylindrical, candle-like, purple or deep blue cones, 5–8cm (2–3½in) long. They exude beads of clear resin like wax dripping down the side of a candle. Eventually they turn a rich brown and break up. *Abies koreana* 'Silberlocke' has leaves that twist upwards revealing their silver undersides.

It is totally hardy, although the foliage of young plants may be scorched by cold, biting winds. It makes a wonderful specimen conifer especially in winter when laden with cones and sprinkled with a dusting of snow.

Propagation is by seed sown fresh in late autumn in a cold frame. Stratify for at least one month. Grow the young seedlings under cover for the first season. Container-grow the plants for their first full year. **JC**

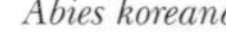
Abies koreana

Abutilon x *hybridum* 'Kentish Belle'

Abutilon x *hybridum* 'Kentish Belle'

FLOWERING MAPLE, PARLOUR MAPLE, INDIAN MALLOW

Type: frost-hardy, semi-evergreen shrub
Soil & situation: well-drained fertile soil/sun or partial shade/best when trained against, or grown beside, a protective wall or fence
North American hardiness zone: 8–10
Height & spread: 2.5m (8ft)
Grow for: extremely long flowering period, sometimes continuously, from early spring to autumn; attractive and unusual mix of warm apricot-yellow and orangey-red flowers; AGM

As these plants are a little on the tender side, both the flowers and the foliage do really benefit from the shelter and warmth of a wall, often trained as an informal fan. I have seen one smothered in flowers, in Bath, just after Christmas, propped up against a slatted fence. It must have been a mild year as they usually stop with the frosts. The flowers are produced singly and are large, bell-shaped and hang from the dark brown/purple shoots. They stand out far more and are better displayed when trained against a wall, particularly a pale-coloured wall.

The young plants benefit from some tip pruning to encourage a good bushy habit. Mature plants can be cut back hard in early to mid-spring to stop them getting over-large or gangly. Dead-heading helps prolong the flowering period, preventing too much energy being taken up with seed production. Abutilons are easy to propagate from either softwood or semi-ripe cuttings in summer. **BG**

Abutilon 'Souvenir de Bonne'

Abutilon 'Souvenir de Bonne'

Type: half-hardy, evergreen shrub
Soil & situation: free-draining soil/full sun or part day sun/winter protection/cannot withstand temperatures below 0°C (32°F)
North American hardiness zone: 8–10
Height: up to 3.5m (11ft)
Spread: 3m (10ft)
Grow for: amazing foliage margined and sometimes mottled in a creamy white, the leaves are a maple shape; soft orange-apricot flowers from late spring to autumn; AGM

I do appreciate the flowers – they are a fabulous colour – but compared to the really over-the-top foliage they rather pale into insignificance. I am not usually a huge fan of rashly variegated plants but this I find agreeable. Generally they are planted out in the late spring, having been heavily cut back, and are almost invariably nearly leafless with me, due to long periods of 0°C (32°F) over winter.

But they quickly gather pace, spread and flower, contributing a fair amount of impact to my sheltered, walled garden. They have other exotic near neighbours – bananas, brugmansias, melianthus and palms – and it is easy to forget that this is the sunny East Midlands.

My specimens generally reach about 1.8m (6ft) by the end of the summer, due to a good cutting back in the spring. Otherwise they would tend to get extremely leggy. As the plants become older, they become less floriferous, so ideally replacement cuttings are taken every four years or so. These are as for *A.* x *hybridum* 'Kentish Belle' (see previous entry). **BG**

Acacia dealbata
MIMOSA OR SILVER WATTLE

Type: half-hardy, evergreen tree
Soil & situation: well-drained, fertile, neutral to acid soil/sheltered site in full sun
North American hardiness zone: 9–10
Height: 6–15m (20–50ft)
Spread: 5–8m (16–25ft)
Grow for: scented winter and spring flowers; AGM

This is the flowering tree the British have nicknamed the 'florist's mimosa'. Its delicate, buttercup-yellow racemes are made up of hundreds of small, rounded, highly fragrant flowers appearing in winter and early spring. When I was a boy every 'decent' bunch of flowers contained some mimosa and it certainly wasn't grown in quantity locally. I used to think it had been sent from Australia, but Cornwall was probably more accurate.

The 12cm (5in) long, fern-like foliage is silvery-green and made up of around 80 leaflets. It dislikes being transplanted so choose a small tree and plant it in its permanent position. A sheltered, sunny wall is ideal. Additional protection from winter wind and frost in the form of a removable screen of horticultural fleece or bubble wrap will guarantee flowers every winter.

In Australia it may grow to 15m (50ft) with a spread of 8m (25ft), but in most northern hemisphere gardens 6m (20ft) in height with a spread of 5m (16ft) is more realistic. **JC**

Bunny adds:
This is a wonderful wall plant, and I find it worth growing even in the East Midlands. It establishes quickly, so if I did lose it in an exceptionally hard winter, its hole could soon be filled with a replacement.

Acanthus mollis
BEAR'S BREECHES

Type: semi-evergreen, hardy perennial
Soil & situation: tolerates a wide range of soils/dislikes the wettest soil/sun or light shade
North American hardiness zone: 7–10
Height: to 1.5m (5ft)
Spread: to 90cm (36in)
Grow for: a superb plant with a bold habit; white flowers with purple-shaded bracts in summer; large, glossy-green basal leaves, evergreen (in most winters) up to 1m (3ft)

This perennial has the rare quality of looking striking throughout the year. Its opulent, shiny leaves remain a feature for most or all of the winter unless you have exceptionally hard frosts. It has the added benefit of producing robust, but delicately coloured flower spikes for several weeks in the summer. These may well be 1.5m (5ft) high and are excellent for dried, winter decorations. *Acanthus spinosus* is famous for the shape of its leaves, which are similar to those of *A. mollis*, but spiny and deeply cut. A stylized form of these leaves is used as a motif in classical and neo-classical ornamentation. *A. spinosus* is generally freer flowering, but tends to die right back in winter.

This plant requires little attention except division and replanting, when necessary, in autumn or early spring. In my experience this is needed only infrequently. I grow them, in repeated clumps, against a 6m (20ft), north-facing, stone-buttressed wall. The lack of sun reduces the quantity of flowers, but not to a worrying extent. The leaves can suffer from slugs and mildew in early summer. If they look unacceptable I remove them and new, perfect specimens replace them swiftly. The spikes are best removed after flowering. These plants can become rampant, so they are best used surrounded by suitable neighbours, as solo performers or in large tubs where they will thrive. When you move clumps of plants, the fleshy roots, which become severed and left behind, may well strike out again on their own so propagation is easy from root cuttings in autumn. Alternatively, seeds can be sown in spring. **BG**

Right: Acanthus mollis

Left: Acacia dealbata

Acanthus sennii

Acanthus sennii

BEAR'S BREECHES

Type: half-hardy, evergreen perennial
Soil & situation: free-draining soil/full sun
North American hardiness zone: 7–10
Height & spread: 1.8m (6ft)
Grow for: flowers from mid-summer to autumn

I've only seen this once and it is absolutely incredible. Rarely mentioned in literature, *Acanthus sennii* grows at Oxford University Botanic Garden and Chelsea Physic Garden, London, is offered by a couple of nurseries and remains a mystery plant. Named in 1940 by an Italian taxonomist Emilio Chiovenda, it is endemic to the Ethiopian highlands between 1,500 and 3,200m (5,000 and 10,500ft), by streams and river banks, in dry forest margins and on open hillsides. The stiff, glossy, dark green leaves in opposite pairs have wavy margins of spiky teeth and prominent veins but it's the striking black bracts and pink to vermilion flowers in clusters towards the top of the stem that are so unusual and eye-catching. I tried to propagate it but failed, now I'm on the hunt for a plant of my own; it's my horticultural Holy Grail!

Look out also for *A. hirsutus*, whose pale greenish-white flowers peep from hairy green bracts; *A. hungaricus* with dense clusters of pink-purple spikes above dull green leaves; *A. dioscoridis* – low growing with beautiful, broad, pink to purplish flowers and long, narrow, grey-green, downy leaves; and *A. d.* var. *perringii* with deeply divided and slightly spiny foliage, grey-green flower spikes and flowers of delicate pink. They all flower from early to late summer. There are several forms in cultivation.

Grow *A. sennii* in milder areas of the UK at the base of a sunny wall, where it may still need winter protection and a 'dry' mulch like bracken in autumn. It is much better grown in a container and over-wintered indoors to protect from frost. It prefers sunshine and deep, fertile, well-drained soil or a loam-based compost. To propagate take root cuttings in winter. **MB**

Acer capillipes

Acer capillipes
SNAKEBARK MAPLE

Type: hardy, deciduous tree
Soil & situation: ordinary garden soil/sun or partial shade
North American hardiness zone: 5–7
Height & spread: 9–14m (30–46ft)
Grow for: curiously striped bark; bright green leaves, attractive form and autumn tints extend its high points to 12 months in a year; AGM

I planted this tree adjacent to our eating-out area and the canopy, although fairly upright and contained, has a few lazier branches, which shade the table like an umbrella. With maturity, it will spread further. It is an undemanding tree but I think quite a special one. It has settled into this dry corner and is a fine young specimen having reached a height of some 6m (20ft) after about 17 years. The bark has vertical, chalky-white stripes running all the way down the trunk, which are always noticeable. They are painted on a green-brown background. The leaves have three pointed lobes and coral-red stems – the same colour as the new young growth. The flowers open in late spring in the form of hanging racemes of a greenish-white colour and are followed by long, drooping bunches of fruit with keys and wings. It is a suitable tree for a medium-sized or, very possibly, even a small garden, depending on position. It is also adaptable – you occasionally see it as a successful street tree.

I, as always, like to see this tree planted small, certainly no bigger than 1.2m (4ft) high if you can get it that size, and with no stake. This way it will quickly overtake any that were planted at a larger size and will form a much better-shaped tree. It is also far less expensive. Bare-rooted trees establish better than container-grown ones. It needs little aftercare, though make sure that there are no grass or weeds growing within 1m (3ft) diameter around the base of the trunk. This way there is no moisture competition and it will grow far faster. Watering in dry periods in the first two to three years after planting, makes all the difference. Feed is much less critical in this initial period. If the bark becomes covered with green algae, a light wash now and again will make the stripes stand out. **BG**

Acer davidii subsp. *grosseri*
SNAKEBARK MAPLE

Type: hardy, deciduous tree
Soil & situation: moist, well-drained, fertile soil/full sun or light shade
North American hardiness zone: 5–7
Height & spread: 14m (46ft)
Grow for: size, shape and bark

Some trees have all the luck and this is one of them. It is trouble-free, grows to a reasonable size, is usually well shaped and has one of the finest barks of any maple.

The green-barked trunk and main branches are streaked with pure white stripes. Mid-green leaves turn to orange and then a buttery-yellow in autumn. Pendent racemes of pale yellow flowers appear in spring and are followed, in autumn, by long, trailing clusters of pink-brown, winged keys or seeds.

Acer davidii subsp. *grosseri*

It will grow well on most fertile soils but the young shoots suffer dieback when planted in waterlogged ground. Large plants transplant well providing they are lifted in late autumn with a good rootball and are watered regularly during the first season after moving.

Occasionally it will produce double leader branches which form a narrow angle. Remove the weakest stem with sharp secateurs and train the remaining leader upright by tying it with raffia to a bamboo cane. Cleaning the bark of a mature tree with a power hose or rubbing with a wet piece of hessian will remove the grime and algae leaving the stripes very obvious. Propagation is by grafting in late summer. **JC**

Acer griseum

Acer griseum
PAPERBARK MAPLE

Type: hardy, deciduous tree
Soil & situation: fertile, well-drained, neutral to alkaline soil/full sun or partial shade
North American hardiness zone: 4–8
Height & spread: 10m (33ft)
Grow for: rich autumn leaf colour irrespective of weather conditions; the spectacular mahogany coloured, peeling bark makes this a 'must-have' tree; AGM

There are too many acers available to select and highlight just one but, for me, weak winter sunlight makes this tree's bark glow. The tissue-thin curls of bark demand little (and large) fingers to peel them off. As the older mahogany bark is stripped the under-layer of cinnamon is revealed. The very thing to perk you up in mid-winter.

Left: Acer palmatum var. *heptalobum*

The dark green leaves are made up of three leaflets, which turn to bright orange, scarlet and crimson in autumn and remain until late in the season. The bright yellow flowers droop gracefully in spring but, because *A. griseum* has separate male and female flowers, the seed is often without an embryo and cannot germinate.

A tree is for life, so don't rush the planting. Dig in lots of old manure or compost. Spread the roots and plant at the same depth as before. Remove low branches if they get in the way of grass cutting or other plants. If they are allowed to thicken then their late removal will result in scarring on the trunk. **JC**

Acer palmatum var. *heptalobum*

JAPANESE MAPLE

Type: hardy, deciduous tree
Soil & situation: moist, humus-rich, well-drained soil/full sun or partial shade
North American hardiness zone: 5–8
Height: 5m (16ft)
Spread: 6m (20ft)
Grow for: elegant form; amazing autumn colour

Every garden should have a Japanese maple. Where there is sufficient space this is one I would recommend for shape and autumn colour. The 5–12cm (2–5in) long, palmate leaves have seven to nine long, tapering lobes with finely toothed margins. In autumn the bright green leaves turn orange and finally scarlet. The foliage is held until late autumn. Small, pendent, purple-red flowers are followed by red-winged fruit in early autumn.

Like most Japanese maples this variety will tolerate alkaline or acid soils providing they are deep and retain moisture. Avoid planting in sites exposed to cold spring winds, which will scorch the young foliage. A woodland situation with partial shade is ideal. Mulch with leafmould every autumn after leaf fall. It is possible to transplant large specimens providing the rootball has been prepared the previous year. Dig a trench 30cm (12in) deep and wide around the plant directly below the outside spread of the tree. Cut any roots and backfill the trench with peat or old compost.

Pruning is only necessary to shape the plant and should be carried out in late summer or early autumn when the sap is falling. Young, strong sideshoots should be shortened in spring. Propagation is by grafting in late winter or budding in late summer. Seed will not come true and the resulting plants will be variable. **JC**

Acer pensylvanicum

Plant of the Week (see page 397)

Achillea ptarmica 'Taygetea'

Type: hardy, evergreen perennial
Soil & situation: any well-drained garden soil/flowers better and lives longer on poorer soils/full sun
North American hardiness zone: 3–8
Height & spread: 60cm (24in)
Grow for: a good border mainstay; the pale lemon-yellow to cream flowers last from summer till early autumn

The name comes from Achilles who, it is said, discovered its medicinal qualities. If you add this plant to an area of planting it scores on several points, adding both good form and colour. The foliage is produced in hummocks of finely cut, long grey-green leaves. When the mass of flowers arrives in summer they are held high above the foliage – on show for all to see. They are very attractive to bees and butterflies. The roots are rhizomatous so it will spread and this can be to its advantage in more natural, larger-scale perennial and grass plantings. Its tolerance of drier conditions also makes it well suited to the hurly-burly of this type of situation. In more traditional border positions, its neighbours should be planned carefully or it may tend to invade them if not kept in check. Another favourite achillea, which is taller (up to 1.2m/4ft) and has flat flowerheads with a strong, gold-yellow colour is *A. filipendulina* 'Gold Plate' (AGM).

This plant does not need staking. It tends to be fairly short-lived but is easy to propagate from division. Unfortunately it can suffer from powdery mildew. It is a fabulous plant for cutting and drying – flowers are best cut when young so that they retain their colour. If you cut them early the plant may well produce a second flush of flowers. **BG**

Achillea ptarmica 'Taygetea'

Coffea arabica

COFFEE

Type: tender evergreen shrub to small tree
Soil & situation: moist, humus-rich soil/light shade/ under cover
Hardiness zone: 10–11
Height: 7m (23ft)
Spread: 3m (10ft)
Grow for: white, jasmine-like scented flowers and red cherry-like berries – you may even gather enough to make a cup of coffee! A striking evergreen subject for the conservatory or greenhouse, and a breath of fresh air in January when not much else is cheerful.

Of great educational interest, as well as being really attractive in leaf and flower, coffee is one of the plants that almost everyone wants to see when I mention I grow it in my greenhouse. To make coffee the berries need to be fermented, cured and roasted in fairly large batches, so one or two plants are unlikely to furnish enough to make a properamount, but it is still really interesting to see the berries form. Some of the original cultivators in Africa ate the berry raw and in the Far East the leaves were used to make coffee, but I can't vouch for the safety of these practices. *C. liberica* is similar and equally worth growing.

Native to the African and Arabian tropics, coffee once formed wild forests in Abyssinia and the Sudan, yet apparently remained unknown to the ancients. First used by the Arabs, it was noted by travellers in the 15th century and introduced to London in the middle of the 17th. Taking coffee quickly became a national vice, to be rivalled – and in the UK outdone – only by tea, which arrived about a decade later and for some reason displaced its forerunner, whereas in the rest of the world coffee triumphed.

Coffee must be grown in a warm greenhouse or conservatory where, like gardenias (see page 187), it likes bright light but not direct sun. It can be quite long-lived – perhaps 25 years – if the cold or mealy bug does not get it. Coffee can be hard pruned in spring when too large.

Sow in warmth with *fresh* seed – old seed is hard to germinate and roasted coffee beans are roasted! The main and most consistent problem is mealy bug – regular jetting down on warm days using a high-pressure hose and a soapy spray will control them. **BF**

Achillea 'Terracotta'

Achillea 'Terracotta'

YARROW, MILLFOIL

Type: hardy, herbaceous perennial
Soil & situation: free-draining soil/sun
North American hardiness zone: 3–8
Height: 75cm (30in)
Spread: 60cm (24in)
Grow for: form and flowers from early summer to early autumn

It's a spectacular change in fortune to rise from being a scruffy lawn weed to become the star of the summer border, yet it's exactly what the yarrow has done. It's mainly because of the interest in natural planting led by the Dutch garden designer Piet Oudolf and others who use the flat flowerheads to provide dabs of colour and form to contrast with other architectural plants like grasses and sea holly (*Eryngium bourgatii*, see page 166). Some achilleas are in single colours, others have flowers with a central eye and many change colour with age. The colour ranges from purple to pale pink, orange, salmon and pale yellow, all with stiff stems and feathery foliage. They are good for cutting and drying; some are fascinating, while others are beautiful!

Achillea 'Terracotta' with its orange-yellow flowers fading to cream is my favourite, but there are lots of others worth trying. *A.* 'Inca Gold' is bright yellow with an orange flush, fading through yellow with pale orange petal tips to pale lemon. *A.* 'Lachsschönheit' is salmon-pink through pale yellow to white-flushed pale pink! It grows to 1.2m (4ft) and needs staking, as does *A.* 'Christine's Pink', which is pink, fading to white with pink eyes. *A.* 'Belle Epoque' is bright red, with faint yellow streaks and a pinkish-white 'eye', it fades through pale yellow flushed dark pink to pale yellow.

Achillea 'Gold Plate'

In the rush for the 'new' we shouldn't forget *A. filipendulina* 'Gold Plate' and *A. f.* 'Cloth of Gold' with their huge bright yellow flowerheads and pale lemon *A.* 'Moonshine', which have been loyal servants for years.

They need full sun in poor, well-drained soil; dead-head after flowering. A. filipendulina and its cultivars are useful plants to give structure in the winter garden. Divide in spring. **MB**

Aconitum carmichaelii

Type: hardy, herbaceous perennial
Soil & situation: prefers moist but well-drained soils/shade or sun
North American hardiness zone: 3–7
Height: 1.5–1.8m (5–6ft)
Spread: 30–40cm (12–16in)
Grow for: exceptionally handsome plants; their strong blue spikes add stature and good strong colour to any border

I think many people are wary of aconitums because of the poison they contain. It is in fact an alkaloid called aconitine, which is one of the most toxic substances found in plants. But strangely enough, compounds derived from *A. carmichaelii* have long been used for medicinal purposes too. (It was mentioned in Chinese literature in AD 200.) Extracts from the roots are used as stimulants for the heart, pain killers and for anti-rheumatic effects. So it's not all evil and it certainly is beautiful.

There are several different forms of *A. carmichaelii.* (*A. fischeri* was the form grown in many gardens as this plant and now is just known as *A. carmichaelii.*) Plant names have never been easy, now they are highly mobile too. Anyway, *A. fischeri* that was is easy, good looking and vigorous, it flowers late, sometimes in October by which time the leaves are just starting to turn. *A. c.* 'Kelmscott' has been awarded an AGM, so it is a safe bet that it is a reliably good plant. It produces tall spires of lavender-blue flowers in early to mid-autumn.

Aconites can sometimes become too crowded and when that happens their propensity for flowering is reduced. However, they do not respond well to being disturbed so only divide them when extra feed and moisture are not triggering a better performance. Division is best done in autumn. They are often quick off the mark in spring so they tend to catch you out if you leave it till then. An annual mulch is good – it helps to retain moisture, which is always appreciated. **BG**

Aconitum carmichaelii

Aconitum hemsleyanum

Aconitum hemsleyanum

Type: hardy, climbing perennial
Soil & situation: moist, humus-rich soils which do not dry out/partial shade or full sun.
North American hardiness zone: 4–7
Height: 2–3m (6½–10ft)
Spread: 45cm (18in)
Grow for: racemes of beautiful, indigo-violet flowers in mid-summer to autumn; scrambling and twining stems

The majority of aconitums are non-climbing but this unusual plant is one of the exceptions, able to climb and intermingle amongst large shrubs in a relaxed, informal way. The intense deep colour of their flowers looks even more vivid when scrambling through a white-flowered plant such as lacecap hydrangea. I always find this an irresistible colour combination. I keep meaning to acquire some *A.* 'Bressingham Spire' (AGM) which has violet-blue flowers, is a non-climbing aconitum and flowers from mid-summer to early autumn. The flowering can be prolonged further by removing the flower spikes once they are past it. It is worth being aware that every part of the aconitum family is highly toxic to people and animals.

As this plant appreciates moisture it is generally far better planted in the autumn. Mulch each spring to help keep soil moisture levels high. Once established these plants will do far better if left undisturbed as their tuberous roots resent movement. Propagate carefully by division; or alternatively it is extremely easy from seed. The colour of the flower varies when it is grown from seed, though you will have to wait until its second year when it starts to flower to find out. I was lucky – mine came a good, strong colour – but do not be dissuaded from having a second try if the first batch are rather a wishy-washy blue. **BG**

Actaea simplex Atropurpurea Group (syn. *Cimicifuga simplex*)

BUGBANE

Type: hardy perennial
Soil & situation: happiest in rich, moist soils, it should not be allowed to dry out during the growing season/prefers light shade
North American hardiness zone: 4–8
Height: 1.5m (5ft)
Spread: 60cm (24in)
Grow for: dramatic foliage plant, with purple leaves, stems and buds; furry, bottle-brush-like, white flowers in autumn

Another of those high-value plants but this one is fussy about moisture levels. My mother grows it in her garden (thin, limestone brash, but heavily adulterated) but she has irrigation, and she is in the wet West Country. In the vast stock beds in her perennial nursery it looks out of this world in the autumn. It has tall, furry, white pokers of see-through flowers and rich, dark purple stems carrying the shiny, green-purple, slightly incised leaves. It is definitely architectural, yet possesses colour, form and flowers – quite a combination.

In less than perfect conditions do what you can to improve the moisture conditions: mulches in spring, organic matter on planting, sheltered site and be at the ready with the watering can when it looks even slightly in want of a drink. To some degree you can mollycoddle it through the first couple of years in less than perfect conditions and then leave it to it, but not if your soil is too sharp-draining and your rainfall low to boot. Apart from this, there is not a lot to be done. It does not require staking despite its stature. It has attractive seedheads, so leave these on so you can enjoy its winter performance too. It is also appealing in flower arrangements. Cut it back when it looks too ragged in late winter/spring. Divide in spring when you have to, which is infrequently. Propagation is often from seed, but the foliage colour will vary, so select out the stunners. **BG**

Actea simplex Atropurpurea Group

Actinidia chinensis

Actinidia chinensis

KIWI/CHINESE GOOSEBERRY

Type: frost-hardy, deciduous, woody, perennial climber
Soil & situation: most soils, moist but not wet/full sun to light shade/prefers warm, sheltered gardens
North American hardiness zone: 7–9
Height: can reach 9m (30ft)
Spread: to 4.5–5m (15–16ft)
Grow for: masses of creamy buff-coloured scented flowers in summer; edible, brown, furry-covered fruits with green flesh in late autumn

The kiwi is firstly a fruiting plant but it has very beautiful young pink shoots; attractive, large, heart-shaped leaves; and such good flowers that it deserves a place in the flower garden. Other species such as *Actinidia arguta* and *A. kolomikta* are similar. They are all closely related to camellias and although the flowers are not as showy, those of most species are sweetly scented – and the edible fruits are rich in vitamins. Coming from China and the Far East, the kiwi has become a major greenhouse crop in many countries where it is grown in surplus tomato houses, but it has been a garden plant for a hundred years. Although normally left to ramble, it can be trained as an espalier, which I have seen done in France.

It needs a tree or strong supports to climb, with tying in and removal of dead wood in winter. To ensure fruiting, you must have both a male and female plant – or buy a new hermaphrodite variety. It can be grown from seed and will fruit in five to ten years. Layer in autumn or take half-ripe cuttings in late summer. Late frosts tend to take off flowers. **BF**

Actinidia kolomikta

Type: hardy, deciduous, climbing shrub
Soil & situation: fertile, well-drained soil/full sun
North American hardiness zone: 5–8
Height: 9m (30ft)
Spread: to 4.5–5m (15–16ft)
Grow for: slightly exotic leaf colouring; fast growing; AGM

I don't really want everyone to plant this climber. It would become common and cease to be a talking point for visitors. Serious questions from adults include queries as to my reasons for painting the leaves.

It is a fast-growing, vigorous, twining climber with 15cm (6in) long, dark green leaves which, when they first emerge, are tinged purple. The top half of the leaf becomes variegated with splashes of white and bright pink. The colour is at its best when grown against a wall in full sun. Clusters of three, fragrant, white flowers appear in early summer. Female plants produce a smooth-skinned, greenish-yellow fruit in autumn.

Keep the root area cool and shaded by mulching annually, in spring, with 10cm (4in) of composted bark. Pruning is usually only carried out to thin the number of climbing stems. When necessary, prune in mid-winter. Plant in a sheltered position, out of the reach of cold winds.

Propagate by softwood cuttings in late summer. Place small cuttings round the inside edge of the pot in an open, gritty compost. They will root quickly, but bear in mind the plant's vigour and don't be tempted to plant out too many. **JC**

Actinidia kolomikta

Aeonium 'Zwartkop'

Aeonium 'Zwartkop'

Type: tender, succulent subshrub
Soil & situation: free-draining soil/partial shade/minimum temperature of 10°C (20°C)
North American hardiness zone: 10–11
Height & spread: up to 2m (6½ft), usually less
Grow for: dramatic purple-black foliage borne in rosettes at the end of branches; AGM

This is a really stunning foliage plant with many uses. It is a good house plant and can be grown in a greenhouse or conservatory, but I think it comes into its own when you put it outside during the warmer months. It looks well in a pot or can be planted into the soil, preferably in a gravel area, so that the distinct form of branches tipped with the amazingly coloured rosettes can be appreciated. *Aeonium arboreum* is similar, but has light green leaves, sometimes they are mottled in a purplish-green. It is not as dramatic but is still a very special foliage plant and may even survive a short, mild frost provided that the compost is on the dry side. It is better in the sun though has a tendency to wilt if very hot.

If growing this in a pot use a gritty, loam-based soil or cactus compost and let it dry out between waterings. When, or if, you plant it outside, plant it in a free-draining moderately fertile soil. To propagate cut off a rosette of leaves, wait till a callus has formed, and then insert the base into a free-draining, gritty compost keeping it on the dry side till it has rooted. **BG**

Aesculus x *carnea* 'Briotii'
RED HORSE CHESTNUT

Type: hardy, deciduous shrub
Soil & situation: deep, moist, fertile, well-drained soil/sun or partial shade
North American hardiness zone: 6–8
Height: 18m (60ft)
Spread: 13m (43ft)
Grow for: wonderful form; autumn leaf colour; eye-catching flowers; AGM

Chestnuts bring back happy childhood memories. The large 'fingered leaves' were probably the first I ever drew (badly) at school; the game of conkers was an important part of playground life; and I was encouraged to grow them from seed with embarrassing results years later when the tree filled our garden and the one on either side.

Aesculus x *carnea* 'Briotii' originated in France and represents beautifully all the charm and grace of the true Parisian. It forms a large spreading tree with glossy, dark green, crinkly edged, overlapping leaflets. Following a hot, dry summer the foliage sometimes displays some red and gold autumn colour. The large, upright, 20–30cm (8–12in) panicles of candle-like flowers appear in early summer. They are deep red with a yellow centre. Very few 'conkers' are produced, the shells of which are less spiny than the white-flowered horse chestnut, *A. hippocastanum*. Warty growths usually appear on the bark of mature trees. They are harmless and should not be removed. When grown as a specimen in parkland the branches will sweep down to ground level. Propagation is usually by bud grafting in summer. **JC**

Aesculus x *carnea* 'Briotii'

Agapanthus praecox subsp. *orientalis*

Agapanthus praecox subsp. *orientalis*

Type: half-hardy, evergreen perennial
Soil & situation: well-drained soil/full sun/some winter protection
North American hardiness zone: 9–11
Height: 90cm (36in)
Spread: 60cm (24in)
Grow for: beautiful blue globe-shaped flowers from mid- to late summer; attractive, glossy leaves

There is quite a variety of different agapanthus; generally the evergreen forms with the broader, strappy bright green leaves are more tender than the hardier forms, such as *Agapanthus* Headbourne hybrids, which are deciduous, and hardy to –15°C (5°F). The flowers of the evergreen forms are bold, beautiful and stunning, whereas the deciduous forms tend to be far less eye-catching, smaller and less freely produced. These plants give an exotic air when shown off in huge tubs, with their sky-blue balls adding a tropical feel. They tell you it really is summer, even when the sky is less than bright blue. The flowers are long-lived and are excellent for cutting.

I grow them in large pots and tend to leave them undivided until they are bursting at the seams. They are said to flower better under crowded conditions, but you do have to make sure that you will be able to get them out without demolishing the pot. (I learnt this one from bitter experience.) In these confined conditions, unless you feed and water them well right up until they have finished flowering, you will find flowering much diminished (also learnt from bitter experience). When you do split them, a simple way is to break the clump into two and re-pot the entire half. This way, flower production the year following splitting is not unduly affected. Winter protection can take the form of a frost-free greenhouse and ensuring that they are watered infrequently, although I tend to just mulch the pots heavily in winter, and provided the position is sheltered, that seems to do the trick. **BG**

Agave americana 'Marginata'

Agave americana

Type: tender, evergreen, succulent perennial
Soil & situation: free-draining soil/sunny position/protection needed in winter, except for large specimens in milder climates
North American hardiness zone: 9–11
Height: 2m (6½ft)
Spread: 3m (10ft)
Grow for: architectural plants with pale green to grey leaves growing in spreading, relaxed rosettes; AGM

I have grown this plant for about four years now, in containers. My specimens are 40cm (16in) high and I have not covered them in winter or even moved the pots back against a wall. I am one of those gardeners who does take chances, but so far I have got away with it in the East Midlands. I am kinder to my variegated version, *A. americana* 'Marginata', also potted, but only a mere 20cm (8in) high, as I pull it in under a south-facing porch when the evening skies and temperatures tell me to watch it. Agaves look perfect in large containers or in gravel. I got sucked into them when I designed a tropical garden for Chelsea, and spent intoxicated hours browsing around specialist nurseries looking at exotica. They are succulents and have characteristic fat, juicy-looking leaves with slightly wavy edges and spines all the way up. Try to avoid coming into too close contact with these if you ever re-pot them. One or two of their leaves bend back, like a swan's neck. As the new leaf slowly opens out it leaves a curious wavy imprint on its old bedfellow. These plants are called 'the century plants', supposedly because they are a great age before they flower. Mine have not yet, but apparently some species take about eight years, others a mere 30 or 40. I am not sure if I want them to flower though, as the energy required often kills them. The flowers can grow to a height of 9m (30ft), are pale yellow and are borne in panicles.

Grow these plants in bright sunlight, and if potted, feed them with a low nitrogen but high phosphate and potash element. As they grow really large you may need to remove the lower leaves and suckers to balance the look of the plant. Propagation from the suckers is simple – if roots are not already formed they soon do when the base is immersed in a free-draining compost. **BG**

Agrostemma githago

Plant of the Week (see page 193)

Ajuga reptans 'Catlin's Giant'

Type: hardy, evergreen perennial
Soil & situation: any moderately fertile soil/partial shade/will tolerate sun or full shade
North American hardiness zone: 3–9
Height: 1.5m (5ft)
Spread: 1m (3ft)
Grow for: useful, evergreen ground cover which dwarfs other bugles; leaves are a smart shade of purple about 15cm (6in) long; AGM

This is one of those low-maintenance, ground-cover plants. That phrase tends to make me think it should belong in a supermarket car park rather than a garden, but this is not so mundane. I used it in large sheets intermingled with ferns, for the Wind in the Willows garden, my first ever Chelsea garden, and it looked stunning. The flowers are produced on stout spikes, they are a bright, fresh blue set off by the rich, shiny, fluted leaves below. Again it is a plant that you need to be generous with, perhaps as a bold edge to a border or in repetitive clumps. Try mixing it with other higher-accent plants spangled amongst it to really enhance the level of interest – then it really comes into its own.

Ajuga reptans 'Catlin's Giant'

The leaves do reduce in size after flowering so it is worth cutting off the flowerheads, when they are past it, to negate this effect as far as possible. If the plant starts to run in unwanted directions, it may require reining back every so often. Otherwise it is a simple beast to maintain and look after. To propagate, you simply separate the rooted stems or take softwood cuttings in early summer. **BG**

Akebia quinata

Akebia quinata
CHOCOLATE VINE

Type: hardy, semi-evergreen climber
Soil & situation: moist, well-drained, fertile soil/full sun or partial shade
North American hardiness zone: 5–9
Height: 10m (33ft)
Spread: 9m (30ft)
Grow for: a graceful, fast-growing climber with delicate flowers, semi-evergreen leaves and strangely shaped fruits

Although this climber is a vigorous, rampant grower it gives the appearance of a delicate plant which isn't likely to be invasive. Given the right situation it will out-pace *Clematis montana* and most of the honeysuckles, at the same time managing to look graceful and desirable.

The dark green, rounded leaves are made up of five leaflets notched at their tips. The underside is blue-green turning purple-green in winter. The spicily perfumed clusters of red-purple flowers remind me of vanilla. They appear in late spring and early summer with the male and female flowers in the same 12cm (5in) pendent raceme. The male flowers are paler and are concentrated at the tip of the cluster. After a hot summer it will produce unusual sausage- shaped purple fruits up to 10cm (4in) long with a white pulp holding jet-black seeds.

Pollination will be improved if two plants are growing in the same location. Where there is likely to be late frosts give it some protection to reduce the risk of damage to the early flowers. Pruning is only necessary to tidy the plant and keep it within the available space and should be carried out immediately after flowering has finished. Propagate by sowing seed as soon as it is ripe or by rooting small 5cm (2in) semi-ripe cuttings in summer. Alternatively, where there are suitable low stems, layer some in a peat/grit mixture *in situ*. Large, well-rooted layers should be replanted as soon as possible after digging up. **JC**

Alcea rosea 'Nigra'

Plant of the Week (see page 217)

Alchemilla conjuncta

Type: hardy, herbaceous perennial
Soil & situation: any well-drained soil/sun or partial shade
North American hardiness zone: 3–7
Height: 40cm (16in)
Spread: 30cm (12in)
Grow for: attractive foliage and delicate flowers

Because *Alchemilla mollis* (see next entry), with its lovely lime-green foliage is such an attractive plant and is so easy to grow to the point of being invasive, other related species tend to be overlooked. All of those mentioned below have smaller leaves but still collect the droplets of dew and rain that make them so delectable.

I love pretty little clump-forming *A. conjuncta* with its deeply lobed, mid-green leaves with silvery hairs below, which provide a sheen to the margins. The closely related *A. alpina*, Alpine lady's mantle, is a creeping woody rootstock and forms a dense carpet of rounded leaves with up to seven deep lobes with toothed margins. The tiny yellow-green flowers appear from early to late summer on stems only 12cm (5in) long. It grows to 12cm (5in) x 50cm (20in) and looks very pretty in a rock garden. *A. erythropoda* has grey to blue-green, strongly toothed leaves with deep lobes, dense hair on the leaf stalks and lime-green flowers. It grows to 20cm (8in) each way. These are all worth considering as alternatives. They are ideal for edging or filling gaps in paths and a combination of several species creates an interesting texture.

They need a moist, humus-rich soil in sun or partial shade but tolerate most soils. Divide in early spring or autumn; transplant self-sown seedlings. Dead-head to prevent excessive seeding.
Slugs and snails can damage young foliage. **MB**

Alchemilla mollis

LADY'S MANTLE

Type: hardy, deciduous perennial
Soil & situation: moist, humus-rich soil/full sun or partial shade
North American hardiness zone: 4–7
Height: 60cm (24in)
Spread: 80cm (32in)
Grow for: excellent ground cover making it very useful for the front of the border; the prettiest sight after rainfall; AGM

Left: Alchemilla conjuncta

Alchemilla mollis

I have a circle of this perennial outside my front door. In summer, after heavy rain, when everything is soggy, it cheers me up. Droplets of water rest and move like beads of mercury on its pale green, pleated leaves with one large drop securely held at the base of each leaf. The masses of frothy, greenish-yellow flowers appear in summer lasting well into autumn. They are carried on long stems, which topple over the foliage like boiling lemon curd.

If you remove the spent flowerheads before seed is set you will save yourself hours of weeding. The seed germinates readily and will grow in every crevice of the garden. Remove all of the foliage at the same time cutting it close to the ground. Water and feed with a liquid tomato fertilizer, then sit back and watch a second batch of new leaves unfurl.

This is a good ground-covering plant for impoverished soil and is drought tolerant. Propagation is by seed sown fresh or, where it has self-sown, lift and transplant the young plants in the spring. Large clumps may be divided in late autumn or early spring. The flowers are excellent for use in flower arranging. **JC**

Bunny adds:
This adaptable plant may prefer moist, humus-rich soil, but as John says it is also great for impoverished soil and is drought-tolerant. Basically it grows anywhere! Dead-head the flowers to encourage further flushes during the summer.

Mahonia japonica

Type: hardy evergreen shrub
Soil & situation: any well-drained soil/light sun to heavy shade
Hardiness zone: 7–8
Height & spread: may reach 1–2m (3–6½ft) all round
Grow for: glossy, dark green, distinctive evergreen with scented yellow flowers in the depths of winter; occasional blue-black berries; AGM

All the mahonias are good plants, with their fresh, spiky, usually glossy foliage making them look like a holly on steroids, and their cheerful yellow racemes of flowers in mid-winter giving off gorgeous lily-of-the-valley-like perfume. I love the way they perfume my front drive for weeks on end. *M. aquifolium* is a near contender for my favourite as it bears edible blue-black berries more reliably and more prolifically, giving it the name Oregon grape – they make a very tasty jelly.

Originally thought to belong to the genus *Berberis*, the 75 or so species of mahonia are natives of North America and the Far East, and do not have spiny stems like berberis. They are named after Bernard MacMahon, an early American botanist. *M. japonica* is a species but has often been confused with the rarer, similar *M. bealei* and also with many hybrids such as *M. bealei* x *napaulensis*; it makes very little difference which of these you end up with as they are all so similar and delightful. In other words if you can scarcely tell them apart it don't much matter!

As long as the soil is well drained they are happy, even on chalk, but they are not so keen in full sun, really doing best under deciduous trees, which give shelter to their winter flowers. They can be cut back in late spring if getting old and leggy. As this is a species you can sow the seed at just about anytime, take half-ripe cuttings in mid-summer or layers almost anytime. They are usually problem free. **BF**

Allium cepa

Allium cepa

JAPANESE ONION

Type: hardy, biennial, bulbous vegetable
Soil & situation: rich soil with plentiful moisture/full sun, no shade
North American hardiness zone: 5–8
Height: vertical leaves up to knee height
Spread: none, but sow at least 5cm (2in) apart
Grow for: one of the earliest onion crops

I find this an extremely valuable crop, as it ripens weeks before either sets or spring-sown seed, just when the stored onions have run out and the bought ones are at their most expensive. Japanese onions do not store well themselves, so should be used up first.

Introduced from Japan, these have almost totally replaced traditional autumn-sown onion varieties. In the East it is said that when Satan left the garden of Eden onions sprang from where his right foot stepped and garlic from his left.

Plant in firm, potash-rich soil in full sun with wide spacing. Must be sown in situ in late summer. Give cloche covers in very hard winters, and do not transplant. Slugs love these young onions, so I mix in the seed of Buffalo onion, which they prefer, leaving Japanese sorts relatively untouched. **BF**

Allium hollandicum 'Purple Sensation'

Type: hardy, bulbous perennial
Soil & situation: fertile but well-drained soil/ full sun
North American hardiness zone: 4–10
Height: up to 1m (3ft) high
Spread: 7.5cm (3in)
Grow for: dramatic, deep violet 8cm (3½in) spheres on tall green wands in mid-summer, followed by attractive dried heads, which persist well into the winter; AGM

This is another plant with a name change – it was formerly known as *A. flatuense*. I always associate it with the Chelsea Flower Show, where large quantities of them are regularly produced for the occasion. They are breathtaking when they arrive, massed together in the van, with their beautifully dramatic, globular flowers on top of the tall, leafless stems. It is, of course, a luxury to be able to position the flowering plant, threading them through other plants and see the planting being 'lifted' as you work with them. In 'real' gardens they work pretty much the same, except of course, you have to imagine how they will look the following summer. Also as the flowers start to emerge, the silvery-tinted foliage at the base withers, so the ideal is to conceal it with low planting that is not too dense to overly shade it. Thankfully, these plants do not smell too onion-like, because they make an amazing cut flower.

Plant the bulbs about 10cm (4in) deep in the autumn. They will self-seed and spread happily on some soils. On others, like mine, I tend to bulk up the numbers with new bulbs when they start to look thin. Alternatively, for the perfectionist with time, you can use them as bedding, lifting them and drying them off once they are past their best, ready for replanting the following autumn. **BG**

Allium hollandicum 'Purple Sensation'

Allium schoenoprasum
CHIVES

Type: herbaceous, clump-forming, perennial vegetable
Soil & situation: any soil with plentiful moisture/full sun to light shade
North American hardiness zone: 3–9
Height & spread: up to 45cm (18in) in rich soil; less in poor soil
Grow for: good edging plant, beautiful purple flowers, edible

There are few plants that make a quicker or neater edging for a vegetable bed. Chives are very beautiful in flower, which benefits many insects; they are also indispensable in soups, stews and salads, especially when egg is an ingredient, and as a garnish. Incidentally, it is more commonly grown in continental Europe than in the USA.

Chives are remarkably adaptable, but for the best results give them a rich, moist soil with plenty of sun. Dead-heading will prevent self-seeding and encourage more new leaves to appear. Propagate by sowing seed or by dividing clumps in spring. At almost any time it can be forced under cover for an earlier crop. Chives are prone to the same diseases as other alliums, especially rusts and moulds (see under Pest and Diseases, page 404). Dig up and burn infected plants and then start with new stock. **BF**

Allium schoenoprasum

Alnus cordata

Alnus cordata
ITALIAN ALDER

Type: hardy, deciduous tree
Soil & situation: fertile, well-drained soil/full sun
North American hardiness zone: 5–7
Height: 25m (80ft)
Spread: 7m (23ft)
Grow for: an attractive fast-growing tree for shelter; AGM

Of the three alders commonly grown this is the one I would consider attractive. The others, *Alnus glutinosa* (common English alder) and *A. incana* (grey alder) are dull but useful for windbreaks and planting in wet sites. *A. cordata* takes its common name from the fact that its timber was used for the piles that still keep Venice afloat. It grows well along river banks and close to water but unlike the other species it tolerates a dry soil. A fast-growing tree, it makes an excellent shelter belt.

The small, oval, finely toothed leaves are a bright, glossy green. Pendent, brown-yellow, male catkins 7.5cm (3in) long appear before the leaves in late winter and early spring. The cones are green, 3cm (1in) long, egg-shaped and occur in groups of three in summer. By winter they have turned black. Alders are the only broad-leafed trees to produce conifer-like cones.

Pruning is necessary only to maintain the tree's shape. Cutting should be completed by mid-winter before the sap starts to flow. Propagation is by fresh seed or rooting hardwood cuttings in early winter. **JC**

Aloe vera

Aloe vera

Type: long-lived perennial but tender succulent
Soil & situation: well-drained compost/moist in summer, dry in winter/greenhouse, conservatory or windowsill/full sun, no shade
North American hardiness zone: 10–11
Height & spread: in a big pot 60cm–1m (2–3ft)
Grow for: a tough survivor with attractive leaves year round; the rare flower is interesting and impressive; AGM

Aloe is a superb survivor for that sunny windowsill where it will tolerate neglect and yet always be architecturally attractive. Its thorn-free, grey-green, starfish-like appearance makes it interesting in an exotic, tropical sort of way. And, of course, *Aloe vera* is a fantastic plant for medicinal purposes; its soothing sap can be applied to burns, rashes and skin eruptions.

It is native to South America, though its name comes from Arabic. It has been introduced to many countries for its bitter sap, which was exported as a dried brown resin for medicinal use (and for putting on babies' thumbs to discourage sucking).

The site must be frost free, in full sun. Cut leaves for use, leaving a big stump remaining to allow withering and prevent rotting off. The easiest way to propagate is by the frequently found offsets, which can be detached to make new plants. It can also be grown from seed, but with difficulty. Do not let its compost become waterlogged, especially not in winter. **BF**

Aloysia triphylla (syn. *Lippia citriodora*)
LEMON VERBENA

Type: frost-hardy, deciduous perennial, shrubby but semi-herbaceous in habit
Soil & situation: well-drained soil outdoors or moist compost indoors/full sun outdoors but will tolerate some shade indoors/in a pot give plenty of moisture when in growth
North American hardiness zone: 8–11
Height & spread: forms a clump up to 2m x 1m (6½ft x 3ft)
Grow for: scented foliage throughout spring, summer and autumn; scented flowers in summer; AGM

I just love the true lemon sherbet perfume this plant carries – it is said that a leaf folded away in a book still smells decades later! I like to use small amounts in cookery and I'm always pulling off leaves and sniffing them. It can also be used in potpourris or to make teas and tisanes. It is a native of South America, where more than 30 species exist. *Aloysia triphylla* is the only one that can survive outdoors in more temperate climates.

It is a wonderful plant for a warm site or greenhouse, conservatory or windowsill. Ideally plant in a well-drained soil with some light cover against hard frosts; it will then overwinter and come again in spring, much like many fuchsias. However, it may be lost in hard winters, so take cuttings as back up, either in autumn with heat or in spring once growth commences. It can also be grown from seed. A bit prone to aphids and red spider mites when pot-grown undercover, but these disappear if it is planted out for summer or when it is permanently outdoors. **BF**

Aloysia triphylla

Amaranthus caudatus 'Fat Spike'

Amaranthus caudatus 'Fat Spike'

LOVE-LIES-BLEEDING OR TASSEL FLOWER

Type: hardy annual
Soil & situation: infertile, moist soil/full sun
North American hardiness zone: annual
Height: 90cm (36in)
Spread: 45cm (18in)
Grow for: a bushy plant with upright spikes of purple-red flowers; very useful for summer bedding

The traditional love-lies-bleeding *Amaranthus caudatus*, with its long, red or yellow tassels of flower is a great plant for summer bedding. This variety is different and eye-catching. The spikes are upright but every bit as showy.

The 15cm (6in) long, light green leaves on pale yellow-green stems form a bushy plant. The small, densely packed, dark purplish-red flowers, produced during summer and autumn, are held in an upright, spike-like cyme 30–45cm (12–18in) long on a branched stalk. The spike of flowers is 7cm (2¾in) thick at the base tapering to 2cm (¾in) at the tip. It is particularly useful for filling gaps in the border or as a centre dot plant to give height in a bedding scheme. The branched spike is excellent fresh or dried in a flower arrangement.

It will flower better when grown in a poor soil with no added fertilizer. Watering in summer will extend the flowering period. Propagation is by seed sown in a heated propagator in mid-spring. It may also be sown directly into the soil where it is to flower in late spring. Thin the seedlings to 45cm (18in) apart. **JC**

Amelanchier 'Ballerina'

SNOWY MESPILUS, JUNEBERRY

Type: hardy, deciduous tree
Soil & situation: moisture-retentive but not waterlogged, acid soil/sun or partial shade
North American hardiness zone: 5–8
Height: 6m (20ft)
Spread: 7m (23ft)
Grow for: attractive flowers, edible fruit and brightly coloured autumn foliage; AGM

If I had to decide on only one tree for my garden *Amelanchier* 'Ballerina' would be in a short shortlist. It provides interest for most of the year with flower, fruit and leaf colour. The star-shaped, white flowers appear in early spring forming long arching racemes just before, or at the same time as the new, young foliage. Opening a bronze-green the foliage turns a glossy mid-green in summer. In autumn it again changes to deep red-purple lasting until the first hard frost.

The edible fruit is sweet and juicy, red at first, ripening to a dark blue-black. You have to be quick to beat the birds or else net the tree. *A.* 'Ballerina' is a hybrid of *A. laevis*, an open-headed spreading tree which our American cousins call the Allegheny service-berry.

Propagation is by semi-ripe cuttings in summer. Pruning is necessary only to keep a tidy shape. Remove crossing branches in late winter when they are still dormant. This tree is recorded as being prone to fire blight disease, but I have never met anyone who has experienced the problem. Of more importance is its dislike for alkaline soil. **JC**

Amelanchier 'Ballerina'

Ameleanchier lamarckii

Amelanchier lamarckii

Type: hardy, deciduous large shrub or small tree
Soil & situation: moist, rich, well-drained, acid soil/sun or partial shade
North American hardiness zone: 3–7
Height: 10m (33ft)
Spread: 12m (40ft)
Grow for: young leaves, flowers and autumn colour; AGM

Act I begins in spring when the pure white flowers, like a mass of snowflakes, appear in loose open clusters at the same time as the coppery-pink, silky young leaves are emerging. It is a truly magnificent sight, particularly when you consider this plant is not a fancy prima donna but a tough, durable, trouble-free plant that is happy to put on a show anywhere, from cities and industrial sites to soft suburban gardens. As if exhausted by the effort it sits quietly through the summer then emerges again in autumn awash in rich red and orange; its performance in shade where yellow is the dominant colour is comparatively muted. It is rather promiscuous and hybridizes freely with other species, producing sweet black fruits that are devoured by birds. It has been naturalized in the UK for over a century and was once cultivated for its fruit in cottage gardens of Holland and northwest Germany. It is naturalized there too and known as the 'currant tree', as the fruits were dried and used as currants or stewed and made into jam.

It needs moist, well-drained, acid soil in sun or partial shade but tolerates poorer conditions. Pruning is only necessary to keep it within its allotted space. It can be grown as a single or multi-stemmed tree; prune accordingly. Propagate from fresh seed or by semi-ripe cuttings in summer, or by layering. If sowing is delayed it may become dormant and take two years to germinate. **MB**

Amsonia tabernaemontana var. *salicifolia*
BLUE STAR

Type: hardy, herbaceous perennial
Soil & situation: any fertile soil/sun
North American hardiness zone: 3–9
Height: 60cm (24in)
Spread: 40cm (16in)
Grow for: pale blue flowers from mid-spring to mid-summer

This herbaceous gem produces a clump of dark green, narrow-leaved stems that are tar-black towards the tip with slightly drooping, rounded flowerheads. The powder-blue petals are slate-blue below but to appreciate their fine qualities you have to stoop down low! The species, from eastern North America, has broader leaves and is more familiar in gardens than *A. t.* var. *salicifolia*; sadly neither is particularly common. A relative, *Amsonia orientalis* from northeast Greece and northwest Turkey, struggles further still, ironically it is freely available in commerce – and almost extinct in the wild!

The reasons for growing it are for its fascinating colour combination and the interminably long rambling name; it seems overblown for something so subdued!

Here's something about its origin. *Amsonia* was named for Dr Charles Amson, an 18th century-physician from Virginia, USA. *Tabernaemontana* was named for Jakob Theodor von Bergzabern, physician to the Count of Palatine in Heidelberg, West Germany who Latinized his name to Tabernaemontanus! He wrote a herbal called *Neu Kreuterbuch* (1588–91) and in 1590, published the illustrations separately using over 1,500 woodcuts copied from illustrations in other books! These were later acquired by a London printer from his colleague in Frankfurt and were used to illustrate John Gerard's 16th-century *Herball*, one of the most famous 'Old English' writings on medicinal plants.

Amsonia tabernaemontana var. *salicifolia*

A. t. var. *salicifolia* (meaning 'willow leaved') needs moist, well-drained, fertile soil in full sun; it tolerates some drought. Cut back dead foliage, feed with general fertilizer and mulch in spring. Divide in autumn or spring; take basal or softwood cuttings in early summer. **MB**

Ananas sativus
PINEAPPLE

Type: short-lived, very tender, herbaceous perennial
Soil & situation: well-drained compost/warmth/full sun, no shade
North American hardiness zone: 10–11
Height & spread: up to 1m (3ft) each way in a big pot; in a small pot it will survive and throw a pineapple chunk!
Grow for: good year-round indoor foliage plant; staggering red flowerhead with violet petals; superb fruit

Although it takes three years to flower and fruit from a rooted crown, it is worth the wait. Few tasks give as much sense of achievement, or taste so divine, as growing then eating your own pineapple! In a big pot kept in a warm greenhouse or conservatory you can expect to produce a fruit weighing up to 3–4kg (8lb) and tasting better than any you have ever bought.

A native of the New World, first seen by Europeans in 1493, pineapple took the Old World by storm. It was first successfully grown in Britain from the beginning of 18th century and is now grown in all warm countries. Eat it as the last of all fruits at the table as the flavour makes those coming after seem insipid.

It needs warmth and a well-drained compost, but keep it moist during summer heat and dryish for the rest of the year. After fruiting, remove and pot up sideshoots to replace old plants; bottom heat greatly improves rooting, growing and fruiting performance. Do not water when ripening. Never grow from seed; instead root the crown from healthy fruit or use offsets from existing plants. Pineapples are prone to red spider mite, scale and mealy bug but can be kept clean with soapy sprays. Beware – the leaves have small, sharp thorns. especially near the tips. **BF**

Ananas sativus

Andromeda polifolia
BOG ROSEMARY, MARSH ANDROMEDA

Type: hardy, low-growing, evergreen shrub
Soil & situation: moist, humus-rich, acid soil/sun or partial shade
North American hardiness zone: 2–6
Height: 40cm (16in)
Spread: 60cm (24in)
Grow for: dainty flowers in late spring or early summer

In the UK this is a native of squelchy sphagnum peat bogs in central England, Wales and Scotland, but rather than tramping through bogs where the water always goes over your wellies, you may prefer to grow it in the comfort of your own garden. It's a low-growing, wiry-stemmed, evergreen shrub and the clusters of slender, glaucous green foliage suit the name bog rosemary perfectly. The pretty white flowers in late spring are enchanting, like dainty lanterns suffused with a soft pink blush. They are ideal for moist pockets in rock or woodland gardens and for the margins by streams

Andromeda polifolia

and ponds. Andromeda was the mythological daughter of Cepheus and Cassiope, who was chained to a rock as an offering to a sea monster but was rescued by Perseus. *Polifolia* means grey-leaved. The first name was given after Carl Linnaeus, who assigned the plant its Latin name, had an amusing experience while discovering the plant – but I can't find out the secret!

Forms of *Andromeda polifolia* include 'Alba', which has a straggly habit, glaucous foliage and pure white flowers; 'Microphylla' with broad leaves and bright pink flowers; and the compact 'Nikko'.

Andromeda needs moist, acid, peaty soil in full sun or partial shade. Protect from scorching summer sun. Mulch annually in spring with leafmould. It succeeds better in the ground, with 3–5cm (1–2in) of sphagnum moss around to act as a sponge. To propagate, sow seed in spring or root softwood cuttings in early to mid-summer. Pot suckers or rooted layers in autumn. **MB**

Anemone blanda

Type: hardy tuberous perennial
Soil & situation: free-draining soil, preferably quite moist and humus-rich/sun or partial shade/after flowering copes well with dry conditions for summer dormancy
North American hardiness zone: 4–8
Height & spread: 15cm (6in)
Grow for: beautiful blue, mauve, white or pink solitary flowers from late winter to spring; will quickly form bright carpets of colour in areas with light, alkaline soil; will naturalize in turf; AGM

These delightful, early spring-flowering plants are so easy to grow, and quickly form satisfying, large swathes of colour at a bleak time of year. They are also ideal for colonizing difficult, dry shade. After the flowers die off the whole plant disappears without trace, so ferns, foxgloves and other woodland plants can spread out and fill in the spaces.

If your soil is not too rich but is poor, limy and light, these vigorous plants are well worth establishing in the turf. They appear well before the grass starts to grow and look their best growing in extravagant, colourful drifts. There are many different cultivars. A particularly good white one is 'White Splendour', a good strong grower with punchy, large flowers.

There is not a lot that needs doing to these plants. They can be divided up when they become overcrowded and this should be done in summer when the tubers are dormant. **BG**

Matt adds:
The iridescent pink and blue forms make excellent companion plants for shrubs with grey or silver foliage like lavender and sage. The multi-petalled flowers open only in the sun.

Among the other varieties I would recommend, 'Ingramii' is a sumptuous deep violet-blue, with buttermilk stamens. This is the darkest flowered form, first found on Mount Parnassus in southern Greece. *A. blanda* var. *rosea* is pale pink to purple with darker foliage. 'Radar' has intense magenta flowers with a contrasting magenta centre.

Anemone blanda

Anemone coronaria Saint Brigid Group

Anemone coronaria Saint Brigid Group

Type: hardy, tuberous perennial
Soil & situation: light, gritty, well-drained soil/full sun
North American hardiness zone: 8–10
Height: 30cm (12in)
Spread: 15cm (6in)
Grow for: pretty flowers in a variety of rich, velvety colours in spring or summer

This plant more than any other reminds me of my youth. Flower sellers used to sit outside the City Hall in Belfast and for 6 old pence (2.5 new pence or about 0.04 euro) you could bring your mother home a mixed bunch of 'Saint Brigid' flowers.

The crinkly foliage looks like parsley and the flowers are carried on long, bare stems. The almost flat flowers have a double layer of petals and are available in deep, velvety shades of red, violet, blue and white with paler zones and a centre 'button' of dark stamens. Anemone De Caen Group are similar but with single flowers. The hard, dark, knobbly tubers should be soaked overnight in water to soften the skin and speed up growth. They can be planted at most times of the year, spring being favoured in colder areas when they will flower in summer. Autumn-planted tubers will flower in early spring. Covering the buds with glass will protect them from the worst of the weather and prevent rain splashing mud onto the flowers. In heavy, wet soil they should be lifted after the foliage has died down and stored in sand. **JC**

Monstera deliciosa

SWISS-CHEESE PLANT

Type: tender, perennial, evergreen climber
Soil & situation: any compost/full sun to heavy shade
Hardiness zone: 10–11
Height & spread: to several hundred feet if you let it...
Grow for: enormous, uniquely holey, glossy leaves; amazing flowers and edible fruits. This is one of the most enduring houseplants, at its best at any time of year.

These are the most abused plants in the world, found in every dark corridor and grim office, every dingy net-curtained alcove and sitting in waiting rooms with their pot full of cigarette butts. Yet they survive, despite the vicissitudes of human nurture being less reliable than the tropical rains. However if you take one of these poor abusees and give it a big tub of good, moist compost and put it in the sun in a frost-free place you get the most amazing, very large, white, arum-like flowers. The flowers die and about a year later the central spathe ripens to become a ceriman. The fruit tastes like a pineapple banana on a stick. It is only edible when fully ripe, when the fruit swells, shedding its skin in little thick platelets, leaving the engorged flesh adhering to the central support – delicious. These can even be hardened off and used for summer bedding – it looked impressive to have a few of these interspersed with sugar cane here in Norfolk!

The Swiss-cheese plant is known for its leaf holes resembling that country's cheese. The Latin name is possibly from *monstrifer* for monster bearing, but that's doubtful. However, the *deliciosa* is for the fruit, which is indeed delicious and enjoyed in many countries. The plant comes from Central America where it climbs tropical trees and covers the rainforest floor like ivy, and in such places it is indeed monstrous.

Ideally this likes a large root run in moist, humus-rich soil in a conservatory or frost-free greenhouse in full sun. It can go out on the patio in summer. Be careful not to sunburn a plant by moving it from cool shade indoors into windswept, full sun; harden it off first. It can be hacked into bits and every chunk with a leaf, and especially those with roots already, will root; it can also be grown from seed with some warmth. Very rarely suffering from any problems, these masochists just ask to be neglected and ignored, but don't let them – drag them into the light. **BF**

Anemone x *hybrida* 'Honorine Jobert'

Anemone x *hybrida* 'Honorine Jobert'

JAPANESE ANEMONE

Type: hardy, herbaceous perennial
Soil & situation: normal garden soil/prefers moist soil/dappled shade or part sun
North American hardiness zone: 4–8
Height: up to 1.2m (4ft) high
Spread: indefinite
Grow for: copious white flowers from summer to mid-autumn; AGM

This is an invaluable perennial. The vine-shaped leaves form handsome clumps, which come into growth relatively late on in spring. Later, single white flowers with golden stamens are produced on wiry stems, and these charming flowers look fresh and glowing throughout their fabulously long flowering period – most welcome at a time when things tend to look parched. You may wish to utilize the spare soil between the slowly-developing foliage in spring: tulips or alliums are ideal temporary fillers. I also find that it takes a few years for the clumps to fill out and have that fully-established air about them, but that might be because with me they are growing on 15cm (6in) of thin topsoil above hardcore, certainly not what the books recommend. Despite this, they give a magnificent show, without fail. They last long as cut flowers too – a real star. There are other good Japanese anemones in various shades of pink: *A. huphensis* 'September Charm' has soft pink flowers that are freely produced.

This indispensable plant can be left untouched for years; the only time you will probably have to divide it up is when friends are transfixed by it and beg a clump. If you want to propagate, root cuttings are the usual method or, if you can afford the stock, division. **BG**

Anemone nemorosa 'Robinsoniana'

WOOD ANEMONE

Type: hardy, rhizomatous perennial
Soil & situation: organic, rich, free-draining soil/sun or partial shade
North American hardiness zone: 4–8
Height: 15cm (6in)
Spread: 30cm (12in)
Grow for: mid-spring flowers; AGM

It's a pleasure to include a selection of one of my favourite 'native' plants. *Anemone nemorosa* is found throughout the UK carpeting deciduous woodlands before the trees are in leaf. Copy this at home by creating a jewel-spangled carpet under deciduous shrubs or trees or 'naturalizing' them in rough grass that doesn't need to be cut until mid-summer when the leaves die back. The flowers open only in the sun.

There's a host of desirable varieties. 'Royal Blue' is possibly the deepest blue with veronica-blue flowers. 'Robinsoniana' has large flowers of delicate wisteria-blue and deep green leaves. 'Bowles' Purple' has shiny, dark purple buds, paler than 'Allenii', darker than 'Robinsoniana', with a purple exterior. *A. nemorosa* has white flowers, sometimes with a delicate lilac or pink hue, which have the daintiness of snowflakes settled on a filigree of foilage. 'Leeds' Variety' is white with a purple-pink reverse, about 5cm (2in) in diameter. 'Alba Plena' originated before 1771 and has double flowers and a large central cluster of white 'petals'. For nature's aberrations, try 'Green Fingers' – the white flowers have a ruff of tiny green leaves in the centre, as they unfurl the petals become pale pink. 'Virescens' is surreal! Every anther, petal and style has become a finely cut leaflet; it looks like the 'Green Man' of legend. It flowers from early to late spring, survives in dry shade and is sometimes labelled 'Viridiflora'.

They grow in almost any soil or situation, preferring dappled shade and well-drained soil enriched with compost or leafmould. Soak the rhizomes overnight in cool water, before planting horizontally at a depth of 3–5cm (1–2in). They take time to settle and may not bloom well in the first year. Keep the area weed free, top dress in autumn with well-rotted organic matter and leave them undisturbed. Anemones seed freely but can be lifted and divided from late summer to autumn when the soil is warm, or after flowering in spring. **MB**

Anemone nemorosa 'Robinsoniana'

Anemone rivularis

Type: hardy, herbaceous perennial
Soil & situation: moist soil/sun or dappled shade
North American hardiness zone: 6–8
Height: 60cm (24in)
Spread: 30cm (12in)
Grow for: delightful flowers from early to late summer

This wondrous plant is native from Kashmir and northern India to Tibet and southwest China, and was introduced to the UK in 1840. Mention the name of this unspeakably beautiful plant and I go weak at the knees so let me sit down and describe it to you! They are dazzling, with pure, glossy white flowers about 3cm (1in) across, with steel-blue anthers; the same colour diffuses from the sepals over the back of the flower, which hovers on stiff stems in clusters of three to five above a mass of dark divided leaves.

Phew! I've made it, perhaps you can understand my predicament by looking at the picture. Plant several in a group for added impact or simply plant one and admire it endlessly!

As the name suggests, *rivularis* means growing by streams. This species tolerates most moist garden soils, and flourishes where they are humus-rich and beside water. Dig in plenty of well-rotted organic matter if necessary before planting, keep them moist throughout the year and water during drought. They flourish in conditions from full sun to dappled light, even tolerating shade.

Cut back the foliage when it dies down in autumn and mulch with a thick layer of well-rotted organic matter. Divide every few years to revitalize the plant and share the pleasure by giving pieces to friends! Propagate by sowing seed immediately when it ripens in summer or divide in late summer or early autumn after it dies down. **MB**

Anemone rivularis

Angelica gigas

Angelica gigas

Type: hardy biennial
Soil & situation: moist soil/partial shade
North American hardiness zone: 4–7
Height: 2m (6½ft)
Spread: 1.2m (4ft)
Grow for: sculptural form, interesting colour and unusual flowers from early to late summer

It may appear dramatic in the flower border but I wouldn't fancy meeting one on a dark night – it looks like the type of plant that would feature in a cheap Japanese horror movie from the 1950s! It bursts from the ground in a sinister fashion unfurling huge, bright green, deeply lobed leaves; everything else is deep plum-purple – the main stems, sideshoots and flowers. Extraordinary! The sheaths spilt open to reveal a dark compressed bloom that gradually unfolds to a typical domed flowerhead, pale beetroot in colour and up to 20cm (8in) wide.

Good in borders, naturalized or as an architectural specimen plant, it is a native of north China, Korea and Japan, mainly from damp woodland meadows. The great plantsman Dan Hinkley of Heronswood Nursery in the USA suggests planting it with bright yellows and golds, but those of us who are less ambitious should settle for a pale background or leave it lurking against dark backgrounds to surprise passers by. I'd love to have a small group spotlit to create a living nocturnal sculpture; one day, one day!

It needs deep, rich, moist soil in dappled shade or sunshine. It self-seeds, but not to the point of becoming a menace. Sow seed in containers in a cold frame as soon as ripe a few weeks after flowering, transplant while small as older plants resent disturbance; it may take two or more years to reach flowering size. It dies after flowering so plant seeds successionally for a regular supply of flowers. It is prone to slug damage. **MB**

Bunny adds:
This is a great plant visually, but can be awkward to grow well. It seems sometimes to do well and sometimes not, for no apparent reason, so is not that dependable.

Anthemis nobilis 'Treneague' (syn. *Chamaemelum nobile* 'Treneague')

CHAMOMILE

Type: hardy, herbaceous, semi-evergreen, prostrate perennial
Soil & situation: moist soil/full sun to light shade
North American hardiness zone: 6–9
Height & spread: prostrate, especially if walked on; an individual plant will eventually reach 25cm (10in) each way.
Grow for: excellent ground cover for small areas, for example a seat; gorgeous scent; occasional flowers can be used for tea

Other chamomiles (there are more than 80 species in the genus) are more use for medicinal or culinary purposes but this is the one for mixing into a lawn or putting in crazy paving, as it is a creeping prostrate plant, likes being trodden on and rarely flowers. The smell is divine and it is apparently included in the lawns around Buckingham Palace, so ought to be good enough for me!

Native to Britain, it has long been believed to be the 'plant physician' – chamomile is said to heal sickly plants brought near it, and it is still much used in herbal medicine. It also flavoured beer and was smoked before tobacco became available.

Chamomile likes full sun and sandy soil, which needs to be well watered in spring and early summer. Dead-heading is useful as it prevents self-seeding, which produces wrong forms. It must be kept well weeded and rolled if not regularly trodden, and clipped if it gets too straggly. The true sort cannot be grown from seed, it must be propagated by division in spring. It's hard to keep a large area such as a chamomile lawn weed-free as grasses, for instance, creep in. **BF**

Anthemis nobilis 'Treneague'

Anthemis punctata subsp. *cupaniana*

Anthemis punctata subsp. *cupaniana*

DOG FENNEL

Type: frost-hardy, evergreen perennial
Soil & situation: free-draining soils/low or moderate fertility/almost neutral or alkaline/sunny position
North American hardiness zone: 6–9
Height: 30cm (12in)
Spread: 90cm (36in)
Grow for: easy, fast-growing, evergreen ground cover; aromatic, mounded, finely cut leaves; masses of long-lasting, simple, white daisy-like flowers with tight, yellow centres in early summer; AGM

If you are looking for rapid-to-establish, charming ground cover that has a bumper flowering period and evergreen foliage, you may well find this is the one that fits the bill. The pretty flowers are held well above the silver-grey foliage on slender stalks. In winter the foliage is less silver, more grey-green. In one garden, my client did not share my passion for it as she found it swamped too many other plants. As everything was planted in one fell swoop, the anthemis was in overdrive before the other plants had got off the starting blocks. If you pop it into established plantings it is easier to manicure if necessary. I am still a big fan however, and its rampant nature is easy to keep in check with a sharp snip from the secateurs. The flowers, apparently, can be preserved using glycerine.

To keep this plant flowering for even longer periods, cut off the dead heads. If it becomes straggly, trim back the foliage so as to get a more manicured, compact plant.

Being fast-growing, it is also short-lived, often having exhausted itself from over-exertion. Cuttings where the stems root themselves into the soil are easy to establish: I usually do this *in situ*, in spring. Be prepared to give them the odd drink if it is too warm and they look as if they may shrivel. **BG**

Anthemis tinctoria 'Sauce Hollandaise'

YELLOW CHAMOMILE, DYERS' CHAMOMILE

Type: hardy, evergreen perennial
Soil & situation: range of situations/sharp drainage/sunshine
North American hardiness zone: 3–7
Height: to 60cm (24in)
Spread: 40–60cm (16–24in)
Grow for: many pale, lemon-cream flowers which fade to creamy-white from late spring to autumn; attractive finely cut dark green foliage

Anthemis tinctoria is the traditionally used 'dyers' chamomile', also sometimes known as yellow chamomile, the golden marguerite and the ox-eye chamomile. It is a clump-forming perennial, which is naturalized in the UK. It has pungent, bright golden to cream flowers, the foliage is mid-green on top with a greyer green below. Its capacity to compete with the grasses and its long flowering season make it a wonderfully useful plant for growing in flowering meadows.

The variety *A. t.* 'Sauce Hollandaise' is far less vigorous but certainly not timid either. It is often included in mixed or herbaceous borders for its ability to produce copious quantities of flowers of a soft, subtle colour. It makes a superb container plant, where you can see the combination of good foliage and simple, but charming flowers shown off to their full advantage. There are other great forms of *A. tinctoria*, such as 'E.C. Buxton', another strong favourite of mine, with exquisite-coloured, light lemon flowers and mid-green leaves.

Plant care is as for *Anthemis punctata* subsp. *cupaniana* (see previous entry). **BG**

Anthemis tinctoria 'Sauce Hollandaise'

Anthriscus cerefolium
CHERVIL

Type: hardy annual salad herb
Soil & situation: almost any soil, kept moist but not waterlogged/full sun in winter, shade in summer
North American hardiness zone: annual
Height: to 1m (3ft) in good soil when flowering
Spread: 15cm (6in) in good soil
Grow for: incredibly useful culinary herb, with cloche or cover available for 52 weeks of the year

Closely related to the wild cow parsley, chervil has wonderful green leaves with a jagged ferny appearance; if grown as a singleton it can get quite big, but when grown for culinary use it's normally crowded into rows. The sweet, parsley-like flavour has a hint of aniseed and I use chervil in almost every savoury dish I cook – and every salad. It is an essential component of a good bouquet garni and has been in widespread use since Roman times, if not earlier.

A native of Europe and Asia, *Anthriscus cerefolium* is one of 20 species. It is closely related to parsley, but has a sweeter flavour. There is also a rare turnip-rooted variety, which I find easy to grow if I can get the damn seed to germinate! Be warned.

A rich soil is ideal but not essential; too dry a site will cause a miserable red-yellow appearance and rapid bolting, especially in full sun. In winter chervil can be grown under cover, but needs a sunny spot. It can be cut back hard to prevent flowering and also to get a new crop of leaves, if the soil is kept moist. Sow once or twice a month from spring to late summer outdoors, or any time except mid-winter under cover.

Chervil makes poor growth if parched by hot sun or dry soil, and it suffers from carrot root fly in open ground, so grow under horticultural fleece or cloches. **BF**

Anthriscus cerefolium

Antirrhinum majus Tahiti Series

Antirrhinum majus Tahiti Series
SNAPDRAGON

Type: hardy, short-lived perennial
Soil & situation: fertile, well-drained soil/full sun
North American hardiness zone: 9–11
Height: 20cm (8in)
Spread: 15–30cm (6–12in)
Grow for: summer bedding display

As a child, were you shown how to gently squeeze the sides of the flower with finger and thumb to make its mouth open? Just occasionally I still do.

The 8cm (3½in) long, lance-shaped, glossy, deep green leaves are carried up the branched, stiff stems. The upright racemes of slightly fragrant flowers are produced in summer and autumn. They have two lips with rounded upper and lower lobes in pink, orange, white and red. The variety *Antirrhinum nanum* 'Tequila Sunrise' produces flowers in a range of bright colours all with bronze leaves. The Rocket Series flowers at 1.2m (4ft) and makes excellent cut flowers.

Dead-heading the spent flowers extends the period of flowering. If there is a particular colour you like, leave the plant in the ground. Protect it from winter wet and cold winds with horticultural fleece and it will not only flower next year but it will be earlier.

Sow seed in early spring and harden off in a cold frame before planting out. Autumn sowings can be overwintered and planted out after all risk of frost is over for an early display of flower. The foliage is rust resistant, which is a feature of modern varieties. In the past whole bedding schemes were disfigured by an attack of rust disease. **JC**

Arachis hypogaea

Aquilegia canadensis

Plant of the Week (see page 87)

Arachis hypogaea

GROUNDNUT, PEANUT

Type: tender annual vegetable crop
Soil & situation: almost any loose soil/moist when young/warm position in full sun
North American hardiness zone: annual
Height & spread: can form a clump about 30cm (12in) all round, larger in right conditions
Grow for: great botanical interest; pretty clover-like leaves and yellow flowers; edible nut

Not only are peanuts a useful crop, but they are also one of the prettiest, and as they are legumes they enrich the soil. Most importantly they are one of the few plants that can catch a young person's interest; their unique habit of burying the flowerhead after blooming to swell their seeds underground makes them a good introduction to gardening, even if the yields are small.

A native of South America but now widespread in all warm countries, peanut causes allergic reactions, especially if old and mouldy, in many people. *Arachis* comes from an old Greek word for plant and *hypogaea* means underground.

Start off peanuts in small pots, then plant them out in loose border soil or in very big wide trays or boxes in a greenhouse or conservatory, or possibly in a very warm sheltered garden after the last frost. In a pot the seedhead can't be buried by the plants, so border soil is best if you want to harvest the nuts. Sow in early spring in pots in the warmth. No problems other than cold (and do not try sowing roasted or salted nuts, as only the fresh ones in their husks will be able to grow).

BF

Aralia elata 'Aureovariegata'

JAPANESE ANGELICA TREE

Type: hardy, deciduous tree
Soil & situation: fertile, moist, humus-rich soil/light shade
North American hardiness zone: 4–9
Height & spread: 5m (16ft)
Grow for: dramatic form and foliage, and billowing heads of small flowers

My tree has a bad habit of drawing my blood on its spiny stems, but that is a small price to pay for its bold architectural shape of open, spreading branches and big leaves.

The very spiny stems bear large – 1.2m (4ft) long – two-pinnate leaves made up of as many as 70 leaflets. The mid-green foliage is margined golden-yellow fading to cream as the leaves age. The tiny, white flowers appear in late summer and autumn in large, spreading, open umbels up to 60cm (24in) long and are followed by small, round, black fruit.

This aralia needs a bit of space. It will flourish if sited in woodland or beside a stream or pond. Provide shelter from strong winds, which tend to shred the large leaves. Where plants are growing strongly feed with a high-potash fertilizer in early autumn to firm up the shoots before the winter frosts. Prune in late winter to remove crossing branches. Occasionally it will produce suckers with all green leaves. Dig them out by the root before they become large and a nuisance. Propagation is by grafting onto a rootstock of the green-leafed *Aralia elata.* **JC**

Aralia elata 'Aureovariegata'

Araujia sericifera (syn. *Physianthus albens*)
CRUEL PLANT

Type: perennial, half-hardy to tender, semi-evergreen, twining climber
Soil & situation: well-drained, humus-rich soil, not limy/full sun/moist all summer
North American hardiness zone: 10–11
Height & spread: to 6–7m (20–23ft)
Grow for: very long flowering period; gorgeously scented chalice- to salver-shaped, usually white, moth-catching flowers; attractive pear-sized, pear-shaped, green seedpods burst to release silky stranded seeds

I love this cruel plant, also sometimes wrongly known as the silk vine, as it has good foliage and the most wonderful perfume, one of the strongest. Although it was thought to be tender I have grown it for many years on a warm wall where it has withstood a fair few hard frosts. The habit of trapping moths by their tongues and holding them until late morning seems cruel, but ensures pollination and the moths seem to come to no actual harm. A fascinating bit of natural history in action.

Araujia comes from Brazil and the Argentines, and is one of a group of tender climbers to which it is worth giving hothouse treatment. However, grown from seed you can select far hardier strains that can endure outdoors or grace a conservatory year round.

It prefers loamy, peaty soils and some frost protection in exceptionally hard winters. Remove dead wood and seedpods, and if grown in pots nip out tips in spring and early summer to keep bushy. Sow in early spring, grow on under cover and plant out several seedlings the following year in late spring; hardy ones will survive if lucky or grow in a big pot under cover. *Araujia* suffers no common problems other than disliking cold winters. **BF**

Araujia sericifera

Arbutus unedo 'Elfin King'

Arbutus unedo 'Elfin King'
STRAWBERRY TREE

Type: hardy, evergreen tree
Soil & situation: fertile, humus-rich, well-drained soil/full sun
North American hardiness zone: 7–9
Height: 2m (6½ft)
Spread: 1.5m (5ft)
Grow for: ornamental bark; glossy foliage; clusters of flowers; strawberry-like, red fruit

A most unusual tree and a favourite of mine. The fruit is remarkably like a strawberry and is edible. A translation of *unedo* is 'I eat only one' and this is probably true, since they are vile tasting.

Even as a young plant *Arbutus unedo* 'Elfin King' flowers and fruits well. It forms a gnarled, compact, bushy tree with coarse, shredding, red-brown bark and 10cm (4in) long, glossy, mid-green, slightly toothed leaves. The urn-shaped, lily-of-the-valley-like flowers are white with a hint of pink. They hang in clusters during autumn at the same time as the fruit of the previous year's flowers ripen. The 'strawberries' are red with warty, rough skin.

A. unedo is the hardiest of the species and will tolerate most conditions but needs protection from cold winds. It grows well in coastal areas, being native to Southwest Ireland and the Mediterranean coast.

Although ericaceous it will tolerate an alkaline soil. As it dislikes being transplanted when large, plant in its permanent position as a young plant with shelter from frost for the first season. Pruning is best carried out in late winter but is seldom necessary. Propagation is by seed sown in autumn and over-wintered in a cold frame. Pot the seedlings as soon as they are large enough. Semi-ripe cuttings are easy to root in late summer with bottom heat. **JC**

Arisaema sikokianum
Plant of the Week (see page 185)

Arisarum proboscideum
MOUSE PLANT

Type: hardy, herbaceous perennial
Soil & situation: moist, organic soil/dappled shade
North American hardiness zone: 7–9
Height: 15cm (6in)
Spread: 30cm (12in) or more
Grow for: novelty flowers from early to late spring

Excuses for buying plants. Number one, 'I've bought this for the children!' As you can imagine, it just didn't work. OK, so I bought this for me and the children are interested honest! Roy Lancaster first introduced me to this fun-packed plant – rummage among the mats of arrow-shaped leaves and you'll find lots of long thin 'tails' often with a twist at the end! Dig further and you'll see they're attached to the pretty dark brown 'mice' with pure white and chocolate stripes at the base. It looks just as if hundreds of tiny rodents have dived into the foliage to take cover! I've just been into the garden and dissected a flower. At the top of the spadix is a lump of tissue that looks exactly like a fungus. It's there to attract fungus gnats that live in moist, organic-rich soil, where the plant likes to grow. They see the 'fungus', lay their eggs on and it's pollinated! Fantastic!

In the wild it is found in moist, shaded woodland, particularly in marshy areas under cork oaks in southwest Spain and central and southern Italy. It is ideal for the woodland or rock garden where it establishes large colonies. Plant 8cm (3½in) deep in organic-rich, moist soil in partial shade. If necessary, dig in plenty of well-rotted organic matter before planting; mulch in autumn to protect over winter. Sow seed from the greenish berries in spring; divide from autumn to spring. **MB**

Arisarum proboscideum

Aronia x *prunifolia* 'Viking'
CHOKEBERRY

Type: hardy, deciduous shrub
Soil & situation: any soil/full sun or part shade/moist site but not waterlogged
North American hardiness zone: 5–9
Height & spread: 2m (6½ft)
Grow for: easy, problem-free vitamin-C-rich alternative to blackcurrants; masses of white flowers in spring; fantastic autumn colour

Chokeberry is one of the great unknowns that ought to be in every garden. It is problem free and easy to multiply; the flowers are much loved by insects; and the fruits make a delicious blackcurrant/myrtle-type conserve with a hint of pine. The autumn leaf colours are among the best of all plants. Indeed, it is more often grown for this leaf colour than for the fruit.

Originally grouped with pears, this native of North America has, as the name suggests, a styptic puckering quality, but once made into conserve it is a great source of vitamins, many times richer than oranges or blackcurrants. *Aronia* comes from the Greek name for sorbus, which has similar fruits.

It does not like dry, limy soils and prefers full sun, but will survive in shade, although the autumn colouring will be less impressive. Protect fruits from birds! The species can be grown from seed but varieties grown for their fruit, such as 'Viking', must be propagated by layers, hardwood cuttings or division. No real problems with this easy subject. **BF**

Aronia x *prunifolia* 'Viking'

Artemisia abrotanum

Artemisia abrotanum
LAD'S LOVE, SOUTHERNWOOD

Type: hardy, deciduous shrub
Soil & situation: dry, sandy soil/full sun to light shade
North American hardiness zone: 5–8
Height & spread: to about 1–1.2m (3–4ft)
Grow for: very good edging plant for large borders or specimen for difficult dry sites with poor soils; aromatic smell; gorgeous grey-green appearance even in droughts; AGM

This plant smells so sweetly of lemon-pine toilet cleaner that it is always worth having it near a door or gate where you can brush past it. Although it rarely flowers, when it does it can be covered with small yellow buttons. *Artemisia absinthium* 'Lambrook Silver' flowers more easily and has more silvery leaves. Easily multiplied, it makes a good informal hedge up to a metre or so high, or it can be trimmed tight back and kept quite compact and low more easily than lavender, which is a much laxer shrub.

Southernwood has been widely used for medicine since ancient times. A native of Europe, it has also been loved in gardens, and put to good use in homes where its stems were placed among clothes as its smell is reputed to keep away moths. Also used for strewing and for pot pourris, and a handful stuffed into your pillow is supposed to help you fall asleep if it doesn't poke your eye out!

In dry sandy soil lad's love is long lived, but in damp shady places it dies away. To keep it compact cut back hard in spring just before growth commences. The seed is rarely offered but cuttings in spring take easily, or divide an old clump if it's multi-stemmed. No real problems with this plant. **BF**

Artemisia dracunculus
FRENCH TARRAGON

Type: hardy, perennial herbaceous herb
Soil & situation: poor dry sandy soil/full sun
North American hardiness zone: 3–7
Height & spread: 30cm (12in); may reach 50cm (20in) in a good spot
Grow for: pleasing foliage from late spring to mid-summer with a superb, unique flavour

'French' tarragon is the herb to make a wonderful vinegar for use with fish; the commoner 'Russian' is miserable and coarse, but far more widely available as it endures so much longer and is easier to propagate.

Natives of Europe, other artemisias, such as *A. absinthium*, have long been used medicinally and are not so useful as edible herbs. However, they were once included in absinthe, an addictive alcoholic liqueur. Weirdly it is named after the Greek god of chastity.

Tarragon must be grown in dryish sandy soil in full sun or it will be very short lived. It dies back in autumn so needs tidying; protect the crown with sharp sand or grit. If offered seed, refuse as it will be the 'Russian' form. To ensure a true variety propagate by root division in early spring. Tarragon must be divided and replanted every third year, or it dies away! **BF**

Artemisia dracunculus

Arum italicum 'Marmoratum' *growing with snowdrops.*

Arum italicum 'Marmoratum'

LORDS AND LADIES

Type: hardy tuberous perennial
Soil & situation: well-drained, moisture-retentive soil/sun or shade
North American hardiness zone: 6–9
Height & spread: 30cm (12in)
Grow for: broad, spear-shaped leaves exquisitely marbled in grey-green in late autumn; an excellent foliage plant, ideal for Christmas decorations; bright red berries in summer when the foliage has died down; AGM

The beautifully marked leaves of this plant look as though they have been deftly hand-painted. They look perfect and pristine through many of the winter months – what could be more endearing? If they do get a little affected by the frosts in extremely cold sites, new growth quickly appears to replace them. (This has not happened yet to mine.) They are hardy to about –10°C (14°F), and will survive lower temperatures still with the insulation of a protective mulch. I grow them intermingled with a range of ferns, and they are extremely complimentary neighbours, with the arums stealing the scene in the late autumn as the ferns start to look a little tired. The roles are reversed in late spring as the lush, emerald foliage of the ferns hides the slowly shrivelling arums.

This plant comes pretty true from seed, though do not become disenchanted if young plants look plain, the markings take a couple of years to develop. It is worth selecting out the particularly stunningly marked plants. **BG**

Asparagus officinalis

ASPARAGUS

Type: half-hardy, herbaceous, perennial vegetable
Soil & situation: rich, well-drained, moist soil/full sun
North American hardiness zone: 4–8
Height: fern may reach 1.2–1.5m (4–5ft)
Spread: crown may grow to 1m (3ft) across, when the roots will extend by ten times as far
Grow for: simply the finest of all vegetable crops, which happily comes when few others are ready; the fern is also attractive in ornamental areas

Any gourmet gardener has to have a bed of this luxury as it is so much better when fresh cut, although patience is required to build up the crown's strength for three years before cutting – it is worth the wait. Also, only six weeks or so of cutting is possible each year as the remaining shoots must be left to form fern to replenish reserves for the following year.

The attractive fern and the pretty, red berries on the female make it easy to fit it into the ornamental border. Do not get all male versions, as I reckon females give bigger buds and they give free plants everywhere as they self-seed fiendishly.

A wild seashore plant from the Mediterranean, asparagus has been grown since Roman times and is little changed in form or even name; indeed, ours appears identical to theirs in every way. It is said to be an aphrodisiac, which is possible, but it certainly gives the consumer's urine its own distinctive aroma. In the markets asparagus is commonly referred to as sparrow grass.

Asparagus officinalis

Asparagus needs a well-prepared site as it may last for 20 years or more. Tidy up dead fern once it's died down and keep the bed scrupulously weed free, but do not thickly mulch as this makes for a late, light crop. Best sown *in situ*, or transplanted as one-year-old crowns but no older. Take care not to damage buds on the crown or the fleshy roots, which need spreading out just under the soil surface. Asparagus beetle is best controlled by hygiene and strong, soft soap sprays when the 'grubs' are seen eating the fern. **BF**

Asparagus officinalis

Asphodeline lutea
KING'S SPEAR, YELLOW ASPHODEL

Type: hardy, evergreen perennial
Soil & situation: any moderately fertile soil/sun or dappled shade
North American hardiness zone: 6–9
Height: 70cm (27½in) although often taller
Spread: 30cm (12in)
Grow for: dense racemes of fragrant, yellow flowers with conspicuous buff/reddish-brown bracts from late spring into summer; stout, leafy stems above the evergreen whorls of interesting, rather thin, grassy, grey-green foliage

This is a fine plant which is rapidly increasing in popularity as it associates well with grasses and large-scale perennial planting. It will naturalize well in these sort of situations – it occurs naturally in scrubby meadows and on rocky slopes. It is also highly suitable for mixed or herbaceous borders. Its individual, star-like flowers are up to 3cm (1in) across. They open after midday at uneven intervals up the spike for several weeks, giving the plant an unusual, rather outlandish look.

These plants are not so successful in rich soils but otherwise tolerate a range of conditions. They can be increased by seed or division but the latter needs care, making sure that the fleshy rhizomes have two or three growing points on each piece. This is best carried out in late summer or early autumn. It benefits from an autumnal mulch in colder areas. **BG**

Asphodeline lutea

Asplenium scolopendrium

Asplenium scolopendrium
HART'S TONGUE FERN

Type: hardy, evergreen fern
Soil & situation: happier in alkaline soils/will tolerate neutral or more acid conditions/prefer well-drained soils/full or partial shade/less than 3 hours sunshine a day, otherwise they get a yellow discoloration of their leaves or brown lesions can be burnt into their fronds
North American hardiness zone: 6–8
Height: to 70cm (27½in)
Spread: to 60cm (24in)
Grow for: simple but highly attractive foliage, which contrasts well with the heavily divided fronds of most ferns; AGM

The hart's tongue is a highly adaptable fern. I have seen it many times growing out of shady free-standing walls, reasonably high above ground. In natural woodlands it forms beautiful evergreen carpets studded with the occasional foxglove. This idyllic scene is easy to recreate in a garden situation by breaking up the clumps of strappy fronds, to a greater or lesser extent, with wild-looking colour from white epilobiums, comfrey, camassias and such like.

Their leaves are ever-present and highly attractive throughout the winter but start to shrivel as the young fronds start to unfurl in spring. It has many different cultivars with crinkled leaves in a variety of shades of green, for those who find the common form too common. But I think you can't beat it and I hope my garden is never without it, no doubt exploiting new cracks and crevices all the while.

Care for this plant as for *Dryopteris filix-mas* (see page 154). **BG**

Astelia chathamica

Astelia chathamica

Type: half-hardy, herbaceous perennial
Soil & situation: moist, humus-rich soil/dappled shade
North American hardiness zone: 8–9
Height: 1.2m (4ft)
Spread: 2m (6½ft)
Grow for: striking, silvery, sword-shaped leaves; AGM

Now here's a rarity: a bold architectural plant with silvery foliage that thrives in dappled shade! It forms a large clump of sword-like leaves, each terminating in a sharp point, which are silvery above and completely white below. Wow! The colour, shape and form lend themselves to contemporary planting schemes. Try it with the silver bramble *Rubus cockburnianus*, the black-leaved ground cover of *Ophiopogon planiscapus* 'Nigrescens', or the large bronze leaves of *Ajuga reptans* 'Catlin's Giant' or *A. r.* 'Pink Surprise', which have the bonus of blue and pink flowers respectively. It also looks wonderful as a feature plant in a black or blue container with crushed glass mulch! Think minimalist; concrete, glass, stainless steel and ceramics – a complete contrast to its home among the leafy forest margins of the Chatham Islands off the Pacific Coast of New Zealand! *A. nervosa* forms a denser clump of narrower, even more metallic leaves.

It needs dappled shade in constantly moist, humus-rich, acid soil; incorporate leafmould or peat substitute if necessary. Do not plant in frost pockets, as they cannot withstand long periods of sub-zero temperatures but have survived snow and are probably more cold tolerant than is supposed. Propagate by detaching rosettes from a parent plant in spring. The problem is that astelias hate disturbance and the only way to divide is to lift the whole plant and detach a rosette complete with its own roots; it is less risky to buy new micro-propagated plants. Pests: queues of people asking for divisions! **MB**

Aster x *frikartii* 'Mönch'

Type: hardy, herbaceous perennial
Soil & situation: well-drained, neutral to slightly alkaline soil/sun
North American hardiness zone: 5–8
Height: 90cm (36in)
Spread: 40cm (16in)
Grow for: gorgeous lavender-blue flowers from mid-summer to mid-autumn; AGM

Although spring has a joy and vibrancy of its own I'm a great fan of late summer and early autumn, particularly those days when the humidity has gone and it's still, warm and sunny without being unbearably hot and sticky. It's the time of year when asters come to the fore, enriching the garden with their bold splashes of colour. They come in a range of colours and sizes from the cerise pink *Aster novae-angliae* 'Andenken an Alma Pötschke' to the tiny-flowered, *A. ericoides* 'Golden Spray' with its bold centres and *A. amellus* 'King George', a reliable old rich purple cultivar. One of the best, however, is *A.* x *frikartii* 'Mönch'. It begins its display much earlier, in mid-summer producing masses of soothing, cool lavender-blue flowers up to 8cm (3½in) across, which cover the plant; it is utterly beautiful. Christopher Lloyd, that great garden writer, enthuses about it as an 'essential' plant for every garden. It is also America's favourite aster. It's good to know I'm not alone!

They need a sunny position in neutral to slightly alkaline, well-drained soil. Incorporate well-rotted organic matter, horticultural grit or sharp sand if necessary; grow in raised beds on clay. Feed with general fertilizer and mulch in spring. Although the stems are thin, they rarely need staking and are drought resistant, but they must be watered over long periods without rain. Divide every two to three years in autumn or spring, or take softwood cuttings from mid to late spring. They are mildew resistant. **MB**

Aster x *frikartii* 'Mönch'

Astilbe 'Fanal'

Type: hardy, herbaceous perennial
Soil & situation: moist, fertile, humus-rich soil/full sun or light shade
North American hardiness zone: 4–9
Height: 60cm (24in)
Spread: 90cm (36in)
Grow for: a dazzling display of crimson flowers making a feathery spire; easy to grow

Given the right soil conditions this perennial will perform well with little or no imput from the gardener. It needs no special treatment and is easy to grow. It will flower profusely for up to four years without being in serious need of dividing. The glossy, dark green leaves are toothed along their margins. They make a contrasting backdrop for the dense panicles of small, dark crimson flowers, which form a feathery spire. Long-lasting, they flower for weeks in early summer.

Astilbe 'Fanal' prefers a moist soil in full sun. If it is planted in a soil that dries out it will do better if it is shaded for the hottest part of the day. Where the ground is clay based and prone to drying out in summer it will not thrive. It is a good plant for the bog garden or at the edge of a pond with its feet close to water.

Propagation is by division in winter or early spring. Small rooted pieces should be potted up in a free-draining compost and kept under glass for the winter, or planted out in the border straight away. Flowers that have not been dead-headed will over-winter on the plant, gradually turning an attractive deep brown. **JC**

Astilbe 'Fanal'

Astilboides tabularis

Astilboides tabularis

Type: hardy, herbaceous perennial
Soil & situation: soil should be fairly rich/should drain but not dry out/enjoys moisture, so bog gardens, pond margins or damp borders are the order of the day/part shade
North American hardiness zone: 5–7
Height: up to 1.5m (5ft)
Spread: 1.2m (4ft)
Grow for: stunning architectural plant; bold foliage; attractive flowers in mid-summer

Although this plant is fairly unusual, it is definitely worth finding a spot for if you have suitably moist conditions. A piece of moist and lightly shaded woodland is ideal. If not, it may be well worth considering making a bog garden to accommodate it, together with several other exciting moisture-loving plants. Do not make the bog garden too small – the leaves are huge and may be up to 90cm (36in) long. The colour is a good, bright green, and the leaves have long stalks and are sharply lobed. It flowers in early to mid-summer, with spectacular panicles of tiny white flowers on tall flowering stems that reach to 1.5m (5ft) high.

It is as well to mulch the plants annually in spring to conserve water, and further watering maybe necessary in dry periods. Propagation is by division in spring. **BG**

Astrantia major 'Hadspen Blood'

Astrantia major 'Hadspen Blood'

MASTERWORT

Type: hardy, herbaceous perennial
Soil & situation: fertile, moist soils/sun or part shade
North American hardiness zone: 4–9
Height: up to 90cm (36in)
Spread: 45cm (18in)
Grow for: fabulous dark red flowers surrounded by co-ordinating dark red bracts from late spring to summer.

These striking, papery-looking flowers are shaped like mini-pincushions and have a charming simplicity about them. The stems are wiry and hold the colourful flowers above the mounded, deeply cut leaves. The flowering period is fairly prolonged so you can be generous and plant extravagant drifts of them, allowing them to hold the fort for well over a month, if not two. If you can bear to cut them, they dry extremely well for winter decoration. I also like *Astrantia major*, which has white flowers. It is more vigorous than the red forms, but less dramatic.

Astrantia major

Unless you have rich, moist soil to maintain these plants in tip-top condition they will need frequent division and re-planting into a good, nourishing soil. Propagate by division in spring. **BG**

Athyrium niponicum var. *pictum*

JAPANESE PAINTED FERN

Type: hardy, herbaceous perennial
Soil & situation: moist, humus-rich soil/dappled shade
North American hardiness zone: 5–8
Height: 38cm (15in)
Spread: 35cm (14in) plus
Grow for: beautifully marked leaves; AGM

This is an exquisite fern, arguably the most beautiful you'll ever see; it's elegant, stylish and has a delicious colour scheme, even by the exalted standards of the plant world. It has soft, metallic grey-green leaves with mauve-purple midribs, the mauve diffusing into the leaf blade. It is worthy of a prominent place at the edge of a border; plant it in the spotlight where it cannot be missed, then go and view it regularly for a contented life! Plant with arisaemas (see page 185) and other woodlanders or combine with arisaemas and black bamboo for a display of contemporary class!

Selected forms include *Athyrium niponicum* var. *pictum* 'Cristatoflabellatum' which has 'crests' at the frond tips and ends of the leaflets; the fronds are slightly narrower. 'Kokage Nishiki' has larger, broadly triangular green fronds flecked with cream.

They tolerate full sun (with sufficient moisture) to deep shade but prefer dappled shade and winter shelter. Those in good light develop the richest colours. They flourish in moist, humus-rich soil; dig in plenty of well-rotted organic matter, preferably leafmould, before planting. Ideal for planting by ponds and in bogs. Propagate by division in spring.

Here are several other colourful ferns that are worth growing. *A. otophorum* (eared lady fern) has lance-shaped, pale green fronds with a burgundy midrib and veins. It is deciduous but holds its leaves into the autumn. *A. vidallii* has green leaves with a dark red midrib and veins. *Adiantum aleuticum* 'Japonicum' (Japanese maidenhair fern) has beautiful rose-pink foliage with contrasting black stems. It needs shelter. *Dryopteris erythrosora* has brick-red new fronds, fading to bronze, then becoming green. Its evergreen leaves turn yellow in winter. Wonderful! See also *Asplenium sclopendrium* on page 50 and other recommended *Dryopteris* on page 154. **MB**

Azara microphylla

Plant of the Week (see page 55)

Athyrium niponicum var *pictum*

Azara microphylla

Type: hardy evergreen shrub to small tree
Soil & situation: any well-drained, preferably humus-rich soil/full sun to light shade. Needs warmth in cold areas.
Hardiness zone: 8–10
Height: can reach 12m (40ft) in a perfect site, smaller in UK
Spread: 3m (10ft)
Grow for: evergreen, box- or cotoneaster-like leaves year round; highly perfumed flowers which emerge before most others, at the end of winter; occasional orange berries; AGM

Azara microphylla (below) is not unpleasing as a foliage shrub but rarely catches the eye. However, in late winter until early spring it produces the most amazingly powerful scent of vanilla and chocolate from tiny, yellow, powder puff flowers on the underside of the leaflets. The scent is almost addictive and I have completely defoliated my specimen as high as I can reach snipping bits off to take indoors.

A native of South America, its generic name comes from a Spanish patron and the species name from its small leaves. It is one of a dozen species, most of which are too tender for Britain except in warm coastal areas – I can't grow the gorgeous *A. lanceolata*, pictured left, but it's fine against a warm wall in milder parts of the country. *A. microphylla* is tough enough to endure winters in my Norfolk garden, even without a warm wall. Some other species flower in autumn.

Apart from its tenderness, *Azara* is obligingly easy. The only real problem is biting cold winds. It can get drawn up and leggy so needs pruning back every few years to keep it compact and also to remove dieback after searing winds or frosts. It's not easy to obtain, or to grow, the seed, and other methods of propagation are not easy either; the best method is to use mature sideshoot cuttings in autumn or by layering – oh go on, buy a plant! **BF**

Begonia sutherlandii

Type: half-hardy tuberous perennial
Soil & situation: moist, organic-rich compost/dappled shade
North American hardiness zone: tender in most areas; normally grown as an annual
Height & spread: 45cm (18in)
Grow for: form and foliage from spring to autumn; flower in summer; AGM

When you put out houseplants for their 'summer holiday' they are usually left randomly on the patio or dispersed to hide in the garden; however, they look much better incorporated into an exotic plant display. Place larger foliage plants together for a 'jungly' effect and smaller plants in groups with other summer-flowering containers.

Begonia sutherlandii, a native of southern Africa where it grows among rocks by humid forest streams is a demure little plant and a study in elegance and form. It has slender trailing stems, bright green, red-veined leaves and hanging clusters of pale orange flowers; it is perfect for shady patios or resting in a bed of ferns or among terracotta pots where its earthy tones combine. Its trailing habit makes it ideal for a plinth, a hanging basket, or anywhere you need a soothing summer display.

Although it is of borderline hardiness, unless you live in a mild area, it is safer to dry it off over winter and store in peat substitute. Repot in multi-purpose compost in spring, gradually increase watering as the stems appear; use tepid, never cold water. Feed every two weeks with general fertilizer, changing to high-potash fertilizer at flowering.

During the first year remove developing flowers; start into growth in mid- to late winter under cover, then harden off before moving outdoors once there is no danger of frost. It needs shade to dappled light, away from scorching sunshine. It produces small bulbils in the leaf axils in late summer – collect and store over winter, and sow the following spring. It can also be propagated by stem cuttings in summer. It is susceptible to mildew, so keep the compost moist and avoid stagnant air. **MB**

Begonia sutherlandii

Berberidopsis corallina

Berberidopsis corallina
CORAL PLANT

Type: half-hardy, evergreen, twining climber
Soil & situation: moist, acid to neutral soil/shade/shelter
North American hardiness zone: 8–9
Height & spread: 6m (20ft) or more
Grow for: flowers from mid-summer to early autumn

This treasure was first discovered in February 1860 by Richard Pearce, one of 22 collectors employed by the great nurserymen Veitch & Co., who found it in a forested ravine in the province of Arauco in Chile where the Mapuche Indians still use the stems to make baskets. The species was described by Joseph Hooker in 1862, later to become a director of Kew, who wrote 'it is not a little remarkable that so striking a plant should hitherto have escaped the notice of all botanists and collectors who have explored a region now so well known as Chile'. The limited natural distribution has been badly affected by forest clearance for commercial timber production and it is now an endangered species. Many of the populations have been reduced or destroyed and even though it's available in nurseries, there is little genetic variation among the plants. The dark green leaves are heart shaped, leathery with spiny margins; the flowers on long stems from the upper leaf joints are rounded with overlapping petals and deep coral-red flowers like bunches of luscious cherries. Have you room for one in your garden? It is a priceless opportunity to grow a beautiful plant and to conserve it in cultivation, even if it is threatened in the wild.

It needs a sheltered, shady wall in well-drained, moist, light, neutral or acid soil; it tolerates some alkalinity. Make sure it gets protection from frost; it flourishes in parts of the UK influenced by the North Atlantic Drift and in sheltered gardens. Plant in early spring, mulch annually to protect the roots and tie in new shoots as required. Prune in spring to remove damaged growths or to tidy up the plant. Propagate by semi-ripe cuttings from mid-summer to early autumn, or by layering in early spring. **MB**

Berberis darwinii

Berberis darwinii
BARBERRY

Type: hardy, evergreen shrub
Soil & situation: moist soil; tolerates chalk/sun or partial shade/shelter
North American hardiness zone: 7–9
Height & spread: 3m (10ft) or more
Grow for: glossy foliage; orange flowers in mid- and late spring; AGM

This robust, attractive Chilean native was discovered by Charles Darwin in 1835 when he was naturalist on the *Beagle*, but not introduced to the UK until 1849 by William Lobb who was collecting for Veitch's Nursery on the island of Chiloe.

It is a joyful sight in spring festooned with hanging clusters up to 5cm (2in) long of as many as 30 flowers. The massed, glossy, holly-like, evergreen leaves with three spines at the tip are the perfect backcloth for the flowers, which are a spectacular striking tone of orange with reddish stems. Like all berberis and mahonias, the stamens are touch-sensitive, springing inwards on contact and coating the head of visiting insects with pollen. In common with many plants, they often stage another smaller flowering display in autumn and are followed by plum-coloured fruits. I planted many of these in the miry Leicestershire clay and undeterred, they still glowed radiantly year after year. It is one of my favourite shrubs, good for creating barriers and as a border specimen. The cultivar *B. d.* 'Flame' has broader leaves with rich orange-red flowers.

Although tolerant of most conditions, except regular drought, it prefers moist soils in a sheltered position, protected from strong wind. It even grows well on chalky soils – how accommodating! Trim in late winter to keep within its allotted space, rejuvenate by removing older stems and encouraging those growing up from the base. Grow from seed in late winter to early spring, or heeled nodal cuttings. Berberis sawfly may be a problem. **MB**

Berberis linearifolia 'Orange King'
BARBERRY

Type: hardy, evergreen, upright shrub
Soil & situation: any moist, well-drained, fertile soil/full sun or light shade
North American hardiness zone: 6–9
Height & spread: 2m (6½ft) each way
Grow for: an excellent, evergreen, spring-flowering shrub

There are superb berberis and then there are the common types much used in local authority landscape plantings throughout Europe to deter vandals and hold, trapped in public gaze, every bit of litter in the vicinity. *B. linearifolia* 'Orange King' is a true aristocrat, flowering royally with the minimum of attention. It is a vigorous plant with lengthy, arching shoots and 5cm (2in) long, thin, glossy, dark green leaves. The clusters of orange-apricot flowers appear in late spring weighing down the stems. Early visiting bees go mad for the blossom. Small blue-black fruits appear in early autumn.

After planting, clip the plant, removing 30 per cent of the growth, to encourage it to form sideshoots. If allowed to grow unchecked, the base of all the branches will become bare of foliage. As it is a surface-rooting shrub, a deep mulch of composted bark will help retain moisture and prevent the ground drying out.

This is a shrub that seldom requires pruning. Remove individual branches that are spoiling the shape in early summer after flowering. When grown as a hedge, trim lightly every year after the flower has faded. Propagate by semi-ripe cuttings in mid-summer in a gritty compost. **JC**

Berberis linearifolia 'Orange King'

Berberis temolaica
BARBERRY

Type: hardy, deciduous shrub
Soil & situation: most soils/sun or partial shade
North American hardiness zone: 6–9
Height & spread: 3m (10ft)
Grow for: uncommon deciduous shrub with red fruits and good autumn colour

I bought this at a county show at Hever Castle in Kent, simply because I'd never heard of the species and the name sounded unusual. It's rather like buying a car because you like the colour; how serendipity has triumphed! The small plant I carefully carried home has now settled into my heavy clay and is showing glimpses of its full glory, and will be wonderful when it reaches its full height. The arching stems are an unusual whitish-grey at first, later becoming purple and shiny brown. There are few spines and the pale yellow flowers in late spring are followed by red, egg-shaped fruits covered with a delicate bloom; I must have missed them last year, but not the fiery orange and yellow autumn colour, which would not look out of place on 5 November. It was first discovered by Frank Kingdon-Ward on the Temo La in Tibet in 1924. I wonder if my plant came from that area or from seed collected by Ludlow, Sherrif and Taylor from the nearby Tsari district in 1938. I don't know, but whatever its origin, in one corner of my garden there's a piece of that Hallowed Kingdom.

Berberis temolaica thrives on most soils including those that are dry and shallow, but dislikes waterlogging. A sunny site encourages fruiting. Regular pruning is not required, just trim it in late winter to keep it within its allotted space and regenerate by removing older stems and encouraging those growing up from the base. Grow from seed from late winter to early spring or take semi-ripe cuttings with a heel. **MB**

Berberis temolaica

Berberis valdiviana

Berberis valdiviana
BARBERRY

Type: hardy, evergreen shrub
Soil & situation: most soils/sun or partial shade
North American hardiness zone: 6–9
Height & spread: 4m (13ft)
Grow for: robust, handsome evergreen; flowers in late spring

See a specimen at maturity and you can only admire its bulk standing there nobly and defiant like Goliath, daring anyone to challenge it! Three-pronged spines, almost hidden by the elegant glossy leaves, sprout from the stems, waiting to trap the unwary. How strange, then, that this plant should produce such fine orange-yellow or saffron flowers in clusters of 20–30 that hang like pendent earrings, up to 5cm (2in) long. Is it having an identity crisis or just a laugh? I've yet to decide, but what is certain is that it is a fine plant in leaf and flower, as the one by Victoria Gate at the Royal Botanic Garden Kew amply demonstrates. I'm sure it would be planted more often if it were freely available. It was discovered in the Valdivia province of southern Chile in 1856 and could easily be mistaken for a holly (see *Desfontainia spinosa* on page 142 and *Osmanthus heterophyllus* on page 283).

It thrives on a sheltered, sunny site on most soils including dry and shallow, but dislikes waterlogging. Good as a wall shrub or in a sheltered corner. Regular pruning is not required, just trim in late winter to keep it within its allotted space and regenerate by removing older stems and encouraging those growing up from the base.

Grow from seed from late winter to early spring or take semi-ripe cuttings with a heel. Be warned – it is extremely difficult to propagate from cuttings. It can suffer from leaf spot with purple-black spots on the leaves, which is disfiguring rather than debilitating. Beware of berberis sawfly. **MB**

Bergenia 'Beethoven'
ELEPHANT EARS

Type: hardy, evergreen perennial
Soil & situation: moist, well-drained soil/sun or partial shade
North American hardiness zone: 3–8
Height: 45cm (18in)
Spread 60cm (24in) or more
Grow for: architectural foliage and early spring flowers

I've never worried about my 'elephant ears', they suit me rather well. Some people pass comment, others laugh, but I think they're very nice; OK, they may go red in cold weather but so does my nose – to me that is part of their charm!

I don't know why bergenias aren't planted more often. They can look untidy (so tidy them up!), but make excellent evergreen ground cover with their bold, green, glossy leaves; even when the older leaves die they turn yellow and scarlet.

There's character in the thick creeping rhizomes, and the early flowers and stems are beautiful. If you have an 'elephant's ear' for music, *Bergenia* 'Beethoven' is beautiful with dark green leaves and spikes of bell-shaped, pure white flowers with

Bergenia 'Beethoven'

a red to greenish-pink flush on the reverse and red or purple stems; you may well find yourself in harmony. 'Bach' has rounded, deep green leaves and pink-flushed flowers – 'Brahms', 'Bizet', 'Bartok', 'Britten', 'Mozart', they all know the score. There's plenty to choose from, and I'm relieved that 'Eroica' has missed her 't'!

The foliage and flowers last well in indoor displays. They need moist, well-drained soil in sun or partial shade. An open site on poorer soil improves their winter colour. Frost may damage early flowers. Divide every three to four years; root young rhizome sections with one or more leaf rosettes after flowering or in autumn in open ground. They are susceptible to slugs, and snails; leaf spot may be a problem. Dry brown rot may affect the rhizomes; remove infected parts and dust with fungicide. **MB**

Beta vulgaris esculenta 'Burpee's Golden'

BEETROOT

Type: hardy, herbaceous, biennial root vegetable
Soil & situation: rich, moist soil/full sun or very light shade
North American hardiness zone: normally grown as an annual
Height & spread: to 30–45cm (12–18in) each way; when flowering can reach almost 2m (6½ft) x 60cm (24in)
Grow for: unusual, golden, turnip-shaped root with attractive yellowy-green foliage; if left to bolt when fully grown it produces a magnificent flower spike of small flowers with a sweet, mawkish scent

Most beetroot are red and grown purely for the table, but this old variety has a different appearance in root and leaf so can be used in the ornamental garden to good effect. It is sweeter than many red cultivars and makes an excellent preserve in vinegar or as pieces in piccalilli. The leaves are more palatable than those of the red sorts and can be eaten as a spinach.

Almost unknown to the early Romans, beet were developed as a fodder crop in the Dark Ages in Europe, probably from the native maritime plant, and seem to have come from Germany. Originally they were cooked in ashes or fried but now they are invariably boiled or pickled.

The soil must be rich and moist or beet may bolt; they enjoy the addition of seaweed products and wood ashes. To further avoid bolting space widely and do not let them dry out. Sow seed from early spring to early summer. Beet seed is in a 'pellet' of several, so single them out in rows at least 12–15cm (5–6in) apart. Birds eat young leaves unless protected. **BF**

Beta vulgaris esculenta 'Burpee's Golden'

Beta vulgaris esculenta 'Crosby's Egyptian'

Beta vulgaris esculenta 'Crosby's Egyptian'

BEETROOT

Type: hardy, herbaceous, biennial root vegetable
Soil & situation: rich, moist soil/full sun or very light shade
North American hardiness zone: normally grown as an annual
Height & spread: as for *Beta vulgaris esculenta* 'Burpee's Golden' (see previous entry)
Grow for: the best beetroot for pickling; if left to bolt produces a flower spike similar to that of 'Burpee's Golden' but more red than yellow.

This old variety may bolt more readily than some newer sorts, but in my trials it performed well when grown, and when pickled in vinegar it kept its colour, taste and texture the longest. It can be used in the ornamental garden to good effect, and the leaves can be eaten like spinach, but they are less palatable than those of 'Burpee's Golden' or white sorts, such as 'Albina Vereduna'.

As an old variety 'Crosby's Egyptian' has a flattish bottom and is not as globular or cylindrical as modern sorts. Beet is very valuable nutritionally as it is rich in minerals but this makes the demand on the soil far heavier than most crops, so it must be rotated each year.

The soil must be rich and moist or the beet may bolt. Give wide spacing to avoid bolting. The same problem can occur if sown in a cold period, so wait until no more than a fortnight before the last frost is expected. Beet can be sown from early spring until early summer; seed is in a 'pellet' of several so either give very wide spacing, 30cm (12in) each way, and leave in natural clumps of three or five, or thin to singletons in a more closely packed row at say 10cm (4in) apart. Protect young leaves to deter birds from eating them. **BF**

Betula utilis var. *jacquemontii*

HIMALAYAN BIRCH

Type: hardy, deciduous tree
Soil & situation: moist, well-drained soil/full sun or partial shade/tolerates exposure
Hardiness zone: 5–7
Height: 18m (60ft)
Spread: 10m (33ft)
Grow for: an elegant, fast-growing tree with striking white bark, shown to best advantage in wintry gloom.

I love all birch, but this is my favourite. The pure white bark heading into the uppermost limbs creates a ghostly effect on a dull afternoon in mid-winter. The 12cm (5in) long, oblong, dark green, double-toothed leaves turn to buttery-yellow in late autumn. In early spring pale brown, male catkins the same length as the leaves appear. In the slightest breeze they dispense clouds of bright yellow pollen.

It is fast growing with the bark colouring early. Sited correctly, it is an ideal specimen tree for drawing your eye and highlighting one part of the garden. It will grow and thrive in damp ground but isn't partial to waterlogged soil. They dislike being moved, but asmall, bare root tree up to 1.8m (6ft) high will transplant without too much fuss, providing it is planted as soon as it loses its leaves. It may also be planted just as it is about to come into leaf in the spring. Plant at the same depth as before and water frequently for the first season. I admit to washing the bark every winter to remove the older, peeling bark and green algae and as I pass by the main trunk I usually give it a pat.

Other varieties worth growing are *Betula utilis* var. *jacquemontii* 'Doorenbos' with white bark peeling to reveal pale orange new bark. *B. utilis*. var. *jacquemontii*. 'Jermyns' has 17cm (6¾in) long male catkins. The variety 'Silver Shadow' is, if anything, whiter than *jacquemontii* but I think my plant is brilliant. **JC**

Beta vulgaris 'Ruby Chard'

Beta vulgaris 'Ruby Chard'

Type: hardy, biennial vegetable
Soil & situation: good, deep, fertile but well-drained soil
North American hardiness zone: normally grown as an annual
Height & spread: 45cm (18in)
Grow for: ornamental foliage; culinary purposes lasting right through the winter till late spring the following year; highly productive, easy to grow and very resistant to bolting

The foliage on this plant is highly decorative: it has dark purple-green, puckered leaves with intense, almost florescent red stems and veins. Admittedly, I value it far more for its appearance than its taste. The midribs and stalks can be steamed and taste like a watery asparagus, while the young leaves can be treated as spinach but are not so good. The best culinary use, I think, is to pick the leaves young and use them to add splashes of colour and some bite (a mild, peppery, spinach flavour) to a salad. It is a strong enough plant, visually and culturally, to be used as a container plant. Indeed a winter window box full of these would certainly outdo the Jones' jaded pansies next door. There are excellent different types available. *Beta vulgaris* 'Bull's Blood' has exceptionally deep red-purple, glossy leaves and the young leaves can be used as a cut-and-come-again, though the purple colour intensifies as the plant matures and autumn approaches. 'Bright Lights' is so bright it looks unreal with its yellow, cream, orange or red midribs and veins amongst the leaves – an exceptional plant. Leaves of this in a Christmas salad are very festive.

These cut-and-come-again vegetables have the edge for busy (and forgetful) gardeners – you cut them to 2.5cm (1in) above the soil and in a few days they produce new leaves. You can do this at least four or five times before you exhaust them. To prolong their life you can 'pick them round' which means instead of stripping all the leaves off you leave half the leaves around the plant. Make two sowings a year, one in mid-spring and one in mid- to late summer and you will have leaves almost throughout the year. Thin the plants to about 23cm (9in) apart when they are large enough to handle. **BG**

Betula pendula 'Youngii'

YOUNG'S WEEPING BIRCH

Type: hardy, deciduous tree
Soil & situation: fertile, moist, well-drained soil/full sun or light shade
North American hardiness zone: 2–7
Height: 8m (25ft)
Spread: 4m (13ft)
Grow for: a beautifully shaped weeping tree with smooth, silver-grey bark when young

When the poet Samuel Taylor Coleridge referred to the birch as 'the lady of the woods' he was not thinking of 'Youngii'. A better description for this highly desirable tree would be 'the little old lady of the garden'. When mature, it forms a mushroom-shaped head. Quite often a vigorous branch will grow out at right angles to the trunk before deciding to weep. Its side branches may do the same, giving the tree a lopsided appearance. Densely twiggy, its weeping outline is apparent all year round. The silver-grey bark eventually turns a dark brown with deep cracks. The diamond-shaped leaves are mid-green turning buttery-yellow in autumn.

If you want to attract leprechauns to your garden and space allows, plant a group of three *Betula pendula* 'Youngii' 4m (13ft) apart and underplant with the hardy *Cyclamen hederifolium* (see page 136). This is exactly the quiet, calming environment they love to hide in. If they don't settle no matter, you will enjoy it!

Pruning may be necessary to maintain a tidy weeping shape. Branches should be cut in early winter before the sap starts to rise otherwise wounds will 'bleed' for days, soaking the ground. Propagation is by grafting in winter. **JC**

Betula utilis var. *jacquemontii*

Plant of the Week (see page 61)

Betula pendula 'Youngii'

Billbergia nutans

Billbergia nutans
FRIENDSHIP PLANT

Type: tender, evergreen perennial
Soil & situation: warm, moist, rich compost/full sun/under cover
North American hardiness zone: 10–11
Height & spread: clump-forming, can reach 45cm (18in)
Grow for: a very tough bromeliad house or conservatory plant with attractive multi-coloured, though not large flowers coming out of evergreen, wide, rush-like foliage

This is a real survivor, hard to kill with neglect or even with over-watering and a good plant to start off a child's interest. The long, narrow leaves strongly resemble the well-known (unvariegated) spider plant without the little 'spiders'. Once pot bound and a big enough clump, billbergia throws out flower spikes of green, blue and yellow blooms from bright pink shoots at any time of year. It can go out on the patio in summer. Big clumps make excellent conservatory subjects.

Named after a Swedish botanist, this plant is almost hardy and may grow outdoors in very sheltered, warm gardens near the coast. It has survived for several years in my Norfolk garden at the base of a hedge in a dry, sunny spot but it does not flower very well there – probably because it is too dry, but any wetter and it would rot in winter.

A perfect houseplant, it can live for many years despite bad treatment. It flowers better when a little pot bound; remove dead flowers, though, as they're unsightly. Seed is not widely available, so use division as the simplest method of propagation, which can be done at almost any time. Otherwise remarkably problem free. **BF**

Brachyglottis monroi (syn. *Senecio monroi)*

Type: hardy, evergrey shrub
Soil & situation: sharp draining soil/hardy to about –10°C (14°F), maybe more/needs a little protection in a cold, first winter/tolerates windy conditions/thrives in seaside locations/sunny position enhances the grey of their foliage/leaf colour becomes more green than grey in dappled shade
North American hardiness zone: 9–10
Height and spread: 1m (3ft)
Grow for: exquisite foliage, neater and more compact than the better known *B.* Dunedin hybrids; leaf has an attractive wavy edge; yellow flowers in summer but very much secondary to the foliage effects; AGM

This plant has a good dense habit, forming a well-mounded dome of foliage. The tops of the leaves are a green-grey, and because the wavy edges of the foliage, which look as if they have been cut with blunt crimping scissors, turn upwards slightly, it pleasingly accentuates the contrasting silver-white undersides of the leaves. The young shoots and flower stalks are also silver-white. The main problem with this plant is that having lived with it you tend to turn up your nose at the commoner *B.* Dunedin hybrids or *Senecio greyi*, as it used to be called. This is larger, generally coarser, with a tendency to sprawl, and seems to be mobbed by the rather vicious yellow-coloured, daisy flowers for too long in the summer. And to think I used to think it a not unattractive, good-tempered plant.

I prefer this plant without the flowers and with a good tight habit, so I cut it hard back in spring, shortening the shoots by about a third. If you like the flowers, then do this procedure after flowering. It is easy to propagate from cuttings, and semi-ripe ones in summer work well, but you could probably succeed at most times of the year. It is that obliging. **BG**

Brachyglottis monroi

Brassica oleracea var. *italica*

Brassica oleracea var. *italica* (syn. *B. o. botrytis cymosa*)

BROCCOLI ROMANESCO

Type: near-hardy, herbaceous, semi-woody, biennial vegetable
Soil & situation: very fertile, moist, lime-rich soil/full sun
North American hardiness zone: normally grown as an annual
Height & spread: up to 60cm (24in)
Grow for: totally unique appearance, somewhat like a cauliflower but lime-green and pointy with an exquisite flavour

The sprouting and heading forms of broccoli and the true cauliflowers are two very similar types of brassica. The former are hardier and will usually over-winter, whereas true cauliflowers are more tender and rarely make it through the winter.

Despite being called a broccoli, romanesco more closely resembles a cauliflower, as it is grown from a spring sowing to crop in late summer/early autumn, and once the main head is taken it rarely produces many sideshoot heads. Although a little tricky to grow, this native of Italy is a gourmet vegetable with a wonderful flavour and a fine melting texture, making it nearly as luscious as asparagus and almost certainly more nutritious. The head warrants close examination with a hand lens, as its form of tight, pointed spirals is aesthetically pleasing and quite unique.

The soil must be rich and moist or romanesco will bolt and give minute heads that are of little use. Break and bend over big leaves to protect the ripening curd from the sun. Sow only in spring, preferably *in situ,* or move on at a very early stage from individual pots or cells. Transplanting from a seedbed is often unsuccessful as plants may then bolt. For good heads give them at least 60cm (24in) each way.

Romanesco suffers all the usual brassica pests and diseases: white moths/flies and various caterpillars are kept off by growing plants under horticultural fleece; slugs are best thinned out with slug pubs of fermenting beer; sowing *in situ,* under plastic bottle cloches also keeps away many of the pests otherwise attracted by the smell given off by seedlings bruised when transplanted. **BF**

Brassica oleracea 'Noisette' (syn. *B. bullata* var. *gemmifera* 'Noisette')

BRUSSELS SPROUT

Type: hardy, herbaceous, semi-woody, biennial vegetable
Soil & situation: rich, moist, firm soil/full sun or light shade
North American hardiness zone: normally grown as an annual
Height: 1m (3ft)
Spread: 30–60cm (12–24in)
Grow for: when in England, you have to have sprouts for Christmas and this is one of the best

'Noisette' is a small, firm hazelnut-sized sprout that rarely gets big and blowsy like some sorts, and it does not have the same rank taste as many unless it's grossly overfed with manure. There are other sprouts bred to have a sweeter, less mustardy flavour but this old variety is still best to my taste, although the red Brussels sprout, *B. oleracea* 'Rubine', is a good alternative.

From the name and lack of reference to it by the ancients, it is commonly believed to have been bred from a Savoy-type cabbage in Belgium in the late Middle Ages. Some say it is derived from the same ancestor as the Jersey tree cabbage, which is much like a very tall (2m/6½ft plus) kale. Indeed, if a cabbage of almost any sort has its head removed then small sprouts may form on the stem and, likewise, the head of a Brussels sprout can be eaten just like a loose cabbage or kale.

A rich, moist soil is essential but most important is to plant the seedling quite deep and to ensure the soil is firmed down hard. Removing the head will cause the sprouts to form sooner; they are said to taste better after a frost has hit them. Sow in early spring in several batches and transplant the best seedlings by late spring/early summer, spacing them at least 60cm (24in) apart each way. Sprouts suffer all the usual brassica pests and diseases (see previous entry), although slugs and caterpillars are less of a problem than with most of the others in the family. Sprouts tend to be loose and blowsy if grown shallow or in uncompacted soil. Keeping the soil moist will deter the flea beetle, which can be a problem when prolific. **BF**

Brassica oleracea 'Noisette'

Brassica oleracea var. *capitata* 'Grand Prize'
SUMMER CABBAGE

Type: half-hardy, herbaceous, semi-woody, biennial vegetable
Soil & situation: rich, moist, limy soil/full sun to light shade
North American hardiness zone: normally grown as an annual
Height & spread: 60cm (24in)
Grow for: it grows big easily, and is significantly sweeter and better flavoured than all the other summer cabbages I've tried

Although I have chosen several cabbages as my favourite plants you may find it surprising to know that I am not very fond of cabbage as a vegetable. However, I do like it in coleslaw and my choices all depend on their suitability for this purpose. This cabbage is really superior in flavour, and I strongly suggest any 'cabbage-phobes', like me, try this one for its almost nutty taste. I even quite like it steamed!

There are many different sorts of cabbage and summer cultivars are distinctly different to the spring and winter varieties, most obviously in that they are far less hardy so are probably related to the old Roman varieties. The Romans believed the cabbage was created from the divine perspiration of Jupiter when he was trying to solve contradictory oracles, and they attributed great healing powers to cabbage, as well as thinking it prevented drunkenness. However, they probably only had loose-leaf cabbages as it is still hard to get them to form hard heads in warmer climates. The art of growing a hard head was most likely not developed until the times of the Norman conquest, as the first references appear after 1066.

Summer cabbages need to be grown quickly and smoothly so they need a rich, moist, limy soil or they may bolt. They are not very hardy and must be gathered before the frosts return. If the cabbage head is removed and a cross cut made across the stem several smaller, looser heads will form, which can be used in succession. Also it is not necessary to take the whole head at once; half can be removed and the remaining half covered with foil or plastic wrap, as it will stay fresher on the stem than if cut and stored in a refrigerator.

Summer cabbage can be started off in pots or cells under cover and planted out after the frosts, sown *in situ* or transplanted out from a seedbed, or use all three methods to give a spread of ripe heads from early summer until the frosts. It suffers from all the usual brassica pests, but is hit harder than other cabbages as it grows when pests are at their most prevalent. However, the crop rarely fails entirely but it can be messy to clean plants. Growing under horticultural fleece prevents a lot of problems and slugs can be thinned by using slug pubs; flea beetles are best kept off the seedlings by maintaining a moist soil. **BF**

Brassica oleracea var. *capitata* 'Spring Hero'
SPRING CABBAGE

Type: hardy, herbaceous, semi-woody, biennial vegetable
Soil & situation: rich, moist soil/full sun or light shade
North American hardiness zone: normally grown as an annual
Height & spread: not much more than 30cm (12in)
Grow for: a significantly better (harder, more densely packed) spring cabbage than older, more pointed sorts

Spring cabbages have to be really tough and hardy to over-winter. Most of them have pointed, fairly loose conical heads, but 'Spring Hero' has a round-shaped head, which is hard enough to use for coleslaw and comes in many weeks before the summer cabbages are ready for the same use. It is a significant improvement and worth the eating. The pointed-headed conical spring cabbages are thought to have some Chinese cabbage blood in them, although others suggest they may derive from the Savoy group of loose-headed cabbages – either way they are much tougher than but not as good to eat as the summer sorts. 'Spring Hero' is a new hybrid with the toughness of the old sorts but with almost the eating quality of the summer ones.

A rich, moist soil in full sun is essential. In winter if it is really cold protect young plants with cloches; in spring give water and shade if there is a sudden hot, dry spell while the plants head up to prevent splitting and bolting. A dose of nitrogen-rich liquid feed in early spring as the soil warms up will help promote an earlier crop. Sow mid- to late summer, preferably *in situ* or transplant out from individual cells or pots in early autumn, or over-winter in a cold frame and plant out in early spring. They can be squeezed in together more than summer or winter cabbages as they are usually more compact and they form a microclimate, helping each other to keep out the cold wind.

It suffers all the usual brassica pests and diseases (see *Brassica oleracea* var. *italica*, page 64). Slugs may be an especial menace as they climb up inside in winter and do their damage unseen. Luckily these cabbages often escape the summer caterpillar and whitefly attacks as they are cropped and gone by the time the pests are in force. They will need extra protection and care when first sown, but this is easy as they are still small. **BF**

Brassica oleracea var. *capitata* 'Spring Hero'

Daphne odora 'Aureomarginata'

Type: frost-hardy, variegated, evergreen shrub
Soil & situation: rich, moist, well-drained soil/full sun to light shade
Hardiness zone: 7–9
Height & spread: 1m (3ft), but maybe more
Grow for: similiar leaves to *Daphne tangutica* (see page 141), but with a silvery-gold narrow margin; gorgeously scented clusters of reddish-purple (outside) and white (inside) flowers opening for a long period. Like many daphnes, it brightens the late winter garden with its scent; AGM.

Daphne odora 'Aureomarginata' has the best perfume in this sweet-scented family. Of all the daphnes it is the toughest, one of the most attractive and even nearly the longest lived, though that is still only about as long as a good-quality automobile! The scent is amazing, in that it often projects itself across the garden and can be smelt strongly upon approach, only to disappear and reappear as you get closer to the small flowers.

D. odora, a neat and very attractive Chinese and Japanese evergreen shrub, was introduced to the UK in 1771 but always proved miffy and not hardy unless given some protection. This superior form, unusual for a variegated plant, is tougher and more vigorous than the plain and survives longer in much less comfortable conditions.

It is the least demanding of a difficult family and does best in rich, moist, humus-rich, limy soil in light sun. Do not prune and do not move once established. You may get 10 or 15 years, but even if it only makes five it will be worth it. It can be layered and is among the easiest of this family to root from cuttings taken in early summer. All daphnes get virus infected and die away, so never prune them. If aphids become a problem, spray with soft soap. **BF**

Daphne mezereum

MEZEREON

Type: hardy deciduous shrub
Soil & situation: moist, preferably slightly chalky soil, partial shade
Hardiness zone: 5–6
Height & spread: to 1m (3ft)
Grow for: early flowering with purple-red scented flowers from February, attractive foliage, red fruits in autumn (which are poisonous). Like *D. odora* 'Aureomarginata' (see page 67), its scented flowers are a late-winter joy.

Although the mezereon is notoriously short-lived and prone to virus infections that make it just fade away, it is still a very good garden plant. The flowers are delightful, come very early in the year and have a sweet orange-flower-like perfume that is most pleasing. There are improved selections such as 'Rosea', 'Grandiflora' and the white-flowered form 'Alba' (top right), which gives yellow berries, but the common mezereon is quite good enough for most people.

A native of Europe and the Middle East, this daphne's name comes from the Persian Arabic *mazarjun*. The plant used to be used as a 'cure' for alcoholism: enough poisonous berries were forced on the miscreant to only make him rather sick; but if he then also drank alcohol he would become really sick – do not try this at home…

Daphne mezereum likes a moist soil in partial shade on a woodland's edge with some chalk in it and it will then last up to a decade or so. Never ever prune it or it will die back. It is best grown from seed; those sown fresh, *in situ* so that they are never moved, do best of all. It may get the occasional aphid attack, but generally no curable problems other than being short-lived; the cure for that is to buy or sow another. **BF**

Brassica oleracea var. *capitata* 'Dutch White'

Brassica oleracea var. *capitata* 'Holland Late'/'Dutch White'

WINTER CABBAGE

Type: frost-hardy, herbaceous, semi-woody, biennial vegetable
Soil & situation: rich, moist, limy soil/full sun or light shade
North American hardiness zone: normally grown as an annual
Height & spread: 60cm (24in) each way
Grow for: the best cabbage to store for winter use

There are many different cabbage varieties that can be available in the coldest months of the year: some summer cabbages can be stored for early winter use and the curly-leafed Savoy Group are hardiest and will stand outside most winters. The latter are not hard headed, really not much better eating than kales and they are useless for coleslaw, whereas 'Holland Late' is perfect and will keep for months. Taken up by the roots it can be hung upside-down in a shed or garage for winter use, though I find it best stored in a dead refrigerator (with the door shut to keep out air and rodents) after liberally dusting it with salt to prevent the slugs moving around and causing further damage. The cabbages go horrible on the outside in the store but clean up nicely.

'Holland Late' or 'Dutch White' is one of the longest developed varieties and has been selected by cabbage growers for several centuries to grow late into the autumn; it will stay in good condition for some months after lifting. Traditionally it would have been stored in a clamp under a layer of straw and soil, likewise it can be kept fresh in the garden by covering it with a large plastic bag stuffed full of straw to keep out the frost. Red cabbage is closely related and grown and stored in much the same way, but is most often used for pickling in vinegar.

Like the majority of brassicas these varieties need full sun and moist, rich, limy soil to be able to grow big, hard heads. As the stumps often come through a winter if left after the head is cut then it is worth cutting a cross in the top of the stem and removing diseased leaves but leaving the healthy ones, in the hope of getting bonus heads in spring. Sow in spring in pots, cells or a seedbed and transplant out in late spring/early summer. Make sure the soil is firm, as uncompacted soil produces loose heads which do not store so well.

As with all brassicas there are many pests and diseases – rotation and hygiene cope with lots of these, and growing under horticultural fleece deters several pests, such as white moths/flies and various caterpillars, while moist soils prevent heavy flea beetle damage. **BF**

Brassica oleracea var. *gongyloides* 'Superschmelz'

KOHL RABI

Type: half-hardy, herbaceous, biennial vegetable
Soil & situation: rich, moist soil/full sun to light shade
North American hardiness zone: normally grown as an annual
Height & spread: 45cm (18in)
Grow for: amazingly versatile; huge variety; easier to grow than turnips in adverse conditions

In light soil or in hot, dry weather it is easier to succeed with kohl rabi than it is with turnips. It can be used either cooked as turnips or raw as a crudité or in a salad. But I am no fan of most kohl rabis, as the majority of varieties attain only tennis-ball size before, like turnips, they become hot and woody.

'Superschmelz' is the exception. It is of Dutch origin and attains an astronomic size; I have grown it to bigger than a football and yet inside the flesh was as sweet and crisp as many a supermarket apple. Moreover this variety can be taken up in autumn and stored for several months without deteriorating as rapidly as some sorts of cabbage, especially if kept in cool conditions such as in a dead refrigerator. It is then available for making kohl slaw all winter.

Kohl rabi is an odd vegetable that has been developed to have a huge swollen stem and is probably derived from the old marrow cabbage. It first appeared in the 16th century in Italy, though the name suggests a more central European origin, and it is claimed to be from the Italian cavoli rape, meaning cabbage turnip. In France there are ornamental varieties with cut and frizzled leaves, and another with artichoke-like leaves apparently once favoured by confectioners for decoration!

It will grow in poor, dry conditions but does best in rich, moist, limy soil. Kohl rabi is not very hardy, so is best sown after the last frost and lifted before the first frost in autumn. Sow ideally *in situ* or in pots or cells from late spring into early summer. Space the plants 45cm (18in) apart when transplanting or thinning out, or more if going for big roots. Although closely related to the other brassicas, kohl rabi – once established – is remarkably unaffected by most of their problems. However, flea beetles can almost destroy small plants, so keep the soil moist. **BF**

Brassica rapa chinensis
PAK CHOI

Type: half-hardy, herbaceous, biennial vegetable
Soil & situation: rich, very moist soil/full sun/under cover in winter and light shade outdoors in summer
North American hardiness zone: normally grown as an annual
Height & spread: may reach 30cm (12in), or more when flowering
Grow for: one of the few vegetables to be available for 52 weeks of the year, and especially useful under cover in winter

Pak choi is like a cross between celery and a loose-leaf cabbage and is incredibly fast growing – even in winter if kept under cover. It is full of valuable minerals and vitamins and easy to use as a spinach, for braising like celery and in stir fries. The closely related *Pe-tsai* has less celery-like stems and more cabbage-like leaves and is probably the most slug-attractive plant in the garden.

It was not known to Europeans until the Victorian period. The Chinese have a whole series of brassicas, many of them closely resembling our European ones, but whereas ours come mostly from the wild coleworts, such as found on the chalk cliffs of Dover, the Chinese developed theirs from the very similar and closely related mustards; indeed, the seed can be ground into a mustard condiment.

Brassica rapa chinensis

Pak choi needs rich, moist soil with plentiful lime. It is prone to bolting if crowded, too hot or too dry – keeping the soil moist is crucial. It can be successionally sown in situ all year round under cover and outside from mid-spring until late summer. It is possible to cut back or pull off leaves to get renewal growth and also to detach and transplant small offshoots. Pak choi can be started off in pots and planted out with care – space plants at least 30cm (12in) apart each way.

It is very prone to slug damage and suffers the same pests and diseases as most other brassicas, many of which can be kept off by growing it under cover or under horticultural fleece. Flea beetle attacks this less than other brassicas, as the soil is always kept so moist. **BF**

Briza maxima
QUAKING GRASS

Type: hardy, annual grass
Soil & situation: any free-draining soil/sun
North American hardiness zone: annual
Height: 30cm (12in)
Spread: 25cm (10in)
Grow for: dainty flowers from late spring to mid-summer

This is such a pretty plant and dainty in every way. From late spring to late summer it forms dense, tufted clumps of narrow, pale green leaves only 20cm (8in) long that dry to become straw-coloured later in the season. However, the finest feature are the loose, open flower clusters that hang from arching, hair-fine stems. The tiny, heart-shaped 'spikelets' like pearlescent lockets, 1cm (1/2in) long, dance enthusiastically to the sound of the leaves rustling in the wind; they start light green, become mid-green and turn pale straw-yellow, like the leaves, as they mature.

It is possibly one of the earliest grasses grown for any use, other than edible purposes. *Briza minor* and *B. maxima* will self-seed and in good conditions can become weeds, but they are excellent for drying and should be picked immediately once they are fully developed, which sorts out the 'weed' problem too.

Briza maxima

There are other quaking grasses worth considering:

B. media is taller and perennial, the flower stems developing from a thick tuft of 'grass' from early to late summer. In Yorkshire, it is known as 'Trimmling Jockies' or 'Doddering Dickies' and it is used in pest control. It's said 'A trimmling jock i' t' house and you weeant hev a mouse'. Precisely!

B. minor is a short, dainty annual only 20cm (8in) tall, with tiny spikelets 5mm (1/4in) long. It flowers from early summer to early autumn. All need a sunny position on free-draining soil. Sow seed outdoors in spring or autumn in the position where it is to flower. **MB**

Brugmansia aurea

Type: evergreen shrub or small tree
Soil & situation: good, but well-drained soil/sunny position/minimum temperature of 7°C (45°F) in winter/fair amount of moisture when in growth
North American hardiness zone: 10–11
Height: 5–10m (16–33ft)
Spread: 2–4m (6½–13ft)
Grow for: copious quantities of huge, yellow to apricot hanging trumpets from summer to autumn; large, ovate leaves add a tropical feel to the garden

You can guarantee that the sight of these in full bloom will cause a stir among gardeners and non-gardeners alike. Those who do not grow them will think that you are really clever to grow such exotic-looking plants and to get them to flower so prolifically. But they are dead easy. The only possible stumbling block is whether you are able to lug them into a frost-free greenhouse, if you have one. They can be grown outside in a warm garden in the milder areas of the country, and in areas which receive little or no frost they will bloom for most of the year. They do get huge very fast – too huge – but it does not cause a problem as in spring you can cut them down to within 15cm (6in) of the ground or to any convenient height, and they burst back forming a grand multi-stemmed flowering shrub. I usually maintain mine at a height of 3m (10ft) at which size they look stately and impressive. The exotic flowers are scented at night and I have been told that if you inhale the fragrance it triggers hallucinogenic dreams – not surprising then that *Brugmansia* spp. are cultivated for their narcotic properties! I play safe though and stick to a glass of wine and have never dared let it give me a whirl.

Brugmansia aurea

Assuming you do not have the luxury of frost-free conditions outside, grow it in a large pot, or, for better results, plant it directly into the open border in late spring. If pot-grown, re-pot – or at least top dress – each spring, and water and liquid feed during growth. Slugs and snails will decimate the foliage, so in this respect pot growing is superior as you can easily control them. But in other respects, apparently, they do better in the border. At the end of autumn I drag it in (if grown in the border then pot it up), and because my temperatures are low, the leaves yellow and drop. This is to be expected unless you have bags of warmth. I keep it on the dry side over winter but as soon as everything starts to move in spring, I increase the food and water as it extends its growth. **BG**

Brugmansia suaveolens (syn. *Datura suaveolens*)

ANGELS' TRUMPETS

Type: tender, perennial, semi-woody shrub
Soil & situation: rich, moist compost/full sun/under cover in winter, outdoors in summer
North American hardiness zone: 10–11
Height & spread: best as a 'small tree' in a tub at 1.5–1.8m (5–6ft) each way, but can get twice as big
Grow for: a profusion of very big, scented, funnel-shaped flowers; AGM

A native of Brazil, the group's name was changed from the closely related *Datura* to *Brugmansia* when Queen Victoria was a virgin. We haven't taken to it yet. Nomenclaturial botanists, a plague on them and their dirty habits!

Angels' trumpets is a relatively reliable and impressive specimen for your patio or conservatory, which looks a million dollars but grows as easily as a fuchsia. Indeed, daturas can be thrown under frost-free cover and forgotten about until spring and will nearly always recover. The pure white forms of the soft, funnel-shaped, hanging flowers have the strongest most sweet perfume; other colours have been selected, but these are not as sweet. *Datura metel* and *D. meteloides* are more tender, and therefore better suited to the greenhouse or conservatory rather than the patio; both have upright funnels. Similar but smaller is *D. stramonium*, the thornapple, and it is a weed!

Brugmansia suaveolens

Best confined in a tub, put out for summer and returned under cover all winter. Water heavily during the growing season. Plants can go on many years, but they are easy to replace anyway. Prune back hard to form a standard with a small head when it's taken in at the end of the growing season or in spring before growth commences. Over the winter keep it almost bone dry and frost free. It can be grown from seed but cuttings are easy any time of year, indeed too easy as these plants multiply on you. Daturas seem to get a host of aphids, whiteflies, red spider mites et al but this never seems to stop them. Don't eat any parts as they are all toxic. **BF**

Buddleja fallowiana var. *alba*

Type: frost-hardy, deciduous shrub
Soil & situation: well-drained soil/will often grow in thin, stony, poor soils/if they are being pruned back annually, they do better in a fertile soil/sun/warm, sheltered environment/hardy to −10°C (14°F)
North American hardiness zone: 8–9
Height & spread: 3m (10ft)
Grow for: handsome white-felted foliage; secondary bonus – creamy-white, fragrant flowers from late summer to early autumn; AGM

This buddleja has elegant, white-felted shoots and very long, lanceolate, silver-green leaves, which are covered in white felt below. The flowers are usually the main reason for growing these shrubs, their fat, densely packed, flowering panicles being produced in large quantities, often heavily fragrant and stuffed with nectar. This one has more slender flowers on long, arching wands so they do make less impact than the flowers on many buddlejas. The eye is orange, creating an unusual, almost quaint appearance. But then, most things about this buddleja are different from the run-of-the-mill purple-flowered job that you more frequently see. But that is why I like it!

The pruning is best carried out in early spring as the buds begin to swell. Simply cut back all the wood to within 5cm (2in) of a low, permanent framework which you make in the first two to three years after planting, or cut back harder to ground level. It is a good idea to give it a thick, protective mulch in the winter. Propagation is very easy – you simply take hardwood cuttings in autumn. **BG**

Buddleja fallowiana var. *alba*

Buddleja 'Lochinch'

Buddleja globosa

Plant of the Week (see page 145)

Buddleja lindleyana

Type: half-hardy, deciduous shrub
Soil & situation: free-draining soil/sun/shelter
North American hardiness zone: 8–9
Height: 3m (10ft), or higher against a wall
Spread: 2.5m (8ft), sometimes taller
Grow for: elegant flower spikes in mid- and late summer

This plant with ecclesiastical connections reminds me of three splendid gentlemen: the Rev. Adam Buddle, an English botanist and vicar; John Lindley, a great horticulturist, administrator and writer; and a great friend of mine, Father Hugh Flower, a Kew-trained horticulturist turned parish priest who gave me the plant. What a wonderful gift! It's a plant with immense finesse; the sleek, gracefully arching stems are tipped with slender flower-spikes, up to 20cm (8in) long, of rich deep purple-violet to lilac flowers; each curved flower is covered on the outside with fine hairs, creating a velvety lavender sheen. In flower there's a cascade of blooms, like an exploding firework. Even the leaves, an attractive dark green, are narrow, tapered and elegant with a simple network of impressed veins; they are the perfect foil to the cinnamon-coloured older stems. Butterflies (and hummingbirds) love it!

In milder climates, grow against a sheltered, sunny wall, or in a cool greenhouse where weather conditions are more extreme. It thrives in moist, fertile, well-drained soil; feed and mulch in spring. It will become chlorotic if under-fed. As a shrub, cut back the previous year's shoots in early or mid-spring to one or two pairs of buds at the base. It can be fan trained against a wall, but the stems are rather stiff. Cut them back to within one or two pairs of buds of the framework of old wood; remove the oldest stems at the base and replace with new growth. Propagate by semi-ripe cuttings. **MB**

Buddleja 'Lochinch'

Type: hardy, deciduous shrub
Soil & situation: well-drained fertile soil/full sun
North American hardiness zone: 6–9
Height: 2.5m (8ft)
Spread: 3m (10ft)
Grow for: superb pewtery, green-grey foliage greening with age; beautiful lavender-blue 20cm (8in) long panicles, which arrive at the end of the summer, staying for many weeks; AGM

This is my favourite buddleja and a really stunning hybrid. It is, in fact, a cross between *B. davidii* and *B. fallowiana*. The flowers are produced in substantial numbers and the strong, but subtle, blue of the flower (it has an orange eye) tones well with the grey-green of the foliage and they have a sweetly scented fragrance too. It has a good bushy form and the structure of the bare plant in the winter is an asset too – not that common in deciduous shrubs.

Prune it back hard each year to keep growth compact and encourage better flowering. It is well worthwhile cutting back the flowerheads to a pair of leaves as they go over – this prevents them seeding around and can, if you are lucky, result in a second flowering. **BG**

Buddleja lindleyana

Buddleja x *weyeriana* 'Sungold'

Type: hardy, deciduous shrub
Soil & situation: fertile, well-drained soil/full sun
North American hardiness zone: 6–8
Height: 4m (13ft)
Spread: 3m (10ft)
Grow for: fragrant orange-yellow flowers in summer and early autumn; AGM

I have to admit I, as well as butterflies, love the large, solid flower panicles of *Buddleja davidii* and its cultivars. The rounded flower clusters of *B. globosa* 'Orange Ball' are also appealing.

B. x *weyeriana* is a cross between the two and the result is an improvement on both parents. *B.* x *w.* 'Sungold' has long arching branches and 20cm (8in) long, lance-shaped, mid-green leaves. The rounded clusters of fragrant, dark orange-yellow flowers are spaced along a grey-white stem to form a loose 30cm (12in) terminal panicle. The flowers are produced in summer and the plant will often still be in flower in late autumn.

Pruning should be carried out in spring, removing all last year's flowering shoots to within several centimetres of the older wood. Enormous growth of up to 2m (6½ft) will be made before summer, when it will produce flowers. Old, neglected shrubs can be rejuvenated by cutting into the old wood. Water and feed with a general fertilizer in late spring and the stumps will send out new growths. Propagate by softwood cuttings in early summer or hardwood cuttings inserted in the ground outside in late autumn. **JC**

Buddleja x *weyeriana* 'Sungold'

Buxus sempervirens
BOX

Type: hardy, evergreen shrub
Soil & situation: wide range of soils, providing it is well-drained/will tolerate a pH range from about 5.5–7.5/sun or light shade
North American hardiness zone: 6–8
Height: up to 8m (25ft) but usually grown as a multi-stemmed shrub to 1m (3ft) or less
Spread: to 8m (25ft)
Grow for: evergreen with small neat, shiny leaves; excellent for clipping and topiary work; AGM

Box has come back into vogue big time in the last 20 years or so. It is much used for giving some formality and structure to gardens whether with clipped forms, hedges, parterres or topiary, in classic or contemporary styles. Since the end of the 20th century, it has suffered from box blight, a disease which has affected several notable gardens including Sir Roy Strong's, The Laskett, but there are certain factors which reduce this risk. For low hedges, *B. sempervirens* can be used – it is less susceptible than the 'edging box', *B.* 'Suffruticosa'. I prefer the larger form anyway as it forms a plumper hedge but admittedly may need a second trim later on in summer due to its vigour. In the moister, more westerly parts of the country it is far more likely to be susceptible to blight than in the drier east. Apparently in Victorian times they used to rip it up and re-plant it at 12-yearly or so intervals – I think possibly because it grew to be too dense and so disease became more of a problem.

If the drainage is not good, do put this right before you plant. If I am planting a low hedge of this, I plant at 6 or 7 per metre (3 feet) run. This will form a recognizable, bushy hedge in three years or so (assuming you put in bushy liners), providing you trim the sides and top to get it to bush out. The best time to trim it used to be Derby Day in early summer, but with the milder winters if I waited this long I would have a scruffy looking hedge for longer than I want, so I tend to do mine in late spring, and if a heavy frost looms, I bring out the fleece or pray. I usually give it a secondary cut in late summer/early autumn to neaten it up before winter. Try not to water it overhead, this is thought to be one of the main factors that encourages the dreaded box blight. **BG**

Buxus sempervirens 'Handsworthiensis'
BOX

Type: fully hardy, evergreen shrub
Soil & situation: fertile, well-drained soil/sun or partial shade
North American hardiness zone: 6–8
Height & spread: 5m (16ft)
Grow for: the dense habit provides an excellent background for more colourful plants, and makes it ideal for hedging or screening

When the specification calls for a tall, dense, evergreen hedge for maximum privacy, use this plant. Kept clipped, not even an x-ray machine could see through it.

The dark, sage-green, cupped leaves are 4cm (1½in) long on stiff, upright stems. Box will withstand regular, close clipping to keep it in shape. It is tolerant of deep shade, making it ideal undercover in woodland. Left unclipped it will eventually form a large, straggly, multi-stemmed tree or shrub. In spring the foliage on the new growth is pale yellow turning to yellowish-green before it is due its next short back and sides. Terminal shoots are orange-tinted in autumn. The tiny, yellow-green spring flowers are insignificant.

The foliage exudes an unusual aroma, not unpleasant but immediately recognizable for what it is – box hedging. Rabbits, while catholic in taste, invariably leave box unnibbled. Snails, on the other hand, consider it their personal hotel. Within the branches there are likely to be hundreds, complete with their mobile homes – a point worth considering before you plant box hedges round fancy vegetable plots.

It is not a deep-rooted plant – most of its fibrous roots lie close to the soil surface. A combination of dry soil and full sun stunts growth causing sickly foliage. This is a common occurrence with pot-grown box. An annual mulch of bark or rotted farmyard manure applied to the base of the hedge in spring will prevent the soil drying out. Propagation is by softwood or hardwood cuttings.

It will be noticed I avoided mentioning its use for my pet hate, topiary. If you must and bearing in mind its stiff, upright nature, 'Handsworthiensis' will allow you to clip a full-size giraffe! **JC**

Buxus sempervirens 'Handsworthiensis'

Caiophora lateritia

Type: tender, annual or perennial climber
Soil & situation: free-draining soil/hot sunshine
North American hardiness zone: normally grown as an annual
Height & spread: 3m (10ft)
Grow for: weird flowers from mid-summer to early autumn; weirder seedpods

I first saw this in the garden at Red Gables, a house just outside Evesham, southwest England, where Derek and Rowlatt Cook, a brother and sister with an infinite enthusiasm for plants, were growing this through the spiny stems of a berberis in a potential 'double whammy' of pain! It was probably the only way to 'cage' their caiophora and deter passers-by from touching this fascinating plant! The grey-green leaves are covered in soft, bristly hairs; stroke them and you'll recoil in pain as hidden among them are sharp, stinging spines!

The brick-red, apricot or white flowers, with unusual keeled petals and tufts of anthers projecting along the centre, hang like hovering flying saucers waiting to land. It looks wonderful scrambling through silver-foliage shrubs like cotton lavender, but avoid planting it through sage, though I have seen it done, as you might need the leaves for flavouring! The seedpods look like screws with an irregular wing and a spike at the end, but having seen the flowers it's no surprise that they're strange!

Treat as a tender annual or biennial. Sow under glass in early spring and plant out before it starts to twine, after the danger of frost has passed. The stinging hairs are usually (!) ineffective on young plants at transplanting time. It needs a warm, dry, sunny position and free-draining soil; incorporate grit before planting if necessary. Grow in mild, sheltered climates as a short-lived perennial, mulching with straw or bracken over winter. Alternatively, grow it in a container and over-winter in a conservatory. **MB**

Caiophora lateritia

Calendula officinalis

Calendula officinalis
POT MARIGOLD

Type: hardy, herbaceous, semi-evergreen annual/biennial
Soil & situation: any soil/preferably full sun to light shade
North American hardiness zone: normally grown as an annual
Height & spread: 30cm (12in) each way in good soil
Grow for: attractive year-round-foliage; striking orange flowers; easy, reliable and edible

This multiple-value plant is fast and easy to grow; it retains its foliage in all but the hardest winters; it isn't prone to pests or diseases; and its pungently scented flowers add flavour to stews and salads, and can be dried for winter use. The leaves have the same flavour as the flowers and can be used when none are available, but they do have an even more pungent taste. Indeed, it is a classic 'children's plant'.

A native of Europe and North Africa, calendula has been known for millennia and is so named because it was always to be found in flower on the *Kalends,* the first day of each month, which it can do in warmer countries than Britain. In the Middle Ages it was called Mary-buds and dedicated to the Virgin, as it was allegedly always in flower on her holy days. In the past marigold petals were used for turning grey hair yellow and the leaves for treating wounds.

They can be almost left to themselves as they self-sow happily, but for a guaranteed year-round supply sow some under cover where they will flower constantly. They are reputed good companions as they attract beneficial insects. Dead-heading promotes more flowers and is worth doing to prevent excessive self-seeding. Sow, preferably *in situ,* from early spring onwards and they will start flowering within 10 to 12 weeks, making them among the fastest annuals to bloom. They suffer no problems at all apart from self-sowing everywhere. **BF**

John adds:
The flowers may be single or double and up to 10cm (4in) across, flowering from early summer to autumn. Colours include cream, orange, yellow and gold. There are many varieties including bicolours such as 'Fiesta Gitana'. 'Indian Prince' is excellent for flower arrangements and grows to 80cm (32in) with dark orange-brown tinted flowers.

Calendula officinalis 'Indian Prince'

Callicarpa bodinieri var. *giraldii* 'Profusion'

Callicarpa bodinieri var. *giraldii* 'Profusion'

BEAUTY BERRY

Type: hardy, deciduous shrub
Soil & situation: fertile, well-drained soil/full sun or light shade
North American hardiness zone: 6–8
Height: 3m (10ft)
Spread: 2m (6½ft)
Grow for: small, astonishingly coloured, deep violet fruits that resemble beads sprayed with metallic paint; AGM

If this shrub likes you and your garden it will out-perform most other berrying plants. It may, however, sulk, in which case give it a ride in the wheelbarrow to a different site. Even as a big plant it transplants well. The bead-like fruit are a special treat in winter.

The 15cm (6in) long, young leaves are bronze, turning dark green as they age. Clusters of pale pink flowers appear in summer from the leaf axils and are followed by groups of small, metallic-looking, deep violet fruit. The colour is so non-gardening they look artificial. They will fruit better after a long, hot summer. Provide shelter from cold, drying winds.

Prune in early spring, cutting back the older stems to the main framework. Old, neglected plants may be hard pruned to within 45cm (18in) of the ground. Feed with a high-nitrogen fertilizer and water well all summer after a hard pruning. New, strong flowering shoots will grow to replace the old branches. Propagation is by softwood cuttings in late spring or semi-ripe cuttings pulled off with a heel and rooted in a heated propagator during summer. **JC**

Matt adds:
This is an unusual plant mainly because its ideas of colour co-ordination, based on violet-purple and tawny, could have come straight from the 1970s. It's fascinating how nature combines the most unusual colours and they are still visually acceptable; if they were artificially reproduced in paints or plastics it would look hideous! That's probably because the 'tones' and 'shades' are always perfect.

What's in a name? In this case, plenty! The Greek *kallos*, meaning beauty and *karpos*, fruit, and two missionaries Emile Marie Bodinieri from France and Guiseppe Giraldi from Italy, who were both avid plant collectors. And 'Profusion'? Just grow it and wait until you see the mass of berries! This plant was especially selected for this feature and its bronze-purple young leaves. The insignificant, pale pink flowers appear in mid-summer in evenly spaced dense clusters wrapped round the stem. They are followed from mid- to late autumn onwards by clusters of dark violet fruits spaced along the tawny-coloured branches. The berries look remarkable, particularly when you add the deep rose-purple autumn colour of the leaves.

Callistemon citrinus 'Austraflora Firebrand'

BOTTLEBRUSH

Type: half-hardy, evergreen shrub
Soil & situation: moist, well-drained, fertile, neutral to acid soil/full sun
North American hardiness zone: 9–11
Height: 2m (6½ ft)
Spread: 4m (13ft)
Grow for: crimson flower spikes that make an excellent focal point

The bottlebrushes are so wonderfully exotic in flower, they grab the attention and hold it over a long period. The silvery flower buds form like a string of pearls, opening to the familiar 'brushes' and finally there is a decorative cylinder of hard, woody seedpods. The habit of growth is low and spreading, forming a wide, medium height, bushy plant. The 10cm (4in) long, lance-shaped, dark green leaves open from young, silvery-pink shoots. Bright, crimson flower spikes are 10–15cm (4–6in) long and freely produced during late spring and early summer.

Pruning is necessary only where branches are spoiling the shape. The shrub continues to grow beyond the flower spike. Eventually each branch has a series of 10–15cm (4–6in) lengths of dead, woody, seed cases strung along the stem. Bottlebrushes tolerate hard pruning to rejuvenate old plants. Propagation is easy by semi-ripe cuttings in late summer. Sow the fine seed on the surface of a moist, loam-based compost in late spring. Keep the temperature at 18°C (64°F). **JC**

Callistemon citrinus 'Austraflora Firebrand'

Helleborus orientalis

LENTEN ROSE

Type: hardy evergreen perennial
Soil & situation: limestone or chalky soils/light or moderate shade in damp woodland/tolerates sun, though dislikes exposed conditions
Hardiness zone: 4–9
Height: to about 50cm (20in)
Spread: 45cm (18in)
Grow for: exquisite, usually white or greenish flowers from late winter to spring; various cultivars in a range of colours from black-purple, through purple to pink, from yellow-white to white and green; evergreen foliage, except in exceptionally cold winters. Called the Lenten rose because its blooms are usually at their best just before Easter.

Many people, understandably, become enchanted by the hellebore flowers and there are numerous cultivars, which have been selected and named, with stunning flowers, such as 'Phillip Ballard', which is a dark purple, and 'Cosmos', which is pale pink with attractive purple spots. The plants exhibit their flowers rather discreetly – you have to make a special visit to the plants to admire them properly, but it is definitely worth it.

The flowers apart, hellebores are good for their foliage, too. The deep, glossy, green basal leaves are handsome and look very presentable even in late winter after a regular battering of snow, frost, winds and wet. They self-sow freely, a big asset, and it is exciting to see what amazing colour flowers the new seedlings will produce, as they are a promiscuous bunch. Take care that the seedlings do not submerge the parent plant, especially if it is a special named cultivar. It is worth trying a choice plant like this in different places, for instance in a meadow setting – in light shade where the grass is not too dense a sward – or in a window box where the plants can be admired regularly at close quarters. Hellebores do not take too kindly to being moved. If you do need to divide up an old plant, it is best done in winter or spring when it is in flower and while the roots are fairly dormant. Then cosset it until it re-establishes itself. **BG**

Callistephus chinensis 'Ostrich Plume'

ANNUAL ASTER, CHINA ASTER

Type: hardy annual
Soil & situation: fertile, moist, neutral to alkaline soil/full sun
North American hardiness zone: annual
Height: 60cm (24in)
Spread: 30cm (12in)
Grow for: summer bedding in a range of bright colours

As a boy I used to sell these as cut flowers to earn money to buy my first greenhouse. The only problem was they lasted for more than a week in water and I only did my selling on a Saturday morning. I still think they are hard to beat.

The mid-green leaves are 8cm (3½in) long and toothed. The daisy-like flowers are held on long, branched stems well clear of the foliage during late summer and all autumn. They are mainly in shades of pink and crimson with feathery, reflexed, double flowerheads. The Milady Series are more compact, growing to 30cm (12in) in a wider range of colours including white, blue, scarlet, pink, rose and red. The double, daisy-like flowerheads are rounded.

Dead heading extends the flowering season. They prefer a moist soil and shelter from cold winds. Water regularly in summer to prevent the soil drying out and the plant's growth slowing down. Propagation is by seed sown in early spring in a cool greenhouse or in late spring *in situ*. China asters are more resistant than most other asters to aster wilt but are very prone to aphid attacks in the young foliage. **JC**

Callistephus chinensis 'Ostrich Plume'

Caltha palustris

Caltha palustris

KINGCUP, MARSH MARIGOLD, MEADOW BRIGHT, MAY-BLOB

Type: hardy perennial
Soil & situation: shallow water to a depth of 15cm (6in)/bog gardens/prefers a sunny site/will grow happily in part shade
North American hardiness zone: 3–7
Height: to 40cm (16in)
Spread: 45cm (18in)
Grow for: golden-yellow, large, long-lasting, waxy, cup-shaped flowers on long stems in spring; after flowering, glossy green leaves carry on growing, providing particularly good foliage effects for waterside areas; AGM

This is a stunning native plant, with its giant, buttercup-like flowers and large, shiny leaves. As it is a native, it is pretty easy to please, so decent groups quite quickly establish to form a good display along the water margins, both in water and in boggy patches. It will also survive being planted in border situations if the soil is moisture retentive and the situation is shady. *Caltha palustris* var. *palustris* is different in habit: its stems are creeping and it roots as it goes. As such it is useful for spreading over damp banks, marshy areas and in shallow water. The leaves are smaller, but the flowers are large initially and then reduce in size later on. The often grown *C. palustris* 'Flore Pleno' (see next entry) has double, yellow flowers and is often admired, but I prefer the native, single-flowered kingcup.

Depending on where it is positioned, this plant may be established in large aquatic baskets or straight into the the ground or planted on the pool base in spring or autumn. It likes a good rich organic soil and so mulching in spring, when grown in land situations, pays dividends. If grown in baskets, it is best divided and re-potted with additional fertilizer and organic matter as soon as it looks confined. It is easily propagated by division in spring, but can also be grown from seed, sown in summer under cover. Apparently American forms of *C. palustris* will self-sow in suitable conditions. Mine, alas, have not done so. **BG**

Caltha palustris 'Flore Pleno'

Caltha palustris 'Flore Pleno'
KINGCUP, DOUBLE-FLOWERED MARSH MARIGOLD

Type: hardy, aquatic, deciduous perennial
Soil & situation: rich, boggy soil/full sun
North American hardiness zone: 3–7
Height & spread: 30cm (12in)
Grow for: interesting shaped leaves; cheerful double yellow flowers in spring; perfect for damp, boggy ground; AGM

I saw a remarkable planting of the double-flowered marsh marigold many years ago in the Netherlands. The owner had planted it on both sides of a narrow dyke in front of his house. It was in full flower. There was a blue sky and when I looked along the length of the dyke the picture on the still water was of two solid lines of gold with a narrow reflected strip of blue sky in between.

The kidney-shaped, toothed, dark green leaves appear in early spring and can be up to 10cm (4in) long. *Caltha palustris* 'Flore Pleno' produces waxy, double, buttercup-yellow flowers in spring on 25cm (10in) bare stems. Before the flowers fully open the centre of each bloom has a greenish tinge. A second flush of flowers may appear in the early autumn. The variety *C. p.* var. *alba* is more compact, flowering in early spring before the leaves appear. It produces solitary, single white flowers with bright yellow stamens.

C. p. 'Flore Pleno' tolerates growing in water for short periods but prefers to be in boggy, constantly wet soil at the side of a stream or pond. Propagation is by division of the large clumps in late summer or, in cold areas, in early spring before flowering. **JC**

Camassia quamash
QUAMASH

Type: frost-hardy, bulbous perennial
Soil & situation: rich, deep, moisture-retentive soils/sun or part shade
North American hardiness zone: 4–9
Height: to 90cm (36in)
Spread: 5cm (2in)
Grow for: deep blue starry flowers produced in racemes in late spring

This plant is a vigorous clump former, with linear, green leaves about 40cm (16in) long and 1cm (½in) wide. In late spring it produces bright blue flowers which are shown off to their best advantage in slightly wild or natural-looking areas. This particular camassia is a strong grower and is often highly successfully naturalized in grass. I often also use it in open woodland areas where it will get sun for part of the day. *Camassia leichtlinii* subsp. *leichtlinii* (AGM) is also a useful plant but is slightly taller and has white flowers. The flowering period is short though, and it is not so able to compete with grasses in a meadow situation.

This plant does not give of its best in drier, poorer soils – the flowering period will be reduced (or even non-existent). It produces seed freely, which usually ripens by mid-summer. It is ideal to propagate by this method or you can take offsets in summer. **BG**

Camassia quamash

Camellia 'Cornish Snow'

Camellia 'Cornish Snow'

Type: hardy, evergreen shrub
Soil & situation: neutral to slightly acid soil (between pH 5–7), moist but well-drained and humus-rich/sheltered site either shaded, partially shaded or sunny/hates exposed, cold, windy sites/avoid east-facing walls unless shaded
North American hardiness zone: 7–9
Height: 3m (10ft)
Spread: 1.5m (5ft)
Grow for: superb evergreen foliage; small, single, white flowers from mid-winter to late spring; AGM

This plant is a hybrid between *C. cuspidata* and *C. saluenensis* and is an excellent, hardy, faster-growing camellia. It has slightly pendent branches and 5cm (2in) long, lance-shaped, bold, glossy leaves which are bronze-purple when young, later turning dark green. It is free flowering, producing multitudes of the petite, white flowers which are pink-tinged on opening, along the stems. These smaller flowers are far less susceptible to frost and wind damage than the very large-flowered forms. Camellias are often thought to be successful in more shady sites but when grown on a south or west wall they do flower more readily – as long as they still get the necessary moisture and their roots are cool, they will not suffer from bud drop. They are ideal for growing in containers.

These are fantastically long-lived plants, so it is important to find the right position where they will always be appreciated. Dense shade will inhibit bud formation; early morning sun, late frost and sunshine on frosted flowers will damage them. We did use a digger to move a mature specimen some two years ago and it re-established afterwards with no apparent ill effects. Camellias are best purchased as larger plants, about 60–90cm (24–36in) high and planted with lots of rotted organic matter. They need little pruning, just trimming lightly to shape the plant, only if needed, and the removal of dead and damaged young growth in spring before growth starts. Neglected plants will take hard pruning back into old wood. **BG**

Camellia japonica 'Bob Hope'

Camellia japonica 'Bob Hope'

Type: hardy, evergreen shrub
Soil & situation: moist, acid soil/sun or dappled shade/sheltered position
North American hardiness zone: 7–9
Height: 3m (10ft)
Spread: 2m (6½ft)
Grow for: glossy foliage and deep red flowers; AGM

I was visiting a camellia nursery when a glorious specimen at the far end of the greenhouse caught my eye. I ran down the path, picked up the plant and claimed it as my own, imagining a romantic name that conjured up images of the orient and vast hillsides clothed with camellias. Then I saw the label – 'Bob Hope'. I've nothing against him, but how could such a wonderful camellia be called 'Bob Hope'? So now Bob, a chance seedling from a nursery in California, stands in a large pot by my back door, displaying his spectacular, deep red, semi-double flowers and a boss of golden stamens. One day he'll be allowed into the garden; I hope he doesn't leave divots in the lawn!

It needs a sheltered position away from cold wind, and in bright light or dappled shade; avoid sites that get the early morning sun as it can damage the blooms. Grow in acid soil, dig in plenty of well-rotted organic matter if necessary before planting, do not plant too deeply, and mulch in spring with well-rotted compost, forest bark, pine needles or similar. Keep the soil moist, particularly from mid-summer to mid-autumn when next year's flower buds are being formed; use rainwater during dry periods.

It can be grown in a container during its early years; use multi-purpose or ericaceous compost, and feed with liquid fertilizer every three weeks. Prune if necessary immediately after flowering. Propagate by leaf bud, or by semi-ripe cuttings from late summer onwards. It is susceptible to aphids, scale and sooty mould – check plants regularly. **MB**

Camellia x *williamsii* 'Anticipation'

Camellia x *williamsii* 'Anticipation'

Type: hardy, evergreen shrub
Soil & situation: moist, well-drained, humus-rich, acid soil/partial shade/shelter from morning sun
North American hardiness zone: 7–9
Height: 4m (13ft)
Spread: 2m (6½ft)
Grow for: glossy, evergreen foliage and lovely double flowers in spring; AGM

It is difficult to set one camellia on a pedestal when there are so many excellent varieties. However *Camellia* x *williamsii* 'Anticipation' was my first camellia, a present from a great nurseryman, Leslie Slinger of Slieve Donard nursery, at the foot of the Mourne Mountains, Northern Ireland. It is still my favourite. It forms a tight, upright shrub with glossy, bright evergreen leaves. The large, deep rose-pink, double flowers, appearing in late winter and early spring, resemble those of a peony.

While the plant is totally hardy, its flowers are easily damaged in spring after a frost. If the morning sun thaws out the frozen flowers quickly they turn brown. The secret is not to plant spring-flowering camellias where they would be hit by the early sun. In the right site it makes a great wall plant and is equally at home in the shrub border or in a woodland situation.

C. x *williamsii* is one of the best hybrid shrubs. All its cultivars, including 'Anticipation', are free flowering, ranging from the single, white-flowered 'Francis Hanger' and the single pink flowers of 'Saint Ewe' to the double-flowered 'Water Lily' (bright pink) and 'Bow Bells' (deep rose).

Incorporate as much humus, in the form of leafmould, rotted farmyard manure or home-made compost, into the soil as possible. Plant at the same depth as in the pot with the rootball close to the surface. Mulch with composted bark every spring to retain moisture in the soil. Water during dry spells, especially in the autumn. If, at this time, the soil dries out, the camellia will drop its unopened flower buds. **JC**

Campanula persicifolia 'Telham Beauty'

WILLOW BELL, PEACH BELLS, PEACH-LEAVED BELLFLOWER

Type: hardy perennial
Soil & situation: moderately, fertile and well-drained soil/sun or light shade
North American hardiness zone: 3–8
Height: 90cm (36in)
Spread: 30cm (12in)
Grow for: a strong and vigorous plant, a mainstay of the herbaceous border; single, very large, good blue flowers in summer, which repeat again in autumn; attractive to bees and butterflies; foliage of evergreen leaves; an excellent cut flower

Lovely, graceful flowers are produced which fit into various parts of the garden. They are highly effective when inter-planted with shrub roses, as they all flower together and are two good ingredients of those much sought-after, classic, colourful mixed borders. They thrive equally well in light woodland and in bold groups looking relaxed and informal with lace-cap hydrangeas, ferns and the like. They work well, too, when mingled with other perennials in large sweeps of planting with their tolerance to light shade and sun, making them come into their own. They look almost animated in full flower in dappled sunlight. The white form, *C. persicifolia alba* is equally good.

There are many other good cultivated and wild campanulas, such as *C. latiflora*, which is available in different varieties, colours and heights; they tend to seed and have similar evergreen foliage. I also have the native harebell, *C. rotundifolia*, which is a really beautiful wild flower, growing in the meadow.

If your soil is thin and light this plant will not produce the goods so, if this is the case, it may be worth bulking up your soil. It does not require staking unless it is grown in an extremely exposed position. Propagation can be from division, basal cuttings and seed. It will seed around fairly actively. **BG**

Campanula persicifolia 'Telham Beauty'

Campanula zoysii

Campanula zoysii

CRIMPED BELLFLOWER

Type: hardy, semi-evergreen perennial
Soil & situation: well-drained, gritty, alkaline soil/full sun
North American hardiness zone: 5–7
Height: 5cm (2in)
Spread: 10cm (4in)
Grow for: an unbeatable plant for the rockery – cushion forming with lavender-blue flowers

When it comes to plants suitable for a rockery scree bed this gem is the number-one contender. It will thrive in a soil which is almost totally composed of grit.

It forms a cushion with small, glossy, mid-green leaves. Flowers appear in summer on short, erect stems. Each carries several tubular, lavender-blue flowers, almost totally enclosed at the mouth as if they have been crimped. It will survive only in very well-drained soil and hates winter rain, needing a sheet of glass overhead to act as an umbrella. Alternatively it may be grown in a container and plunged into the rockery for the summer, then lifted and moved under cover for the winter.

Propagate by seed sown in autumn and over-wintered in a cold frame with lots of ventilation but protection from rain. Root softwood cuttings in early summer in a heated propagator, removing the growing tip to prevent it trying to produce flowers. **JC**

Campsis x *tagliabuana* 'Madame Galen'

TRUMPET CREEPER

Type: frost-hardy, deciduous climber
Soil & situation: fertile but moist well-drained soil/sunny and warm wall with support/requires a little time to 'settle in' and start flowering/needs protection in the first two years during cold periods
North American hardiness zone: 5–9
Height & spread: 10m (33ft)
Grow for: exotic-looking, highly vigorous climber; brilliant salmon-red trumpet flowers over a long period from late summer to autumn; AGM

I must admit I have not yet grown this plant but have admired it in a friend's garden. She has it clambering up the front of her London terrace house and the massive production of the extraordinary brilliant tuber-like flowers causes passersby to stop and gawp. With her it has survived some very cold periods and I have it on my list for the garden here, confident that the tropical appearance belies its hardiness. The foliage has pinnate, dark green leaves which are up to 30cm (12in) long, so it is not a delicate-looking plant in any way, but bold and quite headstrong both in appearance and growth. This fact makes it suitable for spreading over a roof of an outbuilding or up a dead tree. Campsis is also used as a free-standing bush or hedge but needs heavy pruning to keep it in shape.

This plant is one for a spring planting in a sharp-draining site. A couple of layers of fleece at the ready for those sharp frosty nights and a good mulching over the roots should get it through those first two winters. When the plant has grown to fill the allotted space, pruning should be carried out in late winter or early spring, and consists of cutting back the previous season's growth to two or three buds of the framework. It may well require a fair bit of tying in as it clings on by aerial roots. **BG**

Campsis x *tagliabuana* 'Madame Galen'

Canna 'Durban'

Canna 'Durban'

INDIAN SHOT PLANT

Type: tender perennial
Soil & situation: rich soil, plenty of moisture/sun
North American hardiness zone: 7–10
Height: 2m (6½ft)
Spread: 60cm (24in)
Grow for: fabulous foliage and flowers from early summer to autumn

Cannas are amazingly easy to grow in containers or sunny borders, look magnificent in big groups and are wonderful when lit by the evening sun; they are 'must have' plants for the 'tropical' garden. I visited one of the National Collection holders, Keith Hayward, and his small plot was packed with plants of all shapes, sizes and colours; there's an incredible choice. At the time of writing he has well over 200 cultivars; there must be one for you!

Canna 'Durban' has bronze foliage and pink stripes in a herringbone pattern; the leaves gradually turn green and yellow. The flower is big, bold and orange! Wow! *C.* 'Australia' has dark bronze foliage that deepens to almost black by summer with red flowers. I've just bought one and so has my mate Mike, in Florida. 'Fatamorgana' has spectacular dark pink flowers and 'Alaska' has cream-coloured flowers. Where space is limited, there are smaller cultivars for pots on the patio. 'Flameche' is about 30cm (12in) tall with green leaves and pale orange flowers; 'Gnom' has rich pale pink flowers.

They need a sheltered site, fertile soil and full sun. Dig in a generous amount of well-rotted organic matter, provide plenty of water and feed regularly with a high-potash fertilizer. They need good, rich soil and a rich diet; it is impossible to over-feed! Dead-head regularly. In autumn, when frost blackens the foliage, lift the rhizome, cut stems back to 10cm (4in) from the base, store in slightly moist peat substitute or similar in frost-free conditions. Divide when necessary at replanting time, ensuring each division has at least one strong bud. Re-plant into pots in early spring and start them off in a greenhouse; water sparingly, increasing as more growth appears. Plant out when there is no danger of frost.

Slugs and snails bite through young foliage while it is 'scrolled'. One that was brought to *Gardeners' Question Time* looked as if 666 had been etched on the leaf – it provided plenty of laughs! Who says molluscs don't have a sense of humour? **MB**

Canna iridiflora (syn. *Canna* x *ehemanii*)

Plant of the Week (see page 257)

Capsicum annuum

SWEET PEPPER

Type: tender, annual/semi-perennial crop
Soil & situation: rich, well-drained compost/full sun in warm position
North American hardiness zone: normally grown as an annual
Height: 1m (3ft) or more
Spread: at least 30cm (12in)
Grow for: attractive-looking crop of great value economically and nutritionally

Almost every gardener grows tomatoes but few grow sweet peppers. Yet given a greenhouse they are actually easier to grow as they require less nipping out, less support and less watering in smaller pots to produce a respectable crop, which is worth far more than tomatoes in cash value and in vitamins. Green peppers usually turn red as they ripen and become less indigestible – the green are reputed to cause wind. There are hundreds of varieties, including some that ripen from orange to purple, each with a slightly different flavour.

Capsicum comes from the Greek word *kaptos*, meaning to bite. Natives of tropical America, sweet peppers were ignored until recent times when they have become valued for their vitamin content and their colour, which is always welcome on a plate, especially in salads and on pizzas.

They need a warm, light spot, so are better in pots on staging than down in the cold border soil, unless it's a hot summer. They can live for several years if given the right conditions. Spread shoots and nip out tips to encourage bushier plants when small, as the fruits are borne at the joints. Over-winter to crop in the second or even third year, when they will produce fruit earlier than a seed-grown plant. Sow in early spring in individual pots in the warmth, and keep the soil moist but never let it get waterlogged. You may succeed with them outdoors in a very warm sheltered garden, but they are really only worth cropping under cover. Aphids are always a problem especially when the plants are young, but soft soap sprays will cure them. Slugs may damage ripening fruits. **BF**

Capsicum annuum

Capsicum chinense (syn. *C. tetragonum*) Habanero Group

CHILI PEPPER

Type: tender, annual/semi-perennial crop
Soil & situation: very well-drained, rich compost/full sun in warmth – not for the open garden in Britain
North American hardiness zone: normally grown as an annual
Height & spread: 1m (3ft) each way in good conditions
Grow for: extremely expensive to buy, yet fairly easy to grow

All chili peppers, including *Capsicum frutescens*, which is used to make tabasco, are even better value to grow than tomatoes or sweet peppers as they are expensive to buy, yet not difficult to grow given a greenhouse or even a sunny windowsill.

This particular group is known as Habanero or Scotch/grannies bonnet peppers, well beloved by much of South America, the people of Jamaica and other Caribbean islands. They give a fierce heat but also an aromatic flavour, whereas most chilies give more heat than flavour. All chilies are much interbred and there are hundreds of sub-varieties, so you can find Red Habanero, Orange Habanero, Chocolate Habanero, Scotch Bonnet Red and Scotch Bonnet Yellow. The true Habaneros are best eaten raw, while the true Scotch Bonnets are better for cooking.

Most hot or chili peppers were introduced long before the sweet sorts, probably to substitute for the increasingly expensive black and white pepper brought from the East Indies, which was needed to spice up a bland diet of dubiously valid meat. (The modern *chinense* appellation is a misnomer, as it is definitely of South American origin.)

If grown in a well-drained compost in warm, light conditions the plant may live for two or three years but it usually dies after the first grim summer. Sow in early spring in individual pots and keep in a warm, very light place. Do not let the compost become waterlogged or allow it to stand wet in cool or cold weather. Aphids need spraying with soapy water. **BF**

Capsicum chinense

Cardiocrinum giganteum

Cardiocrinum giganteum

GIANT LILY

Type: hardy, bulbous perennial
Soil & situation: rich, moist, organic soil/dappled shade
North American hardiness zone: 7–9
Height: 4m (13ft)
Spread: indefinite
Grow for: flower spikes from mid- to late summer

The elegant spires of flowering cardiocrinums are one of the most glorious spectacles in gardening. Huge, heart-shaped, glossy leaves, up to 45cm (18in) across, diminish in size towards the apex of the stem as a fanfare of as many as 20, fragrant, white, trumpet-shaped flowers up to 15cm (6in) long with a reddish-purple staining in the throat sound their triumphal crescendo. In the dappled light of a woodland glade against a background of dark-leaved rhododendrons they look magnificent.

Tragically this majestic display is their final reveille. They die after flowering but produce up to six offsets that flower after two to three years; the secret is to plant bulbs of different sizes, or a new one each year for a display over several years.

Cardiocrinum giganteum var. *yunnanense* has slightly shorter black stems with bronze young leaves.

They need cool, moist growing conditions and shade to protect the roots; ideally they should be surrounded with small shrubs or mulched with straw in colder areas to protect them from spring frosts.

Dig in old growbags, multi-purpose compost, leafmould, well rotted manure and anything organic to create a cool, moist soil at least 60cm (24in) deep. Plant the bulbs immediately, no less than 1m (3ft) apart when they arrive in autumn (do not let them dry out), position their tips level with the surface and cover with a thin layer of leafmould. Given space and time they naturalize. Alternatively, after they have flowered, dig up and replant the young bulbs in a new position or leave the sausage-like fruits to burst, then sow the seed; they take between six and eight years or more to flower. The old flower stems make an attractive feature in the garden and home. Slugs can damage young leaves. **MB**

Bob adds:
This is not an easy plant to keep happy but when/if you do it is formidable. Stately, magnificent, impressive, highly scented enormous flowers make it a tangible garden status symbol.

Aquilegia canadensis

COLUMBINE, GRANNY'S BONNET

Type: hardy, herbaceous perennial
Soil & situation: cool, moist, fertile, well-drained soil/sun or dappled shade
Hardiness zone: 3–8
Height: 90cm (36in)
Spread: 30cm (12in)
Grow for: dainty spring flowers and foliage; AGM

Tiptoe among the sun-dappled, silent woodlands and damp shady banks and you may see fairies. You may not see them or believe in them, but that doesn't mean to say that they don't exist! From east Canada heading south to New Mexico, the Canadian columbine is one of the ultimate fairy flowers. Like so many *Aquilegia* species, everything about it is delicate and ethereal. Its leaves, a filigree of the finest dark green 'maidenhair' float silently in the breeze. Hovering above them on dainty stems are clouds of fairies dressed in dainty bell-like skirts of lemon-yellow with deep red or scarlet wings.

Its relatives are just the same: *A. elegantula* swoops, its spurs follow like beams of pale red; *A. formosa* var. *formosa* has a pale orange-red trail, like a cluster of shooting stars. Fairies in the forest? You would almost believe it was true!

They need cool, moist, fertile, well-drained soil in sun or dappled shade; dig in plenty of well-rotted organic matter if necessary. They are perfect for woodland gardens, planted on banks for easier viewing or in borders, though their dainty flowers may be lost without equally delicate companions.

Sow seed in containers in a cold frame as soon as they are ripe or in spring; you can divide plants but they dislike disturbance and take a long time to re-establish. Cut back foliage in autumn or spring and mulch. Keep moist during dry weather. Susceptible to powdery mildew in dry conditions. **MB**

Carex comans 'Frosted Curls'
SEDGE

Type: hardy, evergreen sedge
Soil & situation: prefers moist soil in sun or partial shade
North American hardiness zone: 7–9
Height & spread: 30cm (12in)
Grow for: swirling coloured leaves all year round

There are lots of super sedges for the garden and many of them come from New Zealand, the land of the 'Long White Cloud'. It's a wonderful country and I've visited it several times; my wife comes from there and the children have dual nationality, so I'm happy to promote the place and particularly its plants! *Carex comans* 'Frosted Curls' is a New Zealand introduction. I love the dense tufts of arching, pale silvery-green, hair-like leaves that twist and swirl. I've seen it hanging like Rapunzel's hair from a pot on a plinth and used to create swirling 'water' in a wonderful seaside garden. But it's not alone, there's plenty more!

C. comans has narrow, dark chocolate coloured leaves. *C. comans* bronze, the familiar form, has the habit of 'Frosted Curls' but is rusty-red. *C. c.* 'Kupferflamme' has copper-bronze flowers from mid-summer until autumn. *C. buchananii* is stiffly upright but arches with age and has narrow, rich reddish-brown leaves to 60cm (24in). It does best in sun. *C. flagellifera* is a real beauty, with greenish-chestnut leaves and light brown flower spikes which reach over 1m (3ft) as the seeds mature. Variants in cultivation often have red-brown foliage and grow to 72cm (28in) x 90cm (36in). *C. testacea* forms a tussock of narrow olive-green leaves tinted bronze and orange, particularly in winter. *C. t.* 'Old Gold' turns golden-yellow in winter.

They need sunshine or partial shade and are happy in most soils, but dislike extreme wet or dry conditions. Divide frommid-spring to early summer. Aphids sometimes infest the stem bases. **MB**

Carex comans 'Frosted Curls'

Carpinus betulus

Carpinus betulus
COMMON HORNBEAM

Type: hardy, deciduous tree
Soil & situation: most soils, including clay and chalk/withstands exposure/tolerates sun or part shade
North American hardiness zone: 4–8
Height & spread: to 20m (66ft), possibly more
Grow for: beautiful foliage especially when it first opens and has attractive clusters of fruit; fast growing; will tolerate poor soils; can be used as a specimen tree, a woodland tree, a supreme hedge and for pleaching and forming into bowers, arbours and the like; AGM

Hornbeam is a fine parkland specimen tree with a good broad head and a grey, fluted trunk. It is more often grown as a hedge and is frequently confused with beech, though hornbeam does not turn russet in autumn. It just drops its leaves. I think it far superior to beech but some would argue the toss. I frequently specify it for forming pleached screens. These are rather like hedges on stilts, and if you had one in Tudor times, it was a sign that you had 'arrived'.

Today, with problems of privacy from neighbours, hornbeams are unbeatable for forming higher-level screens in confined spaces. With modern hedgecutters, once trained they are simple to maintain. I have also used them for forming 'porches' to highlight a front door and arbours. With these I get a simple metal framework made up and plant the plants around the edge and clip them to it. Similarly I like 'green' garden houses and make a wooden, trellis structure and train the hornbeam around the edge. When the trellis rots, I have the living version.

Although hornbeam, unlike beech, does tolerate being planted at standard size, I always plant small, between 60cm–1.5m (24in–5ft), depending on what I am going to do with it. I have planted ready-made pleached trees on jobs for impatient clients, but they take ages to settle in and do not form a good leafy, thick screen for several years, whereas when I grow them from trees a metre (3 feet) or so tall, they settle in and soon get going. As always, keep all grass and weed competition away from the base and water in dry periods. **BG**

Caryopteris x *clandonensis* 'Arthur Simmonds'

BLUE SPIRAEA, BLUEBEARD

Type: hardy, deciduous shrub
Soil & situation: light, free-draining soil/sun
North American hardiness zone: 6–9
Height: 1m (3ft)
Spread: 1.2m (4ft)
Grow for: soft foliage and blue flowers from late summer to early autumn; AGM

This valuable late summer-flowering shrub forms a rounded mound of aromatic leaves which are dull dark green above and silvery-grey below. Clusters of soft blue flowers appear towards the tips of the stems in the leaf axils from late summer to early autumn, encircling one side of the stalk, hence the common name Bluebeard. They are excellent grouped together or combined with santolina and rosemary, and are attractive to butterflies; they can also be used as cut flowers. Arthur Simmonds found this hybrid in his garden in West Clandon, Surrey, southeast England.

There are several cultivars of *Caryopteris* x *clandonensis*, most with minor differences, and it is not unusual for 'Arthur Simmonds' to be sold as 'Heavenly Blue'. 'Ferndown' has darker leaves and flowers than 'Arthur Simmonds'. 'Heavenly Blue' is more erect and compact, with a slightly deeper flower colour. 'Kew Blue' has slightly darker flowers than 'Arthur Simmonds'. 'Worcester Gold' has yellow foliage and lavender-blue flowers. 'First Choice' is dense and compact, up to 1m (3ft) each way, with tiny, very dark green leaves, tightly clothing the stems, making the perfect foil for the lavender flowers. Flowering starts in mid-summer.

It needs a hot, sunny position on moderately fertile, free-draining soil, protected by a wall in cooler climates. It thrives on chalk and tolerates drought. From early to mid-spring, remove the stems to a strong pair of buds just above ground level. Propagate from greenwood or semi-ripe cuttings. Growth tips and flower buds may be attacked by capsid bugs. **MB**

Caryopteris x *clandonensis* 'Kew Blue'

Caryopteris x *clandonensis* 'Arthur Simmonds'

Cassiope 'Edinburgh'

Cassiope 'Edinburgh'

Type: hardy, evergreen shrub
Soil & situation: well-drained, humus-rich, acid soil/partial shade
North American hardiness zone: 2–6
Height & spread: 30cm (12in)
Grow for: pretty pendent flowers that bring welcome cheer to a spring garden; AGM

Given the right conditions this little plant is the best-behaved shrub in the garden. It is ideal in a rock garden or as a dot plant among heathers. A group of three or more in an open woodland site will brighten the whole area. It forms an upright shrub with whipcord-like stems closely wrapped in small, lance-shaped, overlapping leaves. The white, bell-shaped flowers have contrasting red-brown calyces in late spring. They are produced in the leaf axils at the tips of the stems, nodding in the slightest breeze.

In full sun the plant seems to be less happy, remaining 'sulky' and refusing to grow. A late frost may damage the flowers, browning those which are fully open. Mulching with leafmould every autumn close to the plant will keep the soil moist and encourage the stems to re-root – a source of free, ready-rooted cuttings.

Propagation is by fresh seed sown in the autumn and over-wintered in a cold frame. Semi-ripe cuttings taken in summer root best in a mist propagator. Pot the rooted plants in an ericaceous compost. My plants never seem to suffer from pests or diseases but the dreaded vine weevil has been known to cause havoc to young plants, destroying their root system. **JC**

Catalpa bignonioides

Catalpa bignonioides
INDIAN BEAN TREE

Type: hardy, deciduous tree
Soil & situation: moist, well-drained soil/full sun
North American hardiness zone: 5–9
Height & spread: 10m (33ft)
Grow for: an impressive specimen tree; AGM

In this case, the common name of Indian refers to native Americans. *Catalpa* is Indian rather than Latin and means 'winged head', describing the flower shape. Whatever, it makes a magnificent specimen tree on a lawn.

The 25cm (10in) long, heart-shaped leaves unfurl purple turning to a rich mid-green with an unpleasant odour when crushed. Upright, pyramidal trusses of flowers appear on mature trees in summer. Each bell-shaped flower is white with purple and yellow spots and frilled edges. The flowers are followed in autumn by 40cm (16in) long, thin, green, bean-like seedpods which ripen to dark brown and hang long after the leaves have fallen. *Catalpa bignonioides* 'Aurea' has sulphur-yellow leaves and makes a smaller tree.

It prefers a well-drained site in full sun, sheltered from strong winds. The branches are pithy and brittle and subject to breaking in strong winds. Wind will also shred the large leaves. Although it makes a large tree it may, if it is pollarded, be grown in small gardens.

Every year the tree is cut to a stump in late winter. The shoots it will send up are thinned to one to three and allowed to grow. They will reach a height of 3m (10ft) in one season, with enormous leaves up to 45cm (18in) across. The operation is repeated in subsequent years. Alas there will be no flowers the year it is pruned.

Propagation is by fresh seed in autumn in a cold frame. Softwood cuttings root in a gritty compost in summer. Root cuttings can be propagated in early winter. **JC**

Ceanothus 'Concha'
CALIFORNIA LILAC

Type: frost-hardy, evergreen shrub
Soil & situation: fertile, well-drained, alkaline soi/full sun
North American hardiness zone: 9–10
Height & spread: 3m (10ft)
Grow for: a breathtaking vision of blue in early summer; AGM

There are white- and pink-flowering ceanothus but blue is the colour most commonly associated with this shrub. Of all the shades of blue, for me, 'Concha' stands out with its deep, non-fading, Oxford blue. It forms a dense, rounded shrub with arching branches and 5cm (2in) long, finely toothed, dark green leaves. In late spring and early summer deep red-purple buds open to dark blue flowers in tight, rounded terminal heads.

It is prone to damage from biting, cold winds in spring. Grown against a sheltered, sunny wall it will present a memorable sheet of blue. Little pruning is necessary but for training on a wall, prune after flowering, shortening the sideshoots by half.

Ceanothus are short-lived shrubs, especially in the wetter parts of the UK. Where necessary dig in lots of coarse grit and 13mm (½in) gravel to assist drainage. They dislike being transplanted and should be purchased as small plants with a good root system which isn't pot bound.

Propagate using semi-ripe cuttings with a heel in late summer in a propagator with bottom heat. **JC**

Ceanothus 'Concha'

Cedrus libani

Cedrus libani
CEDAR OF LEBANON

Type: hardy, evergreen tree
Soil & situation: a wide range of pH/acid and alkaline soils/tolerates shade early on, then soon needs full sun and light to form a good specimen/space
North American hardiness zone: 7–9
Height & spread: 30m (100ft)
Grow for: a majestic tree with a sculptural form that few trees can rival, its initial conical outline spreading to form the characteristic, tiered-plate arrangement; AGM

It is thought that this tree was introduced to England around 1645, and it has been hardy here since 1740 when a frost to –30°C (–22°F) killed nearly every tree. Capability Brown did not approve of exotic trees in his landscapes, quite rightly, but he did, wise man, plant this one. It does grow faster than you would think, often 9–10m (30–33ft) in 20 years, 15m (50ft) in 30 years, and after 100 years it will take on its familiar, mature, characteristic appearance. Your children may well be able to appreciate it in its full glory, if you do not.

This is definitely a plant worth planting at a small size: 45–60cm (18–24in) is plenty big enough. Avoid the 'specimen' trees in large containers at 2m (6½ft) plus – they need so much more care in terms of irrigation and staking, and undoubtedly will take far longer to get away than the smaller specimens which will quickly overtake them. If it should happen to send up a double leader, remove the weaker shoot in autumn. It is equally important to keep the ground free of all vegetation around the trunk in a good 1m (3ft) diameter for four to five years after planting. This removes moisture competition from grass. It is definitely better planted without a stake, but if the leader grows away from the vertical, a temporary cane may be necessary. **BG**

Centaurea cyanus
CORNFLOWER

Type: hardy annual
Soil & situation: well-drained soil/sun
North American hardiness zone: annual
Height: 80cm (32in)
Spread: 15cm (6in)
Grow for: blue flowers from late spring to midsummer

This was long regarded as a pestilent weed. The poet and countryman John Clare wrote of 'the blue "cornbottle" crowding their splendid colours in large sheets over the land and troubling the cornfields with their destroying beauty'.

Considering the colour and the fact that it must have been growing with other plants like corn cockle and red field poppies, it must have made an impressive sight. It was last seen on a large scale between the First and Second World Wars, but by the end of the 1970s, with the widespread use of herbicides, it became scarce. Happily it has returned with the advent of the 'set aside' policy for agriculture. The juice from the flower, mixed with alum is used by watercolourists; it is also the traditional flower of Harrow School.

It is upright with narrow, lance-shaped leaves and dark blue flowerheads with violet inner florets. It is attractive to bees. There are several cultivars, including 'Baby Blue', a dwarf with stems to 30cm (12in); 'Black Ball' grows to 1m (3ft) and its double, dark, rich chocolate-coloured flowers look almost black on cloudy days; 'Blue Diadem' has double flowers and stems to 1m (3ft); 'Frosty' (also known as 'Frosted Queen') reaches 50cm (20in) and is mixed, with some flowers having a white rim on the florets; 'Polka Dot' is also mixed; its stems are dwarf and bushy and grow to 40cm (16in). *C. moschata* 'Dairy Maid' is yellow, good for cutting and smells of chocolate.

They need well-drained soil in full sun. Sow from early to late spring for flowers from late spring to early autumn; in early autumn to flower from early to late summer the following year. Plants will self-seed, or collect seed and sow it *in situ*. Powdery mildew may be a problem. **MB**

Centaurea cyanus

Centaurea macrocephala

Centaurea macrocephala
GLOBE CORNFLOWERS, HARD HEADS, KNAPWEED

Type: hardy perennial
Soil & situation: well-drained soil/will tolerate poor, limy soils/sun or partial shade
North American hardiness zone: 3–7
Height: 1.5m (5ft)
Spread: 60cm (2ft)
Grow for: distinctive yellow flowers in summer

This is a robust, charismatic perennial, with tall leafy stems supporting the firm thistle-type knobs. These knobs are topped with a mass of deep orange-yellow florets. One, or preferably several, clumps of these in a border will definitely add some punch. I wish it had a longer flowering season, but maybe that is partly why it makes so much impact. It is especially useful because it will thrive in poor conditions. If you have the space it is worth growing extra plants for cutting as they make a spectacular cut flower and are also great for drying.

This plant is easy, no staking, little feeding, just cut back the dead material in winter or spring. If it is over-vigorous – it tends to get a little carried away in good soils – split it up when necessary to keep it under control. Propagation is easy by division in spring or autumn. **BG**

Centranthus ruber 'Albus'
WHITE VALERIAN

Type: hardy perennial
Soil & situation: thrives in thin chalky soils/poor, free-draining soil/sun
North American hardiness zone: 5–8
Height & spread: up to 1m (3ft)
Grow for: large, dense cymes of white, fragrant flowers over an exceptionally long flowering season in summer; a plant which performs well and looks healthy even in extremely poor conditions

The attraction of this plant lies in the cottagey feel it conveys, perhaps because of its obvious similarity to the red valerian which can be seen all over country villages in England, perched on top of tall, stone walls or growing in invisible spaces at the edge of pavements displaying, as often as not, a profusion of rosy crimson flowers. The white form is more elite, with its eye-catching white flowers. But they both have the characteristic greeny, glaucous, almost fleshy, lance-shaped leaves. Writing this in late winter, I can see lush, thick, attractive foliage through the window even though we have had snow and hard frosts. I have seen it successfully used in borders, where the staying power of its flowers is particularly welcome, and it maintains a better, more compact habit than in an infertile, dry position. Perhaps though, the most fetching positions are the unexpected: growing out of walls, flowering from under large boulders, on a summer house roof, where you are astounded at its *joie de vivre*. It is highly useful, too, for covering steep, awkward banks where most other plants would protest.

To prevent this exuberant plant colonizing your entire garden, it is best to keep cutting it back after flowering. That way you will have flowers all summer long and it will be unable to seed it itself in its accustomed prolific manner. If you need to propagate it, then seed is the easiest, but division is perfectly feasible. Plants are short-lived and are best replaced every three or four years. **BG**

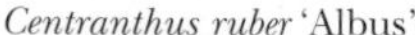

Centranthus ruber 'Albus'

Cephalaria gigantea

Cephalaria gigantea
GIANT SCABIOUS, YELLOW SCABIOUS

Type: hardy perennial
Soil & situation: wide range of soils/prefers a sunny site/will tolerate partial shade
North American hardiness zone: 3–7
Height: to 2m (6½ft)
Spread: 80cm (32in)
Grow for: giant of a plant, with magnificent soft-yellow flowers for a long period in mid-summer

This species of cephalaria is the one most frequently seen in cultivation. The yellow scabious is huge, but whereas traditionally it would be recommended for large herbaceous borders only, I think it can work superbly in smaller areas too.

Tall elements can look dramatic in little spaces, providing a mass of flowers and foliage at eye level and at fairly close quarters, making a huge impact. It helps create a more lax, burgeoning feel. It is also a good plant for naturalizing in wilder parts of the garden, coping with competition from grasses and other wilder-type planting. It does not need staking despite its thin, wiry and rather erect stems.

Another gem of a plant that is easy and flowers well, sometimes thoughout the summer. It can be propagated from seed, though apparently some strains are infertile. The fertile ones though are not aggressive self-seeders. It can also be propagated by division. Both seed and division are best done in spring. **BG**

Ceratostigma willmottianum
HARDY PLUMBAGO, CHINESE PLUMBAGO

Type: hardy, deciduous shrub
Soil & situation: well-drained soil/sun
North American hardiness zone: 6–9
Height & spread: 1m (3ft), sometimes 30cm (12in) taller
Grow for: stunning mid-blue flowers from mid-summer to late autumn; AGM

Miss Ellen Willmott was a formidable, intelligent woman who spent vast sums of money creating a magnificent garden at Warley Place near Brentwood in Essex. At its peak, she employed 104 uniformed gardeners and one nurseryman confided that from 1890 to 1900, she spent £1,500 a year at his nursery alone. Several beautiful plants are named for her, including this one – she raised two *Ceratostigma willmottianum* plants from seed sent to her by the great plant collector Ernest Wilson, who found it growing in the semi-arid Min Valley of Western Sichuan in China.

It produces lance- to diamond-shaped leaves on a mass of wiry stems, tipped with clusters of tightly packed, pale to mid-blue, plumbago-like flowers from mid-summer until mid- or late autumn, depending on the weather. In autumn the foliage develops bright red tints making a pleasing contrast with the flowers. *C. plumbaginoides* is herbaceous, spreading with rhizomes, with remarkable dark blue flowers and it reaches a height of 50cm (20in).

Ceratostigma willmottianum

It needs a sheltered, sunny position on light, moist, moderately fertile, free-draining soil. Grows well on chalk or against a wall. Mulch well over winter. From early to mid-spring, remove the stems to a strong pair of buds just above ground level. Propagate from soft tip cuttings in spring, or semi-ripe cuttings in summer or layers. **MB**

Bunny adds:
Although this is a shrub, in cold situations you can simply treat it as a herbaceous plant, cutting it down to ground level in the spring and away it goes again. It will flower later when treated this way, perhaps not until early autumn, so reducing its flowering period. Otherwise, when flowering on old wood, it will come into flower in midsummer.

Cercidiphyllum japonicum
KADSURA TREE

Type: hardy, deciduous tree
Soil & situation: prefers deep, moist, fertile soil; tolerates some lime/dappled shade
North American hardiness zone: 4–8
Height: 20m (66ft)
Spread: 15m (50ft)
Grow for: form, delicate foliage, autumn colour and fragrance; AGM

In autumn as the leaves change colour, it's the wonderful smell of burnt sugar that alerts you to the presence of this elegant tree long before it comes into view. The delicate, almost heart-shaped leaves with finely scalloped margins turn soft golden-yellow and fall to create a carpet of colour. It's very hardy but prefers a continental climate with long hot summers (don't we all!) and the climate in the UK makes a small- to medium-sized tree. Timber is light, highly valued and used for house interiors and furnishings in Japan. Because of its floral characteristics, scientists have long debated whether this plant is a relic of some primitive flowering plant that has ceased to exist. Inevitably, they still disagree!

Cercidiphyllum var. *magnificum* is a rare, medium-sized tree with smoother bark and larger, broader leaves with coarser serrations on the margins, and yellow autumn colour. *C. japonicum* f. *pendulum* has long hanging branches and has been cultivated in Japan for many years.

They need a sheltered position where the young leaves are protected from frost and cold winds. Soils should be deep, moist and humus-rich and although they tolerate some lime, autumn colour

Cercidiphyllum japonicum

is better on acid soils. Mulch in spring with plenty of well-rotted organic matter until they are well established. Prune when dormant just to remove dead, diseased, dying, crossing, rubbing, damaged or weak branches. They are often multi-stemmed but can be pruned to make a single stem. Propagate by sowing seed under glass as soon as possible after ripening or by taking basal cuttings in late spring/early summer. **MB**

Cercis siliquastrum
Plant of the Week (see page 153)

Euphorbia myrsinites March

Type: frost-hardy, evergreen perennial
Soil & situation: very free-draining soil/sun
Hardiness zone: 5–8
Height: 10cm (4in) or more
Spread: 30cm (12in) or more
Grow for: sculptural form and long-lasting flowerheads from mid-spring to late summer and beyond. We've put it in March because that's when the flowers first appear, but like many of the plants in the this book it is at its best for several months; AGM.

My garden's being taken over by aliens! Every time I pass the euphorbias I hear robotic voices saying 'Take me to your leader'! I'm sure they arrived from Mars as stowaways on a passing spaceship! They're all utterly bizarre; this one is no exception! It's a seething mass of semi-prostrate stems to 30cm (12in) long, with spirally arranged almost lance-shaped, succulent blue-grey leaves.

As if to confirm my paranoia it produces 8cm (3½in) clusters of strange flowers, like glowing acid-green eyes that gradually become pink after staring into the sun for several weeks. I'm sure they're on the move too; they love to bask on sunny banks or by the edge of borders and in my garden one hanging over a low wall looks as if it is about to metamorphose into a snake and slither away. I have a love-hate relationship with these plants: I marvel at their surreal form and flower and see their strange beauty – but I'm sure they're out to get me!

It needs light, free-draining soil in hot, baking sunshine and dislikes shade. Add grit or sharp sand to the soil if necessary to improve the drainage. Mulch with gravel to prevent the leaves and stems from rotting in winter. The sap can be an irritant, so avoid contact with the skin and eyes. Wear gloves when handling. No regular pruning is necessary; cut back old or damaged stems to the base in spring. Divide in spring or grow from seed. **MB**

Cereus grandiflorus (syn. *Nyctocereus grandiflorus*)
QUEEN OF THE NIGHT

Type: tender, perennial, evergreen, trailing cactus
Soil & situation: well-drained, gritty, humus-rich compost with some lime/full sun or light shade/under cover in warm greenhouse or conservatory
North American hardiness zone: 9–10
Height & spread: flowers up to 30cm (12in) across. The plant can be confined to 1.2–1.5m (4–5ft) each way in a big pot or hanging basket, but reaches 3m (10ft) in nature
Grow for: staggering flowers, which are also the prettiest and the most sweetly scented of almost any houseplant. Angular, pliable (within reason) and tough stems, but without significant thorns, make this a pleasant house companion, unlike so many other cacti.

Cereus grandiflorus is a knock-you-over plant when in flower but, unfortunately, the immense flowers only open once, late at night and close again for ever in the morning. However, all through that one night, the white and gold flowers with a hint of pinky-chocolate on the outside, which resemble enormous exotic dahlias or water lilies, give off puffs of the most incredibly strong vanilla-like perfume. The other species are similar but not as imposing, and some of them carry spines. One of about half a dozen species from the Caribbean and Central America and obviously suited to dense forests, these are trailing, scrambling plants, most often seen grown at ground level. I have found that this plant does supremely well in a hanging basket under cover.

Cereus grandiflorus

Cerinthe major 'Purpurascens'

Given a big pot or basket of well-drained compost, it can make an imposing plant, especially as even a small one can carry up to a dozen of the enormous flowers at one time, if well watered. It can live for many years. The compost needs to be kept nearly dry in winter, but water regularly and heavily once growth commences in spring, giving a weekly light feed in the water. It can be grown from seed but cuttings are easy to root in summer in a sandy compost. Mealy bug can be a problem, so wash it off with soapy water. **BF**

Cerinthe major 'Purpurascens'
HONEYWORT, WAXFLOWER

Type: hardy annual
Soil & situation: wide range of soils/sun or partial shade
North American hardiness zone: annual
Height & spread: to 60cm (24in)
Grow for: early and long-flowering annual; dark smoky, purple-blue flowers; pewter-blue fleshy foliage; lasts through one winter in many areas

This annual has become increasingly admired as its undemanding nature and chic appearance has led to it being a deservedly populist plant. You will probably find that some over-winter so they flower even earlier the following year along with the irises in late spring. Spring-sown plants will come into bloom later on in mid-summer. This plant comes from the Mediterranean, enjoying hot sunny conditions particularly. Bees can be seen working the tubular, nodding flowers and are said to obtain wax from the flowers, hence its common name. It is one of the best flowers for cutting.

Cerinthe is usually sown *in situ* early on in the spring, depending on temperature. The soil should be 7°C (45°F), at least. They can be sown the previous autumn and in colder areas over-wintered as young plants in a cold frame. This gives them a head start in spring when planted in their final position. It is more than likely that these beauties will self-sow for you. If you want more control of what goes on you can gather your own seeds and will find that these can be collected from those flowers that have set seed at the base of the plant while the higher flowers are still performing. The seed is short-lived though, so it is best to sow it immediately. **BG**

Chaenomeles japonica – fruit in this condition will be great for jam.

Chaenomeles japonica

JAPANESE QUINCE

Type: hardy, woody shrub
Soil & situation: any soil/sun to heavy shade
North American hardiness zone: 5–8
Height & spread: to 3m (10ft) in rich soil
Grow for: an abundance of very early cheerful flowers and edible (well, once cooked) fruits with pleasant aromatic odour and flavour

There are many different varieties of the Japanese quince, with flowers varying from cream to scarlet. My favourite is *Chaenomeles* x *superba* 'Boule de Feu' as it was given to me as a cutting by Cherry Hills, the wife of the founder of the Henry Doubleday Research Association, on the day I was admiring it on their house wall at Bocking, Essex. However, many other varieties are as good and some have large, more usable fruits, making them more of a crop than an ornamental.

Not introduced until 1815, but now one of the more common ornamental plantings where durability is required, it is said you can knock a nail in with the fruits, but they soften once cooked to make a delicious jelly. Strangely the name comes from the Greek *chaino*, to gape, and *melon*, for apple, as it was completely misunderstood (only by nomenclatural botanists no doubt) to be a fruit that split when it was ripe.

It is a robust, long-lived plant for almost any site, with little attention ever needed. It should be trimmed immediately after flowering. It can be grown from seed but propagate the best varieties only by layers, cuttings or suckers. There are no problems other than the unruly habit, which makes it difficult to train. **BF**

Chaenomeles speciosa 'Nivalis'

JAPANESE QUINCE, FLOWERING QUINCE, JAPONICA

Type: hardy, deciduous shrub
Soil & situation: moist, free-draining soil/sun or partial shade
North American hardiness zone: 5–8
Height: 3.5m (11ft)
Spread: 7m (23ft)
Grow for: pure white flowers from early to late spring, and fragrant fruit

The Latin *nivalis*, snowy or snow-like, is the perfect description for the pure white flowers. This plant's a rule breaker. It usually flowers from early to late spring but doesn't seem to care; it can be earlier – Christmas – or later – June – depending on the location and weather. As a shrub it's no beauty: the leaves are moderately attractive but the stems grow out at ungainly angles and it easily becomes an unkempt mass of interwoven, sparsely spiny stems. Even the fruits are awkward. They are round or pear shaped, glossy greenish-yellow when ripe, speckled and fragrant. When used for jellies or jams, just wash and cook the fruits; don't try to peel them. I did, they're rock hard and I came off worst! But all is forgiven when it flowers.

It grows in any aspect except in a cold, shady spot, but prefers sunshine. Good as a specimen shrub, in open borders, as an informal hedge or fan trained against a wall, it can also be trained as an espalier. It needs moist, fertile, free-draining soil.

For a wall shrub: prune the current year's growth to four to six leaves in early to mid-summer (unless it's needed to fill gaps); cut back secondary growth from these to two to three leaves in early autumn. When the framework becomes congested, cut back summer-pruned growth to two to three leaves in winter. For free-standing shrubs: cut back sideshoots to two to three buds at the base after flowering; remove some of the oldest growths at the base in winter. Propagate by semi-ripe cuttings, layering or removing suckers. Aphids can be a problem. **MB**

Chaenomeles speciosa 'Nivalis'

Chaenomeles x *superba* 'Crimson and Gold'

QUINCE, CYDONIA, JAPONICA

Type: hardy, deciduous, bushy shrub
Soil & situation: well-drained, fertile, neutral to acid soil but tolerant of a little lime/full sun or light shade
North American hardiness zone: 5–8
Height: 1m (3ft)
Spread: 2m (6½ft)
Grow for: attractive flowers in late winter; good for training against a wall; AGM

Growing this plant against a warm, sunny wall I can enjoy the flowers from late winter, long before the leaves emerge, until mid-summer. It forms a mass of spiny branches which can be thinned out after flowering. The clusters of five-petalled, dark red flowers show off their conspicuous golden anthers. Glossy, mid-green leaves appear after the first flush of flowers. Rock hard, green fruit turns yellow-green and aromatic in autumn, hanging long after leaf fall. It is too hard for garden birds to handle, and although the fruit is edible it is only palatable once cooked. While *Chaenomeles* x *superba* 'Crimson and Gold' is my favourite variety, there are many others in contention: 'Cameo' with fully double, peach-pink flowers, 'Rowallane' is scarlet and low growing, and 'Pink Lady' produces early, deep pink flowers. *C. speciosa* 'Moerloosei', sometimes labelled 'Apple Blossom', has large white flowers, flushed deep pink.

When trained against a wall the sideshoots should be shortened to two or three leaves. The quickest way to propagate is to layer a suitably low branch. It will be well rooted within one year. Chaenomeles is prone to canker, so prune out any dead or sickly branches and burn. **JC**

Left: Chaenomeles x *superba* 'Crimson and Gold'

Chamaecyparis pisifera 'Filifera Aurea'

GOLDEN THREAD-LEAF CYPRESS

Type: hardy, evergreen conifer
Soil & situation: moist, well-drained, neutral to acid soil/partial shade
North American hardiness zone: 4–8
Height: 8m (25ft)
Spread: 6m (20ft)
Grow for: year-round interest, especially its striking winter foliage; AGM

This beautiful, slow-growing conifer gives me pleasure every day of the year. The thin, bright yellow, pendulous, summer foliage deepens to a golden yellow in winter. In 16 years it has played host to more birds' nests than it has grown in feet. *Chamaecyparis pisifera* 'Filifera Aureovariegata Nana' is a variety with which it is sometimes confused but, as the name suggests, 'Nana' is quite dwarf.

The foliage will scorch if planted in full sun. A situation where there are evergreens positioned to block the afternoon sun is ideal. If planted in front of dark green conifers, holly or rhododendron, it will, during the dark days of winter, stand out like a golden beacon.

Clipping in late spring will keep young plants in shape. A mature tree can be pruned to prevent it from becoming straggly or too large for its position. Prune in late spring after all risk of frost is past. Propagation is by semi-ripe cuttings taken from the leading shoots. If taken from side branches they will, in their early years, grow into globose plants later reverting to type. These conifers are often erroneously labelled and sold as 'Filifera Aurea Nana' – be warned! **JC**

Chamaecyparis pisifera 'Filifera Aurea'

Cheiranthus cheiri

Cheiranthus cheiri (syn. *Erysimum cheiri*)

WALLFLOWER

Type: hardy, herbaceous biennial/perennial
Soil & situation: any soil with some lime/sun to light shade/moisture useful while young but will survive in dry cracks in a wall!
North American hardiness zone: usually grown as an annual
Height & spread: can make a bush up to 60cm (2ft) high by 1m (3ft) across, but usually half this size, or less if crowded
Grow for: very good value as it is cheap and easy to grow, and its red and yellow flowers are among the most powerfully scented in the garden

This is a must for every garden, useful as a short-term filler, as well as for the mixed border. Wallflowers give a lot of flower and scent for very little effort and have been bred to a vast number of varieties. I prefer the dark red colours as I reckon their scent is the sweetest, although some whites are close; and double-flowered forms the more so and their flowers are longer lasting. Native to Europe, the wallflower is closely related to the brassicas and has been very popular since Elizabethan times. It was so common in nosegays and posies that it was given the Latin name *cheiranthus*, which means hand-flower.

It needs a lime-rich soil, to be sown early, transplanted early and well established by the first frosts, if it is to make a good show of flowers the following spring. It is a short-lived perennial but in the UK is usually treated as a biennial. Dead-heading makes the plant flower for longer and, in most cases, live for another year. Usually grown from seed but propagate by layers and cuttings for the choicest varieties. Sow in mid-spring, transplant into a seedbed in early summer and to its final site by late summer, giving it masses of water. Wallflowers can suffer the same pests and diseases as the rest of the cabbage family (see page 64), but rarely do so badly. **BF**

Chimonanthus fragrans (syn. *C. praecox*)
WINTERSWEET

Type: hardy, deciduous shrub
Soil & situation: any soil, especially limy/sun or part shade
North American hardiness zone: 7–9
Height & spread: up to 3m (10ft) each way
Grow for: crimson and yellow waxy petals give off a wonderful perfume all winter

The standard wintersweet may not be the most attractive or impressive shrub in summer, but through the depths of winter it produces flushes of gorgeously scented flowers with the perfume of violets. The leaves also have a slight smell. The form *Chimonanthus praecox* 'Grandiflorus' has the biggest flowers but is less fragrant, and *C. p.* var. *luteus* flowers later with clear yellow blooms.

A native of China, wintersweet was introduced to Britain in 1766. Three of the species are closely related to the allspice, *Calycanthus floridus*, and they are distantly related to the divine true lemon verbena – now, an inter-genus hybrid of these would really be something special.

Rather like a camellia it prefers a moist, rich soil and shelter from cold winds, so is good sited on a sunny wall where it should be long lived. Removing the seedheads prevents the plant wasting its energy and gives more flowers the following year. Propagating from seed is very slow, cuttings are not easy and the best option is to layer in spring. Do not cut many stems of flowers as these are borne on the back of old leaf axils and will remove too much flowering wood; instead pull off individual blooms and float them in a saucer and their perfume will fill the room. **BF**

Chimonanthus fragrans

Chionodoxa forbesii

Matt adds:
I find this needs a sheltered, sunny wall (preferably by a window or door) on deep free-draining soil; it thrives on chalk. It can take over five years to flower, but the wait intensifies the sense of anticipation! They open well in water, so do cut some for indoors. The Chinese in their wisdom use the flowers with linen the way we use lavender.

Chionodoxa forbesii
GLORY OF SNOW

Type: hardy, bulbous perennial
Soil & situation: moist to moderately dry soil/sunshine or dappled shade
North American hardiness zone: 3–9
Height: 10cm (4in)
Spread: 55cm (22in)
Grow for: bright flowers in late winter and early spring

This is the bulb you'll often find wrongly named in garden centres and catalogues as *Chionodoxa luciliae.* In fact several species in commerce are wrongly named and as it's a challenge trying to unravel them, I'm going to leave it to the experts and bury my head in the sand!

Tiny but tough, this little gem flowers early in the year high on the mountains of the Greek island of Crete, western Turkey and Cyprus, often pushing itself through the snow to reveal its glory against a glistening white background. An impressive achievement when you consider it's barely 10cm (4in) tall! The star-shaped, lilac-blue flowers in compact clusters are only 2cm (3/4in) across with white centres; they pop up from the cold soil in early spring, accompanied by two green leaves. It's a bright and beautiful reminder that spring is on its way.

They look wonderful at the edge of borders or as blue streams flowing under shrubs where they spread and self-seed freely; plant them anywhere that remains undisturbed. *C. forbesii* 'Pink Giant' has an attractive spike of pretty, soft pink flowers 1.5cm (5/8in) across with white centres. It is 13cm (5in) tall.

Plant them in sunshine or partial shade where they will not dry out too much in summer. The soil should be well drained; fork in leafmould and sharp sand or grit in heavy conditions or partial shade. Propagate by lifting and removing offsets in summer and sowing seed in containers. **MB**

Choisya ternata
MEXICAN ORANGE-BLOSSOM

Type: hardy, evergreen shrub
Soil & situation: fertile, well-drained soil/full sun
North American hardiness zone: 7–9
Height & spread: 3m (10ft)
Grow for: clusters of fragrant, white spring blossom and glossy foliage; AGM

I love this shrub. It has never annoyed me or let me down. It looks good all year with guaranteed flower and fragrance. The glossy, dark green leaflets are grouped in threes and when crushed they are strongly aromatic. The wonderfully fragrant clusters of white flowers are reminiscent of orange blossom and appear in late spring. Most years there will be a second flush of bloom in early autumn. *Choisya ternata* 'Sundance' has bright yellow, young leaves when grown in a sunny site. In light shade the leaves become pale green-yellow.

I have found *C. ternata* ideal for supporting summer-flowering clematis. It is happy for the visitor to scramble through its stems, close enough to the new growths for the flowers to poke their heads out through the foliage.

Pruning is seldom necessary. Where branches need to be removed to retain a good shape cut them in early summer after the main flowering period. Large, mature shrubs will form an outer shell of leaves with bare branches on the inside. Old plants respond well to a hard pruning and will quickly regrow. Remove one third of the stems each year.

Propagate by softwood cuttings in summer, rooting them in compost or in water. Large branches respond well to layering, being well rooted within 12 months. Snails love to hide within the plant and regular visits to remove them, shell and all, will reduce the population significantly. **JC**

Choisya ternata

Chrysanthemum chinensis

Chrysanthemum chinensis
SHUNGI-KU

Type: hardy, herbaceous annual
Soil & situation: any soil/sun or light shade
North American hardiness zone: annual
Height: to 1m (3ft)
Spread: 60cm (24in)
Grow for: easy to grow; bright yellow and white flowers and healthy, green, edible, ferny foliage

Also known as chop-suey greens, shungi-ku is little known to British gardeners but is rather valuable as it can be sown successionally to give young leaves for stir fries throughout most of the year. The flowers are cheerful, beneficial to insects and can be used for cutting, while the petals are also delicious in salads. This tough, easy-to-grow plant gives a lot of show from a spring sowing or three.

There are about 200 species in the chrysanthemum family, including ox-eye daisy, a native of Britain. Most have a less than pleasant scent, often resembling that of stale perspiration, but, fortunately, shungi-ku tastes better than those. In the East it is esteemed as a good companion to brassicas – its scent seems to help prevent many pests of that family locating them. *Chrysos* is the Greek for gold and *anthos* for flower, so chrysanthemums are gold-flowers.

Moist soil is necessary in the early stages but otherwise it is an easy plant to grow. It can be cut back hard to get renewal growths for stir fries but tastes best in the first six weeks from seed. Sow successionally from late winter under cover, through spring and summer outdoors and under cover again in autumn for a winter crop. Remarkably problem free. **BF**

Cirsium rivulare 'Atropurpureum'
PLUME THISTLE

Type: hardy perennial
Soil & situation: moist, fertile soil/sun or partial shade
North American hardiness zone: 4–8
Height: 1.2m (4ft)
Spread: 60cm (24in)
Grow for: elegant stems and flowers from late spring to autumn

This came to prominence after starring at the Chelsea Flower Show one year and briefly became a name that was on everyone's lips. It still has its admirers, including me. It is a striking, upright, 'architectural' plant and is wonderful for designs using a naturalistic style or in large borders where it needs plenty of space. It is a plant with poise.

The smooth, almost leafless stems are self-supporting and topped with flowers which are dense, soft tufts of burgundy appearing singly or in clusters. It has a rather vicious basal rosette of elegant but spiny leaves like the teeth of a swordfish – wear gloves if you're thinking of going near them! Flowering can be erratic – they are good some years and not others – but they bloom intermittently over a long period from late spring to mid-autumn, making them a valuable garden plant. Their colour combines well with blues, purples and silvers. The winter seedheads attract birds. It is incredible to think that these are related to thistles that can be such a problem in the garden.

The Latin *rivulare* means 'brook loving' and its natural habitat is in damp meadows, usually on acid soils. Ideal in rich, moist, well-drained soil in sun or partial shade. Clear the foliage in spring. Propagate by division from autumn to spring. Mildew can be a problem. **MB**

Cirsium rivulare 'Atropurpureum'

Cistus ladanifer

Cistus ladanifer

GUM CISTUS OR SUN ROSE

Type: hardy, evergreen shrub
Soil & situation: free-draining soil; tolerates chalk/sun/shelter
North American hardiness zone: 8–10
Height & spread: 1.5m (5ft)
Grow for: scented foliage and stems; flowers in early and mid-summer; AGM

I once worked in a garden where *Cistus ladanifer* flourished on a sunny bank. On scorching, cloudless summer days, I could smell their sweet fragrance long before I reached them. It was so beguiling; it even made hoeing a joy! Perfumers have long valued the fragrance; the young branches are the main source of a sticky resin called 'labdanum' which is still used in cosmetics, aromatherapy and potpourri. In ancient times, it was combed from the beards of goats that browsed among the foliage and in the Middle Ages it was a major ingredient of pomanders.

Their fragrance is not their only attribute. In early and mid-summer the bush is smothered by a succession of simple, tissue-thin, white flowers, up to 10cm (4in) across, each delicately crumpled petal with a deep blood-red blotch at the base. They last only a short time and before long the ground round the bush is covered with a layer of 'confetti'. The form *C. ladanifer* var. *albiflorus* lacks the coloured blotch.

Cistus flourish on chalk or poor, free-draining soil in hot, sunny conditions and are wind and maritime tolerant. Frost hardy to around –7°C (20°F), cistus need shelter in colder areas. They dislike being transplanted; buy small plants and avoid root disturbance. Prune from mid- to late spring to remove dead, diseased, dying or weak shoots and keep plants within their allotted space. Do not hard prune. Propagate from softwood, greenwood or semi-ripe cuttings from mid-summer until they are almost hard in autumn. **MB**

Omphalodes cappadocica 'Cherry Ingram'

NAVELWORT

Type: hardy, evergreen perennial
Soil & situation: best in moist, moderately fertile soil/light shade
Hardiness zone: 6–8
Height: about 25cm (10in)
Spread: about 40cm (16in)
Grow for: good evergreen ground cover with forget-me-not-like blue flowers in early spring; AGM

This is not only an extremely useful, woodland ground cover but also a bit of a show stopper in its own right in springtime. At this time of year it produces abundant, large, true-blue flowers on stems about 35cm (14in) tall. After this it may produce more flowers intermittently. It is a clump-forming plant and makes attractive leafy mounds that are present for 12 months of the year. I find it useful for enhancing the character of open woodland – it is particularly effective when used in decent-sized groups. It will tolerate quite heavy shade and also a fair amount of sunshine, so is versatile, although it does not appreciate dry situations. *Omphalodes verna* is much quicker to establish but does not flower for so long and I find is more deciduous than semi-evergreen.

These are plants that can be slow to settle down and get going as they do not like being moved, but once they do get going they are extremely good value, requiring little attention. They will form good, dense ground cover, ideal for interspersing with foxgloves, ferns, white epilobium and woodland grasses. Most of the omphalodes do appreciate moisture so, if your soil dries out in high summer, you will need to give them some moisture to prevent them looking sad and shrivelled. Propagate by division in early spring. **BG**

Citrullus lanatus

Citrullus lanatus (syn. *C. vulgaris*)
WATERMELON

Type: tender, herbaceous, scrambling, annual fruit
Soil & situation: moist but well-drained, sandy soil/full sun under cover
North American hardiness zone: annual
Height: 30cm (12in)
Spread: 3m (10ft)
Grow for: the challenge!

I am determined not to be defeated by what ought to be an easy subject, but growing watermelons in Britain is a lot more difficult than I ever imagined – if you live anywhere warmer it is easier. But when I have succeeded the quality and sweetness of the flesh have amazed me, even if I have raised fruits of only about 3.2–3.6kg (7–8lb), whereas they should be reaching up to 45kg (100lb)! A very healthy food, and if you eat the seeds it is more nutritious than spinach.

Natives of Africa, they seem not to have been known to the Romans and remained relatively unknown to Europeans until the New World was explored when the watermelon proved very happy in its new home. Now you can find them in every part of the warmer world and in many colours, inside and out!

It must be grown in warm, free-draining, yet moist soil and in full sun under cover. Pollinate the fruits by hand and limit each vine to one or two at most Stand fruits on a wooden board to prevent the underside rotting. Do not stop the vines as for other melons, but let them run. Sow from mid-spring under cover, pot on and grow in large pots of compost or in a warm border under cover; never overwater and do not feed heavily. It is very prone to red spider mite, so use the commercially available predators or lose the plants! Also be prepared to fail in cool, dim years. **BF**

Citrus x *meyeri* 'Meyer'
LEMON

Type: tender, woody, evergreen shrub to small tree
Soil & situation: well-drained, lime-free soil/full sun/kept moist in summer, drier in winter when it needs to be under cover
North American hardiness zone: 9–10
Height & spread: 60cm (24in) in a tub
Grow for: striking green foliage year round; gorgeously scented white pink-stained flowers in several flushes; a continuous supply of fruit; AGM

All citrus make good conservatory or greenhouse subjects, especially for their divinely scented flowers and their edible fruit. *Citrus* x *meyeri* 'Meyer', or the Chinese lemon, is one of the most reliable, amazingly compact and highly productive of all the citrus and is rarely out of bloom or out of fruits. Its flavour is not so acid as some varieties. It is one of the easiest of the genus to root from cuttings and one of the hardiest. No wonder it's popular.

The lemon reached Egypt and Palestine in the 10th century and was cultivated in Genoa by the middle of the 15th century. The new fruits were soon spread around the warmer parts of Europe and they are now mainly grown in California, Florida, Israel, Spain and South Africa, though every warm to tropical area produces their own and more. Unripe lemons are often sold as limes, which are more spherical-shaped fruits.

It must be grown in well-drained, gritty, lime-free, humus-rich compost in a large tub. Given careful watering and feeding it may live for hundreds of years. To prevent the plant getting too big it can be pruned hard in early spring as growth commences. Once frosts are over it prefers to be outdoors. It can be grown from seed and may occasionally come true, but it will take a decade or two to fruit; cuttings in spring may take with bottom heat or ideally bud onto seedling stocks. Aphids, mealy bugs, scale insects and red spider mite all infest the plants, but a sojourn outdoors and soft soap sprays keep them under control.
Matt adds: I find lemons need a lot of care. Here are some guidelines to add to what Bob has suggested. They prefer constant temperatures and humidity. Winter temperatures should be moderate; they dislike being too wet, dry or hungry. Low light, low temperatures or erratic watering prevents flowering. Mist with soft water early in the morning or stand on a tray of expanded clay aggregate filled with water to the bottom of the pot. Dry air and under-watering causes flowers to drop.

Feed with liquid or foliar feed all year round with citrus fertilizers or high-nitrogen fertilizer with trace elements in summer; general feed in late autumn to winter. Apply weekly to leaves and roots when the plant is growing strongly, otherwise fortnightly or not at all.

Outdoors: when there's no danger of frost or cold wind. Stand in partial shade, wrapped in horticultural fleece; bring indoors at night for 7-10 days. At the end of the summer reverse the process. Put them in a sunny spot; excessive heat bakes them.

Pinch out shoots to retain shape. Prune mature plants in late winter or early spring. Repot every two or three years; flowering is better when restricted, so do not over-pot.

Citrus x *meyeri* 'Meyer'

Citrus reticulata

Phew.

Of the many other varieties available, 'La Valette' is compact, prolific and has medium-sized fruit. 'Garey's Eureka' (aka 'Quatre Saisons') is heavy fruiting.

Citrus reticulata
TANGERINE ORANGE

Type: tender, woody, evergreen shrub to small tree
Soil & situation: well-drained, lime-free soil/full sun/kept moist in summer, drier in winter when it needs to be under cover
North American hardiness zone: 9–10
Height & spread: 3m (10ft) x 2m (6½ft), but smaller in a tub
Grow for: striking green foliage year round; gorgeously scented flowers in several flushes; a Christmas supply of fruit

Whatever you call this small, loose-skinned orange, it is among the best for eating as it is so easily peeled. It is highly productive and gives far more fruits than a sweet orange tree of the same size and about as many as a lemon. These delicious fruits also conveniently ripen for Christmas, which is also when they are most often found in the shops.

It comes from Cochin China, and is known by several names and sub-varieties such as mandarin, satsuma, tangerine or clementine, whatever you will. These names are frequently confused and interchanged for several small, sweet, easily peeled and segmented sorts of sweet orange.

For plant care and propagation, see previous entry. **BF**

Citrus sinensis 'Valencia'
SWEET ORANGE

Type: tender, woody, evergreen shrub to small tree
Soil & situation: well-drained, lime-free soil/full sun/kept moist in summer, drier in winter when it needs to be under cover
North American hardiness zone: 9–10
Height & spread: can reach 6m (20ft) x 3m (10ft), but not in a tub
Grow for: striking green foliage all year round; gorgeously scented pure white flowers in several flushes; delicious fruit

I love all citrus for their scented flowers, their aromatic foliage and their fruit. *Citrus sinensis* 'Valencia Late' is my favourite as it fruits for me at Christmas time and is to my mind the best, though others are good such as *C. s.* 'Jaffa', which is large, thick-skinned and seedless, and *C. s.* 'Washington Navel', which is nearly seedless. Blood oranges, such as 'Maltese', are sweet oranges with a red tint to their flesh.

Native to China and South East Asia, the citron was known to the Romans, but oranges did not reach Arabia until the ninth century. It is said that St Domine planted an orange in Rome in 1200 and a Spanish ship full of these fruits landed at Portsmouth, England, in 1290. However, all of these may have been bitter oranges as many think the sweet orange did not reach Europe until 1421 when it arrived at Versailles. Another planted in 1548 in Lisbon became the 'mother' of most European sweet orange trees and was still living in 1823.

For plant care and propagation please see *Citrus* x *meyeri* 'Meyer' on page 104. **BF**

Citrus sinensis 'Valencia'

Clarkia amoena

Clarkia amoena (syn. *Godetia*)

Type: hardy annual
Soil & situation: fertile, moist, well-drained, acid soil/full sun or partial shade
North American hardiness zone: annual
Height: 75cm (30in)
Spread: 30cm (12in)
Grow for: excellent cut flowers

I have always been used to calling these flowers godetia. It sort of rolls off the tongue, so I will continue to do so. They are one of the easiest annuals to grow from seed, providing a continuous flower show all summer.

The 5cm (2in) long, lance-shaped, mid-green leaves are held on erect stems. The single or double fluted flowers are 5cm (2in) wide and available in shades of pink, lilac and a deep pink-red, all with paper-thin petals. They form clusters at the tips of the leafy shoots from early summer until mid-autumn. They are excellent as cut flowers lasting for at least a week in a vase. Strip the leaves off the portion of the stem which will be immersed in water.

The Grace Series of godetia have single flowers with contrasting centres growing to 45cm (18in) high.

Avoid dry soil and humid conditions. Excess nitrogen will result in leafy growth and fewer flowers. Propagation is by seed sown *in situ* in autumn or spring in open ground. They dislike being transplanted. If it is necessary to thin the seedlings, dump the thinnings. Seedlings from an autumn sowing will need to be over-wintered under a cloche and protected from winter frost. **JC**

Claytonia perfoliata (syn. *Montia perfoliata*)

MINER'S LETTUCE/WINTER PURSLANE

Type: hardy, herbaceous, annual salading
Soil & situation: any moist soil/light shade/preferably under cover
North American hardiness zone: 5–7
Height & spread: 30cm (12in)
Grow for: good winter ground cover and green manure, but mainly because it's a delicious, mid-winter salad vegetable

Few plants grow in the depths of winter but this one thrives in moist shade year round and is especially good for growing in the winter greenhouse border when little else will do there. Not only does it produce masses of tasty greens, which can be eaten raw or cooked as a spinach, but it is easy to pull up and eradicate. It makes a superb ground cover, excluding weeds, and provides quite a bulk of material for incorporating, composting or feeding to hens. Claytonia also has a unique shovel-shaped leaf with the flower stalk coming out of the middle and even when flowering the whole plant is still edible and not hot or fibrous – it is even liked by children!

Originally from North America, this one of half a dozen species was introduced to France in the 18th century, when it was known as Cuban spinach. The closely related species are also edible but not as palatable. Little known in the rest of world, miner's lettuce really ought to be grown everywhere. It is named after John Clayton, an Englishman who after 1705 became described as the greatest botanist in America.

Allow it to self-sow in your greenhouse border and it will be there for ever. If the soil is too dry it does poorly – it needs copious moisture and thrives in partial shade. Sow *in situ* from late autumn and leave some plants uncut to self-sow. Individual sporadic plants in open ground attract slugs underneath them – if they start looking miserable and pinkish, it's time to investigate. **BF**

Claytonia perfoliata

Clematis armandii

Clematis armandii

Type: frost-hardy, evergreen climber
Soil & situation: any aspect, as long as it is sheltered/wide range of soils, but dislikes poorly drained, heavy soils
North American hardiness zone: 7–9
Height: up to 6m (20ft)
Spread: 2–3m (6½–10ft)
Grow for: fast and strong-growing evergreen climber; highly fragrant, creamy-white flowers in early spring

This plant is far tougher and more vigorous than it is generally given credit for. It has thrived in my garden for many years and survived through cold periods below −10°C (14°F). I first saw it transforming a north-facing trellis in the Midlands in full flower, where it engulfed the whole courtyard garden with its powerful, almond-scented fragrance. The leaves are large, up to 15cm (6in) long, shiny, green and will cover sizeable stretches of wall. The downside is, I suppose, the rather gnarled appearance as it ages. But this can be dealt with using a bit of know how and secateurs.

Plant as for *C.* 'Warszawska Nike' (see page 108). A good annual mulch of compost or farmyard manure helps this vigorous climber keep in good health. This clematis is in pruning group 1, which means it is not essential to prune it at all but if you feel the urge a little snipping does help it keep looking trim. This simply involves removing any dead, dying or diseased stems after flowering and shortening any lengths that have outgrown their allotted space. However as it becomes gnarled with age, it becomes the plant to remove one or two thick stems right back to ground level after flowering. When new, reinvigorated shoots are well on their way, replacing the removed wood, tackle another stem or two. **BG**

Clematis x *durandii*

Type: hardy, deciduous climber/scrambler
Soil & situation: cool, moist, well-drained soil/sun
North American hardiness zone: 6–9
Height & spread: 3m (10ft)
Grow for: beautiful flowers from early summer to early autumn; AGM

Blue is my favourite colour, particularly at the end of the spectrum where shades of deep and grey-blue abound. It's no surprise, then, that these colours appear regularly in my plant selections or that *Clematis* x *durandii* is one of my favourite flowers. The four, broad sepals of dark indigo-violet with textured midribs, wavy margins and a central boss of yellow stamens are up to 10cm (4in) across. These sumptuous aristocratic blooms are big, but not blowsy and look even better resplendent on a bed of silvery foliage, notably *Brachyglottis compacta* x *monroi* 'Sunshine' (what a horrible, lumpy name!) or *Nepeta* x *faassenii* or draped over plants with dark purple leaves like *Cotinus* 'Grace'. Planted in the middle of a border it scrambles through surrounding plants, but can also be used as ground cover or tied into trellis as a climber with a backcloth of mid-green leaves. It has valuable cut flowers too.

It needs moist, cool, free-draining soil in sunshine. Dig in organic matter before planting and mulch well. It is fast growing and free flowering; ensure that there's a plentiful supply of moisture; feed with slow-release fertilizer in spring and mid-summer. Prune in late winter or early spring, cutting back the stems to at least 1m (3ft) from the ground. When planted in spring, water well in dry periods until established.

Propagate by internodal cuttings in spring. It is prone to mildew if grown against hot walls or fences and performs much better growing through other plants. Avoid mildew by keeping the soil moist and improving air circulation. **MB**

Clematis x *durandii*

Clematis heracleifolia 'Wyevale'

Clematis heracleifolia 'Wyevale'

Type: hardy, woody-based perennial
Soil & situation: well-drained fertile soil/sun or part shade
North American hardiness zone: 3–8
Height: 90cm (36in)
Spread: 1.2m (4ft)
Grow for: scented racemes of deep azure-blue flowers in late summer to autumn; AGM

At home I grow this plant in repeated clumps under my pleached hornbeams, where they get enough light to produce strong splashes of colour at the end of the summer. Their flowers are small, hyacinth-like, and in clusters on erect stalks. The foliage is bold and vine-like. The plant spreads, not rampantly but usefully, enabling you to divide it up to make more. I can only think that the reason it is not more popular is that people assume it is a climbing, twining clematis and are not sure what to do with it. It is a self-supporting ground cover, though not one that leans or romps through other plants. I use it regularly in a variety of schemes in various situations from formal borders to semi-wild areas – in fact anywhere that will benefit from this late-summer, rather natural-looking beauty.

Apparently some gardeners do stake this plant but I have certainly never had to. I can only assume that it may be necessary on extremely rich soil. The dead growth should be removed in late winter or spring (they flower on the current season's growth). This plant is easily propagated from layers and I have also grown *Clematis heracifolia* from seed. Herbaceous clematis do not suffer from wilt. **BG**

Clematis x *jouiniana* 'Praecox'

Clematis x *jouiniana* 'Praecox'

Type: hardy, deciduous climber/scrambler
Soil & situation: cool, moist, well-drained soil/sun
North American hardiness zone: 4–9
Height & spread: 3.5m (11ft)
Grow for: masses of beautiful flowers from mid-summer to autumn; AGM

Life is full of odd couples! It's remarkable that the handsome yet rather coarse UK native 'Old Man's Beard' should pair up with a gorgeous Oriental, *Clematis heracleifolia* var. *davidiana*. Thankfully, the offspring aren't as rampant as their father and have inherited both parents' good looks!

The stunningly beautiful mid-summer to autumn-flowering *C.* x *jouiniana* 'Praecox' and its relatives should be more widely grown. Scrambling rather than climbing, they cover low walls, mounds or tree-stumps and can be used as ground cover or tied into trellis. That great gardener, Christopher Lloyd, recommends it for herbaceous borders, rambling over perennial plants; the clouds of small, white, lavender-blue tinted, star-shaped flowers combining well with asters. Although the flowers are not scented, they are attractive to butterflies. The species flowers from early to mid-autumn, *C.* x *j.* 'Praecox' from July to October; other selections, like the azure-blue *C.* x *j.* 'Côte d'Azur' from August onwards.

It needs deep, moist, cool, free-draining soil in sunshine. Dig in organic matter before planting; mulch well. It is hungry, fast growing and free flowering; ensure that there's always plenty of moisture and feed with slow-release fertilizer in spring and mid-summer.

Prune in late winter or early spring, cutting back the stems to at least 1m (3ft) from the ground or prune to keep within its allotted space. Propagate from hardwood cuttings about 10cm (4in) long, in late winter. Take a slice of rind 3cm (1in) from the stem, then plant in pots of cutting compost in a cool greenhouse or cold frame. **MB**

Clematis 'Warszawska Nike'

Type: hardy, woody, deciduous climber
Soil & situation: best on alkaline soils/will grow on sunny aspect but enjoys a cool, shady root run/needs some support be it shrub, fence or pergola
North American hardiness zone: 4–9
Height: 2–3m (6½–10ft)
Spread: 1m (3ft)
Grow for: exuberant, large, beautiful, dark purple-crimson, velvety flowers from mid-summer well into the autumn; free-flowering; AGM

There are several reasons I particularly like this clematis: the flower colour is a good intense wine which contrasts obligingly with the yellow anthers; the large flowers (10cm/4in across) seem to keep coming and coming; and in my experience it is a fairly robust, high-performance clematis. I grow it climbing into *Trachelospermum jasminoides* (see page 381), where it twines elegantly through this ideal support, the dark purple, white and racing green working well together earlier on, and the clematis flowering on its own later on. It will also work well on any aspect, whereas many light-coloured, flowering clematis go a dirty grey on a south wall. These darker colours do lighten a bit but they are still good colours. It is also ideal for climbing over and through shrubs, bringing them to life.

Many failures with clematis are because gardeners find them difficult to establish but they are much easier when you know how. The successful growth of clematis depends a lot on planting. Firstly make sure you buy a plant in at least a 2-litre pot so you are starting off with a decent volume of roots. Ideally plant it in the autumn so it can get its rooting system started over the winter. Plant deeply, with the surface of the compost 8cm (3½in) below the soil level. Mulch it with gravel to retain the moisture and deter slugs and snails, possibly using a sunken plastic pot rim to contain the gravel. I never use stones as these attract snails which love clematis. Make sure you water well during the first summer in dry periods. Leave all the growth on it for the first winter and then cut back to about 30cm (12in) above ground level, just above a good, strong pair of buds. For subsequent pruning, as this plant is sometimes is listed as a group 2 and sometimes a group 3 clematis, I think it is best in late winter or early spring to cut the plant back to about 1m (3ft) from the ground, discarding the less healthy growth. When grown amongst a shrub you just cut it back to the top of the shrub – if you take it right back to the ground it wastes too much energy climbing back up and flowers less well. **BG**

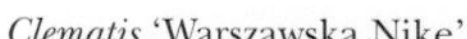

Clematis 'Warszawska Nike'

Cleome hassleriana

Cleome hassleriana (syn. *Capparis spinosa*)

AMERICAN SPIDER FLOWER

Type: half-hardy annual
Soil & situation: light, fertile soil/thrives in sandy, free-draining soils/warm, sheltered sunny position
North American hardiness zone: annual
Height: to 1.5m (5ft)
Spread: to 45cm (18in)
Grow for: exotic, colourful and decidedly different annual; spikes of spidery pink, mauve or, my favourite, white flowers perform for an amazing length of time; bold foliage

This is an annual I grow most years. You are pushed to find something that makes such a statement as this or can match its long period of colour (sometimes mine go on till late autumn) and before this arrives you have the added plus of the bright green leaves. There are three main cultivars, 'Cherry Queen', 'Violet Queen' and 'Helen Campbell'. I am not a fan of the mixed packets and have never grown 'Cherry Queen', which is not cherry pink at all but more of a knicker-pink – insipid and not my shade. 'Violet Queen', though, while again not really violet but more of a mauve which fades off to a blush-white, is quite a sight when mixed with deep purples. But the white 'Helen Campbell' is always spectacular and will keep a planting looking fresh even late in summer. The foliage, apart from being armed with spines, is sticky and is an unexpected asset before the flowers swipe your attention. These annuals look great in containers and are useful for cutting. Bees also appreciate them.

Sow the seeds under glass in single pots in mid-spring, ready for planting out about eight weeks later, once the risk of frosts has passed. Dead-head with care (as there are painfully sharp spines at the base of the leaves) to prolong flowering. These plants should not need staking. **BG**

Clerodendrum trichotomum var. *fargesii*

Type: hardy, deciduous shrub or small tree
Soil & situation: rich, well-drained soil/sunny, sheltered position
North American hardiness zone: 7–9
Height & spread: 6m (20ft)
Grow for: fragrant flowers from late summer to early autumn; unusual fruits; AGM

Clerodendrum trichotomum is an upright small tree or shrub, with bold oval leaves, to 20cm (8in) long that are larger on younger plants than older ones. The sweetly fragrant, waxy, star-like, white flowers, with long projecting stamens, five narrow petals and maroon calyces are produced in long-stalked clusters. They make an impressive sight but are overshadowed by the extraordinary bright turquoise metallic-blue fruits that are backed with a maroon, fleshy calyx. The leaves are malodorous when crushed and smell of cats. *C. t.* var. *fargesii* was introduced to France from China, it flowers more freely and is hardier than the species.

The Latin name *Clerodendrum* comes from the Greek *kleros*, which translates as chance, and *dendron*, meaning tree; it is supposed to be a reference to the variable medicinal qualities of the group.

The young shoots and leaves of the species are cooked and eaten! The leaves are used for many ailments including dermatitis, rheumatoid arthritis and joint pain. When used in a clinical trial, the blood pressure of 81 per cent of the group dropped significantly – the problem returned when treatment was stopped. The crushed seeds are used to kill lice.

It needs fertile, humus-rich, well-drained soil in sunshine, and protection from cold wind and frosts which can damage young growth. Feed with general fertilizer and mulch in early spring with well-rotted organic matter; water regularly during drought. Prune in late winter to remove dead, diseased, damaged, crossing, rubbing or weak branches and any spoiling the shape of the plant. Propagate by semi-ripe cuttings from mid-summer to early autumn, or root cuttings in autumn. **MB**

Clerodendrum trichotomum var. *fargesii*

Ulex europaeus 'Flore Pleno'

DOUBLE GORSE, WHIN, FURZE

Type: hardy, evergreen shrub
Soil & situation: well-drained, impoverished soil/full sun
Hardiness zone: 6–8
Height & spread: 2m (6½ft)
Grow for: masses of yellow flowers with a wonderful scent; perfect for a barrier hedge. Good all year round, but particularly lovely in early spring; AGM.

I love wild gorse. The first thing you see when you fly into Northern Ireland is mile upon mile of bright yellow hedges separating the fields. There is no difficulty finding plants in flower at any time of the year. Bob Flowerdew will tell you 'when gorse is out of flower, love is out of fashion'.

Ulex europaeus 'Flore Pleno' is double flowered and without seed. The freedom from nuisance seedlings elevates it to a class of its own. This evergreen shrub with sharp-tipped shoots and pointed, spiny leaves makes a wonderful barrier hedge. The bright, deep yellow, double, pea-like flowers are deliciously scented of coconut. There is more good news. It is happy to grow in the most miserable, impoverished soil you can find. It will do best in a well-drained, gravelly site in full sun.

Prune half of the branches hard after flowering every few years to encourage new growth. Propagate in summer using firm current year's growths in a free-draining, gritty compost. There are no pests or diseases that would dare to annoy it.

Warning: old bushy plants retain their dead, tinder-dry leaves, making them a fire risk close to property. **JC**

Clethra alnifolia

SWEET PEPPER BUSH, SUMMERSWEET

Type: hardy, deciduous, suckering shrub
Soil & situation: moist, acid soil/from full sun to deep shade
North American hardiness zone: 3–9; *C. arborea* 8–9
Height: 2m (6½ft)
Spread: variable
Grow for: fragrant, white flowers in late summer and early autumn when the leaves turn yellow and orange

My first introduction to this genus was the evergreen *Clethra arborea*, a native of Madeira where, heaven forbid, they use the foliage as cattle fodder! While visiting the Quinta do Palheiro, a magnificent garden near Funchal, I detected a spicy fragrance and followed it round the corner to find a young tree in full bloom. Sadly it's suitable only for sheltered gardens in mild areas of the UK so try *C. alnifolia* instead. It's a handsome, deciduous shrub covered in late summer with upright terminal spikes of fragrant, white flowers and in autumn with yellow and orange leaves. In good conditions it forms large colonies. *C. barbinervis*, a deciduous shrub or small tree up to 3m (10ft) high, is similar but does not sucker and is not as hardy.

There are several cultivars of *C. alnifolia*, including: 'Paniculata', which is considered to be the best of all the hardy clethras. 'Rosea' has very glossy leaves and pink tints to the buds and flowers. 'Pink Spire' grows to 1.2m (4ft) and has rose-pink tinted flowers. 'Ruby Spice' has deep rose-pink flowers and will reach 1.5m (5ft). 'Hummingbird' is only 38–95cm (15–38in) tall with white flowers.

Clethra alnifolia

It is very adaptable, preferring moist, acid soil but tolerates wet or dry conditions. It is surface rooting so mulch in spring to preserve moisture. Remove older stems in winter to maintain the shape; rejuvenate by cutting back hard and feeding in spring. Propagate by seeds or detaching suckers in spring, layers in late autumn or early spring, or semi-ripe cuttings with a heel and bottom heat. **MB**

Clianthus puniceus 'Red Cardinal'

LOBSTER'S CLAW, PARROT'S BILL

Type: frost-hardy, evergreen shrub
Soil & situation: well-drained soil/full sun/shelter from cold winds
North American hardiness zone: 8–9
Height: 4m (13ft)
Spread: 3m (10ft)
Grow for: looks phenomenal in flower

With plants I can be very persistent and I can prove it. Over the past 30 years I have planted a total of six clianthus. All in my own garden with each one following the death of its predecessor. They are not frost hardy and every so often a hard frost teaches the plant and me a lesson. One reason I admit to my weakness is to encourage everyone to try growing this super plant. You may have to wrap it up every winter and it will eventually die but for a few, or more, seasons you will enjoy its full glory in flower.

Given support it will grow on trellis or against a wall, with 15cm (6in) long, dark green leaves and numerous narrow leaflets. The pendent racemes of brilliant scarlet flowers appear in late spring and early summer. When open, each 7.5cm (3in) flower resembles a lobster's claw or parrot's beak. These are followed by pea-like seedpods. Other good varieties include *Clianthus puniceus* 'Albus', white flushed green, and *C. p.* 'Roseus', deep rose-pink.

Planted in well-drained soil on a sunny wall and sheltered from cold winds it will quickly make a large shrub. Protect the base of the plant in winter with a deep mulch of straw or bracken. If cut back by frost it may well throw new growths

Clianthus puniceus 'Red Cardinal'

from the base in spring. Immediately after flowering prune the shoots back by one third. Old plants dislike hard pruning. Propagation is by seed sown in spring. Semi-ripe cuttings can be rooted in a free-draining compost with extra grit in summer. **JC**

Clivia miniata

KAFFIR LILY

Type: tender, evergreen perennial
Soil & situation: loam-based compost with added grit/frost tender/minimum temperature 10°C (50°F)/tolerates low light levels and dry atmospheres, making it a useful house plant/shady conditions outside/fairly high levels of water when in growth
North American hardiness zone: 10–11
Height: 45cm (18in)
Spread: 30cm (12in)
Grow for: strappy foliage in a good bright green; magnificent orange, fragrant blooms from spring to summer; AGM

This South African plant does look difficult to grow, with its huge, glamorous, scarlet-orange, funnel-shaped flowers and broad leaves, often up to 7cm (3in) wide. The foliage is distinctive enough to be grown for that alone, looking splendid if several plants are crammed together in a large pot. Because of its low requirements for humidity and light it copes well with central heating and indoor light levels so it is, in fact, a surprisingly undemanding plant that is well worth getting hold of to accommodate in the house in the cooler months and to use as a superb pot plant, adding an exotic flavour to the garden in the warmer months.

Although this plant dislikes root disturbance, periodically it will be necessary to divide it. This is best carried out in late winter or early spring. Only do this when they become very crowded as they do flower far better when they are more confined. They also look better when you see generous clumps of leaves. Feed the plant with a liquid feed when the flower buds appear, and then cut down the spent flowerheads after flowering. I put my pots outside in early summer in a fairly shaded spot and bring them in in autumn when the weather starts to turn. **BG**

Clivia miniata

Cobaea scandens

CUP-AND-SAUCER VINE, CATHEDRAL BELLS

Type: half-hardy perennial, usually grown as an annual
Soil & situation: free-draining soil/hot sunshine
North American hardiness zone: annual
Height & spread: 4m (13ft) or more
Grow for: unusual flowers from mid-summer to mid-autumn

Here's a few fascinating facts! The branched tendrils are tipped with tiny hooks that hang onto the branches and twist tightly to drag the stems towards the branches; the hooks are so effective they will hold onto your skin. The large, open-mouthed, solitary flowers at the end of stalks up to 25cm (10in) long are at first creamy-green with an unpleasant smell and are fly pollinated, ageing to deep violet with a honeyed scent and are bee pollinated. Finally, they darken further and are believed to be bat pollinated. The plant is always covered with flowers at different stages of maturity. Now there's something to tell your friends while you're cooking the barbecue!

Cobaea scandens f. *alba* has white flowers, ageing to creamy-white. *C. pringlei* from eastern Mexico has dainty, greenish-white cups on elegant flower stalks. I have seen it growing outside in a sheltered London garden where it looked magnificent.

Although this can be grown in conservatory borders or containers as a perennial, here it is treated as a half-hardy annual. Soak the seeds overnight in tepid water and sow from early to mid-spring; plant out when there is no danger of frost in a sheltered, sunny position on moderately fertile, free-draining soil. Rich soils promote foliage at the expense of flowers. Pinch out the growing tips to encourage bushiness then trim to keep under control. It is excellent trained over a shed or trellis. **MB**

Cobaea scandens

Cobaea scandens

Codonopsis clematidea

Codonopsis clematidea
BONNET BELLFLOWER

Type: hardy, herbaceous climber
Soil & situation: moist, free-draining soil/full sun
North American hardiness zone: 7–9
Height & spread: 1.5m (5ft)
Grow for: pretty flowers from mid-summer to early autumn

Some plants like to tease and this is one of them! It's a delicate twining climber with brittle slender stems and grey-green leaves. Viewed from a distance, it seems so refined but when you get closer, there is a slight odour that gets much worse when the foliage is touched. Gently upturn the nodding pale blue flowers (taking care not to touch the foliage!) and its true beauty is revealed. There, as if painstakingly inked with golden-yellow, blue, purple and black are the most exquisite markings. There are many good reasons for growing this delicate, delectable plant – just remember not to touch the leaves!

Codonopsis convolvulacea has saucer-shaped, sky-blue flowers with circular purple markings inside. The bud expands like a small balloon, bursting open to reveal the flower. *C. lanceolata* is bell shaped, slate-mauve and greenish-lilac with violet spots, stripes and veins inside.

C. pilosula has large green bells with purple markings; its roots are used extensively in Chinese medicine.

They need light, moist, humus-rich, well-drained soil in sun or light shade, and shelter. Dig in plenty of well-rotted organic matter before planting, if needed. It grows best through shrubs, dark leaves providing an excellent background. Alternatively create brushwood supports using birch twigs, or similar, and allow them to scramble through. Plant near paths so they can be easily seen.

Pinch out shoot tips to encourage bushiness. Cut back to 30cm (12in) in autumn and to ground level in spring. Mulch in autumn. To propagate divide established plants in spring or sow seed. They are susceptible to slugs and snails. **MB**

Coffea arabica
Plant of the Week (see page 25)

Colchicum speciosum 'Album'
NAKED LADIES, AUTUMN CROCUS

Type: hardy, cormous perennial
Soil & situation: deep, fertile, well-drained soil/full sun
North American hardiness zone: 4–9
Height: 20cm (8in)
Spread: 10cm (4in)
Grow for: it is hard to beat the sight of dozens of autumn crocuses in flower; AGM

A border full of naked ladies, well I never! The way to appreciate autumn crocus is as a large drift in full bloom. Without their leaves, individual flowers do look a bit naked whereas, en masse, they make a spectacular display.

The 20–25cm (8–10in) long, lance-shaped, thick, dark green leaves of *Colchicum speciosum* 'Album' appear in late winter and last until mid-summer. The corm produces one to three goblet-shaped flowers on long stems (perianth tubes) in late autumn. The tepals are pure white with yellow anthers. Fortunately, they are unaffected by adverse weather.

C. 'Waterlily' produces up to five fully double, pinkish-lilac flowers in autumn on long stems. They are followed by erect, 20–25cm (8–10in) long leaves during winter and spring.

The corms should be planted 10cm (4in) deep in late summer or early autumn. Soils which tend to dry out in summer will need additional leafmould or well-rotted farmyard manure to help retain sufficient moisture. Propagation is by fresh seed sown as soon as it is ripe. Keep in a cold frame over the winter and early spring. Corms may be divided in summer when the foliage has died down. Replant them immediately. **JC**

Colchicum speciosum 'Album'

Colletia hystrix

Colletia hystrix (syn. *C. armata*)

Type: hardy, spiny shrub
Soil & situation: free-draining, preferably sandy soil/sun
North American hardiness zone: 7–10
Height & spread: 4m (13ft)
Grow for: sculptural form; curiosity value; fragrant flowers from early to late autumn

Roll up, roll up, see the weird and wonderful in a grotesque horticultural freak show full of fascination and fear! These bizarre botanical specimens, direct from the scrubby hillsides of temperate South America, have shed almost all their leaves, exposing a naked mass of flailing stems, covered with vicious spines. Grey-green *C. hystrix* has opted for tight clusters of short, rounded spikes. In sharp contrast to this ungainly mass of vegetative violence, tiny, white, sweetly scented flowers appear directly on the stems from late summer to autumn. There is even a pale pink form called 'Rosea'.

C. paradoxa (syn. *C. cruciata*) is similar, but the spines are even more intimidating with all the appeal of living razor wire! For defence and attack they have pairs of triangular, fin-like, flattened stems, each topped with a short sharp spine. Each pair is set alternately and at right angles to the previous one, right down the stem – there is no escape! Clusters of small, white, fragrant flowers dare to appear among this armoury, proving that there is beauty in these beasts; tangle with them at your peril!

I find them strangely beautiful and would love to plant either species in a stainless steel pot to be illuminated at night as living sculptures; it's the perfect piece of haughty culture! It needs shelter on well-drained, even poor soil in full sun. In cooler climates, grow in containers and protect from frost. Propagate by semi-ripe cuttings of sideshoots in late summer. **MB**

Convallaria majalis
LILY-OF-THE-VALLEY

Type: hardy, herbaceous perennial with creeping roots
Soil & situation: moist, humus-rich soil/light sun to light shade
North American hardiness zone: 2–7
Height: less than 30cm (12in)
Spread: indefinite
Grow for: even people who find many scented flowers too strong or overpowering love the pure white, scented spikes of lily-of-the-valley; AGM

Flowering in late spring and early summer there are few flowers more welcome – the little one-sided spikes of hanging white bells are attractive enough, but their scent is divine. The creeping roots can make this plant invasive where it is happy, but who cares as it is better than almost any alternative. It can also be made into a hanging-basket subject, as was popular in Victorian times. There is a rare double form and rarer still a pink form and I have even read there was a red variety, long since lost to us. A native of the northern temperate zone in England, it used to grow wild and in profusion on Hampstead Heath, London, and at Lee, Essex, but is now almost only found in gardens. The name is from the Latin *convallis*, a valley.

Given a moist, humus-rich soil in light shade this plant can become a weed and in such a site it will endure for centuries. Because of its creeping habit careful weeding is essential but it's not easy, so mulches really are of double benefit. It can be grown from seed, but lifting and dividing roots each with a bud before growth starts in spring is the best option. Lily-of-the-valley is not at all happy in dry conditions, especially in full sun. **BF**

John adds:
When it comes to ground cover that tolerates deep shade, most woodland plants smell a bit fusty or worse. Lily-of -the-valley is in a class if its own. The perfume of my favourite variety, *C. m.* 'Flore Pleno', is magnificent. Picking flowering stems for the house evokes pleasant memories of years gone by and they last well in water. *C. m.* 'Albostriata' is unusual, with bright leaves longitudinally striped in creamy white. The mauve-pink flowering *C. m.* var. 'Rosea' is not to my liking, but it is different.

Convallaria majalis

Convolvulus cneorum

Type: hardy, evergreen shrub
Soil & situation: impoverished, gritty, well-drained soil/full sun
North American hardiness zone: 8–10
Height: 60cm (24in)
Spread: 90cm (36in)
Grow for: early summer colour in the heather bed; AGM

If you want a Mediterranean garden, this is a good plant with which to start. It loves it hot and dry, forming a compact, rounded, bushy shrub.

I delight in the foliage of this plant. The 5cm (2in) long, silvery-green, silky leaves shimmer like old silver in the afternoon sun feeling smooth and polished. They contrast beautifully with its ivory-white, funnel-shaped flowers which are 4cm (1½in) across. Flowering from late spring to mid-summer, each bloom, opening from a shell-pink bud, has a splash of bright yellow in its centre. A great plant for the rock garden or scree bed, it looks cool dotted through a mixed heather and dwarf conifer planting.

Convolvulus cneorum

In areas with cold, wet winters it should be grown in a container and given the protection of a cold greenhouse. To keep the plant in shape, shoots which have flowered may be trimmed back after flowering. It dislikes hard pruning. Propagation is easy in late spring with softwood cuttings or in summer using semi-ripe shoots. **JC**

Cordyline australis
TORQUAY/TORBAY PALM

Type: half-hardy, perennial, evergreen palm
Soil & situation: most soils/full sun/preferably moist
North American hardiness zone: 10–11
Height: 12m (40ft)
Spread: 2m (6½ft)
Grow for: unusual palm-like appearance; attractive, long, sword-like leaves; enormous foamy white panicles of highly scented flowers; AGM

There are few true palms hardy enough to survive in the UK and although this is not a true palm it closely resembles one. Famous along the southwest coast of England, it prefers mild coastal districts but can survive further inland; I have two in my Norfolk garden and despite getting battered by the weather they survive, and a large one in a neighbouring garden thrives and flowers most years. It is a big plant when it reaches flowering size so often a set of steps is needed to smell the beautifully perfumed flowers.

Cordyline australis

A native of New Zealand where it is called the cabbage tree, it has been taken all over the world. The name is from the Greek *kordyle*, meaning a club, for which use it would be of no use as the wood is light and fibrous, not hard or even very rigid.

Although it likes moisture in the growing season, cordyline dislikes waterlogged soil in winter; given good conditions it can become quite big and then is much tougher than smaller specimens. Avoid searingly cold windy spots. If the growing point is destroyed it sometimes bifurcates but more often dies back and new stems come up from the base. Protect young small specimens from hard frosts, but be careful not to smother them.

Although it is possible to propagate from seed, offsets taken in spring are more sure – take big ones rather than small as the latter rarely survive.

Cats can cause immense damage to the stems as they use them as the most appealing scratching posts – wrapping with galvanized chicken netting stops them. **BF**

Coriandrum sativum 'Santo'

Coriandrum sativum 'Santo'

CORIANDER, CHINESE PARSLEY

Type: hardy, annual herb
Soil & situation: free-draining, warm soils which are not too rich/sunny position
North American hardiness zone: annual
Height: 1m (3ft), including flower
Spread: 20cm (8in)
Grow for: home-grown supply of this divine, distinctively flavoured leaf, an asset to any cook and many dishes

This plant can zap up a salad, barbecue or plain bit of fish or meat, transforming it to new heights. When grown commercially this herb tends to have lower levels of flavour, either because it is produced under polythene or fleece with reduction in sun and light or because it is irrigated to maximize yields. Home grown is superior. People seem to have problems getting this plant to produce decent quantities of leaf before running to flower. The main factor I think is variety. For several years I have been growing 'Cilantro', a variety that is resistant to bolting but now it is no longer recognized as a distinct form.

My seed suppliers, Tozer Seeds Ltd, who supply many commercial growers and do variety trials, recommend that 'Santo' is the best variety for leaf production. They make the point that it is very early days in terms of selection of good varieties as this is a relatively new commercial crop over here. So keep on the look out for good new forms. Another form is 'Bilbo': commercial growers use this one for pot-grown supply to supermarkets as it is compact and does not flop over the pot (good news at point of sale). It quickly bolts, so is no good for leaf production. 'Moroccan' is the variety recommended for seed production. The RHS's AGM is also awarded for excellent varieties of vegetables and herbs but as yet they have not awarded one for coriander.

This plant germinates quickly and can be broadcast or sown *in situ* in drills from early spring onwards, at about three-weekly intervals, depending on weather. You can thin the plants to about 25cm (10in) which probably helps them resist bolting as there is less moisture stress when it is hot and dry. Commercially they cut the complete row, plough it in and start again, but for gardeners it far better to use it as cut-and-come-again picking, if possible, a few leaves of each plant rather than stressing it by shearing it to a couple of centimetres or an inch off the ground. If you are trying to grow for seeds though, watch carefully as the seeds drop as soon as they are ripe. For some dishes I also use the green seeds which are softer and full of flavour. **BG**

Cornus alba 'Sibirica'

Plant of the Week (see page 17)

Cornus controversa 'Variegata'

WEDDING CAKE TREE

Type: hardy, deciduous tree
Soil & situation: fertile, moist, well-drained soil/full sun or light shade
North American hardiness zone: 6–9
Height & spread: 7m (23ft)
Grow for: an excellent specimen tree with a horizontal structure; AGM

A cornus with attitude. When mature and in leaf this tree will leave you speechless. It is a tree of rare beauty which refuses to conform to normal tree shape. The branches spread out horizontally, forming tiers, sufficiently far apart to allow light and shade to affect the lower foliage. Its tiers have resulted in the common name of wedding cake. It makes a marvellous specimen on a lawn underplanted with blue-flowered, spring bulbs such as grape hyacinth.

The 15cm (6in) long, oval leaves are shiny green, margined with creamy-white or yellow. In early summer a mature tree will produce flattened clusters of small, ivory-white flowers, followed by blue-black fruit.

Avoid planting in sites subjected to biting, cold winds as the young leaves are emerging in spring. It dislikes waterlogged soil. There is seldom any need for pruning but, when necessary, it should be undertaken in early winter before the sap commences to flow. When it is planted in grass it may be necessary to remove the lowest tier of branches to accommodate a lawn mower. If the tree is planted when it is small it will only require staking for one or two seasons. Propagation is by grafting in winter. **JC**

Cornus controversa 'Variegata'

Lunaria annua

HONESTY, MOON PENNIES

Type: hardy biennial
Soil & situation: fertile, moist, well-drained soil/partial shade or sun
Hardiness zone: 3–8, but often grown as an annual in North America
Height: 90cm (36in)
Spread: 30cm (12in)
Grow for: flowers from mid- to late spring; seedheads through the winter. In most years April is the month when the flowers first appear.

The name honesty was apparently adopted in the 16th century because you can see right through the seedheads; I prefer moon pennies, which is a more romantic description of the ethereal, translucent seedheads. It is a robust plant with coarsely toothed leaves, upright stems and sweetly scented reddish-purple to white flowers from late spring to early summer. The seedheads start off deep lime-green, become tinted purple and then dry to form rounded 'moons' with three or more seeds like flattened currants that dry and rustle in the wind. Cut for decoration after a dry day, as soon as they mature; they look lovely in winter displays. In Guernsey it is believed to be good luck to hang a dried bunch in the wardrobe; in Yorkshire it is considered bad luck to have it in the house or garden! I think I'll go to Guernsey! They are excellent for naturalizing on banks, borders or in wildlife gardens.

Lunaria rediviva is similar but perennial with pale lavender flowers. *L. annua* var. *albiflora* has white flowers; *L. a.* var. *a.* 'Alba Variegata' has cream variegation and margins, and white flowers; and *L. a.* 'Munstead Purple' has deep reddish-purple flowers, and was selected by Gertrude Jekyll. The leaves of *L. a.* 'Variegata' are variegated and margined creamy white and the flowers are purple or red-purple.

They prefer fertile, moist, well-drained soil in partial shade or sun. Dig in plenty of well-rotted organic matter if necessary. Sow seed in a prepared seedbed from spring to early summer for planting out early the following year. Alternatively, sow *in situ* or allow it to self-seed. Any pests or diseases affecting the family Cruciferae, including clubroot, can be a problem. **MB**

Corydalis flexuosa 'Père David'

Type: hardy, herbaceous perennial
Soil & situation: moist, humus-rich soil/dappled shade
North American hardiness zone: 6–8
Height: 30cm (12in) or more
Spread: 20cm (8in) or more
Grow for: turquoise flowers from mid-spring to late summer

This glorious species was first introduced to the UK in 1986 from the Wolong Panda Reserve in China. Mixed forest shelters this society beauty and its classy companions *Cardiocrinum giganteum* var. *yunnanense* (see page 85) and *Paris polyphylla* (page 287). I like to believe that occasionally the flowering may overlap – can you imagine what that would be like? Botanical ecstasy!

The form 'Père David' is vigorous with grey-blue, oval leaves with blood-red markings. They appear in autumn, remain over winter (where conditions allow) and become dormant in summer. From early spring to early summer it is covered in slender, brilliant blue, 3.5cm (1¼in) long flowers gliding over the foliage like a shoal of exquisite tropical fish. For any blue addict, it's just bliss! At first they are densely packed, then gradually disperse until they finally swim away to oblivion. Rather than being beautiful and temperamental, this is beautiful and obliging; what a wonderful plant to grow!

Corydalis flexuosa 'Père David'

Other cultivars of *Corydalis flexuosa* include: 'Balang Mist' whose flowers are pale with a blue flush; the leaves of 'Blue Panda' are pale blue-green and the flowers sky-blue; 'Purple Leaf' has reddish-purple leaves and stems, and deep blood-red markings at the base of the leaflets; and 'China Blue' has greenish to sky-blue flowers and brownish-green leaves with small red blotches at the base.

They need partial shade and moderately deep, fertile, humus-rich, moist, free-draining soil. Dig in plenty of well-rotted leafmould if necessary. They tolerate both alkaline soil and drier soils. Divide in late summer when autumn growth is about to begin. Slugs and snails can be a problem. **MB**

Corylus avellana/C. maxima
COBNUT, RED-SKINNED FILBERT

Type: hardy, deciduous, woody shrub
Soil & situation: well-drained, poor soil/full sun to light shade
North American hardiness zone: 3–9
Height: 7m (23ft)
Spread: 3m (10ft)
Grow for: catkins in late winter, delicious nuts in autumn and useful for pea sticks

All the hazel family are good shrubs for the wild garden, though most are not attractive enough for an ornamental planitng. In the orchard they are very valuable as the tasty nuts are generously produced almost every year without fail. The catkins are gorgeous in late winter and the wee red female flowers, like tiny crimson starfish, are a joy to behold on a bright late winter's day. I grow several varieties but the most flavoursome, and slightly more compact, red-skinned filbert is by far and away the tastiest. The husks and shells are also useful as I save these up and use them for smoking cheese.

The hazel is a native of the UK but foreign blood has been introduced to the cobs and filberts. Once an important crop in Kent, the plants were ruthlessly trained and pruned to a wheel-shaped base with a cylinder of fruiting stems rising from the rim – sadly this intensive method has now passed and most nuts for sale are imported.

Corylus avellana

Hazel is long lived in a dry, gravelly, poor soil which few other crop plants enjoy. Prune to remove congested internal growths and strong vertical shoots, which are always useful to have in the garden anyway. Plants can be bought impregnated with truffle fungus on the roots but so far I've not had any success with mine, nor heard of any one who has, and they were not cheap! Seed does not come true, cuttings are difficult, layering is not easy, so I find inarching onto seedlings the best option. Without doubt, the only major problem is the squirrels who steal most of my crop and they will get yours too. **BF**

Bunny adds:
I grow a lot of hazel – they are ornamental in themselves and of course you can cultivate carpets of other plants around them. I often use them for screening children's areas; they create useful cover for children to play in, too, and great dens can be made between and from the sticks. We have no squirrels, but the Jack Russell pinches the nuts, cracks them open and eats them!

Corylus maxima 'Purpurea'

Corylus avellana 'Contorta'

Corylus avellana 'Contorta'

CORKSCREW HAZEL, HARRY LAUDER'S WALKING STICK

Type: hardy, deciduous shrub
Soil & situation: fertile, well-drained, alkaline soil/sun or partial shade
North American hardiness zone: 3–9
Height & spread: 3m (10ft)
Grow for: mad twisted stems which are its main claim to fame – I'm old enough to remember the famous twisted walking stick

I include *Corylus avellana* 'Contorta' in lots of planting plans. Perhaps it is because it looks so ludicrous in winter with its bare stems contorted, as though following the silvery trail left by a drunken snail. An edging of blown snow to highlight the shapes makes a chilly, winter garden walk worthwhile. Bright yellow 5–8cm (2–3½in) long catkins appear in winter and early spring, ahead of the mid green leaves which turn pale yellow in autumn. Another hazel I wouldn't be without is *C. maxima* 'Purpurea' (the purple-leafed filbert), which makes a big shrub with rounded, deep, deep purple leaves.

C. a. 'Contorta' is grafted onto *C. avellana* rootstock. Suckers must be removed where they join the main stem or root as soon as they appear (and they will). Left to grow, the faster-growing common hazel will overpower and smother 'Contorta'. I prefer to thin the branches in spring to prevent them forming a tangled mass. This also allows the contortions to be better admired. The prunings are much sought after by flower arrangers. The easiest form of propagation is by layering a low branch. It will tolerate most soils but dislikes waterlogged or acid conditions. **JC**

Cosmos atrosanguineus

Type: tender perennial
Soil & situation: well-drained but moisture-retentive soil/full sun/protection over winter in many areas
North American hardiness zone: 7–10
Height: 75cm (30in)
Spread: 45cm (18in)
Grow for: stunning, small, solitary, rich chocolate-maroon flowers from summer to autumn; with a strange, strong, dark chocolate fragrance

This wonderful plant is well worth the effort involved with winter protection – the exquisite flowers are velvety, and look like mini dahlias. The leaves are green, sometimes with reddish-brown midribs. The long stems are often reddish too, topped with the individual flowers that are produced for months from summer to autumn. At the start of the season the growth is upright, later spreading out. If your soil is too rich you may find masses of vegetative growth is produced at the expense of flowers.

These plants start into growth very late in spring, so in warmer areas you can get away with leaving the mature tubers to over-winter outside providing the soil is well-drained and you add a protective mulch. If the tubers are planted deeply, about 15cm (6in) below the soil surface, they are also in with a far better chance of survival.

Otherwise, either lift the plants in the autumn and over-winter them under glass in frost-free conditions or lift and store the small tubers as you would for dahlias. The mature tubers are hardier, so for the first year at least, even in warm, sheltered areas, it is advisable not to chance it. If you want to propagate them, take basal cuttings from the tubers as for dahlias, but a hormone rooting powder is worth it as they tend to be a little tricky. **BG**

Cosmos atrosanguineus

Cotinus coggygria

Cotinus coggygria

SMOKE TREE, VENETIAN SUMACH

Type: hardy, deciduous shrub
Soil & situation: well-drained soil/sunny or partially shaded position/generally an easy plant to please and grow.
North American hardiness zone: 5–8
Height & spread: to 5m (16ft)
Grow for: bushy shrub with wonderful translucent, bright green foliage; autumn tints a spectacular red; flowers form a smoke-like blur all over the shrub in summer; AGM

I inherited a magnificent specimen of this plant – more like a multi-stem tree, it must be 5m (16ft) going on 6m (20ft), with five large limbs spreading from a short leg about 30cm (12in) high and with a diameter of the same order. This and an elderly, but delicious, greengage were the only inhabitants of my small walled garden, even though the house dates back to the thirteenth century. My new design was superimposed around them, and the cotinus has risen to the occasion and become more spectacular each year. The winter profile of its fine, comely multi-stem habit is as good as its dramatic performance of flowering in summer, then its seasonal turn in autumn is a show-stopper and for the rest of the year its stature and foliage command centre stage. I would never have planted it for this position, not having the wit, patience or foresight to know that it would be such a specimen. Normally it makes up a mixed border as a large and decorative shrub. The purple-leafed form *C. coggygria* 'Royal Purple' has dark purple leaves that can look heavy, but equally can be dramatically offset by brighter limes and vivid oranges.

Cotinus coggygria is fairly fast growing and so, with a little patience, could be positioned and planted as a specimen tree. On the other hand, if a more compact, smaller plant is desired, pruning it back to a permanent framework each spring, before growth begins, produces larger foliage and restricts the size. For a more laid-back approach, just remove the undesirables – dead, dying, crossing limbs and anything that is getting too big – in late winter or early spring. **BG**

Cotinus 'Flame'

SMOKE BUSH

Type: hardy, deciduous shrub
Soil & situation: moist, well-drained soil/full sun or light shade
North American hardiness zone: 5–8
Height: 6m (20ft)
Spread: 5m (16ft)
Grow for: a fine-looking shrub with amazing orange-red foliage in the autumn; AGM

To see this plant in late summer and then in early autumn is one of the wonders of a garden. The contrast in leaf colour inside a few days is magical.

It forms a tree-like, bushy shrub with 10cm (4in) long, light green leaves. In autumn the foliage turns a brilliant orange-red. The 15cm (6in) long, fruiting panicles are pale purple in late summer. *Cotinus* 'Flame' can tolerate light shade but the autumn leaf colour will not be so spectacular. *C.* 'Grace' is similar with brilliant, translucent, bright red leaves in autumn. Powdery mildew can seriously mark the foliage of both varieties.

Cotinus 'Flame'

Cotoneaster bullatus

Shelter from strong winds is essential as its brittle stems will break off, spoiling the overall shape. Pruning in spring by reducing all the branches back to a few buds of the main framework will result in new growth with large leaves. Propagation is by softwood cuttings in summer. Where there are suitably low branches layering will result in large, rooted plants within 18 months. **JC**

Cotoneaster bullatus

HOLLY BERRY COTONEASTER

Type: hardy, deciduous shrub or small tree
Soil & situation: most soils/full sun or partial shade
North American hardiness zone: 6–8
Height: 5m (16ft)
Spread: 3m (10ft)
Grow for: flowers in early and mid-summer; autumn fruits and colour; AGM

I can't help admiring plants that combine the attributes of physical toughness and attractive features. Cotoneasters fall into this category, yet they are cursed by being regarded as 'municipal' and consequently undervalued as garden plants;

Cotoneaster 'Rothschildianus'

they make good hedges, ground cover and specimen plants. A particular favourite of mine is *Cotoneaster bullatus*, a large shrub with an open arching habit and big oval to oblong corrugated leaves which are soft bronze when young. The flat clusters of up to 30 rose-pink coloured flowers are followed by bunches of large, bright, glossy red berries, which often weigh down the branches, and magnificent autumn colour of orange or red.

Other recommended plants in this genus include *Cotoneaster microphyllus*, a low-growing evergreen with stiff stems and masses of tiny leaves, flowers and red berries; and *C. franchetii*, semi-evergreen with pale green leaves and small clusters of orange fruits. *C. horizontalis*, the deciduous 'herringbone cotoneaster', is magnificent when massed with white flowers, in red autumn colour and fruit, and when covered with frost in winter. I also love *C. salicifolius* 'Rothschildianus' (see next entry).

It needs sunshine to partial shade in moist, free-draining soil, however it tolerates anything except waterlogged soil; nurture until established in drier soils. Prune in summer, if necessary. Propagate by semi-ripe cuttings in early autumn. Sow seed outdoors when ripe in autumn or stratify in damp sand and sow under glass in spring. It is subject to many of the pests which afflict apples, including aphids, scale and silver leaf. Prune from the start of late summer and early autumn. **MB**

Cotoneaster salicifolius 'Rothschildianus'

Type: hardy, evergreen shrub
Soil & situation: fertile, well-drained soil/full sun or light shade
North American hardiness zone: 6–8
Height & spread: 5m (16ft)
Grow for: a mass of golden-yellow berries in autumn; AGM

You couldn't have too many big cotoneasters but it is nice to ring the changes and with golden-yellow berries this one is worth the money.

Tree-like, this vigorous, upright shrub has arching branches. The 10cm (4in) long, pale green leaves are narrow and lance-shaped. Clusters of small white flowers appear in summer and are followed in autumn by golden-yellow fruits, which last well into winter or until eaten by birds. If planted close to a path and allowed to grow over, it will resemble a covered walkway with clusters of pendent berries on arching stems.

It will grow well in light shade but dislikes cold, drying winds. Prune in early spring to keep it in shape. When necessary large branches may be cut hard to encourage new, strong shoots from low down on the plant. Propagation is by semi-ripe cuttings in late summer. Pot the rooted plants during the following summer and allow to grow for a season before planting out. **JC**

Crambe cordifolia

GREATER SEAKALE

Type: hardy perennial
Soil & situation: well-drained soil/will tolerate some shade and poor soil/sunny position
North American hardiness zone: 6–9
Height: up to 2m (6½ft)
Spread: 1.5m (5ft)
Grow for: dramatic, large, cabbage-like leaves followed by a vast froth of tiny, white, honey-scented flowers in late spring to early summer; AGM

This plant is a relative of the edible seakale and is a fun plant for borders providing you have the space. It will rapidly swallow up 1m (3ft) of ground, so is fairly imposing. The superb flowers, carried in branched panicles, are equally imposing in the vertical plane. If the plant sets seed, it remains attractive for a good long period and is a useful structure for encouraging another plant to weave itself into. If this is not the case, soon after the flowering is finished the leaves start to go yellow and die back as all the resources are taken back to the tap root. This leaves you with a large space to fill, which may be was just what you wanted, but more likely not. With their huge stature and relaxed feel they are easier and perhaps better suited to other situations – for instance in wilder spaces or in summer-flowering meadows, where the higher cut later on in the year will not harm them.

On a wet, poorly drained soil this plant tends to succumb to bacterial rots. Propagate these plants by root cuttings in winter, division in spring or by seed. **BG**

Crambe cordifolia

Crambe maritima

Type: hardy, herbaceous perennial
Soil & situation: light, free-draining soil/sun
North American hardiness zone: 6–9
Height: 75cm (30in)
Spread: 60cm (24in)
Grow for: tasty shoots; ornamental leaves and white flowers in summer; AGM

Seakale was harvested from beaches in the UK long before it came into cultivation; the shoots were blanched by heaping sand around them, then cut and carried to market. In the late 16th century, John Gerard in his *Herball* described seakale like this: 'It groweth naturally on the bayches and brimmes of the sea where is no earth to be seen, but sande and rolling pebble stones.' By Victorian times it had swept by a tide of enthusiasm into the garden and was regarded as an aristocrat among vegetables. The young shoots, blanched using terracotta forcers, burst from the ground as if twisted and contorted by a supreme effort. It was lightly boiled and served on folded napkins or pieces of toast with a sauceboat of lemon-flavoured melted butter or simply drenched in white bechamel or hollandaise sauce. Now there's an incentive to grow it!

Blanch by covering the crowns in late winter. It needs sunshine and deep, rich, moisture-retentive, light soil. Add plenty of well-rotted organic matter or sharp sand if necessary the winter before planting. Water regularly; feed with general fertilizer in spring.

In the vegetable garden, seakale needs a permanent bed, like asparagus. Plant crowns or root cuttings or pencil thick 'thongs', 7.5–15cm (3–6in) long, in late autumn or early winter; make a horizontal cut at the top and a slanting cut at the base so you don't plant them upside down and store in sand in a cool shed until early spring. Make a hole with a dibber and plant cuttings 3cm (1in) below soil level, 38cm (15in) apart each way. They need at least a year to establish before harvesting. Beware of club root; flea beetle damages the leaves. **MB**

Bunny adds:
A great vegetable for the ornamental kitchen garden, but I have to say I think it looks better than it tastes, though I adore the hollandaise sauce. Removing any flowering stems before they develop helps it establish and become more productive. In my garden I usually let it flower though, as we do not eat that much and the flowers are a real asset.

Crambe maritima

Crataegus spp.
HAWTHORN, QUICKTHORN

Type: hardy, deciduous woody shrub to small tree
Soil & situation: any soil/in full sun or shade
North American hardiness zone: 5–8
Height & spread: grows to a small tree but if regularly clipped it can be kept to 1m (3ft) x 50cm (20in)
Grow for: the thorns and bushy habit make this a stock- and people-proof hedge

The congested habit makes the appearance of a well-clipped hawthorn hedge look like a piece of coarse tweed, even when out of leaf. Hawthorn is overlooked because of its presence everywhere – it is one of the finest of hedges and if it ever gets too big and unwieldy it can be laid, pleached and worked up again, which is more than can be done for many others.

A native of Europe it has been used since time immemorial for hedging fields and has been and still is used on a vast scale. The wood is hard and it was known to the Greeks as *kratos*, from which we derive our name.

It will do almost anywhere and has no special needs but if total impenetrability is required then plant two offset rows, each plant at less than 30cm (12in) apart and start trimming early on. Shear at least once a year, or twice if exquisite neatness is required. The young plants are not so tough as an established hedge so protect them with guards or windbreak netting. Quickthorn is easy to strike from cuttings but in the UK because of its wholesale use by farmers can be bought by the hundred or thousand very cheaply indeed. Sometimes webber caterpillars or similar may defoliate a piece but it usually soon recovers. **BF**

Crataegus hedge

Crataegus laevigata 'Paul's Scarlet'

Crataegus laevigata 'Paul's Scarlet'

HAWTHORN, PINK THORN, MAY HAYTHORN

Type: hardy, deciduous tree
Soil & situation: any soil other than waterlogged/full sun or partial shade
North American hardiness zone: 5–8
Height & spread: 8m (25ft)
Grow for: mass of flowers in spring whatever the weather; AGM

All the 'thorns' are highly desirable plants. They are tough, well able to withstand icy blasts, salt-laden winds, impoverished soil and still manage to look good while preventing livestock from trespassing. The species is sometimes known as *C. oxycantha.*

The tree forms a rounded, compact shape with many thorns on all branches. In windswept sites it will bend with the wind, appearing lobsided. The 5cm (2in) long, glossy, mid-green leaves have three to five shallow lobes. They don't colour much in autumn and differ from the dark green, deeply lobed English hawthorn, *C. monogyna*, which is commonly grown as a field hedge.

Irrespective of the weather, in late spring *C. laevigata* 'Paul's Scarlet' is covered in clusters of up to ten deep pink, double flowers. It seldom produces berries but I am prepared to overlook this one small fault to be able to sit under a mature, gnarled tree laden with birds' nests and covered in rich blossom. There are two schools of thought about the English saying 'Don't cast a clout until May is out.' Either don't remove any clothes before the end of the month of May or else wait until the hawthorn is in bloom. You can please yourself, but if you are cold put your coat back on.

Propagation is usually by bud grafting onto a crataegus rootstock. Plant with the graft union above soil level. Remove suckers as close to the root as possible when they are still small. **JC**

Crataegus monogyna 'Biflora'

GLASTONBURY THORN

Type: hardy, small, spreading, spiny, deciduous tree or shrub
Soil & situation: moisture-retentive, free-draining soil/sun or partial shade
North American hardiness zone: 5–7
Height: 10m (33ft)
Spread: 8m (25ft)
Grow for: white flowers in mid-winter and late spring; red fruits; autumn colour

This fascinating and mystical plant flowers not only in late spring, like the common hawthorn, but in mid-winter too! Tradition says that it flowers on Christmas Day; I've seen it blooming then and on 7th January, 'old' Christmas Day. Depending on the weather, it blooms any time from late autumn until mid-spring.

There are many variations on the legend that tells of Joseph of Arimathea preaching Christianity in England and here is one of them. He went to Glastonbury, then called the Isle of Avalon, which at that time was surrounded by water. Tired from travelling and his preaching being ignored he rested on 'Weary-all Hill', and prayed for a miracle to convince the doubters. His prayer was answered; the staff he was leaning on, being thrust into the ground, burst into leaf and flower; it was Christmas Day and the miracle is said to be repeated each Christmas. Sprays are sent to the Royal family as decoration for Christmas Day; Queen Elizabeth II is said to have hers on the breakfast table; the late Queen Mother placed hers on a writing desk. It flowers only moderately in late spring.

One of the hardiest and most adaptable trees, tolerating sun to moderate shade and waterlogged or dry soil once established. It thrives in industrial and windswept sites. Pruning after flowering in spring will be necessary to keep the plant within its allotted space. Rejuvenate it by cutting hard after flowering in spring. Propagate by grafting or cuttings. Remove stems affected by cotoneaster webber moth; in dry seasons it may suffer from powdery mildew. Keep the soil moist as a preventative measure. **MB**

Crataegus monogyna 'Biflora'

Paulownia tomentosa

EMPRESS TREE, FOXGLOVE TREE

Type: hardy, deciduous tree
Soil & situation: well-drained, fertile soil/full sun/shelter from cold winds
Hardiness zone: 5–8
Height: 12m (40ft)
Spread: 10m (33ft)
Grow for: stunning, foxglove-like flowers; massive leaves; a compact tree for any size garden. If you are lucky, the flowers burst into bloom at this time of year; AGM.

This is one of my all-time favourite flowering, deciduous trees. It isn't rare but, in my book, deserves to be planted in every garden. It comes in two sizes: big and, when managed, small enough.

The felted, tan-coloured buds appear in autumn. From mid- to late spring, if these have escaped frost damage, the tree is covered in showy, 5cm (2in) long, fragrant, pale violet, foxglove-like flowers, marked with purple and yellow on the inside. The soft, hairy, bright green leaves are up to 30cm (12in) long, unfurling as the tree flowers.

It produces stumpy, thick branches, quickly forming a compact, round-headed tree. In a small garden you may sacrifice the flowers for enormous 60cm (24in) leaves by pollarding (cutting) the main stem close to the ground every spring. Allow one or two shoots to grow and these will quickly reach 3m (10ft) with huge leaves – the result looks stunning and makes quite a talking point.

Paulownia tomentosa prefers a sunny site, sheltered from biting, cold winds. It is totally hardy, although frost may damage soft growths and flower buds. Sow fresh seed in autumn and over-winter in a cold frame or propagate by taking root cuttings in winter. Powdery mildew may cause early defoliation. **JC**

Crinodendron hookerianum

Crinodendron hookerianum

CHILEAN LANTERN TREE

Type: half-hardy evergreen shrub or small tree
Soil & situation: cool, moist, acid soil/partial shade/shelter
North American hardiness zone: 9–10
Height: 10m (33ft)
Spread: 6m (20ft), or more
Grow for: unusual, lantern-like flowers opening in late spring; AGM

One of two species of glossy, dark-leaved evergreens from the temperate rainforests of southern Chile, where there is over 250cm (100in) of rain a year and the locals probably have webbed feet! *Crino* (lily), *dendron* (tree) was named for Sir William Hooker, the first director of the Royal Botanic Gardens, Kew and was introduced in 1848 by a Cornishman, William Lobb (1809–63), who was the first plant collector to be employed by the famous nurserymen Veitch & Co. The best specimen I ever saw was in Dublin, where it made a wonderful sight, reaching about 10m (33ft) tall and festooned with masses of red 'lanterns'. It shares with *Stachyurus praecox* (see page 371) the habit of producing flower stalks in autumn which bloom the following year; the flowers open in late spring and last for about six weeks – tap them and they rain yellow pollen. Atchoo!

C. hookerianum 'Ada Hoffman' has pink flowers; *C. patagua* has white, bell-shaped flowers in late summer and is more tender than *C. hookerianum*.

Plant in a sheltered, partially shaded spot or the leaves will be scorched by cold, drying winds or sun in cool, moist, acid soil. Shelter is vital as they are susceptible to winter damage. Mulch in spring and keep them constantly moist. They flourish in mild, moist regions of the UK like Cornwall and the west coast of Scotland. Plants grown in pots in the greenhouse in ericaceous compost should be watered with rainwater and fed with fertilizer for acid-loving plants. Containerized plants flower when young. Trim after flowering to keep within its allotted space. Propagate by semi-ripe cuttings from late summer to early autumn. **MB**

Crinum x *powellii* 'Album'

WHITE CAPE LILY

Type: hardy, bulbous perennial
Soil & situation: deep, moisture-retentive but well-drained, fertile soils/full sun
North American hardiness zone: 7–10
Height: 1.2m (4ft)
Spread: 30cm (12in)
Grow for: heavy umbels of highly scented, white flowers from late summer till autumn; AGM

You often see these glamorous plants being grown in large pots, which does show them off extremely well and gives you the advantage of being able to move them to a highly visible position when they are at their peak. This way you do not necessarily have to view the rather gangly leaves for too long. They are also fairly dramatic in the border, especially when you see impressively large clumps in full bloom. It is a surprisingly versatile plant – it can also be grown as a marginal plant in shallow water where the leaves look better than in the border.

This hybrid is hardier than many people think. Plant in spring, not too deeply: the neck of the bulb should just be at soil level. It is then best to leave them uninterrupted as they take some time to become established and reach their full potential. Once settled, they will spread by offsets quite quickly, become more congested and it is this which really helps them to produce those much sought-after blooms. **BG**

John adds:
When I first started growing these magnificent bulbs it was a love-hate relationship. I loved the big funnel-shaped pink or white flowers but hated the enormous, strap-like leaves.They tumbled over, smothering all nearby plants. In late autumn the leaves were still green but quite tattered. The solution was an accident. One clump was overplanted with *Cotoneaster* 'Coral Beauty', by mistake.This evergreen shrub has small leaves and is mound-forming, holding the crinum leaves in place as they grow through the stiff stems.

Crinum x *powellii* 'Album'

Crocosmia x *crocosmiiflora* 'Emily McKenzie'

Crocosmia x *crocosmiiflora* 'Emily McKenzie'
MONTBRETIA

Type: hardy, cormous perennial
Soil & situation: damp conditions/well-drained but moisture-retentive soil/shelter from exposure/sun or dappled shade
North American hardiness zone: 6–9
Height: 60cm (24in)
Spread: 10cm (4in)
Grow for: strident, bright orange flowers with mahogany markings in the throats in late summer; mid-green leaves are also attractive, lance-shaped with pleats or ribs

If you visit Portmeirion Gardens in Wales in the late summer, you see montbretias in abundance – huge clumps of pleated foliage and masses of burnt-orange-red flowers. I think it must be *C.* x *crocosmiiflora*, which is a parent of this cultivar. It is too vigorous for most gardens. 'Emily McKenzie' has larger, downward-facing flowers and is not invasive. It has a definite exotic flavour and both leaves and flowers last well in water, making this an excellent plant for cut flowers.

The plant forms chains of corms as new corms are formed from old ones and stay attached. When they become too congested the clumps should be divided, but you should leave the old corms intact as they provide the initial food source. The best time to do this is in autumn, and they regularly do not flower in the first year after planting. Very dense colonies tend to flower less, so you will find it pays dividends to watch the congestion stakes and act accordingly. **BG**

Crocosmia 'Solfatare'

Type: hardy, cormous perennial
Soil & situation: moderately fertile, humus-rich, well-drained soil/sun or partial shade
North American hardiness zone: 6–9
Height: 75cm (30in)
Spread: 23cm (9in)
Grow for: elegant foliage; flowers from mid-summer to early autumn; AGM

As the long hazy days of summer roll seamlessly into autumn with its cooler mornings and warm, still days, plants like this gorgeous *Crocosmia* 'Solfatare' come to the fore. It provides the perfect link between the seasons, the hot colours of summer and rich yellows, oranges and reds that dominate autumn colour. It is an elegant plant; the streamlined, sword-shaped, bronze-tinted leaves stand stiffly to attention, among them pure pale apricot to yellow trumpets appear on arching, wiry stems that are delightful in bud, accentuating the herringbone pattern of the flowerhead. Those nearest the base open first creating the shape of a bird's beak and as the flowers fade and fall all that remains is an ordered row of peg-like seedheads. The flowers are good for cutting.

While thinking of crocosmias, it is impossible to ignore 'Lucifer': reaching 1.2m (4ft) x 30cm (12in) it makes a bold clump for the larger garden; its big spikes of brilliant red flowers look like a cluster of birds' beaks above the foliage. *C.* 'Bressingham Blaze' is better for the smaller garden. These and several others were raised by the great nurseryman Alan Bloom.

They need moderately fertile, light, free-draining soils in sun or partial shade; fork in sharp sand or organic matter where necessary. In cooler areas, *C.* 'Solfatare' should be protected over winter with a layer of dry mulch, like bracken or straw, or planted by a wall. Plant 8–10cm (3½–4in) deep in spring. Lift and divide congested clumps in spring just before growth starts. **MB**

John adds:
'Solfatare' is my favourite variety, but I prefer to grow it on its own to let it show off its particular colour combination of flower and foliage.

Crocosmia 'Solfatare'

Crocus 'E.A. Bowles'

Crocus 'E.A. Bowles'

Type: hardy, spring-flowering, cormous perennial
Soil & situation: gritty, well-drained, reasonably fertile soil/full sun
North American hardiness zone: 3–8
Height: 7cm (3in)
Spread: 5cm (2in)
Grow for: rich yellow flowers with purple feathering; a cluster gives a cheerful display

I love all crocuses. They are dainty little flowers in a wide range of colours. They can be forced for early indoor flowers, grown in containers or in the rock garden and be naturalized even in good lawns. Then they quietly disappear without fuss for another year. When they are forced for early indoor display only bring them into the warmth when the flower buds are showing colour, otherwise the flowers may abort.

Of them all, *Crocus* 'E.A. Bowles' is my favourite. Flowering in spring it produces compact, bright lemon-yellow flowers. The outer tepals (petals) appear to be hand-painted with purple feathering on a bronze base. Belonging to the chrysanthus hybrids, each corm displays up to three flowers. The 15cm (6in) long, narrow, grey-green leaves appear at the same time as the flowers. Within six weeks they are yellowing and can be removed.

Plant corms in early autumn 5–8cm (2–3½in) deep. They will increase quickly and clumps can be lifted and divided in early autumn. **JC**

Crocus sativus

SAFFRON CROCUS

Type: hardy, cormous perennial
Soil & situation: very free-draining soil/warmth/sunshine
North American hardiness zone: 5–8
Height & spread: 5cm (2in)
Grow for: flowers and delicate stamens

The large, lilac-purple flowers with dark purple veins appear with the leaves in mid- to late autumn. Each bloom has three deep red stigmas, up to 3.5cm (1¼in) long sometimes hanging over the flower; they are the source of saffron. Spain provides 70 per cent of the world's saffron; it takes 250,000 flowers to produce 2.2kg (1lb) and they are all harvested by hand! No wonder it is such a precious commodity!

Arabs spread the plant throughout the Mediterranean; Phoenicians brought it to England and traded it for tin. From the 11th to the 14th century penalties, even death, were imposed on anyone who adulterated it. In the UK it was grown in Cornwall, the Cotswolds and of course Chipping Walden, later renamed Saffron Walden. It dyed the yellow robes of ancient Irish kings, it is still used in liqueurs, notably chartreuse, for colouring rice and in paella. As a medicine it is a mild sedative and was once used as a cure-all; this may have some basis, as it is a very rich source of vitamin B.

It needs a warm, sunny position in preferably alkaline, free-draining soil and plenty of moisture in autumn for flower production and spring for growth. In the UK the best chance of success is to plant it 12–18cm (5–7in) deep so it dries out in summer, and replant every three to four years from early to late summer on soil enriched with rotted farmyard manure well before planting. Feed with sulphate of potash in autumn and spring. Saffron is sterile; increase by division in spring. **MB**

Bob adds:
Saffron is one of the most expensive plant products yet is not difficult to grow, although as you collect and dry only the three minuscule stigmata the yields are necessarily small. It is wonderful to grow your own, and educational as well. In the ornamental garden the plant is rather small and needs a special raised bed where you can look at it closely. Please do not confuse this crocus with other autumn-flowering croci, especially the colchicums, which are very poisonous! In other words, buy the corms or seed from a reputable seller and do not collect from self-identified plants.

Crocus sativus

Cucumis melo 'Extra Early Nutmeg'

Cucumis melo 'Extra Early Nutmeg'
MELON

Type: tender, herbaceous annual
Soil & situation: rich, moist, limy soil/full sun/under cover
North American hardiness zone: annual
Height: 30cm (12in)
Spread: 2sq m (22sq ft)
Grow for: there is no melon as sweet nor so perfumed as one ripened on the vine

Nearly all fruits taste better when home-grown but with melons they're are not just better but vastly improved. Allow them to fully ripen on the vine until they drop into the net. Then chill and slowly warm up a bit immediately before serving so the perfume in the green flesh develops, but does not go over. Many newer melons are a little more reliable but most lack the flavour of this really old variety, which I have cropped without any real difficulty under glass and plastic. Failing this, 'Jenny Lind' is similar and if anything even sweeter and more perfumed, but it needs slightly better conditions.

Cucumis melo 'Extra Early Nutmeg' was known in the USA before 1835 and to the great French gardener Vilmorin-Andrieux as 'Melon Muscade des Etats Unis'. It is a very reliable variety with a distinct pear-like shape with barely more than a sort of splattering of netting. It requires a rich, moist, loamy soil with both plenty of humus and lime. Stop the vine after the third or fourth true leaf to form up to four sideshoots which bear sooner than an unstopped vine. Leave no more than two or three fruits per vine. Female flowers may need pollinating by hand. It can be started a couple of weeks before the last frost and grown on under glass or plastic, even in a cold frame as long as it is kept frost free, and it can be planted outdoors under a plastic sheet in early summer. It is prone to red spider mite and slug damage. **BF**

Cucumis sativus (syn. *C. pepo*) 'Petita'
CUCUMBER

Type: tender, herbaceous annual
Soil & situation: rich, moist, limy soil/full sun/under cover
North American hardiness zone: annual
Height: 30cm (12in)
Spread: 2sq m (22sq ft)
Grow for: mini-cucumber is now one of the quickest and easiest crops to grow in a warm greenhouse

Cucumbers used to require more heat and humidity, and were hard to grow well. They were prone to diseases and pests, and needed all males ruthlessly removing every day. Now they are easy to grow. There are many small-fruited, all female cucumbers and every one of them is good, but I especially like this one as in most years it gives me something fresh to eat way before anything else is ready for cropping.

Cucumbers were known to the ancients and seem to have come from India – certainly they have been cultivated for thousands of years. In the past, believe it or not, they were eaten when fully ripe and yellow; our taste for green cucumber is recent.

They need to be grown in a humus-rich, moist, loamy soil with plenty of lime, under cover in the warmth. Pick fruits before they ripen and swell, as they stop more forming. They can be started from the New Year if given extra heat and will crop within three months or so. Other varieties known as ridge and Japanese can be planted outdoors under a plastic sheet in early summer. Cucumbers are prone to red spider mite and slug damage. **BF**

Cucumis sativus 'Petita'

Cucurbita pepo

Cucurbita pepo
PUMPKIN

Type: tender, herbaceous annual
Soil & situation: rich, moist, limy soil/full sun
North American hardiness zone: annual
Height: 60cm (24in)
Spread: 1.8–6m (6–20ft)
Grow for: Halloween would not be the same without a pumpkin and it is a good plant to get children interested in gardening

I am not a great fan of pumpkin pie but I love making the lanterns. I also find that winter-storing pumpkins are really good value for little labour and the flesh is handy in soups, while the seeds are good roasted.

Seeded varieties with no hull can be grown just for the seeds and others such as the acorn squashes are for storing late into winter. Spaghetti squash has amazing vegetable spaghetti-like flesh and I always grow some, but I still prefer the real stuff. Other pumpkins for winter storage are the Hubbard sorts and these belong to *Cucurbita maxima*; my favourite is 'Gold Nugget', which is almost like a sweet potato.

It needs a rich, moist, loamy soil with plenty of humus. It can be started a couple of weeks before the last frost and grown on under plastic or in a cold frame until there is no risk of frost, then planted outdoors; or sow *in situ* under a plastic sheet in early summer. If you want champion-size fruits then fill a car-size hole with well-rotted manure and plant in that under a plastic sheet held up on sticks. Prone to slug damage. **BF**

Cucurbita pepo

Cucurbita pepo
COURGETTE MARROW

Type: tender, herbaceous annual
Soil & situation: rich, moist soil/full sun
North American hardiness zone: annual
Height: 60cm (24in)
Spread: 1 sq m (11 sq ft)
Grow for: no crop so productive so easily, that's such great value too

There is no crop so impressive as a row of courgette plants; they can give you a fruit or two apiece every day for weeks, if the soil is right for them and the sun is kind. Any surplus courgettes are easily frozen after frying in oil and they can be made into ratatouille with surplus tomatoes. A good plant for kids to grow.

Courgettes are really small marrows, and zucchini are exactly the same thing. Indeed, if accidentally left on the plant you get marrows, which are not as much use in the kitchen but do store for some weeks. Only a few years ago courgettes were all trailing sorts but now they are all more compact, bushy forms.

It needs a rich, moist, loamy soil with plenty of humus. Keep removing courgettes as fast as they form, daily is not too often – small ones are much better eating! It can be started a couple of weeks before the last frost and grown on under glass or plastic, even in a cold frame as long as it is kept frost free. Plant or sow directly outdoors in early summer. It is prone to slug damage and often suffers from cucumber mosaic virus in warm, damp years; destroy the plant if the fruits are blotchy and distorted. **BF**

x *Cupressocyparis leylandii*
LEYLAND CYPRESS

Type: hardy, evergreen conifer
Soil & situation: most well-drained soils (tolerant of some chalk)/full sun to light shade
North American hardiness zone: 6–9
Height & spread: if trimmed it can be kept to 2m (6½ft) x 60cm (24in); if left it will reach 50m (165ft)
Grow for: the fastest-growing hedge which is neat, tidy and a boon to over-wintering insects, particularly ladybirds who love its dry interior; tolerant of salt-laden winds; AGM

Although yew and holly make as good a hedge in time, they take years more to reach the same size. x *Cupressocyparis leylandii* is very quick and beats all others, even similar species such as *Chamaecyparis lawsoniana*. Once trimmed in mid-summer it is very neat and as perfect a backdrop for flowers as you can find. There is a yellower form, x *Cupressocyparis leylandii* 'Castlewellan' that is slightly less vigorous but of pleasing appearance. x *C. leylandii* was raised as a hybrid between *Chamaecyparis nootkatensis* and *Cupressus macrocarpa* at Leighton Hall in Montgomeryshire, Wales in 1888.

For a hedge space the plants 60cm (24in) apart and prune back fairly hard, but only to green wood, in the early years in mid-spring; later trim annually in mid-summer. To stop it from reaching 50m (165ft), which it can do in very little time, it must be trimmed back hard. Leylandii hedges suit most soils that are not bone dry or waterlogged but are unhappy on thin chalk soils or heavy clay. It is fairly shallow rooted so is not suited to very windy sites with thin soil. If well established and regularly trimmed it will have a long life. It cannot be grown from seed and is best propagated from cuttings in early spring. Sometimes the plants die back; there are attacks on hedges giving rise to dead brown patches thought to be spread by aphids. There is no cure, and they cannot be cut back hard into 'dead' wood as it never re-sprouts. **BF**

x *Cupressocyparis leylandii*

Cupressus cashmiriana

Cupressus cashmiriana
KASHMIR CYPRESS

Type: half-hardy, evergreen conifer
Soil & situation: most moisture-retentive, free-draining soils/sun
North American hardiness zone: 6–9
Height & spread: 30m (100ft) x 10m (33ft) in its native habitats; considerably smaller in the UK
Grow for: the most graceful of all conifers; AGM

Perhaps it's cheating to include a plant that is so tender it can be grown outdoors only by the privileged few, but I have done so because you may be one of them! Style, elegance, grace and every flattering superlative are packed into this one glorious conifer! In the UK it is small to medium sized and usually container grown in a conservatory in John Innes no. 3 compost. I have only ever seen one growing outdoors in this country, at the Hillier Arboretum in Hampshire in a very sheltered spot, and another in Christchurch Botanic Gardens, New Zealand that's worth seeing if you're passing that way!

Conical when young, it becomes broader with age with good-looking, fibrous, red-brown bark but it is the weeping, pale blue-grey foliage hanging in long, flat, lacy branchlets that makes it so irresistible. It was first discovered growing in Buddhist temples and has never been found in the wild in Kashmir, only in a single locality in Bhutan. If you can't grow this outdoors, the similar *C. torulosa* is marginally hardier but nothing compares to the Kashmir cypress.

It must be grown in deep, fertile soil in a very sheltered position in the south or southwest of England or areas affected by the North Atlantic Drift. It really needs longer hotter summers than we have in the UK and it cannot tolerate frost or cold. No pruning is necessary. Propagate by seed in spring or semi-ripe cuttings from mid-summer to early autumn. Plants grown in containers produce cones from a very early age. **MB**

Cycas revoluta
JAPANESE SAGO PALM

Type: tender cycad (tree with a palm-type appearance)
Soil & situation: moist but free-draining soil/prefers full sun/in really strong sun requires some shade/winter protection/sheltered position
North American hardiness zone: 9–11
Height: up to 2m (6½ft) or more
Spread: 1–2m (3–6½ft)
Grow for: highly dramatic evergreen foliage; long, glossy, pinnate leaves up to 1.5m (5ft) long.

This plant is usually grown in a pot and positioned outside to add an exotic, jungle-type feel to the garden. It will survive temperatures marginally below 0°C (32°F), but only for short periods and if the crown is well protected with straw and sacking. I imagine as it gets larger it also becomes hardier, but as it is extremely slow growing (and therefore expensive) I would be loath to risk years of cosseting just to lose one's investment to an unexpected, extreme frost. Mature plants (but none that I've seen) produce woolly, honey-brown flowers, the males smelling of pineapples, the females producing oval yellow fruit about 3cm (1in) long. Do not get too excited as they are rarely produced by plants in pots. But with or without these extras, it is a truly tremendous palm that looks great on a kitchen window sill in its early years. When it outgrows the creature comforts of home it can be housed in a greenhouse for the winter – I put mine outside from late spring to autumn.

Pot this on using a free draining compost, part soil-based, part loamless and with added grit and charcoal. A slow-release fertilizer also speeds it on its way. Water infrequently in winter but in the summer give it a moderate amount. It suffers from mealy bug and scale insects so keep a watchful eye on this, ready to wipe off the early invaders with a detergent wash. **BG**

Cycas revoluta

Cyclamen coum

Cyclamen coum

Type: hardy, tuberous perennial
Soil & situation: moisture-retentive, free-draining soil/sun or partial shade
North American hardiness zone: 5–9
Height: 8cm (3½in)
Spread: 10cm (4in)
Grow for: flowers from early winter to early spring; beautifully marked foliage; AGM

Small but perfectly formed rounded leaves ease themselves above the soil in late autumn after the flower buds have appeared. Then, springing one of winter's fabulous floral surprises, the tiny flowers open towards the end of winter, brightening the days with jewel-encrusted cushions. The flower colour is variable but always with a dark stain around the mouth. They combine well with winter-flowering heathers, rhododendrons, snowdrops and aconites but don't let them become overpowered by their companions.

Among this species and its forms there's an incredible range of leaf marking and zoning in silvery grey; flowers range from deep carmine to pink and white; the leaves are striking until late spring when the rest period begins. Do not buy plants that have been collected from the wild. Pewter Group has leaves that are almost entirely silver and carmine flowers. Silver Group has silvery leaves with a dark rim and flowers in tones of pink. 'Maurice Dryden' has pewter leaves with a dark green midrib and edge and white flowers.

They need shelter in sun or partial shade and prefer neutral to alkaline, but tolerate all except waterlogged or dust dry soil; they should be kept moderately moist in summer. Improve drainage by adding plenty of grit and well-rotted leafmould to at least 15cm (6in) deep. Plant tubers in early autumn or late spring, cover with 4cm (1½in) of loose leafy soil. In autumn, mulch with well-rotted leafmould; in poor soils, apply bonemeal; and propagate the species from seed. **MB**

Fritillaria imperalis

CROWN IMPERIAL

Type: hardy, spring-flowering bulb
Soil & situation: fertile, well-drained, alkaline soil/full sun
Hardiness zone: 5–9
Height: 1.2m (4ft)
Spread: 25cm (10in)
Grow for: large, handsome, orange, bell-shaped flowers on tall stems; statuesque form. Just coming into flower at this time of year.

A spectacular late spring-flowering bulb made all the more interesting by a story that just might be true. The sultan wrongly accused his sultana of infidelity and had her executed. The crown imperial fritillary saw what happened and cried. It has been crying ever since. Look up inside the pendulous flowerhead and you will see a clear, liquid 'teardrop' at the base of each petal. Why don't they run down? Touch them and they flow!

The flowers are carried on strong, bare stems up to 1.2m (4ft) high and the glossy, light green, lance-shaped leaves are arranged in whorls. Umbels of three to six pendent, bell shaped, orange flowers are topped with an odd-looking cluster of upright, strap-like bracts. There are several other good colours. *Fritillaria imperialis* 'Lutea' (right) is bright yellow and *F. i.* 'Aurora' has orange-red flowers. *F. i.* 'Aureomarginata' has variegated leaves.

The fragile, hollow-crowned bulbs have an unpleasant foxy odour. They are prone to rotting in poorly drained soil. Plant them at least four times their own depth with a 5cm (2in) layer of washed 13mm (1/2in) gravel in the base of the planting hole.

In a windy site it may be necessary to stake the flower stems. The cane or stake should be inserted before planting to avoid spearing the bulb. Where there is good drainage the bulbs can be left in the ground over winter. Otherwise, lift the bulbs as soon as the foliage turns yellow. Cover the soil surface with a mulch of composted bark. Water if necessary in spring to keep the soil moist and as the weather warms up watch out for slugs and the bright red lily beetle. **JC**

Bob adds:
Clearly a plant that attracts legends: another version says that they were blooming near the Crucifixion of Christ and have shed a tear every year since. Originally from the Himalayas, this was introduced to Europe by Clusius in 1576. Often seen haunting old gardens where the drainage is good, they persist long after most garden subjects have passed on.

Cyclamen europaeum (syn. *Cyclamen odoratum*)

Plant of the Week (see page 361)

Cyclamen hederifolium (syn. *Cyclamen neapolitanum*)

Type: hardy, tuberous perennial
Soil & situation: fertile, humus-rich, well-drained soil/partial shade
North American hardiness zone: 5–9
Height: 10cm (4in)
Spread: 15cm (6in)
Grow for: an ideal plant for a woodland garden, eventually forming a carpet of colour in autumn; AGM

This is a wonderful small plant for the woodland garden. It may look fragile, but it is as tough as old boots and well capable of ignoring bad weather.

The 5–15cm (2–6in) long, heart-shaped, mid- to dark green leaves are patterned in shades of green. Occasionally they are purplish-green on the underside. Fragrant flowers are produced in various shades of pink with maroon marks at the mouth and appear during autumn, before or just as the leaves appear.

They dislike soils that dry out in summer and are best grown in an area shaded from full sun. Plant the tuber 5cm (2in) deep. Apply an annual mulch of leafmould after the leaves die down.

Propagation is by fresh seed sown in a peaty compost. It will self-seed in the immediate area of its leaves. Trouble comes from mice and squirrels who eat the tubers and vine weevil who go for the roots, causing the plant to collapse when in flower. **JC**

Cyclamen hederifolium

Cydonia oblonga 'Vranja'

Cydonia oblonga 'Vranja'

QUINCE

Type: hardy, deciduous fruit tree
Soil & situation: moist soil/full sun to light shade
North American hardiness zone: 5–9
Height: 6m (20ft)
Spread: 4.5m (15ft)
Grow for: attractive flowers; fragrant, pear-shaped fruit; eye-catching autumn colour; good small specimen tree; AGM

This true quince, unlike the *Chaenomeles* sort (see pages 97–98), blooms very late so usually misses all the frosts. The flowers are like little barber's poles or more accurately strawberry ripple ice-cream cones; all white with a pinky-red stripe. The quinces are large, yellow, fragrantly aromatic and as hard as stones; once cooked they keep some texture and add flavour to fruit pies and other puddings. The leaves turn a lovely yellow-gold in autumn and the grey-black framework has a certain form and appeal in winter.

A native of Southern Europe and the Middle East, it may be the original Biblical apple and was probably first cultivated in Persia. *Cydonia* is from the Latin *kudonea*, meaning a small tree, and it was certainly known to the Romans, indeed it was well suited to their climate. It is likely that quince comes from Old French *coine* or *cooin*, derived from the Latin *cotoneum cydoneum*. Quinces often occur in gardens where an old pear tree has died, as they were and still are used for the rootstock which may outlive the graft.

Quince trees can be long lived in well-drained but moist soil in a sheltered spot, but they are not so happy in exposed positions. They tend to make congested, twisted growth so may need early pruning to form a well-shaped framework. Seed does not come true; a poor variety can be had by taking almost any pear rootstock sucker, but the best named varieties of quince must be grafted. Otherwise remarkably problem free. **BF**

Bunny adds:
I think this in my favourite tree – I have four in the courtyard outside my office window, and they are attractive for many months of the year. We use all the fruit they produce, mainly for quince jelly. They are growing in extremely poor soil, virtually hardcore as it is an old crew yard, but they seem happy enough. They are very easily propagated from the suckers they produce, and the young trees make highly prized presents. In recent years people have complained of quince leaf blight, which is a fungus that causes the leaves to turn first yellow, then brown, and fall prematurely. This can be treated by removing infected parts and spraying with a copper-based fungicide in early spring as the leaves break.

Cydonia oblonga 'Vranja'

Cymbopogon citratus

Cymbopogon citratus
LEMON GRASS

Type: tender, perennial, evergreen, herbaceous weed
Soil & situation: any soil/full sun to light shade/will stand drought and will stand in water
North American hardiness zone: 9–11
Height & spread: 60cm (24in) each way in preferred soil
Grow for: unusual bedding plant for summer; lemon-scented foliage; essential for Eastern cookery and expensive to buy

When I worked out how much each piece cost me at the supermarket and I realized it grew like a weed, I never bought it again. Lemon grass can be grown on any warm windowsill, almost anywhere by anyone. It is always handy to have a fresh supply. The base of each offset is the part used; trim off the leaves and roots and split it into quarters lengthwise before including it in the dish.

Lemon grass is a common weed of dry stony places and ditches in much of the Far East, where it is an essential part of the cuisine. It is used to give the flavour of lemon but its texture is also liked by some people who enjoy chewing tough food. I treat it like a bay leaf or herb sachet and retrieve it before serving. There are several other closely related lemon-scented 'grasses' commonly found in warm countries, but none of them with such a fine flavour as *Cymbopogon citratus*.

Lemon grass is not very long lived if you use it faster than it multiplies, so have several plants. One of the few houseplants that can stand waterlogging, even though it often grows wild in dry places; I have one clump in a pot floating in my indoor garden pool with sodden soil and it thrives. It can be grown from seed but supermarket bits will root in a glass of water. The edges of the leaves are razor sharp, so take care when handling the plant. **BF**

Cynara scolymus
GLOBE ARTICHOKE

Type: hardy, herbaceous, semi-evergreen, perennial vegetable
Soil & situation: rich, moist, well-drained soil/full sun or light shade
North American hardiness zone: 7–9
Height & spread: 2m (6½ft) each way in preferred soil
Grow for: highly ornamental, silver-green foliage; attractive purple flowerheads on some forms; huge azure-blue flowers; AGM

It is one of the few vegetable crops that can be decently and sensibly grown in an ornamental situation. The nearly evergreen leaves rise in autumn to fall again the next and the purple flower buds make delicious eating, but if left to go over and open are full of a sky-blue to azure fuzzy thistle which has a pleasing perfume redolent of the barley harvest. The flower is immensely attractive to solitary bees.

Cynara is native to the Mediterranean coast and was known to the Romans who ate the blanched stems and leaves, as the French still do today, but of the form grown as the cardoon. The globe artichoke was not developed from this until the 15th century, and the huge flower buds now formed would have been esteemed by the ancient gourmets. Sadly they are still only a little known nowadays as they make some of the finest eating in the world.

A moist, rich soil is needed to grow good specimens and the crowns will need dividing and replanting after five to ten years. Tidy up decaying stems in autumn and protect bases and new leaves against hard frost with loose straw or bracken covering. It can be grown from seed: de-flower in the first year, choose the best in the third year and from then on multiply by dividing off 'thongs' or part-rooted sideshoots in mid-spring. Hard frosts can knock back topgrowth, waterlogging quickly kills, and geese and slugs can do heavy damage to young shoots. **BF**

Cynara scolymus

Cytisus battandieri
BROOM

Type: hardy, semi-evergreen shrub
Soil & situation: most soils/full sun to light shade
North American hardiness zone: 7–9
Height: 4.5–5m (15–16ft)
Spread: 2.5m (8ft)
Grow for: attractive clover-like foliage nearly all year round; deliciously scented, pineapple-shaped, yellow flowers; AGM

One of nature's natural beauties, this stately wall shrub is hardier than we used to think and survives unaided in several nearby gardens. I have mine on a wall where it is near evergreen in mild winters. The flowers are outstanding, and look and smell like small pineapples. The stems, once dried, are as hard as bamboo and have some use in the garden as sticks.

Not introduced to Britain until 1922, this tall member of a native European family closely related to gorse comes from the Moroccan coast of North Africa and was thought, at first, to be a greenhouse subject, then a wall plant and it is now grown as a free-standing specimen in most areas. Even if the top is lost it can come again from lower down if planted as a stool.

Cytisus battandieri needs a sheltered position in well-drained soil in full sun, against a warm wall in colder areas. Remove dead flowerheads and prune after flowering if necessary. If grown on a wall tie in over the winter. Watch for rootstock suckers with laburnum leaves and prune these out as soon as identified. It can be grown from seed, but it is normally budded onto laburnum seedling. Cuttings are not easy and neither are layers. It may be killed by hard weather. **BF**

Matt adds:
This plant fascinates me because plants from Morocco are rarely represented in gardens. It's found at an altitude of 1,500–2,000m (5,000–6,600ft) in the sun-scorched Atlas Mountains among venerable Atlas cedars and regal oaks. Is it the joker in such majestic company? Absolutely not. No other plant combines bright golden-yellow flower clusters 10cm (4in) long with an enticing pineapple fragrance or has laburnum-like tri-lobed leaves cloaked with a sheen of silky white hairs that are particularly prominent and tactile when young.

The variety 'Yellow Tail' has flower spikes 15cm (6in) long, sometimes more. Suckers form when it's pruned close to the ground; allow several branches to develop and prune back to them.

Bunny adds:
I used this favourite in my tree-house garden at the Chelsea Flower Show. We planted it in full flower against a Tuscan pink wall which we had adulterated with sponge painting, algal deposits and lime to convey that faded, been-around look.

The combination of the various muted pinks of the wall, the yellow of the flowers and the silvery green silky leaves was mouthwatering. This is a very special plant, though, that does look stunning in many situations. In one garden we grow it as a standard. It is a cold garden some way north of me, but the plant is in a sheltered nook and looks very dramatic like that.

Cytisus battandieri

Dahlia imperialis

Dahlia imperialis
TREE DAHLIA

Type: half-hardy, herbaceous perennial
Soil & situation: rich, moist soil/sun/shelter
North American hardiness zone: 9–10
Height: to 6m (20ft)
Spread: to 4m (13ft) or more
Grow for: giant foliage and spectacular stems

I'd read the garden guide before visiting the Quinta do Palheiro in Madeira for the first time and among the plants listed was *Dahlia imperialis*. Further research told of a dahlia with a sheaf of stems to 6m (20ft) tall and 7.5cm (3in) in diameter that looked like a giant bamboo with leaves up to 60cm (24in) long. I could hardly believe my eyes! Could a dahlia really be so huge? In my excitement I ran down the garden, and there to my left stood a dahlia on steroids, a pumped-up muscle bound giant, 4m (13ft) tall and topped with unmistakable, hanging, rose-purple flowers – what an awe-inspiring sight! The long stems were used by the Aztecs to pipe water from mountain streams and the direct translation of their word for 'dahlia' is 'water pipes'. Although unlikely to flower outdoors in the UK it is a worthy 'architectural' plant and your friends will never believe its identity!

It needs a sheltered, sunny position, on rich, well-drained soil. Dig in organic matter the autumn before planting. Plant once the danger of frost is over, mulch with organic matter, water and support the young stems. Protect from late frosts with straw or horticultural fleece. In autumn, cut the stems back to 15cm (6in), lift and store in a cool, frost-free place; the tuber eventually becomes massive too.

Ideally, start it off early in pots. In a frost-free polythene tunnel it may flower in late autumn or form buds for the following spring. Propagate in spring by division or stem cuttings. **MB**

Dahlia 'Moor Place'

Type: half-hardy, tuberous perennial
Soil & situation: fertile, humus-rich, well-drained soil/full sun
North American hardiness zone: 8–9
Height: 1m (3ft)
Spread: 60cm (24in)
Grow for: rich red pompom flowers make this an impressive sight in the border

Dahlia flowers come in all shapes and sizes. When you see them at a flower show they range from tiny buttons to giant 'cactus' flowers up to 25cm (10in) across. Others are as big and as round as footballs in every colour with the exception of black, green and blue. As cut flowers they haven't lost their popularity in 100 years.

The 20cm (8in) mid-green leaves are pinnate with toothed-edged leaflets and rounded tips. The 5cm (2in) diameter, wine-red, pompom flowers are perfectly round with incurved florets. They enclose the stem completely, flowering from mid-summer until the first frosts. Each stem is branched, carrying two to five flowers. For larger blooms take off the two flower buds immediately below the top flower. Removing spent flowerheads will result in more flowers, which will continue to appear until the first frosts. Dahlias benefit from a weekly application of a high-nitrogen liquid fertilizer from early to mid-summer, switching to a high-potash feed from then until early autumn.

In mild areas they may be left in the ground over winter with a deep, dry mulch of straw or coarse bark mounded over the soil surface. In cold gardens or where the ground is wet and heavy it is necessary to lift the tubers and store them in a frost-proof shed until late spring. Check them regularly for signs of rot and dump those affected.

Propagation is by division of the fleshy tubers in spring, retaining a shoot on each piece. Basal shoot cuttings can be taken in late winter from the tubers and rooted in a propagator. Slugs are a serious pest of dahlias, devouring shoots overnight. **JC**

Dahlia 'Moor Place'

Daphne bholua 'Jacqueline Postill'

Daphne bholua 'Jacqueline Postill'

Type: hardy, upright, evergreen shrub
Soil & situation: moist, well-drained, preferably acid soil/sun or partial shade/shelter
North American hardiness zone: 7–8
Height: 4m (13ft)
Spread: 2.5m (8ft)
Grow for: tight clusters of sweetly fragrant flowers from early winter until early spring; AGM

For many years visitors and passersby alike were beguiled by *Daphne bholua* 'Jacqueline Postill' as she leaned seductively by a friend's front door. They would not fail to comment on her beauty and fragrance, then take note of her name so their love affair could begin; I too fell for her delectable charms. In winter she was at her most comely when to the surprise and delight of her admirers she would adorn her deep green robes with dense clusters of jewels with a rose-purple flush. Postman and plant lover alike adored from afar or pressed their nose to the flowers to inhale more deeply of the sweetly intoxicating fragrance. Alain Postill named me after the woman he loved, she whispered breathlessly, telling tales of her home high in the mountains of eastern Nepal where she lived under the protective shadow of giant rhododendrons.

Her brother *D. b.* var. *glacialis* 'Gurkha', a hardier soul, is stripped of his raiment in winter yet still wears similar heirloom jewels and those of *D. b.* 'Darjeeling' are smaller but appear even earlier, from late autumn to late winter. This is a plant to treasure!

It tolerates full sun or partial shade on cool, moist, well-drained soil. It flourishes in a sheltered position, protected from cold winds, but even then it may lose the leaves and possibly the flowers in severe conditions. It dislikes pruning but trim minimally, if necessary, after flowering to keep within its allotted space. It resents being moved so transplant when still young. Propagate by grafting in late winter to very early spring. It can suffer from leaf spot; remove affected leaves and dispose of them. **MB**

Daphne blagayana

Type: hardy, dwarf, spreading, evergreen to semi-evergreen shrub
Soil & situation: humus-rich soil/partial shade
North American hardiness zone: 7–9
Height: 40cm (16in)
Spread: 1m (3ft), or more
Grow for: sweetly fragrant flowers in spring

Count Blagay originally discovered this gem in 1837 on his estate in Slovenia, growing alongside *Erica carnea*, a lime-tolerant heather. Planted in a border with the cultivar *E. carnea* 'Vivellii' it creates a glorious contrast of creamy white and deep carmine. The prostrate branches root as they spread, terminating in rafts of leaves bearing rounded clusters of 20–30 gorgeously scented, creamy white flowers in early and mid-spring. There are records of a plant at Glasnevin Botanic Gardens in Dublin, 6m (20ft) across and covered with flowers; alas it is no more! My first meeting with this glamorous ground cover was in a raised bed outside the refectory at horticultural college. As I waited in line for my meals, its sweet, powerful fragrance was the perfect antidote to the assorted odours emanating from the kitchen!

Daphne blagayana

Daphne x *burkwoodii* 'Somerset Gold Edge'

Plant in acid or alkaline soil; in its native habitat *Daphne blagayana* ranges over layers of leafmould in limestone areas. Mimic this in the garden with a layer of leafmould in semi-shade on alkaline or acid soil, and make sure there is plenty of space for it to roam. Raised beds make the flowers easier to appreciate.

Prune to keep within its allotted space immediately after flowering. Propagate from seed sown when ripe, or by soft-wood or semi-ripe cuttings or layering. It layers naturally; weigh down the previous year's growth with a stone when the young shoots are a few centimetres long and detach after a year. Weighting the stems also encourages the plant to spread. **MB**

Daphne x *burkwoodii* 'Somerset Gold Edge'

Type: hardy, semi-evergreen shrub
Soil & situation: rich, moist, well-drained soil/light shade
North American hardiness zone: 5–8
Height & spread: 1m (3ft) each way
Grow for: from late spring to early summer the golden-edged, neat, finger-shaped, nearly evergreen leaves are covered in masses of heavenly-scented, pink flowers – this is a masterpiece and among the best plants in the garden

This variegated hybrid is quicker growing than most daphnes, reaching full size in five years or so, and it gives the most impressive display in and out of flower. In flower it is a stunner, out of flower it is still attractive. A 'must have' when you see and smell it.

A cross between *D. caucasica* and *D. cneorum* by the famous Burkwood, it has two sisters, *D.* x *burkwoodii* and *D.* x *burkwoodii* 'Somerset', which lacks the stripe but is more vigorous and is the biggest, longest-lived plant of the three.

D. x *burkwoodii* 'Somerset Gold Edge' is one of the more demanding but faster-growing daphnes. It does best in rich, moist, humus-rich, limy soil in light shade. Do not prune and do not move once established. It will have a short life but a glorious one. It can be propagated by layers or half-ripe woody cuttings but it's not easy. Go on buy one! All daphnes get virus infected and die away so never prune them. If aphids are on the attack spray with soft soap. Nip out tips in early summer if it looks straggly. **BF**

Daphne mezereum

Plant of the Week (see page 69)

Daphne odora 'Aureomarginata'

Plant of the Week (see page 67)

Daphne tangutica

Daphne tangutica

Type: hardy, evergreen shrub
Soil & situation: rich, moist, well-drained soil/light shade
North American hardiness zone: 7–9
Height & spread: up to 1m (3ft) each way, but probably less
Grow for: healthy, diamond-shaped, neat, leathery leaves and heavenly scented clusters of purple (outside) and white (inside) flowers; AGM

Daphnes are short-lived, expensive to buy, hard to propagate and impossible to move. However, many are also incredibly neat, compact, attractive, evergreen shrubs with a range of similar scented flowers each with a different, and in some cases overwhelming, perfume. *D. tangutica* is among the toughest of the family and one of the sweetest smelling. It is very similar to *D. retusa* but quicker growing and it has slightly longer leaves.

This neat, tough (for a daphne) Chinese shrub was introduced to the UK at the end of the Victorian period by E. H. Wilson. You should consider getting a collection, as their perfumes are superb.

D. tangutica is one of the least demanding of a difficult bunch. It does best in moist, humus-rich soil in light shade. Do not prune and do not move once established. Give a dressing of leafmould in summer and water in droughts and you may get a decade of pleasure from this plant. Most daphnes are species and can be grown from seed – it took me five years to produce a good flowering plant. They may hybridize, which doesn't matter as they're all wonderful. Pest and disease care is as for *Daphne* x *burkwoodii* (page 140). **BF**

Daucus carota 'Panther'

CARROT

Type: biennial, semi-evergreen, root vegetable
Soil & situation: deep, moist, uniform soil/full sun to light shade
North American hardiness zone: usually grown as an annual
Height & spread: 30cm (12in) each way
Grow for: the foliage is surprisingly attractive if seen unbiasedly; the root is tasty and good for you – this one is the most tasty

Unlike many other vegetables, carrots are not much detested; moreover, they are very good for us. I have grown many varieties and although reliability is important, flavour is crucial, and to my mind 'Panther' is the best. It has the odd habit of tapering the wrong way occasionally – these ones are even tastier!

Daucus carota 'Panther'

Carrots were known to the Romans and seem to have come from Afghanistan. It appears there used to be more interest in the white and violet forms which are now reappearing; the orange was first reported about AD500 and achieved almost total exclusivity between AD1500 and 2000. Gourmets are now trying some of the other colours again, but not often repeating the experiment.

The soil must be uniform with no big stones, lumps, voids, or raw manure so the tap roots can run straight down, and preferably moist but never waterlogged. If you cut the shoulder and crown off a root and trim back the leaves, then stand it in a saucer of water on a windowsill, fresh green leaves will appear – well, it's cheerful and much cheaper than a houseplant or a bunch of chrysanthemums. Sow thinly *in situ* in early spring, cover sparingly and firm down. Protect with horticultural fleece supported on sticks to stop root fly. Slugs can also be a problem. **BF**

Davidia involucrata

DOVE TREE, HANDKERCHIEF TREE OR GHOST TREE

Type: hardy, deciduous tree
Soil & situation: fertile, moist, well-drained soil/sun or light shade/shelter from cold winds
North American hardiness zone: 6–8
Height: 15m (50ft)
Spread: 9m (30ft)
Grow for: dramatic show of flowers in late spring; AGM

This is not a tree to be rushed. It may take ten years of growing before you see a dove, ghost or hankerchief but if you have the space then plant one for later.

It forms a conical head with 15cm (6in) red-stalked leaves, light green above and softly hairy on the underside. They are sharp pointed and toothed with a heart-shaped base. In late spring large white bracts appear, one on either side of the small male flowers with their red-purple anthers. The bracts are uneven in size. Seen fluttering in a breeze against a blue sky it is easy to see how the tree gets its various common names. Pendent, pale brown, ridged fruit with a red stalk appear in autumn, hanging long after leaf fall.

When E. H. Wilson went to China in search of this tree in 1899 he was given a map of the region in which it had been seen. The search area was larger than England. When he did find the tree there was only the stump remaining. It had been cut down to build a house. Fortunately he found other ghost trees close by.

Davidia involucrata

Desfontainia spinosa

It does best in a sheltered site in full sun. The variety *D. i.* var. *vilmoriniana* is better suited to cold areas. Its leaves are green-yellow on the upper surface and dark green and hairless underneath. Propagation from seed is slow. Sow the whole fruit in autumn. It may take two years to germinate, whereas hardwood cuttings will be well rooted in less than 12 months. **JC**

Desfontainia spinosa

Type: half-hardy, evergreen shrub
Soil & situation: moist, peaty, acid soil/partial shade
North American hardiness zone: 8–10
Height & spread: 2m (6½ft)
Grow for: holly-like leaves and drooping, scarlet and yellow flowers, which are almost guaranteed; AGM

For me this is like a holly with airs and graces. It loves a moist climate with lots of rain and that just about includes the northern half of the British Isles. I have a seven-year-old-plant and it has never refused to flower.

Slow growing, it forms a dense, bushy shrub with 5cm (2in) long, glossy, spiny, dark green leaves. The similar length, pendent, tubular flowers are produced from mid-summer to late autumn. They are a bright scarlet with a golden-yellow mouth. Feeding high-potash liquid fertilizer in late spring increases the quantity of flowers and seems to heighten the flower colour.

When planted in gardens with a dry atmosphere it is necessary to provide a sheltered site with no risk of cold winds. A mulch of composted bark or leafmould in late winter will help to conserve moisture in the soil. Pruning is not normally necessary. Propagation is by semi-ripe cuttings in summer in a peaty compost. Cover the tray with clear polythene and place out of direct sunlight. Pot the rooted cuttings the following spring. **JC**

Matt adds:
D. spinosa is native to Central and South America, from Costa Rica to Cape Horn where the climate is moist and temperate. In the north, it's found in cool mountain cloud forests, descending further south to the fjords and islands of the Pacific coast. The best conditions in the UK are in the west coast of Scotland and Northern Ireland, where the North Atlantic Drift influences the climate. In central Chile it grows alongside *Drimys winteri* (see page 151), *Fuchsia* (page 182), *Gaultheria* (page 188) and *Pseudopanax* – a fascinating combination, and firecrown honeybirds pollinate the flowers.

The delightful form 'Harold Comber' has larger flowers of rich vermilion, up to 5cm (2in) long.

Deutzia gracilis

Type: hardy, deciduous, bushy shrub
Soil & situation: fertile, moist, well-drained soil/full sun or light shade
North American hardiness zone: 5–8
Height & spread: 1m (3ft)
Grow for: an abundance of pretty, fragrant flowers

My earliest memory of this delightful shrub was armfuls of branches wreathed in fragrant, white flowers. They were being used for indoor decoration for an early spring wedding. The plants had been forced in large earthenware pots. It forms a bushy shrub with erect branches and bright green, 5cm (2in) long leaves. The sweet smelling, star-shaped, pure white flowers are produced on upright 5–10cm (2–4in) long racemes in spring and early summer. Plant it in a position sheltered from the morning sun to prevent the flowers being damaged by spring frosts. The flower colour will fade more quickly if exposed to full sun.

Prune out the shoots that have finished flowering, cutting them back to within 5cm (2in) of the previous year's wood. Give it a high-nitrogen feed after pruning. Apply a high-potash feed in early autumn to harden up the new growths. Propagation is by softwood cuttings in summer or hardwood cuttings outside during winter.

D. x *hybrida* 'Mont Rose' has dark green leaves and grows to 1.2m (4ft). Star-shaped, pink-purple flowers with wavy petals and yellow anthers are carried in panicles in early summer. *D. scabra* makes a large shrub at 3m (10ft) with upright panicles of honey-scented, single, white flowers in mid-summer. *D. scabra* 'Pride of Rochester' produces double white flowers tinged with pink. **JC**

Deutzia gracilis

Dianthus caryophyllus

Dianthus caryophyllus
CARNATION

Type: hardy, evergreen perennial
Soil & situation: well-drained, limy soil/full sun
North American hardiness zone: 7–10
Height: 60cm (24in)
Spread: 1.2m (4ft) if not tied up
Grow for: attractive flowers with glorious clove perfume

The sea-green foliage is unusual, the flowers are attractive and freely produced, but the perfume, oh the perfume, is so tangible you want to eat it. The scent of cloves does not describe its sweet lusciousness. There are indoor carnations but they are not as easy as the hardy border forms. The name carnation comes from coronation, as the flower was used for garlands. A native of the Mediterranean, where wild carnations grow in pockets of soil in broken limestone formations. Transferred to gardens early on in history, carnations have become widely grown around the world for the cut flower trade. *Dianthus* 'Fenbow Nutmeg Clove' was rediscovered in 1960 in a garden where it was recorded as originally growing in 1652. It dates from the 14th century and was used to flavour wine; it is fragrant, crimson-maroon and double, though small.

Drainage is crucial, not just under the plant, but the soil must itself be open, and full sun is essential; even so the plants do not last long. As they are short lived, get into the habit of taking slips and rooting them every year. If you do not want to pick the broken stems up, then stake and tie the plants early. The varieties that can be sown from seed are nowhere near as good as the many selected forms, most of which are double. The latter are propagated by slip cuttings in spring or summer. The main problem is slugs! **BF**

Buddleja globosa

ORANGE GOLFBALL TREE

Type: perennial, semi-evergreen, woody shrub
Soil & situation: lime-rich, well-drained soil/full sun or light shade
North American hardiness zone: 7–9
Height & spread: 3.5m (11ft)
Grow for: striking orange golfball flowers with a pronounced honey scent, appearing up to two months earlier than other hardy varieties; AGM.

All buddlejas are good garden plants (see other recommendations on pages 73–74). Many are lumped together and called butterfly bushes as they are scented, full of nectar and attract countless insects to their flowers. Although really deciduous, most of them hold their leaves until the depths of winter and *B. globosa* is particularly hardy, losing its leaves only in the hardest winters. Its bright orange, uniquely spherical flowers make it the best of all.

B. globosa is one of 70 species from subtropical Asia and America named after the 18th-century English botanist and cleric Reverend Adam Buddle, all of them floriferous and scented, easy to keep compact and able to make a good windbreak. *B. globosa* was first introduced to Britain in 1774, well over a century before most of the others arrived, but has not naturalized in the same way.

Other than not liking waterlogged soils, buddlejas are really easy to grow in most garden soils and situations. If it must be pruned, do so in early spring when growth gets under way, as the hollow stem can fill with water, freeze and rot if autumn pruned. Other species can be pruned back very hard to a stool, if desired, but I find *B. globosa.* resents really tough treatment. Although it is possible to grow buddlejas from seed, they do not always come true and hardwood cuttings in autumn are remarkably easy. It is best to strike a cutting *in situ* where the new plant is wanted, because although it is easy to move a small plant it is difficult to shift a large one. Buddlejas suffer from no problems worth mentioning. **BF**

Dianthus gratianopolitanus

Dianthus gratianopolitanus
CHEDDAR PINK

Type: hardy perennial
Soil & situation: well-drained, neutral to alkaline soil/full sun
North American hardiness zone: 3–8
Height: 15cm (6in)
Spread: 45cm (18in)
Grow for: pretty, pink, fragrant flowers

You can see sheets of this little plant growing on the rock face of Cheddar Gorge in the Mendip Hills in Somerset, England. It is one of the prettiest wild flower scenes I have been privileged to see; AGM

It is mat forming with a dense layer of 5cm (2in) long, grey-green leaves. In flower during early summer, the solitary, deep pink, very fragrant, single flowers have attractively toothed petals and are carried on short, stiff stems.

When planting make sure the soil is well drained. This species is usually pot grown so plant anytime that the soil is suitable. Do not plant deeply, but keep the collar of the pink above the surface. Feed with a liquid tomato fertilizer in late spring. Dead-head to prolong flowering and help the plant retain a compact habit.

Propagation is by seed sown in autumn and over-wintered in a cold frame. Small, non-flowering shoots root well in summer. Reduce the length of the leaves of the cutting by half to lessen transpiration. Insert the cuttings around the rim of a pot of gritty, free-draining compost, then water in and cover with horticultural fleece. It is an excellent plant for the rockery, especially if the rocks are limestone as in its native Cheddar Gorge. **JC**

Dianthus 'Mrs Sinkins'
PINK

Type: hardy, evergreen perennial
Soil & situation: well-drained soil/particularly happy on thin, stony, alkaline or chalky soils/sun/protection from rabbits and pigeons
North American hardiness zone: 5–9
Height: 45cm (18in)
Spread: 30cm (12in)
Grow for: highly perfumed, white flowers over the whole summer

It is thought that this plant, a charming, traditional and old-fashioned pink, originated from a workhouse garden in Slough, Berkshire. However, no one I know seems to know who Mrs Sinkins was. There is a *Dianthus* 'Miss Sinkins' too, but not nearly as well-known, and only two or so nurseries in the RHS *Plant Finder* stock it.

Anyhow, whoever she was, I think the double, white flowers of this deservedly popular plant are rather endearingly shaggy-looking, which is why I like it better than many. Some of the more modern pinks look a bit too perfect and regular, but there are many superb ones to choose from, and they are an extremely useful cut flower.

If straggly shoots are produced, just tuck them in under the soil, firming them in well, and then it is likely that they will form a new, bushy plant. Regular dead-heading prolongs the flowering greatly. These plants are so easy from cuttings that it makes a lot of sense to renew your stock every two or three years. They do seem to flower themselves out. The cuttings are best taken from non-flowering shoots any time in summer. **BG**

Dianthus 'Mrs Sinkins'

Dianthus plumarius

Dianthus plumarius
PINK

Type: hardy, herbaceous, evergreen perennial
Soil & situation: well-drained, limy soil/full sun
North American hardiness zone: 4–7
Height: 15cm (6in)
Spread: 30cm (12in)
Grow for: neat hummock of grey-green leaves and good-looking flowers with glorious clove perfume

Slightly tougher than carnations, the grey-green foliage is neater, the flowers are as attractive, if smaller, and more freely produced and the perfume, oh the perfume, is so tangible you want to eat it, again. Pinks were brought over with William the Conqueror and all the early varieties that survive are single flowered and deliciously scented. There are dozens of pinks in many colours and forms and most have that wonderful clove perfume.

The name *dianthus* comes from the Greek *dianthos*, as it was the Flower of Jove. There is a native UK pink is *D. gratianopolitanus*, Cheddar pink (see left), but most of our garden sorts are natives of southern Europe and the Caucasus Mountains, where wild pinks grow in abundance.

Drainage is crucial, not just under the plant but the soil must itself be open, and full sun is essential, even so the plants do not last long. As they are short lived, though slightly tougher than carnations, take slips and root them every year. Those that can be sown from seed are nowhere near as good as the selected forms of which many exist, these are propagated by slip cuttings in spring or summer. As with carnations, the main problem is slugs. **BF**

Dicentra spectabilis 'Alba'

BLEEDING HEART, LADY'S LOCKET, LADY IN THE BATH, DUTCHMAN'S BREECHES

Type: hardy, herbaceous perennial
Soil & situation: cool, moist soils/shady conditions
North American hardiness zone: 3–8
Height: 1m (3ft)
Spread: 45cm (18in)
Grow for: excellent foliage and flowers: foliage is a cool, soft green and much divided, and flowers, from late spring to summer, are locket-shaped, hanging in lines from pendent stems; AGM

The unusual-looking flowers have given rise to the string of folksy epithets. The rather ornamental appearance of this plant makes it better suited to more cultivated woodland or shady borders – it is perhaps too showy-looking for wilder parts. It is also not that vigorous and so would not hold its own that well with the more hearty woodlanders. Having said that, this form is more robust and longer-lived than the species. You can prolong the flowering period by not letting the soil dry out.

This plant does not appreciate strong winds, and will perform better if tucked into a snug situation. Do not be deceived by its rather delicate form – it is tougher than it looks. The dicentras can be propagated by division: their rather fang-like, fleshy roots are brittle, as are the shoots, so a little care is needed. As they like moist soils, I find the splitting up is better done in autumn rather than spring. It can also be propagated from root cuttings. **BG**

Dicentra spectabilis 'Alba'

Dicksonia antarctica

Dicksonia antarctica

Type: tree fern
Soil & situation: prefers slightly acid conditions, with moist, peaty soil/sheltered, fairly humid conditions with lots of water during the growing season/will not tolerate temperatures below -5°C (23°F)/needs some winter protection if left outside
North American hardiness zone: 9–10
Height: 6m (20ft)
Spread: to 4m (13ft)
Grow for: one of the most majestic plants with magnificent fronds sometimes reaching up to 3m (10ft) long; AGM

This is not a plant I would like to be without, although my natural soil conditions and climate are not at all conducive to its well-being. When the plants are small and easily portable I grow them in pots and over-winter them in my greenhouse. When this becomes too much of a chore I find it simpler to plant them into the soil, heavily modified soil in my case, with lashings of leaf mould. I planted them in a sheltered spot against a north-facing wall. Tree ferns feature widely in television garden make-overs. This is not surprising really, as the moment you wheel in a few of these they will totally change the set – a sort of organic equivalent to mobile scenery. The problem is they are exacting in their requirements and if you can not meet these they will be wheeled out shortly afterwards – only in the direction of the bin this time! In the garden a shady position saves regular hosing down of the trunk. If you are not of the frame of mind to have heavily wrapped up plants in your winter garden, grow them in containers instead. They do not require huge volumes of soil and are adaptable as long as you give them lots of water in the summer. They will grow at a snail's pace admittedly, but robustly.

I am embarrassed to say that I forgot to wrap up my tree fern this winter. It has been growing in its position for a good year, protected by a wall, and in late winter it is still looking as pleased as punch. Whew! In their native habitat they are subject to snow and some clones are hardier than others, particularly those from Tasmania, so maybe I have just struck lucky. I should have packed the trunk and crown with insulating material such as straw, with polythene to hold it in place and keep out too much wet. This should, ideally, be removed in mild periods. Treated like this you can keep them happy to about –15°C (5°F). The fronds may die, but they are soon replaced in spring. The larger the plant, the hardier it is, so do not be in too much of a rush to plant it outside. **BG**

Dictamnus fraxinella (syn. *D. alba, D. albus*)

DITTANY, DITTANDER, BURNING BUSH

Type: hardy, herbaceous perennial
Soil & situation: well-drained soil/sun
North American hardiness zone: 3–8
Height: 1m (3ft)
Spread: 60cm (2ft)
Grow for: attractive lemon-scented foliage, followed by a spike of exotic, orchid-like, white flowers with purple veining; AGM

It's amazing how many otherwise knowledgeable plants-people don't know this old garden favourite. The foliage has a delicious aroma but dittany has one of the most distinctive, memorable and imposing flowers with a haunting orchid-like beauty, and if you don't yet know it, go out there, find one and grow this superb bloom for yourself.

The name is a corruption through French of the Greek *diktamnon* which was reputedly a great wound herb as apparently goats ate it to expel arrows! (This herb was probably an oregano, but that's beside the point.) This is also a genuine burning bush as on hot days an oil is generated which can be lit – I have often tried this is England but the great heat required to liberate the oil has been lacking.

Dittany likes a well-drained soil in full sun where it will slowly grow to a goodly clump. It can be divided in spring or root cuttings taken in early winter and grown on in a cold frame. Seed is slow to germinate unless it is fresh, and plants take quite a while to reach flowering size. The only problem is slugs eating the emerging shoots. **BF**

Dictamnus fraxinella

Dierama pulcherrimum 'Blackbird'

Dierama pulcherrimum 'Blackbird'

ANGEL'S FISHING ROD OR WANDFLOWER

Type: hardy, evergreen, cormous perennial
Soil & situation: humus-rich, well-drained soil/full sun
North American hardiness zone: 7–10
Height: 1.5m (5ft)
Spread: 1m (3ft)
Grow for: nodding, dainty flowers on wiry stems and grass-like leaves; a great addition to the border

In the summer of 1966 I saw a field of dierama at the Slieve Donard Nursery, Co. Down, Northern Ireland, where Leslie Slinger was producing new varieties. He gave them the names of birds, hence 'Blackbird'. It was an incredible sight and I presume every angel in Ireland was fishing in that field!

The 1m (3ft) long, thin, grass-like, grey-green, basal leaves remain erect for most of the year. In summer tall, arched 'wands' carry pendent spikes of bell-shaped, deep wine-purple, 5cm (2in) long flowers. They are followed by dangling strings of 'beads' with shiny brown seeds.

The corms resemble those of gladioli but each year the new corm grows on top of the previous one forming a chain of old corms. They should be planted 7.5cm (3in) deep in spring in free-draining soil. Water regularly during the first summer. Clumps may be divided in spring taking care to dig deeply to avoid breaking the brittle roots. Young plants are slow to become established after moving.

Seed should be sown fresh in the autumn and over-wintered in a cold frame. Dierama will frequently self-seed in the area and may be mistaken for seedling grass weeds. Used as a dot plant in a mixed border, a clump of dierama immediately becomes the centrepiece. Please plant one close to the edge of the pond and make some little angel happy. **JC**

Digitalis ferruginea

RUSTY FOXGLOVE

Type: hardy perennial/biennial
Soil & situation: moisture-retentive soil/partial shade
North American hardiness zone: 4–7
Height: 90cm (36in)
Spread: 50cm (20in)
Grow for: flowers in early and mid-summer; architectural form; AGM

Compared to the romantic cottage garden foxglove which has been enjoyed by gardeners for centuries, *Digitalis ferruginea* has only recently found its way into the hearts and minds of gardeners. In a relatively short time it's become a favourite among those who favour the naturalistic style of perennial gardening. From the basal rosette, the leaves become narrower and hang gracefully as they climb the stiff, elegant spires, as if supporting them on thin air. Take a close look at the flowers: the colour and markings are fascinating, they're tightly packed in leafy spikes

Digitalis ferruginea

and a golden honey-brown with red-brown veins on the inside. It is the perfect horticultural exclamation mark. From flowering in early summer, they gradually decline and die, becoming deep brown. Over winter they slowly fall, projecting like angled iron spikes from among the surrounding foliage and look simply gorgeous when dusted with frost.

D. ferruginea 'Gelber Herold' is larger and has golden-yellow flowers. *D. f.* 'Gigantea' reaches 1.5m (5ft) and has stiff yellowish-brown spikes. I must not forget to mention *D. parviflora* with its wonderful, silvery-haired, narrow leaves and dark chocolate-brown flowers with a purple-brown lip. (I love anything that reminds me of chocolate!) It is sculptural, elegant and deliciously understated.

Very accommodating, *D. ferruginea* prefers moisture-retentive soils in partial shade but also grows in dry shade and full sun, if the soil is moist. It is a short-lived perennial that can be grown as a biennial. Sow from mid-spring to mid-summer *in situ* or in containers in a cold frame. It self-seeds freely. Its leaves are susceptible to leaf spot. **MB**

Digitalis purpurea

Digitalis parviflora

Digitalis purpurea
COMMON FOXGLOVE

Type: herbaceous biennial
Soil & situation: light, humus-rich soil/sun or light shade
North American hardiness zone: 4–8
Height: first year rosette to 30cm (1ft), second year spike to 1.8m (6ft)
Spread: 50cm (20in)
Grow for: a most impressive native wild flower with a tall spike of orchid-like blooms

The common foxglove, especially the wild purple, is such a flower of childhood wonder – who has never slipped a bloom upon their finger? It is so much flower for so little effort, and if you sow them two years running and let them be they will self-seed like weeds and can come up everywhere, forever. There are more refined varieties, all-white travesties and dingy near relations, but nothing approaches the common foxglove for sheer exuberance. I once saw these advertised in a scurrilous limb of the Sunday press as 'Lakeland Orchids' at a price to match and no mention of their humble ancestry or more common name!

Named after the Latin *digitus*, a finger, for the thimble-shaped flower, foxgloves would often appear on the dirt spoil from a fox's lair in woodland, thus becoming associated with the predator. However, the English name was first applied to *Atropa belladonna* and not to *Digitalis purpurea* until the 14th century. The foxglove is, of course, infamous for being the source of one of the earliest powerful cardiac drugs. It is also said to be a good companion to many plants. It will grow almost anywhere, but needs a good site to do well; add plenty of leafmould and moisture. If the spike is removed before it has finished flowering, several smaller ones may follow it. Sow *in situ* any time or transplant when very small. Don't eat the leaves or any other part of the plant! **BF**

Dipsacus spp.
TEASEL

Type: hardy, herbaceous, biennial weed
Soil & situation: any soil, preferably moist/sun or shade
North American hardiness zone: 5–8
Height & spread: first year rosette to 30cm (12in) each way, second year flowering stem 2m (6½ft)
Grow for: imposing stately plant in second year; educational; good for wildlife

The teasel is not staggeringly beautiful, but it is statuesque, and the flowerhead, with its violet-blue sheen of flowers, is intricate, delicately made and loved by bees and butterflies, who visit it all summer. The leaf joints trap pools of water for birds and insects, and mosquitos too if the climate warms up!

In autumn the seedheads attract small birds and the dried, hollow stems can be cut up to make good wildlife shelters or, if a bundle of them is rolled in a tube of paper, a wonderful hibernation home for even more insects.

Dipsacus spp.

The name comes from the Greek *dipsa,* for thirst, as the teasel leaf base holds water. The teasel was used by fullers and weavers to draw up the nap of a fabric well into the industrial times, as the spiky flowerheads have prickles with recurved tips that were difficult to replace by man-made substitutes.

Being a biennial it needs a rich, moist soil to make a good-sized root to flower the next year and die. It can be transplanted when small, but this is not recommended as it is hard to dig up the tap root as one piece. Ideally sow *in situ* in autumn or spring. Avoid handling plants as they're prickly all over. **BF**

Doronicum pardalianches
LEOPARD'S BANE

Type: hardy, deciduous, perennial rhizome
Soil & situation: moist, humus-rich soil/part shade
North American hardiness zone: 4–8
Height: 90cm (36in)
Spread: 60cm (24in)
Grow for: ideal for a shady corner and quick to fill a gap in the border

Doronicum pardalianches

This is a great spring-flowering herbaceous perennial for a shady corner. It thrives on neglect, forming large clumps in open woodland. The 7–12cm (2¾–5in) long, heart-shaped, basal leaves are softly hairy and mid-green. The stem leaves are lance shaped. Large, pale yellow, daisy-like flowers are carried on stiff, branching stalks, above the foliage, from late spring through to early summer and are excellent for use in flower arrangements. It is one of the best perennials for filling gaps in shrub borders where it quickly forms a dense clump. *Doronicum* x *excelsum* 'Harpur Crewe' is slightly smaller with large, golden-yellow, daisy-like flowers on branched stems.

Propagation is by division of the clump in autumn or early spring. In a damp situation protect the emerging shoots from slugs and snails. Where exposed to wind support the stems as they come into flower. **JC**

Dracunculus vulgaris
DRAGON ARUM

Type: hardy, tuberous perennial
Soil & situation: free-draining soil/sun
North American hardiness zone: 7–10
Height: 1.2m (4ft)
Spread: 30cm (12in)
Grow for: curious flowers in mid-summer

This fantastic plant is a typically strange member of the arum family. The dark purple blotched stems, up to 1m (3ft) tall, formed from flower stems and leaf stalks are topped by an elegant, mid-green, umbrella-like leaf with up to 15 segments. The fun starts in mid-summer when it produces a revolting, floppy, cowl-like spathe,

45cm (18in) long, in rich velvety-maroon with a shiny, erect, deep maroon spadix protruding suggestively from the centre. Their disgusting, pungent odour pervades the atmosphere, encouraging clouds of excited flies that buzz round the flower or wait, rubbing their forelegs with glee, for the slightest opportunity to sip nectar from the malodorous chalice. If they are successful, pollinated plants produce an oblong head of rounded fruits. It's the type of plant which is beloved by small boys of all ages! There is a white-spathed form found occasionally on Crete and one from the Canary Islands. I understand both are now in cultivation! Yippeee!

They flourish against a sheltered, sunny wall on free-draining soil or among low shrubs that provide protection in winter. In the wild cistus bushes are their companions. In colder areas they should be covered with a layer of bracken or straw for winter protection. Propagate by offsets, lifting and dividing clumps in late winter and replanting at 15cm (6in) deep. Where conditions are good, they are inclined to spread, particularly if they find their way into gravel paths. **MB**

Dracunculus vulgaris

Drimys winteri

Drimys winteri

Type: frost-hardy, evergreen shrub or small tree
Soil & situation: fertile, moist, well-drained soil; tolerates chalk/sun or partial shade
North American hardiness zone: 8–10
Height: 15m (50ft)
Spread: 10m (33ft)
Grow for: attractive leaves, stems and flowers; AGM

In late spring and early summer *Drimys winteri* produces rounded clusters of simple, ivory, jasmine-scented flowers at the tips of young growth backed by a ring of tough, glossy dark green leaves that are blue-grey below. I made the mistake of eating them once, they're ferociously peppery – a good deterrent to predators, but rich in vitamin C, like the bark. The genus commemorates Captain William Winter who travelled with Sir Frances Drake through the Magellan Straits on the southern tip of South America. It was 'very useful to his ship's crew instead of other spices, adding it to their meat and as a medicine, it was very powerful against scurvy'. It's a symbol of peace to several South American tribes, as we use the olive branch.

D. winteri var. *andina* is compact and slow growing; it flowers when 30cm (12in) tall with a height and spread of 1m (3ft). *D. lanceolata* is a medium to large shrub with coppery young growth, beetroot-red stems, dark green leaves and small creamy-white flowers in mid- to late spring.

It flourishes in sun or partial shade in moist, mild, climates, usually sheltered by a wall or in a woodland garden among other trees and shrubs. It's not reliably hardy but tolerates some frost. It needs moist, fertile, free-draining soil and copes with chalk, but not with dry or shallow soils. Cut out dead or damaged wood in spring. Plants in this genus are resistant to honey fungus.

Propagate from semi-ripe cuttings or by layering; sow seed in autumn, over-wintering in a cold frame. **MB**

Cercis siliquastrum

JUDAS TREE

Type: hardy, deciduous tree
Soil & situation: moist, fertile, well-drained, loamy, alkaline soil/full sun or light shade
Hardiness zone: 6–9
Height & spread: 10m (33ft)
Grow for: a mass of colour in spring with its profusion of pink flowers

The story persists that this is the tree from which Judas Iscariot hanged himself but, in truth, in France the tree is called 'l'arbre de Judée' translating as 'the tree from Judaea'.

When mature it becomes a spreading, multi-stemmed tree. The new growths form a zigzag pattern, changing direction at each leaf joint. The heart-shaped leaves are bronze when they first appear, turning a glaucous blue-green in summer and finally becoming primrose-yellow in autumn.

There can be a variation in flower colour from pale pink to magenta or pink-purple, with the occasional plant producing white flowers. My plant has what I would call icing-sugar pink flowers and looks as good as any cake, flowering on my birthday. The clusters of small flowers cover the tree before, and at the same time as, the leaves. They have the unusual habit of appearing directly from the bark of old branches. The flowers are followed by clusters of pendulous, flat, deep purple seedpods.

Young plants and the new shoots of established plants are prone to damage from cold winds and late frosts. Feeding with a high-potash liquid feed in autumn will harden up the shoots before winter. Purchase small, container-grown plants. Large plants dislike being transplanted and may die in the first season. Propagate from fresh seed sown in autumn and over-winter the trays in a cold frame. Semi-ripe cuttings are supposed to root easily in summer but it has never worked for me. **JC**

Dryopteris filix-mas

Dryopteris filix-mas
MALE FERN

Type: hardy, deciduous fern
Soil & situation: a wide range of conditions – sun or shade/moist, humus-rich soil but will tolerate dry conditions once established
North American hardiness zone: 4–8
Height & spread: 1m (3ft)
Grow for: stunning looks as the fronds are unfurling in late spring; stays looking great into early winter; valuable for use in areas which are too dry, too alkaline or too sunny for other ferns to grow; AGM

This, together with bracken (*Pteridium aquilinum*), is the commonest British fern. In moist, semi-shaded conditions it will look amazing as the fronds, which form a circle around the crown of roots, stretch up to over a metre (3ft) in height and spread. Needless to say, in my dry-as-a-bone soil, where they furnish the woodland floor around the children's play area, they are about half this height – they still look good though. I have also used them to clothe the dry banks of a massive natural looking waterfall which we made on a 6m (20ft) high south-facing bank, and again they convey that lush, damp feel even though it's bone dry. They will self-seed freely once they get going, coming up in a beguiling fashion and transforming a space in a way you had not thought possible.

If you are establishing these ferns in less hospitable conditions, they will need extra moisture for maybe the first year or two until they get their roots down. Each spring, as the new foliage emerges, cut away the dead fronds.

Sparsholt College – the agricultural and horticultural college near Winchester where *Gardeners' Question Time* has a garden – showed me a really simple way to propagate ferns, which they developed and I can highly recommend it. Put a frond with spores (usually in mid-summer) on a tray of moist, gritty compost with the underside touching the compost; seal the whole tray in a polythene bag and leave in a cool greenhouse; check periodically that it has not dried out too much or not is rotting. After perhaps three months (but it can be up to nine months) you will eventually see the tiny prothallus start to grow on the compost. Leave the bag on and next you will see the first true leaf develop from the prothallus. As more proper leaves develop you can start to wean the plants off the bag. To get a true fern it usually takes about two months after the formation of the prothallus. Using this method you can get a good fifteen ferns or so from one tray. **BG**

Dryopteris wallichiana
BUCKLER FERN, WALLICH'S WOOD FERN

Type: hardy, deciduous fern
Soil & situation: humus-rich soil/dappled shade/shelter
North American hardiness zone: 5–8
Height : 90cm (36in) or more
Spread: 30cm (12in) or more
Grow for: attractive form and elegant fronds; AGM

Ferns are elegant, stylish and graceful and this is an example of them at their glorious, majestic best. A regal fern with a 'shuttlecock' of stiff, dark green fronds and regularly spaced opposite leaflets that are golden-green when young. It is the midribs with the dark, chocolate-brown scales that are so inviting and a wonderful contrasting colour. I have only ever seen them growing singly or in small clumps, but it would be wonderful to see a huge group of them flourishing together in the manner of the shuttlecock or ostrich fern (*Matteuccia struthiopteris*). Dream on!

D. wallichiana is named for Nathaniel Wallich (1786–1854), born Nathan Wolff, a Danish botanist who went to India as a surgeon to the Danish settlement at Serampore. He was briefly imprisoned by the British before becoming superintendent of the Calcutta Botanic Garden. He went on several expeditions and encouraged collectors in India, Nepal and Burma, including Edward Garner, a British resident of Kathmandu, who sent the seeds of the first Himalayan rhododendrons to Kew packed in tins of brown sugar. Wallich also introduced the magnificent *Amherstia nobils* into European cultivation – it was named for Lady Amherst, the Governor General's wife, and there is a beautiful pheasant named for her too. He returned to England with a collection of over 8,000 specimens.

This plant needs a sheltered spot and moisture-retentive, humus-rich, well-drained soil in dappled to deep shade. Divide in spring or autumn or sow spores. **MB**

Dryopteris wallichiana

Ecballium elaterium
SQUIRTING CUCUMBER

Type: half-hardy perennial usually grown as an annual
Soil & situation: very free-draining soil/sun
North American hardiness zone: 8–10
Height: 23cm (9in)
Spread: 2m (6½ft)
Grow for: explosive fruits

This is another fun plant for children of all ages! It is found throughout southern Europe and has escaped into Africa; I saw it growing by the city wall in Tangiers. Although it is a cucumber it cannot climb but makes a large patch of dense ground cover when flourishing. The triangular leaves with the texture of rough sandpaper are upright with wavy edges. Nodding, pale yellow flowers are found on separate short stems in the leaf joint, the females singly, the males in small clusters! The hairy fruits are about 5cm (2in) long and when ripe the slightest touch sends out a jet of seeds and 'goo' from the fruit. It squirts at an average angle of 50–55 degrees; mathematically the ideal angle for distance is 45 degrees but the extra accounts for the leaves that would obstruct the seeds if they flew too low. The pressure inside the fruits reaches six atmospheres (6kg/sq cm or 84lb/sq in) and the seeds are projected up to 12m (40ft) at 10m (33ft) per second! Now that's impressive!

Warning: the juice is a powerful purgative, do not eat the fruit and wash your hands after touching it. Take care too when triggering the explosive seedpods, you would not want to be hit by squirting seeds. Otherwise just have fun!

Ecballium elaterium

Echinacea purpurea

It prefers a sunny site and free-draining soil, but flourishes in most soils exept waterlogged ones. It is a perennial, treated as an annual, and can survive warmer winters outdoors; mulch with straw or bracken to protect the roots. Sow under glass and plant out in early summer when the soil is warm and there's no danger of frost. It self-seeds freely in your garden and next door's! **MB**

Echinacea purpurea
CONE FLOWER

Type: hardy perennial
Soil & situation: occurs naturally in dry habitats, so is ideal for free-draining soils/deep, humus-rich soils/sun or partial shade
North American hardiness zone: 3–9
Height: 1m (3ft)
Spread: 45cm (18in)
Grow for: eye-catching daisy-like flowers in a luminous shade of purple-red, with prominently domed, dark orange-bronze centres; long flowering period during the summer; attracts bees and butterflies

Not only is this plant adaptable in terms of soil type and situation but it is also adaptable in terms of the effects you can achieve with it as it has a relaxed, casual feel, a good strident-coloured flower and a significant winter silhouette. The traditional use, ever popular, is in the herbaceous border, not staked but ready for action from mid-summer to early autumn. More recently it can be found sprinkled and threaded through prairie plantings mixing with coreopsis, monardas and the like. It is also in vogue now to mix it with ornamental grasses, especially *Calamagrostis*, *Molinia* (see page 267) and *Stipa* (page 372) and, along with umbellifers and other bold perennials. Truly not a plant I would be without, although it has not yet been awarded an AGM.

These plants need cutting down in early spring. They can be left alone for years, quite happily, but if you want to divide them, spring is the time. They can be propagated by seed, root cuttings in winter or division in spring or autumn. I did mine from seeds, as being greedy I wanted lots and lots. They are dead easy but the seedlings are variable, so you simply discard the less intense shades. The amount of reflex on the petals varies too. In natural-type plantings it is a bonus to get ones that come out at different times, are a range of shades and look subtly different – you do not always want a shipment of soldiers. If you are being extravagant and buying in, *E.* Bressingham hybrids are a strong colour with less variation of both colour and form. **BG**

Echinops ritro

Echinops ritro
GLOBE THISTLE

Type: hardy perennial
Soil & situation: well-drained garden soil/sun or partial shade
North American hardiness zone: 3–9
Height: 60cm (24in)
Spread: 45cm (18in)
Grow for: eye-catching globes of blue flowers in late summer; AGM

This is an old favourite that I would not like to be without. The metallic blue balls look almost sculptural sitting on top of tall, pale silvery-green, rigid stems and last for a month or so. The leaves are extremely spiny, stiff and leathery, dark green on top and white underneath. It is definitely a plant with character that looks good in the wilder areas or, as I grow it, in a more formal courtyard garden. However, it needs clever siting as it does look a bit too informal when the flowers start to go over. Mine sits behind a low, but buxom, box hedge. As soon as the flowers start to go over, cut them back and you may get a second flush. This is an excellent plant for cutting and drying, but cut it before the tiny, starry flowers are open.

These plants will thrive on a poor, thin soil: on heavier soils it is worth adding grit to help drainage before planting. They do not need staking, and if you do not want to dead-head in the hope of a second flowering, you can leave the dead flowerheads intact until they start to look over-scruffy. Echinops are easily propagated by division in autumn or spring or by root cuttings in winter. **BG**

Matt adds:
Because of their shape, I always imagine banging kettle drums with a pair of these! The flowers are irresistible to bees, who arrive en masse to forage for nectar; moths take over at night. It forms a wonderful combination with *Stipa gigantea* (see page 372) and orange and yellow kniphofia (pages 228–229 and 345); it is also useful in flower arrangements.

Echinops ritro 'Veitch's Blue' is repeat flowering with darker blue flowerheads. *E. bannaticus* 'Blue Globe' has dark blue flowerheads to 6cm (2½in) across; it blooms for a second time if the stems are cut back after flowering. *E. b.* 'Taplow Blue' has rounded, powder-blue flowers on prominent silvery-white stems from mid-summer to early autumn.

John adds:
I much prefer to plant 'Veitch's Blue' in a large group of at least five. When it comes into flower the mass of 'globes' looks spectacular. Dead-head the spent flowers to prevent them self-seeding. Left alone they can become a nuisance weed. The species *Echinops giganteus* lives up to its name. The spherical, grey-blue flowerheads are up to 20cm (8in) across and it will reach a height of 5m (16ft).

Echinops ritro 'Veitch's Blue'

Echium vulgare 'Blue Bedder'

Echium vulgare 'Blue Bedder'

Type: annual or biennial
Soil & situation: wide variety of soils, not too fertile/especially suited to free-draining soils/sunny position
North American hardiness zone: 9–10
Height: to 40cm (16in)
Spread: to 30cm (12in)
Grow for: fast-growing, easy but most attractive infiller; large quantities of charming blue flowers

Try not to be put off this plant by the name 'Blue Bedder'. It may not conjure up a plant that is in any way inspirational or exciting, but this is a peak performer. It is an old variety that is not commonly grown but it will produce for you, for several weeks, a good, bushy, soft-looking plant with copious blue, bell-shaped flowers. It looks particularly good when mixed with other simple annuals such as flax and cornflowers, to form a more natural-looking, yet cohesive, planting.

This plant is best treated as an annual. Either sow the seeds *in situ* in spring or under glass. I find it far more successful to sow the seed in small 7cm (3in) pots inside and then to plant them out when they are ready. Although this is not in anyway essential for this plant, I find the results superior. Planted out at just under 10cm (4in) centres, you will get a good density of its foliage knitting together to from a colourful mass. If the soils are too fertile, too much foliage will be produced and fewer flowers. Once they are past their best and form a totally knitted tangle, clear the space – unless you wish to leave them to self-sow, which they frequently do. **BG**

Edgeworthia chrysantha
PAPER BUSH

Type: half-hardy, deciduous shrub
Soil & situation: rich, moisture-retentive, fertile soil/sun/shelter
North American hardiness zone: 7–10
Height & spread: 1.5m (5ft)
Grow for: scented, rich yellow flowers from late winter to mid-spring

I first came across this plant while looking for daphnes in a flower border at the Royal Botanic Garden, Kew; it's amazing how something that looks so fragile flowers early in the year. The dense, hanging clusters at the end of every twig are only 3–5cm (1–2in) wide, yet contain up to 50 fragrant, rich cowslip-yellow flowers, each clothed with a layer of white silky hairs. The young shoots are incredibly supple and can be tied into knots without breaking them, while the older branches are covered with papery bark that in Japan is carefully peeled off and used for making paper for currency. It's native to the forests and streamsides of the Himalayas, South Korea and southwest China and was named for Michael Pakenham Edgeworth (1812–81), an employee of the East India Company and keen amateur botanist.

A form with vivid red-orange flowers is known as *Edgeworthia chrysantha* 'Red Dragon' and is sometimes labelled f. *rubra*. There is also a selection *E. c.* 'Grandiflora' which is larger in growth and flowers.

E. chrysantha needs a warm, sheltered position among other shrubs in a sunny border protected from frost, on well-drained, moisture-retentive, loamy soil enriched with plenty of well-rotted organic matter; mulch in spring. In colder areas grow in a cool greenhouse in loam-based compost, watering freely and feeding monthly when in growth; reduce watering in winter. Prune if necessary after flowering. Propagate by seed or semi-ripe cuttings in summer. **MB**

Edgeworthia chrysantha

Elaeagnus pungens 'Maculata'

Elaeagnus pungens 'Maculata'

Type: hardy, evergreen, bushy shrub
Soil & situation: well-drained, moderately fertile, neutral to acid soil/full sun
North American hardiness zone: 7–9
Height: 4m (13ft)
Spread: 5m (16ft)
Grow for: variegated foliage with large splashes of golden yellow

This shrub is largely grown for its foliage. The shiny, dark green, oval leaves are generously splashed with golden yellow. Even on the darkest day of winter it seems to brighten the whole garden. During and immediately after rain each leaf collects and reflects light.

In autumn small, very fragrant, white flowers appear followed by shiny red, edible fruits. *Elaeagnus pungens* 'Maculata' is one of my favourite shrubs for seaside sites. It withstands sea spray, harsh winds and is very tolerant of a dry, gritty soil.

It is prone to reversion where vigorous branches with all green leaves appear. They should be cut out when young or they will take over the plant at the expense of the variegated growth. Do take care as it occasionally produces a few spines, not many, but it only takes one to cause injury. Plants are usually grafted so remove any emerging suckers as close to the main stem or root as possible. As a shrub it is indispensable but as a tough, variegated hedge it is memorable. Another excellent variegated relation is *E.* x *ebbingei* 'Gilt Edge' with leaves bright green in the centre and broad golden margins. **JC**

Embothrium coccineum
CHILEAN FIRE THORN OR FLAME FLOWER

Type: hardy, evergreen tree
Soil & situation: moist, well-drained, fertile, neutral to acid soil/full sun or partial shade
North American hardiness zone: 8–10
Height: 10m (33ft)
Spread: 5m (16ft)
Grow for: an unbeatable specimen tree for its scarlet flowers

In flower, this tree has no equal. Seen as a specimen tree on the lawn it seems to be on fire with its red flower.

It often forms a multi-stemmed tree with numerous suckers. If these are not removed they will eventually form a copse. The lance-shaped, mid- to dark green leaves are 12cm (5in) long. They almost disappear under a sheet of scarlet flowers carried in 10cm (4in) long racemes and produced in late spring and early summer. Occasionally they carry yellow flowers but I have never seen it happen.

Plant in a sheltered situation well protected from biting, cold winds. Pruning is not normally necessary but where branches have to be removed, in order to retain the shape of the tree, cut them out in winter before the sap starts to rise. Propagation is by seed sown in a heated propagator in spring. Softwood cuttings can be taken in early summer or semi-ripe cuttings in late summer with bottom heat in a propagator. Pieces of root can be used for propagation in winter. If you carefully dig around a sucker at a depth of 20–30cm (8–12in), you can remove it with a section of the main root complete with fine hair roots. Pot it up in a loam-based compost watering regularly.

Embothrium Lanceolatum Group 'Norquinco' has narrow leaves and is hardier in cold areas. **JC**

Embothrium coccineum

Enkianthus perulatus

Type: hardy, deciduous shrub
Soil & situation: humus-rich, well-drained, neutral or acid soil/full sun or light shade
North American hardiness zone: 6–8
Height & spread: 2m (6½ft)
Grow for: a mass of white, urn-shaped flowers and the most amazing autumn-leaf colour; AGM

I am delighted to be able to grow this shrub. The flowers are pretty in spring but wait until you see its autumn colour. Grown in very peaty soil the leaves turn to a brilliant bright red, every year without fail.

The stems of the young growths are red tinted. The 5cm (2in) long, mid-green leaves are toothed and are mainly at the ends of the branches, leaving bare stems beneath. The autumn colour can be breathtaking. In mid-spring umbels of up to ten small, urn-shaped, pure white flowers dangle like drop pearl earrings.

Pruning is seldom necessary unless there is a crossing branch spoiling the overall shape. If so, it can be removed in winter. This is a great shrub for planting in light shade in woodland or in a copse where there is acid soil and a deep mulch of leafmould. From a distance the autumn colour will resemble a fire. Propagation is by seed sown in heat in early spring or semi-ripe cuttings in summer rooted under clear polythene. Low branches layered in autumn will be rooted and ready for transplanting within 18 months. **JC**

Enkianthus perulatus

Epilobium angustifolium 'Album'

Epilobium angustifolium 'Album' (syn. *Chamerion angustifolium* 'Album')

WHITE ROSEBAY WILLOWHERB

Type: hardy perennial
Soil & situation: many different conditions/prefers sun or light shade/well-drained, moisture-retentive soil
North American hardiness zone: 3–6
Height: to 1.5m (5ft)
Spread: 1m (3ft)
Grow for: racemes of white flowers which can enhance more natural plantings or wild areas

This white form of rosebay willowherb is not as invasive as the native variety – it only spreads by its stolons and rarely by seed, as it sets very little, if any, viable seed. Occasionally people encounter forms that do set copious quantities of viable seed, but I have yet to. It is fabulous to use in wilder spaces and it can really lift those less tamed parts of the garden by imparting charm, colour and life. The common pink form used to be known as 'Fireweed' as, after the fires following the blitz in London, it swiftly colonized vast areas both by seed and its running white roots. It is too invasive for the garden though. Not so the white form. Gardeners have often asked how to bulk it up quickly, but unfortunately, there does not seem to be a speedy route. So do not be mean but buy several, if not many, plants initially. And do cut it back after flowering so you get maximum value for money. My mother says she finds it too leafy in richer soils – certainly not my problem though.

This plant can be cut back by half after flowering and it will produce lots of new flower spikes later in the season. It can be obstinate to propagation by division: I find it more successful carried out in spring and I give it fair bit of 'TLC' afterwards until it starts to grow. **BG**

Epimedium stellulatum 'Wudang Star'
BISHOP'S HAT

Type: hardy, herbaceous perennial
Soil & situation: humus-rich, moist soil/dappled shade
North American hardiness zone: 5–9
Height & spread: 35cm (14in) or more
Grow for: attractive young leaves and flowers in spring

In 1983, Roy Lancaster found this plant in the walls of the Purple Clouds Temple in the Wudang Mountains of central China. Professor William Stearn, a world authority on epimediums, identified it as *E. sagittatum* and Roy named his introduction 'Wudang Star'. However, after further communication, his discovery was found to be even more exciting – the plant was new to science! In 1993, Professor Stearn renamed the species to *E. stellulatum*, meaning 'flight of little stars'; it describes the flowers perfectly.

It's clump forming, with arrow-shaped leaflets, bright pink young growth flushed with crimson in spring and arching stems to 30cm (12in) long, which explode in a star-burst of up to 40 white flowers with orange-brown sepals and prominent yellow stamens. They're exquisite – how can anything be so beautiful?

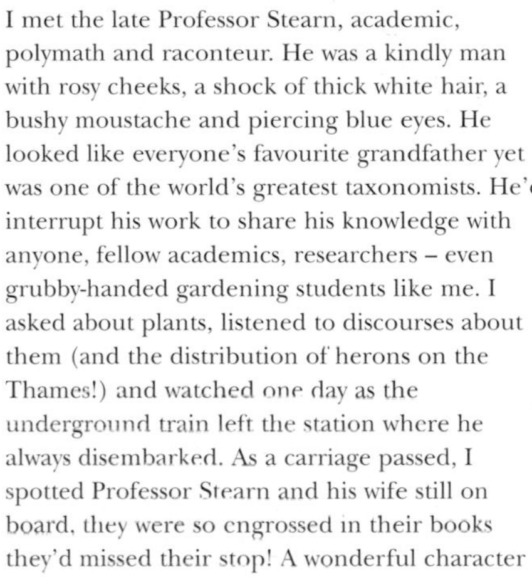

I met the late Professor Stearn, academic, polymath and raconteur. He was a kindly man with rosy cheeks, a shock of thick white hair, a bushy moustache and piercing blue eyes. He looked like everyone's favourite grandfather yet was one of the world's greatest taxonomists. He'd interrupt his work to share his knowledge with anyone, fellow academics, researchers – even grubby-handed gardening students like me. I asked about plants, listened to discourses about them (and the distribution of herons on the Thames!) and watched one day as the underground train left the station where he always disembarked. As a carriage passed, I spotted Professor Stearn and his wife still on board, they were so engrossed in their books they'd missed their stop! A wonderful character and a great man!

It needs moist, fertile, humus-rich, well-drained soil in a sheltered, partially shaded position but grows in any soil, sun or shade. Divide in autumn or after flowering. **MB**

Epimedium stellulatum 'Wudang Star'

Eranthis hyemalis

Eranthis hyemalis
WINTER ACONITE

Type: hardy, tuberous perennial
Soil & situation: moist, free-draining soil/sun or dappled shade
North American hardiness zone: 4–9
Height: 8cm (3½in)
Spread: 5cm (2in)
Grow for: cheerful flowers and foliage in mid- and late winter; AGM

If you need something to cure the winter blues, it's here! Don't just put in a few, think 'big' and plant huge swathes through borders, under trees and over lawns so their golden-yellow beams illuminate winter's dullest days; why not add a few snowdrops too? Individually, winter aconites are fascinating, with deeply cut leaves and yellow, balloon-like buds that burst open to form cup-shaped blooms sitting on top of a ruff of leaf-like bracts. There's a bold hybrid between two species, *E. cilicia* and *E. hyemalis*, called *E.* x *tubergenii* 'Guinea Gold' that I've seen with bronze-tinted foliage and flowers like golden bowls; it tolerates more sunshine than *E. hyemalis*. *E. cilicica* has bronze-tinged leaves, larger flowers and more lobes on the leaves.

Tubers are normally bought dry; soak them overnight in cool water before planting. They can also be bought and planted in full leaf immediately after flowering, this is known as 'in the green' and they establish more successfully. Several specialist nurseries sell them this way.

They like any soil providing it is not waterlogged, stagnant or dry; dig in plenty of organic matter then leave undisturbed to form colonies; they flourish in alkaline soil. Cool, moist soil below deciduous trees and shrubs is ideal. Plant the knobbly tubers about 5cm (2in) deep. Divide after flowering; sow seeds of the species in spring. Birds may damage the flowers; aphids disfigure and cause sooty mould.

Legend has it that in England they bloom only where Roman soldiers have shed their blood. **MB**

Smilacina racemosa

FALSE SPIKENARD, TREACLE BERRY

Type: hardy, herbaceous perennial
Soil & situation: any soil/sun or shade
Hardiness zone: 4–9
Height: 90cm (36in)
Spread: 30cm (12in)
Grow for: hosta-like leaves; foamy, feathery, fragrant, white flowers and occasional, apparently edible, sweet, aromatic, glossy red berries. The freshness of the flowers heralds the change from spring to summer; AGM.

I am always on the look out for edible 'wild' fruits that could be improved – after all, the modern strawberry is enormous compared to those before Victoria's reign. This delightful plant has a red berry that was eaten by the native North Americans and called the treacle berry for its sweet taste. These are not prolifically produced so a bigger berried, heavier cropping selection would be wonderful. Especially as this lily relative has a neat habit, is not invasive and exudes a wonderful perfume from the flowerheads. A really good plant, and what's more it grows in shade…

This is a small genus of North American herbaceous plants that strongly resemble polygonatums (see page 302) in growth though not in flower. The name is because it allegedly, in some faint way, resembles smilax, which is itself rather dubiously named after a green briar.

Smilacina is not fast growing but is fairly tough and will endure many sites, preferring moist, leafmould-rich soils in light shade. It can be tidied once the stems wither. Sow seed in spring or divide the roots in autumn. It has no problems and is a good alternative to hostas, as slugs avoid it. **BF**

Eremurus stenophyllus subsp. *stenophyllus*

DESERT CANDLE, FOXTAIL LILY

Type: hardy perennial
Soil & situation: rich fertile, well-drained sandy soils/acid or alkaline/sharp, cold winter temperatures/sunny positions
North American hardiness zone: 6–9
Height: 1.2m (4ft)
Spread: 60cm (24in)
Grow for: amazing, tall, upright stems densely packed with bright yellow flowers in early summer

When I was working in northern Japan recently, I saw masses of different flowering eremurus, flowering far better than they do, even in the books, over here. This brought home to me how well these plants really respond to the cold winter (they will easily get –17°C/1°F there) and strong sun in the summer. The flowers are far bigger and better, and last longer too. Sheltered sites are definitely worth seeking out, as you can then get away without the need to stake them. The taller *Eremurus himalaicus* reaches 2m (6½ft) and is white, flowering in early May. Both this and *E. robustus*, which is taller still, towering to 2.4m (7½ft) and is pink, are equally brilliant plants.

On a sheltered site you may get away without staking the taller types. If you do need to stake, it is best to insert a stout peg into the ground at planting to avoid damaging the crown of fleshy starfish-like roots. To make sure you have good enough drainage, you may need to plant the crown on – and cover ot with – sharp sand or grit, or plant it in a raised bed or on a bank. The leaves have mostly shrivelled up by flowering time, so disguise them with other planting, bearing in mind they love the sun. Reduce congestion in crowded groups by lifting them in early autumn when they are dormant. This involves sorting out the knitted roots to separate the crowns and then replanting individually, just below the surface of the soil. Place some grit or sand on top to stop slugs, snails and stray forks damaging the plants. **BG**

Eremurus stenophyllus subsp. *stenophyllus*

Erica arborea 'Estrella Gold'

TREE HEATH

Type: hardy, evergreen shrub
Soil & situation: moist, free-draining, gravelly soil/full sun/shelter from cold winds
North American hardiness zone: 9–10
Height: 1.2m (4ft)
Spread: 1m (3ft)
Grow for: total reliability; scented, white flowers; very useful for the border; AGM

Erica arborea 'Estrella Gold'

Heathers have a place in every garden and among the best of them are the tree heaths. They add character and height to any border all year round. I have never known a tree heath to refuse to flower.

Erica arborea 'Estrella Gold' is slower growing than *E. arborea* with lime-green, needle-like foliage tipped bright yellow in spring. Later, in summer, it will darken to golden yellow. Early spring, white flowers are honey-scented, appearing in long, spiky racemes. It has an upright habit with stiff branches.

Usually, the only pruning required is to clip the plant over after flowering removing the dead flowerheads. Large, overgrown plants may be pruned hard in late spring when all risk of frost is past. In early summer feed with a general, balanced fertilizer and mulch the soil surface. Propagate by rooting semi-ripe cuttings in summer in a gritty compost. In late spring pinch out the tip of young plants to encourage them to branch low down, forming a bushy plant. **JC**

Erica carnea 'December Red'

WINTER HEATH OR HEATHER

Type: hardy, evergreen shrub
Soil & situation: well-drained, fertile, acid soil/full sun or light shade
North American hardiness zone: 5–6
Height: 20–25cm (8–10in)
Spread: 60cm (24in)
Grow for: deep green foliage which contrasts with the long-lasting, rose-red flower spikes, making a cheerful display from mid-winter until mid-spring; superb ground-covering plant

Flowering times of *Erica carnea* depend on the variety, starting in late autumn until mid-spring. Colours range from white through pink to purple. The flowers of *E. c.* 'December Red' open a pale pink gradually deepening to a warm rose-red colour. Totally hardy, it loves the wind in its hair and will sit under a blanket of snow, emerging in full bloom. It manages to cheer me up on a cold day when the rain is dripping down my neck.

It is at its best in an open, free-draining soil with added humus. It prefers acid conditions but, providing there is a good depth overlying chalk, it is tolerant of alkaline soil. Regular mulches will encourage surface roots, thus extending the life of the plant. A general clip over after the colour has faded to remove the dead flowers will keep the plant compact. Planted in groups and spaced 45cm (18in) apart, they will soon join up to form a weed-suppressing carpet. **JC**

Erica carnea 'December Red'

Erica x *darleyensis* 'Silberschmelze'

Erica x *darleyensis* 'Silberschmelze'

DARLEY DALE HEATH

Type: hardy, vigorous, busy, evergreen shrub
Soil & situation: moist, well-drained soil/tolerates alkaline conditions/full sun
North American hardiness zone: 7–8
Height: 38cm (15in)
Spread: 90cm (36in)
Grow for: very reliable winter- and spring-flowering heather with pure white flowers

I love its habit of growth where it not only spreads well but is taller and more dense than most of the other varieties of *Erica* x *darleyensis*. The tiny, lance-shaped leaves are tipped with pale-cream in spring, turning a deep green in summer and tinged a rusty-red in winter. The urn-shaped, fragrant, white flowers that cover the plant in the dead of winter are so white they make virgin snow look grey. It trades under two other names, 'Silver Beads' and 'Molten Silver', both of which are good descriptive terms for this plant.

E. x *d.* 'Silberschmelze' is a good companion plant for dwarf conifers and, planted 80cm (32in) apart, forms a dense ground-covering mat which smothers most annual weeds.

An annual mulch of compost worked or washed into the centre of the heather will encourage the stems to root. Clip the plant over removing the dead flower stems as soon as it has finished flowering. It is sufficiently hardy for the coldest areas of the UK and is happiest in an exposed, windy site. Propagation is by 5cm (2in) long semi-ripe cuttings in early summer. Pot the cuttings up in late summer the same year to allow them to establish fresh roots in the compost before winter. **JC**

Erigeron karvinskianus

MEXICAN DAISY

Type: evergreen perennial
Soil & situation: sharp-draining, moderately fertile soil/naturalizes in stone walls/sun or part shade
North American hardiness zone: 5–7
Height: 15–30cm (6–12in)
Spread: 1m (3ft) or more
Grow for: a plant rarely out of flower in the summer; colonizes in gaps in paving or stone walls as it seeds itself freely; AGM

This flower must be one of the longest-flowering plants around and will perform from late spring to late autumn which is a real feat. The flower looks very like that of a lawn daisy, except they are not always white with a yellow centre. They start white or pink (with a yellow centre) and then finally end up red-purple. It is a star plant in terms of performance and, if you too like simple charm, then I think it is also a star plant in terms of appearance. When it colonizes a gridwork of cracks in paving, a dry stone wall or a stone roof it creates something totally different, away from the norm, which really lifts your spirits.

This is one of those plants that either takes a real shine to you or looks the other way. One major factor is drainage – if you have heavy, wet soil then you must lighten it up a lot. Apart from this, if you want it in copious quantities, I think the secret is to grow it from seed in spring, in 7cm (3in) pots, and then plant it out in late spring. Once you have it well established, it benefits from a hard cut back in early spring. This keeps it looking smart and natty right through to the end of flowering in late autumn, when you can leave the heads on for maximum seed dispersal. **BG**

Erigeron karvinskianus

Eriobotrya japonica

Eriobotrya japonica
LOQUAT/JAPANESE MEDLAR

Type: frost-hardy evergreen shrub to small tree
Soil & situation: any soil/full sun to light shade
North American hardiness zone: 8–10
Height: 9m (30ft)
Spread: 6m (20ft)
Grow for: very large, firm, leathery, evergreen foliage; hawthorn-scented flowers; AGM

The loquat first came to my attention as a student abroad. I ate the delicious fruit but never saved the seed, thinking the plant would not be hardy. Then years later I saw an old specimen in a friend's garden in Norwich where I first mistook it for a rare rhododendron, because of its impressive leaves. I have since grown many myself as evergreen foliage plants; they are easy from seed, and I have found them surprisingly tough. The exotically perfumed (well, hawthorn-like) drooping clusters of flowers come, sporadically, throughout winter if it is mild following a hot summer. Just occasionally fellow growers have reported fruits setting – these are like chewy apricots.

A native of China and Japan, it was introduced in 1787. It is named after the Greek *erion*, for wool, and *botrys*, for grapes, describing the woolly clusters of flowers. Loquat, comes from the Cantonese name, *lu-kywit*, for its orange fruits.

Any well-drained soil in full sun will suit this plant and it will survive for many decades in a sheltered position. Nip out the growing tip to make it into a bushy shrub, because as a tree it gets too leggy and windswept unless on a wall. It can be grown from seed but then you will only get a species, not an improved fruiting variety – which is fine in Britain where it is grown only for its ornamental value. Or take cuttings in late summer. No problems other than occasional wind burn. **BF**

Eruca vesicaria
WILD ROCKET

Type: annual herb
Soil & situation: rich, well-drained but moist soils/will grow satisfactorily on a range of soils, but bolting may be encouraged in lighter soils/shade protection or a shady position can prolong leaf production
North American hardiness zone: annual
Height & spread: to 1m (3ft), usually less
Grow for: an essential spicy leaf for salads; harvestable leaves six to eight weeks from sowing; one sowing will generate a good five cuttings if not more; sown in very early autumn it will have leaves for cutting from mid-autumn right through to spring, with a bit of luck

Wild rocket is different in appearance from salad rocket, having thinner, smaller and darker leaves and a stronger taste, but the big advantage is that it will produce leaves for about twice as long as other rockets. It is also slower growing. It has been used since at least the first century AD for medicinal purposes, but now is a hot favourite in salads. It is a constituent of mesclun, which is a very tasty mixed salad of small leaves which originates from around Nice in the South of France. You should cut the leaves before the flowering stem is produced, as they become overpoweringly strong after this point.

Sow from mid-spring. Thin to about 15cm (6in) apart to stop the plants bolting prematurely.

Eruca vesicaria

Continue sowing till mid-summer and cover with fleece, if necessary, to prevent flea beetle attack. If you sow in late summer or early autumn, flea beetle is not a problem, and there is often foliage for picking from mid-autumn to spring. Cut the leaves to about 2.5cm (1in) above the ground, and carry on doing this till they bolt. Plants in a sunny position have more pungent leaves than those growing in shady spots, as happens with most herbs. **BF**

Eryngium agavifolium

Type: frost-hardy, evergreen perennial
Soil & situation: a wide range of soil types from poor gravelly to limy and rich loams/free-draining moderately fertile soils are optimum/ full sun
North American hardiness zone: 6–9
Height: flowers to 1.3m (4ft), basal leaves to 45cm (18in)
Spread: 60cm (2ft)
Grow for: amazing looks through the winter months with its striking silhouette iced with frost; evergreen clumps of foliage through which protrude several tall spikes supporting many rounded, teasel-type heads about 1cm (½in) in diameter

Eryngium agavifolium

This rather exotic plant will fit into many places in the garden. Because of its year-round appeal, I grow it in my entrance courtyard where the beds are edged in box. The garden is a funny mix of traditional and contemporary and this plant is a bit like that too. The thin, strappy leaves can be up to 75cm (30in) long, are slightly fleshy-looking, edged in neat little spines on both sides and form bold, solid clumps that look good right through the grey, cold winter months. The greenish-white flowers appear in late summer. They are perfect plants to grow as specimens in gravel, mixed with ornamental grasses, in containers, as part of prairie schemes, or more traditionally, with a dark green hedge behind them. How versatile can you get? They are superb for drying to use in winter decorations.

These plants do not appreciate root disturbance and I have left mine untouched for many years. One day, when they get too large, I will split the clumps in spring, as opposed to autumn, as they might well tend to sit and rot through the winter months if done earlier. They will be slow to re-establish. Propagate by root cuttings in winter or by seed. **BG**

Eryngium bourgatii 'Picos Blue'
SEA HOLLY

Type: hardy, herbaceous perennial
Soil & situation: moist, free-draining soil/full sun
North American hardiness zone: 5–9
Height: 45cm (18in)
Spread: 30cm (12in)
Grow for: sculptural form and foliage; flowers from mid-summer

Now here's a conundrum! The genus is commonly called 'sea hollies', you'd think they were thistles but what are they? Carrots! It just proves that appearances are deceiving. I'd like to include them all as they're such wonderful plants. *E. b.* 'Picos Blue' is one of several with blue flowers and stems, but it's arguably the bluest and best. It has a basal clump of deeply cut, dark green leaves and a stiff candelabra of flowerheads and stems of deep metallic blue. The flowers are nectar rich, beloved by bees and other insects; cut at their peak and hung upside down, they dry and retain their colour.

E. bourgatii has deeply cut, silvery-grey, white-veined leaves and silvery-green bracts. *E. bourgatii* 'Oxford Blue' has darker silvery-blue flowerheads. *E. alpinum* has attractive foliage and a mass of large, feathery, blue bracts surrounding the flowerheads. *E.* 'Jos Eijking' is intense steel blue. *E. proteiflorum* is a challenge: a deep pot and frost-free conditions is the solution in most gardens. It is silvery-white with an amazing ruffle of bracts about 15cm (6in) in diameter.

Eryngium bourgatii 'Picos Blue'

Their best colour develops in full sun on cool, moderately fertile, slightly moist, light, well-drained soil; they grow well on poor alkaline soil. Remove dead leaves in winter and put a gravel mulch round the crown of the top plants; they are ideal for gravel gardens. Propagate by root cuttings in summer, disturbing the plant as little as possible. Some cultivars are protected by 'Plant Breeder's Rights'. They can suffer from powdery mildew and crown rot in wet soil. **MB**

Eryngium maritimum
SEA HOLLY

Type: hardy, herbaceous perennial
Soil & situation: most light soils of good depth/full sun or light shade
North American hardiness zone: 5–8
Height & spread: 30–60cm (12–24in)
Grow for: startling, spiny, whitish glaucous foliage; spiky heads of pinkish-blue; edible parts

This is a beautiful plant – not large, quite compact, yet perfectly formed as if die cast in white metal. There are many other species often planted in the garden and most of these are more showy, but *Eryngium maritimum* has edible parts. The young shoots can be eaten as asparagus, before the spines of the holly-like leaves harden, and the roots may be candied – which I keep intending to do but I lose the plants too quickly. This is unusual as they are normally long lived. The flowerheads and stems if cut in their prime and dried carefully become everlasting, which makes them even more valuable.

A native maritime plant, the roots were thought to be an aphrodisiac when prepared by candying and were called eringoes. They are mentioned by Falstaff, 'let the sky rain potatoes…hail kissing comfits and snow eringoes'. *E. giganteum*, a close but larger relation, is known as Miss Willmott's Ghost as she had the appalling arrogance and inconsideration to surreptitiously sow seeds of this weed in every garden she visited.

E. maritimum prefers to be on a sandy shoreline, even washed by the sea! So give it a light, sandy, well-drained soil in full sun. Most of this family can be easily propagated by root cuttings, but this one is easiest from seed. Sow *in situ* or in small pots and transplant ASAP to its final site before the deep tap root forms. Slugs, or so it would seem, have made off with mine on several occasions – be warned! **BF**

Eryngium maritimum

Erysimum 'Bowles' Mauve'

Erysimum 'Bowles' Mauve'
PERENNIAL WALLFLOWER

Type: hardy, herbaceous perennial
Soil & situation: moderate to poor soil/sun
North American hardiness zone: 6–8
Height: 75cm (30in)
Spread: 60cm (24in)
Grow for: compact form and flowers from mid-spring to late autumn; AGM

Edward Augustus Bowles (1865–1954) lived at Myddleton House in Enfield, North London. He was an educated and enthusiastic gardener and plantsman with a kindly personality. Before gardening, he was interested in entomology and it was on a moth and caterpillar hunting expedition to Wicken Fen in Cambridgeshire that he noticed part of a clump of native *Carex elata* with bands of bright yellow which he removed and planted in his garden; it became *Carex elata* 'Bowles' Golden'.

Another plant named after him, *Vinca minor* 'Bowles Variety', was found in a French churchyard and *Milium effusum* 'Aureum' or 'Bowles Golden Grass' came from Birmingham Botanic Garden. Sadly, he almost certainly didn't grow *Erysimum* 'Bowles' Mauve', the reliable bushy wallflower with grey-blue foliage and masses of mauve flowers from mid-spring to late autumn. He never mentioned this fine plant in his books nor was it recognized by any of his gardeners who were later questioned about its origin. It is a really good performer and worthy of being one of the seventeen plants that bear his name. Given shelter, it flowers all year round.

While we're talking 'wallflowers' I'd like to sneak in a mention of another particular favourite of mine called *E.* 'Jacob's Jacket' with purple and bronze flowers, turning orange and finally lilac. It's wonderful!

Flourishing in poor to moderately fertile, well-drained, neutral to alkaline soil in full sun, in a sheltered position, these are ideal plants for those difficult dry sunny spots. Take nodal or heeled softwood cuttings in spring or summer. It is worth having a replacement plant standing by, as it dislikes cold, wet winters; protect from severe frost. **MB**

Erythrina crista-gallii
CORAL TREE, COCKSPUR CORAL TREE

Type: tender, deciduous perennial
Soil & situation: moderately fertile, well-drained soil/sun
North American hardiness zone: 8–10
Height & spread: 2.5m (8ft) x 1.5m (5ft), as a perennial
Grow for: extraordinary flowers from late summer onwards

Looking for an exotic? Then here's the real McCoy. Forget tree ferns and hardy tropical lookalikes, bring a touch of the Copacobana into your British back garden! This elegant beauty has spiny stems, trilobed leaves and waxy, deep coral-red flowers, each one about 6cm (2½in) long on flower spikes reaching a staggering 60cm (24in)

Erythrina crista-gallii

long. All the best gardens have one! The specimen at Oxford University Botanic Gardens has its roots in a greenhouse, escaping under the glass to flower outside; at the Royal Horticultural Gardens, Wisley, it is treated as a herbaceous plant; there's one at Sissinghurst Castle in Kent too. Mine is in a pot, it's growing well and is yet to flower.... There's a bottle of champagne waiting!

Plant outside against a sheltered, sunny wall in southern areas of the UK. It needs moderately fertile, well-drained soil and tolerates temperatures down to –10°C (14°F), providing the base is heavily mulched with leafmould or compost then covered with bracken. Cut back the stems from mid- to late spring once the danger of frost is over and the new shoots should flower by late summer. Alternatively, grow it in a pot, in a free-draining loam-based mix, like John Innes no. 3 with added sharp sand. Overwinter under glass and put it outside after the last frost. Reduce watering in winter and re pot or top dress when growth begins in spring. Propagate by seed or 7.5–10cm (3–4in) cuttings of young shoots in spring. **MB**

Erythronium 'Pagoda'

TROUT LILY

Type: hardy, bulbous perennial
Soil & situation: moist but free-draining soil/ partial shade
North American hardiness zone: 4–9
Height & spread: 35cm (14in)
Grow for: both for its foliage and flowers; attractive leaves are mottled, glossy and dark green and appear in late winter to early spring; the flowers, borne in mid- to late spring are yellow and last for several weeks; strong growers and spread quickly; AGM

Easy, very vigorous and undemanding to grow *Erythronium* 'Pagoda' spreads quite quickly, even in my dry soil. Even though I have read several times that it likes moist, acid conditions, I know of several dry, alkaline gardens where it copes admirably. Never believe everything you read in books! The leaves are large, elliptical and mottled with bronze and make quite a show. The tall stems each carry up to ten, pale sulphur-yellow flowers which hang way above the leaves.

Although the stems seem delicate, the flowers, like the plant, are robust and are not perturbed by inclement spring weather. I grow it in large drifts under my hazel bushes, with primroses, ivies and ferns. It competes surprisingly well even with the ivy. I think it looks best growing in a

Erythronium 'Pagoda'

naturalized way rather than in clumps in the border, which then leaves you with a gap as the leaves die down in summer. Another way to grow them is around the base of trees where the empty space in summer does not register so much. I am going to try them naturalized in thin, woodland turf where apparently it also does well. It is another of those plants that makes you wonder why it is not grown more.

This plant establishes well from dry bulbs but do plant them promptly on arrival. They look like a large canine fang, hence one of its common names is dog's tooth violet. If the clumps become congested you can either split them when the foliage starts to die in summer or just as the flowers are going over. **BG**

Escallonia 'Pride of Donard'

Type: hardy, evergreen shrub
Soil & situation: fertile, well-drained soil/full sun
North American hardiness zone: 8–9
Height: 1.5m (5ft)
Spread: 2.5m (8ft)
Grow for: a dense, compact shrub with an abundance of flowers in summer: AGM

I have a particular liking for escallonia. As an informal hedge they are in flower over a long period. Of the many varieties available, *Escallonia* 'Pride of Donard' is my favourite.

In maturity it forms an upright, dense, compact shrub with 3cm (1in) long, glossy, dark evergreen leaves. The short terminal racemes of bright, pink-red, chalice-like flowers are carried in profusion during summer. It is an excellent seaside plant tolerating sea spray and coming into flower earlier than when planted inland. Another good choice is *E.* 'Iveyi' with conical panicles of pure white, highly fragrant flowers and growing to 4m (13ft) high.

As a hedge, clip immediately after flowering and apply a general fertilizer to encourage growth. When it continues to flower into early autumn it is necessary to clip it over before it has finished flowering. Lightly prune free-standing shrubs in spring when all risk of frost is over. Old, neglected plants may be hard pruned in late spring, cutting into the old branch system. They will soon recover sending up strong, new shoots from the base.

Propagation is by softwood cuttings in early summer, semi-ripe cuttings from late summer to autumn or as hardwood cuttings taken in early winter. **JC**

Eschscholzia californica

Plant of the Week (see page 281)

Escallonia 'Pride of Donard'

Eucalyptus pauciflora subsp. *niphophila*

SNOW GUM

Type: hardy, evergreen, spreading tree
Soil & situation: moist, fertile, well-drained, neutral to acid soil/prefers sun
North American hardiness zone: 8–10
Height & spread: 6m (20ft)
Grow for: something pleasing in all its stages – graceful when young and in old age, which seems to come early, it becomes dome-headed, open and gnarled; AGM

A native of Australia, it is one of the hardiest eucalypts. Seed from trees growing at high altitude in New South Wales appears to be immune to frost and cold winds.

The mature bark has been likened to a python's skin but in case, like me, you are happy never to have seen a python, I will describe the trunk. Cinnamon brown, flaking to reveal green, grey and yellow patches, the latter turning to a creamy white.

The young shoots are covered in a waxy, white bloom. Adult foliage is leathery, grey-green and lance-shaped with the characteristic pungent aroma when crushed. The umbels of creamy-white, petalless flowers appear from late spring through to summer in clusters of between three and seven. The flower buds resemble acorns – each a small urn with a lid. The stamens push the lid off and fully expand.

Eucalyptus pauciflora subsp. *niphophila*

Eucomis bicolor

Where space is restricted the snow gum can be coppiced annually by cutting the tree down to within 30cm (12in) of the ground in the late spring. The resultant seasonal growth can be as much as 2–3m (6½–10ft) with juvenile, pale green, rounded leaves. Propagation is by seed which germinates easily after an eight-week period of cold, winter weather. Plant the young tree in its permanent position as soon as possible. Larger than 1.2m (4ft) high, and it will always be unstable, its roots staying in a ball rather than spreading in search of nutrients. If left lying, dead eucalyptus leaves will mark a patio surface, leaving a brown stain. **JC**

Eucomis bicolor

PINEAPPLE LILY, PINEAPPLE FLOWER

Type: hardy bulbous perennial
Soil & situation: well-drained fertile soil/full sun
North American hardiness zone: 8–10
Height: 60cm (24in)
Spread: 20cm (8in)
Grow for: unusual and charismatic flowers on thick stalks, surrounded by a cylinder of starry blooms, topped with a spout of leafy bracts in late summer to early autumn and, as their name implies, looking a little like pineapples; AGM

I have seen these plants growing in a thick colony all the way along the base of a mature yew hedge. It was facing due south and obviously in a very dry position, but the plants looked rather handsome and exotic. They are supposedly a little tender, but mine have survived outside for several years. If you are in a colder area, they can be planted out each spring, but they look best when they are well and truly established in thick clumps or ribbons.

You plant these bulbs in autumn, about 15cm (6in) deep, and I have to admit I do not think I have ever done anything to these plants in my life after planting them, except admire them. If I was not so reckless, I would give them a mulch in winter to ensure protection against the frost, though mine are in a narrow border running along the house and are fairly snug against the stone walls. I could also water them in active growth, which no doubt would spur them on. A feed too, would also have this effect, and be appreciated when they become active quite late in spring. **BG**

Eucomis comosa

PINEAPPLE FLOWER

Type: hardy, bulbous perennial
Soil & situation: moist but free-draining soil/full sun
North American hardiness zone: 8–10
Height: 1m (3ft)
Spread: 60cm (24in) or more
Grow for: attractive form, flower, foliage and fruit

The first specimen described in England was in 1732 by Dillenius, Professor of Botany at Oxford University who named it *Corona regalis lilii folio crenato* meaning 'crown royal lily with crenate (scalloped) leaves'. And you thought the current

Eucomis comosa

Latin names were difficult! *Eucomis* is from the Greek *eu*, meaning good, and *kome*, hair or tuft, describes the 'good tuft' of leaf-like bracts that top the dense head of waxy, star-shaped flowers.

Although all the eucomis are impressive, this is perhaps the most dramatic, reaching 1m (3ft) tall in a range of flower colours from pale green to cream, pink and purple. The developing fruits glisten and are suffused with burgundy tints like tiny beetroot and the stem is flecked and striped! It makes a wonderful specimen on a patio, particularly when it flowers in late summer and early autumn.

The most common of the others is *Eucomis bicolor* (see previous entry). *E. pole-evansii* is a giant, reaching a staggering 2m (6½ft) tall in warmer climates (it's not quite as enthusiastic in ours!), while *E. zambesiaca* is comparatively small at 20–30cm (8–12in) with white, coconut-scented flowers fading to green. There are plenty to choose from!

They need a sheltered, sunny position, against a wall or fence on free-draining, moist soil; dig in plenty of well rotted organic matter before planting, water well in summer. Mulch in autumn to protect from frost. In cooler parts of the UK they are better grown in containers and overwintered in a cool greenhouse or shed. Propagate by division or seed in spring. **MB**

Eucryphia x *intermedia* 'Rostrevor'

Plant of the Week (see page 305)

Euonymus europaeus 'Red Cascade'

Plant of the Week (see page 357)

Euonymus fortunei 'Emerald 'n' Gold'

Type: hardy, evergreen, bushy shrub
Soil & situation: moist, well-drained soil/full sun or light shade
North American hardiness zone: 5–9
Height & spread: 1m (3ft)
Grow for: attractive leaves; neat, low hedge; AGM

When you need to fill a gap this is a good and easy filler. It will grow in any soil providing it isn't

Euonymus fortunei 'Emerald 'n' Gold'

waterlogged. Its small, shiny green leaves are delightfully edged in bright yellow. The variegation is more pronounced in a sunny site and when the weather turns cold the whole plant takes on a pink tinge. It forms a compact plant when mature, throwing the odd long, sparsely-leafed stem.

Trim lightly in late spring to keep it in shape and remove any green stems that appear. Planted close together and clipped regularly it will form a tight, attractive, low hedge. Planted against a wall it will go vertical, making 2m (6½ft) without support. A good companion plant is the cream-and-green variegated *Euonymus* 'Emerald Gaiety' with a spread of 1.5m (5ft).

E. fortunei 'Emerald 'n' Gold' dislikes biting, cold winds, preferring a sheltered sunny situation. Propagation is easy with softwood or semi-hardwood cuttings in a gritty compost. Cuttings where the stems root themselves into the soil are a quick way to increase stock. **JC**

Euonymus fortunei 'Silver Queen'

Type: hardy, evergreen climbing shrub
Soil & situation: huge range of soils/useful on dry, shady sites/also grows well in full sun on poor dry soils
North American hardiness zone: 5–9
Height: up to 2.5m (8ft)
Spread: 1.5m (5ft)
Grow for: useful and decorative foliage, leaves have a broad cream margin and in prolonged cold periods take on 'bottle-nosed pinkish tints', as aptly described by Christopher Lloyd in his book *The Well-Tempered Garden*; excellent against walls and fences; more usually grown as ground cover.

Although not a great fan of variegated plants, I do think of this as a really choice plant and accordingly use it on a regular basis. The natty, compact foliage is well-behaved and will do what you tell it, be it scrambling up trees or fences (albeit slowly), forming sheets of classic, smart green and white ground cover or, clipped and trained, forming huge, solid but vivid topiary balls. It adapts to look appropriate to its neighbours somehow. In one very special garden, we have used it in a green and white border mixed with white *Gladiolus callianthus* (see page 194), *Rosa* 'Gruss an Aachen' (page 334), *Choisya ternata* 'Aztec Pearl' and others, all grown in repeated groups. The effect is simple and refreshing. Another big plus in its favour – it grows pretty much anywhere you tell it, lightening up rather dark, dry shade, or baking on a sun-soaked terrace.

These plants need little care except if you would like them to climb, and then support will be necessary. Otherwise you just shape them if their growth is lopsided or whatever, but this is hardly likely to offend anyway. I think it would be difficult to kill or damage them, whatever time of year you cut them, except perhaps by cutting too early or late in the year and so encouraging new growth at a time when it could be frosted. It is ever so easy to propagate by cuttings taken any time between early summer and mid-autumn. **BG**

Euonymus fortunei 'Silver Queen'

Exochorda x *macrantha* 'The Bride'

PEARL BUSH

Type: hardy, deciduous shrub
Soil & situation: moist, fertile, well-drained soil/full sun or light shade
Hardiness zone: 5–9
Height: 2m (6½ft)
Spread: 3m (10ft)
Grow for: an abundance of large, white flowers, at their best in mid-spring; AGM

A lovely woman and a great gardener, Jane Higginson of Comber, near my home in Northern Ireland, has a matching pair of these wonderful shrubs, one either side of a path. In flower they are spectacular.

It forms a compact mound of arching branches. The 7cm (2¾in) long, pale green leaves are produced early in spring. Racemes of up to ten, pure white, five-petalled flowers on short, leafy stems appear in late spring and early summer covering the branches. It makes a wonderful plant in a mixed shrub bed or grown as a specimen in an open situation where its arched branches will reach the ground.

Another species, *Exochorda racemosa*, is one of the parents of 'The Bride'. It is an equally classy shrub but is more fussy, needing an acid soil. It will succeed in all soils but will become chlorotic (yellow leaves) in shallow chalk soils.

Prune back the branches that have flowered to healthy buds. Neglected shrubs may be severely pruned in late spring, removing a quarter of the old branches close to the base each year. This will encourage new, strong shoots. Propagation is by softwood cuttings in summer. Take short cuttings and remove most of the leaves. **JC**

Eupatorium rugosum 'Chocolate'

Eupatorium rugosum 'Chocolate'

Type: hardy perennial
Soil & situation: moderately fertile soil/responds well to moist soil/sun or part shade
North American hardiness zone: 4–9
Height: to 1.2m (4ft)
Spread: 25cm (10in)
Grow for: deep green foliage heavily tinted with a burgundy-brown colour; AGM

This plant is a new and unusual perennial, a selection from the white snakeroot, *Eupatorium rugosum.* However the main difference is the distinctively-coloured foliage which happily, is also fairly bushy and maintains a good colour throughout the growing season. Corymbs of good-looking white flowers are produced in late summer and last for just about a month, if you are lucky. They are much appreciated by bees and butterflies.

Another favourite is *Eupatorium purpureum* subsp. *maculatum* 'Atropurpureum' (AGM). This is a grand plant, towering to over 2m (6½ft) high. It produces intense reddish-purple flowers which last into the autumn, and are often a hive of activity with bees and butterflies.

This plant responds well to good moisture levels, so if necessary add good volumes of organic matter prior to planting, and maybe water a little in dry periods until it really gets its roots well down. Cut down in late winter or spring. Propagate by division. **BG**

Euphorbia amygdaloides 'Purpurea'

WOOD SPURGE

Type: hardy, evergreen perennial
Soil & situation: ordinary garden loam/tolerates moist conditions/sun or shade
North American hardiness zone: 6–9
Height: up to 70cm (27½in)
Spread: 30cm (12in)
Grow for: year-round, purple foliage and stems; lime-green flowerheads in spring/summer

This plant is a real favourite of mine. I first became intimate with it when I included it in a ruby-coloured planting scheme for a Chelsea Flower Show garden, and managed to take it home afterwards for 'safe keeping'. It did me proud at Chelsea and has done my garden proud for the next two years to date. My major concern is that apparently it is short-lived but as it comes true from seed, hopefully I will have some offspring to remember it by when the fateful day eventually comes. The stems grow quite upright in their first year and usually flower in their second year. As I write about it in winter, following a period of snow and frost, the foliage is still in pristine condition and looks as showy as ever. It manages to thrive in a dry and shaded spot with me, although moist conditions are its preferred choice. I also grow *Euphorbia amygdaloides* var. *robbiae,* a useful evergreen plant for colonizing awkward dry shady places but not a show stopper like 'Purpurea'. One small downside to be aware of: all euphorbias have milky, white sap, which is toxic if eaten and an irritant to the skin and eyes.

Euphorbia amygdaloides 'Purpurea'

It is a good idea to remove stems after flowering which provides space for new stems to grow. This plant is easiest propagated from seed but as the seeds are released explosively, remember to encase the flowerheads in paper or light fabric just before the seeds are released. If using stems for flower arranging, seal the ends with boiling water or a flame, to prevent the sap bleeding.
BG

Euphorbia griffithii 'Dixter'

Type: hardy, herbaceous perennial
Soil & situation: rich, moist soil/sun or partial shade
North American hardiness zone: 5–9
Height: 1m (3ft)
Spread: 60cm (24in) or more
Grow for: colourful stems; flowerheads from late spring to mid-autumn; AGM

Yet another euphorbia that is highly sought after by Martian landscapers! Continuing in the generic tradition, it seems to have forgotten that it is supposed to be a plant and has absent-mindedly transformed itself into a piece of outrageous surrealist art. It looks more like a coral than a vegetable; particularly those extravagant flowerheads and stems during the early stages of growth.

As it explodes out of the ground like angry asparagus, the narrow, dark green-purple leaves folding out from the stems are edged and veined with orange-red. The massed stems make a wonderful architectural plant as the leaves cluster like a starfish round the stem. Topping each stem, the flowerheads resembling masts packed with satellite dishes have obviously decided that traditional 'lime-green' isn't ostentatious enough and glow brick-red instead; in autumn, the rest of the plant joins in the fun and the colour on the leaves and stems is incredible.

It is a spectacular plant, displaying all the creative flamboyance of the legend that is Christopher Lloyd; he selected this from a group of seedlings at Washfield Nurseries in Kent, and named it after his garden and home.

Euphorbia griffithii 'Fireglow' is more invasive, has green leaves with a red tinge and brick- to tomato-red flowers. It makes an impressive bold statement anywhere!

They need deep, humus-rich, moist soil in sun or partial shade. Colour is better in rich soil and sunshine. They are good in woodland gardens; cut back and mulch in spring. They can cause dermatitis, so wear gloves when handling. Divide in spring, take basal cuttings in spring and early summer; dip the cuts in warm water or charcoal to prevent bleeding. **MB**

Euphorbia myrsinites

Plant of the Week (see page 95)

Exochorda x *macrantha* 'The Bride'

Plant of the Week (see page 171)

Euphorbia griffithii 'Dixter'

Fabiana imbricata f. *violacea*

Fabiana imbricata f. *violacea*

Type: hardy, evergreen shrub
Soil & situation: well-drained, impoverished, neutral to acid soil/full sun
North American hardiness zone: 8–10
Height & spread: 2.5m (8ft)
Grow for: mauve-lavender flowers that cover the plant in early summer; AGM

This plant resembles a well-grown tree heather. Given a sheltered site in full sun or planted against a sunny wall it will thrive. The branches are stiff and upright with sideshoots emerging horizontally covered in small, needle-like, dark green leaves. The single, tubular, mauve-lavender flowers appear in early summer. While it will eventually become too large for a container, a young plant looks good in an earthenware pot. A matching pair at the front entrance can be impressive. *F. imbricata* 'Prostrata' is lower growing at a mature height of 1m (3ft). It produces white flowers in summer.

Prune in late spring, removing stems which spoil the overall shape. Propagation is by softwood cuttings in early summer or semi-ripe heel cuttings in late summer. Seed may be sown in autumn and over-wintered in a cold frame. **JC**

Fagus sylvatica 'Purpurea Pendula'

PURPLE WEEPING BEECH

Type: hardy, deciduous tree
Soil & situation: well-drained soil/full sun
North American hardiness zone: 5–7
Height & spread: 3m (10ft)
Grow for: good looks all year round as a specimen tree or in a large border

I am a firm believer in the saying, 'Every garden should have at least one tree', and there are few gardens too small to accommodate this lovely weeping beech.

It manages to look good all year round. In winter its mushroom-shaped head weeps gracefully on thin stems with shiny, pointed buds. The glossy, deep purple-black leaves emerge in late spring with a hint of green. It holds the leaves until late autumn when they turn to a rich brown before leaf fall.

It is tolerant of most soil types including thin soil over chalk but dislikes waterlogged conditions. Plant in a position in full sun and sheltered from cold winds. When planted in light shade the leaf colour is less intense with more bottle-green visible.

It is a well behaved tree but being top grafted it may occasionally produce all green shoots down the stem below the grafted head. Rub these off when they are young or cut thicker shoots as close to the main trunk as possible to prevent regrowth. Pruning may be necessary in the early years to shape and balance the tree. The weeping stems may be shortened by one third of the previous year's growth. They will produce several sideshoots, thickening the canopy of branches. Where staking is necessary to hold the tree, use a short stake with 45cm (18in) above ground level. Remove it as soon as the tree can stand on its own feet.

Tip: when selecting a purple weeping beech choose the tallest one possible. It may look a bit skinny and top heavy but in future years you will have a taller weeping specimen. **JC**

Fagus sylvatica 'Purpurea Pendula'

Fallopia baldschuanica

RUSSIAN VINE, MILE-A-MINUTE

Type: hardy, deciduous climber
Soil & situation: moderately fertile, moist, well-drained soil/full sun or partial shade
North American hardiness zone: 5–9
Height: 12m (40ft)
Spread: indefinite
Grow for: extremely fast growing; an abundance of small flowers covering long stems

Russian vine frequently gets a bad name and is laughed out of the garden when recommended as a climber. If the plan calls for a fast-growing climber to take over a miserable-looking tree and transform it for the summer, good old 'mile-a-minute' has the last laugh.

The 10cm (4in) long, heart-shaped leaves are dark green and from spring to autumn they camouflage the vigorous, woody, twining stems. The panicles of funnel-shaped, tiny, pink-tinged white flowers cover the plant in late summer and autumn. They appear on the new growth and seem to overflow the climber like froth or soapsuds. To see long stems covered in 'froth' trailing out of a big old tree is fairly dramatic. Small, pink-white fruits follow in late autumn.

It is no exaggeration to state that this climber is rampant. So much so I suggest you strengthen the supporting trellis before planting one. The tree it is going to climb and take over, and the support needs to be well anchored into the ground. The top growth high up in the tree will act as a sail, offering resistance to any wind. Pruning consists of teaching it who is boss. After flowering or in early spring, it can be hard pruned to stay within its allocated space. Allow for 3–4m (10–13ft) of growth in one season. Try to keep the stems clear of the ground as they will root where they touch the soil. Propagation is by seed in spring. Semi-ripe cuttings, taken in summer with a heel, root quickly. Hardwood cuttings in autumn will be well rooted by the following winter. Space the cuttings at least 30cm (12in) apart to prevent the new growth tangling. **JC**

Fallopia baldschuanica

Fascicularia bicolor

Fascicularia bicolor

Type: half-hardy, evergreen perennial
Soil & situation: extremely poor, very free-draining soil/sun or shade
North American hardiness zone: 9–10
Height: 45cm (18in)
Spread: 60cm (24in)
Grow for: fascinating form and flower from summer to autumn

Bromeliads, those spiny structures inhabiting deserts and rainforests, are rarely grown in gardens but this, one of nature's fantastic living sculptures, makes a fabulous novelty plant. It looks so 'spidery', I always expect it to get up and walk away!

The rosette, an arching, multi-layered mass of spiny-toothed stems is green for much of the year. At flowering time the insignificant central cluster of pale blue flowers seemingly strains, shoulder to shoulder in a united valiant effort to shine but all it can do is raise itself slightly and smile wanly at passersby. The leaves take pity on their shy, retiring friends and decide to help by lining their lips with glossy red lipstick and glowing like giant beacons. 'Hey, fancy some pollination?' they cry out to passing insects. Over the years, more rosettes appear, collectively there's more 'lippy' than at a tart's convention! It may be bold and brassy, but you have to say it's a 'tart wiv an 'eart'!

Given poor, very free-draining soil in sun or shade, it withstands light frosts. Plants produce offsets and colonies soon develop. They are long lived and over the years the leaves just grow longer.

How tough is it? E. Charles Nelson and Jorg Zizka in *The Plantsman* describe how a rootless rosette was left on a dry dark office floor for three weeks without water. It was finally planted in peat and left outdoors with no further care or water. Within two months it was growing strongly! Divide in spring or summer. **MB**

Fatsia japonica
JAPANESE ARALIA

Type: hardy, evergreen shrub
Soil & situation: moist, well-drained soil/full sun or partial shade
North American hardiness zone: 7–10
Height & spread: 3–4m (10–13ft)
Grow for: an unbeatable shrub for its architectural qualities; AGM

It is old fashioned and smacks of 'Victoriana' but it is still one of the very best architectural shrubs for the garden. On top of that, it flowers in late autumn. It forms a rounded, open shrub which readily suckers within the overall clump.

The large, 20–45cm (8–18in) long, glossy, dark green leaves are hand-shaped with between seven and eleven 'fingers'. Each lobe is wavy edged giving the leaf a crinkled appearance. The tiny, creamy-white flowers appear in autumn and form long-stalked umbels which are part of a larger loose umbel. They are followed by small, rounded, jet black fruit.

Aralia dislikes cold, drying winds. A sheltered woodland site in light shade, where its evergreen foliage can brighten a dull corner, is ideal. There are several variegated varieties, all of which require a shaded site. *Fatsia japonica* 'Aurea' is slow growing with golden variegation. *F. j.* 'Marginata' has creamy-white margined, deeply lobed leaves.

Prune in late spring removing low and crossing branches. Remove heavy falls of snow from the leaves before the weight breaks branches. Propagation is by seed sown in a heated propagator in spring. Softwood cuttings taken in early summer root well providing the leaves are trimmed by half to reduce transpiration. Air layering of young stems in summer is good fun, resulting in a large-rooted plant. **JC**

Fatsia japonica

Feijoa sellowiana

Feijoa sellowiana (syn. *Acca sellowiana*)
PINEAPPLE GUAVA/FRUIT SALAD TREE

Type: frost-hardy, perennial, evergreen shrub
Soil & situation: light, well-drained, moist soil/full sun to light shade, or under cover in winter in a tub like citrus
North American hardiness zone: 8–10
Height & spread: makes a wall shrub up to 5m (16ft) each way
Grow for: evergreen, well evergrey, foliage with white felt underneath; bright red, paintbrush-like, edible flowers; delicious, well interesting, fruits

Feijoa sellowiana is closely related to the guavas and is just hardy. Although it can be fruited easily under cover, it is tough enough for most sheltered gardens in the warmer parts of the UK where it is an attractive, healthy shrub. The flowers when they unfurl are amazing, with sticking out red and white petals (which are edible and taste of cinnamon, sort of), and exceptionally decorative. The egg-shaped and egg-sized fruit, which occasionally sets outdoors, has a taste somewhat redolent of pineapple if you are generous or a tin of macedoine, or mixed fruit salad, if cynical. It is never seen for sale, so if you want to try it you must grow it!

A native of Brazil, it was not introduced to the UK until 1898. Still rarely known in this country, there are improved fruiting varieties such as 'Coolidge', 'Nazemetz' and 'Edenvale Supreme' available in the USA. These, however, deserve to be under cover so they can fruit.

Without doubt this needs a warm wall where it might then fruit, but it also makes an excellent cool conservatory subject and does well in similar conditions to citrus (see pages 104–105). It may need hand pollinating if you want fruit. I have some fine specimens grown from seed, but improved types need taking from cuttings or by layering. If you grow from seed or have older types you must have at least a pair of plants to get fruits to set, though the latest cultivars from the USA are, as they put it, 'self-fruitful'. **BF**

Tulipa 'Magier'

May

Type: hardy, spring-flowering bulb
Soil & situation: good garden loam/sunny position
Hardiness zone: 4–7
Height: 60cm (24in)
Spread: 15cm (6in) as an individual plant
Grow for: beautiful white flowers edged with pinky-violet rims; an excellent border tulip. As a Single Late-Flowering type, it is at its loveliest at this time of year.

A superb tulip for leaving in from year to year, this is also a most attractive flower with its smart coloured rim and occasional flecks of pink or violet on the white. It was raised in 1951 and flowers in late spring; the flowers last exceptionally well. 'Shirley', also a Single Late-Flowering, which is white with narrow purple margins, has been bred more recently and although it is now more readily available than 'Magier', is neither as good nor as bold. I think it might be more popular on the lists because of its better performance for commercial cut-flower growers – but they are often after different criteria to gardeners. 'Magier' used to be called 'Magician', but is rarely listed as such now.

Another tulip I use a lot is *T.* 'Purissima' (AGM). It is a sturdy number, only 35cm (14in) high, and has long-lasting milky-white flowers in spring.

Care for this tulip as you would for *Tulipa* 'Queen of Night' (see page 385). **BG**

Festuca glauca

Festuca glauca
BLUE FESCUE, GREY FESCUE

Type: hardy, perennial grass
Soil & situation: prefers light, well-drained soil/easily grown in many soils except those with winter damp/sunny position
North American hardiness zone: 4–8
Height: up to 35cm (14in)
Spread: 25cm (10in)
Grow for: neat, strong, textural, grey-blue tussocks of ever-grey-blue foliage; small, open flowerheads in summer which later become pale tan or beige

This is one of those plants that looks presentable for 12 months of the year, and as such, has become extremely popular, possibly too popular. Probably its most common use is as a low edge to the front of a border. Frequently it is planted in gravel areas where it can also be used in generous clumps, which may well increase as it self-seeds around. But beware, many seedlings will not come true. There are many cultivars available; 'Elijah Blue' is one of the most intense blues of all the fescues. It is worth trying to use this grass in different ways to stop it becoming a cliché. It could be used for a small area of lawn – it will tolerate being mown with the blades set as high as they will go – but this would be more of an ornamental lawn rather than one for a game of rounders. It would also require higher maintenance, with the clumps being divided every fourth year or so.

When the clump becomes overcrowded it will start to die out in the middle and then it is necessary to lift and divide. This will probably be every three or four years. To maintain the vivid, blue foliage, the plants should be clipped in spring and summer. Dead leaves should also be removed. Propagation is best by division; seed is feasible but as the species readily hybridizes, the results are not always predictable. **BG**

Ficus carica 'Brown Turkey'
FIG

Type: hardy, deciduous shrub or tree
Soil & situation: for good fruit a sunny, preferably south-facing wall in the warmer parts of the country and restricted root growth/any ordinary garden soil, not too rich and preferably more or less neutral (with a pH between 6 and 7.5)
North American hardiness zone: 7–10
Height: 3m (10ft)
Spread: 4m (13ft)
Grow for: stunning foliage and the well-established atmosphere it conveys to a garden; delicious fruit in late summer or autumn; AGM

'Brown Turkey' is a smaller growing variety of fig, so much so that some say it is not necessary to restrict its root growth on planting by confining it to a tub within the soil. This is frequently recommended with figs so that the plant produces less vegetative growth and is encouraged to fruit. Often, if grown in paving by a house wall it is hardly in clover anyway. Figs are easy to grow but less easy to site in order to get regular, good crops of fruit. It is also said that figs should just be grown in the south but I know of many happily fruiting figs, including mine, in the Midlands. With the climate changing as it is, it is worth chancing your arm in many more northern areas too. If some years you are figless, you still have an amazing plant. 'Brown Turkey' is usually reckoned to be the most reliable variety for outdoor culture. I think the taste takes a lot of beating and the smaller size makes it more manageable.

Figs bear ripe fruit on last year's ripened growth. Therefore, do not go and hack it back in winter to reduce the size or you will remove prospective fruiting wood. Instead cut the growing ends that are getting into places that they should not be in summer, leaving the parts bearing fruit untouched. You can just, very gradually, thin out the remaining growth to keep it in bounds, at any time – when the mood takes you is always best.

Ficus carica 'Brown Turkey'

Watering in dry periods as the fruit is swelling does seem to help plump up the crop, and protecting the near-ripe fruit individually, with bags or gauze, is often recommended to stop squirrels, blackbirds and wasps consuming them first. Apparently you then check them every few days to see if they have gone that amazing dark brown-purple colour. I have never had to do this, I can only think the cats guard them for me. True fig aficionados often talk about the volume of work needed to produce great figs, but the best crops I have seen are in neglected, walled gardens, where they have been left untouched for years. Get the site and variety right and you are there. **BG**

Foeniculum vulgare 'Purpureum' (syn. *F. vulgare* 'Bronze')
BRONZE FENNEL

Type: hardy, perennial herb
Soil & situation: undemanding of soil type providing it is well drained/sunny position
North American hardiness zone: 4–9
Height: 1.8m (6ft)
Spread: 45cm (18in)
Grow for: flavoursome use in cooking; excellent foliage plant with its part smoky-purple and part green-grey foliage

Bronze fennel is a huge bonus to many plantings; it looks particularly beguiling in early summer with its foamy, subtly coloured, fluffy foliage produced in a comely, voluminous manner. It establishes quickly and forms a strong presence, contrasting well with fresh lime greens and bold foliage. The flowers are, I think, secondary to the foliage – they are mustard yellow and borne in umbels.

The ordinary green form, *Foeniculum vulgare*, is also attractive and looks exceptional in naturalized types of perennial plantings. In winter its silhouette is good but then you may well find the plant becomes too pernicious, seeding and spreading too much for the garden's good. It occurs naturally in southern Europe, particularly in sunny, seaside areas.

This plant is a prolific self-seeder and its young seedlings put down deep, penetrating roots with terrific speed. If this is going to cause you problems (be warned – it usually does), it is well worth cutting off the flowering stems to prevent them setting seed. You can shear the whole plant down to the ground at this point as new foliage will be reinstated before the end of the season, giving a fresh new look to that part of the planting. **BG**

Foeniculum vulgare 'Purpureum'

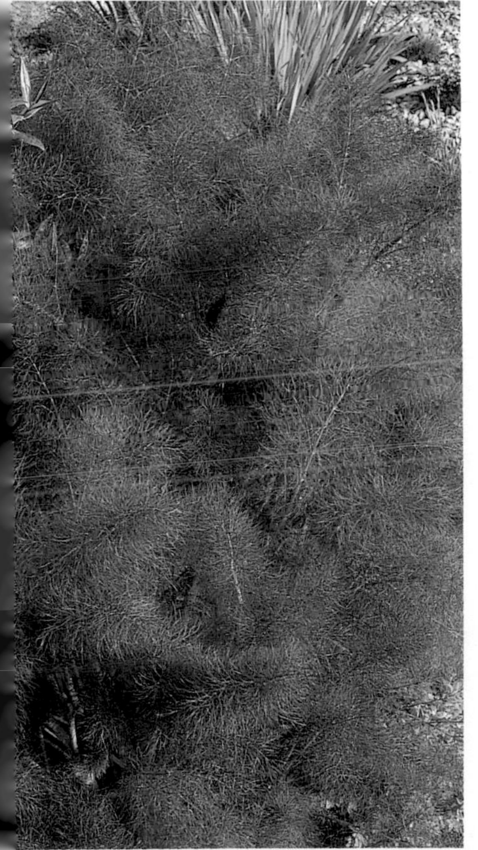

Forsythia x *intermedia* 'Karl Sax'

Forsythia x *intermedia* 'Karl Sax'

GOLDEN RAIN

Type: hardy, deciduous shrub
Soil & situation: moist, well-drained, fertile soil/sun or light shade
North American hardiness zone: 6–9
Height & spread: 2.5m (8ft)
Grow for: an abundance of yellow flowers from late winter to early spring

It has to be said forsythia is a common plant but only because it is easy to grow, flowers profusely every year and roots like a weed. I wish more plants were common! *Forsythia* x *intermedia* 'Karl Sax' in flower is slightly less well known. Its four-petalled flowers are a deep buttery yellow rather than a bright golden colour. They appear in late winter and continue making a show of themselves until mid-spring. The 10cm (4in) long, dull, mid-green leaves appear after the flowers and turn to shades of purple or red in autumn.

Forsythia is a surface-rooting shrub and benefits from an annual mulch in spring to retain moisture. I have seen mature plants wilt during a dry period but, being a professional performer, a drink soon revives them. Flowering on the previous year's growth it should be pruned immediately after flowering. Old plants can be rejuvenated by a severe pruning over two years, cutting half of the branches to within 30cm (12in) of the ground each spring. Propagation is by softwood cuttings in summer or hardwood during winter.

For early flowers for indoor arrangements cut branches as soon as the flower buds swell. Crush the base of the stem, place in water and they will open. **JC**

Forsythia x *intermedia* 'Lynwood'

Type: hardy, deciduous shrub
Soil & situation: fertile, well-drained soil/sun
North American hardiness zone: 6–9
Height & spread: 3m (10ft)
Grow for: bright yellow flowers in early and mid-spring; AGM

Tone down your forsythia, it's too loud! Start by planting the next one down the scale. *Forsythia* x *intermedia* 'Lynwood', a sport of *F.* x *i.* 'Spectabilis', is bold, but not as brash and slightly more refined; the large, rich yellow flowers are a vibrant, warming sight. It was discovered in a Miss Adair's cottage garden in Cookstown, Co. Tyrone, Northern Ireland in 1935 and I've seen it romantically described in French catalogues as 'Mimosa de Paris'. At the other end of the scale try *F. suspensa* or its form *atrocaulis,* with dark purple stems and pale yellow flowers. *F. giraldiana* has pale yellow flowers in late winter or early spring, while *F. ovata* reaches only 1.5m (5ft) tall.

Forsythia grows happily in most soils but prefers well-drained, fertile soil in full sun; flowering is reduced in shade, but it will flower on shady walls. Prune immediately after flowering, removing flowered stems to young, vigorous growth lower down the main stems and any thin or weak growth. If the plant is congested remove up to a third of the older stems at the base. Mulch in spring.

Propagate by semi-ripe cuttings in summer in a cold frame; or hardwood cuttings in winter, sealing the top and bottom of the stems with wax; plants layer naturally. Cut stems for the house for an earlier display will root in water and can be planted out by early summer. Forsythias suffer from galls and branches should be removed well below the gall. Spray if there is any sign of capsid bugs. If it is suffering from leaf spot, collect and dispose of leaves in autumn. **MB**

Forsythia x *intermedia* 'Lynwood'

Fragaria hybrids

Plant of the Week see page 233

Fragaria vesca

ALPINE STRAWBERRY

Type: hardy, herbaceous, semi-evergreen perennial
Soil & situation: any soil/sun or shade/moist or dry
North American hardiness zone: 5–9
Height & spread: 50cm (20in)
Grow for: cheerful foliage; small but pretty flowers; fruits all summer and autumn; good companion plant

Few plants flower for so long and, although these are only small plants with small flowers, they make very attractive, neat mounds of healthy foliage. *And* their delicious little fruits are produced for about half the year, without pause. Birds do not eat these fruits like they do the big ones, so they can be grown without nets or jars. I also love them as ground cover, for they are dense with bone dry centres much favoured by ground beetles and devil's coach-horses.

The alpine strawberry, unlike the wild strawberry of our woods, does not produce runners, but spreads everywhere by seed. This is not a problem as they are so useful and transplant easily. Natives of Europe, these have been improved by the French with varieties such as 'Baron Solemacher', but the standard sorts are wonderful enough anyway. They thrive in any soil, almost anywhere not bone dry and, besides, they only live for a few years. I pick the fruits over the entire season, freezing those I don't eat on the spot; once I have enough I shake the frozen berries to remove the seeds and then make them into the tastiest jam I know – try it! Sow in pots and plant out at any time; from then on move self-sown seedlings in early spring or autumn. Remove virus-infected, 'miffy'-looking plants to prevent the spread of disease and replace all old ones after a few years. **BF**

Fragaria vesca

Fraxinus ornus

MANNA ASH

Type: hardy, deciduous tree
Soil & situation: fertile, moist, well-drained, acid or alkaline soil/full sun
North American hardiness zone: 6–9
Height & spread: 15m (50ft)
Grow for: panicles of fragrant flowers; generally problem free; AGM

This tree is the source of manna sugar, a mild laxative obtained from the sap. It has no connection with the manna of the Old Testament which, incidentally, may have come from *Tamarix gallica*, a pink-flowering shrub that during the night exudes a honey-like nectar which solidifies on the ground.

A mature manna ash differs from other ash trees, forming a broad tree with a domed head. The grey bark is smooth and winter buds are fawn-brown rather than jet black. The pinnate, 20cm (8in) long, glossy, dark green leaves are tulip-like as they unfurl. They are made up of five to nine leaflets turning an attractive, deep red-purple in early autumn. Large panicles of fragrant, creamy-white flowers are produced in late spring and early autumn. The flower also separates it from the common ash, *Fraxinus excelsior*, which, being wind pollinated, has no need for petals or scent.

Fraxinus ornus

In Europe, *F. ornus* is generally free of pests and diseases. Unfortunately in America it suffers from borers and oyster scale. The former may kill the tree but the scale is more troublesome than deadly. Propagate by bottom grafting onto common ash. **JC**

Matt adds:
As there aren't many large trees with prominent flowers, it's a lovely surprise to see the abundance of blooms in late spring, appearing in large fragrant, creamy white clusters all over the tree. It's an amazing sight! Mulch young plants and water until established. Prune in late winter, particularly in the early years, so that only one leading stem develops. It can also be propagated from chilled seed in spring.

Fremontodendron californicum

Fremontodendron californicum
FLANNEL BUSH

Type: frost-hardy, evergreen shrub
Soil & situation: infertile, moist, well-drained, neutral to alkaline soil/full sun
North American hardiness zone: 8–10
Height: 6m (20ft)
Spread: 4m (13ft)
Grow for: excellent for a sunny wall; long flowering season

Given a warm wall, this is an easy shrub to grow and guaranteed to flower for longer than most of the opposition. Against a red brick wall it is as pretty as a picture. Fast growing, it forms an upright shrub.

The 5–10cm (2–4in) rounded, dark olive-green leaves have between three and seven lobes. The bright, buttercup-yellow, shallow, saucer-shaped flowers are 7.5cm (3in) across. The flower buds form immediately behind the newest growth and can be in flower within 10cm (4in) of the tip of the stems. Flowering kicks off in spring and goes on until late autumn. Its close neighbour from over the border, *Fremontodendron mexicanum*, is similar with slightly larger, deep golden-yellow flowers tinged an orange-red on the outside. As the flower dies it becomes a brick yellow.

Plants which are growing very quickly will benefit from a liquid feed of high-potash fertilizer to harden up the growth before winter. Plant where there is protection from cold winds. Pruning is not usually necessary apart from training on wall wires or removing crossing branches and it should be carried out in winter before growth commences.

Propagation is by seed in spring. Softwood cuttings root readily in early summer. The young shoots and backs of the leaves are coated with a mealy grit which is a skin irritant. **JC**

Fritillaria imperialis
Plant of the Week (see page 135)

Fritillaria meleagris
SNAKE'S HEAD FRITILLARY

Type: hardy, perennial bulb
Soil & situation: moist, rich soil/sun or shade
North American hardiness zone: 3–8
Height: 30cm (12in)
Spread: 15cm (6in)
Grow for: unique claret-red to purple flowers with distinctive whitish-green variegation; the only bloom that has a chequer-board pattern

This is a beautiful flower, fragile and delicate with a most delightful patterning that makes you wonder why? It is easy in moist sites but not happy in dry, windswept spots so I have to go to great pains to keep them going in my Norfolk garden. Of course, although I found it hard to grow deliberately, one managed to self-sow and grow a bulb to flowering size beside a leaky water butt, which only seems to indicate its desired conditions.

A European native, it used to be common but is now found wild only in a few sites. The name obviously refers to the unique pattern, though it once was also known as the guinea hen flower for the same reason. The pattern is not actually truly square in most cases and there are also some plain white ones.

It needs a moist, rich soil, as in water meadows, and prefers really damp conditions during the growing season, plus lashings of leafmould as a mulch. It can be grown from seed in pots in a cold frame and planted out later, or plant bulbs in autumn. Voles steal flowers and eat them – I should know as I've had it happen. **BF**

Fritillaria meleagris

Fuchsia spp.

Fuchsia spp.

Type: frost-hardy to hardy, woody, perennial shrub
Soil & situation: any soil/sun or shade/loves moisture
North American hardiness zone: varies according to species, but roughly 7–10 (some more tender species 9–10)
Height & spread: depends on local climate, some may reach 1.8–2.2m (6–7ft) each way
Grow for: very good value as the cheerful white, scarlet, red and violet or purple flowers bloom from summer until the end of the year, plus the berries are edible

Most flowering shrubs are blooming in spring but far fewer are good from mid-summer through to the frosts, and there aren't many so easy to keep compact enough to grow in pots or even hanging baskets. In the mildest areas hardy fuchsias remain shrubs and are often used for a hedge. In such mild climates wet soil seems not to be a problem and the plant may become almost evergreen. They also remain evergreen under cover, when they often last in fair condition until growth starts again. Many sorts do not set very many berries but when they do these can be collected and used to make a good jelly. I wish someone would breed a sweet, big berried, hardy form – with scent!

Originally from South America, fuchsias took the early 19th-century gardeners by storm; the colours and robustness of the plants amazed them and still does us. There are hundreds, if not thousands of indoor tender varieties and many of these will survive outdoors; even if cut down by frosts they will come back from their roots, if these are well protected.

Unless the soil is free draining fuchsias may rot while dormant. For over-wintering success choose a warm, sheltered spot. Trim back when the first frosts take off foliage and cover roots with loose straw or bracken in colder areas. The seed is minute and not easy to get to set or to germinate, and the young plants damp off easily; luckily each and every cutting is likely to take. Under cover the young plants are prone to aphids and whitefly, but when they go outdoors for summer these pests are no longer a problem. **BF**

Fuchsia magellanica 'Riccartonii'

Type: hardy, deciduous shrub
Soil & situation: fertile, moist, well-drained soil/full sun
North American hardiness zone: 7–10
Height: 2.5m (8ft)
Spread: 2m (6½ft)
Grow for: exquisite flowers and in a sheltered area may be grown as a hedge; AGM

The beauty of living on an island is the amount of coastline. As islands go the climate of Ireland is quite mild. When you combine these two facts you have a place where *F. magellanica* 'Riccartonii' grows like a weed. It forms high natural hedges and in Counties Down, Donegal and Mayo is accepted as part of the rural scene.

It forms an upright shrub with dark green, bronze-tinted leaves. The single flower is typically 'ballet dancer' shape with a scarlet tube and sepals. The 'under skirt' of the corollas is purple.

Fuchsia magellanica 'Riccartonii'

Fuchsia procumbens

Although it is deciduous, the mass of bare winter twigs provides considerable shelter by filtering the wind. Plants that have suffered from hard frosts may look dead but if they are left undisturbed until early summer they generally produce new shoots from the base. The dead branches can then be cut back and the new shoots allowed to take their place. A deep, dry mulch of coarse bark over the crown of the plant in winter will be sufficient protection in all but the coldest areas or where the soil is heavy and damp.

Propagation is by softwood cuttings in early summer. Semi-ripe cuttings can be rooted in autumn in a propagator with bottom heat. Autumn-rooted cuttings should be left undisturbed until the following spring after they have come into leaf. **JC**

Fuchsia procumbens

Type: half-hardy, deciduous scrambler
Soil & situation: fertile, free-draining soil/sun
North American hardiness zone: 9–10
Height: 15cm (6in)
Spread: 1.2m (4ft)
Grow for: pretty flowers and fruits in summer

This trailing or creeping fuchsia is worth growing for its novelty value and unusual coloured flowers, though you will need a magnifying glass to study them closely! It is a fine example of the diversity of fuchsias and the fascinating flora of New Zealand. You'd perhaps expect it to be a shrub, but it's a carpeting species that scrambles over the ground. Its tiny leaves are a rounded heart shape only 2cm (¾in) long. In summer it produces small flowers with greenish-yellow tubes that fade to banana-yellow then pale orange. Purple-tipped green sepals take the place of the petals. The stamens, when mature, release bright blue pollen and the flowers are followed by vivid red fruit, like tiny plums, with a glaucous 'bloom'. It's found on the North Island coastline in rocky, sandy places right on the shore above the high-tide mark, so it's no surprise that it is a good rockery and maritime plant.

Fuchsia excorticata, also from New Zealand, is a deciduous shrub with attractive papery bark, green and purple flower tubes and blue pollen.

Fuchsia procumbens needs a sheltered position in full sun or partial shade on moist, fertile, well-drained soil. Plant the base of the stem 5cm (2in) below the soil surface, mulch in winter. Shelter from cold, drying winds or grow in pots in cooler climate; it is frost tender and ideal for sheltered gardens. In pots, feed monthly when in growth with a liquid general fertilizer. Grow from seed and cuttings. Take cuttings annually in autumn in case plants are lost. **MB**

Galactites tomentosa

Type: annual or biennial
Soil & situation: any free-draining soil, light or heavy, slightly acid or calcareous/self-seeds into waste ground, gravel cracks in pavements or wherever/sunny position/ tolerates some shade
North American hardiness zone: usually grown as an annual
Height & spread: up to 1m (3ft)
Grow for: exquisite evergreen foliage; fetching thistle-like pink-purple flowers in summer

Galactites tomentosa

This is possibly my favourite biennial and I haven't a clue why everybody does not have it.

The broad, thistle-like leaves are beautifully marked: the background is dark green and it has eccentric veining patterns picked out in pale verdigris. They form decent-sized rosettes, about 30cm (12in) across, sometimes more, often less. Beautifully evergreen, these rosettes crop up out of gaps in paving you did not think existed. They are surprisingly spiny. Then in mid-summer, or whenever it feels like it, it shoots up into flower with its perfect, thistle-like flowers. Another of its virtues is that it is not so prolific as to drive you mad, but I hope, prolific enough for you to keep and enjoy for ever. It was given to me by Molly Wheatley, a renowned local gardener with an interesting garden in Clipsham.

I suppose if it did ever get a little out of hand you could cut off the flowers as they were about to set seed, but I have never had to do this. I just leave it to do its own thing totally, and simply follow it around and see what new sites it has recently acquired. Its a useful plant for taking to friends as, no matter whether they are keen or indifferent gardeners, it is easy to grow and easy to appreciate. But do transplant it into a pot when it is very small as it has a long tap root. **BG**

Galanthus reginae-olgae subsp. *reginae-olgae*

Type: hardy, bulbous perennial
Soil & situation: moist, free-draining soil/some sunshine
North American hardiness zone: 6–9
Height: 10cm (4in)
Spread: 5cm (2in)
Grow for: fragrant flowers in mid and late autumn

This, the earliest flowering snowdrop, comes from southern Greece. At one time it was called 'Octobrensis' because it flowers so early, before the delicate leaves which are marked with a single silver stripe. It is dainty, delicate, absolutely beautiful and needs a warmer, sunnier, more sheltered position than most snowdrops. Plant with *Cyclamen hederifolium* (see page 136) and they will flower at the same time. Mix sharp sand and leafmould to improve the drainage if necessary. It should be kept quite dry during summer dormancy; at the front of a sunny border is ideal. Plant at 5cm (2in), but if the soil is very light go down to 8cm (3½in).

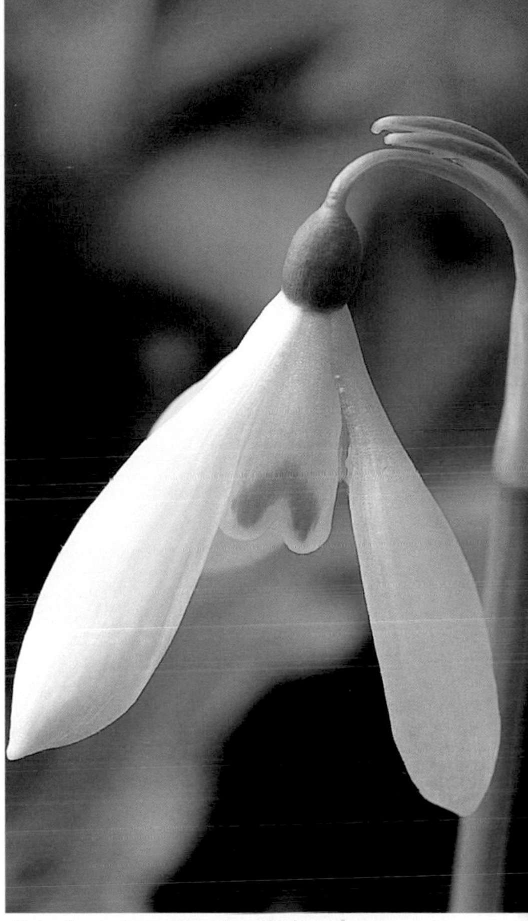

Galanthus reginae-olgae subsp. *reginae-olgae*

Divide and replant after flowering. Slugs and snails can damage petals and grey mould the foliage. Remove badly infected bulbs and dispose of them or drench them with fungicide and replant elsewhere.

Someone once said to me, 'All snowdrops look the same to me'. Wrong! Here's a few examples of different shapes, sizes and colours.

Galanthus reginae-olgae subsp. *vernalis* has a silver striped leaf; it appears early in the New Year and lasts for about four weeks. *G. plicatus* 'Wendy's Gold' has good size and vigour for a yellow snowdrop. The colour of its petals and ovary is acid yellow. *G.* 'Hippolyta' is double flowered and has more than one flower per stem. *G. nivalis* 'Lady Elphinstone' is double with a pale apricot ovary and markings. *G. n.* 'Viridapicis' has green markings on both its outer and inner petals. *G.* x *allenii* smells of bitter almonds. **MB**

Arisaema sikokianum

COBRA LILY

Type: frost-hardy, tuberous perennial
Soil & situation: moist, humus-rich soil/dappled shade
Hardiness zone: 5–9
Height: 60cm (24in)
Spread: 15cm (6in)
Grow for: extraordinary leaves and flowers, at their weirdest in late spring

'Only blokes buy arisaemas,' the nurseryman told me. Perhaps he'd already spotted the distant look in my eyes and was moving in for the kill. I'd picked up several pots that day and only bought one, but now, the more I see, the more I weaken! My dream is to become rich enough to plant drifts of *A. sikokianum* through a woodland garden; it is a typical case of *Arisaema* addiction!

Look at the picture and you may understand why I'm vulnerable; if you do, then you are too! The hood is delicately marked and deep chocolate brown suffused with green, but the most extraordinary features are the thick, club-like spadix and throat, painted in pure, glossy, brilliant white. Aren't they amazing?

Here are a few of the many species. *A. candidissimum* is hardy and attractive with pale pink flowers with a white striped cowl, produced just before the leaves; it tolerates sun and shade; the leaves do not emerge until early summer. *A. consanguineum* has a dark purple spathe with white pinstripes and is up to 20cm (8in) long. It does best in semi-shade. *A. griffithii* is dark and sinister, deeply veined, has a broad hood and is positively reptilian!

Plant in dappled shade in humus-rich, well-drained soil. Add plenty of well-rotted leafmould or organic matter before planting about 15cm (6in) deep. They need protection from frost early in the year; mulch over winter with well-rotted organic matter. Propagate from seed in autumn or by detaching offsets, which may form on the tubers. **MB**

Galanthus 'S. Arnott'
SNOWDROP

Type: hardy, bulbous perennial
Soil & situation: moist, well-drained soil with added leafmould/partial shade
North American hardiness zone: 4–9
Height: 20cm (8in)
Spread: 8cm (3½in)
Grow for: early fragrant flowers that tolerate frost, snow, wind and rain; AGM

For me snowdrops are not so much harbingers of spring as a useful reminder that the worst of the winter is still to come. I love all snowdrops but 'Sam Arnott', as it is sometimes called, is a favourite. It exudes a strong honey fragrance which, on a calm winter's day, is a delight in any garden. This is one of the snowdrops much admired by galanthophiles.

The grey-green foliage appears in early winter growing to 15cm (6in) in height. The large, rounded, pure white flowers, 3–3.5cm (1–1¼in) long, are carried on 20cm (8in) stems. They have an inverted green 'v' mark on each of the inner tepals (petals). It manages to look delicate and frail yet it is as tough as old boots, tolerating extreme winter weather.

Avoid planting in soil which dries out in summer. Dig in leafmould and well-rotted farmyard manure to help retain moisture. Snowdrops self-seed and spread quickly but are often reluctant to grow from dry bulbs purchased in autumn. Lift and transplant the bulbs 'in the green' when they are still in leaf. **JC**

Galanthus 'S. Arnott'

Galega orientalis

Galega orientalis

Type: hardy, rhizomatous perennial
Soil & situation: prefers moist soils, but grows fairly well in drier, poorer soils/sun or part shade
North American hardiness zone: 5–8
Height: up to 1.2m (4ft) high
Spread: 60cm (24in)
Grow for: intense violet-blue flower spikes produced from mid- to late summer

This is an extremely rewarding plant to grow. It thrives (probably a bit too much) on moist soils and in these conditions may be considered invasive, spreading by creeping underground rhizomes. But otherwise, in a drier soil, it is a gentle, good-natured plant that performs well (Legumes are usually a good bet for poorer conditions). The flower spikes are held upright, making the beautiful, long-lasting (a good month or so) flowers more prominent. The foliage is deeply divided and forms a good substantial mass. My mother grows repeated clumps of it through a throng of apricot-flowered shrub roses and the colour combination works exceptionally well. She divides her galega every two years, to keep it at its best. Other gardeners just seem to leave it growing untouched for years, the excuse being that legumes are not that agreeable to being moved. But I think it is such a good doer that the check goes pretty well unnoticed.

This will need regular division if you want to keep it in check in richer soil conditions. Otherwise it really requires little looking after, except for cutting it down in winter or spring and dividing it up when the mood takes you. Propagation is by division but it does set seed and from my experience seems to come true from seed. Soaking the seed for 12 hours or so speeds up the process. **BG**

Galium odoratum
SWEET WOODRUFF

Type: hardy, rhizomatous perennial
Soil & situation: frequently occurs on alkaline soils but does tolerate a range of pH/cool, shady situation/tolerates dry conditions/becomes scorched in sunshine
North American hardiness zone: 5–8
Height: 45cm (18in)
Spread: indefinite
Grow for: superb native plant that will colonize the wilder parts of the garden with a thick carpet of attractive vegetation; clusters of small, starry, white flowers from late spring to mid-summer enjoyed by bees and butterflies

This is one of my favourite native wild flowers. It used to be called *Asperula odorata*, because it contains asperuloside – even if you do not recognize the name, you will the smell. It produces a compound which gives rise to one of the best smells in the world – that of new-mown hay – as the foliage dries. Try picking some and hanging it up to dry. It wafts out that wonderful fragrance, but only when dry, not just for one year but for several. Vita Sackville-West recommended making bags of it to hang in your cupboards to keep moths away or sleeping with it under your pillow. It certainly beats a well-used tissue.

The leaves are bright emerald green, lance-shaped and produced in whorls. The flowers are borne in large quantities, and while they are not showy, they are definitely appealing. It is the sort of plant to grow where not much else will grow: in the shade or under the drip of trees where it will colonize the space and stop weeds coming through.

If you require quantities of it, seed is ideal or else you can divide it and every bit of root will grow. **BG**

Galium odoratum

Garrya elliptica 'James Roof'
SILK TASSEL BUSH

Type: frost-hardy, evergreen shrub
Soil & situation: moderately fertile, well-drained soil/full sun or light shade
North American hardiness zone: 8–10
Height & spread: 4m (13ft)
Grow for: eye-catching clusters of catkins from winter to spring; AGM

This is one of a group of shrubs ignored by passersby for most of the year, but when they 'dress up' everyone takes notice. It has an upright habit, making it ideal as a free-standing shrub for planting in front of a wall. The leathery, dark sea-green leaves form a perfect backdrop for the pendent, dense clusters of silver-grey male catkins. These can be up to 20cm (8in) long, made up of hundreds of petalless flowers. They appear in mid-winter and last until early spring. Male and female catkins are on separate plants, the female being less noticeable but producing purple-brown berries in summer.

Garrya elliptica 'James Roof' is tolerant of poor, dry soil (usually to be found at the base of a wall) but dislikes cold, biting winds. When grown as a hedge it forms a great shelter for a seaside garden. Pruning is carried out after flowering and is only necessary to keep the plant in shape. Propagate by seed sown in autumn or by short, semi-ripe cuttings in a gritty compost in summer. *G. e.* 'Evie' is also a male variety with crinkly leaves and catkins 30cm (12in) long. **JC**

Garrya elliptica 'James Roof'

Gardenia augusta

Gardenia augusta (syn. *G. florida, G. jasminoides*)
CAPE JASMINE, FLORISTS' GARDENIA.

Type: tender, evergreen shrub
Soil & situation: loamy, lime-free compost/light shade/under cover
North American hardiness zone: 8–10
Height & spread: 2m (6½ft) each way, if you are patient and lucky
Grow for: gorgeous flowers with fantastic perfume on glossy evergreen foliage; AGM

Gardenia has one of the most opulently luscious perfumes, almost decadent in its undertones yet, somehow, retaining a sense of purity. The flowers are like miniature loose cabbage roses with layers of creamy-white petals, and the leaves behind them are so glossy and richly green. They make exquisite conservatory subjects along with citrus (see pages 104–105), as they need similar conditions and their perfumes complement each other. I must admit, they are hard to grow on from the forced specimens you can buy, but once re-established in a new home they are immensely rewarding with flowers from summer until winter.

Named by Linnaeus after a Dr Garden of Charleston, it's a big genus with mostly tropical members which are nearly all evergreen trees and shrubs, although several are used as houseplants. It needs lime-free, leafmould-rich compost kept moist but never wet, in a humid atmosphere and light shade such as under citrus trees. Mist regularly and, if necessary, disbud to preserve the shape. Never move a gardenia!

The species can be grown from seed. Control red spider mite by misting and using commercially supplied predators. Bud drop is best prevented by misting and not moving the plant. **BF**

Gaultheria mucronata (syn. *Pernettya mucronata*)

Type: hardy, evergreen shrub
Soil & situation: peaty, moist, neutral to acid soil/partial shade
North American hardiness zone: 8–9
Height & spread: 1.2m (4ft)
Grow for: glossy foliage, pretty flowers and eye-catching fruit

A great plant which isn't afraid to show off its fruit in a range of colours set against dark green leaves which, in size, are no competition. It is necessary to grow male and female plants together to guarantee fruit.

It forms a bushy, compact, suckering plant with small, sharp-pointed, glossy, dark green leaves. Pendent, urn-shaped, white or pink-tinged flowers appear in late spring and early summer. They are followed, in autumn, by fruits which often persist through winter until the next season's flowers appear. Colours range from white, pink, red and crimson to deep purple-red. *Gaultheria mucronata* 'Wintertime' has pure white fruit and *G. m.* 'Edward Balls', which is male, has light green leaves.

Full sun is tolerated where the ground is constantly moist. It can be grown as an ornamental, informal hedge by lightly clipping the plants after they have finished flowering. Propagation is by semi-ripe cuttings in summer, though a quicker method is to dig up the rooted suckers in spring. Line them out in a moist shaded site for a year before planting in their permanent positions. **JC**

Gaultheria mucronata

Gaultheria procumbens

Gaultheria procumbens

CHEQUER BERRY, WINTERGREEN, TEA BERRY

Type: hardy, creeping ground cover
Soil & situation: moist, acid soil/shade to full sun
North American hardiness zone: 3–9
Height : 15cm (6in) or more
Spread: 90cm (36in) or more
Grow for: evergreen leaves; flowers in mid- and late summer; bright red winter berries; AGM

This is one of my favourite shrubs. For some reason it makes me smile, particularly when it's fruiting. Perhaps it's a response to the bright red berries; it must be a cheerful, happy plant so I should be happy too! The elliptic leaves sprout from creeping stems that spread to create a lush, deep textured carpet of dark, glossy green. In mid- and late summer it produces masses of lily-of-the-valley-like, urn-shaped, white or pale pink flowers followed by aromatic bright scarlet fruit to 1cm (½in) across, remaining until spring. Oil, extracted from the plant, possesses stimulating and tonic properties; the same oil is found in a birch, *Betula lenta*, and is used for Deep Heat, a muscle-relaxing cream, and other similar products. The crushed leaves smell strongly of Germoline, an antiseptic cream. Partridges like to eat the berries – they must be hungry; I can confirm that they taste as bad as they smell!

It is a native of eastern North America and makes excellent ground cover in moist, acid soil in shade and a container plant for winter displays with skimmias and heathers. It needs moist, acid soil, enriched with leafmould, peat substitute or well-rotted organic matter, in a sheltered, shady position. It tolerates full sun with extra moisture. Mulch in spring, water with rainwater and feed monthly with a fertilizer for acid-loving plants. Prune to remove dead wood and weak growths whenever they appear. Trim to keep it within its allotted space. Propagate by seed, division or semi-ripe cuttings from mid-summer. **MB**

Gazania Daybreak Series

Type: half-hardy, evergreen perennial
Soil & situation: light, sandy, well-drained soil/full sun
North American hardiness zone: normally grown as an annual
Height: 20cm (8in)
Spread: 30cm (12in)
Grow for: stunning flowers; a great plant for the patio

Unfortunately I have to grow this plant as an annual or else go to a lot of trouble molly-coddling it over the winter. It is well worth the expense of new seed each year with spectacular flower colour in summer and autumn. It is ideal in containers for patio use and it is one of the best plants for use in a coastal bedding display.

The 15cm (6in) long, glossy, dark green leaves are silky white on the underside. Flowering commences in early summer with short-stemmed, solitary flowerheads in a blaze of colours including white, yellow, orange, pink and bronze. Often they are zoned in contrasting colours such as white-pink and orange-bronze.

Although the Daybreak Series is my favourite, members of the Talent Series have a lot going for them too – they are vigorous with silvery leaves and a good range of colours. 'Talent Yellow' is a deep yellow, flowering at 25cm (10in) high.

Dead-head immediately after flowering to prolong the display. Propagation is by seed sown in a heated propagator in late winter. Take basal cuttings in autumn in a free-draining, gritty compost. Overwinter the rooted cuttings and do not pot on until spring. **JC**

Gazania Daybreak Series

Genista lydia

Genista lydia
BROOM

Type: hardy, deciduous shrub
Soil & situation: impoverished, light, well-drained soil/full sun
North American hardiness zone: 6–9
Height: 60cm (24in)
Spread: 90cm (36in)
Grow for: form and colour that will brighten up the border; AGM

Whether you want it to or not, *Genista lydia* always forms itself into a dense, compact mound. A single plant appears to have been clipped into shape. When planted as a group at 1m (3ft) spacing and in flower they resemble a lovely, large, bright, golden-yellow inkblot. The slender, grey-green, arching branches are pointed at the tip with thin, blue-green leaves. In late spring and early summer it produces masses of bright yellow, pea-like flowers which smother the plant.

Another excellent genista, which will spread to 1.5m (5ft), is *G. hispanica*, the Spanish gorse. It forms a dense mound of spiny stems, covered in golden-yellow flowers in early summer.

G. lydia performs best in a poor, undernourished, free-draining soil. It does not thrive in a heavy clay or badly drained soil. Avoid feeding or mulching. It tends to be a short-lived plant, but its useful life can be extended by annual pruning to remove the previous year's growth as soon as it has finished flowering. Don't cut into the older wood. Propagation is by semi-ripe cuttings in summer in a gritty compost. **JC**

Gentiana acaulis
TRUMPET GENTIAN

Type: hardy, evergreen perennial
Soil & situation: moist, humus-rich, well-drained, alkaline soil/sun or partial shade
North American hardiness zone: 5–8
Height: 8cm (3½in)
Spread: 30cm (12in)
Grow for: the most vivid blue flowers – a must; AGM

Anyone who dislikes gentians has got a problem. Even those unfortunates who find them difficult to grow keep on trying in the hope that gentians will come to like them. Quickly forming a dense mat of pointed, glossy, dark green rosettes of leaves, in late spring and early summer it produces single, 5cm (2in) long, trumpet-shaped flowers, a deep, vivid blue, spotted green on the inside. Flowering may be erratic, seemingly having an occasional 'off year'.

In areas lucky enough to have long periods of bright sun, site the plants in light shade, but in cool, damp climates they will need all the sunshine they can get. Propagate by fresh seed sown in autumn and overwintered in a cold frame or unheated greenhouse. Clumps may be divided in spring but it is essential they are planted firmly in reliably moist soil with added leafmould and grit. Watch out for attacks by slugs and snails. A collar of coarse grit around the plants will offer some protection. **JC**

Gentiana acaulis

Gentiana asclepiadea

Gentiana asclepiadea

WILLOW GENTIAN

Type: hardy perennial
Soil & situation: deep, moist, humus-rich soil/dappled to full shade
North American hardiness zone: 6–9
Height: 90cm (36in)
Spread: 60cm (24in)
Grow for: elegant arching stems of flowers from late summer to early autumn; AGM

This delightful gentian with elegant willow-like leaves has been grown in gardens in the UK since 1629. It's a small, bushy plant with graceful, arching stems and leaves in pairs. Clusters of two to three deep blue flowers, sometimes with a white throat, project from the leaf joints towards the top of the stems. It's perfect for borders, large rock gardens or naturalized in woodland. It is reliable, long lived and very, very beautiful.

Reginald Farrer, a writer, plant collector and tough-talking Yorkshireman, was also renowned for his lyrical prose and described it thus: '...flowers like a summer sky at dawn...its long, bending sheaves of graceful blossom make a famous loveliness in late summer...inclining this way and that beneath the burden of its beautiful sapphire trumpets'. He was obviously besotted!

The specific name comes from the Latinized form of the name of the Greek god of medicine, Aesculapius; he was usually portrayed with Hygieia, the goddess of wise living, and Panakeia, goddess of cure-alls. Gentian root has long been used as a tonic.

There are several forms of this lovely plant. *G. asclepiadea* var. *alba* has white flowers with greenish-cream throats. *G. a.* 'Knightshayes' has deeper blue flowers and a more upright habit. There are also pink, pale blue and yellow selections.

They flourish in dappled to full shade in cool, deep, moist, humus-rich soil and are lime tolerant. Water during dry periods, and cut back the stems and mulch with well-rotted organic matter in spring. Take basal cuttings in spring.
MB

Gentiana sino-ornata

Type: hardy perennial
Soil & situation: moist, acid soil/bright light
North American hardiness zone: 5–7
Height: 7cm (2³/₄in)or more
Spread: 30cm (12in) or more
Grow for: azure-blue flowers from early autumn to early winter; AGM

Gentiana sino-ornata

I'll never forget the first time I saw the magnificent display at Sheffield Park in Sussex, southeast England, where a green carpet of foliage was almost submerged in a sea of deep blue, white-striped, trumpet-shaped flowers. This delicate beauty comes from northwest Yunnan and Tibet where it grows in wet ground high in the mountains, where only the strong survive. The colour is mesmeric, life's not the same without them, and every time I see them I suffer another case of the blues!

It needs moist, acid soil and can be planted among paving slabs or in drifts at the front of borders. On alkaline soil, make your own compost using peat substitute or well-rotted leafmould and grit and grow them in shallow pans, pots, troughs, raised beds or 'acid' pockets in rock gardens; surely there's some space in your garden. It associates well with rhododendrons.

Grow in bright light and in humus-rich, moist, well-drained neutral to acid soil on an open site away from the 'drip line' of trees. Keep the compost moist using rainwater. Plant in spring, or autumn when it is in flower; handle it carefully as it resents root disturbance. Divide in early or mid-spring. It dies back in winter to fleshy 'crowns'.

Aphids, red spider mite, slugs and snails can be a problem. Gentian rust causes brown spotting on the leaves; remove infected stems immediately, spray with fungicide, destroy badly infected plants. Take off dead or damaged material in spring with a sharp knife to reduce problems with pests and diseases. **MB**

Geranium himalayense 'Gravetye'

Type: hardy, evergreen perennial
Soil & situation: huge variety of soils, except ones that dry out or are waterlogged/sun or partial shade
North American hardiness zone: 4–7
Height: 30cm (12in)
Spread: 60cm (24in)
Grow for: highly useful, long-flowering geranium in summer; neat, attractive evergreen foliage; AGM

It is easy to be perplexed by the many hardy geraniums. Most of us include one or several different ones in our garden but I think this is one of the best. It has very divided leaves and it slowly spreads to form neat mats. The flowers are a good, clear blue fading to white at the centre

Geranium himalayense 'Gravetye'

and they attract bees and butterflies. Two reasons that this plant stands out are the length of the flowering period and the most agreeable-looking flowers.

After flowering it is best to cut the foliage right back, which will stimulate new, fresh-looking leaves, and most likely, another crop of flowers. It can be propagated by seed or division. **BG**

Geranium phaeum
MOURNING WIDOW

Type: herbaceous perennial
Soil & situation: any soil/sun or shade
North American hardiness zone: 4–8
Height & spread: rounded clumps to 50cm (20in)
Grow for: good ground cover and distinctive purple, almost black flowers over many weeks

Also called the dusky geranium or dusky cranesbill, this excellent and reliable plant has deeply toothed, lobed leaves which always look healthy. Some strains have an attractive blotch in the middle of the leaf. Above the neat foliage it displays a profusion of blackish-purple, flat, crinkley-edged flowers for many weeks. It will grow in almost any soil or site, and makes good ground cover in front of wall trees or for filling large areas that need a fairly low but neat and attractive plant. It combines well with *Alchemilla mollis* (see page 33), which it resembles in form and height and complements in colour. The genus gets its name from the Greek for cranes, *geranion*, for the resemblance its carpels bear to cranes' beaks.

It seems to do well anywhere – in both dry and moist spots, and in sun or shade, but prefers moist shade. It can be grown from seed, in pots or a seedbed, and it's easy to divide in spring or autumn. It suffers from no problems at all. **BF**

Geranium psilostemon
ARMENIAN CRANESBILL

Type: hardy, herbaceous perennial
Soil & situation: many types of soils/sun or shade
North American hardiness zone: 5–8
Height: 60–120cm (2–4ft)
Spread: 60cm (24in)
Grow for: vivid magenta flowers produced over a long period in summer; uninspiring but worthwhile delicately cut, bright green foliage, red in spring and colouring up again in autumn; AGM

There are many acceptable geraniums to choose from but I tend to use *G. psilostemon* far more than most. I think this is because many herbaceous geraniums tend to be background fillers that you stroll past, whereas this one will make you stop in your tracks. It is taller than many geraniums, too, which also makes it more noticeable. The flowers have a black centre and veins which enhances the strident colour of the petals. Because it has quite a bold presence it is a useful plant to grow in repeated clumps in a border as a cohesive element. It is also well adapted to growing in rough grassy areas, due to its height and vigour.

If the plant looks a little tatty after flowering, cut it down to the ground and then it will regenerate and possibly give you a good repeat flowering. It can be easily propagated by division, basal cuttings or seed. **BG**

Geranium phaeum

Geranium psilostemon

Geranium renardii

Type: hardy, herbaceous perennial
Soil & situation: most soils/ sun or shade
North American hardiness zone: 6–8
Height & spread: 30cm (12in)
Grow for: beautiful softly textured leaves in deep grey to olive green, with a prominent mosaic of veins; white or bluish flowers in early summer; AGM

I frequently use this plant having been inspired by it at Hidcote. There they use it in large drifts and the low grey-green olive mounds of foliage look simple but stunning. The flowers are a pleasant extra, also quite simple, but they do have conspicuous blue veins. There is apparently an excellent selection of this plant called *G. renardii* 'Whiteknights', the name commemorating the campus of the University of Reading, where it originated. This plant is said to have exceptional grey, felted foliage and impressive lilac-blue flowers. It is on my list. The other geranium I use predominantly for foliage is 'Ann Folkard'; this has lush, golden-green, young leaves followed by bright purple flowers which are freely produced. Cut away any tatty foliage in autumn or spring. It is easily propagated by division, basal cuttings or seed. **BG**

Geranium renardii

Agrostemma githago

CORN COCKLE

Type: hardy annual
Soil & situation: poor, dry soil/sun
Hardiness zone: annual
Height: 90cm (36in)
Spread: 30cm (12in)
Grow for: flowers from early to late summer

Is it right to try to rationalize the reasons why I adore this flower? As with many emotions, it's easier to accept that attraction in any form is indefinable, the same 'must have' desire that makes people fall for anything; art, gardens – even each other! In this case I'm beguiled by the sleek willowy elegance of the stems up to 90cm (36in) long that sway gracefully in the caressing breeze; seduced by the shape and colour of the delicately flecked, magenta-purple flowers balancing like saucers on top of stiff stems; and enchanted by the elegant narrow sepals. In other words, I go weak in the presence of beauty!

In times past it was persecuted as a cornfield weed because the bitter seeds tainted flour, but it is now very rare in the wild. It is a good nectar plant for insects and butterflies, the perfect plant for cottage gardens; the flowers are excellent for cutting and the seeds are short-lived. It was originally introduced to the UK with grain from the eastern Mediterranean.

There are several cultivars, including *Agrostemma githago* 'Milas,' with dark plum-pink flowers; 'Ocean Pearl', with white flowers flecked with black; and 'Pink Pearl', with soft, pale pink flowers.

Dead-head to prolong flowering, but allow a last seed crop to self-sow. It prefers poor, well-drained soil in full sun but survives in most moderate to light soils. Sow *in situ* in early spring, thinning to 23–30cm (9–12in) apart. For containers, sow in autumn, over-winter in a cold frame and plant out the following spring. The seeds are toxic. **MB**

Gilia tricolor

Gilia tricolor
BIRD'S EYES

Type: annual
Soil & situation: any dryish soil/full sun
North American hardiness zone: annual
Height: may reach 60cm (24in), but often only half as much
Spread: 15–30cm (6–12in)
Grow for: excellent filler; very pretty; totally reliable; problem-free; and a funny scent

Bird's eyes is often given to children as it is so easy. A good filler for gaps seen in spring and an excellent bloomer, it bears masses of cheerful (yellow-inside, violet-purple-outside) flowers for weeks with almost no care or attention. I first grew this as it was alleged by a perfidious seedsman to have the scent of chocolate. In trials I conducted the commonest description given was of 'burning rubber' or by some as 'a mint chocolate dropped on a barbecue!' Do not let this put you off; it is a lovely little gem.

The genus was for some unknown reason named after an obscure 18th-century Italian astronomer. There are about 120 species, all natives of North America, and this sweet plant comes from California, where it carpets the wild hillsides with flowers all summer.

It is obliging and will grow almost anywhere, but does best on a loamy soil with plenty of space to each plant. Sow *in situ* in spring. It is easy and has no problems. **BF**

Ginkgo biloba
MAIDENHAIR TREE

Type: hardy, deciduous conifer
Soil & situation: fertile, well-drained soil/sun
North American hardiness zone: 5–9
Height: 30m (100ft)
Spread: 8m (25ft)
Grow for: bright green leaves; long life; lovely autumn colour; AGM

Think about this fact. This tree was growing quite happily over 160 million years ago. The notched leaves with fan-shaped veins are found as rock fossils in many countries, including England (near Scarborough in Yorkshire), and are identical to the leaves produced today. The pale green 12cm (5in) wide leaves are pendulous on long stalks with deep notches that almost split the young leaves. In autumn they slowly turn to a beautiful butter-yellow, providing a variegated appearance until all the green fades.

Male plants produce 7.5cm (3in) long, yellow catkins at the same time as the new leaves appear. The female flowers are small and pale green. They are followed by plum-shaped, green-yellow fruits, which when ripe have a most unpleasant smell. The variety *G. biloba* 'Princeton Sentry' is more upright, with a height of 20m (66ft) and a spread of 5m (16ft). It is a male variety with no fruit and no bad smell.

It is quick growing in a moist, fertile, well-drained soil in full sun. It can tolerate an exposed, windy situation. Propagation is by seed sown as soon as it is ripe. Semi-ripe cuttings will root in summer. **JC**

Ginkgo biloba

Gladiolus callianthus

Gladiolus callianthus (syn. *Acidanthera murieliae*)

Type: half-hardy, cormous perennial
Soil & situation: fertile, well-drained soil/full sun
North American hardiness zone: normally grown as an annual
Height: 60–90cm (24–36in)
Spread: 20cm (8in)
Grow for: a wonderful display of highly fragrant spikes of white flowers in late summer

I preferred it when it was called *Acidanthera*. It doesn't really look like gladioli as I think of them. It is deliciously delicate-looking with scented flowers that dance in the slightest breeze. It makes a great display in a container for a patio, or in a cool conservatory where its perfume fills the room.

The 30–45cm (12–18in) long, linear leaves are dark green. The flowers appear in late summer and autumn as loose spikes with up to ten flowers per stem. They are 5cm (2in) wide, pure white, with a deep, purple-crimson centre and have a wonderful fragrance. Funnel-shaped, they dangle on long, pale pink tubes.

Plant the corms 15cm (6in) deep on a bed of sand to aid drainage. After flowering remove the stem. When the foliage turns yellow dig the corms, dry them off and store in a frost-proof shed over winter. Propagation by seed is slow, taking up to five years to flower. Separate cormlets from the side of the corm when lifting and grow in containers until they are the size to flower, usually after three years. **JC**

Gladiolus papilio

Type: hardy, stoloniferous perennial
Soil & situation: moist soil/sun
North American hardiness zone: normally grown as an annual
Height: 90cm (36in)
Spread: 8cm (3½in)
Grow for: subtle flowers from late summer to mid-autumn

Well possums! Dame Edna Everage and Morrissey from the rock band The Smiths love gladioli for their artistic exuberance, but they're not all gaudy and gauche; some, like this one have elegance and charm.

Its sword-shaped leaves to 45cm (18in) long have arching stems of up to ten hooded flowers of yellow-green, marked on the back with dusky purple and in the throat with dusky-purple and yellow. The first time I saw the colour combination I thought it was insipid rather than subtle – for some reason it reminded me of marzipan – but now I've grown to admire its poise and understated beauty. *Gladiolus papilio* is difficult to place because of its colour, but plant it by a path for a closer view of the flowers or against a plain dark background to highlight colours that would be overwhelmed by brighter blooms.

Its home is in southern Africa, particularly in damp grassland around Transvaal and Natal. *Gladiolus* means sword shaped, referring to the leaves; the name *papilo* (butterfly) was given by Sir Joseph Hooker, one of the great directors of Kew Gardens. It's the perfect description. There are a few cultivars, one of which is 'David Hills'. At the time of writing, I've only seen photographs, but it has amazing red flowers. I hope this is a true representation!

G. papilio needs cool, moist, humus-rich soil in sunshine and is ideal for gaps in borders or rock gardens. It is hardy in most parts of the UK and unlike many gladioli, does not need lifting and replanting every year. In poorer soils it spreads but does not flower. It spreads by underground runners, which can be lifted and divided in autumn, and replanted in spring. Often damaged by slugs which eat new shoots underground. **MB**

Gladiolus papilio

Glaucium flavum

Glaucium flavum
YELLOW HORNED POPPY

Type: Hardy, biennial or short-lived perennial
Soil & situation: free-draining soil/thrives along sandy sea-shores but sometimes comes inland too/sunny position
North American hardiness zone: 6–9
Height: to 60cm (24in), sometimes taller
Spread: 45cm (18in)
Grow for: good foliage in the form of extremely glaucous rosettes; enchanting yellow flowers from late spring to late summer

Although this poppy is native to southern coastal Britain, it has been in gardens for centuries, usually popping up between cracks in paving or sowing itself serendipitously in a pebbly corner. It is one of those plants for which there is always a bit of space, however full your garden. The grey foliage, which has toothed lobes, is slightly rough and sends up grey stalks of the charming golden-yellow, papery poppies. These are produced in the first year when grown from seed. The seedpods are decorative too – long, curved and adorned with tiny warts. The down-side is their short lifespan. Some say they can be long lived, but I find that after three years they give up the ghost and this seems to be the norm.

G. flavum f. *fulvum* is a form of the species well worth obtaining. It produces bright orange flowers in summer and has the same attractive, glaucous, almost cabbage-like foliage of the species. It is also nicely robust.

Sow the seed for this plant in spring or autumn, either *in situ* or if you are more neurotic, like me, in small 7cm (3in) pots. It does not like being transplanted, so if it does self-sow it is not always possible to move it to your chosen position. **BG**

Gunnera magellanica

Type: frost-hardy, herbaceous perennial
Soil & situation: moist, humus-rich soil/open, sunny site
North American hardiness zone: 8–9
Height: 20cm (8in)
Spread: indefinite
Grow for: its pretty carpet of leaves from spring to autumn.

Life is enriched by contrasts. I just love the giant *Gunnera manicata* (see next entry) but what I find even more fascinating is that its relative is so tiny: the giant and the dwarf! Unlike its monster herbaceous cousin, it has rounded leaves only about 9cm (3³/₄in) across that are cupped and pleated when young and with wavy, toothed margins. They appear on 8–20cm (3½–8in) stalks that develop from stems that creep above and below the ground, rooting at leaf joints as they spread to form a dense leafy carpet; except in winter when frost kills the foliage!

Male and female flowers occur on different plants, most in the UK are males (females are rare in their native habitat too!), flowering just above the leaves in red-tinted clusters in spring. One of my ambitions is to visit Chile, the natural home of *G. magellanica*, for the plants, wine and scenery! Roy Lancaster has seen it in the wild from 1,200m (4,000ft) above a ski lodge in the Chilean Lake District down to the coastline by an iceberg-strewn sea in Patagonia – an impressive range of performance for such a little plant.

It prefers a moist, humus-rich, acid soil in an open position and could always be planted as ground cover around its larger cousin. It tolerates drier sites but tends to form mounds rather than sweeping carpets. I've seen it flourishing by garden ponds, in bog gardens and stream margins.

Gunnera magellanica

Gunnera manicata

Keep plants within their allotted space by reducing clumps in autumn or spring; simply dig them out with a spade – they are not deep rooted. Propagate from division any time of year. Keep new divisions well watered in summer. **MB**

Gunnera manicata

Type: hardy, deciduous perennial
Soil & situation: deep, permanently wet soil/sun or partial shade
North American hardiness zone: 7–10
Height: 3m (10ft)
Spread: 4m (13ft)
Grow for: huge, lush, jungle-like leaves; AGM

This is not a perennial for the herbaceous border. It is bold, dramatic, architectural and big enough to swamp its neighbours. I have a large clump close to a woodland path. In spring, as the leaves closest to the path grow, they are propped upright with long-handled brushes. The soft brush head prevents the stems being damaged. By summer they form a waterproof canopy overhead. The sun shines through the leaves and the rain is directed to the other side of the path.

Its dark green, lobed, kidney-shaped, heavily veined leaves can be 2m (6½ft) long and almost as broad. They are carried on 2.5m (8ft) long, prickly stalks. In summer 1m (3ft) long, vertical panicles of tiny red-green flowers appear in the centre of the clump and are followed by brown-green fruit. Since it is herbaceous, the absence of winter foliage causes a blank spot in the garden. Underplanting with yellow-flowered winter aconite (*Eranthis hyemalis*) and deep blue *Anemone blanda* 'Ingramii' will provide a carpet of colour in late winter and spring.

It won't tolerate a soil that dries out and is happy in boggy ground with its feet close to water. Planted at the edge of a stream or big pond it will quickly form a large clump. In cold areas the crown needs protection in winter but it provides its own cover. As the leaves die in autumn bend them over the centre of the plant. They certainly won't blow away!

Propagation is by seed sown fresh and over-wintered in a cold frame. Germination is slow. Large, basal buds can be removed in early spring. These are often well rooted on the underside. Pot up in a moisture-retaining compost and keep well watered for the first season. **JC**

Hacquetia epipactis

Type: hardy, herbaceous perennial
Soil & situation: moisture-retentive, humus-rich soil/dappled shade
North American hardiness zone: 5–7
Height: 15cm (6in)
Spread: 30cm (12in)
Grow for: unusual green 'flowers' in late winter and spring; AGM

I first saw this in the northeast of England in a rock garden that was mulched with grey gravel; it was the colour contrast that attracted my eye. It is a small plant with a mass of long-lasting blooms formed from a ruff of tiny green bracts, with a dense cluster of yellow flowers in the centre; both the flowerheads and ruff can be red-tinged in sunnier positions. It is a miniature version of the structure that is found in flowering dogwoods, *Davidia involucrata* (see page 114) and poinsettias.

It has pretty, shiny leaves divided into three segments with lobes at the toothed or rounded margins; the veining can be paler green. Looking at the colour I suppose that it's not surprising that it's in the celery family! It makes good ground cover under shrubs and a wonderful association in the rock garden with *Gentiana acaulis* (see page 189) and other plants with early blue flowers such as *Hepatica nobilis* (page 206). It is long lived, slow growing and a true harbinger of spring. As you might expect from something so unusual, it stands alone; there are no other species in the genus.

It needs humus-rich, well-drained but moist, neutral to acid soil in dappled shade. Ideal for woodland or rock gardens. Mulch in autumn and water during drought. To propagate divide in spring, take root cuttings in winter and sow seed when fresh (it usually seeds prolifically); it takes about two years to flower. Slugs and snails can damage young growth. **MB**

Hacquetia epipactis

Hamamelis x *intermedia* 'Jelena'

WITCH HAZEL

Type: hardy, deciduous shrub
Soil & situation: moist soil/sun
North American hardiness zone: 5–9
Height & spread: 4m (13ft), or more
Grow for: flowers in mid- and late winter; autumn colour; AGM

Hamamelis x *intermedia* 'Jelena'

Witch hazel's spidery blooms are traditionally tones of yellow, but I like those with red and orange hues, particularly *H.* x *intermedia* 'Jelena', which was named for Jelena de Belder at Kalmthout Arboretum in Belgium. It has wonderful fiery autumn colour and petals with yellow tips diffusing down to red at the base. Look out too for these varieties of *H.* x *intermedia*: 'Orange Peel', with sharp orange petals; 'Orange Beauty', with orange flowers; 'Aphrodite', with large burnt-orange flowers; and 'Diane', red with good autumn colour.

They prefer a sunny position but tolerate dappled shade; excessive shade reduces flowering. Grow in any moist soil except thin soil over chalk; improve the drainage on clay; mulch and water in drought. Feed in spring with Growmore, chicken pellets or fish blood and bone at 40g/sq m (2oz/sq ft).

I read an article about witch hazels by Chris Lane, a *Hamamelis* enthusiast, that included new information about cultivation and pruning, and I'm sure that if what he said reached a wider audience it would encourage more people to grow these fabulous plants. Cut back the previous season's wood to two growth buds annually in winter unless they have only made a little growth. There is normally a cluster of flowers at the base of the growth and the growth buds are above these. Using this technique Chris had 14-year-old plants that were only 1.5m (5ft) x 1.5m (5ft). They lack the wide spreading habit but it allows them to be grown where there's minimal space. If space is not a problem, restrictive pruning is not necessary. It can be propagated by grafting, but it's easier to buy a plant from a nursery in late winter. **MB**

Hamamelis mollis 'Coombe Wood'

CHINESE WITCH HAZEL

Type: hardy, deciduous shrub
Soil & situation: neutral to acid, well-drained soil/full sun or partial shade
North American hardiness zone: 5–9
Height: 4m (13ft)
Spread: 5m (16ft)
Grow for: fragrant, unusually shaped, yellow flowers in winter; buttery-yellow autumn leaf colour

If you want a plant to brighten your day in the middle of winter this funnel-shaped shrub has a lot going for it, including a powerful, freely given fragrance. The individual flowers look like delicate, finely peeled lemon zest but are tough enough to withstand the worst of weather. Appearing before the leaves, the massed flowers resemble a yellow cloud against a washed-out wintery sky. Sited close to the house, its winter perfume will come looking for you through an open window.

There are other good species and varieties of witch hazel, but it is hard to beat *Hamamelis mollis* 'Coombe Wood' for fragrance and size of flower. Another favourite is *H.* x *intermedia* 'Jelena', but Matthew has chosen that one (see previous entry)! *H. virginiana*, from North America, flowers in late autumn and is the commercial source of witch hazel used in medicine.

Witch hazel is what I would call a 'kind' plant. It rarely suffers from pests or diseases, is fully hardy and requires minimal pruning. Cut out crossing branches in early winter to maintain a good shape. Plant in deeply dug, well-drained ground. It dislikes heavy clay soil. Layering is the easiest method of propagation, but leave the branch for two years to allow a good root system to form. **JC**

Hamamelis mollis 'Coombe Wood'

Hebe albicans

Hebe albicans

Type: frost-hardy, evergreen shrub
Soil & situation: range of free-draining soils, even very thin ones/coastal areas/sun or light shade/hates winter wet and very cold areas
North American hardiness zone: 9–10
Height: 60cm (24in)
Spread: 90cm (36in)
Grow for: dense, glaucous foliage; neat humpy habit; reasonably pretty white flowers, spotted with their chocolate-coloured anthers in early summer; AGM

Hebes are useful fillers in the garden. They root quickly from cuttings and rapidly establish into neat hummocks of foliage. This hebe has a particularly dense habit. The leaves are about 2cm (3/4in) long and are a pale, soft grey-green – a fabulous foliage colour that works well with purples and mauves, oranges and whites. It does not seem to get all woody and open and leggy at the base like many hebes do if you do not cut them back regularly. Many people admire 'Red Edge', which is similar and the leaves have exactly what the name implies, but I do not like it half as much as this beauty.

You can, as with many hebes, clip them over annually in spring, but I find that the natural form is so dense, it is unnecessary. When the plant eventually does get leggy, it may well respond to a hard cutting back into old wood in spring but sometimes an aged specimen will give up the ghost. Generally I find they are so simple to propagate from cuttings, that this is the simplest method of rejuvenating the border. Semi-ripe cuttings can be taken in the summer. Beware if you are on a wet, heavy soil with lots of organic matter – hebes can suffer from Phytophthora, which is a rotting of the roots, so add lots of grit before planting to lighten things up a touch. **BG**

Hebe x *andersonii* 'Variegata'

Type: nearly hardy, evergreen shrub
Soil & situation: moist, well-drained, neutral or alkaline soil/full sun or partial shade
North American hardiness zone: 10–11
Height & spread: 2m (6½ft)
Grow for: bold, variegated, evergreen foliage and summer flowers

This hebe, while it needs mollycoddling, has a lot going for it. Larger-growing and less dense in habit than many others, it has beautiful, big, 10cm (4in) long, dark green leaves streaked grey-green in the centre and margined in creamy-white. It flowers all summer and into the autumn with 8cm (3½in) long spikes of pale violet which fade to blue-white as they age.

It needs a sheltered situation or a place against a warm, sunny wall. It makes a spectacular display facing a red brick wall. Avoid cold, windy sites. If it does get hit by cold leave it untouched until early summer. Prune it back to 30–45cm (12–18in) from ground level and it may reshoot from the base.

Propagation is by softwood cuttings taken in early summer. It roots easily and rooting a few every year as replacements means you will never be without one of the best varieties of hebe. **JC**

Hebe x *andersonii* 'Variegata'

Hedera helix 'Congesta'

Hedera helix 'Congesta'/ *H. h.* 'Erecta'/*H. h.* 'Conglomerata Erecta'

Type: hardy, perennial, evergreen shrub
Soil & situation: any soil/sun or shade
North American hardiness zone: 5–10
Height & spread: can slowly make a mound up to 1–1.5m (3–5ft)
Grow for: distinctive geometric form

Most ivies are clinging, creeping plants, but this one is an upright-growing shrub. Quite different to normal ivy, it is composed of vertical growing spikes covered with spirally formed leaves, giving a strange, somewhat alien look that is offset by the healthy dark green of the spade- to arrow-shaped leaves. On warm spring days this plant appears to be covered in small, bright red flowers, but on closer examination these turn out to be ladybirds just out of hibernation from inside the dry interior. As a uniquely sculptural plant it can be used in 'artistic' situations, such as combined with a large stone or old tree trunk.

Although given separate Latin varietal names these are very similar plants, differing in leaf shape but all with amazing architectural form.

Any soil or site suits this tough shrub which persists for many years, slowly increasing in size, though it is happiest in rich, moist, alkaline soil and partial shade. It is rather brittle so be careful when handling the shoots. It cannot be grown from seed, but cuttings taken in autumn and set in a cold frame are easy. In hot, dry sites it can suffer from red spider mite, so keep it misted. **BF**

Hedera helix 'Cristata' (syn. *H. h.* 'Parsley Crested')

Type: evergreen climber
Soil & situation: prefers shady conditions/does particularly well in limy soils
North American hardiness zone: 5–10
Height: 2m (6½ft)
Spread: indefinite
Grow for: a wonderful, rumpled green leaf, crumpled and twisted around the margins; a good climber; highly attractive plant.

This ivy stands out with its weird but rather wonderful leaf. The leaves do not look in any way poxed or diseased because they are fairly uniformly affected and the crimps look rather delicately applied. They are almost rounded, bright green and prominently veined. It will branch and trail as it grows and I have seen it sprawling neatly over a low wall in a fairly compact way, creating a bit of organic sculpture or green architecture. Ivies are multi-purpose, versatile tools suitable for topiary on wire frames, making solid, evergreen 'walls' from chain-link-type fences (which take up only a smidgen of space and form magnificent 'fedges') and of course for camouflaging monstrosities. On the whole I tend to use *Hedera helix* 'Conglomerata' or common or garden English ivy, *H. helix*. I am not a fan of those scores of bicoloured, brash-looking ivies, which you regularly see plastered against eyesores – obviously the intention was to conceal, not reveal, but their appearance is so artificial it works the other way.

This ivy is unlikely to become large and bulky and so cause problems to its support in the way that many vigorous ivies can in trees, roofs, fences and the like. If you want it to form a denser, flatter line then regular clipping of sideshoots helps create a more solid mass of vegetation. I saw a superb, arched 'porch' around a front door created entirely of ivy. This was regularly clipped over to give a flat, green surface. It not only transformed an otherwise unremarkable house, but was home to a robin and scores of insects too.

To propagate ivy, take cuttings of young shoots any time during the growing season. If you are forming and growing your ivy topiary in pots, do not forget to feed and water them. They are incredibly tolerant of neglect but really thrive with a bit of love and care. **BG**

Hedera helix 'Cristata'

Salvia sclarea var. *turkestanica* June

BIENNIAL CLARY

Type: hardy biennial or short-lived perennial
Soil & situation: free-draining light soils/copious sunshine
Hardiness zone: 5–9
Height: 75cm (30in)
Spread: 30cm (12in)
Grow for: highly dramatic when in pink and white flower from late spring to summer, and this drama is good and prolonged; orderly, felted foliage is highly agreeable; will usually seed itself around

A few, repeated clumps of this architectural, yet colourful, perennial will pull any planting up a good couple of notches in the summer. The flowers are white and pink and have highly conspicuous, pale, red-purple bracts. These, together with stout pink stems, form hunky candelabras, which look sensational for a good few weeks. The leaves are a good size (about 25 x 12cm/10 x 5in), ovate and a deep, sagey green.

The ordinary clary is also known as 'clear eye' and 'muscatel sage', though it is far less colourful than *S. sclarea* var. *turkestanica*. It is in widespread cultivation for medicinal and culinary uses and is reputedly an aphrodisiac. Parts of it are used externally in eyewashes and also to flavour Rhine wines with a muscatel bouquet, hence the alternative common names.

I am not always prepared to make the assumption that this plant is going to self-seed where I want it, and as it is such a strong statement I think it is well worth positioning where it gives maximum impact. It is a good idea to sow a few seeds on the window sill in early spring or *in situ* in late spring – it is so easy from seed. If it dies out and I have forgotten to grow my own, I regret it so much so that I have even been known to buy in some replacements! After flowering, leave on some spent heads for seed and cut down the remaining spikes so that the plant recovers. This, with an annual spring mulch, helps it to be more perennial in nature and boosts performance. They are far shorter-lived and more miserable in appearance when subject to winter wet. No need to stake. **BG**

Hedera helix 'Goldheart'

Type: hardy, perennial, evergreen climber
Soil & situation: any soil/sun or shade
North American hardiness zone: 6–10
Height & spread: will eventually cover any area
Grow for: the cheerful golden splash in each evergreen leaf makes this a useful wall or ground covering

Most ivies are somewhat funereal; yes, they are good covers for trellis, hiding tree stumps or clinging to unsightly walls, but they are undeniably grim, and more at home in the graveyard or the dark woods. However *H. h.* 'Goldheart' is cheerful, the yellow splash in the centre of each leaf redeems this plant so it can be used in narrow alleys or small courtyards without making them seem dungeon-like. It can even be grown as ground cover if the area is initially well weeded, but it does want to climb.

A native of Europe and the Near East, ivy has long been growing in gardens but has not necessarily been grown in gardens! *Hedera* is the Latin name for ivy, and the plant was held sacred to Bacchus, the god of wine.

Ivy is long lived and prefers a moist, alkaline soil in partial shade. It may be slow to start with but once it gets a hold it is in for good. It can be sheared back in spring to keep it flat against a wall. *H. h.* 'Goldheart' cannot be grown from seed but cuttings or layers are easy in autumn. It can get red spider mite on hot, dry walls and the answer is to spray with water on hot days. **BF**

Hedera helix 'Goldheart'

Hedera helix f. *poetarum* 'Poetica Arborea'

Hedera helix f. *poetarum* 'Poetica Arborea'

POET'S IVY, ITALIAN IVY

Type: hardy, evergreen, climbing shrub
Soil & situation: moist, humus-rich, well-drained, alkaline soil/full sun or light shade
North American hardiness zone: 5–10
Height: 3m (10ft)
Spread: 1m (3ft)
Grow for: excellent bush ivy with orange fruit

Ivies have many attributes, being excellent evergreen coverers for horizontal and vertical situations. They have attractive juvenile foliage and late-season flowers which are beneficial to insects.

This variety is grown for its orange-coloured fruits. Usually sold as a bush or 'tree ivy', it is propagated by cuttings from adult arborescent growths. Pliny, in his *Natural History*, in the first century AD wrote 'One kind has black seed and another the colour of saffron, the latter is used by poets for their wreaths and its leaves are not so dark in colour'. I must admit my main interest is that it is unusual and makes a show in winter.

The 5–8cm (2–3½in) long, five-lobed leaves are pale green. The fruit are small, dull, deep orange and persist all winter. It is tolerant of most soils with the exception of waterlogged conditions but prefers alkaline soil. Pruning consists of clipping to keep the bush tidy and under control. Propagation is by softwood cuttings with a heel in a gritty compost under horticultural fleece. Trim the leaves of the cutting to reduce transpiration. Trailing stems may be layered in the open ground and should be well rooted within six months.

If you know a poet, don't risk buying him a plant in case he knows the original story of the use for 'poet's ivy'. **JC**

Helianthemum apenninum

WHITE ROCK ROSE, SUN ROSE

Type: hardy, evergreen, spreading shrub
Soil & situation: well-drained, neutral to alkaline soil/full sun
North American hardiness zone: 6–8
Height: 45cm (18in)
Spread: 80cm (32in)
Grow for: excellent ground-covering plant with small, pure white flowers

Rock roses are dependable plants. They are guaranteed to flower no matter what, weather wise, has gone before. They are excellent for ground cover either in a rockery or tumbling down a steep bank. This species is native to the UK and can still be found in at least one part of Devon.

It forms a loose mat of branching stems with small, narrow, grey-green leaves. From late spring until mid-summer the plant is covered in small, five-petalled, saucer-shaped flowers. They are pure white with a centre of conspicuous, deep yellow anthers.

Pruning is essential every year to prevent the shrub becoming woody and leggy with little growth at the base of the plant. Clip it over after flowering to remove most of the young growth. Avoid cutting into the old wood of neglected plants as they may not produce new shoots. Propagation is by fresh seed sown thinly on the surface of the compost in autumn and over-wintered in a cold frame. Softwood cuttings root readily in early summer in a gritty, free-draining compost. Cover the cuttings with horticultural fleece rather than polythene. **JC**

Helianthemum apenninum

Helianthus annuus 'Teddy Bear'

Helianthus annuus 'Teddy Bear'

SUNFLOWER

Type: half-hardy annual
Soil & situation: moist, well-drained, humus-rich, neutral to alkaline soil/full sun
North American hardiness zone: 5–7
Height: 45cm (18in)
Spread: 20–30cm (8–12in)
Grow for: a perfect size for children; adds colour, interest and height to the border

You don't have to be a child to appreciate growing your very own giant sunflower, but growing one with flowers at face level, such as *Helianthus annuus* 'Teddy Bear', must be satisfactory when you are small.

The hairy stems form a compact plant and carry 20cm- (8in-) long, heart-shaped, mid-green, hairy leaves. The fully double, golden-yellow flowers are 15cm (6in) in diameter and are produced during summer and autumn. *H. a.* 'Teddy Bear' is ideal as a dot plant in the centre of a container or en masse in a sunny border. It is useful for wildlife – bees love the nectar and the spent flowers can be left to produce seed which is much enjoyed by birds.

Sunflowers need a long, hot summer to flower well so plant a row along the base of a sheltered, sunny wall where they are in full sun. Propagation is by seed sown in late winter in a propagator. They may be sown outside where they are to flower when all risk of frost is over. Protect the young plants from slugs and snails, which can destroy a whole crop overnight.

If size matters, then grow the variety *H. a.* 'Russian Giant' with large, bright yellow, 25cm (10in) diameter flowers all summer. It grow to 3.5m (11ft) high and needs to be staked to prevent the wind felling it. **JC**

Helianthus tuberosus
JERUSALEM ARTICHOKE

Type: hardy, herbaceous perennial
Soil & situation: any soil/sun or shade
North American hardiness zone: 4–9
Height: up to 3m (10ft)
Spread: 25cm (10in)
Grow for: an instant windbreak with scented flowers and edible tubers

You have to learn to love Jerusalem artichokes, as once you've got them you can rarely get rid of them. This does not matter, as they can be relegated to an out-of-the-way place where they will look after themselves. Like a magic soup-pot, plant some tubers and walk away – there'll always be some there, giving you an ever-present source of food. The stems reach an amazing height in good sites and can quickly hide a garden eyesore or give privacy this summer, not in five years' time. The flowers are just like miniature sunflowers and have a warm vanilla-chocolate scent in some strains. (You can find the tubers in knobbly, very knobbly, white, pink and red colours.)

It is a native of North America and came to the UK in 1617, where it was thought to be a wonderful new crop to feed the poor but, unfortunately, it was not as palatable as the potato. (The dahlia was similarly introduced as a crop and only later became seen as a flowering plant for the garden.) The botanical name comes from the Greek *helios*, meaning sun, and *anthemon*, a flower. The English appellation Jerusalem is alleged to be a corruption of the Italian *girasole* (to turn with the sun) and artichoke, as it was thought to taste similar to the globe artichoke.

Helianthus tuberosus

It will grow almost anywhere! For ever! Tidy up the dead stems in winter. Leave the crop in the ground until required as it stores badly once lifted. Plant tubers 10cm (4in) deep in moist, rich soil 30cm (12in) apart, and stand back. Tubers are quite tasty but cause dreadful wind, which is appropriate for a windbreak plant. **BF**

Helleborus foetidus Wester Flisk Group
STINKING HELLEBORE

Type: hardy, evergreen perennial
Soil & situation: rich, well-drained soil/dappled shade
North American hardiness zone: 6–9
Height: 1.2m (4ft) in flower
Spread: 50cm (20in)
Grow for: sculptural form and colour; flowers from mid-winter to mid-spring

Mrs Mamie Walker discovered this plant with unusual reddish tints when she moved to the rectory at Wester Flisk on the Firth of Tay, Scotland, in the early 1970s. By a process of seedling selection she and others have produced plants with an even stronger, more widespread red stain. So where did this form come from? It is a scarce UK native, but does not grow around the Firth of Tay. However, from 1811 to 1832, the Reverend Dr John Fleming, a professor at both Aberdeen University and Queen's College, Edinburgh, lived at the rectory. An enthusiastic botanist, he may well have introduced the plant through the Botanic Gardens in Edinburgh or Aberdeen or had a special interest in the flora of Spain, where similar forms are found. There is also a double snowdrop growing in the woods nearby! I suspect that the professor did it!

It has narrow finger-like leaves and fascinating colouring. I find it a bit weird yet intriguing, like modern art! The crushed dark foliage is malodorous. Plant with snowdrops, bugle (*Ajuga reptans*), lungwort (*Pulmonaria officinalis*), silver-foliage plants or *Narcissus* 'February Gold'.

It flourishes in rich, well-drained soil, preferably alkaline, in dappled shade, but will also grow in dry shade or full sun. Mulch in spring; tall plants may need staking. Thin out older leaves and stems in winter to encourage new growth from the base and cut out the flower stems at ground level as they deteriorate. Sow seed in containers in a cold frame as soon as ripe. Divide after flowering, in early spring or late summer. It comes true from seed if isolated from other cultivars of *H. foetidus*. Prone to snails, aphids, leaf spot and black rot. **MB**

Helleborus foetidus Wester Flisk Group

Helleborus niger 'Potter's Wheel'
CHRISTMAS ROSE

Type: hardy, evergreen, clump-forming perennial
Soil & situation: heavy, neutral to alkaline soil/light shade
North American hardiness zone: 4–8
Height: 30cm (12in)
Spread: 45cm (18in)
Grow for: beautiful, cup-shaped, white flowers in mid-winter

Miss Davenport-Jones, who named this plant, decided on 'Potter's Wheel' because every flower was perfectly round. What a lovely common name. It comes into flower with the minimum of fuss and, like the snowdrop, manages to flower in spite of adverse weather. When it was given the AGM in 1958 the flowers were described as follows: 'The immense flowers measure from 4–5 inches across with broad, glistening white, overlapping sepals, the bases of which, together with the nectaries, are a deep, clear green.'

The leaves are a glossy, dark green and the flowers are held on 23–30cm (9–12in) stems well clear of muddy rain splash. Unfortunately it seldom flowers for me on Christmas Day, but a few weeks later it is in bloom and continues to produce flowers until early spring. As a table decoration the simple flowers are exquisite. The secret to growing the 'Christmas rose' is choice of site and soil. It will love you if you provide it with moist, alkaline, humus-rich soil away from full sun. The base of a shady wall would get you brownie points. Whenever possible buy plants which are in flower. There are a lot of seed-raised plants on the market which, while white flowering, are inferior imposters. **JC**

Helleborus niger 'Potter's Wheel'

Helleborus odorus

FRAGRANT HELLEBORE, SWEET-SCENTED HELLEBORE

Type: hardy, herbaceous perennial
Soil & situation: rich, moist, loamy soil/light shade
North American hardiness zone: 6–9
Height & spread: clump of 30–60cm (12–24in) or so each way
Grow for: pleasant pale green, lightly striped foliage; large, similarly coloured flowers with strong sweet perfume

This is the only perfumed member of the genus. I notice that we have almost all chosen a hellebore as one of our favourite plants, yet they are not commonly grown. I think this is because they are not easy to establish as big plants and few amateurs want to grow them from seed or buy tiny plants, when big ones are available. Also many of them are a disappointment in comparison to their catalogue descriptions; for example, the typical label of 'red flowers' is misleading, because in fact the blooms

Helleborus odorus

are a pale wan red. Secondly the flowers droop, so you do not even get to see their beauty. It would be ideal if hellebores could live on top of a wall, so you could look up at them, but they can't.

A group of a dozen or so species, hellebores are among the oldest medicinal and garden plants. They were first recorded as early as 1500BC when they were used to cure the daughters of Proteus, King of Argos, of insanity. *Helleborus odorus* is a late arrival, introduced in the 19th century from Hungary, and still not common.

Hellebores are very long lived and if undisturbed in light shade may pass a century or more. Never ever try to move large or established plants; only small ones will take well. Grow from seed in individual pots in a cold frame or *in situ*. Particularly nice strains can be root divided after flowering but never make as good a plants as seedlings. Beware – poisonous plants! **BF**

Helleborus orientalis

Plant of the Week (see page 79)

Helleborus x *sternii*

Type: hardy, herbaceous perennial
Soil & situation: moist, free-draining soil/sun
North American hardiness zone: 6–9
Height: 35cm (14in)
Spread: 30cm (12in)
Grow for: fascinating form and winter flowers

This is a hybrid between *Helleborus argutifolius*, a hardy green-leaved and green-flowered species, and *H. lividus*, a tender species with short veiny leaves and unusual pink flowers. They combine to produce a clump-forming perennial which looks sometimes like one parent, sometimes the other. Those that are more like *H. argutifolius* are less ornamental; those with more *H. lividus* are beautiful but not as hardy. It has smooth or spiny leaves with cream-coloured veins and strange pink-purple leaf stalks and main veins. If that isn't crazy enough the green flowers to 5cm (2in) across are also creamy-green with a pink-purple tinge. They appear in clusters from late winter until mid-spring.

There are several selected groups and cultivars. *H.* x *sternii* 'Boughton Beauty' has grey, strongly veined foliage with pink stems and leaf bracts. *H.* x *s.* Blackthorn Group are dwarf with purple stems, silver-grey leaves and green flowers with a pink tinge. Some are only 30cm (12in) tall and *H.* x *s.* dwarf is even smaller.

They tolerate most soils but prefer one that is neutral to alkaline and free-draining; incorporate leafmould or organic matter at planting time and add spent mushroom compost to acid soils. They prefer full sun but need to be protected from scorching sunshine; they tolerate dappled shade. Mulch in autumn. In colder climates grow strongly pink forms in containers and protect from hard frosts. Remove some of the leaves during autumn and early winter, particularly those showing signs of blackening. Just before they are in full flower, take off all the rest of the leaves. On windy sites, remove them entirely to prevent wind rock. Divide after flowering in late spring or early summer; self-seeds freely. They are susceptible to snails, aphids and black rot. **MB**

Helleborus x *sternii*

Hemerocallis flava
DAYLILY

Type: hardy, herbaceous perennial
Soil & situation: any soil/anywhere
North American hardiness zone: 3–9
Height: up to 60cm–1m (2–3ft)
Spread: a clump of 2–25cm (1–10in)
Grow for: pleasant, wide, flat, rush-like foliage; attractive, large, yellow flowers over many weeks with a warm sweet smell of honeysuckle

This is a marvellous plant for many reasons. Daylilies do best in moist, light shade, but they will succeed almost anywhere a weed will grow, making them very useful as a filler. The succession of blooms lasts right through the summer, and they need no dead-heading. Their scent is very pleasant and I have even taken to eating the petals in salads. They are also problem free with no serious pests or diseases, and if the leaves are left to wither down they naturally form a weed-suppressing mat. Yellow daylilies have perfume but *Hemerocallis fulva*, orange ones, do not; thus the hybrids, of which there are many, may have scent, especially if they are more yellow than orange.

Hemerocallis comes from the Greek *hemera*, meaning day, and *kallos*, beauty, and the plant was given this name as individual blooms last but a day, though they are continually produced for weeks on end.

Hemerocallis flava

Hemerocallis 'Prairie Blue Eyes'

The daylily can be long lived in a rich, moist, lightly shaded site. It can be grown from seed, preferably autumn sown, but root division is easier and quicker. Every bit of root with a bud can be divided off and will soon make another clump. These tough survivors suffer from no problems at all. None. **BF**

Hemerocallis 'Prairie Blue Eyes'
DAYLILY

Type: hardy, semi-evergreen perennial
Soil & situation: fertile, moist, well-drained soil/full sun
North American hardiness zone: 3–9
Height & spread: 75cm (30in)
Grow for: a continual show of flowers for a lengthy time in the summer

The good news is, however short-lived each flower may be, there are lots of them, making a show for between four and six weeks in mid-summer. Long, narrow, arching, strap-like leaves are mid-green and will over-winter on the plant in mild climates. The star-shaped, 13cm (5¼in) wide, maroon-purple flowers have a greenish-yellow throat. The unopened flower buds are edible, adding colour to salads. Daylilies are low-allergen plants, making them suitable for allergen-free gardens.

A mulch of bark on clumps which die down in late autumn will see them through the winter. Slugs and snails are a constant problem, especially in spring when they devour the new shoots as fast as they grow. Weekly liquid tomato feeds from spring until the flower buds appear will strengthen the plant. If abnormally fat buds appear in late spring it will indicate an infection of gall midge. They should be picked off and burned, and the plant should be removed and destroyed in autumn.

Propagation is by division of the clump every two to three years in spring. Take care not to damage the fleshy roots. It can be grown from freshly sown seed in autumn but it will not come true. But, who knows, you may raise some good, new varieties. **JC**

Hepatica nobilis

Type: hardy, herbaceous perennial
Soil & situation: moist, organic-rich, free-draining soil/sun or dappled shade
North American hardiness zone: 5–8
Height: 10cm (4in)
Spread: 15cm (6in)
Grow for: pretty early spring flowers; AGM

In Japan the hepatica is known as *Yukiwariso*, which translated means 'herb of the snow', as they often emerge through snow cover in spring. It is found from Europe and Scandinavia east to Japan where it shows an incredible diversity of flower and form, not found anywhere else in its range. Capitalizing on this natural inclination, Japanese enthusiasts breed 'fancy' varieties and by 1995 almost 550 cultivars had been registered. Although they have been cultivated in Japan since 1730, it is only in the last 25 years that they've been developed for showing. Propagation is slow

Hepatica nobilis

and rare and unusual varieties are sold for huge sums of money; strangely for a member of the buttercup family, the rarest colour is yellow! There are doubles, triples and even 'thousand-layered' flowers and a range of pattern and colour classifications that includes nail-coloured and sprayed or wrinkled. A pot called *Tanba-Yaki* has been specifically designed for growing them.

The species is a simple, pretty little flower and ranges in colour from white to pink, blue and purple. It withstands low temperatures but not winter waterlogging and is ideal for scree and rock gardens; it flourishes in limy soil. Mulch in autumn and feed regularly, particularly in spring after flowering and in autumn when the flowers are formed. For perfect plants, grow in alpine houses in pots. Propagate from fresh seed; it may take 12 months to germinate. It is prone to slugs. **MB**

Hermodactylus tuberosus

WIDOW IRIS, SNAKE'S HEAD IRIS

Type: hardy, tuberous perennial
Soil & situation: very dry, free-draining soil/sun
North American hardiness zone: 7–9
Height & spread: 40cm (16in) or more
Grow for: unusual scented flowers from early to late spring

This bashful plant seems almost embarrassed by its own good looks! You could easily walk past the tussocks of leaves without realizing that hiding among the grey-green, grassy foliage are sombre, almost translucent greenish-yellow, iris-like flowers, about 5cm (2in) across with velvety black outer segments and an alluring perfume. They are so inconspicuous that some argue that, to appreciate them fully, they are better displayed in a vase! Perhaps they feel ashamed that they are not as bold as the iris, a group to which they once belonged, but there is no real reason to hide – this is a plant for those who appreciate subtle charms and the longer you look, the more you find.

John Gerard (1545–1612), the herbalist and gardener, described it thus: 'The lower leaves [petals] that turne downward, are of a perfect blacke colour, soft and smooth as is black velvet, the blackness is welted about with greenish yellow, or as we terme it, a goose turd greene, of which the uppermost leaves [petals] do consist'. Charming!

Hermodactylus tuberosus

Flowering is better after long, hot summers and it combines well with silver-foliaged shrubs or against a light-coloured wall. It comes from the dry slopes in rocky regions of southern Europe, North Africa, Israel and Turkey. Plant 6–10cm ($2\frac{1}{2}$–4in) deep in a hot, dry, sunny situation at the base of a wall in preferably alkaline soil. It must be very free draining and it's one of few plants that would be delighted if builders buried their rubble in your garden; if they haven't, throw in a few half bricks and gravel yourself! In areas where the soil is not regularly disturbed, it spreads happily.

Lift and divide in late summer and early autumn at the end of its summer dormancy. Slugs and snails can be a problem. **MB**

Hesperis matronalis

DAME'S VIOLET, SWEET ROCKET

Type: hardy perennial
Soil & situation: fertile, well-drained soil/sun or partial shade
North American hardiness zone: 4–9
Height: 90cm (36in)
Spread: 45cm (18in)
Grow for: flowers for about six weeks in late spring and early summer

This is a quintessential cottage-garden flower in shades ranging from purple to lavender and white. Robust, wholesome with a simple beauty and fragrance that pervades the garden in the evening, this pretty plant was introduced from Europe in the 16th century and is naturalized throughout the UK. Gertrude Jekyll in her book *Annuals and Biennials* writes that 'it looks best in a half-shady place, such as the edge of woodland or the beginning of a wood walk. The double kinds, of which the pure white is the best, should be treated as biennials'. William Robinson in *The English Flower Garden* notes that this is 'a popular old garden plant, and one of the most desirable of hardy flowers…the double kinds are much more valued'; an honest appraisal of a fabulous flower from two gardening 'greats'.

Hesperis matronalis var. *albiflora* is the best, with pure white flowers. It comes true from seed if isolated from other colours. *H. m.* var. *albiflora* 'Alba Plena' is a white, double-flowered form. *H. m.* 'Lilacina Flore Pleno' has dense spikes of fragrant, double, lilac-coloured flowers.

The single forms grow in any fertile, moist, well-drained soil in sun or partial shade; double forms need a little more pampering, preferring better drainage and additional well-rotted organic matter.

Treat as biennials or short-lived perennials; the first flush of flowers are nearly always the best. Divide every two years as flowering diminishes with age, and take basal cuttings in spring for planting out the following year. Slugs and snails can be a problem. **MB**

Hesperis matronalis

Meconopsis x *sheldonii* 'Slieve Donard'

BLUE POPPY

Type: hardy herbaceous perennial
Soil & situation: humus-rich, moist, well-drained, neutral to acid soil/partial shade
Hardiness zone: 7–8
Height: 1m (3ft)
Spread: 30cm (12in)
Grow for: beautifully shaped, long-lasting, rich blue flowers, which may appear earlier in the summer but are at their best now; AGM.

I love all the blue poppies, but this is truly the best blue. Also I met my wife in Newcastle, a seaside town at the foot of Slieve Donard 'where the mountains of Mourne sweep down to the sea'. As perennials go, this is a show stopper. A hybrid of *M. betonicifolia* and *M. grandis*, it is blessed with the best of its parents. In early summer flower stalks 1m (3ft) high carry large, bright, rich blue nodding flowers made up of four long, pointed petals. The drooping flower buds open slowly, allowing seemingly bright blue tissue paper to squeeze out. The lance-shaped, dark green, smooth-edged leaves have the decency to stay below flowering level.

Sometimes blue poppies tend to be monocarpic (they die after flowering). There is less risk of this if they are grown in a moist soil and are prevented from flowering for two years. Removing the flowerhead before it sets seed also helps to prolong the life of the plant. It prefers a deep, fertile, lime-free soil with good drainage. Add lots of leafmould to help retain a moist root area without waterlogging. Choose a sheltered site in partial shade such as a woodland glade. In cold areas protect the crown with bark mulch in winter. Propagation is by seed, preferably sown fresh in autumn. Use a soilless seed compost. Don't cover the seed as light is required for germination. Keep the seedlings under cover in a greenhouse or cold frame during winter and watch for any sign of damping off disease. **JC**

Bunny adds:
A fantastic plant, certainly, but difficult to grow unless you live in a moist part of the country.

Hesperis steveniana

Type: hardy, herbaceous annual/biennial/perennial
Soil & situation: moist soil/sun or light shade
North American hardiness zone: 4–9
Height & spread: first year rosette to 15cm (6in), second year spike to 60cm (24in)
Grow for: lots of beautiful violet blooms attracting masses of insects and smelling divine

Hesperis steveniana is very similar to the larger and better known dame's violet, *H. matronalis* (see previous entry), both resembling bluey-violet wallflowers. In the day it is magnificent with a mass of violet (or white, as there are always a few) blooms smelling of, well, violet. But in the evening return again and now the violet is augmented by a clove perfume, heavenly! It goes well with wallflowers as it comes into bloom with them and is not so huge as *H. matronalis*, but has a much longer flowering season.

A native of Europe, *Hesperis* has always been popular in gardens. The genus name is from the Greek for evening, when they are most highly perfumed.

H. steveniana does well in dryish soil in full sun, but is always short lived. Like wallflowers, some plants, especially if dead-headed, become short-lived perennials. Sown in early spring, they will flower, and probably die, like an annual; sown in a seedbed in late spring or early summer, many will become biennial and can be transplanted while dormant to flower the following year. **BF**

Hesperis steveniana

Hibiscus sabdariffa var. *sabdariffa. The photograph was taken in Thailand – most of us would need a greenhouse to achieve this result.*

Hibiscus sabdariffa var. *sabdariffa*

Type: tender, annual crop
Soil & situation: rich, well-drained compost/full sun/under cover
North American hardiness zone: 10–11
Height: 1–1.5m (3–5ft)
Spread: 25cm–1m (10in–3ft)
Grow for: something completely different, and delicious

OK, this is an enthusiast's or gourmet's plant. Indian sorrel or roselle is grown in the tropics but in the UK it can be grown in a warm greenhouse. It is closely related to okra and needs similar bright light, heat and well-drained, fertile soil. The actual crop is the dark red calyces which surround the yellow flowers. These fleshy parts are dried, then in winter made into a tea, jelly, pudding or punch. Roselle has a wonderful taste of cloves, cinnamon and spices all. If that wasn't enough, you can also use the leaves as spinach or salad!

Hibiscus is a big genus with 300 members all in the warmer zones. Barely any have scented flowers as they are pollinated by hummingbirds, who find them by their bright colours. Roselle comes from India where it is used in a multitude of ways and it is very popular in the West Indies. Incidentally, the reason you so often see the large hibiscus flowers used in hotels and as decorations in the tropics is that they don't wilt for the whole of the day on which they are picked.

Not easy as it likes a hot, bright environment with a fairly low humidity. It takes many months to grow, won't flower readily without daylight-length manipulation, and will bolt while small if you're not careful. Don't stare in wonder at the ripe calyces when they arrive – use them before they rot. Sow in warmth in late winter and grow on in warmth, pot on into large pots or a greenhouse border and keep the air fairly dry once flowers set in autumn. To grow these you need to like a challenge! **BF**

Hippophae rhamnoides
SEA BUCKTHORN

Type: hardy, deciduous shrub or small tree
Soil & situation: moist, well-drained, alkaline, sandy soil/full sun
North American hardiness zone: 3–8
Height & spread: 6m (20ft)
Grow for: excellent as a hedge; good for seaside areas; impressive fruit; AGM

Hippophae rhamnoides is one of the best shrubs for coastal planting and will grow in sand close to the hig- water line. It makes an efficient shelter belt and windbreak. When grown as a hedge the vicious thorns are a deterrent to animals.

The 5cm (2in) long, thin, grey-green leaves remain on the plant well into early winter. Male and female plants need to be close by for pollination. The small, insignificant, greenish-yellow flowers appear in spring. They are followed in autumn by masses of round, orange-yellow berries. The fruit is juicy but sufficiently acid to deter birds, thus allowing the shrub to hold its berries until early spring.

Older branches become brittle and have a habit of splitting. Hard prune in late summer, removing 50 per cent of the oldest branches. The following summer prune the remaining branches in the same way. This will encourage new shoots to grow from the base. Propagation is by seed sown as soon as it is ripe in autumn. Allow it to stratify in a cold frame. Examine the base of the parent plant for self-sown seedlings. Semi-ripe cuttings root in summer. Hardwood cuttings are rooted outside in the ground in autumn. Layering works well, forming large, rooted plants quickly. **JC**

Hippophäe rhamnoides

Hoheria sexstylosa 'Stardust'

Hoheria sexstylosa 'Stardust'

LONG-LEAVED LACE BARK, NEW ZEALAND LACE BARK

Type: hardy, evergreen tree or shrub
Soil & situation: tolerant of most soils except heavy clay, prefers a well-drained loam/sun/shelter
North American hardiness zone: 8–10
Height: 8m (25ft)
Spread: 6m (20ft)
Grow for: evergreen foliage; masses of white flowers in mid- and late summer; AGM

My wife Gill planned a surprise party for my fortieth birthday – what a treat! I arrived home from work and was delighted – and shocked – to find a host of friends had come to join the celebrations. Among them were Roy Lancaster and his wife Sue, who came bearing plants! Their trays of treasures included *Hoheria sextylosa* 'Stardust', a plant Roy had named. It's compact, columnar, vigorous, appears to be hardier than the species and flowers freely from an early age – mine has already produced a few blooms, and I can't wait until it matures when the great mass of mid-green foliage will be star-spangled with dense clusters of white flowers. They are so pretty that I'm growing mine as a shrub for optimum flower power!

Other selections include the weeping form *H. sextylosa* 'Pendula' and two related species *H. lyallii* and *H. populnea,* not as robust but very beautiful; there are plenty of spectacular New Zealand plants, but these are among the best.

Although hardy throughout the UK, it flourishes in damp, mild climates and is suitable for seaside planting. Planted against a wall in a sunny position with shelter from drying winds is ideal. In cold winters it can lose its leaves but rapidly recovers with the onset of spring. Prune to tidy up in the spring after the last frosts. Propagate by layering from late autumn to early spring, or by semi-ripe cuttings in late summer. **MB**

Hosta 'Gold Standard'

Plant of the Week (see page 241)

Humulus lupulus

HOP

Type: hardy, herbaceous, climbing crop
Soil & situation: rich, moist soil/full sun or light shade
North American hardiness zone: 4–8
Height: 6m (20ft)
Spread: 3m (10ft)
Grow for: decorative, aromatic leaves; interesting, scented flowers; and a useful crop

The hop is a strange plant, wreathed in mystery, closely related to cannabis and used in beer ostensibly as a flavouring and preservative. Just to grow it is educational, but to use it to excess detrimental. The young shoots, which can be eaten like asparagus (in the manner of; they are stringy and bitter) writhe from the ground like snakes. They climb at an amazing speed, reaching over 6m (20ft) given the support, then they burst into gorgeous cascades of golden-green panicles of scented flowers surmounting the grapevine-like, aromatic foliage. Glorious.

A UK and European native, hops were allegedly known to the Romans but did not become widely used for beer making until the 15th century. Our name *Humulus* is a Latinized form of the old European name *hummel,* while *lupulus* is Latin for small wolf, from its habit of choking whatever it comes upon. Male and female flowers are usually borne on different plants and only the female ones are of any use or value. Improved specialized varieties are used for serious beer making.

It prefers a rich, moist old meadow, well-manured soil, and plenty of sun and strong supports. To use this plant to its potential you need tall supports – and then a tall ladder! Leave only three or so shoots per plant if you want crop production and nip off rest. It can be grown from seed but improved known female varieties only from rooted offsets in spring. Hops can have devastating attacks of aphids. **BF**

Humulus lupulus

Hyacinthus orientalis 'Lady Derby'

Hyacinthus orientalis 'Lady Derby'
HYACINTH

Type: hardy, spring-flowering bulb
Soil & situation: moist, well-drained, fertile soil/sun or partial shade
Height: 20–30cm (8–12in)
Spread: 8cm (3½in)
Grow for: pretty, rose-pink, fragrant, spring flowers

Spring wouldn't be the same without the bowls of bright, perfumed flowers and the huge areas of hyacinths bedded out in our parks. Then there are all the primary school windowsills filled with glasses, each holding a flowering bulb and showing a mass of white roots in murky water. *Hyacinthus orientalis* 'Lady Derby' is my favourite pink-flowering hyacinth. Neither too dark nor too pale, its single rose-pink flowers make up a 20cm (8in) raceme of up to 40 flowers. The lance-shaped, channelled, bright green leaves continue to grow after flowering to a height of 30cm (12in).

Specially prepared bulbs are available in late summer to force for early indoor flowering. Avoid waterlogged compost in containers or a heavy, clay border soil. They may be lifted immediately after flowering to clear the bed for other plants. Remove the dead flower and heel the bulb, complete with leaves, into damp sand or peat until the foliage has died. Always use gloves when handling hyacinths to reduce the risk of skin allergies. **JC**

Hydrangea anomala subsp. *petiolaris*
CLIMBING HYDRANGEA

Type: hardy, deciduous climber
Soil & situation: moist, fertile, well-drained soil/sun or shade
North American hardiness zone: 4–9
Height: 25m (80ft) if grown in suitable trees, usually much smaller
Grow for: attractive foliage, early summer flowers and peeling bark in winter

In the UK I'm often asked to recommend a climber for a north-facing wall; my answer is '*Hydrangea anomala* subsp. *petiolaris*' and the conversation goes something like this: 'Hang on, doesn't everyone plant that, it's a bit boring, isn't it?' to which I reply, 'Well yes, lots of people plant it, but I wouldn't say it's boring; dependable, more like with fresh green, serrated leaves in spring, beautiful lace-cap flowers in early summer and bronze peeling bark on the older stems in winter, year after year after year. Would you be able to retain such freshness and good humour after labouring at the coal-face for a life time? I doubt it'! There are few better plants for a shady wall, they are self-clinging but need some support until the roots 'get a grip' and can be trained as espaliers and free-standing shrubs too. The most impressive displays, however, are when they clamber up giant trees, holding on by their finger tips, then flaunt their lacy garments to be viewed from afar.

It thrives in fertile, moist, well-drained soil, high in organic matter. When planting, ensure that it is at least 60cm (24in) away from the base of the foundations. Tie the stems to a cane leaning against the wall during the early years and moisten the brickwork occasionally with a sprayer to encourage the roots to stick. Mulch and feed in spring with a balanced fertilizer. Prune in spring to encourage branching and to keep it within its allotted space. Propagate by layering or semi-ripe cuttings from mid-summer. **MB**

Hydrangea anomala subsp. *petiolaris*

Bunny adds:
This is one of only a few self-clinging climbers, so it is highly useful to millions of more sporadic gardeners. Not only useful, it also has exquisite white lace-cap-like heads of sumptuous greenish-white flowers in summer. I do find that in certain gardens (mine for instance) where the dry conditions are not totally to its liking and the exposure levels are high, it is slow to get off the ground, but who can blame it? But in other conditions, it is up and away in no time. It clings adroitly, by its aerial roots. Hilliers catalogue mentions that it is picturesque when grown as a shrub, which had never occurred to me, but it seems like a great idea.

Hydrangea arborescens 'Annabelle'
Plant of the Week (see page 273)

Hydrangea aspera subsp. *sargentiana*

Type: hardy, deciduous shrub
Soil & situation: light, humus-rich, moist, fertile soil; tolerates chalk/bright, sheltered position
North American hardiness zone: 7–8
Height: 3m (10ft), or more
Spread: 2.5m (8ft)
Grow for: overall appearance; flowers in mid- and late summer

This sumptuously dressed, rather haughty, aristocratic shrub whose young stems are clothed in hairs and bristles and with leaves of the finest 'velvet' would not look out of place in a Victorian costume drama. Remarkable flat flowerheads up to 23cm (9in) across appear in mid- and late summer; the fertile flowers are lilac-rose, surrounded by guardian sterile florets, just over 3cm (1in) across, of pinkish-white. A well-grown, mature plant is magnificent, yet I find them slightly sinister. They combine elegance and serenity with an air of 'gothic' menace that's unmatched by any other; a compelling but unsettling plant!

This hydrangea is hardy but in need of shelter and protection, and although often grown in woodland gardens it is unhappy with competition from surrounding plants. It is reasonably tolerant of chalky soils and needs humus-rich, well-drained soil with plenty of well-rotted organic matter and an annual mulch in spring, when a top dressing of fertilizer is beneficial. Position in good light but protected from the scorching midday sun. Prune in spring to maintain the shape.

On established plants, young growth can be damaged by late frosts but it recovers very quickly producing a more resistant second flush, so the plant is often restored to health within four weeks. Younger plants are much more vulnerable and should be protected from frost. Propagate by layering in spring or semi-ripe cuttings in summer. **MB**

John adds:
If the flowerheads are allowed to remain they offer some frost protection to the new growths. The individual sterile flowers gradually deteriorate, becoming filament-like and see-through. Old plants may become leggy with all the leaf growth at the top of the plant. In late winter prune half the branches down to 45cm (18in) above ground level. Strong new shoots will appear from the stumps. The remaining branches can be cut the following year.

Hydrangea aspera subsp. *sargentiana*

Hypericum perforatum

Hydrangea aspera Villosa Group

Type: hardy deciduous shrub
Soil & situation: moist, but well-drained soil/fair amount of organic matter/part shade or sun/does not like windy conditions.
North American hardiness zone: 7–9
Height & spread: up to 4m (13ft)
Grow for: fantastic lilac-blue and whitish flowers in late summer; attractive, dark green leaves covered with soft down on their undersides and slightly downy on top; AGM

This hydrangea looks perfect in areas of light woodland or shady mixed borders. Although it grows exuberantly in the wetter and more acid areas of the country, *Hydrangea aspera*, together with *H. involucrata* 'Hortensis', are the most tolerant hydrangeas for growing on chalky soils. It is also a surprisingly strong-growing shrub which will settle in fairly rapidly and get on with life. Because hydrangeas come into growth early on, young shoots can get damaged by late frosts. After this initial setback, they quickly carry on producing their large, beautifully felted leaves. It is an ideal plant to grow in a prominent position against a shady wall: the protection from full sun is necessary to maintain the superb flower colour. If you are growing this plant on a thin, more impoverished soil, it is worthwhile adding lots of organic matter at planting and regularly applying a good mulch in autumn. Little pruning is required, the main task being to remove crossing shoots, diseased or unhealthy wood and anything that looks too eccentric. This is best done in late winter or early spring. **BG**

Hypericum perforatum
ST JOHN'S WORT

Type: herbaceous perennial
Soil & situation: moist soil/light shade
North American hardiness zone: 3–8
Height & spread: clump to 60cm (24in)
Grow for: good ground cover in shade, with dark green foliage and small yellow flowers

The most common member of this genus, *Hypericum calycinum*, the rose of Sharon, is everywhere; it fills supermarket and municipal car-park borders and even comes up as a weed. *H. perforatum* is much more civilized, and is effectively herbaceous, so can be cut back hard each winter and kept really neat. The flowers are yellow and small but welcome, and it is said the leaves taken internally under medical supervision relieve depression.

Hypericum is one of 160 species native to copses and woodlands in the UK and Europe. The Latin name is from the Greek *hyper*, meaning above, and *eikon*, picture, as the flowers were hung above icons to ward off evil on St John's day, June 24th, thus also giving it the common name of St John's wort. The *perforatum* part is from the tiny oil glands that appear as punctures through the leaf and can be seen if a piece of foliage is held up to the light. The French call it 'thousand punctures plant'. These oil cells make it an invaluable medicinal plant but not for home use, and have led to the breeding of varieties with a high oil content.

St John's wort copes quite well with a dry site, but will be long lived in moist, loamy soil in partial shade. Avoid handling because the oil gives this plant smelly leaves. It can be cut back like any herbaceous plant once the flowering stems wither. Sow in spring or divide established clumps. It suffers no problems. **BF**

Hyssopus officinalis

Hyssopus officinalis
HYSSOP

Type: small, tenderish shrub
Soil & situation: well-drained soil/full sun
North American hardiness zone: 6–9
Height: 60cm (24in)
Spread: 60cm (24in)
Grow for: a beautiful, semi-evergreen, bright blue flowered shrub

I find hyssop annoying as I keep losing it and having to replace it, but it is fairly easy to propagate and, occasionally, I even find odd seedlings self-sown. The azure-blue flowers are small but mass themselves over the entire bush, emitting a powerful fragrance on warm days, which attracts every bee in my garden. Some of the best honey too! Hyssop can be kept pretty tidy and is good for edging as long as it is not shaded or exposed. It has useful culinary properties – the petals have a sort of tangy minty-piney flavour and I use them in moderation in salads and stews.

The name hyssop stems from the Latin, which comes from the Greek *hussopos* and the Hebrew *esob* or *ezob*, holy herb, which is all very confusing because the hyssop of the Bible was probably actually what we know as marjoram. Introduced in the Middle Ages, hyssop has never been much improved, though there are pink, and white, miffy forms.

Even in a well-drained, light, warm soil and position hyssop is not long lived as it soon succumbs to a bad winter. Trim to keep it neat and tidy as growth commences in spring. To propagate, sow seed in spring or divide the roots, or take summer cuttings. Hyssop can be lost in very cold weather so back up with half-ripe cuttings with a heel rooted in a cold frame in the summer. **BF**

Ilex aquifolium 'J.C. van Tol'
HOLLY

Type: hardy, evergreen tree
Soil & situation: moist, well-drained, humus-rich soil/full sun or partial shade
North American hardiness zone: 7–9
Height: 7m (23ft)
Spread: 4m (13ft)
Grow for: guaranteed clusters of bright red berries; AGM

With this holly there is no need to wonder if there will be a good crop of berries. Being hermaphrodite, it carries male and female flowers on the same plant ensuring pollination.

The 7.5cm (3in) long, glossy, dark green leaves are slightly puckered with few or no spines. The young shoots are dark purple. Small clusters of creamy-white flowers appear in early summer and are followed, in autumn, by bright red fruit.

Don't plant it in a site where the soil dries out in summer and avoid biting cold, drying winds. Once established, it dislikes being disturbed. Planting and transplanting should be carried out in late winter or early spring. Birds love the berries and to be sure of a supply for winter decoration you will have to secure them early by covering the clusters with muslin bags.

Prune in late winter to remove vigorous stems that are spoiling the shape. Where there are two erect branches, competing for leader and making a narrow angle, remove the weaker stem. A row of *I. aquifolium* 'J.C. van Tol' makes a wonderful hedge and it should be trimmed in early spring. Propagate by semi-ripe cuttings in late summer or early autumn in a heated propagator. **JC**

Ilex crenata 'Convexa' (syn. *I. c.* 'Bullata')
BOX-LEAVED HOLLY, JAPANESE HOLLY

Type: hardy, evergreen shrub to small tree
Soil & situation: most soils except waterlogged/sun or shade
North American hardiness zone: 5–7
Height: up to 2.5m (8ft)
Spread: to 2m (6½ft)
Grow for: tiny, neat, evergreen leaves; useful for hedging and shaping; white flowers followed by glossy, black berries in the autumn; AGM

Ilex aquifolium 'J.C. van Tol'

Ilex crenata 'Convexa'

The first time I was aware of this plant was when I saw a magnificent, cloud-pruned specimen that was about 1.5m (5ft) high. The leaves, being only about 1cm (less than ½in) long, make it an ideal plant to clip, shape and train. Because of the diminutive leaves, you would not necessarily know it was a holly – the leaves are elliptically shaped, curved and a mid-dark green colour. Several gardeners I know of, whose gardens have suffered from box blight disease, have replaced the dwarf hedges with this holly and it seems to work a treat. The downside is that it is more difficult to get hold of than box, but then it is not so much of a cliche. Hollies, as a rule, do not like being moved much, so they can take a little time to settle down and get into their stride.

The species *Ilex crenata* is also useful for low hedges, but the leaves are larger, about 2–3cm (1in) long, so not so neat-looking.

If shaping the plant, cut it in late summer so that you are cutting the shoots before they are fully ripened. If you cut before this, you may well get further new growth the same year, causing you to carry out a further cut to keep it looking pristine. Berries are formed on two-year-old wood and are black and glossy. When planting all hollies, reduce the stress as much as possible in the first few years. Although they tolerate exposure well, they hate it before they are established, so temporary shelter netting, adequate moisture in dry periods and no weed competition help dramatically to get this plant going. Propagate by cuttings in late summer. **BG**

Impatiens omeiana

Type: hardy, herbaceous perennial
Soil & situation: moist soil/dappled shade
North American hardiness zone: 7–8
Height: 50cm (20in)
Spread: indefinite
Grow for: beautiful foliage; unusual flowers from late summer to late autumn

American plantsman Don Jacobs found this treasure growing at 2,440m (8,000ft) among rhododendrons and tiarellas on Mt Omei in Sichuan, China in 1983. It was the first discovery of a plant that was previously only known as a lifeless two-dimensional specimen, pressed to a sheet of stiff paper in a herbarium (a scientific collection of pressed plants). To find it alive and flourishing must have been incredibly exciting! Now this delightful exotic is in cultivation; it is excellent ground cover for damp shade and perfect for a moist spot in a woodland garden, gradually spreading where conditions allow. Its crowning glory is the fabulous foliage that looks like that of a New Guinea impatiens. The leaves are long and narrow, purple to olive-green with yellowish-green ribs and a more prominent central vein and are arranged in circles around the stem. The apricot-yellow flowers appear in late summer or early autumn, hanging like elongated trumpets or plump goldfish – depending on your imagination! – from stems in the leaf axils. It looks good in a pot in a 'tropical' garden.

It needs full or part shade in moist, well-drained soil; mulch in spring. It is hardy – the weather in its natural habitat can be fairly chilly; cut back stems and protect with a layer of mulch over winter. Propagate by seed, division in spring or cuttings in spring or early summer. **MB**

Impatiens omeiana

Impatiens tinctoria

Impatiens tinctoria

Type: tender, tuberous perennial
Soil & situation: moist, free-draining soil/sun/shelter
North American hardiness zone: 9–10
Height: 2.2m (7ft)
Spread: 1m (3ft)
Grow for: unusual flowers from late summer to mid-autumn

Impatiens tinctoria is not your average blowsy busy Lizzie (don't mention the name in its presence!). This spectacular species comes from mountainous forests, shady, shrub-filled gullies on damp banks and by streams from eastern Zaire and southern Sudan to Ethiopia and northern Uganda – exotic locations that conjure up an air of magic and mystery!

It's a lush, vigorous, upright plant that forms bold clumps of stout fleshy stems, each with large lance-shaped leaves to 20cm (8in) long, which look perfect in a 'tropical' garden. The remarkable, fragrant flowers hang on long upright stalks, like giant, pure white butterflies flitting above the foliage. The two lower petals are landing pads for visiting insects and the rounded throat is marked with a bold splash of colour ranging from violet to burgundy and magenta that trickles down onto the petals. It's a fabulous plant for the garden, with magnificent foliage but it's those amazing flowers that really make it a plant to savour.

It needs moist, humus-rich soil that is well drained in winter. Dig in plenty of well-rotted leafmould and grit in heavier soils. Ideal for a warm, sheltered corner by a wall or greenhouse in mild climates where it can be long lived. Cut back the stems in autumn and protect with dry mulch, like bracken or straw, until there's no danger of frost. In colder areas, treat it like a dahlia by lifting and over-wintering in a cool, frost-free place. Divide in spring, adding plenty of organic matter to the soil before planting. **MB**

Alcea rosea 'Nigra'

HOLLYHOCK

Type: hardy perennial
Soil & situation: sharply-drained soil/sunny position.
Hardiness zone: 3–9
Height: 2.4m (7½ft)
Spread: to 60cm (24in)
Grow for: the archetypal cottage garden plant; unusual, wine-coloured flowers, which give this well-loved flower a more extravagant air and last from early to late summer, sometimes longer

There is always room for these lofty beauties, which are easy and fun to grow. The single flowers are, of course, not black, but a rich, maroon-wine colour and have a yellow throat – quite a combination. The papery flowers are arranged all the way up the towering spires. I like them best growing against a building, preferably near a door, where you can get up close to them.

They will set seed in the most impenetrable-looking cracks that are rarely in intolerable positions. The far better known *A. rosea* comes in red, white, yellow and pink forms, and these too are fetching. They all form really striking cut flowers.

The problem with these beauties is, of course, rust. It is recommended that preventative measures are taken by spraying from late spring before the outbreak occurs. If it does occur, you get rid of the plant. However, in some areas rust is less prevalent. I do not spray routinely but remove them if they get attacked and plant new plants elsewhere the next year. As they are easy from seed this is no huge loss. They can be sown in summer and then planted out into their final position in autumn to flower the following summer. You can, of course, treat them as biennials and hopefully avoid a lot of the rust altogether. They may need staking, especially if your soil is fertile, but I tend to get away without having to do so. **BG**

Imperata cylindrica 'Rubra'
JAPANESE BLOOD GRASS

Type: hardy, deciduous perennial
Soil & situation: moist, slightly acid, humus-rich soil/back-lit by sunshine
North American hardiness zone: 4–9
Height: 40cm (16in)
Spread: 30cm (12in)
Grow for: blood-red leaves

Take one bright green grass, dip the tips in blood red then watch it slowly diffuse down the stems until mid-summer and beyond. By autumn, it is completely crimson. It's incredible how so many unusual and beautiful plants come from Japan; *Salix gracistylis* 'Melanostachys', the willow with 'black' catkins (see page 347), 'fancy' hepaticas (page 206) and this spectacular grass. There have also been some complete duffers, like the horrendous *Salix integra* 'Hakuro-nishiki', which is weak, insipid and looks like a pile of vomit. This, however, is one of the best and most beautiful. Placed so that it is back-lit by the evening sun, it becomes bathed in a rich red glow and is a spectacular sight. This spreading, shallow-rooted plant emerges late and creates an excellent contrast between softer colours and arching grasses like *Stipa tenuissima*. I would place it in a pot on a plinth at eye level, rather than ground level, so that every centimetre could be savoured!

It needs moist, well-drained, fertile, slightly acid, humus-rich soil in full sun or light shade, though it tolerates some drought once established. It is also happy on clay. Not reliably frost hardy, grow in containers if your garden is exceptionally cold or in a frost pocket; over-winter in a cool, frost-free place. Cut back plants in spring and mulch with well-rotted organic matter. Divide in late autumn or spring. Aphids, slugs and snails can be a problem. **MB**

Imperata cylindrica 'Rubra'

Indocalamus tessellatus f. *hamadae*

Type: hardy evergreen perennial
Soil & situation: moist soil/partial shade
North American hardiness zone: 8–11
Height & spread: 3m (10ft), or more
Grow for: architectural form and leaves

There's always been an interest in bringing a tropical touch to the garden and anything with big bold leaves or unusual flowers is usually welcomed with open cheque book. It's inevitable that among the spiny cacti and hardy palms there are also some big bamboos and this is one of the best for its massive, delicately ridged leaves.

Formally known as *Indocalamus hamadae* but now classified as a form of *I. tessellatus*, this is a real beauty. The elegant stems, to 1.5cm (over 1/2in) thick, support noble leaves, usually about 40cm (16in) long, sometimes longer, and 8–60cm (3 1/2–24in) wide. It's native to Kyushu in Japan, where the leaves were used for wrapping rice balls. *I. tessellatus* has long leaves too, consistently reaching 60cm (24in). It forms dense thickets of slender, bright green canes with a waxy bloom that simply collapse under the weight of the leaves to form a low mound. Both are stunning, just make sure that you have the space for them to grow.

They prefer partial shade on moist, humus-rich soils. They can be grown in pots but need regular division. Plant in a hole 90cm (36in) wide and 45cm (18in) deep. Dig in plenty of well-rotted manure or garden compost. Thoroughly soak the bamboo in a bucket before planting a little deeper than it was in the pot. Water well. It does not spread too far, but you can put in a plastic barrier about 10cm (4in) below the ground. Mulch annually in spring and keep the ground moist. Thin out the canes to keep them under control. Divide in spring. **MB**

Ipomoea batatas
SWEET POTATO

Type: tender, perennial, semi-evergreen climber
Soil & situation: rich, moist soil/full sun/under cover
North American hardiness zone: 9–11
Height: climbs to 3m (10ft)
Spread: 3m (10ft)
Grow for: attractive, ivy-like, edible foliage; very pretty flowers; edible roots

Sweet potatoes have slowly been improved and it is now possible, given a good summer, to grow them outdoors even in the UK. Young plants are actually being sold commercially. However they do much better under cover in a greenhouse or conservatory, though they can go out on the patio in the height of summer. The heart-shaped leaves have a healthy, vigorous, dark green luxuriousness which makes this a beautiful climber for a big tub. Many varieties flower with pretty bindweed-like blooms in pink, white and purple, and if they have done well at the end of the season you have a load of delicious sweet potatoes to eat as well!

A native of South America, sweet potatoes came to Europe even before the more common 'Irish' potato, which also came from the South America. The latter triumphed because the sweet is more frost tender and it is hard to over-winter the tubers. It has to be over-wintered as rooted layers or slips, which is not convenient. There are several strains; the yellow-fleshed and the white with pink, purple, red or orange skins. Don't confuse these with yams, which are another genus – *Dioscorea*.

It needs well-drained but moist, rich, limy soil preferably in a big tub or greenhouse border. Nip out tips and tie runners to a pole or strings to keep them off the ground – if they touch the soil they root everywhere and waste energy on making sweet potato spaghetti. Root tips as layers in early autumn and over-winter plantlets in the warmth. Alternatively force a supermarket tuber and detach shoots when a finger or so long, pot up and grow on in the warmth, potting up regularly, and as the new season gets underway move or plant outdoors a few weeks after the last frost. Tubers may get nibbled by rodents! **BF**

Ipomoea batatas

Iris 'Brown Lasso'

Iris 'Brown Lasso'

Type: hardy, perennial rhizome
Soil & situation: well-drained soil/sun
North American hardiness zone: 3–9
Height & spread: 55cm (22in) x 30 cm (12in), or more
Grow for: striking flowers in early summer; sword-shaped foliage; AGM

Beware of being seduced by the pictures in a magazine; they glamorize reality and the only limit is your imagination. The first time I saw this glamorous iris, it had made the front cover and everything I imagined about it was true! There are so many beautiful irises that it takes something extraordinary for one to stand out from the rest, here, the colours are irresistible – it seems that however unusual the colour combination, in nature, it seems to work. We are not worthy!

The three upright petals are deep butterscotch while those hanging downwards are light violet with caramel-brown margins and a yellow beard. The description is simple, the impact, stunning! 'Brown Lasso' is a border bearded iris, flowering in early summer and good for small gardens and windy sites. It is beautiful, robust and a good grower too. Some have everything; others, nothing. It's just not fair!

It needs free-draining soil and full sun, but tolerates partial shade. Dig in sharp sand or gravel on clay soils and grow in raised beds; add organic matter or leafmould to lighter soils. If possible plant so the cut end of the rhizome faces south and the fan north so the rhizome is not shaded. It needs a good baking in summer; don't let the rhizomes get weedy; remove dead leaves and spent flowers to save energy.

Divide every two to three years to keep plants vigorous; the top of the rhizome should be only 1cm (½in) below the surface. Feed with high-potash fertilizer at half rate when planting and in early spring to help flowering. It can be affected by aphids and rot in poorly drained soils. **MB**

Iris danfordiae

Type: hardy bulb
Soil & situation: free-draining soil/sun
North American hardiness zone: 5–8
Height: 15cm (6in)
Spread: 7.5cm (3in)
Grow for: bright yellow flowers from late winter to early spring

This bulbous iris, a relative of the elegant *Iris reticulata* (see page 221), is a true harbinger of spring. It is always a pleasure to greet the small, bright yellow flowers about 5cm (2in) long that illuminate the winter border. Study it closely to enjoy the green tints and spots in the centre along a deep orange ridge; the upright petals or standards at the top of the flower have almost disappeared, all that remains are tiny bristles. It is found in the mountains of Turkey along the snowline and pushes its way through the snow to flower, as it sometimes does here in the UK. The glowing yellow flowers are a wonderful sight against the pure white background of snow and a sure reminder that springtime and sunshine are not far behind. It is good at the front of rockeries, in borders, containers or among silver-foliage plants. Combined with blue chionodoxas it is a thoroughly uplifting sight.

It is cheap and is better treated as an annual. According to Brian Mathew, an expert and connoisseur of bulbs, it has a habit of splitting into a tiny group of non-flowerings bulbs. He has been successful in establishing a group by planting them at least 10cm (4in) deep and feeding with high-potash fertilizer in early spring and autumn. Why not try it too?

It needs sunshine, ideally a good summer baking, and free-draining, preferably alkaline soil; dig in sharp sand or grit if necessary before planting. When growing as an annual don't worry about the soil, providing it is not waterlogged. **MB**

Iris danfordiae

Iris foetidissima

Iris foetidissima
STINKING IRIS

Type: hardy, evergreen perennial rhizome
Soil & situation: moist, well-drained soil/partial shade
North American hardiness zone: 7–9
Height: 60–90cm (24–36in)
Spread: indefinite
Grow for: summer flowers; interesting seeds in autumn; AGM

It really isn't fair to call it stinking. It is not the flower but the leaf which has the unpleasant smell, and only when it is crushed. Most of us could go through life without crushing an iris leaf!

Vigorous growing, it has tufts of 80cm (32in) long, dark green leaves. The 5–8cm (2–3½in) wide, mat, purple-yellow flowers are produced in early summer on long branched stems each carrying up to five blooms. They are followed in autumn by large, club-shaped capsules, which split to reveal bright, orange-red seeds. Occasionally the seeds are yellow, scarlet or white. It is good for a woodland situation or on a shady bank close to a pond.

A deep surface mulch of composted bark in spring is beneficial. Propagation is by seed sown in autumn or spring without protection or by division of the fleshy rhizomes in early autumn and replanting immediately. The plant is poisonous to livestock, which is a very good reason for keeping cows out of your garden! **JC**

Bunny adds:
A useful plant for its leaves and the long-lasting and eye-catching seeds. It seeds freely all round my garden, and seems fairly happy in sunny situations too.

Iris germanica var. *florentina*
ORRIS ROOT

Type: hardy, herbaceous perennial rhizome
Soil & situation: dry, limy soil/full sun
North American hardiness zone: 3–9
Height: 50cm (20in)
Spread: indefinite
Grow for: attractive, sword-shaped, light green leaves; palest pastel decorated white flowers with heavenly scent; good for stuffing mummies and cleaning your teeth; AGM

Iris are often overlooked as 'common' and so they are, loads of them in all sorts of colours and sizes. They are adaptable and some variety or other will grow in every different place, usually putting on a good show. *Iris germanica* var. *florentina* is delicate, needing a warm, sheltered spot but then it is delightful. It is nice in leaf and the finely sculptured blooms are lightly scented of the finest soap, but it is the roots that captivate. Once dried they become orris root, which is used in potpourri, perfumes and toiletries and has been since ancient times. The smell of violets from the roots gets stronger as they dry and wither.

Iris is the Greek goddess of the rainbow. It was thought to come from Florence, and even though it is in fact from southern Europe, it was first known to be grown in gardens in 1500BC in Egypt, where it is shown distinctly on tomb walls at Karnak.

Iris germanica var. *florentina*

Iris pseudacorus 'Variegata'

In dismal weather it may not be very long lived and, anyway, it needs replanting every few years to keep up its vigour. Iris are hard to plant as their rhizome needs to be above the soil and the roots (few as there are) must not be buried deep or straight down, thus it is difficult to anchor with the green leaf on top; I use two bricks to temporarily hold down the roots under a thin layer of soil and pushed up to either side of the rhizome, thus still exposing it to the sun. The books say plant these rhizomes in mid-summer, but I have also split and replanted mine in spring just as they started into growth. It is not happy if shaded, cold or wet. **BF**

Iris pseudacorus 'Variegata'
FLAG IRIS

Type: hardy, perennial rhizome
Soil & situation: permanently moist, humus-rich, deep, acid soil/full sun or partial shade
North American hardiness zone: 5–8
Height: 75–90cm (30–36in)
Spread: 45cm (18in)
Grow for: bold, architectural leaves; perfect for waterside planting; AGM

I used to grow large quantities of this plant for sale. In spring the 1-litre black plastic pots of young, creamy-white striped, variegated, sword-like leaves were an instant buy. There were always a few plants with pure white variegation and they were highly sought after. I grew it because I liked it.

The variegation remains as the leaves lengthen and they continue to be rigid and upright. In mid- to late summer each branched stem produces between four and eight bright yellow flowers. Strong-growing, it spreads quickly by

Iris reticulata

thick rhizomes. This moisture-loving plant looks well positioned beside water and it can be grown in pots in shallow water but its growth is more restricted. Planted beside a strong-flowing garden waterfall it tolerates the water splash while providing camouflage for a change in levels.

Propagation is by lifting and dividing large, overgrown clumps. Re-plant straight away in their permanent sites. Healthy rhizomes can be cut into lengths retaining one shoot per length and rooted in trays of wet peat and grit mixed. Once rooted they are potted on for a season before planting out. The principal pests are slugs, which damage the young leaves and the flowers. **JC**

Iris reticulata

Type: hardy, spring-flowering bulb
Soil & situation: moist, free-draining, neutral to slightly alkaline soil/full sun or light shade
North American hardiness zone: 5–8
Height: in flower 5–10cm (2–4in); after flowering, foliage 30cm (12in)
Spread: 5cm (2in)
Grow for: bluey, fragrant flowers in winter; makes a fine show in a group; AGM

If you make it happy *Iris reticulata* can be in flower in mid-winter but more usually from late winter to early spring. The fragrant flowers come in various shades of blue, from Wedgewood through to deep velvety purple. The true wild form is a deep purple-blue with an orange-yellow raised stripe along the centre of each fall (petal). The thin, four-ribbed leaves appear to be square in section. After flowering they continue to grow to 30cm (12in).

Ideal in groups in a rockery, scree bed or container, they dislike being forced for early indoor show. Choose bulbs which are firm and packed in sawdust to prevent them drying out. Check the skin is creamy-white and free from the black blotches of ink spot disease, a fungus which first shows as yellowing foliage. The bulbs eventually turn black and rot. There is no control other than burning infected bulbs.

When grown on heavy, wet soil the bulbs often split after flowering and refuse to flower the following year. Planting in a raised bed in autumn in well-drained soil with extra grit prevents this problem. Lift and divide every few years when fully dormant, re-planting 10cm (4in) deep.

There are many selections of the species, including 'Harmony', which is blue and yellow, 'Cantab', pale blue and yellow, 'J. S. Dijt', red-purple with orange markings, and 'Natascha', pure white with a butter-yellow strip. **JC**

Iris 'Superstition'

Type: hardy, perennial rhizome
Soil & situation: prefers very well-drained soil that is fairly neutral/will tolerate alkaline soil/hates acid soils and poor drainage/sun
North American hardiness zone: 3–9
Height: 90cm (36in)
Spread: 15cm (6in)
Grow for: beautiful dark wine-purple to black flowers during the early summer; foliage is grey-green and not unattractive; AGM

There are so many different irises to choose from it is not always easy to know which is the best for you. If you are keen on the exotic dark purple, almost black colour range, then you need look no further than Iris 'Superstition'. It is a difficult colour to find in plants generally, but bearded irises seem to come up trumps here. The whole plant is a good, strong, robust grower with the flowers carried on stout stems above the leaves. It is generally a good, healthy plant despite its truly exotic flower colour. My cousin, Claire Austin, who was an illustrator before starting her nursery where she now grows more than 400 different irises, describes this one far better than I could, 'in texture its falls are glossy as silk, and its standards are silkier still. The beard is dark purple, and the whole flower is ruffled and scented.' So you can see it is a difficult one to resist.

If your soil is wet it is worth considering growing irises in raised beds, or else digging a large hole and adding free-draining material, prior to planting. When you plant the rhizomes (assuming they have arrived bare rooted) the top of the rhizome should be just above the soil and the roots spread out to anchor it. If you have bought pot-grown plants, remove the potting compost before planting. Water the plant in gently with a sprinkling of water. Divide the irises once every three or four years: this is best done in late summer or autumn, discarding the older bits. Re-plant and cut the foliage back to about 15cm (6in), otherwise the routine care calls for removing any manky leaves in autumn to prevent the spread of disease. **BG**

Itea illicifolia

Itea illicifolia

Type: hardy, dense evergreen shrub
Soil & situation: moist, fertile, free-draining soil/sun or partial shade
North American hardiness zone: 7–9
Height & spread: 5m (16ft)
Grow for: foliage and catkins of mellifluous flowers in late summer and early autumn; AGM

Yes, it's another holly 'doppelgänger'! You could easily be misled by *Itea illicifolia* until closer scrutiny reveals that the leaves are thinner and not as glossy or undulating and the young growth is coppery in colour. Long racemes of tiny, greenish-white flowers burst from the arching stem tips in late summer and early autumn, lengthening as the season passes until they hang like lamb's tails between 15–30cm (6–12in) long, barely moving in the passing breeze. At dusk and overnight, a heady, honey-sweet fragrance pervades the atmosphere around them, enticing moths in great numbers to come and sip of their nectar. Place a chair nearby and just sit and enjoy it too!

A related species, *I. yunnanensis,* is similar but the leaves are longer and not as spiny or rounded, the white flowers in hanging clusters up to 18cm (7in) long. *I. virginica* is a smaller, upright, deciduous shrub growing to 2.5m (8ft) with creamy-white, fragrant flowers in mid-summer. It often has good autumn colour, is hardier than the other two and needs good, constantly moist soil.

Prune at any time to keep within its allotted space. Propagate by softwood or semi-ripe cuttings from late summer to early autumn. It needs a warm, sunny position in fertile soil. In colder climates where it is not hardy, the shoots can be frosted and it even loses its leaves; it is best to train *I. illicifolia* along wires or grow it as a shrub against a sheltered, sunny wall. Protect and mulch plants in winter until they are established. **MB**

Jasminum nudiflorum

WINTER JASMINE

Type: hardy, deciduous shrub
Soil & situation: fertile, well-drained soil/full sun or light shade
North American hardiness zone: 6–9
Height & spread: 3m (10ft)
Grow for: colour in the winter garden; AGM

I have a soft spot for the winter jasmine. While it doesn't have the fragrance of other summer-flowering jasmines, its bright yellow flowers on leafless stems are a welcome sight in winter. Arching, dark green stems are coated with small lateral branches. The dark green leaves are divided into three, 3cm (1in) long leaflets. The solitary, six-petalled, bright yellow flowers appear in winter and early spring from the leaf axils. The tight flower buds are tipped red, making a contrast with the open flowers. They are immune to inclement weather. Left to its own devices it will scramble about forming a low, untidy mound of stems. Planted against a wall or trellis and given support it can display its winter charm.

Annual pruning after flowering will prevent stems becoming bare from the base upwards. Cut the flowered shoots to young growths lower down the stem. With small plants trim back to healthy buds. Mature, straggly plants should be hard pruned removing one third of the growths at ground level. Tie in the new shoots as they grow.

Propagate by semi-ripe cuttings in summer. Make the lower cut immediately below a pair of leaves. Stems layered in autumn will be well rooted and probably in flower by the following winter. **JC**

Jasminum nudiflorum

Jasminum revolutum

Jasminum revolutum (syn. *J. humile* 'Revolutum')

Type: frost-hardy, near-evergreen shrub
Soil & situation: any soil/sun to light shade
North American hardiness zone: 8–9
Height: 2m (6½ft)
Spread: 1m (3ft)
Grow for: unusual and very beautiful shrub with fragrant yellow flowers; AGM

Everyone knows the common jasmine, many know there are numerous other climbing jasmines, tender and hardy, but few gardeners know or grow any of the shrubby species. In fact, there are around 200 jasmines in all. *J. revolutum* is almost evergreen, although in severe weather it will drop its leaves. It has fragrant yellow flowers over a long season and is amenable to being neglected, but is more suited to the damper, milder west of England than in the east where I live. However, I had one for years until I foolishly moved it.

This jasmine is one of several shrubby species almost all of which have deciduous foliage and yellow flowers. *J. revolutum* was introduced to the UK from China in 1814 and is closely related to the more deciduous and inferior *J. humile*, but is not to be confused with the scentless *J. nudiflorum*, which flowers through winter. The name *revolutum* refers to the flowers having rolled-back edges.

It is happy in most soils and positions, but not in waterlogged or windy, exposed sites. Trim it in early spring if you need to remove wind-burnt leaves. It can be layered, otherwise try semi-ripe cuttings in summer with bottom heat. **BF**

Jasminum x *stephanense*

Type: perennial, deciduous climber
Soil & situation: most soils/full sun
North American hardiness zone: 8–10
Height: 8m (25ft)
Spread: 1–1.5m (3–5ft)
Grow for: young foliage in spring gives the striking effect of a ball of fire, then changes to yellow-green until the autumn; pink, scented flowers all summer

Common white jasmine, *Jasminum officinale*, is a well-known garden plant needing a sunny spot to thrive in evergreen glory and scented white flowers. It has dozens of relations, including *J. beesianum*, which has small carmine-coloured flowers. The cross between these two, *J.* x *stephanense*, was raised in France in the 1920s and is the only jasmine hybrid. The leaves are similar to both parents, less evergreen and more decidedly deciduous, and have fantastic colours when first unfurled, looking quite simply as if the foliage is on fire in red, yellow and cream. Later the foliage settles down to a pleasant lemon-green and the flowers take over. Masses of them for weeks; stupendous.

J. officinale has been grown from early times and is originally from the area between Persia and China, yet made it to England in time to be popular with the Tudors. The Arabic name was *yasamyn*, the Chinese *yeh-lse-ming*, and we made it sweet jessamine or jasmine and Latinization makes it *jasminum*.

Jasmines can be long lived in a sunny sheltered site with a well-drained soil and the addition of some lime. They may need shearing back one year in ten. I have sown seed of *J. beesianum* crossed with *J. officinale* and grown half a dozen plants all very similar to *J.* x *stephanense*; otherwise propagate by layers. It has no problems. **BF**

Jasminum x *stephanense*

Jeffersonia dubia

Jeffersonia dubia

Type: hardy, herbaceous perennial
Soil & situation: organic-rich, free-draining soil/dappled shade
North American hardiness zone: 5–7
Height: 20cm (8in)
Spread: 15cm (6in)
Grow for: flowers in late spring and early summer

If you're looking for delicate beauty, this is another 'must have'. This 'woodlander' from the forests of Manchuria has kidney-shaped or rounded, two-lobed leaves, blue-purple when first unfolding but gradually turning to green with deep purple tints. Appreciate the simple, dainty flowers of soft lavender-blue while you can, as they only remain open for two days, then gradually fade away – how transitory is beauty!

Its North American cousin *Jeffersonia diphylla* (rheumatism root or twinleaf) is found on limestone woodland near rivers and is very rare in the wild. It grows to 20cm (8in) plus x 15cm (6in) and has more petals than *J. dubia* and white flowers with a central boss. The leaves hover over the white like giant green butterflies protecting the tender flowers. It has been used extensively in herbal medicine as the name suggests, for anything from diarrhoea to cancer. The Shakers used it for several ailments including spasms and cramp.

This genus is named for Thomas Jefferson, third President of the USA, who was also a great gardener, landscape designer and agriculturist. In 1811 he wrote, 'No occupation is so delightful to me as the culture of the earth and no culture comparable to that of the garden'. Hear! Hear!

Grow in light to moderate, moist, well-drained soil in dappled shade. Add plenty of well-rotted organic matter, preferably leafmould, before planting if the soil is lacking it. Mulch around the plants in spring, if necessary. They are slow-growing in ideal conditions, where they make large clumps. They can be divided in early spring but resent disturbance. Sow seed as soon as possible in a cold frame. Prone to slug and snail damage. **MB**

Plectranthus argentatus

Type: tender, evergreen shrub
Soil & situation: medium fertile soil/sun or light shade/frost-free conditions in winter
North American hardiness zone: 9–10
Height & spread: 1m (3ft)
Grow for: a stunning foliage plant with silver, hairy leaves. Good at any frost-free time of year, but a perfect foil for summer flowers; AGM

Plectranthus argentatus is one of my most admired foliage plants. It has eye-catching (up to about 15cm/6in) grey-green leaves covered with silver hairs. These in turn are supported by downy, ascending, pinky-purple stems. The undersides of the ovate leaves are paler than the top. The flowers admittedly are less significant than the foliage. They are carried on 30cm (12in) racemes, are a not unattractive bluish-white and are shown off to their advantage against the pretty coloured stems. I use this put adjacent to plants like *Dahlia* 'Bishop of Llandaff', where the silvery leaves contrast with the purple, almost fern-like leaves. It is also a great plant for a summer container – something a bit different and rather good.

Although technically a shrub, it is usually treated as a tender perennial; small, rooted cuttings in spring will quickly form a presentable plant, whereas a larger shrub with its spreading habit will need annual cutting back to keep it in shape and take up too much precious greenhouse space during the winter. It is extremely easy to root from cuttings from new growth, which can be taken at any time of the year. **BG**

Juglans regia 'Franquette'

Juglans regia 'Franquette'

WALNUT

Type: hardy, deciduous tree
Soil & situation: well-drained soil/sunny position
North American hardiness zone: 3–7
Height: 30m (100ft) or more
Spread: 15m (50ft)
Grow for: fragrant leaves, beautiful form, edible nuts

Walnuts make big trees and are only suited to large sites, although the variety 'Franquette' is, for a walnut, compact and early bearing. In fact it cropped for me after only a few years, possibly because I knew that to pollinate the female flowers with saved up male catkins, which also flower early, would aid cross-pollination. It is an old variety, probably French, with a long, large nut.

A native of southeastern Europe to China, the walnut was introduced to the Romans from Persia and allegedly did not arrive in the UK until the 15th century, when it was prized as much for its timber, which was used for veneers and gun stocks, as for its nuts. The nuts make a very good cooking and salad oil. The name in English comes via Old English from the Low German *walh-knutu* for foreign nut. The botanical is from *jovis* or Jupiter and *glans*, an acorn. They used to be planted near the outside privy, as the scent of the aromatic leaves was thought to keep the flies away. *Juglans nigra* is the American walnut and is similar but faster growing.

Walnuts are very long lived and although not fussy about the soil, they do prefer a heavy, moist one. They should not be planted in a frost pocket. Collect male catkins and keep dry and dust their pollen on female flowers which open a week or two later. Seedlings are easy enough to grow but may not crop for 20 years and could then produce inferior nuts. Grafted plants are necessary for true varieties. Their only real problem – squirrels! **BF**

Juniperus communis 'Compressa'

NOAH'S ARK JUNIPER

Type: hardy, evergreen conifer
Soil & situation: moist, well-drained soil/full sun/shelter from cold winds
North American hardiness zone: 2–6
Height: 80cm (32in)
Spread: 45cm (18in)
Grow for: dot plant in scree bed or stone trough; AGM

This little gem is the best conifer ever to have graced a rockery, sink or alpine scree bed. It is slow growing, forming a dense, compact column of light to mid-green. The needle-like leaves form an outer shell on a mature plant, camouflaging the brown interior of dead foliage.

Juniperus communis 'Compressa'

Keep the surrounding area weed free and prune back or transplant any other plant that may smother it. Plant a group of these miniatures 1–1.2m (3–4ft) apart on a gravel bed and watch them slowly mature, growing about 2cm (3/4in) yearly. In autumn spiders swing like Tarzan from one to the other, leaving silver threads in their wake.

Juniperus communis 'Compressa' is tolerant of an alkaline soil but will suffer from dieback disease if planted in a heavy, wet soil or exposed to cold winds. Propagate using well-ripened current year's growth as small cuttings in autumn. Examine this conifer from mid-summer onwards for red spider mite. This pest, if not treated, will yellow the leaves and eventually defoliate the plant. **JC**

Kalmia latifolia 'Olympic Fire'

Kalmia latifolia 'Olympic Fire'

CALICO BUSH, MOUNTAIN LAUREL

Type: hardy, evergreen shrub
Soil & situation: moist, humus-rich, deep, acid soil/partial shade
North American hardiness zone: 5–9
Height: 3m (10ft)
Spread: 2m (6½ft)
Grow for: clusters of cup-shaped, pink flowers; AGM

As a child I loved hard icing (I still do). The unopened flower buds of kalmia are identical to the crimped design squeezed out of an icing bag and it is difficult to imagine them opening to cup-shaped flowers. A mature plant forms a dense, bushy shrub with 12cm (5in) long, lance-shaped, wavy-edged, glossy, dark evergreen leaves. Large 10cm (4in) clusters of pink flowers up to 3cm (1in) wide open from tight, dark red buds from late spring through until mid-summer.

Kalmia latifolia 'Dollar Spot' has large white flowers; *K. l.* 'Bullseye' is white with wide, red-purple banding on the outside; and *K. l.* 'Clementine Churchill' has deep pink buds which open to large, pink, waxy flowers.

Water newly planted shrubs regularly for the first season. Mulch with composted bark, leafmould or pine needles in spring before the soil surface dries out. Pruning should be kept to a minimum, only clipping off damaged or misshapen branches. Old specimen plants may be pruned hard in late spring, removing up to 50 per cent of the branches in the first year. Large shrubs will be slow to recover and may not flower for two years. Propagation is by softwood cuttings taken in late spring or semi-ripe shoots in mid-summer. Low-growing branches layered outdoors in late summer will root within 12 months. **JC**

Kerria japonica 'Pleniflora' (syn. *K. j.* 'Flore Pleno')

JEW'S MANTLE

Type: hardy, deciduous shrub
Soil & situation: well-drained, fertile soil/full sun or partial shade
North American hardiness zone: 4–9
Height & spread: 3m (10ft)
Grow for: an easy-to-grow, graceful shrub with golden-yellow flowers; AGM

It is surprising how many people don't know or grow this foolproof flowering shrub. Its suckers can be removed complete with roots, making it ideal for bulking up plant stalls at charity, church and school sales.

It is a vigorous plant, forming a tall, upright shrub. The mid-green, deciduous leaves are held on bright green stems which add interest to the garden in winter. The rich yellow, spring flowers are fully double like miniature chrysanthemum flowers. As they age the petals become paler. *Kerria japonica* 'Golden Guinea' has large 5cm (2in) single, bright buttercup-yellow flowers in early spring. *K. j.* 'Picta' has grey-green leaves edged with creamy white. It is more compact, growing to 1.5m (5ft) in height. I have struggled with this variegated form for three years and it is still only 60cm (24in) high, which may suggest it doesn't like me.

Kerria japonica 'Pleniflora'

After flowering cut out the older branches as close to the base as possible. Younger stems may be pruned back to healthy buds lower down. Dieback will affect the thin tips of flowering stems in winter and early spring. The whitened twigs may be removed. Propagation is by softwood cuttings in summer. Suckers should be taken off in the autumn after leaf fall and planted out in the border or potted up. **JC**

Kirengeshoma palmata

Kirengeshoma palmata

Type: hardy, herbaceous perennial
Soil & situation: deep, moist soil/partial shade
North American hardiness zone: 5–8
Height: 1.2m (4ft)
Spread: 75cm (30in)
Grow for: foliage, form and soft yellow flowers in late summer and early autumn; AGM

Here's another plant that has stolen my heart, though I have to confess I succumbed willingly, and I know I'm not alone! It is a clump-forming perennial from the woodlands of Japan and Korea with flat, slightly lobed leaves, like those of an acer, which appear in opposite pairs along the stiff stems, diminishing in size towards the tips. Those near the flowerheads seem to clasp the dark stems with all their might, the leaf bases overlapping as if supporting each other, terrified that they might slide down the stems and disappear from view. The long, arching flowerheads look as though they are straining under the weight of the plump, rounded buds and soft butter-yellow flowers with thick, waxy petals. I have seen them described as 'loose, airy flights of ivory shuttlecocks…which pervade the entire plant'. Perfect!

The contrast between the pale yellow buds and flowers and the purple-maroon stems is delightful and its deportment, poise and grace, even without the flowers, are utterly enchanting. It is a privilege to grow it in your garden.

It needs deep, moist, fertile soil in shelter and dappled shade. Add plenty of well-rotted organic matter if necessary; it tolerates clay. Ideal in a shady border, woodland garden or a sheltered shady position. Divide in spring when growth starts, handle with care to avoid damaging the young shoots. Cut back the stems and mulch in winter with bracken or straw in colder areas. Slugs and snails attack shoots and leaves. **MB**

Knautia macedonica

Type: hardy perennial
Soil & situation: free draining soil/warm site
North American hardiness zone: 5–9
Height: up to 80cm (32in)
Spread: 45cm (18in)
Grow for: flowers of an extraordinary crimson colour over a long period

This plant has become extremely trendy over the last few years, mainly because of its very long flowering season and the bright, zany shade of its flowers. They are produced on thin, spindly, rather wiry stems, and in my garden reach about 40cm (16in) in height. The flowering season starts in early to mid-summer and will often carry on to late summer to early autumn. It looks far better as it establishes to form good-sized clumps as it can look too weedy and lacking in substance initially. If you are buying it in, it is worth buying well-established plants in 1-litre pots rather than in the smaller 9cm (3³/₄in) pots. They tend to get away more quickly. Some people recommend staking it, but I find it far more attractive to grow the plant between supporting neighbours where it tends to thread itself into them.

The field scabious, *K. arvensis*, grows in meadows, hedgerows and open woodland, often on calcareous soils, and is a charming native for wilder parts of the garden. It is easy to grow from seed and often flowers in the first year (unusual for perennials).

Knautia macedonica is a short-lived perennial, sometimes a biennial. Cut down the plant in late winter, early spring. To propagate, take basal cuttings in spring. **BG**

Knautia macedonica

Kniphofia rooperi

Kniphofia spp.
TORCH LILY, RED-HOT POKER

Type: hardy, semi-evergreen, clump-forming, herbaceous perennial
Soil & situation: most soils/full sun/preferably moist in spring and summer, but dry in autumn and winter
North American hardiness zone: 6–9
Height: compact varieties under 50cm (20in), old-fashioned sorts may reach 1.5–1.8m (5–6ft) when flowering
Spread: 60cm–2m (2–6½ft)
Grow for: summer flowers with spectacular red, orange and yellow heads, and attractive long leaves for most of year

I rarely grow anything that is not either edible or scented, yet none of the kniphofias are known for these attributes. Then some years ago I noticed that the blue tits were feeding on the nectar, much like hummingbirds, so I thought I would have some in my garden just for them. However, I then noticed that if I placed a bowl under the flowerheads and shook them an amazing amount of green nectar fell out. I cannot recommend that you do the same but I have tried drinking this sweet fluid (ten heads can give a wineglass full) with no apparent ill effects. As they are originally from South Africa, it is surprising they survive in the UK at all, as they do not like dry summers and wet winters, preferring the converse.

The soil must be well drained in winter, so raised beds can be of help in heavy soils; do not plant in shade or they die away, and in colder regions position against a warm, sunny wall. Take off the dead flower stems and tidy up decaying leaves in autumn, but do not remove old leaves as these protect stem bases from hard weather. They can be grown from seed but offsets are much quicker, easier and come true; so split clumps in mid-spring as growth commences. They do tend to rot away if in shade, or if damp in winter. Otherwise problem free. **BF**

Kniphofia caulescens
Plant of the Week (see page 345)

Kniphofia rooperi (syn. *K.* 'C. M. Prichard')
RED HOT POKER, TORCH LILY

Type: hardy, evergreen perennial
Soil & situation: deep, fertile, well-drained, sandy soil/full sun or light shade
North American hardiness zone: 7–9
Height: 1.2m (4ft)
Spread: 60cm (24in)
Grow for: a distinctive plant for the border with bright flowers on tall, vertical stems

Once an essential component in traditional cottage gardens, the red hot poker now shares its affections with modern planting designs. I love the bold clump of architectural leaves and its tall, bright, sturdy, late-flowering 'torches' of flower. The long, arching, dark green leaves are wide and pointed, managing to look tidy even in the dead of winter. The broad, stumpy, erect racemes of flowers are held well above the foliage on strong, mid-green stems. The pendent, 5cm (2in) long, tubular flowers are a bright orange-red, becoming orange-yellow and finally a clear yellow. Flowering commences in late summer and continues through to late autumn.

They are a good late source of nectar for bees. After flowering dead-head to prevent seed forming. The leaves form a hotel for snails and frequent examination during the year can reduce the population significantly. In the first winter after planting, protect from frost by covering with bracken foliage or straw, held in place with netting wire. Propagation is by division of established plants in spring. Large, woody clumps produce few rooted sideshoots. They can be taken as basal cuttings in early summer and rooted in a propagator in a gritty compost. **JC**

Koelreuteria paniculata

Koelreuteria paniculata
GOLDEN-RAIN TREE, PRIDE OF INDIA

Type: hardy, deciduous tree
Soil & situation: fertile, well-drained soil/full sun
North American hardiness zone: 5–9
Height: 10m (33ft)
Spread: 9m (30ft)
Grow for: flowers when most other trees have moved on to fruit or autumn foliage; AGM

It may well be the pride of India but this tree originated in China! I wouldn't be without it. It is in flower when most others are relying on fruit or autumn leaves for colour.

The 45cm (18in) long, pinnate leaves have scalloped leaflets. The young leaves open pink-red, turning to mid-green and finally buttery-yellow in autumn. Large – 30cm (12in) – loose panicles of small, golden-yellow flowers appear in early autumn, standing well clear of the foliage. The flowers are followed by bladder-like seedpods, bright pink at first, gradually becoming a rich brown colour.

It dislikes waterlogged ground and cold winds. Remove dead and damaged branches during winter before the sap starts to rise. Propagation is by seed sown thinly in autumn and over-wintered in a cold frame. Root cuttings taken in late winter and inserted upright in pots of soil-based compost will produce shoots the following spring and will be ready for repotting a year later. **JC**

Kolkwitzia amabilis
BEAUTY BUSH

Type: hardy, deciduous, suckering shrub
Soil & situation: fertile, well-drained soil; thrives on chalk/sun and tolerates some shade
North American hardiness zone: 5–9
Height: 3m (10ft)
Spread: 4m (13ft)
Grow for: gorgeous flowers in late spring and early summer

Kolkwitzia amabilis

This is an elegant, hardy, densely twiggy, medium-sized shrub. In late spring and early summer the drooping branches are massed with delightful, white, bell-shaped flowers, with the softest pink flush and a splash of deep golden-yellow in the throat. The broad, mat, dark green leaves are the perfect foil to this graceful display; in winter, the peeling bark is attractive too. It is hard to believe that something which looks so dainty and delicate could be so robust.

Its home is among the rocks along the Han and Yangtse rivers in China at a height of 3,000–3,300m (10,000–13,075ft). It is yet another gorgeous shrub introduced by Ernest Wilson, this time in 1901 when he was collecting for Veitch's Nursery; it first flowered in the UK in June 1910 – what a cause for celebration! I remember it as one of the outstanding plants from my days working on Leicester City Council's Parks Department.

Kolkwitzia amabilis 'Pink Cloud' is pink flowered. Foliage can be damaged by late frosts, so plant in a sheltered border or in dappled shade. Prune out old, damaged or weak shoots at the base immediately after flowering to younger stems lower down on the original branches. On older plants, remove weak growth and about one fifth to a quarter of the oldest stems after flowering in spring. Then feed with a slow-release general fertilizer and mulch. Propagate by semi-ripe cuttings from mid-summer or a sucker detached from mature plants in winter. **MB**

+ *Laburnocytisus* 'Adamii'

+ *Laburnocytisus* 'Adamii'

Type: hardy, deciduous tree
Soil & situation: moderately fertile, well-drained soil/sun
North American hardiness zone: 6–8
Height: 8m (25ft)
Spread: 6m (20ft)
Grow for: curiosity value and unusual flowers

This graft hybrid between *Cytisus purpureus* and *Laburnum anagyroides* occurred in 1825 when Jean Louis Adam accidentally grafted purple broom onto a laburnum at his nursery near Paris. The resulting plant had a core of laburnum wrapped in a layer of cytisus and where it breaks down branches of pure laburnum burst through. Amazingly it produces not only purple or yellow flowers but some that are coppery-pink, an intermediate between the two! It's also known as a chimaera; in Greek mythology this was a monster with a lion's head, a goat's body and a serpent's tail; when it comes to looks, Adam's plant is not far behind!

It is an uncommon occurrence, + *Crataegomespilus dardarii* 'Bronvaux' is a graft hybrid between hawthorn (*Crataegus monogyna*) and medlar (*Mespilus germanica*) with a central core of hawthorn and an outer sleeve of medlar. The leaves and fruits are like a medlar; the flower clusters and spiny branches are similar to the hawthorn but smaller. Another graft hybrid, 'Jules d'Asineres', occurred at the same time, but this has an outer layer of hawthorn. The leaves and flowers are hawthorn but the shoots and calyx are covered with greyish wool, like a medlar; even weirder was a branch of hawthorn that changed to 'Jules d'Asineres' near the tip!

It needs a moderately fertile, deep, well-drained soil in full sun. Buy a plant, as they are propagated by grafting. It may suffer from leaf spot, which is worse in some years than others. **MB**

Laburnum x *watereri* 'Vossii'

GOLDEN RAIN

Type: hardy, deciduous tree
Soil & situation: fertile, well-drained soil/full sun
North American hardiness zone: 6–8
Height & spread: 9m (30ft)
Grow for: long, fine racemes of golden-yellow flowers; AGM

This must be the best-known tree in the northern hemisphere. You don't have to be a gardener to recognize its chocolate-box appearance. Considered by some to be a common plant, I prefer to think of it as popular and much loved. Trained over an arch, it is a spectacular sight when in flower and viewed from underneath. Planted in such a situation, with blue-flowered wisteria (see page 398) scrambling through, it would be breathtaking.

The young shoots are hairy, as are the dark green, three-palmate leaves on the underside. In late spring and early summer 50cm (20in) long racemes of bright, golden flowers trail down like 'golden rain'. It is a well-known fact that its small, black, round seeds are toxic. If enough of them are eaten they could be fatal. This variety of laburnum produces very few seedpods and the seed is usually sterile.

Pruning is necessary only to shape the tree and should be undertaken in early winter when the tree is dormant and before the sap starts to flow. Propagation is by winter grafting or summer bud grafting. Unfortunately laburnum does suffer from diseases. Honey fungus and silver leaf disease will eventually kill even established trees. **JC**

Laburnum x *watereri* 'Vossii'

Lamium orvala

Lamium orvala

DEAD NETTLE

Type: hardy, herbaceous perennial
Soil & situation: moist soil/dappled or full shade
North American hardiness zone: 4–8
Height: 60cm (24in)
Spread: 30cm (12in)
Grow for: flowers from mid-spring to early summer; compact foliage

Not all nettles are nasty; some are civilized and make excellent ground cover, like the forms of *Lamium maculatum*, the dead nettle. *L. m.* 'Beacon Silver' is a real beauty with silvery leaves, narrow green margins and clear shell-pink flowers; *L. galeobdolon* 'Hermann's Pride' has silvery net-like venation on the leaves; but if you want a nettle with an aristocratic aura, look no further – *L. orvala* reigns supreme. It's not bright and bold, that would be soooo vulgar; its qualities are understated and discreet, just take the time to admire. *L. o.* f. *alba* has off-white flowers and the leaves of *L. o.* 'Silva' have a broad central stripe.

L. orvala is a fine, clump-forming foliage plant with square stems and oval to triangular, softly hairy leaves on opposite sides of the stem that combine to create a soft, textured look. The flowers are typical of nettles, but a subtle coppery-pink to rich purple with delicate markings in the throat that draw you down to view. Always walk round the garden with a magnifying glass in your pocket, there's great pleasure in the hidden details of every plant: stamens, petals, bark and bough wait patiently to be appreciated by those passing by. Few take the trouble to view but the reward is pure delight.

It makes good ground cover in borders or among large shrubs. Give it a moist but well-drained soil in deep or partial shade. It is more vigorous in moist, moderately fertile soil; poorer soil reduces its growth. Cut back to ground level and mulch in early spring. Divide in autumn or early spring. Slugs and snails may damage early growth. **MB**

Lathyrus odoratus

Lathyrus odoratus
SWEET PEA

Type: hardy, annual climber
Soil & situation: any moist soil/full sun or light shade
North American hardiness zone: annual
Height & spread: 2m (6½ft)
Grow for: the cut flower; the gorgeous scent and, because it is leguminous, providing nitrogen for other plants

I adore sweet peas – the scent is so edible I can stuff my head into a bunch and just inhale their intoxicating fragrance. I do not like cutting flowers and taking them indoors; they look best where nature placed them. However sweet peas must be cut, as if you leave just one to drop its petals then all is lost; you don't want to see the small green pods because as soon as the seed has ripened the plant will stop producing more blooms and die away. This wild strain is powerfully scented, the flowers are purple and violet and only two or three per stem, but what fragrance! I find that if you self-save seed of almost any mix of sweet peas, within a few years this original form reappears and eventually dominates.

First brought from Sicily at the end of the 17th century, the wild form was good enough to keep everyone happy until the late Victorian period, when they were suddenly widely grown and bred. The flowers became bigger and more fancy, and the process continued until the Second World War when interest waned. This was probably because the highly bred plants had lost their scent and become hard to look after, unlike their wild ancestors.

Rich, moist soil in full sun is essential for a continuity of blooms. Dead-heading is hardly the word, live-heading is more to the point. Do not shirk this! Sow in autumn and over-winter in a coldframe, or sow *in situ* in spring. Plant out early and train onto a support such as a wigwam or trellis. Sweet peas are prone to drought so add more water than you think necessary, unless it's raining. **BF**

John adds:
If, like me, you have a soil which tends to dry out if there is even a hint of summer you should invest a bit of your time digging a planting trench. The deeper the better as sweet peas have an extensive root system. Lay lots of wet newspaper in the base, mixing old farmyard manure and moisture-retentive compost into the soil as you back-fill the trench. Water the soil well a few days before planting.

Laurus nobilis
SWEET BAY TREE, BAY LAUREL

Type: frost-hardy, evergreen shrub or small tree
Soil & situation: well-drained soil/full sun
North American hardiness zone: 8–10
Height: 12m (40ft)
Spread: 10m (33ft)
Grow for: an excellent evergreen and essential for the kitchen; AGM

This is the laurel the ancients made into crowns of glory and that cooks still use today. Bay is often cut into a geometric shape – a pair stands outside every pretentious restaurant like a couple of barber's poles. I love the flavour the leaves give, particularly the aged ones, and use a lot in my cooking – they're expensive to buy. There are male and female trees and only the latter carry the black, inedible berries.

A native of Southern Europe, this was named in Roman times after *laus* or praise as it was used for the victor's laurel and was presumably then introduced to the UK about 2,000 years ago.

In a warm, sheltered spot and a well-drained soil bays can become old and venerable, but on a heavy wet soil and in a windy exposed site get something else, or put it in a tub up against a warm wall. Make sure young plants are given some form of shelter against cold winds, and protect roots in containers against frost. If top growth is seared by wind you can prune back hard in spring and it will come again, if well established. It can be clipped, or preferably pruned to different shapes, which is best done in several stages from spring to late summer.

It can be grown from seed sown in pots in a coldframe in spring, or by hardwood cuttings with a heel in a coldframe in late autumn or winter; layering also works, and occasional suckers can be detached and potted up. Scale insects are often a problem and these are nearly always farmed by ants, so dispose of those first. Honeydew on leaves is caused by scale or aphid infestation higher up; wash it off with a sponge of soapy water. **BF**

Laurus nobilis

Fragaria hybrids

STRAWBERRIES

Type: hardy herbaceous perennial
Soil & situation: rich, moist soil/full sun
North American hardiness zone: 5–9
Height: 30cm (12in)
Spread: 60cm (24in)
Grow for: do I have to tell you?

Whenever I give a talk on gardening I like to pose a few questions to my audience; one is 'How many of you like strawberries?' and another is 'How many of you grow strawberries?' It's odd because although this fruit is almost unanimously liked it is relatively rarely grown, which is crazy as it is one of the quickest and easiest, let alone tastiest crops! To grow it really well is not easy, but to grow and fruit it is fairly simple if you are not after commercial yields. And I know you are supposed to grow it a year before fruiting them, *but* you can crop half of your plants the first summer if you throw them away afterwards. Leave the alternately planted ones you properly de-runnered and de-flowered to grow on and they will make the bed productive for the next few years.

The huge, sweet strawberry available today is a relatively modern fruit. The ancients gathered tiny, wild strawberries, and in the Middle Ages these plants were brought into gardens where they remain almost unimproved. A Victorian hybrid between a North American Virginian strawberry, with flavour, and a South American Chilean sort, with some size, gave rise to the whole gamut of modern strawberries, which can fruit for most of the summer and autumn, but few match those ripening around the longest day, eaten in the warmth of a summer's evening.

Rich, moist soil with added bonemeal suits this hungry crop. Plant in full sun, or cool shade for a successional crop, and replace one-third of the bed every year, re-planting on a new site. Do not remove the leaves until the plants die down, then shear off the residue. In the growing season trim off runners regularly. De-flowering in the first summer will lead to bigger, stronger plants and huge crops later. Do not grow from seed but obtain the first runners of healthy plants, rooted into pots in late spring, and plant in a new bed by mid-summer. Weevils, slugs and miserable weather plague this delightful crop but hygiene, jam jars over the ripening trusses and eternal hope combat these – well, maybe not the last. **BF**

Lavandula angustifolia 'Twickel Purple'
LAVENDER

Type: hardy, evergreen shrub
Soil & situation: moderately fertile, well-drained soil/full sun
North American hardiness zone: 5–8
Height: 60cm (24in)
Spread: 90cm (36in)
Grow for: no garden is complete without it

I cannot imagine having a garden without at least one lavender plant. I can dream of a garden with hundreds of plants in many varieties. Reality is in the middle – I have between 30 and 35 plants in six varieties in my garden. Around 18 *Lavandula angustifolia* 'Twickel Purple' are planted round a weeping pear, *Pyrus salicifolia* 'Pendula' (see page 316), and they form a magic circle.

It makes a compact, rounded, bushy shrub with narrow, 5cm (2in) long, grey-green, aromatic leaves. In mid-summer it bears dense spikes of very fragrant, bright purple flowers on long stalks. The flowers are held above the foliage, providing a wonderful contrast in colour. The variety *L. a.* 'Hidcote' is compact with silver-grey foliage and deep purple flowers. *L. a.* 'Nana Alba' produces white flowers and grows to a height and spread of 30cm (12in).

Annual pruning to prevent the plant becoming leggy is carried out each spring. Cut last year's growth back to within 2.5cm (1in) of the older wood. Lavender tends to be a short-lived plant becoming woody and bare at the base after seven to eight years. This is more likely to occur in heavy soil and moist climates. The answer is simple: pull the old plant out and replace it with another or, if there is space, two more.

Propagation is by semi-ripe cuttings in summer. Insert them in a gritty, free-draining compost and cover the container with horticultural fleece. **JC**

Lavandula angustifolia 'Twickel Purple'

Lavandula pinnata

Lavandula pinnata
LAVENDER

Type: tender, evergreen shrub
Soil & situation: tolerant of many soil types except wet ones/sunny position
North American hardiness zone: 9–10
Height & spread: 1m (3ft)
Grow for: fragrant, strong blue flowers with a hint of purple, ever-present from late spring/early summer to early autumn

This tender lavender is probably one of my top 50 if not top ten plants. I treat it as a bedding plant, planting it into the border in late spring, where it quickly fills out to form an excellent small foliage plant. Come early summer, it starts to flower its heart out and continues till autumn. Then I leave it until it is killed by the frost and quickly discard it. Grown like this, from well-rooted liners taken towards the end of the previous summer, they do not reach 1m (3ft) high, perhaps only 60cm (24in), by the end of the year. But I plant them pretty close together, about eight or ten per square metre/yard so the plants knit together to form a sea of grey-green leaves within a few weeks.

The rather hairy, aromatic foliage supports tall, unbranched stalks topped with the ever-flowering, intensely coloured spikes. Because of their wonderful flowering capacity and their ability to withstand hot dry periods, they are also tailor-made for summer containers – looking particularly good in faded terracotta or lead. I like them best massed together on their own. Simple, stunning and sweet-smelling.

Even though I could never get away with leaving this plant to over-winter outside, I still think it is worth propagating new stock every summer from softwood cuttings, to over-winter under cover before going out the following spring. They will root in a couple of weeks and it speeds up rooting if you keep pinching out the flowers. **BG**

Lavandula 'Sawyers'

Type: hardy, evergreen shrub
Soil & situation: according to Henry Head of Norfolk Lavender, there are three things that lavender needs – 'drainage, drainage and drainage'/sunny position
North American hardiness zone: 6–9
Height: 60cm (24in)
Spread: 80cm (32in)
Grow for: winter colour: exceptional foliage looks attractive throughout the winter with its large leaf and excellent silver colour; attractive two-tone flowers; AGM

Lavandula 'Sawyers'

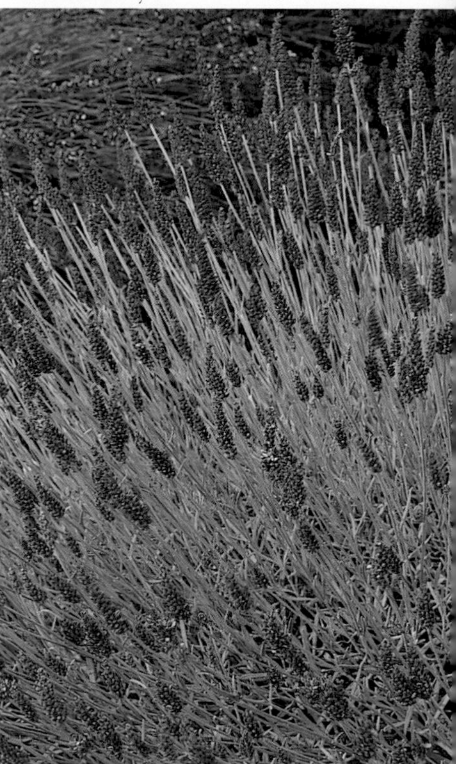

Henry Head recommended this lavender to me and I have to agree it is a star. Looking at my collection of lavender plants, now in late winter, this lavender is head and shoulders above most of them. The large leaves, often 4cm (1½in) long and 5mm (¼in) wide, are a positive presence in the garden rather than looking like tired hedgehogs as most other lavenders do at this time of year. Most people grow lavender not for the foliage but for those summer months when the plant is covered with its captivating flowers. This one has pale purple flowerheads, which are a deeper blue in the centre and flowers from mid- to late summer. *L.* 'Richard Gray' is very similar but has large, rich purple flowers.

Given that drainage is the key to success, if you do not have sharp drainage it is worth digging a large hole and incorporating masses of free-draining material before attempting to plant on top. On poorly drained soil, lavender will probably look good for a mere six years or so and then need replacing, otherwise it will go on for a good 15 years.

Pruning is important in keeping it looking dapper. As soon as it has finished flowering cut back all this year's growth, and if necessary, a little into the hardwood too. Many people recommend pruning in late spring, but the problem here is that they tend to wait too long for fear of new growth being frosted, and so also remove incipient flowerheads, reducing flowering performance. Propagate from cuttings, which will root virtually at any time of year, but early summer is best. **BG**

Lavandula stoechas
FRENCH LAVENDER

Type: hardy, semi-evergreen shrub
Soil & situation: well-drained soil/full sun
North American hardiness zone: 8–9
Height & spread: can make clumps 30–50cm (12–20ft) round
Grow for: neat, whitish-greyish-green evergreen with purple flowers, excellent for edging; AGM

Any lavender is good, but this is the best. It is superbly scented in a spicier way than the old English and although less hardy, it has survived in my Norfolk garden through many a cold winter and has even self-sown. It may lose its verdure in winter but if you rub the greyish foliage or a flowerhead there is that pungent warmth and sweet comfort reminding you of summer. It makes a neater, more compact edging than most lavenders.

Lavandula stoechas

French lavender originates from the tiny island of Stoechas, off the coast of Marseilles, and was introduced into the UK in the 16th century. The name *Lavandula* comes from the Latin word for washing or soap, *lavo*, as the lavender scent extracted even back then was used as a perfume.

The soil must be well drained, ideally with some chalk, and full sun is essential or it just moulds away.... Trim if you must in early spring before growth commences, but preferably just tidy off dead flower stems, and do keep other plants cut back so as not to shade this delicate beauty. In early spring sow in a very chalky, gritty compost in a cold frame, or take root cuttings. Plant out the next spring. This plant sulks in cold, dank springs and grey, damp summers! I feel much the same. **BF**

Lavatera thuringiaca 'Burgundy Wine'

Type: hardy, semi-evergreen subshrub
Soil & situation: light, well-drained soil/full sun
North American hardiness zone: 8–10
Height & spread: 1.2m (4ft)
Grow for: attractive foliage; a profusion of dark purple-red flowers in generous quantities through summer till early autumn

There are several forms of *L. thuringiaca*, perhaps the most widely grown are 'Barnsley', with its pale pink flowers, and *L.* x *clementii* 'Rosea', with bright pink flowers. These two are highly productive, quickly becoming established and bearing huge volumes of flowers in the first couple of years. These are for impatient gardeners. But the only one I grow is 'Burgundy Wine'. This has bags more charm, is more unusual and not as rampant and blowsy as the others. The habit is more compact, but the foliage is still an attractive grey-green and if grown in a sheltered warm spot the leaves will last throughout the year in a mild winter. The flowers are a rich, pink colour, but unfortunately not that of wine. What is more, they are produced for well over a month. They are perhaps not as beautifully textured as the commoner ones and are slightly smaller, but they just hit the right spot for me.

All the subshrub mallows or tree lavateras are fast-growers and with most plants that indicates they are short-lived; these are no exception. If the term 'flowered themselves to death' applied to any plants, it certainly would to these. As they root extremely easily from softwood cuttings in spring and early summer, it is no bother to propagate a new batch every three or four years. Do not be tempted to over-feed them – on a rich soil you will get all foliage and far fewer flowers – but do be tempted to give them a protective autumn mulch and a bit of shelter from cold winds. **BG**

Lavatera thuringiaca 'Burgundy Wine'

Ledum groenlandicum

Ledum groenlandicum
LABRADOR TEA

Type: hardy, evergreen, bushy shrub
Soil & situation: moist, well-drained, humus-rich, neutral to acid soil/full sun or partial shade
North American hardiness zone: 2–6
Height: 1m (3ft)
Spread: 1.2m (4ft)
Grow for: survives terrible weather conditions; small, white flowers

I admire this tough little plant. It is at home in Alaska and Greenland so is quite capable of dealing with the worst of any weather. It is now included in the family *Rhododendron* and its shape resembles a dwarf form. When mature it makes a bushy, open, rounded shrub with pale brown, woolly shoots and 5cm (2in) long, dark green leaves, fawn-felted on the underside. The oblong leaves are recurved along the margins. Small, white flowers with prominent stamens form terminal clusters up to 5cm (2in) across in late spring and early summer.

It is a good companion plant with heathers, pieris and dwarf conifers. I have a 12-year-old-plant and have never had to prune it. I do, however, dead-head it after flowering to prevent seed forming. Propagation is by semi-ripe, short cuttings in late summer or by layering *in situ*. **JC**

Lespedeza thunbergii
BUSH CLOVER

Type: hardy, deciduous subshrub
Soil & situation: fertile, well-drained soil/full sun
North American hardiness zone: 6–8
Height: 2m (6½ft)
Spread: 3m (10ft)
Grow for: a good show of colour in late autumn; AGM

I have this plant in a mixed border and I always forget about it. Suddenly, in late autumn, it reminds me, yet again, how good a plant it is by making a show of itself. Delicate, arching stems carry three palmate, blue-green leaflets, each 5cm (2in) long. The 15cm (6in) long, pendent racemes of small, pea-like, purple-pink flowers appear in autumn. *Lespedeza bicolor* is similar in size, but more upright with dark green leaves. Its purple-pink flowers are produced in mid-summer.

With me, each winter, the stems are cut to the ground by frost. In late spring new shoots appear and by early summer they are quietly draping low-growing plants. Propagation is by seed sown in spring without heat. Softwood cuttings can be rooted in summer under polythene. Mist the foliage over daily to prevent them wilting. Large clumps may be divided in spring taking care not to damage the fine roots. **JC**

Lespedeza thunbergii

Leucojum autumnale

Leucojum autumnale
AUTUMN SNOW FLAKE

Type: hardy, bulbous perennial
Soil & situation: sandy, free-draining soil/sun
North American hardiness zone: 5–9
Height: 15cm (6in)
Spread: 10cm (4cm)
Grow for: dainty white flowers for the whole of autumn; AGM

This is one of the daintiest plants you'll ever see. The flowers, appearing just before the leaves in early autumn, hang like tiny white bells from slender grassy stems only 10–15cm (4–6in) tall. Everything in their world is so tiny I would not be surprised if fairies crept out unseen at night to dance around them and ring their pretty bells!

These delicate relatives of the snowdrop grow in rocky, stony woodland scrub and grassy places in the western Mediterranean. They need careful positioning to ensure that they are visible and you don't stand on them by mistake! Ideally they should be raised up in planting pockets on rock gardens where they are easier to view; dark stone or evergreen shrubs highlight the white flowers and protect them from cold wind too. Alternatively, grow them by dry hedge bases, as edging plants or against a sunny wall and remember that they need a good baking to develop flower buds for the following year; don't shade them with shrubs. *Leucojum autumnale* 'Cobbs Variety' has larger flowers from late summer to mid-autumn.

It needs a sunny position on sandy, free-draining soil. Dig in plenty of sharp sand before planting about 5cm (2in) deep in mid- to late summer. Propagate by division in spring or autumn after flowering. Sow seed when ripe in autumn, in gritty compost. It takes up to three years to produce a flowering bulb. It will also grow in containers of gritty sand. **MB**

Levisticum officinale
LOVAGE

Type: hardy, perennial herb
Soil & situation: naturalized in meadows throughout Britain and Europe/will grow pretty well anywhere in pretty much anything
North American hardiness zone: 4–7
Height: up to 2m ($6^1/_2$ft)
Spread: 1m (3ft)
Grow for: a herb indispensable in cooking; yeasty, celery-like flavour; it can be shredded finely and added to salads; one plant gives ample leaves for the entire growing season; said to have widespread medicinal properties

I grow about five plants of this magic herb in my kitchen garden. It sits in a square of dwarf box, part of a pattern of herb squares that form 'stops' on the corners of all my vegetable beds. This makes the vegetable garden look the business even in mid-winter. More importantly, it stops rushing children and chasing dogs cutting corners over my beds. I need not grow five plants – with this quantity I could supply our local hotel too – but that way the plants are a continual presentable mass. They are not unattractive: their flowers are borne in umbels which look good with the greenish-yellow flowers. I always cut them off, before they look their finest, to favour leaf production. But you can use the seeds for flavouring, as well as the roots and shoots for a vegetable or in a salad, grated, raw or cooked. The dried root has a strange, almost nutty flavour and was once used as a condiment. It is one of those useful plants that the longer you grow it, the more uses you find for its wide-ranging facets. If you grow this herb in shade the flavour will be less intense but as it is pretty, if not extremely punchy, I do not think this is a problem. It is easily propagated from seed or from division in early spring. **BG**

Levisticum officinale

Lewisia tweedyi

Lewisia tweedyi

Type: hardy, evergreen perennial
Soil & situation: humus-rich, well-drained, neutral to acid soil/light shade
North American hardiness zone: 4–7
Height: 20cm (8in)
Spread: 30cm (12in)
Grow for: brightening up the rockery in early summer; AGM

I have to admit that this plant is a bit fussy but then so was my grannie and I loved her. The 10cm (4in) long, fleshy, mid-green leaves form a tight rosette and are often tinted purple. Fully open, the star-shaped flowers can be 5cm (2in) across. They appear from spring to early summer either singly or in clusters of up to four; they are a clean pink-white or a deeper apricot shade. The variety *Lewisia tweedyi* f. *alba* has pure white flowers but is not as readily available. *Lewisia* Cotyledon Hybrids produce panicles of flowers in a range of bright colours including pink, yellow and apricot.

L. tweedyi dislikes being planted in full sun. A site on the shady side of a large rock where it is in the open but out of the sun is ideal. It suffers from winter wet and will rot if not protected. A roof made from a sheet of glass secured on either side of the clump between two bricks will be sufficient protection. Alternatively it can be grown outside during summer in a shallow pot of gritty compost and moved under cover in a greenhouse in winter. Seed can be sown in a cold frame in autumn or offsets may be removed in early summer and rooted in pots. **JC**

Leycesteria formosa

Leycesteria formosa
HIMALAYAN HONEYSUCKLE

Type: hardy, deciduous shrub
Soil & situation: moist, well-drained soil/full sun to light shade
North American hardiness zone: 8–10
Height & spread: 2m (6½ft)
Grow for: provides pendent flowers in summer and autumn followed by purple berries; AGM

I love the bare, bamboo-like stems in winter. The unusual flower resembles something a girl would dangle from her ear.

Of upright habit, this shrub will form a thicket. Its 15cm (6in) long, dark green leaves are held on sea-green, hollow stems. The 10cm (4in) long, pendent spikes of flowers are produced in summer and early autumn. They are white and just visible among the dark claret-red bracts. The flowers are followed by red-purple berries which are loved by birds.

Don't plant in heavy, wet soil or where there are cold, drying winds. A deep mulch in autumn is beneficial, especially if there are likely to be prolonged frosts. It loves the shelter of a woodland garden, providing it is not too shaded in summer.

Pruning is necessary to prevent the plant becoming bulky with non-flowering stems. After flowering, cut the two-year-old stems, which are a dark green, back to a strong sideshoot or low down close to ground level. Propagation is by sowing fresh seed in autumn and over-wintering in a cold frame. Softwood cuttings taken in summer root quickly and may be potted up in a soil-based compost in the autumn. **JC**

Libertia formosa

Type: hardy, rhizomatous, evergreen perennial
Soil & situation: medium loam soil, preferably slightly acid/sun or light shade
North American hardiness zone: 8–10
Height: leaves up to 45cm (18in), flowers to 1.2cm (4ft)
Spread: 1m (3ft)
Grow for: year-round foliage; white flowers in small umbels in spring

This is one of those charming, low-key plants that never knock you out, but you are always pleased to have around. I grow it in a large drift in my orchard where it mingles with masses of ferns. The tough, thick, grassy leaves are evergreen and a good evergreen at that, not tatty but nicely strappy, even in late winter, then at the end of spring a mass of small white flowers appears. I remember featuring it widely in a woodland garden I designed for the Chelsea Flower Show (always at the end of May). It was fun arranging it in wide drifts, and it was a dream to use as it looks at its best then so needed no forcing and little titivating or 'dressing up'. It does look right in light woodland, although is possibly happier in full sun; either way, it will self-seed around.

After a few years the old leaves tend to get congested and the plant responds to being cut back to just above ground level. Alternatively you can start afresh with new seedlings. Propagation can either be by division in spring or seed. **BG**

Libertia formosa

Ligularia dentata 'Desdemona'

Ligularia dentata 'Desdemona'

Type: hardy, herbaceous perennial
Soil & situation: rich, deep, moisture-retentive soil/dappled shade
North American hardiness zone: 4–8
Height: 1.2m (4ft)
Spread: 1m (3ft)
Grow for: bold purple foliage in spring; pale orange daisies in summer; AGM

This is an amazing plant with excellent foliage and flowers. The foliage comes in the form of basal leaves up to 30 x 40cm (12 x 16in), rounded and toothed, which are purple above and below initially and then become a deep green on the top. Because I am on free-draining soil I have positioned them in the shadow of a north-facing wall, having added lots of organic matter, and in dry periods I water. Little sacrifice to grow this spectacular plant. This is the only one I grow, though if I had more favourable conditions I would grow others in wild areas. One other would be *L. tangutica* 'The Rocket', which has coarse, toothed leaves, often blackish stems and flower stems that launch up to a height of 2m (6½ft).

If you have dry conditions, grow this plant in a man-made bog garden and it will thrive. Other suitable places are beside streams, lakes or in naturally marshy places. It does not need staking except in exceptionally exposed conditions.

Beware if you are an allergic gardener – it can cause reactions. My main grouse with this plant is slugs: ligularias are the McDonalds of the plant world, feeding millions at every sitting. Unfortunately they do not produce new leaves quickly when you remove their manky ones but just look ravaged for weeks. Propagate by division or the species by seed. **BG**

Ligularia dentata 'Othello'
GOLDEN GROUNDSEL

Type: hardy, herbaceous perennial
Soil & situation: deep, fertile, moist soil/full sun
North American hardiness zone: 4–8
Height: 90cm (36in)
Spread: 80cm (32in)
Grow for: a particularly handsome perennial plant with a good combination of flower and leaf colour

This is a wonderfully dramatic perennial for the front of a border. The leaf and flower colours contrast beautifully. Unfortunately there is a constant battle against slugs, which seem to prefer the leaves even to those of a hosta. But if you win the war you will have a sight worth fighting for.

Clump-forming, the rounded, 25cm (10in) wide, deep purple-green leaves are purple-red on the underside. The 10cm- (4in-) wide corymbs of deep orange, daisy-like flowers are produced from mid-summer to early autumn on long stiff stems above the foliage.

Ligularias need to be protected from the midday sun. The leaves will droop if there is a shortage of water but soon recover after a shower of rain. They are totally hardy but the foliage is easily shredded in strong winds. Propagation is by division after flowering or in spring. The seed of *Ligularia dentata* 'Othello' will not come true, but the plants will be very similar in appearance.

Whoever named these two varieties was fond of Shakespeare but 'Desdemona' (see previous entry) is more likely to be murdered by slugs! **JC**

Ligularia dentata 'Othello'

Hosta 'Gold Standard'

PLANTAIN LILY

Type: hardy, herbaceous perennial
Soil & situation: fertile, moist, well-drained soil/ light shade
North American hardiness zone: 5–8
Height: 70cm (27½in)
Spread: 90cm (36in)
Grow for: a mass of heart-shaped leaves; excellent for beds and borders in dappled shade. The leaves are lovely throughout the growing season, but the flowers are an added dimension at this time of year.

This hosta produces leaves that improve with age. It is happy growing in the border or in a container where its foliage is better protected from slugs. It is clump-forming with large, 18cm (7in) heart-shaped leaves. When they first open they are splashed green-yellow. As they age they become a brighter yellow, edged with a narrow margin of dark green, then cream before fading to a beige-green. In mid-summer, the long stems carry funnel-shaped, lavender-blue flowers above the leaves. Plant hostas in a situation where they won't suffer from strong, biting, cold winds. Mulch annually in spring using composted bark or leafmould. The new emerging shoots are prone to slug and snail attack, so lay poisons and traps to lessen the numbers in the area. Select a site away from full sun, which will scorch the leaves. Too much shade will cause the leaves to become green.

Propagation is by division in late spring or early autumn. The clumps are dug up and divided into small plants each with their roots attached. With large clumps it is difficult to tease out these small rooted pieces. Where necessary, chop the clumps apart with an axe or sharp spade. Discard the old, woody centre section. Pot them into a moisture-retentive compost in the containers and leave them on a sheltered side of the garden. **JC**

Ligustrum delavayanum (syn. *L. ionandrum*)

Type: hardy, evergreen shrub
Soil & situation: any reasonable soil/sun or part shade
North American hardiness zone: 7–10
Height: just over 2m (6½ft)
Spread: 3m (10ft)
Grow for: a relatively fast-growing, evergreen plant used for topiary and hedging

This useful plant has smallish, elliptical leaves up to 3cm (1in) long, but more usually 1.5cm (⅝in). It does not produce topiary of the calibre of box and yew as the foliage is not so tight, and because of its faster growth rate. This is good in that you get the final result more speedily, but not so good for the guy with the clippers who will need to have them at the ready three times a year (at least) to keep them in trim!

I have often used this plant in gardens, though, because you can get instant topiary specimens in *L. delavayanum* for half or even a third of the price of their slower-growing counterparts and they look pretty good, making bags of immediate impact. I have seen them in Italian nurseries shaped as helicopters, elephants, swans and other bizarre shapes. A lot of preformed topiary shapes are imported into the UK from Italy and Holland. Most frequent are the mop-head standards. Some say they are not so hardy and in a cold winter become more semi-evergreen. I think the answer is that they are variable, but looking at some I planted recently in the Midlands, they are definitely evergreen, even after some very cold winter conditions.

Ligustrum delavayanum

As these plants are not so tall, the mop-head standards often look far superior in a large pot, so the 'mop' can be brought up to eye level. To stop them blowing over and to avoid them being dependent on being watered, I cut the base out of cheap terracotta pots (I usually do a coloured wash over them so they look expensive) with an angle grinder, and put good soil beneath the pot, allowing the plant to root through. This works well in gravel or in soft areas with a 'plinth' of planting around the base. In exposed areas I drive a bar through the pot and into the ground, for initial stabilization. I water for the first year, and then slowly wean them. Clip from late spring to mid-summer. **BG**

Ligustrum lucidum
CHINESE PRIVET, WHITE WAX TREE

Type: hardy, evergreen tree or shrub
Soil & situation: well-drained soil; excellent on chalk/sun
North American hardiness zone: 8–10
Height & spread: 10m (33ft)
Grow for: attractive form, glossy leaves and small white flowers; AGM

I first saw this neat, compact tree with gorgeous glossy leaves in a garden in Fulham. I selected some shoots, carefully took them home and discovered to my enduring surprise that in this part of west London even the privets are posh! Someone with a cultured eye must have selected this plant, not for them the humdrum drudgery of a dull privet hedge but something far more impressive – an elegant, regal tree that bathed in the sunshine and luxuriated in the warmth of London's microclimate. It was a fine specimen standing serenely in the middle of the lawn with long, glossy leaves, attractive bark and bouquets of white flowers in late summer and early autumn. The rest of the year it stands, statuesque and looking divine; it's such a charming plant, my dear, you simply must have one!

Those dressed in contemporary 'haute couture' include *Ligustrum lucidum* 'Excelsum Superbum', which has bright green leaves marked with pale

Ligustrum lucidum

green and edged with yellow and greenish-yellow. It is not as hardy, needing protection from cold winds. The narrow, deep green leaves of *L. l.* 'Tricolor' are prominently marked with grey-green and edged with creamy-yellow, tinged pink when young.

Hardy but unsuitable for cold or exposed areas. It needs a warm, sheltered position, flourishing in warmer parts of the UK, in sunshine or part shade on well-drained soil; it's excellent on chalk. Mulch in spring and water young trees during drought. Prune to tidy in spring. Propagate by semi-ripe cuttings in winter. **MB**

Ligustrum vulgare
COMMON PRIVET

Type: hardy, semi-evergreen shrub
Soil & situation: any soil, poor soils too/sun or part shade
North American hardiness zone: 5–8
Height: to 5m (16ft)
Spread: 3m (10ft)
Grow for: highly useful plant when mixed into native thicket and hedgerow plantings, adding a fast-growing, semi-evergreen element

This is a native hedgerow and woodland plant that is most frequently seen on limestone and chalky soils. I frequently use this invaluable plant for planting on boundaries with the countryside, mixed in with other appropriate natives, for shelter belts, hedges and natural plantings. Its leaves are much smaller than those of the common hedging privet (*L. ovalifolium*), which I rarely use. It has a darker green leaf and in autumn produces conspicuous shining black fruit in long clusters. It

Ligustrum vulgare

rapidly establishes in even quite inhospitable soils where it is windy and cold, and keeps a respectable covering of leaves on to the end of winter in most areas. It is ideal for providing shelter both for us and for the wildlife.

I invariably plant this as a bare-rooted plant, at usually a fraction of the cost of container-grown ones, and strangely enough, it establishes better. It is essential to keep the soil clean at the base of the plant for a good metre (3ft) if possible, as then there is no competition for moisture from grass or weeds and it will grow up to 70 per cent faster. On planting for use in a native hedge, I usually reduce all growth back to 15cm (6in) from the ground and a better, bushier, more vigorous plant is the result. For the next two or three years I reduce the new side growth back to half in spring. Then, when it is the size I want, I just clip over the sides and top it again in spring or when all the berries have been had by the birds and before nesting. **BG**

Lilium candidum

MADONNA LILY

Type: hardy, bulbous perennial
Soil & situation: well-drained, humus-rich, neutral to alkaline soil/full sun
North American hardiness zone: 6–9
Height: 1–1.8m (3–6ft)
Spread: 30cm (12in)
Grow for: the most lovely, fragrant, pure white flowers; AGM

When I see this lily, whether as a single plant, a clump or as cut flowers I can't help but think, WOW. It is perfection in flower.

Broad, lance-shaped, 20cm (8in) long, bright, shiny green basal leaves appear in autumn. Stiff flower stems emerge in spring and carry small, 7cm (3in) long, twisted lance-shaped leaves. Racemes of up to 20 wonderfully fragrant, pure white flowers appear in mid-summer. Each 5–7cm (2–2¾in) long flower is trumpet-shaped with a yellowish base and golden-yellow anthers. They are ideal for growing in mixed borders or as clumps among shrubs or herbaceous plants.

Plant on top of a small mound of coarse grit in the base of the planting hole to encourage good drainage. The tip of the bulb should be level with the top of the surrounding soil. Insert a marker cane or label before planting to avoid spearing the soft, scale-like bulb. Space the bulbs 20cm (8in) apart. They flower better when they are crowded and clumps should only be replanted when they are congested.

Seed will germinate more easily when sown fresh. The first stage of germination is the formation of the root. The seed appears to be dormant until the leaves appear in the following season. Keep the seed trays moist and shaded for at least two years after sowing. **JC**

Lilium candidum

Lilium 'Casa Blanca'

Lilium 'Casa Blanca'

Type: hardy, bulbous perennial
Soil & situation: more tolerant of alkaline conditions/moist, but free-draining soil when growing/sun or part shade/needs less mollycoddling than many people think
North American hardiness zone: 5–8
Height: 1m (3ft)
Spread: 30cm (12in)
Grow for: flamboyant, fragrant, white flowers from mid-summer to early autumn; can be grown in pots or in the ground; AGM

This is a very flashy lily which has an extraordinarily powerful, sweet fragrance and flowers for a good five or six weeks. The exotic, rather flat white flowers have reddish anthers which contrast well with the whitest of flowers. It is ideal for growing in pots where you can give it the exact conditions it demands and position it exactly where you want it when it starts to look its finest. This also helps deal with the slug problem.

It is worth taking a little extra time and trouble with the ground preparation for these lilies. Add a lot of well-rotted, organic matter – ideally leaf-mould and extra grit if your soil is on the heavy side. They hate wind, heavy, poorly drained soils and also over-dry conditions during growth. If you have problems with mice, squirrels and slugs eating them over winter, you can prevent this by planting them individually in 2-litre pots when they arrive in autumn. Keep them in a dryish spot, such as by a wall where winter rains will not drench them, and cover the pots with netting to fend off the rodents. Pop them in the ground (without their pots) in early spring and they will get off to a good start in an ideal compost. You can then leave them in the ground from then on and if the numbers start to dwindle you can bulk them up with new. If the spot is well sheltered those in the border probably will not need staking; those in pots do tend to as the ideal conditions make them taller and floppier. If you want to grow them permanently in pots, lift and divide them in late winter/early spring at least every other year. As long as you top dress and feed well in the year you do not re-pot every year. Dead-heading after flowering is also important to help as much energy as possible to go to the bulb. Remove the flower as soon as it has withered with just the top two or three leaves, no more. **BG**

Lilium regale
REGAL LILY

Type: hardy, bulbous perennial
Soil & situation: well-drained soil/full sun to very light shade
North American hardiness zone: 4–7
Height: 2m (6½ft)
Spread: 20cm (8in)
Grow for: staggering flowers, staggering perfume; AGM

Lilium regale

Limnanthes douglasii

I love this flower and have been fortunate to see one grow to more than 1.8m (6ft) tall with over a dozen flowers. Each bloom is an enormous funnel of pure white, golden within the throat and occasionally flushed with a whiff of burgundy on the outside. The sweet perfume is overwhelming and you wander around with a yellow nose from the golden anthers having given you a good dusting. This is one of the easiest and most obliging of lilies and can flower in only a couple of years from seed.

Although we have had many wonderful lilies since before Biblical times, *Lilium regale* was not found until 1903, when it was stumbled upon by the great plant hunter E. H. Wilson, in a high mountain valley on the border of Tibet and China.

This lily is not particular as to soil, or even planting depth, as long as it is well drained. It likes full sun, but can be planted under or between very low shrubs to keep off early frost damage. Remove stamens and the flowers last for longer. Take off dead flowers to prevent seed forming and weakening the plant. It is remarkably easy to grow from seed, especially self-saved as it is fresh, and no matter how hard you try it seems to resist hybridization and apparently always comes true; or divide bulbs in early spring. Late frosts may twist or damage new growths. **BF**

Limnanthes douglasii
POACHED-EGG PLANT

Type: hardy annual
Soil & situation: any soil/full sun to light shade
North American hardiness zone: annual
Height & spread: mound to 30cm (12in)
Grow for: good ground cover; ferny foliage; cheerful yellow and white scented flowers; attracts beneficial insects; AGM

The poached-egg plant or meadow foam was first recommended to me by Lawrence Hills, the founder of the Henry Doubleday Research Association, who suggested it as a companion plant for attracting hoverflies. I noticed that it was not just a good self-seeder but also seemed to suppress almost all other weeds over winter and yet could be easily stripped off itself. If left it is a mass of flowers for weeks but never gets very tall, so it could even be used under gooseberries.

Their sweet scent fills the air and attracts butterflies and bees by the thousand. It is marvellous value and a sprinkling of the seed can be thrown in every neglected area to advantage – the ferny foliage and pretty yellow and white flowers of this 'cultivated weed' are nicer to look at than real weeds. I now even use it as a green manure to incorporate under a sheet.

Limnanthes douglasii is one of about a dozen species related to geraniums which come from North America, and it hails from California where it gained its sunny disposition. Its name is Latin for marsh flower – *limne* (marsh) and *anthos* (flower) – but meadow foam or poached-egg plant sounds much better. And why a poached egg, when truly a fried egg would be a more accurate a description?

It will grow on any soil, but prefers moist ones. Sow in autumn *in situ* initially, then let it self-sow. It is easy to weed out if unwanted. Sow self-saved seed in spring and early summer for a later flowering crop of blooms. However invasive it may be, it is too beautiful to weed out when you know you should. **BF**

Lippia dulcis

Type: tender, perennial, evergreen, sprawling sub-shrub
Soil & situation: moist soil/full sun or light shade/under cover
North American hardiness zone: 9–11
Height: 30cm (1ft)
Spread: 1.8m (6ft)
Grow for: unique ground cover under cover; interesting scent; weird flowers; super-sweet foliage

I first grew this plant to find out about its super-sweet leaves, which if chewed are really quite impressive and can be used to make a tea. I then noticed that, although tender, it was quite tough and made a good subject for a hanging basket; however, it self-seeded onto the floor, where it made a dense, aromatic carpet. It was full of whitefly initially, but when I introduced the predators the pest almost disappeared, and now the plant remains a source of both the whitefly and the predator, but I rarely see any large outbreaks of the former.

Very closely related to the true lemon verbena, *Aloysia triphylla* (see page 36), they are both native to South America. Named after Lippi, an Italian botanist killed in Abyssinia, the species name *dulcis* (Latin for sweet) is because of the sweetness of the leaves.

Any soil or compost suits this obliging plant; it even works well filling a hanging basket for the summer. It can be sheared back as growth commences in spring. Very easy from seed, layers and cuttings. Whitefly bother it no end, so use commercially available predators, *Encarsia formosa*. **BF**

Lippia dulcis

Liquidambar styraciflua 'Worplesdon'

SWEET GUM

Type: hardy, deciduous tree
Soil & situation: reliably moist, well-drained, acid soil/full sun
North American hardiness zone: 6–9
Height: 20m (66ft)
Spread: 10m (33ft)
Grow for: maple-leaf-shaped foliage and autumn colour; AGM

Liquidambar styraciflua 'Worplesdon'

In North America it is called sweet gum. In the UK it is simply known as liquidambar. As common names go, neither are very descriptive. Glowing torch, flame tree or autumn glory would all suit it better. Perhaps it is a case of once seen, never forgotten.

The bark on the young shoots is often winged and corky. Older bark remains raised and corky. The deeply lobed, glossy, mid-green leaves turn purple in early autumn and then orange-yellow in winter, often persisting until Christmas time. They could easily be mistaken for those of a maple but they are alternate on the stem, while those of maple are opposite each other. Tiny, green-yellow flowers of male and female are carried on the same tree, the males being in groups of three. Small spiky fruits appear in autumn.

L. styraciflua 'Moonbeam' is slow growing, maturing at 10m (33ft) high with a spread of 6m (20ft). The creamy-yellow leaves turn to shades of yellow, red and purple in autumn.
Liquidambar requires a soil which is constantly wet but not waterlogged. Leaf colour will be better when it is planted in full sun. It has brittle, fleshy roots and dislikes being transplanted. Ignore large, containerized trees for sale. Buy small and plant in its permanent position.

Basal suckers may be a problem. Remove them as close to the root as possible. Cutting at ground level will result in even more shoots. Pruning, when necessary, should be carried out in early winter before the sap starts to rise. Propagation is by seed sown and over-wintered in a cold frame. Softwood cuttings will root in summer with bottom heat. **JC**

Lithodora diffusa 'Heavenly Blue'

Type: hardy, evergreen shrub
Soil & situation: well-drained, humus-rich, acid soil/full sun
North American hardiness zone: 6–8
Height: 15cm (6in)
Spread: 60cm (24in)
Grow for: trailing stems covered in deep blue flowers from the end of spring until late summer; perfect for growing over a low wall; AGM

This gem used to be called *Lithospermum diffusum* 'Heavenly Blue'. Then it was a great plant for tumbling over a rock or dwarf wall and it still is. If it is happy with the soil conditions it will flower without fail every year.

It has a prostrate habit, forming a dense carpet and shaping itself to whatever it grows over. The narrow, deep green leaves are noticeably hairy. From late spring until late summer the plant is covered in small, azure-blue flowers. In full sun the effect is quite startling, with the leaves, where they show through the sheet of blue, acting as a metallic backdrop.

Lightly trim with hedge clippers after flowering and feed with a high-potash, liquid fertilizer.

Lithodora diffusa 'Heavenly Blue'

Mulch the crown of the plant in autumn with peat, washing it down around the inner bare stems. This will encourage the plant to re-root. Propagation is by semi-ripe cuttings in summer. Root them in an ericaceous compost, otherwise the leaves will become yellow and rooting will be slow.

Lithodora oleifolia produces sky-blue flowers from pink tinted buds in early summer. It is not as dense with upright stems 20cm (8in) high. Propagation is easy since it readily sends up rooted suckers which should be removed. It requires a neutral to alkaline soil. **JC**

Lobelia cardinalis

Lobelia cardinalis

CARDINAL FLOWER

Type: hardy, perennial rhizome
Soil & situation: fertile, deep, constantly moist soil/full sun or light shade
North American hardiness zone: 3–9
Height: 90cm (36in)
Spread: 30cm (12in)
Grow for: the vibrant spikes of red flowers make a great show; AGM

I think my main interest in this plant is the way it surprises me every year. It is always bigger and brighter than I remember from the previous year. It also gets Brownie points for enjoying a soil which is always moist. The red-purple stems bear 15cm (6in) long, lance-shaped, glossy, bright green leaves with more than a hint of bronzing. In summer and early autumn it produces upright racemes, 38cm (15in) in length, made up of many bright, scarlet-red flowers. Tubular in shape, each flower has two lips with purple-red bracts.

Constant moisture is essential in summer and autumn but, although fully hardy, it can't tolerate heavy, wet ground in winter. Where drainage is poor in winter, lift and containerize the clump, replanting the following spring. My favourite position for the cardinal flower is at the edge of a pond where its reflection resembles the glow from an electric fire.

Propagation is by seed sown fresh in autumn and potted up in a peaty compost when small. Bud cuttings root well in summer. Over-winter in a cold frame and repot in the spring. **JC**

Lobelia 'Hadspen Purple'

Type: hardy, perennial rhizome
Soil & situation: moist, fertile soil/sun or part shade
North American hardiness zone: 5–8
Height: up to 80cm (32in)
Spread: 25cm (10in)
Grow for: a hardy lobelia that will flower from mid-summer well into the autumn; extremely floriferous with striking plum-purple flowers

This plant has only been very recently released, and I have grown it for only a few months. My mother though, sniffed it out at the very early stages, and has been well and truly smitten by it. I am beginning to see why. The flowering spikes

Lobelia 'Hadspen Purple'

are densely covered with masses of an almost luminous colour, and despite the fact that mine were battered with extreme wet and cold weather conditions, they looked perfect for well over a month, almost incongruous amongst the grey, autumnal weather. Although the plant has an upright habit with very leafy stems, there is no need to stake it. It holds its own against the autumn gales.

These plants enjoy moist, fertile soils, so it is worth adding fertile organic matter prior to planting if your soil is on the thin side. Dead growth can be removed during early winter or spring. This plant would also grow as a marginal plant, but apparently would not live so long if submerged. Propagate by division in spring. **BG**

Lonicera etrusca

Lobelia tupa
DEVIL'S TOBACCO

Type: half-hardy perennial
Soil & situation: deep, moist, fertile soil/sun or partial shade
North American hardiness zone: 8–10
Height: 2m (6½ft)
Spread: 1m (3ft)
Grow for: foliage and flowers from late summer to mid-autumn

This, another extraordinary Chilean plant was introduced to the UK in 1824. It's difficult to believe that this is a relative of the plant with little blue flowers that decorates your hanging basket and there are giant lobelias over 2.7m (9ft) tall that grow on Mt Kenya; it's such a diverse group, that anything can happen. It is in the family Campanulaceae, so is related to campanula too. It has earned its common name from the Mapuche Indians who smoked the leaves and used a juice pressed from the foliage to treat toothache.

Lobelia tupa

This is a real gem. I first saw it at Kew Gardens growing against a hot, sunny wall and couldn't believe my eyes – or the label! It's a robust, upright plant with red-purple stems and tactile, oval- to lance-shaped, grey-green, felty leaves. The narrow, tubular, brick-red to orange flowers appear on upright spikes up to 45cm (18in) long from mid- or late summer through till autumn, and a well-grown specimen in flower looks amazing.

It needs a sheltered position in full sun to partial shade, on deep, fertile, constantly moist soil. Hardy in mild climates like the south and west of Britain, it needs to be protected from frost by mulching with bracken or straw. In colder climates, lift in autumn and over-winter in pots or grow as a container plant. It grows tall and usually needs supporting. It may be attacked by slugs; in mild, moist winters the crown is susceptible to rot. Propagate by fresh seed in the autumn, sown as soon as it is ripe; divide in spring. **MB**

Lonicera etrusca
ETRUSCAN HONEYSUCKLE OR GREEK HONEYSUCKLE

Type: hardy, perennial, semi-evergreen climber
Soil & situation: any soil/full sun to part shade
North American hardiness zone: 7–9
Height: 10m (33ft)
Spread: 4–5m (about 16ft)
Grow for: soft, semi-evergreen foliage; purple shoots; glorious blooms with stunning fragrance

I love walking round my garden on a warm summer's eve sniffing the various fragrant delights; I often start and end with this vigorous climber which has engulfed one end of my cottage. I'm loath to cut it back and lose a year or two's flowers, so it continues to rampage. It is so gorgeous in flower with each large bloom opening cream flushed with red and deepening to a golden-yellow, and their scent permeates the whole garden. The foliage is healthy, attractive, pleasant and actually soft to touch as it is downy, while the youngest shoots carry a purple hue – wonderful.

Lonicera is a genus consisting of 80 or more mostly fragrant plants named after Lonitzer, a 16th-century German botanist. The species name, *etrusca,* suggests it comes from Tuscany – Etruria – in Italy and it is in fact a Mediterranean plant, often referred to as the Greek honeysuckle.

It will grow in almost any site or soil, in sun or light shade but preferring some shelter. It is quite rampant so needs good supports; only prune when overgrown. It is slow to come into bloom but once established is very free flowering. As a true species it can be grown from seed but is quicker to flower from summer softwood or autumn hardwood cuttings. It may get aphids but does not suffer as badly as the commoner *L. periclymenum.* **BF**

Thymus spp.

THYME

Type: hardy or nearly hardy evergreen shrub
Soil & situation: well-drained soil/sun
North American hardiness zone: varies from species to species, but roughly 4–9
Height: 20cm (8in)
Spread: 50cm (20in)
Grow for: neat compact plants to fill areas with a magic carpet of white, pink, purple or red scented flowers. They flourish in the warmth of mid-summer.

There are many dozens of thyme species and varieties easily available, all similar, but with different coloured flowers or foliage or scent. The ones illustrated are (left) *T. hirsutus* 'Doerfleri' and (right) garden, golden and silver thyme (*T. vulgaris, T. v.* 'Aureus' and *T. v.* 'Silver Posie'). Each is delightful in itself, but even better if many are massed together to fill one bed as a patchwork quilt. Because they are so flat they can be used where most plants would be too intrusive, such as down the middle of a driveway or in front of a basement window. Sadly the finest varieties for flavour tend to be fairly upright, but still make low shrubby hummocks; others are so prostrate as to cling to the contours of the ground, flowing over large stones like water. Grand, go on, get yourself some.

Most thymes are natives of warmer parts of Europe and Asia and were well known to the ancients. We get our name from the Latin *thymum,* which came from the Greek. Thyme has strong bactericidal properties and has long been used in home remedies; it is also much loved by bees. It needs a well-drained soil, sandy is good but most species need chalk too. Give it full sun. Plants are short lived, so propagate them every year. The species can be grown from spring- or summer-sown seed, or propagated by cuttings most of the year if taken with a heel, and root division is easy in spring or autumn. No real problems other than fiddly weeding. **BF**

Bunny adds:
I find that if you give them sharp drainage and one cutback after flowering, they will look good for several years.

Lonicera fragrantissima

Lonicera fragrantissima

Type: hardy, perennial, semi-evergreen shrub
Soil & situation: any soil/sun or shade
North American hardiness zone: 5–8
Height & spread: to 5m (16ft) if not supported
Grow for: small, fragrant, cream flowers all winter; red berries in summer

This is one of the longest flowering shrubs; the first flower may open before Christmas and the last after Easter. As each flower is small, only the size of a fingernail, and creamy, pale yellow in colour, they seem insignificant but are powerfully fragrant. They also allure bees, who flock to them on sunny days. The flowers are borne along twiggy shoots so it is easy to pick stems to take indoors to perfume a room though, sadly, they do not last long in a vase. Although partially evergreen, it is not a particularly attractive shrub as such and is best hidden at the back of a border.

Lonicera fragrantissima was introduced to the UK from China by Robert Fortune in 1845. Do not be deceived into getting *L.* x *purpusii* (a cross between *L. fragrantissima* and *L. standishii*), the similar but rather disappointing hybrid.

The shrubby honeysuckles are very long lived and vigorous on almost any soil or site. This is a shrub not a climber, but as it is not totally rigid it will need something to lend it support, such as a post or old tree against which it can be tied. It can be grown from seed but summer softwood or autumn hardwood cuttings are quicker to flower. *L. fragrantissima* is not so prone to aphids as the climbing honeysuckles. **BF**

Lonicera periclymenum 'Graham Thomas'

COMMON HONEYSUCKLE, WOODBINE

Type: hardy, deciduous, twining shrub
Soil & situation: moist, well-drained, humus-rich soil/full sun or partial shade
North American hardiness zone: 5–9
Height: 4m (13ft)
Spread: 1.8m (6ft)
Grow for: it speaks for itself; AGM

Summer wouldn't be the same without honeysuckles. A walk down a country lane with the heavenly scent of the woodbine scrambling through the hedges with its nectar-filled flowers is a memorable experience. Did you suck the nectar from the unopened tube? Didn't we all? In autumn the bright, glistening, red berries outshone the red hips and haws of the dog rose and the hawthorn.

Lonicera periclymenum 'Graham Thomas' is a much-improved form of that wild woodbine. The 7.5cm (3in) long, mid-green leaves are glaucous on the underside and carried in pairs on the vigorous, twining branches. From early summer to autumn the plant is covered in whorls of two-lipped, very fragrant, tubular, white flowers, which gradually fade to yellow with a hint of copper, giving the plant a bicoloured appearance. They flower on the previous year's shoots and are best pruned back, after flowering, to some strong, young shoots. *L. p.* 'Belgica' is more vigorous with white flowers that turn yellow with bright red streaks.

Propagate by inserting hardwood cuttings into open ground in early winter and they will be well rooted by the following autumn. Aphids can be a serious problem. When chemicals fail to control them the only solution is to hard prune in summer and allow new clean foliage to regrow. **JC**

Matt adds:
I smoked Woodbines years ago, they never smelt as sweet as this! This variety is named after the late Graham Stewart-Thomas, the garden writer and former Chief Gardens Advisor to the National Trust, who found it in a Warwickshire hedgerow in 1960; it's very free-flowering and typically vigorous. Derrick Cook found just a single seedling under a holly tree in his garden near Evesham and decided to nurture it. It matured to a dark reddish-green leaved plant with dark red flowers that are honey-coloured on the inside; this delightful plant is named after his home, 'Red Gables'. Roy Lancaster was walking along a beach in Sweden when he spotted one with cream and yellow flowers growing in a mound of brambles; Roy named it after his wife, 'Sweet Sue'. Where will you find yours?

Lonicera periclymenum 'Graham Thomas'

Lonicera syringantha

Lonicera syringantha

Type: hardy, perennial, deciduous shrub
Soil & situation: any soil/full sun to light shade
North American hardiness zone: 5–8
Height & spread: makes a lax shrub 1–2m (3–6½ft) each way, or possibly wider
Grow for: arching sprays of stems and neat, grey-green foliage; wonderful, pink, scented flowers; occasional red berries

This is a plant to fool your friends. The grey-green foliage is small, neat and almost geometrical; the lilac-like flowers come in clusters in the axils of the leaves and can coat the stems with a multitude of blooms, each with a daphne-like perfume. Your friends will never guess this is a honeysuckle!

Introduced from China at the end of the 19th century, this beautiful plant was named for the resemblance its flowers bore to those of lilac (*Syringa*).

It will grow in most soils and situations but flowers best in sun. Although shrubby, it is very lax and makes an arching shrub given the space or can be trained to supports. As a species it can be grown from seed but cuttings in summer or autumn are quicker to flower. It has brittle wood, which is easily snapped. **BF**

Lonicera x tellmanniana

Type: hardy, deciduous climber
Soil & situation: moist, well-drained soil/sun or light shade
North American hardiness zone: 7–9
Height: 5m (16ft)
Spread: 45–60cm (18–24in)
Grow for: twining climber; copious clusters of soft coppery-orange flowers in late spring to early summer; AGM

Although this honeysuckle has no fragrance, it is one of my favourites. The tubular flowers are up to 5cm (2in) long, very bold but not brassy and definitely eye-catching. When the plant is grown in light shade it produces its best, but will grow fairly well in full shade too. You can appreciate the vibrant hue of the flowers better in the softer light, they become more intense and fiery. I have not seen it scrambling up a tree but it would be highly suited to that type of situation, and being a fast mover, you would not have to wait too long for the startling results. I grow it twining up and over a dark blue, metal swing-seat with gold leaf finials, and love the strong colour combination of blue, gold and orange – rather exotic.

These are easy plants to grow although they do need a supportive framework of some sort, be it trellis, wires, a fence or the like. They will do better with an annual mulch of organic matter. Too much nitrogen will result in much leaf and little flowering, in which case potash will help redress the balance. Pruning is straightforward: you can just remove the shoots that have flowered immediately they are over; no other attention is necessary. They can be propagated from semi-ripe cuttings in summer or hardwood cuttings in late autumn. **BG**

Lonicera x tellmanniana

Lotus hirsutus

Lotus hirsutus
HAIRY CANARY CLOVER

Type: hardy, evergreen perennial or subshrub
Soil & situation: free-draining, moderately fertile soils/sunny position
North American hardiness zone: 6–9
Height: up to 60cm (24in)
Spread: about 1m (3ft)
Grow for: extremely useful foliage plant with silver grey-green, tiny, hairy leaves; AGM

This is a close-textured, rather natty foliage plant that will form an attractive low hedge or edge to the front of the border; it can also be used as a specimen or group grown in gravel. It is a fairly unusual plant but is easy to grow, easy to propagate and extremely well-mannered. Because it has such fine leaves it is useful for contrasting with more informal, or larger-leaved types. It flowers in summer with not very conspicuous, but typical pea-type flowers that are cream flushed with shell pink. They are just an also ran, not unattractive though, but the prime reason for growing this is definitely the silvery foliage.

Leave on the growth throughout winter (it looks quite presentable) and then cut it down in spring if more bushy growth is required. It is worth growing replacement cuttings every three or four years so you can rejuvenate your stock periodically. Propagation from softwood cuttings is straightforward in summer. It can, apparently, also be propagated from seed but the offspring is variable. **BG**

Lunaria annua

Plant of the Week (see page 119)

Lupinus arboreus

TREE LUPIN

Type: semi-woody, usually evergreen, perennial shrub
Soil & situation: dry or at least well-drained soil/sun
North American hardiness zone: 8–9
Height: 1.8–2.2m (6–7ft)
Spread: 1m (3ft)
Grow for: effectively evergreen; fast-growing, scented, yellow flowers all summer; AGM

I like the usual run-of-the-mill lupins; they are easy and obliging plants that have the biggest aphids I've ever seen and they put on a gaudy show. But the tree lupins are different. This shrubby form is more refined, with greyer more spidery foliage and pale creamy-yellow blooms with a wonderful sweet scent. I like this delicate form, and the fact that it keeps its evergreen, silvery leaves in mild winters is an added bonus. It is a bit like a tree peony, but much quicker growing, positively frenetic by comparison. It is very useful for dry sunny banks and although short lived, it does self-seed.

The name comes from the Latin for wolf, *lupus*, as lupins produce 'peas' fit for a wolf/dog – we refer to unpalatable plants as dog(berry) or horse (...mint). Lupins were well known to the Romans as many of the genus are natives of the Mediterranean, but this one was brought from California in 1793.

Lupinus arboreus

It needs a dry sandy soil and apparently does well by the sea, but I've never seen it growing there. Dead-heading helps to keep them flowering and living a bit longer. As it is semi-shrubby you can try cuttings, but it is easier and quicker to make a spring or autumn sowing. Aphids can be a problem, but nothing like as much as they are with the more herbaceous species. **BF**

Lupinus 'The Governor'

Lupinus 'The Governor'

LUPIN

Type: hardy, clump-forming perennial
Soil & situation: fertile, well-drained, light, slightly acid soil/full sun or light shade
North American hardiness zone: 5–8
Height: 90cm (36in)
Spread: 75cm (30in)
Grow for: the coloured spikes of flowers in early and late summer

When I think of cottage and farm gardens they conjure up images of tall, multi-coloured spikes of lupin flowers standing above dense clumps of palmate leaves, each with a bead of dew at the base above the leaf stalk.

The softly hairy, mid-green leaves are made up of lance-shaped leaflets held on strong, thick, pale green stems. Flowering in early summer, the bicoloured racemes of royal blue and white pea-like flowers are up to 45cm (18in) long. Removing the spike after flowering prevents the plant using its energy to produce seeds. These are contained in numerous small, pea-like pods. Early removal will encourage the plant to send out another flower spike in late summer.

Propagation is by seed sown in autumn or spring. Autumn seedlings need to be over-wintered in a cold frame. Soaking the round, black or brown seed in water for 24 hours before sowing will soften the outer seed coat and speed up germination. Basal cuttings can be rooted in a gritty, free-draining compost in spring. New young shoots are prone to slug damage. **JC**

Luzula nivea

SNOWY WOODRUSH

Type: hardy, evergreen grass
Soil & situation: will tolerate a wide range of soils/best in moist, humus-rich but free-draining soils/sun or shade
North American hardiness zone: 4–9
Height: 60cm (24in)
Spread: 45cm (18in)
Grow for: a useful grass for shady areas such as woodland; low-key but graceful year-round foliage; attractive, fairly long-lasting white flowers in late spring

I was pleased when I first fell upon this plant – 'fell' in the literal sense too! We were in the exhausting period of pulling to bits and removing one of our Chelsea gardens, when I saw a nice clump of *Luzula* in the bottom of the skip, exactly where I was about to dump a huge barrow of hardcore. You can guess the rest. Suffice to say they now are thriving in my woodland garden in bold drifts, jostling next to ferns, arums and primroses. They have a natural-looking habit with loose tufts of thin, strap-like dark green leaves which contrast with the snowy-white flowers borne in relaxed panicles. They have now established well and are tolerant of my dry conditions (which is not what the books would have you believe), though I must admit they are not spreading like wildfire.

The other one I grow, also purloined from a skip, is *Luzula sylvatica*, the greater woodrush. Its leaves are broader and it is a coarser plant generally but grows and spreads in a pleasingly compact fashion. The chestnut flowers are not a patch on the snowy woodrush, but it is a plant I like.

This plant, once established, needs next to no looking after. Because it is a plant often used in

Luzula nivea

rather large, natural-looking drifts, it is a useful one to propagate in quantity. This can be done by division or seed. Division is best done between mid-spring and early summer. Seed can be sown in spring or autumn. **BG**

Lychnis coronaria
DUSTY MILLER, ROSE CAMPION

Type: hardy biennial or short-lived perennial
Soil & situation: prefers free-draining soil but will grow in any moderately fertile soil/sun or partial shade
North American hardiness zone: 4–8
Height: up to 80cm (32in)
Spread: 45cm (18in)
Grow for: incredible, intensely bright magenta flowers in mid-summer lasting over a month; basal rosettes of ever-grey, felted foliage; AGM

This is an old cottage-garden plant, but none the less is highly versatile because the vibrant hue of the flowers can be used to give a high-voltage effect to many a colour scheme. It is tolerant of extremely poor soil conditions too, and sets seed freely all around the edges of my gravel courtyard – it is growing in lines against north- and south-facing walls. It is also fine in borders and if it sets seed next to an unsympathetic neighbour and the colour combination sets your teeth on edge, it is simple to whip out. In truth I never notice whether my plants are biennial or perennial because they are not over-invasive but always there, a much appreciated presence. There is a white form, *L. c.* 'Alba', for those who find the magenta too much or too common.

To prolong flowering you can dead-head these adaptable plants. After flowering, they look a bit seedy. They are simple to remove and I either cut them down to leave the basal rosettes or just pull out the whole plant if I want to put in some later, temporary colour. The seedlings are adaptable and if I would rather they were elsewhere they can be moved with little setback. Propagation is easy with fresh seed sown immediately after flowering or in spring. **BG**

Lycopersicon esculentum 'Aromata'
TOMATO

Type: tender, annual scrambler
Soil & situation: rich, moist compost/sun/under cover
North American hardiness zone: annual
Height & spread: up to 3m (10ft)
Grow for: delicious good-looking fruit packed full of vitamins; an easy and highly reliable greenhouse plant

In the UK we have one of the highest levels of amateur greenhouse ownership in the world and in most tomatoes are grown. There is an unbelievable number of tomato varieties, each with its own characteristics and virtues. However I am recommending 'Aromata', and in second and third places 'Moravi' and 'Merlot', as the most outstandingly reliable croppers of round red tomatoes throughout the year. Not only do these grow well, crop well and not show any tendency to problems such as greenback, they have proved resistant to the majority of diseases that plague greenhouse-grown tomatoes.

The original tomatoes were ribbed and somewhat flattened in shape and the spherical tomato was not noticed or bred until about 1700. This is not surprising, as in Europe we only really started showing much interest in the tomato as a food at about that time and indeed, a century later most people were still unfamiliar with this new fruit.

Indoor tomatoes should be grown in an enriched border soil rather than in pots or bags of compost as they do better and require less attention with a big root run. At the end of the growing season if you do not heat your greenhouse through winter or when the light levels fall, the plant will wither and mould; at this point carefully take off the ripening and green fruits and put them in a warm place to ripen. Sow in individual pots in the warmth in late winter, pot on and plant out in the greenhouse border as soon as it can be kept frost free. Remove excess sideshoots; these can be rooted to make more plants. 'Aromata' avoids many of the diseases suffered by other tomatoes but may come under attack from aphids and whitefly; soft soap sprays prove effective. **BF**

Lychnis coronaria

Lycopersicon esculentum 'Dombito'

Lycopersicon esculentum 'Dombito'
TOMATO

Type: tender, annual scrambler
Soil & situation: rich, moist compost/sun/under cover
North American hardiness zone: annual
Height & spread: up to 3m (10ft)
Grow for: an excellent large salad tomato

Having suggested indoor tomatoes for reliability I now want to recommend two for using as salad, beefsteak or slicing tomatoes. There are bigger beefsteaks – the old 'Marmande' is very good but really does better outdoors in a warm climate – but 'Dombito' was bred to be a modern, large, greenhouse tomato. Fairly reliable and on the whole disease resistant, and although it isn't early it does give a lovely crop of huge, round, sweet fruits. These peel like a peach, which is very handy, and do not get the corky, greeny-white, tough ring of poor flesh called greenback, which so many greenhouse tomatoes suffer from if exposed to heat stress. Of course if you want an old-fashioned, hard to peel and unreliable beefsteak with an incomparable flavour, grow 'Pink Brandywine', but be prepared for disappointing plants and crops in cool damp years.

Our larger tomatoes, such as 'Marmande' and 'Pink Brandywine' often revert to the ribbed and slightly flattened shape of older varieties. 'Dombito' is a significant improvement and the nice-looking fruits still have a good flavour.

Indoor beefsteak tomatoes are better off in an enriched border soil than in pots or bags of compost, as they do better and require less attention with a big root run. These big tomatoes need more care than others: add more wood ash to the soil, water diligently and foliar feed with seaweed sprays. Remove all excess shoots and reduce each truss to only a few fruits. At the end of their growing season carefully take off the ripening and green fruits and take these into a warm place to ripen. Sow in individual pots in the warmth in late winter, pot on and plant out in greenhouse border as soon as it can be kept frost free. 'Dombito' avoids many of the diseases but may still suffer from aphids and whitefly; soft soap sprays prove effective. **BF**

Lycopersicon esculentum 'Gardener's Delight'
TOMATO

Type: tender, annual scrambler
Soil & situation: rich, moist soil/sun/shelter
North American hardiness zone: annual
Height: 2m (6½ft)
Spread: 30cm (12in)
Grow for: I defy you to find a better flavoured tom!

In almost every taste trial of outdoor tomatoes that has taken place over the last few decades 'Gardener's Delight' has come out a clear winner. It can be grown indoors but tastes the best when grown outdoors. Being a cherry-sized fruit, it is quick and easy to crop and not very prone to pests or disease, except blight. The small, bite-sized fruits have a delicious flavour with a pronounced acidity that makes them thirst quenching.

The cherry varieties, like 'Gardener's Delight', seem to have as old a lineage as the original ribbed tomatoes and were probably grown in South America alongside the larger sorts.

Outdoor tomatoes are better off in an enriched border soil than in pots or bags of compost as they do better and require less attention with a big root run. Take off all sideshoots and remove the tip once six trusses of fruit form. At the end of the growing season, before the frosts come, carefully lift the vines and hang them upside down under cover somewhere frost free to let green fruits ripen on the plants. Sow in individual pots in the warmth in early spring, pot on and plant out in a sheltered border once the last frost is over. Outdoor tomatoes avoid many diseases and pests but are plagued by potato blight in damp years; I protect them by keeping them dry under a polythene flysheet. **BF**

Lycopersicon esculentum 'Gardener's Delight'

Lycopersicon esculentum 'Sakura'
TOMATO

Type: tender, annual scrambler
Soil & situation: rich, moist compost/sun/under cover
North American hardiness zone: annual
Height & spread: up to 3m (10ft)
Grow for: a fast, tasty, reliable crop – and not just tasty but TASTY!

I have already recommended an indoor tomato, 'Aromata' (see page 253), for reliable cropping, but it is not the tastiest. One of the tastiest for years was 'Gardener's Delight' (see previous entry); however it never has such a good flavour grown inside as out. This new variety is even better than the old champ when grown indoors, which amazes me as it is also fairly problem free and remarkably quick to crop – a superb, bite-sized cherry tomato.

Cherry tomatoes have been grown nearly as long as the larger ribbed sorts but appear to be of different lineage. They are usually better flavoured, prolific and often early croppers, and some resist diseases better than the larger, more conventional tomatoes. Of course this may be due to more breeding in the big ones, making them miffy.

Right: *Lysichiton americanus*

Indoor cherry tomatoes are better off in an enriched border soil than in pots or bags of compost, as they do better and require less attention with a big root run. However if you are after an extra early crop, then keep them in pots on the staging and do not feed heavily. Sow in individual pots in the warmth in mid-winter, pot on and plant out in the greenhouse border as soon as it can be kept frost free. If you have space it can be left unpruned to ramble, otherwise remove excess sideshoots. 'Sakura' avoids many diseases but may still suffer from aphids and whitefly; soft soap sprays prove effective. **BF**

Lycopersicon esculentum 'San Marzano'

TOMATO

Type: tender, annual scrambler
Soil & situation: rich, moist soil/sun/shelter
North American hardiness zone: annual
Height: 2m (6½ft)
Spread: 30cm (12in)
Grow for: plum tomatoes are the best for cooking and hard to buy fresh

It is impossible to find good, fresh, ripe plum tomatoes so you have to grow them. They are the only tomato to cook alongside bacon and eggs and are invaluable for almost all Italian or Spanish recipes. If you haven't tried fried plum tomatoes, please do – the flavour changes completely as they cook and becomes divine, and is especially good if eaten with some organic smoked back bacon. They are less runny than most tomatoes with a more solid flesh.

Lycopersicon esculentum 'San Marzano'

Plum-shaped tomatoes were developed mostly in Italy where they were originally called, and were more, pear shaped. For planting and aftercare please see *L. e.* 'Gardener's Delight', opposite. **BF**

Lysichiton americanus

YELLOW SKUNK CABBAGE

Type: hardy, aquatic, deciduous perennial
Soil & situation: fertile, humus-rich, deep, moist soil/full sun or partial shade
North American hardiness zone: 7–9
Height: 1m (3ft)
Spread: 1.2m (4ft)
Grow for: fine-looking, bright yellow spathes in spring; ideal for a waterside planting or in a bog garden; AGM

Not so long ago I was admiring hundreds of plants growing in a sheltered, low-lying, water garden in the West of Scotland. The sun was shining and all was well with the world until two passersby came along and proceeded to moan about the problems of the 'imaginary', nearby compost heap. The musky smell of yellow skunk cabbage is only noticeable when there are lots of flowers or when your attention is drawn to it.

The leaves, which appear at the same time as the flower is fully open, are leathery, shiny, dark green and grow to 50–100cm (20–39in) long. Appearing in early spring, each 'flower' comprises a large, bright yellow spathe up to 40cm (16in) long, with a central yellow spadix made up of hundreds of tiny, bisexual, green flowers turning yellow. It is a striking plant for the edge of a pool or stream where its reflection doubles the display. It is also a 'talking point' for those who have never seen it before.

When planting allow adequate room for the leaves to grow, spacing the plants about 1.5m (5ft) apart. Propagation is by seed in wet peat as soon as it is ripe or by pulling offsets from the base of the plant in early summer and potting into a peaty compost.
JC

Canna iridiflora/C. x *ehemanii* July

Type: tender rhizomatous perennial
Soil & situation: moisture-retentive soil/full sun/ winter protection
North American hardiness zone: 7–10
Height: up to 3m (10ft)
Spread: 50cm (20in)
Grow for: highly exotic-looking, dramatic foliage; superb rose-coloured flowers, which appear later than other cannas and are glorious in the bright mid-summer light; AGM

This plant is a real knock-out and will stop you in your tracks. It is a huge plant growing frequently to above 1.5m (5ft) with massive, purple-edged, green leaves and pendulous, relatively small and delicate-looking, yet punchy flowers. Cannas are easy to grow generally. I have tried them in different areas and they invariably just get on with life even in excessively free-draining areas, though I do shovel in the odd wheelbarrow load of compost. Some years odd plants are overlooked and left out; they survive to tell the tale but bloom much later, so I would not do it on purpose. This one is hardier than many and is also grown far less, perhaps because of its size, but in a small garden it would fill the space with zing – very exciting. Another possible reason for its low profile is that it comes into flower relatively late and is worth growing on under glass for a bit longer to bring it forward. The most likely reason though is just that it is difficult to come by, but I do not know why. The more common *Canna indica* and its many cultivars are more widely grown. They are all great assets to the garden, transforming it with their lush structure and vibrant colour.

Do not be put off by the following routine. It is simple and the results are inevitably stunning. I always pop a few extra into pots as they can plug gaps or just stand alone. All cannas need lifting as soon as the frost has blackened their foliage, then their top growth should be cut off. Over-winter them in a cellar, greenhouse or shed, keeping them just slightly damp and frost-free. Do not let them dry out. Plant them back out in late spring or early summer. If the weather is hot and dry give them a good drink to maintain that lush feel and pull off dead flowerheads to encourage more. Slugs and snails are fairly keen on them but I find a thick mulch of cocoa shells adds to the tropical effect, deters pests and retains the moisture. **BG**

Macleaya microcarpa 'Coral Plume'

PLUME POPPY, TREE CELANDINE

Type: hardy, rhizomatous perennial
Soil & situation: wide range of soils/prefers moist conditions/tolerates light shade
North American hardiness zone: 4–9
Height: to 2.5m (8ft)
Spread: 1m (3ft)
Grow for: fabulous bold foliage; beautiful plumed racemes of long-lasting, rich coral flowers in summer; AGM

I grew this plant in my previous garden in deep, rich soil and it thrived, producing increasing quantities of wonderful juicy stems each spring, followed by softly stunning flowers. People are wary of its over-enthusiastic nature. It is on the keen side, so hem it in with sturdy neighbours or just spade through its outer limits each spring and show it who is boss. When I moved to my current free-draining, light soil, I thought its exuberant nature would be over-subdued, but it has come up trumps again. Try to seek out 'Coral Plume', as this clone has warmer hues to its foamy flowers.

Macleaya cordata (AGM) has creamy-white flowers and is another favourite of mine. The foliage has an architectural feel with bold leaves that are up to 20cm (8in) wide, lobed, with a soft olive green colour above but downy white below. I have a big clump of them beside my front door and the architectural leaves complement the chunky stone carving of the quoins around the doorway. Not a plant I would be without.

Macleaya microcarpa 'Coral Plume'

Magnolia liliiflora 'Nigra'

I do next to nothing to this plant – I don't stake it, nor divide it up unless a friend wants a bit – all I do is admire it and cut it down in autumn. Slugs are supposed to go for it, and I have more than my fair share, but they never make it unsightly. **BG**

Magnolia liliiflora 'Nigra'

Type: hardy, deciduous shrub
Soil & situation: moist, humus-rich, well-drained, neutral to acid soil/sun or partial shade
North American hardiness zone: 6–9
Height: 3m (10ft)
Spread: 2.5m (8ft)
Grow for: continuous display of dark purple flowers from late spring and through the summer; AGM

This delightful variety is regarded by many as having the longest flowering period of all magnolias. Plants flower early in life, often the year after planting. It is a vigorous variety with glossy, dark green leaves up to 20cm (8in) in length. The large, chalice-shaped flowers appear in late spring and it can still be in flower in the autumn. Externally they are a dark purple and an ivory-white with purple staining on the inside. As the flowers age, they resemble an untidy tulip with some of the petals peeling back to reveal their inner colouring.

Pruning is not normally necessary with this compact-growing variety. Branches which are crossing or spoiling the shape may be removed in winter when the shrub is dormant. *M. l.* 'Nigra' dislikes being transplanted when large. Check the roots of container-grown plants and if they are congested tease them apart before spreading out in the planting hole. Avoid a site exposed to cold winds or late spring frosts which will blacken the early flowers.

Propagation is by semi-ripe cuttings in late summer. Use small cuttings and cut the leaves in half to reduce transpiration which causes wilting. Layering in early spring is guaranteed to work but can be slow, taking up to 18 months to root well. **JC**

Mahonia japonica

Plant of the Week (see page 33)

Mahonia x *media* 'Charity'

Type: hardy, evergreen shrub
Soil & situation: well-drained, fertile soil/shade or partial shade
North American hardiness zone: 7–8
Height: 4m (13ft)
Spread: 3–4m (10–13ft)
Grow for: fragrant, deep yellow flowers in winter; spiny, architectural, evergreen foliage; blue-black, fruits in summer

Its shiny, dark green, spiny-toothed, pinnate leaves ensure this plant creates interest all year round. From late autumn until late winter it carries long, prominent racemes of small, scented, deep yellow flowers followed by berries. Even the stems and roots are interesting: cut them and you will find the wood is bright yellow.

Mahonias can be divided into two groups: the taller Asian species such as *M. lomarifolia* and the more compact Americans, including *M. aquifolium*. Those from North America can tolerate a more sunny situation. Both parents of 'Charity' are Asian, *M. lomarifolia* and *M. japonica*, resulting in a plant with 45cm (18in) long leaves made up of between 17 and 21 leaflets. *M.* x *m.* 'Charity' has, over many years, proved to be totally reliable.

Mahonias dislike being transplanted, so buy small plants which are not pot bound to avoid disturbing the roots. Dig a generous-sized planting hole and add lots of rotted farmyard manure. Plant firmly and water regularly during the first season. In exposed, windy sites the tips of the young leaves may be scorched. Occasionally it will throw up a long flowering shoot devoid of lower leaves. After flowering remove the shoot close to the ground to encourage new growth.

Mahonia x media 'Charity'

It is seldom troubled by pests or diseases, so for me 'Charity' begins at home. **JC**

Mahonia x *media* 'Lionel Fortescue'

Type: hardy, evergreen shrub
Soil & situation: any soil/partial shade
North American hardiness zone: 7–8
Height & spread: 4m (13ft)
Grow for: architectural form and winter flowers; AGM

There are several excellent hybrids between *Mahonia japonica* and *M. lomariifolia*, collectively known as *M.* x *media*. They have terminal flower clusters surrounded by an umbrella of stiff, glossy, spiny leaves topping upright jointed stems.

Lionel Fortescue at the Garden House in Buckland Monachorum in Devon, southwest England, produced 200 seedlings; five were retained. *M.* x *media* 'Lionel Fortescue' produces masses of branched, bright yellow, fragrant flower spikes up to 40cm (16in) long. From the same batch came M. x m. 'Buckland' with up to 14 upright, branched, arching, spreading flower spikes to 45cm (18in) long. *M.* x *m.* 'Charity' (see previous entry) is another favourite – it was selected by Sir Eric Savill from seedlings raised in Ireland around 1950.

They were busy in America too! *M.* x *m.* 'Arthur Menzies', up to 4m (13ft) x 4m (13ft), is similar, with yellow flowers on upright spreading spikes up to 25cm (10in) long. The leaves can be as long as 45cm (18in). This was selected at the University of Washington Arboretum.

They need moist, slightly acid to neutral soil with plenty of well-rotted organic matter and prefer partial shade. Protect plants from cold winds. When they become spindly and bare at the base, cut the stems back to within 30–60cm (12–24in) of the base after flowering in spring; feed with general fertilizer and mulch. They regenerate with denser growth. Propagate by leaf bud cuttings in late winter. **MB**

Mahonia x *media* 'Lionel Fortescue'

Malus coronaria 'Charlottae'

Type: hardy, deciduous tree
Soil & situation: moisture-retentive, free-draining soil/sun
North American hardiness zone: 5–8
Height & spread: 9m (30ft)
Grow for: delicate, fragrant flowers in late spring and early summer

It took a journey to New Zealand to discover this magnificent *Malus* growing in the pretty garden in Taranaki created by Gwyn Masters. Among all her treasures was a young specimen of *Malus coronaria* 'Charlottae', resplendent in light and shell-pink blooms, perfectly placed by a path so I could press my nose to the fragile, semi-double flowers and inhale a draught of the delicate violet perfume. It's a good 'value for money' tree. The branches are at first upright, then spread with age (I know the feeling!) and the flowers not opening until the end of spring are quite late for a crab apple. The large, lobed leaves often colour brilliantly in autumn to a rich orange-red; the tree also fruits prolifically after long, hot summers. It was found as a chance seedling in the wild in 1902 near Waukegan, Illinois, by Mrs Charlotte de Wolf. Sir Harold Hillier, the great English nurseryman, once remarked, 'In my opinion this is the best of the semi-double American crabs for English gardens with a strong constitution'. What more can I say?

It prefers a sunny position, where autumn colour is better, and moisture-retentive, fertile but not waterlogged soil; it tolerates some shade. Water young trees well to help them establish and mulch in spring. Feed with slow-release fertilizer in spring until mature. Prune in winter to remove dead, diseased or damaged wood. Propagate in winter by grafting or budding. It can be attacked by any pests and diseases that affect apples like powdery mildew, scab and woolly aphid. **MB**

Malus coronaria 'Charlottae'

Malus domestica
RUSSET APPLE

Type: hardy, long-lived, deciduous tree
Soil & situation: any well-drained soil/sun
North American hardiness zone: 5–8
Height & spread: 30cm–18m (12in–60ft), depending on rootstock
Grow for: prolific, pink, scented flowers in late spring; green- or reddy-brown, aromatically flavoured apples in early autumn

There are many apple varieties – over 2,000 different sorts are known – and it is fairly easy to buy several hundred different ones if you want a collection. There is every size, quality and keeping ability, but one group remains unique and that is the russets. While every other apple is glossy and shiny, these have a corky matt skin overall or in large areas. The fruits are usually reddy-brown or even greeny-brown and the skin is tough. The flesh is often more substantial than other apples. It is also drier, which is why they store well, and their sweet, strong, aromatic, even nutty flavour makes them a good choice for the gourmet. The skin is usually scentless, but resists scab well. Indeed, a great many of the best apples have some russet patches, if only as flecks on the skin. 'Brownlee's Russet' was introduced in 1848; it is an upright tree with very prolific pink blossom which is a feature in itself, and the fruits are juicier than most russets and aromatic. They store well, being good all winter up until spring when they come into bloom again. 'Rosemary Russet' is even older (1831), not strong growing but upright and productive. The apples are best from mid-winter till spring.

Ideally any apple wants a rich, moist but well-drained, loamy soil in a warm, sheltered spot but it will thrive almost anywhere not totally barren and windswept. Most russets are not tip bearers and thus can be pruned, or trained; they are best on very dwarfing rootstocks as cordons or espaliers. 'Brownlee's Russet' needs a pollinator and 'Greensleeves' suits it. Plant bare-rooted trees in autumn, preferably as soon as their leaves have fallen. Russets suffer less than many apples from pests and diseases, and crop well regardless. **BF**

Malus domestica 'Court Pendu Plat'
WISE APPLE, WALLATON PIPPIN

Type: hardy, upright, deciduous tree
Soil & situation: all except waterlogged soil/sun
North American hardiness zone: 5–8
Height & spread: depends on growing conditions and rootstock
Grow for: history; flavour; fruit from early winter to late spring

This apple, believed to have originated in Roman times, is still used in breeding programmes because it keeps well and flowers at the end of spring, escaping the frost, hence the name 'Wise Apple'. 'Court Pendu' means 'suspended short', as the stalk is so short the fruit appears to sit upon the branch. Around Herefordshire, it is called garnons because the Cotterell family from Garnons near Hereford grew it without knowing the name; for the same reason it is often known as the 'Wallaton Pippin' because Lord Middleton in Wallaton, Nottinghamshire, lost the label too! It was among the top ten Victorian apples, prized for its looks and fine flavour and its use as a decorative tree for borders or pots when grown as bushes or espaliers.

The small, flat, rounded fruit is dull yellow with a vermilion flush and slight russetting. In the UK leave on the tree until late October if possible; it will then ripen from December to January and store until April/May.

It is full flavoured and fruity with a pineapple-like taste, but mellows to become scented and intensively flavoured. Delicious! Pollination group 3. It needs moist, loamy soil in a sheltered sunny site; mulch in spring and don't let the soil dry out. Grow as cordons or espaliers in small gardens. As it is spur fruiting, prune in winter and mid-summer. It is very hardy, prolific and scab resistant, but suffers from pests and diseases common to apples, including mildew, codling moth and woolly aphid. **MB**

Malus domestica 'Discovery'

Type: hardy, long-lived, deciduous tree
Soil & situation: any well-drained soil/sun
North American hardiness zone: 5–8
Height & spread: 30cm–18m (12in–60ft), depending on rootstock
Grow for: prolific white and pink, barely scented flowers in late spring; brightly coloured red apples in late summer; an early cropper; AGM

Early apples are so delicious; they are such a delight to eat straight from the tree and warmed by the sun on a bright, late summer's afternoon. Of course being early means most of them won't keep, and some go woolly within hours of picking.

Malus domestica 'Russet'

'Discovery' is, however, an early that stays fresh a little longer (that's why it is so common in the shops) and despite this is still a very, very good apple. The sweet crunchiness makes for really excellent eating. I love to stand with a large scarlet 'Discovery' in one hand being heartily munched and to alternate it with fistfuls of Japanese wineberries (*Rubus phoenicolasius*, see page 342) which I collect with the other – yummy!

There are several dozen wild *Malus* species, but most of our domestic tree's ancestry comes from *M. pumila*, a wild crab common all over Europe. Domestic trees were known to the early Romans but not as our modern fruit – they were much closer to the crab; however by late Roman times they had selected over three dozen improved varieties! 'Discovery' was introduced in 1962 and makes an upright tree with healthy foliage, it is fairly resistant to scab and tolerant of late frosts. It is now the most popular early apple.

Ideally an early apple wants a rich, moist but well-drained, loamy soil in a warm, sheltered spot but it will thrive almost anywhere not totally barren and windswept. Most early apples are tip bearers and thus should not be pruned or trained, so are best on very dwarfing rootstocks as small bush trees. 'Discovery' does form spurs as well so can be trained, just. It needs a pollinator; 'Greensleeves' suits it and is a good apple, ripening after 'Discovery'. Plant bare-rooted trees in autumn, preferably as soon as their leaves have fallen. **BF**

Malus domestica 'Winston'

Type: hardy, long lived, deciduous tree
Soil & situation: any well-drained soil/sun
North American hardiness zone: 5–8
Height & spread: 30cm–18m (12in–60ft), depending on rootstock
Grow for: prolific, pale pink and white, lightly scented flowers in late spring; yellowish-green flushed red apples in late autumn; a long keeper; AGM

I want to be able to eat my own apples all year, but even more importantly I want good apples for coleslaw almost all year round. Although 'Winston' is one of the longest keepers of all, I find it also stays as a high-quality apple until well into the early summer of the following year, unlike some others I could name. It is resistant to scab, can be trained and has vigorous growth which overcrops if you are not careful – a first-class choice. There are many late keepers, 'Granny Smith' being one example, but few of them make as good eating as late as 'Winston'. Long-keeping apples were very popular in previous times as they could be taken as ship's stores. However, those that kept for longest (some were claimed to keep two years) were hardly fit for eating, being more akin to hard green crab apples. 'Winston', originally called 'Winter King', was raised in Berkshire in 1920 as a cross between a 'Cox' and a 'Worcester Pearmain'; fortunately it gets its flavour from the former and its habits from the latter – good job it wasn't the other way round.

Ideally it wants a well-drained, loamy soil in a sheltered spot so that the apples can hang on the tree as late as possible. It can be trained but also does well on any dwarfing rootstock as a small bush or medium-sized, freely grown tree. Thin the crop or they will be prolific and small. 'Winston' needs a pollinator and goes well with 'Jupiter' or 'Ellison's Orange', which ripen well before it. Plant bare-rooted trees in autumn, preferably as soon as their leaves have fallen. **BF**

Malus 'John Downie'

CRAB APPLE

Type: hardy, deciduous tree
Soil & situation: fertile, moist, well-drained soil/full sun or light shade
North American hardiness zone: 5–8
Height: 9m (30ft)
Spread: 5m (16ft)
Grow for: cup-shaped flowers, colourful fruits and good autumn colour; AGM

This is one of the best crab apple varieties for fruit. It is a regular and heavy cropper. Even better news is that you can eat the fruit from the tree without it bringing a tear to your eye.

Malus domestica 'Winston'

Malus 'John Downie'

Young trees have narrow heads with upright branches. Eventually it forms a broad-headed tree. The glossy, bright green leaves appear before the clusters of pure white flowers, which open from pink buds in late spring and are followed by 5cm- (1in-) diameter apples. The fruit hangs in bunches on long stalks and their shiny skin colour starts off yellow, ripening through orange to red or deep scarlet. This is the variety with fruit capable of prize-winning crab apple jelly. It dislikes heavy, wet soil where it is prone to apple canker disease. On light, very free-draining soils the crop will be reduced. Avoid sites exposed to cold, drying winds. Low areas prone to spring frosts will damage the blossom.

Pruning is necessary to keep the centre of the tree open for light. Diseased and crossing branches should be removed in winter. Suckers at the base of the tree and up the stem will be from the rootstock and should be removed. Propagation is by budding in summer or grafting in winter. **JC**

Matt adds:
This is a fine tree for small gardens, and its fruits look wonderful in the autumn sunlight. It increases its value by being an excellent pollinator in orchards, it's self-fertile, producing fruit when planted alone and the fruits are good for jellies and winemaking. Some nurseries offer 'family trees' with three or more different varieties all grafted on to the same tree, including other legends like *M.* 'Golden Hornet' with masses of white flowers in mid-spring and golden-yellow fruit, and *M.* 'Red Sentinel' with its pink flowers in late spring and glossy fruits lasting until early in the New Year.

Matthiola bicornis
NIGHT-SCENTED STOCK

Type: hardy annual
Soil & situation: any soil/sun
North American hardiness zone: annual
Height & spread: 50cm (20in), spindly
Grow for: staggering fragrance; pastel, bluey-violet, purple, white evening blooms, usually two-tone

This is a knock-you-down scent, sort of a sensual cruise missile, and if you have not enjoyed the pleasure of this night-flowering bloom you have not lived. It is often overlooked as it is too easy to grow and so given to kids – who are sent to bed before it comes out. This is a hardy plant that can be sown in almost any bare soil and will then flower throughout summer, giving you untold nights of delight. The perfume is so delicious that when I make a clear fruit jelly, such as white currant, I drop petals of *Matthiola bicornis* into it as it cools, capturing that memory of a summer evening. You would hardly call the plant attractive, the grey foliage is scrappy and the flowers only open at night, remaining closed and limp looking all day, so it should be mixed with *M.* Virginian stock, which has no scent but brightly coloured flowers all day. (Virginian stock is another wonderful misnomer, as it comes from the Mediterranean islands!)

A native of southern Europe, night-scented stock is a hardy biennial, but we treat it as an annual more successfully. The genus is named after a 16th-century botanist Mattiola.

Happy on any soil in the sun, it will over-winter for an earlier show of flowers but is often lost to the vagaries of the weather and slugs. It does really quite well in pots. In an outdoor spot it can be sown fairly densely from early spring. Keep weeded and watered, and remember to visit at dusk. This plant suffers no problems. **BF**

Matthiola incana
WILD STOCK

Type: very hardy, short-lived, evergreen, perennial subshrub
Soil & situation: well-drained soil, especially chalky/sun/shelter
North American hardiness zone: 7–8, though may be grown as an annual
Height: 50cm (20in), top heavy
Spread: 30cm (12in)
Grow for: masses of white, highly fragrant flowers through summer and ever-grey foliage

Matthiola bicornis

There are many sorts of stocks and this is the mother of most of them. There are refined garden forms, but this wild original from the Atlas Mountains of Morocco is my favourite. There is no compromise with the scent, which is a heady clove, and given some winter shelter the plant may live long enough to make a fairly big mass of flowers. The grey foliage gets a bit battered in winter but soon revives in spring. They love the same conditions as pinks and carnations (*Dianthus* spp., see pages 143 and 146), lavender (*Lavandula* spp., pages 234–235) and so many other grey-leaved plants that it is worth having a border just for them.

A native of southern Europe and possibly even the UK, as it is apparently wild on the Sussex cliffs in the southeast. It was well known in early gardens and is the parent form from which we get our Brompton, Ten-Week, East Lothian and other series of fragrant bedding stocks, which between them fill the entire year with perfumed blooms.

It must have a sheltered, sunny spot on a free-draining, preferably chalky soil. Dead-heading is worthwhile as the plants may live a few years if they don't seed. It may be cut back to keep it bushy, in theory, but in practice it dies. Sow the seed in pots in late spring under cover, grow on and plant out in early summer. Give it some windbreak protection for the first, and then during the coldest, winters. **BF**

Meconopsis x sheldonii 'Slieve Donard'
Plant of the Week (see page 209)

Melissa officinalis
LEMON BALM
Type: hardy, herbaceous, perennial weed
Soil & situation: any soil/sun or shade/moist or dry
North American hardiness zone: 3–7
Height & spread: forms a 60cm (24in) dome
Grow for: lovely, healthy, bright, scented foliage in an attractive form

I like the smell of lemon balm's scented foliage enough to rub myself with it on a hot day. I also use the leaves in long, cool drinks and I plant this lovely weed in many different places just for its cheerfulness. The variegated form is splashed with bright yellow and gives a spot of colour in many a drab area; it is also quick and easy to chop into chunks and multiply in late winter. Balm is often accused of spreading rampantly by runners like mint, however I have never found this to be so; true, the clump grows, but it is the self-seeding that makes this a lovely weed.

A native of Europe and possibly of the southwest of the UK, this was allegedly introduced in the Middle Ages, but I reckon it was by the Romans for their bees. The name comes for the Greek for

Matthiola incana

bee, as this plant is loved by these insects for its flowers and their nectar, but also for the sweet lemon fragrance. Indeed it has long been held that the beekeeper should grow this plant to keep his bees from straying and also to rub over himself before approaching the hive. I do it and it's true, they seem to like the smell.

This is a remarkably useful plant as it will grow on any site, soil or situation given half a chance. Cut out any reverted all-green shoots and remove seedlings. Dead-heading is worthwhile to prevent self-seeding everywhere. The variegated form is propagated by root division in late winter or early spring; the plain green by seed sown anytime. One particular problem – this is invasive by seed! **BF**

Melissa officinalis

Melittis melissophyllum
BASTARD BALM

Type: hardy, herbaceous perennial
Soil & situation: moist soil/dappled shade
North American hardiness zone: 6–9
Height: 72cm (28in)
Spread: 50cm (20in)
Grow for: attractive flowers in late spring and early summer

This, the largest-flowered native of the mint family and a relative of the deadnettle, is rare in the UK and was first discovered in a wood near Totnes in south Devon. It is found in southwest England and southwest Wales, throughout Europe and east as far as Russia in hedges, scrub and mountain woods.

Melittis melissophyllum

The flowers, appearing towards the top of the stems have pink or purple-mauve lips or spots; there is also a white form. Their fragrance is described by some as 'honey', but others disagree, detecting a more pungent aroma, hence the French name *melisse de punaisse* or bug balm. When dried, it retains its fragrance (or odour) for a long time. This pretty, undemanding plant is ideal for mixed or herbaceous borders or woodland gardens; the flowers are attractive to bees.

When I look at the flowers I always think that they are like opera singers in flowing robes with their mouths open, ready to sing – it's as near as I'll ever get to an opera! The name *Melittis* is a variant of the Greek for honey bee; *melissophyllum* means honey sweet. Considering the Latin name, it is a shame that this pretty little plant isn't called something more flattering like the honey balm.

Plant in organic-rich, moisture-retentive soil in dappled shade. Incorporate plenty of well-rotted organic matter before planting; cut down stems and mulch in spring. Divide in spring. **MB**

Mentha rotundifolia
BOWLES' APPLE MINT

Type: hardy, herbaceous, perennial weed
Soil & situation: any soil/partial sun to heavy shade/loves moisture
North American hardiness zone: 6–9
Height: 1–1.2m (3–4ft)
Spread: 9m (30ft)
Grow for: delicious flavour; good ground cover; pale green, roundish leaves

Mint is a cheap way of covering a lot of shady ground with something other than nettles, and the flowers in autumn are really good for insects. But I grow it because I love mint sauce. I rarely have lamb but often have the sauce with carrots and peas, and especially with new potatoes. I make a delicious sauce by shredding the fresh leaves into a white currant and apple jelly made with vinegar – it is just so gooood! Anyway Bowles' apple mint is the best of all the mints for flavour and it is not so prone to rust as most other sorts.

There are many mints, the majority of them occurring naturally in damp places, and they have been used since time immemorial both in cooking and for strewing on floors. They are mentioned in St Matthew's Gospel. The name is *minthe* in Greek and then, as now, mint was much used for eating with suspicious lamb. (You have to be crazy to buy pre-minted lamb, didn't you see the television programme?)

Mint does not thrive in full sun unless the soil is very moist; it prefers a rich, damp soil and does not like wood ashes or dry chalky soils. Traditionally mint is planted in the ground in a bottomless bucket so the runners are confined. Many mints can be grown from seed but any bit roots and spreads like water. Plant the new roots in autumn or spring; they can also be taken inside in pots for an out-of-season forced crop. If you get rust then cut off all the foliage, burn it and cover the roots with a sterile mulch. **BF**

Mentha rotundifolia

Mirabilis jalapa

MARVEL OF PERU

Type: tender, tuberous-rooted perennial or half-hardy annual
Soil & situation: any well-drained soil/sun
North American hardiness zone: 8–11
Height & spread: to 1m (3ft)
Grow for: amazing striated flowers with strong perfume, One of the many joys of mid-summer.

The Marvel of Peru is not fashionable now but was immensely popular a century ago. I first came across it on clearing an abandoned Victorian conservatory. Among a few surviving plants and a lot of rubbish was a brick-sized tuber of some sort. I took it home and nurtured it back into life, got it to flower and was staggered by the orange, red-striped flowers with such a powerful orange blossom scent. A couple of hand grenade-like seeds were formed and I was able to multiply this old relic. The flowers open at tea time and last a mere day, but what flowers! They really are unique as the striping is not symmetrical or sensible but it is pleasing.

Introduced to the UK in the 16th century from South America, the generic name is the Latin for wonderful and *jalapa* is a distortion of the Mexican place name Xalapan. It is also known as the four o'clock plant, as that is the time when the flowers open.

It needs a free-draining compost or soil and a site in full sun. It can be treated like a dahlia or even a potato, as the large tuber can be dug up in autumn and over-wintered somewhere frost free to be replanted in early summer. Alternatively it can be kept under cover in a pot and allowed to die down over winter to be started again in spring, much like a datura or fuchsia. Or it can be sown under cover in warmth in early spring to be planted out in early summer; it will then flower soon after. A remarkably tough plant, but it sometimes gets aphids – and it is poisonous! **BF**

Mespilus germanica
MEDLAR

Type: shrub or small tree
Soil & situation: most soils apart from boggy or very dry/needs sun
North American hardiness zone: 6–9
Height: to 6m (20ft)
Spread: to 8m (25ft)
Grow for: compact form, attractive flowers and autumn colour; unusual fruits

This robust, no-nonsense fruit tree has been cultivated in British gardens for centuries. It needs an open, sunny site on most soils and makes a small, spiny shrub or small tree. The dark green leaves, which turn yellow in autumn, highlight simple white or pink blush flowers in late spring or early summer. They are followed by small brown fruits with persistent calyces that are 'bletted' (left to rot) until they become edible. It is found in the wild in Asia Minor, was cultivated by the ancient Assyrians and is believed to have been taken to the United States by French Jesuits.

The earliest reference to it in England was in 1270, when the gardener of Westminster Abbey was instructed to provide the monastery with medlars and other fruits. A German book records the wood being used for making the spokes of wheels and the twigs turned into for horsewhips for carters.

Of the several varieties around, *Mespilus germanica* 'Nottingham' has brown fruit 4cm (1½in) across, *M. g.* 'Dutch' crops heavily, ripens in mid-autumn and is ready for Christmas. They are an acquired taste, but is it worth acquiring? Give it a try and find out! **MB**

Mespilus germanica

Metasequoia glyptostroboides

Metasequoia glyptostroboides
DAWN REDWOOD

Type: hardy, deciduous conifer
Soil & situation: open position in moist soil
North American hardiness zone: 5–10
Height: 40m (130ft) or more
Spread: 5m (15ft) or more
Grow for: its elegant form; foliage in summer and autumn; winter silhouette; AGM

This is one of botany's and horticulture's most exciting stories, proving that there are still plants waiting to be discovered. Keep looking! In 1941 this species was described from fossils unearthed in Japan, then the same year living specimens were found by Mr T. Kan in a village in central China but were not collected until 1944, when further trees were discovered. They were not scientifically described until 1948. It is a native of western Huphe and northeast Sichuan on streamsides and ravines and although it was new to science, it had long been cultivated in its native region where it was used to stabilize river banks and paddy fields. The first seeds, collected in 1947, were sent to the Arnold Arboretum in the USA and distributed to gardens in America and Europe, and some of these original seedlings are still flourishing in gardens within the UK.

It is an outstandingly beautiful tree, conical habit when young, with shaggy, fibrous, cinnamon-brown bark, and bright green feathery leaves, that turn pink and gold in autumn in good conditions. It grows rapidly, almost as fast as its popularity! There are several selections available in nurseries, including some that are variegated.

It needs a sheltered position, protection from frost, which can damage young growth, and deep, moist soil; it is slow growing on poor soils like chalk or sand. It flourishes in warm summers and pefers a Continental climate. Propagate by seed, semi-ripe cuttings from mid-summer and hardwood cuttings in winter. **MB**

Mirabilis jalapa
Plant of the Week (see page 265)

Miscanthus sinensis 'Variegatus'

Type: hardy, perennial grass
Soil & situation: moist soil when young/sun or light shade
North American hardiness zone: 4–9
Height: to 1.7m (5½ft)
Spread: indefinite
Grow for: striking, variegated foliage; pink blossom in a warm summer; AGM

This plant, like many of the variegated miscanthus, forms fantastic, dense tussocks of bright, variegated foliage. The leaves will often arch over so the tips touch the ground and it makes an intriguing rustling sound as breezes move through its leaves. Towards the end of a hot summer it will usually send up arching panicles of silky spikelets. These look dramatic and should be left through most of the winter in their bleached, pale straw-coloured form. The flowerheads can be used for cutting, if you can bear to do it.

Miscanthus are also good screens and effective filters for the wind as they can establish fairly fast to form a tallish, attractive barrier that is economical in terms of space. Another use is for aquatic planting: they enjoy a waterside position as long as they are not crowded out by more vigorous neighbours. There are many good ones to choose from; others I like particularly are *M. sinensis* 'Kleine Fontane', which has early and abundant flowers, and *M.*

Miscanthus sinensis 'Variegatus'

sinensis 'Flamingo', with pink flowers and great autumn colour. They tolerate many soil conditions but do particularly well in a more moist soil. A sunny situation is required and they look most effective situated so as to catch the low evening sunlight on their flowerheads. Miscanthus are generally trouble-free. If you leave the stems on for winter effect, cut them to the ground in spring. To propagate, divide in early spring. **BG**

Molinia caerulea subsp. *arundinacea*

TALL MOOR GRASS

Type: hardy, deciduous perennial
Soil & situation: acid soil/dry, sunny position
North American hardiness zone: 5–9
Height: 1.2m (4ft)
Spread: 2.4m (7½ft)
Grow for: elegant stems and seedheads from early summer

These wonderful plants have come to the fore with the introduction of the naturalistic style of perennial planting promoted and developed by Piet Oudolf, Jaques Wirtz and others. They have a graceful habit, attractive foliage and dense to open flowerheads held high above the foliage, and they are bold enough to provide structure, yet 'transparent' enough to make good screens. The flower stems and seedheads move with the slightest breath of air and look wonderful in the low autumn light. They are all magnificent; never malign a molinia!

Molinia caerulea subsp. *arundinacea*

Molinia caerulea subsp. *arundinacea* forms a low, rounded mound; the flower spikes develop in early summer. Varieties worth seeking out include 'Fontane', which has dense heads of dark grey flowers that weigh down the tips of the stems like a fountain, as its name suggests. It grows to 1.5m (5ft) tall, the same height as 'Karl Foerster' which has large dark heads of bronze flowers on stiff upright or arching stems. 'Transparent' is deliciously beautiful. It is 1.8m (6ft) tall and creates the lightest haze of tiny dark flowerheads that catch raindrops and dew. My favourite! 'Windspiel' moves elegantly in the breeze. The stems are upright in flower but arch like a fountain when it's wet. It also reaches 1.8m (6ft).

All need moist, well-drained, preferably acid to neutral soil, in full sun or partial shade. Unlike most grasses, the leaves and stems detach easily from the rootstock in winter. They are slow to establish; buy moderate to large plants rather than smaller ones. Divide in spring and pot up until established. Trouble free of pests and diseases. **MB**

Monarda didyma

BERGAMOT

Type: hardy, herbaceous perennial
Soil & situation: any soil, ideally moist/sun or shade
North American hardiness zone: 4–9
Height & spread: forms a 1m (3ft) dome
Grow for: lovely, healthy, bright coloured scented foliage in an attractive form, with attractive purplish-red scented flowers

This is another plant (see *Melissa officinalis*, page 262) with whose leafy aromatic smell I like to rub myself on a hot day, and I use the leaves and petals in long, cool drinks. I grow this lovely plant in many different places just for its petals, which I put in salads. There is a pineapple-scented form and some with improved flower colours, but I prefer the original as it is a good doer and a useful plant for adding colour to the border all through summer and into autumn.

A genus of half a dozen species native to North America, this was named after a Spanish botanist and was used by the natives for a beverage. I remember my grandmother's shop having packets of Oswego tea made from this very plant. The name bergamot is supposed to be from the bergamot orange, which annoyingly has a totally dissimilar perfume. Oswego is after the town on Lake Ontario where it was noted by a botanist named Bartram who sent seed to the UK in 1745.

This is a remarkably useful plant as it will grow on most soils and situations given half a chance and thrives in damper soils. Deadheading is worthwhile to prevent seeding. The choicest forms are propagated by root division in late winter or early spring, the natural by seed sown any time. It does benefit from splitting and replanting every few years and needs tidying in late autumn. Bergamot has no problems other than being unhappy in drought. **BF**

Monstera deliciosa

Plant of the Week (see page 41)

Monarda didyma

Morina longifolia

Morina longifolia

WHORL FLOWER

Type: hardy, herbaceous perennial
Soil & situation: well-drained, preferably sandy soil/full sun
North American hardiness zone: 6–9
Height: 90cm (36in)
Spread: 30cm (12in)
Grow for: sculptural form; flowers from mid-summer to early autumn

The fact that this handsome evergreen is not bone hardy must be the only reason why it's not more familiar. It is absolutely beautiful; elegant, refined, colourful, charming – we have absolutely nothing in common!

There is a basal rosette of narrow, glossy, lemon-scented, thistle-like leaves diminishing in size and number towards the top of the stem, which provide a perch for tiers of thorny candelabras. The flowers with narrow, arching tubes about 3cm (1in) long and beautifully rounded petals explode from these in a glorious starburst of white, rich rose-pink and crimson. I dislike most shades of pink but here the tones and contrasts are refined, not sickly, the white is pure and the arching flowers and sculptural stems create a wonderful sense of dynamism. In winter, they dry to deep brown, making great decorations for the home; in the garden, they look gorgeous when dusted with frost and delicately embroidered with spider webs.

The plant is used to make incense. The flowers are moth pollinated, but if they haven't been visited by morning the pistil curves over, effects self-pollination and the flower changes colour! It needs humus-rich, fertile, well-drained, moist, sandy or gritty soil in sun. It is not difficult to grow but is short lived, hates waterlogging and rots if cold and wet. It does better in milder climates. It hates disturbance! Propagate by root cuttings in late autumn; sow fresh seed in gritty compost and over-winter young plants in a well-ventilated cold frame. In waterlogged, cold conditions it may be attacked by slugs and rot. **MB**

Morus nigra

Plant of the Week (see page 353)

Musa chinensis

CHINESE/DWARF CAVENDISH BANANAS

Type: tender, herbaceous perennial
Soil & situation: rich, moist soil/full sun/under cover
North American hardiness zone: 9–10
Height & spread: 3m (10ft)
Grow for: impressive subject, large leaves, amazing flowers and sweet edible fruits

If you've got it flaunt it, and you do need quite a lot of space to grow this to perfection. In the ground under cover these make trees – a strange, succulent, soft sort of tree, but really impressive, even more so when the gigantic corn cob of a flowering shoot pops out at the top and hangs down like a triffid, and flowers for weeks and weeks and weeks. The small flowers are stuck on the ends of the wee bananas and the inflorescence carries a smell of tropical rainforest. Months later the bananas start to ripen and then the old stem is cut down (the fruits are ripened on the detached stalk), and another stem grows up to replace the old. If in a pot the plant can go outdoors for summer, but will need a sheltered spot as wind shreds the leaves.

Musa chinensis

Musa basjoo

Originally from China, this small banana is a tough survivor and has become grown all over the world where quality is seen as more important than size, or where sheer size is inconvenient. As it was first grown for the European market in the Canaries it is also known as the Canary banana. Other larger bananas from India have followed and colonized most hot countries. However, it seems not to have been known to the Romans, though early Muslim texts indicate it had already arrived in Arabia. Our word banana comes from Arabic via Spanish or Portuguese.

You've got to have a frost-free light place about 3m (10ft) high, although if you cramp the plant, say in a plastic dustbin, it will stay smaller. Fill a big hole or enormous container with a humus-rich, well-drained compost, and water and feed regularly. Remove all new shoots from the base until the main shoot is nearly full grown, then allow only one to replace it. In the tropics the crown can last for 50 years or more, though each shoot is only there for a couple. Bananas can be grown from seed, but not the good ones such as this. Offsets need be taken in spring with as much root as possible. These do not suffer many problems other than cold and damp causing moulds. **BF**

Matt adds:
I was first introduced to *Musa basjoo* (zone 8–10) as a student when it was flowering in a frost-free greenhouse; observing its long, pendent flower stem, we gave it a nickname that was none too polite! It's since become popular as a patio or border plant for gardeners wishing to add a little 'exotica' to their lives. The narrow stem, made up of old leaf bases, supports several paddle-shaped leaves that emerge from the top of the stem like long cigars. In summer it needs a warm, sheltered spot and plenty of moisture, in winter, the protection of a frost- free shed or greenhouse.

Myosotidium hortensia
CHATHAM ISLAND FORGET-ME-NOT

Type: half-hardy, evergreen perennial
Soil & situation: humus-rich, gritty, moist, well-drained soil/light shade
North American hardiness zone: 8–9
Height: 60cm (24in)
Spread: 80cm (32in)
Grow for: clusters of forget-me-not-like blue flowers; glossy, bright green foliage

On its native Chatham Island, to the east of New Zealand it, while not the first, was one of the earliest plants to see the dawn of the new millennium – a well-deserved honour for one of earth's most beautiful perennials.

Clump forming, the large, 30cm (12in) long, fleshy, bright green leaves are so glossy they appear to have been varnished. They are heart-shaped with conspicuous veins and wavy edges. The dense clusters of small, bell-shaped flowers appear in early summer on strong stems. Pale to dark blue, they are occasionally white-margined.

Myosotidium is not the easiest plant to grow, doing best in damp, cool conditions. A sheltered coastal site would be ideal with an annual spring mulch of seaweed. In cold areas plant in dappled shade under a tree and cover in winter with bracken or straw for frost protection. In late spring remove the old deteriorating leaves at soil level.

If it likes you, it will self-seed in the immediate area. Leave the young seedlings *in situ* until they have produced at least three leaves. Saved seed should be sown fresh and over-wintered in a cold frame. Alternatively it may be propagated by dividing the clump in spring. Slugs and snails prefer this plant to hostas, so be warned and take preventative action. **JC**

Matt adds:
When John says this is not the easiest plant to grow, he isn't joking, at least as far as most British gardeners are concerned. They may march you to a single plant or pot and proudly announce, 'This is my Chatham Island forget-me-not.' The usual response (a combination of admiration and envy!), 'Did you really grow that?' 'But of course,' comes a self-satisfied reply. This plant should be your destination at the end of a red carpet, it should be enthroned, pampered, praised and every demand satisfied in order for it to flourish. I once visited a garden in New Zealand where it was rampant, scattered through a border without a care. Gardening can be so cruel!

Myosotidium hortensia

Myosotis sylvatica
FORGET-ME-NOT

Type: hardy biennial
Soil & situation: moist, well-drained soil/sun or partial shade
North American hardiness zone: 5–9
Height: 30cm (12in)
Spread: 15cm (6in)
Grow for: pretty spring flowers

Forget-me-not is quite a recent name. It is not mentioned in Shakespeare or in the *Oxford English Dictionary* between 1532, when it's mentioned in an old French translation as *une fleur de ne m'oubliez mye*, and 1817, quoting Samuel Taylor Coleridge's poem 'The Keepsake': 'Nor can I find, amid my lonely walk, By rivulet, or spring, or wet roadside, That blue and bright eyed flowerlet of the brook, Hope's gentle gem, the sweet Forget me not.' It was probably inspired by the tale of a German knight and his lady walking by a river: while picking 'water forget-me-nots' the knight slipped and fell in the water. Before he drowned, he threw the flowers to his lover crying, '*Vergisz mien nicht.*' So remember! Don't wear your armour while picking forget-me-nots.

The water forget-me-not, *Myosotis scorpioides*, may have been the earliest garden introduction; most now come from the wood forget-me-not, *M. sylvatica*. There are ten species in the UK. Selections include 'Royal Blue' with rich royal blue flowers; mixed selections with pink, white and blue flowers; Victoria Series cultivars are dwarf, compact and have white, blue or pink flowers. 'Victoria Rose' with bright rose-pink flowers, grows to 10cm (4in).

They need moderately fertile to poor, moist, well-drained soil in sun or partial shade. Water in dry weather; after flowering allow to self-seed before lifting, or lift early to prevent self-seeding. Sow seed in seedbeds or *in situ* for planting out the following spring. Susceptible to powdery mildew, so as a preventative measure keep the soil moist. Slugs and snails may cause damage. **MB**

Myosotis sylvatica

Myrrhis odorata

Myrrhis odorata
SWEET CICELY

Type: hardy, herbaceous perennial
Soil & situation: rich, moist soil/full sun to heavy shade
North American hardiness zone: 3–7
Height & spread: 60cm (24in)
Grow for: healthy, green, ferny foliage from early in the year; foamy white flowers; decorative seedpods; edible salading

This is a multiple-use plant; first it is tough, reliable, and dense enough to be used as ground cover. Then it is early to shoot and looks good when little else does, moreover these shoots are edible along with the ferny soft leaves, which go well in soups and stews, and the foamy white flowers which can be used in salads. The roots are small but, once cooked, are interesting and could be improved by plant breeders. The seedpods add aniseed flavour to liqueurs.

The plant is a native to Europe and the Romans seem to have used it for a pot herb; it was known to the Greeks as *murrhis* in place of the true myrrh which comes from an African tree, and also as *seseli*, which was their name for a herbal umbelliferous plant.

Sweet cicely likes rich, moist soils in cool damp glades. It is not long lived individually but spreads around sufficiently. Dead-heading will stop this self-seeding, though do retain some seedpods as they are nice to use in cooking. Trim and tidy in autumn. Sow *in situ* in spring or in small pots and plant out as soon as possible. Sweet cicely can be troublesome as a self-seeding weed. **BF**

Myrtus communis
COMMON MYRTLE

Type: frost-hardy, evergreen shrub
Soil & situation: free-draining, moist fertile soil/sheltered, sunny position in cold areas
North American hardiness zone: 8–9
Height: up to 4.5m (15ft)
Spread: 3m (10ft)
Grow for: aromatic, polished, evergreen foliage; copious numbers of fragrant flowers in mid- to late summer, followed by black berries; AGM

Myrtle was and is considered a symbol of love, peace and a happy married life, and as such, makes the best wedding present of all. The fragrant foliage and flowers of this plant have long been used in bridal wreaths and garlands. It has been grown in England since the 16th century but not just for ornamental purposes. It has many herbal uses too: the oil is used in perfumery; the leaves can be added to pork and lamb dishes; the fruits are used in the Middle East as a spice, and apparently when ingested, the active compounds are quickly absorbed and give a violet-like aroma to urine within 15 minutes – certainly a fairly dynamic and useful plant!
It is not difficult to grow, but flowers and fruits better in a sunny, sheltered site such as at the base of a warm wall, preferably somewhere where the rich and spicy fragrance will linger and not be wafted away. The thousands of flowers produced on the mature bush have a generous, central burst of long, yellow-white stamens.

For gardens in mild or coastal areas it forms a most magnificent, very special hedge that tolerates clipping well and it can be used to form exquisite and unusual mop-head standards or pyramids.

This plant will tolerate –10°C (14°F) given shelter and sharp drainage, so even if you need to give added protection such as fleece now and then, it is well worth finding the ideal spot for it and cosseting it in its early years.

It is best pruned in spring, but only when needed to maintain the size and shape and remove any frosted growth. It can also be grown as an espalier. I have never seen this, but it would be spectacular for enlivening a dull facade of a house, or for training along a discordant elevation to pull it together. It is easily propagated by semi-ripe cuttings taken in summer. A dwarf form, *M. c. tarentina*, makes a great dwarf hedge. **BG**

Bob adds:
I love myrtle, not for the attractive, neat foliage, nor for the strangely scented creamy-white paintbrush-like flowers that remind me for some bizarre reason of garlic sausage, but for the black berries that make an excellent jam and reputedly a good wine. However, for those of you looking for a neat shrub for a sunny patio or wall, do not be put off by the garlic-sausage smell as it is so faint; instead, rejoice in the healthy appearance of this lovely shrub. I find *M. c. tarentina* attractive but too small for any real use other than as a bonsai specimen; it has white berries. *M. ugni*, the Chilean guava, is similar with pinky bell-like flowers and sweeter purplish berries; it is slightly more tender than *M. communis* and best as a conservatory subject.

Myrtus communis

Narcissus poeticus var. *recurvus*

Narcissus poeticus var. *recurvus*
PHEASANT'S EYE

Type: clump-forming, hardy, bulbous perennial
Soil & situation: rich, moist soil/full sun to light shade
North American hardiness zone: 5–8
Height: 50cm (20in)
Spread: 30cm (12in)
Grow for: beautiful, highly perfumed flowers as spring becomes summer; AGM

I love these flowers as they are the last of the spring bulbs to bloom and their arrival heralds the warmest days a-coming in. Its scent is intoxicating yet fresh and clean, making it one of the few flowers I love to cut and take indoors in quantity. It is also a very personal favourite as when I moved to my garden 20 years ago there was just one small clump of pheasant's eyes and another of the old green and yellow, double daffodilly; I have multiplied and multiplied both of these, and now have long walks lined with these delightful gems.

The pheasant's eye narcissus grows wild around the shores of the Mediterranean, and although undoubtedly known to the Romans was apparently not introduced to the UK until some were brought back after the Battle of Waterloo. The story of Narcissus is alleged to be the name's derivation, and the *poeticus* – well, because poets write about it. The English name comes because, like its namesake, *Adonis annua*, it resembles a pheasant's a*** (oops, sorry, couldn't help myself).

Given a well-drained soil in an orchard or glade, these will naturalize, albeit slowly, as they seldom seed but do clump up and go on for ever. Dead-heading will prevent seed being formed if you want more flowers. Digging and dividing as soon as the leaves die down helps to multiply these more quickly and is especially useful for old congested clumps which cease to bloom. I've not seen the seed offered so plant the bulbs as soon as you can get them. No common problems bother this species very much. **BF**

Narcissus pseudonarcissus
LENT LILY, WILD DAFFODIL, TRUMPET NARCISSUS

Type: hardy, bulbous perennial
Soil & situation: almost any soil/spreads best in a moist well-drained soil/prefers sun or part shade/does not like heavy shade
North American hardiness zone: 4–9
Height: 15–35cm (6–14in)
Spread: 10cm (4in)
Grow for: subtle, beautiful, native daffodils which flower in early spring and naturalize well; AGM

This charming wild daffodil is well suited to naturalizing – it spreads well and looks thoroughly in keeping in wilder areas with its small, but exquisite, nodding, mid-yellow flowers in early spring. It looks so delicate compared to the relatively large, stronger-coloured, rather brash daffodils that you see in most front gardens in spring. Being native, it is a good, hearty plant and looks a dream in large drifts, in orchards, paddocks, meadows and in the more natural garden areas. I am not a fan of daffodils in borders – I would rather pot some up and have a few simple containers of them where I can admire them at close quarters, near a window or doorway.

Plant the bulbs about one and a half times to twice their depth or thereabouts, although you can go deeper in lighter soils. They will increase in quantity if you plant them shallowly, but the resultant bulbs are smaller. Conversely, if you plant deeper you will have bigger bulbs, but the increase is slower. Bigger bulbs generally equate to better, bigger flowers. I never divide bulbs in grass areas, life is too short and they manage perfectly well without my help. But I do not treat them mean! I try never to cut them till a good month or preferably six weeks after the flowering is well on the wane. In some lush springs though, it is difficult to resist. You can almost feel the mower twitch as you try to veer away from the rather sad mess of leaves. These smaller varieties do have less conspicuous, smaller leaves and once the time is up, cutting even green leaves does little harm. Wood ashes added in spring are a useful source of potassium which can help flowering. **BG**

Narcissus pseudonarcissus

Hydrangea arborescens 'Annabelle'

Type: hardy deciduous shrub
Soil & situation: ordinary garden loam/sun or shade
North American hardiness zone: 3–9
Height & spread: 1.2m (4ft)
Grow for: white, spherical flowerheads for a long period from early summer; attractive dried flowerheads in the autumn; AGM

I think hydrangeas are my favourite plants but on my dry soil many do not thrive. This one certainly does, however. I frequently use it in planting schemes in a wide variety of conditions and often the client will be bowled over by it, often after only the first year.

An individual flowerhead may be as much as 20cm (8in) across, though most of the flowers are sterile. The late summer flowering comes at a time when many shrubs have done their bit, and the white looks particularly fresh on a hot summer's day. I leave the dried flowerheads on the plant until they look battered, which may well be in spring when its time to prune it anyway. (It is well worth picking a few flowerheads in their prime and drying them by hanging them upside down somewhere airy.) Another great hydrangea, *H. aspera* (see page 212), tends to wilt on my soil, but if you have a good loam soil I recommend it strongly.

Hydrangea arborescens flowers at the tip of the current season's growth, and you can cut all this back to two or three pairs of buds in late winter or spring. Doing it this way you will get extra-large panicles of flowers. If you just leave it unpruned you will have a taller shrub and smaller flowers. Hydrangeas are hungry, so they respond to a good feed, but do not feed them in the summer as you might well encourage them into late growth, which is susceptible to frost. **BG**

Narcissus 'Yellow Cheerfulness'

DAFFODIL

Type: hardy, bulbous perennial
Soil & situation: moist, moderately fertile, well-drained soil/full sun or partial shade
North American hardiness zone: 4–9
Height: 45cm (18in)
Spread: 15cm (6in)
Grow for: stunning, gold-yellow, double flowers; AGM

The only thing nicer than a single-flowered daffodil is one with double flowers and fragrance. Performing in mid-spring, the strong stems carry clusters of three or four double, golden-yellow flowers. The corona (trumpet) is short, divided and doubled, making an attractive centre. The mid-green leaves are strap-shaped and narrow. In great demand as a cut flower, it is also recommended for growing in containers indoors for early, scented flowers. *N.* 'Cheerfulness' is white with a cream centre and has larger, double, fragrant flowers.

Plant bulbs in autumn at twice their own depth with the 'nose' pointing up. In light, sandy soil and when being naturalized in grass plant slightly deeper. When dividing, usually every three years, wait until the foliage has withered and turned yellow. Dead-head, removing the old flower to prevent the bulb's energy being used to form seed. When naturalized in grass, avoid cutting the foliage for at least six weeks after flowering. **JC**

Narcissus 'Yellow Cheerfulness'

Nemesia strumosa

Nemesia strumosa

Type: half-hardy annual
Soil & situation: moist soil/sun
North American hardiness zone: annual
Height: 30cm (12in)
Spread: 16cm (6¼in)
Grow for: colourful flowers from early summer onwards

It's always in the catalogues and is easy to grow, so why don't gardeners plant them more often? This is such a happy, gay little plant, with bright, cheerful blooms creating a chorus of colour in such pure distinctive tones. They are so mood enhancing; if you feel down, those eager little faces just lift you up; you simply have to smile. So pack them in pots, use them as edging plants for borders or draped like colourful curtains from a window box and take one look three times a day or as prescribed by your doctor.

Here are some of its varieties with intensely coloured flowers. 'Orange Prince' is a vibrant, warming orange; you can almost feel the heat. 'Fire King' is a wonderful rich, iridescent scarlet. 'Sundrops', an award winner, is compact with masses of large vivid yellow flowers and is perfect for containers.

The bicolours are really eye-catching and always provoke comment. 'KLM' reminds me of my visits to Brentford FC, in my student days when they were sponsored by KLM; the flowers are mid-blue and white, the colours of the Dutch National Airline. 'National Ensign' waves the flag of St George in bright red and a white 'lip' – your own 'barmy army'! Just to prove that they aren't all outrageously coloured there are soothing shades like 'Coconut Ice' with a soft fragrance and pink and lilac flowers and 'Pastel Mixed', a lovely selection of lilac, yellow and blue.

They need moist, well-drained, moderately fertile, slightly acid soil in full sun. Keep them well watered and feed with general fertilizer every two weeks until established; change to high-potash fertilizer to encourage flowering. Sow from early to late spring for flowers in early and mid-summer. Harden off before planting out when the danger of frost has passed. **MB**

Nemophila menziesii 'Penny Black'

Type: hardy annual
Soil & situation: fertile, moist, well-drained soil/sun or partial shade
North American hardiness zone: annual
Height: 20cm (8in)
Spread: 30cm (12in)
Grow for: pretty flowers in spring and summer

The name comes from the Greek *nemos*, meaning grove, and *philos*, loving, alluding to their habitat and offers an interesting slant if you have any friends with the surname Lovegrove. It is a delicate carpeting plant found in California from coastal sands to chaparral and redwood forest. In spring and summer it is covered with flowers that have a simple beauty, like those of a herbaceous geranium. There are many forms and selections. The species, commonly known as baby blue-eyes, has pale blue flowers with a white centre; there's a pure white form too. *Nemophila* subsp. *atomaria* is white with minute speckles and spots radiating from the centre that look as though they have been drawn with a fine drafting pen. I favour *N. menziesii* 'Penny Black' (sometimes sold as *N.* var. *discoidalis*) for its unusual colouration; it is predominantly black with a white centre and margins. Another species, *N. maculata*, has pretty violet blotches at the outer edge of each petal. They are ideal as a border edging or for tumbling over the side of a window box.

They need fertile, moist, well-drained soil in a sheltered position in full sun or partial shade; they will grow in an open shady position. Keep the compost moist during hot, dry weather, otherwise they stop flowering. Feed with high-potash fertilizer if necessary to encourage flowering. Sow seed *in situ* in late summer for spring flowering and mid-spring for summer flowering; they self-seed freely. Aphids may be troublesome. **MB**

Nemophila menziesii 'Penny Black'

Nepeta cataria

Nepeta cataria
CATNIP

Type: hardy, herbaceous perennial
Soil & situation: any soil/sun
North American hardiness zone: 3–7
Height & spread: 1m (3ft) to prostrate, well flattened
Grow for: grey-green aromatic foliage loved by cats

The catnips are named because they are attractive to cats. I love my cats and it is a pleasure to feed bits of this plant to them as they go all kittenish and frisky and then drowsy, often enjoying a good roll on *Nepeta cataria* before taking yet another nap. (What do cats dream of while they're sleeping? Of having a nice nap, of course.) *N. cataria* is a UK native often found wild in ditches. *N. mussinii* is quite different – more compact, more colourful and more floriferous, so more widely grown in the ornamental garden – and there are several other interesting species. However, if you love your cats, grow this.

Before our present tea, people drank catnip tea made with milk and sugar in much the same way and the herb was also thought good for a black eye. If you don't like cats then put catnip plants in parts of your garden you can't see easily and thus keep them out of sight. The botanical name is *Nepeta* for a mint-like plant, which in medieval Latin became *nepta*, then in Old English we get cat nepte, changing to catnep and it is now catnip, but should be cat-kip.

Catnip wants to be put in a warm sunny spot, say between paving slabs on a patio so the cats can roll on it comfortably. It will be short lived unless protected when young by an inverted wire hanging basket. Trim off foliage before it dies, then dry it to stuff cushions for cats. Catnip can be sown at almost any time, ideally in pots in a coldframe or you can divide the roots in spring. Its only problem is cats, who nibble and chew it. **BF**

Nepeta x *faassenii* 'Snowflake'
CATMINT

Type: hardy perennial
Soil & situation: enjoys well-drained soil/tolerant of poor soils/full sun
North American hardiness zone: 4–8
Height & spread: up to 30cm (12in)
Grow for: copious white flowers for about five weeks during the late spring and early summer

Nepetas are extremely common garden plants – highly popular as they are good, solid performers that are easy to grow. This one is definitely easy to grow but is quite unusual. The delightful little white flowers, which are produced on spikes, sometimes have a bluish tinge to them. They are frequently enhanced by the presence of a butterfly or two, hard at work around them. The foliage is beautifully compact, being low and spreading. The leaves, also an asset, are tinted grey. *Nepeta cataria* (see previous entry) is said to repel rats - presumably because if you bruise its leaves it releases essential oils that are extremely attractive to cats. But I, for one, do not particularly want cats romping in my borders, so give me *N.* x *faassenii* 'Snowflake' any day. My mother's favourite form is *N.* x *faassenii* 'Walkers Low', which grows to 60cm (24in) and has dark blue-mauve flowers on dark stems. They appear earlier than ordinary catmint, and again the first flowering lasts for about five weeks.

In common with most forms of *N.* x *faassenii*, this plant will give a good flush of second flowers if it is cut back when the first flowers are going over. It is simple to propagate by division in spring or autumn or by softwood cuttings in spring or summer. **BG**

Nepeta x *faassenii* 'Snowflake'

Nerine bowdenii

Nerine bowdenii

Type: hardy, bulbous perennial
Soil & situation: well-drained soil/full sun
North American hardiness zone: 7–10
Height: 45cm (18in)
Spread: 20cm (8in)
Grow for: the most elegant pink blooms late in the season; AGM

Anywhere else this shade of pink would be sickening, but in the garden you can get away with it and what's more it looks and feels right.

Umbels of six or more funnel-shaped flowers on long stalks appear in autumn before the leaves. They are fragrant, icing-sugar pink and 8cm (3½in) across with wavy-edged outer tepals. The strap-like, broad, mid-green leaves are 30cm (12in) long. *Nerine bowdenii* f. *alba* has white flowers which may be flushed a pale pink shade.

They flower best when the bulbs are congested. Plant them in well-drained soil at the base of a warm wall in full sun. Nerines are well suited to growing in containers, making a show late in the season. Protect the bulbs in winter by wrapping the pot in hessian and moving it to a sheltered side of the house. The bulbs should be planted in spring with their noses at soil level. Cover them in winter with a dry mulch of chopped bark or straw for protection from frost.

Propagation is by seed sown as soon as it is ripe in a heated propagator or by division of crowded clumps after they have finished flowering. Nerines are prone to damage by slugs, especially when they are coming into leaf. **JC**

Nerium oleander
OLEANDER

Type: half-hardy, evergreen shrub
Soil & situation: rich compost/sun/under cover in winter
North American hardiness zone: 8–10
Height: 3m (10ft)
Spread: over 2m (close to 7ft)
Grow for: prolific, scented, pink, red or white flowers all summer on handsome evergreen plants

Despite this plant killing and sickening people every year it is such a beauty and so enduring that it is one of the commonest roadside plantings in the south of France. It is ironic that in many tropical holiday resorts there are warnings about this or that dangerous local tree, local plant or local local, but it is rare that this plant is so labelled although I've seen it in all the hotel gardens I've ever visited. I used to grow it myself for its perfume, but in a fit of desperation to make more space it was given a hardiness trial along with some citrus hybrids and other experimental plants, and it did not last. I would soon get several oleanders as they are impressive patio plants but my winter storage space is already overflowing.

Nerium is a genus of mostly tropical shrubs and trees that contains poisonous sap which has been the death of many cattle, and people foolish enough to use the enticingly straight stems for kebab sticks and barbecue skewers.

It can be treated much like citrus or patio fuchsias, being out all summer but going under cover in winter to escape the frosts, though it may survive on a warm wall with occasional covering in severe weather. It needs cutting back to encourage new shoots and this is best done before growth starts in spring, though I used to do it in autumn to squeeze the plants into limited space. It can be grown from seed or take ripe cuttings in autumn to root in a glass of warm water. It can suffer from scale but soapy sponging will clear this up. **BF**

Nerium oleander

Nicandra physalodes 'Violacea'

Nicandra physalodes 'Violacea'
SHOO FLY, APPLE OF PERU

Type: hardy annual
Soil & situation: fertile, moist, well-drained soil/full sun or partial shade
North American hardiness zone: annual
Height: 90cm (36in)
Spread: 30cm (12in)
Grow for: a very attractive late-flowering annual

This plant is supposed to keep flies at bay, hence its common name. Whether it does or not, it is a fine, late, free-flowering annual for the garden. It is a vigorous, upright plant with 10cm (4in) long, wavy-edged and toothed, mid-green leaves. The 4cm (1½in) wide flowers open in the middle of the day and are in flower from summer to late autumn. They are a deep mauve with deep blue and white corollas. The small brown fruits which follow are enclosed in attractive, Chinese lantern-like, papery, deep purple calyces. Its branches can be dried, complete with the fruit and 'lanterns' for indoor winter decoration.

Propagation is by seed sown in a propagator in early spring or outside, *in situ*, in late spring. It will, if allowed, self-seed. **JC**

Nicotiana sylvestris

Plant of the Week (see page 327)

Nigella damascena 'Miss Jekyll'

LOVE-IN-A-MIST, DEVIL-IN-A-BUSH

Type: hardy annual
Soil & situation: most well-drained soils/sun or partial shade
North American hardiness zone: annual
Height: 50cm (20in)
Spread: 20cm (8in)
Grow for: irresistible, long-flowering (if deadheaded), captivating blue flowers, followed by fat seedpods with spidery bracts which are an additional bonus; fine filigree, fresh green leaves which over-winter well

This is an old cottage-garden favourite, coming to England about 1570, purportedly from Damascus. It has many common names including love-entangle and love-in-a-puzzle. It is named after Miss Gertrude Jekyll, the famous gardener, who thought it to be the best garden nigella. The flower starts off pale blue, but matures to a more intense bright, sky blue. Not only is it wonderful to have self-seeding around the garden, but it is a superb cut flower both fresh and dried. It is also ideal for using in wildflower (not native) mixes with grass, where it blends and contrasts handsomely with whites, reds, yellows and other hues of striking annuals and perennials.

Nigella damascena 'Miss Jekyll'

Nymphaea 'Fire Crest'

When sown in autumn the attractive rosettes of foliage can develop well, so the plants come into flower early. These can then be deadheaded, and the subsequent flowers will be larger. Continuation of flowering is ensured with subsequent sowings in early and late spring. Give these beautiful plants a free rein and let them self-seed. Seedlings will transplant, but they do suffer a check. **BG**

Nymphaea 'Fire Crest'

WATER LILY

Type: hardy, aquatic perennial
Soil & situation: undisturbed water/full sun
North American hardiness zone: 4–11
Spread: 1.2m (4ft)
Grow for: a blaze of colour on the water

I have no time for pale, insipid, cheerless waterlily flowers. Bright, sparkling and even a little gaudy in colour contrasts well with still, often dull water. *Nymphaea* 'Fire Crest' is all I could wish for. The rounded, two-lobed, mid-green leaves are 20cm (8in) across. They are purple when they first unfurl. The 15cm (6in) star-like, deep pink flowers have pale pink, inner petals. The inner stamens are orange, and surrounded by a pink outer ring.

Water lilies dislike moving water and can't tolerate a fountain constantly raining water on the leaves. These large floating leaves serve a practical purpose. They shade the water, which is one method of controlling algae growth. Always read the plant label to find which varieties suit your depth of water. If a variety for shallow water is planted too deep, the leaves will struggle to reach the surface and the plant will become exhausted. The tall variety in shallow water will spread its leaves all over the surface of the pond.

Propagation is by division of the fleshy root in summer, keeping an eye on each piece of root. Pot up in an aquatic compost. Place in shallow water, lowering the pot as the leaves begin to extend. **JC**

Ocimum basilicum
SMALL-LEAFED BUSH BASIL, GREEK BASIL

Type: half-hardy perennial to tender annual
Soil & situation: rich, moist soil/sun/under cover
North American hardiness zone: annual
Height & Sspread: up to 30cm (12in)
Grow for: handsome, compact, neat herb with a delicious flavour

I grow most of my own food as I want it fresh and flavoursome, and once I have had fresh basil leaves in a cheese and tomato sandwich I have enjoyed my meal. It is such an essential ingredient for salads and particularly for tomato dishes. In fact I grow the basil with my greenhouse tomatoes as the vines always get bare and leave a bit of space at their base. They are reckoned a good companion, attracting the aphids off the tomatoes – this depends on your point of view: it does work but it's easier to clean the aphids off the tomatoes!

There are over 150 basils and most of them come from Africa and the Far East; the first arrived in the UK in Elizabethan times or before. They are very mixed in habit and parentage and although this is called the Greek, my favourite for its fine flavour and neat habit, which has now been grown in Europe for centuries, it apparently comes from Chile! Basil is named in Greek *basilikon*, the kingly herb, for its strong flavour and medicinal uses.

Ideally grow basil in a greenhouse in a pot on staging but it can be grown in a warm border or even outdoors in summer if given a cloche at the start. Cut and use all the leaves before it flowers and it will regrow until the cold returns. Sow in spring in the warmth, pot on and plant out after the last frosts. Basil is bothered by aphids but these can be jetted off with a hose. **BF**

Ocimum basilicum

Oenothera biennis

Oenothera biennis
EVENING PRIMROSE

Type: hardy, herbaceous, biennial weed
Soil & situation: any soil/sun or light shade/likes moisture
North American hardiness zone: 4–8
Height & spread: first year a prostrate rosette, spreading up to 45cm (18in); second year to 2m (6½ft)
Grow for: prolific yellow flowers from early summer to late autumn

This is another weed – a delightful one I would not be without, but a weed none the less. Good this week, in fact good nearly every week of the summer. This has one of the longest flowering seasons of any plant. It is full of pollen for beneficial insects for although the flowers open at night they remain partly open, if flaccid, early the next day. It comes up for free everywhere, is immune to pests and diseases, and even has edible roots. What more could you want? Well tasty, tender, edible roots would be nice, rather than the strong, coarse fare that's on offer, still they could be improved – bigger, double, sterile flowers, so no self-seeding, and tastier roots please! The seeds are the source of evening primrose oil, a trendy substitute for monkey gland therapy. This is a good plant for cheering up desolate areas.

One of nearly 100 species, mostly from North America, this reached Padua in 1619 and is described by Parkinson in 1629 as the tree primrose. The Latin name is stolen from the Greek for no apparent reason – it was apparently originally applied to a different flower of Greek origin. The common name is too obvious. There are some very nice alternative species with more luxurious flowers and scents such as *Oenothera odorata*, but none is as easy to grow as this thug.

The ideal site is just about anywhere initially; from then on just weed out the ones everywhere else. You have to be crazy not to deadhead this and it does make for more flower spikes. Sow in late spring or early summer *in situ* or in pots in a coldframe and plant out in early autumn. Because they are so deliciously scented in the evening you can't help sniffing them – so please wipe the yellow splodge of pollen off your nose before going anywhere in public. I've forgotten to do this many a time. **BF**

Olearia macrodonta

Olearia macrodonta
NEW ZEALAND HOLLY, DAISY BUSH

Type: hardy, evergreen shrub
Soil & situation: fertile, well-drained soil/full sun/shelter from cold winds
North American hardiness zone: 9–10
Height: 6m (20ft)
Spread: 5m (16ft)
Grow for: wonderfully fragrant flowers cover this shrub every summer; AGM

A neighbour has an enormous, overgrown, unpruned *Olearia macrodonta* in the front corner of her large garden. Every summer it is plastered with white flowers. Without fail, once a year the postman asks me its name and have I noticed its perfume!

The 8cm (3½in) long, leathery, sage-green, holly-like leaves are sharp pointed with a silvery-white underside. Enormous 20cm (8in) panicles of small, daisy-shaped, fragrant, white flowers with yellow centres are produced in summer. The warmer the summer the more flowers are formed.

This is one of the best evergreen plants to use as a windbreak or hedge for screening in exposed, coastal gardens. It thrives on a shallow chalk soil. Prune after flowering, reducing the stems by half their length. Old, neglected plants will tolerate hard pruning in spring and will send out new growths from the old stumps. Propagate by semi-ripe cuttings in summer. If they are not well rooted by autumn leave until spring before potting on. **JC**

Omphalodes cappadocica 'Cherry Ingram'
Plant of the Week (see page 103)

Onopordum acanthium
SCOTCH THISTLE, COTTON THISTLE

Type: hardy, biennial/perennial herb
Soil & situation: free-draining, preferably alkaline soil/sun
North American hardiness zone: 6–9
Height: 3m (10ft)
Spread: 1m (3ft)
Grow for: architectural form; flowers from mid-summer to early autumn

This, one of the best architectural plants, is believed to be the plant chosen by James I as the emblem of Scotland; however, it is uncommon north of the border so we could be wrong! The Latin name *Onopordum* means 'ass's fart'. It's derived from the Greek *onos*, ass, and *porde*, fart, because of the effect it has on their digestive system. If they're growing in your field, don't stand downwind of the donkey!

It stands defiant and proud, with a distinct air of menace that's created by the wide, wavy-edged, spiny wings protecting the silver-grey candelabra. At the top of each stem a dense tuft of pale purple to white, nectar-rich flowers sits on a tight 5cm (2in) diameter globe of spiny projections, scowling threateningly from behind a white cobwebby covering. It is outstandingly beautiful and worthy of the utmost respect. Wear gloves when working nearby and site it away from paths in deep borders, against a dark background to highlight its sculptural form. In the past the down was used for stuffing cushions and pillows and the bracts were eaten like artichokes. I remember filming one for Channel 4's *Garden Club* while in Scotland; because we were recording I missed the only chance I have ever had of seeing an osprey. It appeared briefly over the top of a hill, then disappeared for good! Every Scots thistle I see reminds me of that day!

Grow in fertile, well-drained, preferably alkaline soil in full sun; it tolerates heavier soils and light shade. This biennial or short-lived perennial resents root disturbance; sow *in situ* in summer or in pots to plant the following spring, and avoid knocking the taproot. It may become unstable and need staking. It can self-seed and become a nuisance, so dead-head or collect seed before dispersal. Slugs and snails are a problem. **MB**

Bunny adds:
This is the only plant in my garden that the farmer next door has remarked upon – farmers are notably uninterested in the minuscule scale of gardening, but even he could not help but notice these huge beauties as he whizzed past on his tractor. In the first year they develop large basal rosettes of white-felted spiny leaves. The following year they reach for the sky, sending up a monstrously stout, spiny stem which is much branched. As the flowers begin to colour the plant looks a dream, but as it starts to go over the foliage looks as though you have put it in the wash with a blue towel, and comes out underwear grey. If you want it to self-seed you just have to grin and bear it.

Onopordum acanthium

Eschscholzia californica

CALIFORNIA POPPY

August

Type: hardy annual
Soil & situation: free-draining soil/sun
North American hardiness zone: annual
Height: 30cm (12in)
Spread: 15cm (6in)
Grow for: vibrant shades from early summer to autumn. Still stunning at this time of year, when many other flowers are fading; AGM.

Put on your 'shades', pour an ice-cold beer and crank up the Beach Boys; surf's up, the sun's out and the California poppies are in flower! This party's a riot, you can feel the good vibrations blasting from their blooms, with more tones than the finest Hawaiian shirt. You want colour? Baby, you got it!

The variety 'Ballerina' grows to 40cm (16in) tall and has frilled and fluted semi-double or double red, pink, yellow or orange flowers. Dazzling! 'Dali' is compact with scarlet flowers to 25cm (10in). It has the subtlety of Salvador himself! 'Monarch Art Shades' bears semi-double or double orange-yellow, apricot-yellow, creamy yellow or red flowers with fringed petals. Funky and free stylin'. 'Alba' has smaller flowers that start creamy and become white. Cool! 'Apricot Flambeau' has moderate-sized flowers, semi-double with fluted and ruffed orange petals streaked with red. Blowsy! In 'Cherry Ripe' the flowers are edged with crimson, fading to a pale centre. Sensational! 'Thai Silk Rose Chiffon' has pale pink, double flowers. Hang loose! 'Thai Lemon Silk' is pale lemon and about 20cm (8in) tall. Wicked! The Thai Silk Series has similar flowers at different shades from red and purple to white. Easy!

Buy a packet of each, mix them up and shake out a cacophony of colour. They look great when naturalized in a gravel garden; life's a beach! They need full sun in poor, free-draining soil. They self-seed freely and can become invasive if happy. The short-lived flowers only open in sunshine. Sow *in situ* from mid- to late spring for a continuous display through the summer. Pests and diseases? They wouldn't dare! **MB**

Opuntia ficus-indica

Opuntia ficus-indica
EDIBLE PRICKLY PEAR, INDIAN FIG

Type: just hardy, perennial cactus
Soil & situation: well-drained, dry, sandy soil/sun
North American hardiness zone: 6–10
Height & spread: may make 1m (3ft) in UK; much bigger in warmer climes
Grow for: astounding foliage plant, pretty flowers, edible fruits (you'll be lucky, matey)

This really is a conservatory or windowsill subject, none the less it is hardy. I have grown one outdoors for eight years here in Norfolk and at Kew they have some that are yonks older. There is a spineless form which I have not been fortunate enough to find as these are prickly b******s. The flowers are pretty and the fruits, which are rarely borne even under cover, are sweet and juicy; it's not something you should eat in the dark. I've found the best way to handle cacti pads is with a heavyweight newspaper wrapped around them. This is really worth growing to plant outdoors just to shock your friends – and anyone wandering around in the dark....

Named after a Greek town renowned for its figs, because of the resemblance the fruit bears to a fig, this is a New World plant now so widespread that it is mistaken for a native in many countries. In Australia it was introduced as a cheap stockproof hedge but it naturalized and took over, making incredibly large tracts of land ungrazeable, indeed impenetrable. The plague was ended with the introduction of one of its natural parasitic controls, a moth called *Cactoblastis cactorum*, whose larvae demolished the plants almost totally within a few years.

In either pot or ground, a well-drained, gritty, sandy soil is essential, preferably dry as a bone in winter, and it does best in a sheltered position facing the sun in front of a wall or on a sunny windowsill indoors. There is no need for any care except possibly to keep heavy rain and really hard frosts off with a temporary cloche. Propagate from seed sown on top of a gritty compost indoors in the warmth. Grow on under cover and plant out in early summer when they are about 30cm (12in) or more tall. Then select for the hardiest by waiting. Opuntia will root pads if these are taken off in spring or summer. Although the weather never got my opuntia the slugs did! Under cover watch out for mealy bug and dab them off with an cottonbud soaked in strong alcohol. **BF**

Origanum laevigatum 'Herrenhausen'

Type: hardy, perennial herb
Soil & situation: well-drained soil/sunny position
North American hardiness zone: 7–10
Height: 60cm (24in)
Spread: 45cm (18in)
Grow for: maroon buds and mauve flowers from mid- to late summer; ornamental leaves and shoots, purplish in colour when young and in winter; culinary purposes; aromatic; AGM

I started off growing this in my herb garden, but what a waste! When I saw its beautiful purplish foliage and long season of most appealing pale lilac flowers in large clusters, I propagated it up and now I grow this beauty in large mats under my pleached hornbeams. Not many plants luxuriate in those dry conditions, but this one certainly does. Many gardeners are confused over marjoram and oregano: both belong to the *Origanum* genus, but they are different species. *Origanum majorana* is marjoram, but just to confuse the issue, *Origanum vulgare* (see next entry) is called wild marjoram in the UK.

If you want to propagate this plant from seed, bear in mind that it and many origanums can damp off after germination. To prevent this I put a layer of fine vermiculite, about 1cm (½in) deep, over the potting compost and sprinkle the seeds over it. Then I cover the tray or pots with a sheet of polystyrene and put it/them by a radiator to germinate. As soon as they emerge, I put them on the kitchen window sill, without the polystyrene. Then I water the tray from the bottom to help prevent damping off. In the garden they are pretty well trouble free. The plants are best cut back after flowering as this will stimulate the growth of new rosettes of leaves, ensuring that they look good at the back end of summer. **BG**

Origanum vulgare
GOLDEN MARJORAM

Type: hardy, herbaceous, perennial herb
Soil & situation: any well-drained soil/full sun to light shade
North American hardiness zone: 5–9
Height: 30cm (12in)
Spread: 1m (3ft)
Grow for: wonderful warm yellow foliage from early in the year; purple flowers loved by bees; edible herb

Golden marjoram is hardy and, although pleasant enough to use in many dishes, is really an ornamental plant rather than a valuable herb. However, adding a few leaves to a salad brightens it up and it can be used with tomato dishes. I use it for ground cover between more important plants in the herb garden as it is easy to propagate by cutting it into chunks in spring, quick to recover and the flowers are really loved by bees. It looks its best from spring until summer, after which it becomes less tidy as it flowers, but these can be trimmed off to keep the neat yellow mounds of foliage for longer. There is a plain green form but it's a cheerless soul by comparison.

Origanum laevigatum 'Herrenhausen' *growing with Sedum* 'Autumn Joy'.

Origanum vulgare growing with creeping thyme.

The oregano of pizza fame is *Origanum majorana* or sweet marjoram which is a tender biennial. The Greek for marjoram was *origanum* made up of *oros*, mountain, and *ganos*, joy, for the natural habitat and habit of this wild plant.

This is long lived, growing almost anywhere but preferring well-drained spots in full sun; in shade the leaves stay green. Trim back the dead stems in autumn or earlier for a late show of foliage. Marjoram is easy to grow from seed sown in spring or summer and the clumps can be divided in spring. It suffers no particular problems but the golden form can be burnt by sudden fierce sun after weeks of grim damp dimness. **BF**

Osmanthus x *burkwoodii*

Type: hardy, evergreen shrub
Soil & situation: moist, fertile, well-drained soil/full sun or partial shade
North American hardiness zone: 7–9
Height & spread: 3m (10ft)
Grow for: incredible fragrance; AGM

I fully expect big, blowsy roses and magnolias to have a lot of scent to offer, but I am constantly amazed when tiny flowers exude fragrance by the wheelbarrow full. From mid- to late spring *Osmanthus* x *burkwoodii* does just that. The small, tubular, fragrant, pure white flowers are carried in clusters at the tips of last year's growth. On a calm, spring evening the scent from an informal hedge of *burkwoodii* is magic.

It forms a dense shrub with 5cm (2in) long, glossy, leathery, dark evergreen leaves. No regular pruning is required. If necessary old plants may be rejuvenated by cutting half the main branches to within 30cm (12in) of the ground in the first spring and the remainder the following year. Clip hedges immediately after flowering.

The flowers are impervious to rain and frost, but plant in a site protected from biting, cold, spring winds. Propagation is by semi-ripe cuttings taken in summer, with bottom heat in a propagator. If there is a suitably low branch, you can layer it into the soil in spring or autumn allowing 12 months for it to root. **JC**

Osmanthus x *burkwoodii*

Osmanthus heterophyllus

Type: hardy, slow-growing, evergreen shrub or small tree
Soil & situation: fertile, neutral to acid, well-drained soil/sun or partial shade
North American hardiness zone: 7–9
Height & spread: 5m (16ft)
Grow for: attractive foliage and fragrant flowers in late summer to autumn

Yes, here's another holly lookalike with dark green, glossy, sometimes spiny leaves, and the only apparent difference is that the leaves are opposite whereas in holly they are alternate. The real give-away though, perhaps the most obvious, are the

Osmanthus heterophyllus

sweetly scented, tubular flowers that appear from late summer to autumn. It was introduced to the UK by Thomas Lobb from Japan in 1856. Like his brother William, he collected plants for Veitch & Co., the legendary Victorian nursery, and visited locations from northeast India to Java and its nearby islands.

Osmanthus heterophyllus has several cultivars. 'Purpureus' is the hardiest form and its young growths are deep black and glossy and look as though they've been dipped in bitumen, later turning green with a purple tinge. 'Aureomarginatus' has bold, yellow leaf margins. 'Goshiki' has conspicuously yellow- and bronze-tinted leaves when young. Its name means five-coloured and you'll either love it or hate it! 'Gulftide' has white flowers and leaves that are twisted and spiny or lobed. 'Myrtifolius', the 'myrtle-leaved osmanthus' is neat and compact, with unarmed leaves except for a spine at the tip, just like the mature leaves on the upper part of *O. heterophyllus* and holly. They root easily and do not revert. 'Rotundifolius' is a slow-growing curiosity with round, occasionally twisted leathery leaves with wavy margins.

'Sasaba' is a remarkable form from Japan; its leaves are deeply cut into numerous spine-tipped lobes.

Prune to remove straggly or winter-damaged growth. Trim in autumn to maintain shape when grown as a hedge. Propagate in late summer by semi-ripe cuttings. Layer in autumn or spring. It is susceptible to scale. **MB**

Pachysandra terminalis 'Variegata'
MOUNTAIN SPURGE

Type: hardy, evergreen perennial
Soil & situation: any moisture-retentive soil/sun or partial shade
North American hardiness zone: 4–8
Height: 25cm (10in)
Spread: 60cm (24in)
Grow for: excellent year-round ground cover; AGM

When I'm asked for an interesting ground-covering evergreen, pachysandra is always on the list. In late winter the variegated foliage will add colour even to a deeply shaded garden. Coarsely toothed, shiny, dark green, 10cm (4in) long leaves are clustered at the ends of short, bare stems. Spikes of small, slightly fragrant, white flowers are produced in late spring and early summer.

The type of soil is irrelevant, providing it doesn't dry out, and the good news is that pachysandra is tolerant of chalky soils. It will, however, respond to being planted in a humus-rich, well-drained soil where it will romp away, quickly covering the ground. This plant, together with English ivy (*Hedera helix*), is widely used in the USA as ground cover under trees, speedily forming a dense mat and creating maintenance-free areas. Propagation is by semi-ripe cuttings in summer. Alternatively fork up a clump and remove the stems which have rooted into the soil. Pot them up in a soil-based compost for a season before planting out in their permanent position. **JC**

Pachysandra terminalis 'Variegata'

Paeonia lactiflora 'Sarah Bernhardt'

Paeonia lactiflora 'Sarah Bernhardt'

Type: hardy, herbaceous perennial
Soil & situation: rich, moist soil/sun or light shade
North American hardiness zone: 3–7
Height & spread: 1m (3ft), if not tied
Grow for: attractive, richly coloured foliage with enormous pink fragrant blooms; AGM

Peonies are an old-fashioned plant perfect for old-fashioned gardens. A peony bed is a short-lived display and is not labour free, as the stems need tying up or they flop. However, it is a marvellous thing with massive, soft pink, fragrant blooms borne in profusion on top of good-looking foliage. They go well along the sides of a path. Position them where they are easy to reach, as half the pleasure is in cupping the blooms in your hands and inhaling the sweet perfume. *Paeonia lactiflora* 'Sarah Bernhardt' is one of the finest, a fairly upright grower (still needs tying up) and suitable as a cut flower.

The lactiflora peonies come from China where they were grown for millennia, not arriving in Europe until the 19th century; whereas from ancient times in the West we had *P. officinalis*, the old red-flowered species. The name comes from the Greek for the plant of Paion, the god's physician, as it was used medicinally.

Peonies can be very long lived, often remaining in derelict gardens. They prefer a richly manured, loamy, moist soil and will take full sun or even fairly heavy shade without succumbing. Do not move or divide clumps unless necessary; mulches help immensely as they conserve moisture. Trim dead stems in autumn, stake and tie up new stems early and deadhead. Sow the seed for variable results or divide the roots in late autumn. Their roots are brittle and must be handled with care. They take several years to settle down before they start flowering. **BF**

Paeonia lutea var. ludlowii

Paeonia lutea var. *ludlowii*
TREE PEONY, TIBETAN PEONY

Type: hardy, deciduous shrub
Soil & situation: deep, fertile, moist, well-drained soil/full sun or partial shade
North American hardiness zone: 5–8
Height: 2.5m (8ft)
Spread: 4m (13ft)
Grow for: eye-catching specimen plant – attractive leaves, wonderful flowers and large seedpods

This is the very best in tree peonies. It forms a handsome, open, spreading shrub with no inhibitions regarding growth or flowering. Grown as a specimen plant out on its own it is quite startling in flower.

Bright green, architectural leaves are trifoliate and the large, buttery-yellow, single flowers are up to 13cm (5in) across with four to a stem. They are borne in late spring. Each flower produces two carpels. The seedpods are 7.5cm (3in) long, pale green flushed pink and sausage-shaped, and the seed produced is the largest of all peonies.

Tree peonies are long lived plants so give them plenty of space and they will, over many years, repay you with an annual display. The variety 'Superba' is of similar habit with bronze leaves when young turning to green and yellow flowers flushed with pale pink. The anthers are orange.

It will need protection from cold, drying winds. In its native habitat of Tibet, it grows wild in forests of holly and oak in a gravelly soil at an altitude of 3,000m (10,000ft). Propagation is by semi-ripe cuttings in summer or saddle grafting in winter. **JC**

Paeonia mlokosewitschii

Paeonia mlokosewitschii

MOLLY THE WITCH, CAUCASIAN PEONY

Type: hardy, herbaceous perennial
Soil & situation: rich, moist soil/sun
North American hardiness zone: 5–8
Height & spread: 1m (3ft)
Grow for: attractive buds, leaves and late spring flowers; AGM

This is a plant that everyone raves about but its name can be spelt by hardly anyone. I'll be short on the description and long on planting and aftercare, as you can see from the picture it's an absolute beauty and you'll want to ensure that it flourishes. The glorious bowl-shaped flowers, a full 12cm (5in) across, are cool lemon-yellow with a bold central boss of yellow and pale pink stamens. They're held on stout stems high above a mound of red-stemmed, silvery-green leaves. It's a native of the southeast Caucasus Mountains, growing on sunny slopes in hornbeam and oak forest. You'd never group those together in a garden!

It needs moist, fertile, well-drained soil, at least 30cm (12in) deep in sun or partial shade. Where late frosts occur, avoid positions which get the morning sun and mulch with well-rotted manure or compost around, not over, the crown; if buried too deep, it stops flowering. It is long-lived and a heavy feeder – prepare the ground thoroughly. Dig a planting hole ideally 1m (3ft)each way, incorporate plenty of well-rotted organic matter and wait two weeks to allow for settlement before planting. Plant the crown in early autumn, no more than 3cm (1in), or slightly less, below the surface. Feed with general fertilizer in spring and support with wire hoops or plant supports when foliage is half grown. If necessary, protect with dry mulch during winter. Keep the soil moist during drought.

Prevent peony grey mould with good hygiene, drainage and air circulation. Spray with fungicide as leaves emerge when problems occur. Check plants regularly. **MB**

John adds:
Some nursery-raised plants produce flowers with pink colouring, but the true flower has no discolorization. There also seem to be strains which flower earlier or later which can't be explained by location or climate.

Propagation by seed can be very satisfactory. Make sure the seed is ripe before harvesting. Sow it fresh. A root will form in the first autumn with a shoot appearing the following spring. Stored seed may take two or three years to germinate. Large clumps may be divided in autumn or spring, taking care not to damage the fleshy roots. Root cuttings are easily propagated in winter.

Paeonia suffruticosa 'Rock's Variety'

TREE PEONY

Type: hardy, deciduous shrub
Soil & situation: any well-drained soil/sun
North American hardiness zone: 5–8
Height & spread: up to 2m (6½ft) x 2.5–3m (8–10ft), but may be much less
Grow for: enormous lightly fragrant blooms

I have always loved flowers, more often for their scent than plain beauty but was nearly overwhelmed when I walked through Kew Gardens one day and beheld a tree peony in full bloom. Similar to a peony but shrubby, a bit more like a hydrangea, it was overladen with gorgeous blooms, each with satin-like petals. Then I started looking for these rare beauties, which wasn't easy as they are not much grown because they can be cut back by late-spring frosts, surviving but without flowering. However, a good large specimen in full bloom is wonderful, some are even well scented, but with such beauty that kind of seems irrelevant!

Worshipped in China for thousands of years, tree peonies were originally found in bamboo groves and were developed into double-flowering forms grafted onto other roots before the Norman conquest had even happened. They were introduced to Europe in the 18th century; in the UK we got hold of the first varieties from an American plant collector, Joseph Rock, who introduced many interesting plants (see his sorbus, page 369), and it's because of this that they are often referred to as Rock's tree peonies.

Tree peonies are not so demanding of rich soil as are their herbaceous relatives and are happy in a well-drained soil in full sun or shielded just from the early morning sun to protect the blooms from frost damage. They do better among other shrubs or on a wall than in a windswept site or frost hollow. The named varieties are often smaller more compact selections than seedlings! Tree peonies are long lived unless pruned, but dead-heading is worthwhile, as it saves the plant wasting energy on seed. The species can be started from seed as soon as acquired or it can be layered in spring; commercially the named varieties are grafted onto herbaceous rootstocks. The young shoots sprout early in the year so protect these with fleece or nets if harsh spring frosts or winds are predicted; do not worry about apparent dieback after flowering as it's normal, and do not prune. **BF**

Paeonia suffruticosa 'Rock's Variety'

Papaver orientale 'Patty's Plum'

Papaver orientale 'Patty's Plum'

MRS MARROW'S PLUM

Type: hardy perennial
Soil & situation: deep, fertile but well-drained soil/tend to stop flowering in dry conditions/sun or part shade
North American hardiness zone: 4–9
Height: 78–85cm (31–34in)
Spread: 70cm (27½in)
Grow for: beautiful, papery flowers over a period of about six weeks from late spring to mid-summer; attractive foliage is an asset, but dies down after flowering; reappears with a new crop of leaves in late summer which remain through the winter unaffected by frost

The extrovert flowers of this fabulous poppy are a most unusual shade of sumptuous mauve-plum. The flowers are single (single oriental poppies tend to be less invasive than double-flowered forms) and the stunning colour fades as they age. The stems are stiff and have no leaves immediately below the flowers. Oriental poppies are, understandably, a big favourite generally as they are easy to grow, colourful and with many good varieties in reds, white, salmon and pink to choose from. The individual blooms last for one, two or sometimes three days.

Generally oriental poppies are survivors – once they have established they will be with you for years to come. There are quite a few cultural methods that help maximize the flowering period of these ethereal blooms: it is best to cut the stalk off at the base as soon as it starts to go over, not letting it waste flower power on setting seed; keep them well watered if necessary as they do not appreciate it too hot and dry (contrary to popular belief) because in dry conditions the plants soon cease to produce flowers; the flowers of 'Patty's Plum' and other mauve and purple poppies will last about twice as long if they are grown in part shade so, surprisingly, they are far better in north-, west- or east-facing borders. Some poppies need staking and some do not, but as 'Patty's Plum' has long stems it does tend to need it. Sometimes, unfortunately, if the weather is wet, the flowers fail to open. Propagate by root cuttings; seed will produce mixed results. **BG**

Papaver rhoeas

CORN POPPY, FIELD POPPY, FLANDER'S POPPY

Type: hardy annual
Soil & situation: fertile, well-drained, alkaline soil/full sun
North American hardiness zone: annual
Height: 80cm (32in)
Spread: 15cm (6in)
Grow for: bright red, simple flowers

I have always loved these simple red flowers. They were so common in arable fields when I was growing up but, sadly, today weedkillers have

Papaver rhoeas

Papaver rhoeas 'Cedric Morris'

significantly reduced their numbers. They still appear in profusion after cultivation or where the soil has been disturbed for road works or building. The buried seed can remain viable for decades until it is disturbed and heat, light and moisture allow it to germinate. An example of this ability was demonstrated on the churned up soil of the Somme battlefield in 1916. Since then this memorable little red poppy has been adopted by the British Legion and is worn with pride and poignancy.

When crushed, the bristly stems exude a white sap. The 15cm (6in) long, downy, light green leaves are deeply cut into toothed lobes. Single, flimsy, bowl-shaped, scarlet flowers appear from late spring to early autumn. Occasionally the base of each petal has a black blotch. The stamens are numerous and jet black.

The round seed capsule releases its ripe seed through a ring of open pores rather like a pepper pot. Allow seedheads to form and, when ripe, collect and store dry for next year's flowers. Seed can be sown in spring *in situ*. Sow thinly.

There are selections available including 'Mother of Pearl' in shades of pink. The Shirley Series produce single and double flowers in yellow, orange, pink and red without blotches on the petals. **JC**

Matt adds:
Cedric Morris, a great friend of Lucien Freud and Beth Chatto, was an artist-plantsman who created a wonderful garden at Benton End in Suffolk. He regarded flowers as an extension of his palette and loved species plants; a list found after he died shows that at one time there were over 700 different kinds in his garden. It's no surprise, then, that he scoured the fields and hedgerows for variants of the enchanting field poppy. *Papaver rhoeas* 'Cedric Morris' is his selection of soft ethereal shades of pale pink, white and smoky grey; 'Fairy Wings', 'Angel's Wings' and 'Mother of Pearl' are almost identical but with darker colours, and 'Angels Choir' is a double selection.

Paris polyphylla

Type: hardy, herbaceous perennial
Soil & situation: cool, moist, free-draining soil/dappled shade
North American hardiness zone: 5–8
Height: 90cm (36in)
Spread: 30cm (12in)
Grow for: leaves; flowers from late spring to mid-summer; fascinating fruits

Paris polyphylla (formerly known as *Daiswa polyphylla*) is one of the wonders of the woodland garden. Fascinating and stylish rather than beautiful, if you're looking for a piece of natural contemporary art this is it! It's the perfect lesson in symmetry – look at it from above for maximum impact then go to the side to marvel at how it's stacked up in tiers. There's a ruff of up to 15 lance-shaped, mid-green leaves at the base. Above them at the top of the stem is a single spidery flower comprising narrow, green, arching outer sepals, the finest thread-like filaments that you'd never believe were petals and a boss of yellow to bronze stamens with a dark, almost purple ovary. Wow! As a bonus, it lasts for about three months.

The grand finale is even more bizarre when the capsules burst open grotesquely to reveal their bright red, shiny seeds. The fruits are said to shine out in their native forests in the Himalayas to western China, where they must be a hugely impressive sight. Sadly, because this plant grows slowly, dislikes disturbance and is desirable, it is under threat from over-collection in the wild. If you can't resist, and I hope you can't, please buy yours from a reputable, cultivated source.

Paris polyphylla

Passiflora edulis

Very easy to grow, it needs moist, fertile, well-drained, humus-rich soil, ranging from neutral to acid, in partial shade. Plant 12cm (5in) deep. It hates being divided and produces little fertile seed, but left undivided it spreads naturally and soon makes a fine clump. Slugs may attack rhizomes and young growth. **MB**

Passiflora edulis
EDIBLE PASSION FRUIT

Type: tender, perennial, semi-evergreen climber
Soil & situation: well-drained compost/full sun/under cover
North American hardiness zone: 7–9
Height & spread: 10m (33ft)
Grow for: glossy, lobed foliage; fantastic large flowers for months; edible fruits

I just love this plant. The ease with which it grows from seed, the lovely leaves, the flowers which are just out of this world, then the fruits. I've grown dozens of different passion flowers and they are all fascinating, almost all fantastically flowered – and yet each species is differently fantastically flowered – and nearly all of them have edible fruits. The fruits come in giant forms, miniature forms, different colours and shapes; there is one that looks like a small banana. The fruits have a tough skin surrounding an edible pulp coating the many seeds and this pulp when sieved is delicious in squashes and sorbets. And best of all is the form *Passiflora edulis*, the purple granadilla. You don't need buy the seed – every fruit from the supermarket is full of them. By the way, they're best to eat when wrinkled up.

Passion flowers, and there are hundreds of them, come from the Americas (and Australia – *P. herbertiana* is an Aussie thug I had to machete to death in my polytunnel). The name comes from the allegedly divine signs – each part of the flower supposedly representing the Passion (betrayal, torture and death) of Christ. Unfortunately, it's a fit-up that doesn't work well – for example, the ten petals represent the twelve disciples by leaving out Judas and Peter….

Passion flowers are a bit vigorous for most greenhouses or conservatories unless grown in a tub; they may survive on a warm wall outdoors if well protected in winter. A tub under cover means they can go out in summer, which helps keep them pest free. They need a gritty, well-drained compost kept moist in summer, with a regular high-potash feed in their water, and to be drier in winter. They are easy from seed and can even be cropping the same autumn from an early-spring sowing, or take summer heel or nodal cuttings with bottom heat. Passion flowers are prone to the usual greenhouse pests and mostly pine away if cold and damp. **BF**

Sedum spectabile

ICE PLANT

Type: hardy, herbaceous perennial
Soil & situation: prefers alkaline, free-draining soil/sun
North American hardiness zone: 4–9
Height & spread: 45cm (18in)
Grow for: sculptural form and late summer-autumn flowers; AGM

Butterflies love *Sedum spectabile* – it's a great place to sup in late summer and early autumn; when the sky is blue and the sun shines, it's drinks all round at the butterfly bar! Broad, dense flowerheads, up to 15cm (6in) across, mean easy access and copious nectar for all, the tables are packed with 'shots' and they drink until satisfied from its bountiful blooms. One of autumn's finest sights is a cloud of red admirals and tortoiseshell butterflies out for a drink and at play, dipping and sipping from the tiny chalk-pink flowers. When they have a chance, the bees love it too!

Like so many sedums it's rather surreal, with upright green stems and toothed, succulent, grey-green leaves. It's fascinating in leaf and bud; over winter when the bars close, the tables are bare and they're brown, dried and dusted with frost, it has a wonderful sculptural form. *S. spectabile* 'Iceberg' has bright lime-green foliage and tiny icy-white flowers that burst from striking green buds in late summer. There's a form called 'Stardust' that also has white flowers. *S. s.* 'Brilliant' (right) has flowers with bright pink petals, darker pink carpels and anthers.

They flourish in all garden soils, including clay, in sun or partial shade, but prefer moderately fertile, alkaline soil or sandy soil with added organic matter. Excellent for the front of borders; cultivars of *S. spectabile* are best for butterflies. They are prone to slugs and snails, and may be affected by fungal, bacterial, crown and root rot. **MB**

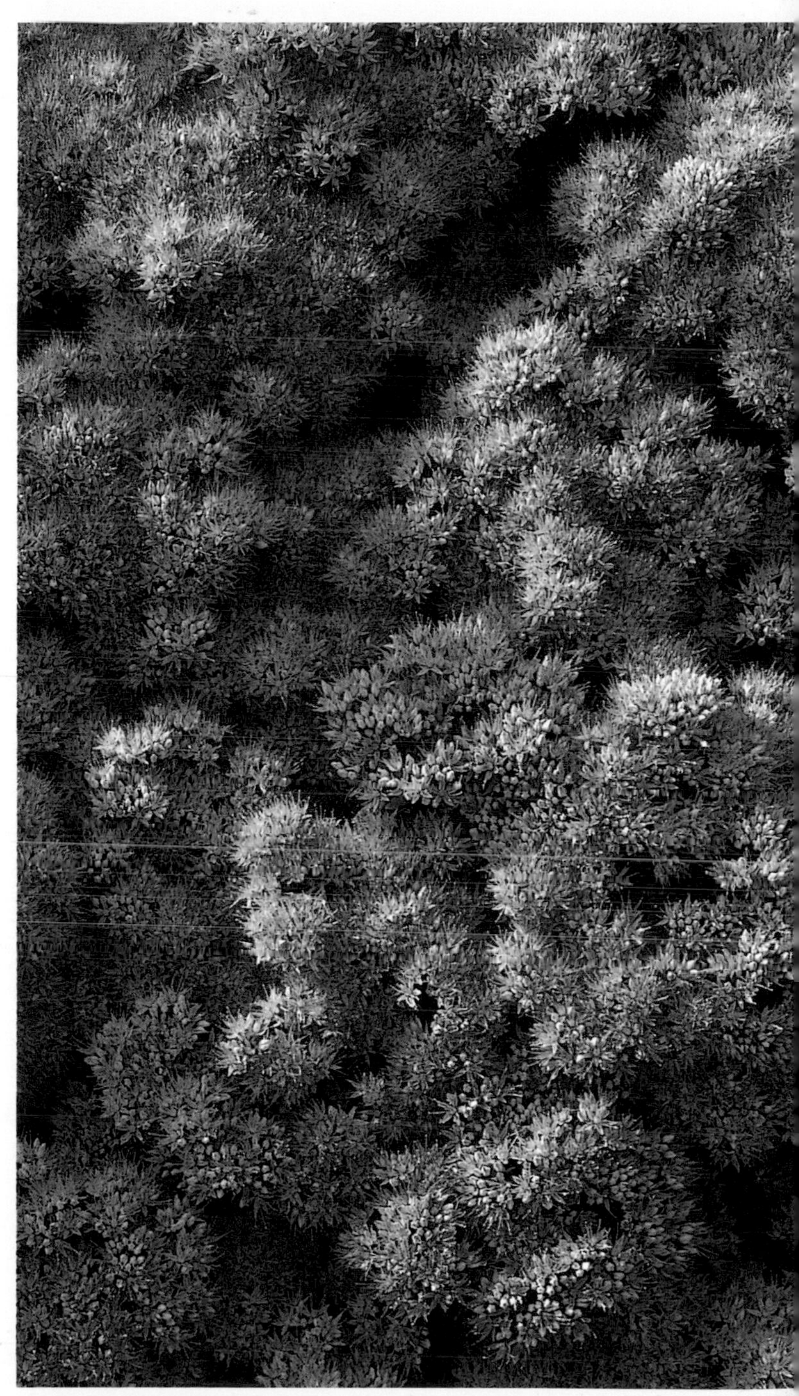

Paulownia tomentosa

Plant of the Week (see page 125)

Pelargonium 'Ardens'

Type: tender perennial
Soil & situation: free-draining compost/sun
North American hardiness zone: 8–10
Height: 30cm (12in)
Spread: 25cm (10in)
Grow for: striking flowers from mid-spring to mid-autumn

It is not difficult to fall in love with this plant – although it does not produce the bold display of so many pelargoniums, the flower colour is simply irresistible.

I first saw this several years ago and for some inexplicable reason didn't buy it. After that I couldn't stop thinking about it, then several months later I saw another at a flower show, I had butterflies in my stomach when I bought it! Is it normal to be so excited about buying a plant? I only have one, but it is beautiful and bright. Imagine a huge pot full outside on the patio, floating on their wand-like stems; here come those butterflies again!

Pelargonium 'Ardens' is my absolute favourite, it has clusters of intense ember-red flowers with darker teardrop markings on each petal topping long, elegant flower stalks and grey-green foliage. It can be used as a cut flower, but you'd need a lot of stems – unless you go minimalist. Force into dormancy and divide in midsummer to create one of life's more difficult dilemmas, do you share them, or keep them all for yourself?

The species and 'primary' hybrids rarely get a mention; so here are a few more to whet your appetite.

Pelargonium sidoides has small, very deep purple flowers with orange pollen from late winter to late autumn, the grey-green leaves have a silvery sheen. There is a black form and a raspberry-coloured form with larger, bright, deep pink flowers. *P. tomentosum* (see page 291) looks great in a large pot. I'd also like to mention *P.* 'Splendide' which has fabulous flowers – the upper petals are red and the lower ones white. Delightful!

Grow pelargoniums in sunshine in John Innes No. 1 compost with added sharp sand. Water moderately and feed with a liquid general fertilizer every two weeks in spring, changing to high-potash fertilizer when flowering. In winter, water sparingly, keeping the compost almost dry. They are not frost hardy. Propagate from non-flowering shoots in spring and summer. Cut shoots just below a leaf joint, put them in warm, moist compost in bright light; do not cover. Beware of whitefly. **MB**

Pelargonium 'Ardens'

Pelargonium 'Lord Bute'

Pelargonium 'Lord Bute'

Type: tender perennial
Soil & situation: free-draining compost/sun
North American hardiness zone: 8–10, but often grown as an annual
Height: 45cm (18in)
Spread: 30cm (12in)
Grow for: handsome flowers from late spring to early summer; AGM

'Lord Bute' is a superb pelargonium for a summer patio display and it certainly lives up to its name as a Regal pelargonium. It's one of the oldest of this type and has a deep blackberry-coloured, velvety flower with fine cherry-red edges and orange pollen. It makes an excellent specimen for a decorative urn or with silver-foliaged plants. It has a distinct flowering period from mid-spring and is in full flourish by early summer; each flower cluster is about 10cm (4in) across. If you remove the spent flowers and feed with high-potash fertilizer like those used for roses or tomatoes, they will flower even longer.

Other dark-flowered Regal pelargoniums include *Pelargonium* 'Noir' with very dark, almost black flowers and mid-green leaves. 'Morwenna' has iridescent, floppy, black flowers. 'Springfield Black' is an almost black dark purple. The blooms of 'Black Velvet' are very dark velvety black with a fine purple margin. 'Marchioness of Bute' has flowers of deep maroon, almost black, with a light margin and exterior. 'Minstrel Boy' is deep mahogany. 'Australian Bute' has dark burgundy, wavy and lobed petals. Cultivate as for *Pelargonium ardens* (see previous entry). **MB**

Pelargonium tomentosum
PEPPERMINT-SCENTED GERANIUM

Type: tender, evergreen perennial
Soil & situation: potted in a free-draining, gritty medium and watered extremely sparsely during the winter months/sunny, sheltered position/needs over-wintering in frost-free conditions
North American hardiness zone: 9–10
Height: to 90cm (36in)
Spread: to 75cm (30in)
Grow for: divine foliage; heart-shaped, peppermint-scented, velvety leaves; AGM

This plant is not nearly as fussy or difficult as it sounds. I leave it out in a sheltered position through the winter, and when we get cold snaps, pull it in under our porch. (Normal people put it in a frost-free greenhouse, but mine is usually too full.) If you keep it on the bone side of dry, it survives. I rate it so highly because it forms a beautiful mound of touchy-feely foliage, spreading and flopping attractively over the pot with its softly hairy leaves, which you stroke it as you go past. Then, whenever you smell your fingers throughout the day, the strong, fresh, organic peppermint lingers on them. It does flower, with small white butterfly-shaped flowers in spring and summer – pleasant but not special. Feed and water this plant as it starts into growth. If you are lucky enough to be given a young, rooted cutting, pinch out the tips to develop a good, bushy shape. Avoid it becoming leggy as it ages – part of the beauty of the plant is a well-rounded form – so prune it back during the growing season to maximize this. It is very easy from cuttings, and a wonderful gift that will be appreciated even by non-gardening friends. **BG**

Pelargonium tomentosum

Penstemon 'Burgundy'

Penstemon 'Burgundy' (syn. *P.* 'Burford Seedling')

Type: hardy, semi-evergreen perennial
Soil & situation: infertile, well-drained soil/full sun or light shade
North American hardiness zone: 7–10
Height: 90cm (36in)
Spread: 60cm (24in)
Grow for: deep red flowers from summer to autumn

Burgundy by name and burgundy by nature. The wine-red flowers provide a long-term splash of colour in the mixed border. It has the decency to use up its allocated space yet not crowd its neighbours.

It quickly becomes a robust, bushy plant with 12cm- (5in-) long, light green leaves. The upright racemes of flowers appear in summer and go on until late autumn. They are bell shaped, 5cm (2in) long and deep red-purple with white stigmas and styles. The throat is white with pale red streaks. The upper lip of each flower consists of two lobes, while the lower lip has three. Dead-heading after flowering prolongs the display.

Avoid a fertile soil which will encourage growth at the expense of flowers and also make the growth lush and soft, prone to frost damage. Covering the base of the plant in late autumn with a dry mulch of coarse bark will help see it through a cold winter.

Propagation is by seed sown in heat in early spring. Take softwood cuttings in late spring or semi-ripe cuttings in summer. Cover with horticultural fleece. Large clumps can be carefully divided in spring discarding the old, woody centre of the clump. Penstemons have their share of problems. Slugs can be a real nuisance. Chrysanthemum eelworm distorts the foliage and infected plants should be dug up and burned. **JC**

Penstemon 'White Bedder'

Penstemon 'White Bedder' (syn. *P.* 'Snowstorm')

Type: frost-hardy perennial
Soil & situation: free-draining but not too fertile soil/sun or light shade
North American hardiness zone: 6–9
Height: 70cm (27½in)
Spread: 30cm (12in)
Grow for: a gloriously long flowering season from mid-summer to early autumn, provided it is dead-headed; freely produced, bell-shaped, pure white flowers; AGM

Not all the penstemons are reliably hardy, but with our milder winters, the range that will over-winter is increasing. For me, the ones that are reliably hardy are indispensable perennials. The foliage of these hardier types is generally evergreen and their free flowering over a period of several months is invaluable. *P.* 'White Bedder', despite its name, is reliably hardy in sharp-draining soil. It has bright green ovate leaves. But, of course, the main reason for including it is its handsome trumpet-like flowers, borne in racemes and of an eye-catchingly large size.

Another excellent new penstemon which I grew for the first time last year is *P.* 'Cassis Royale', a sumptuous dark wine-purple. It was quite hardy with me in its first winter and it is a far better, stronger colour than the widely grown *P.* 'Sour Grapes'.

It is worth tidying up penstemons in early spring with a bit of a cut back. They are generally short-lived perennials and ideally you replace your stock every few years to keep them looking their best. They root very readily from softwood cuttings which you can take from the new growth stimulated from being cut back. Ideally I think it is best to plant them out the following spring, giving them a full growing season to get their roots down before having to endure the frosts. Otherwise there is little more to be done, apart from dead-heading to keep them flowering and a light winter mulch to help them through the frosts. **BG**

Perovskia atriplicifolia 'Blue Spire'

RUSSIAN SAGE

Type: hardy, deciduous subshrub
Soil & situation: poorish, perfectly drained alkaline soils/tolerates slightly acid conditions/useful for coastal conditions/best in sun/will tolerate some shade though may need staking
North American hardiness zone: 6–9
Height: 1.2m (4ft)
Spread: 1m (3ft)
Grow for: excellent foliage and superb flowers; the former is aromatic, grey-green and finely cut; the latter are lavender-blue in late summer and autumn; AGM

This is an excellent, soft, see-through plant with many vertical but airy spires of flowers. It forms a delicate tracery of colour at a time in the year when you really appreciate it. The flowers are carried in effusive quantities and I like mixing it with dark black-purples and oranges, but it is a shade that mixes well in many colour themes. It is also adaptable to how you use it – it looks topical, current and trendy in widespread drifts of perennial plantings; it works particularly well in gravels with expanses of other drought-loving plants and low mounds of grasses; and it is equally at home sunning itself against a house wall, or in a herbaceous or mixed border.

Perovskia atriplicifolia 'Blue Spire'

This plant is easy from cuttings, and they strike really easily if you remove very young shoots with a heel in late spring. These small, new shoots will only be about 3.5cm (1¼in) long, but they will rapidly root at that size. Although this is technically a subshrub, it is most usually grown as a herbaceous plant with the whole plant cut back to ground level when it becomes too ratty-looking in early spring. That way you leave the vertical white, leafless stems to add colour and structure to the winter scene. The new foliage in spring is also far better when treated like this. **BG**

Matt adds:
Perovskia atriplicifolia has a soothing effect when planted with lavender or white-flowered perennials, and contrasts well with late orange or yellow flowers such as *Solidago* 'Goldenmosa'. The branches are an attractive winter feature, particularly in clear, cold frosty weather.

There are several cultivars, possibly hybrids between Russian sage and *P. atriplicifolia* or *P. abrotanoides*, but who cares when they look so beautiful! *P. atriplicifolia* 'Little Spire' is slightly smaller than 'Blue Spire', with a height and spread of 1m (3ft); 'Filigran' has finely cut, almost fern-like leaves. But I agree with Bunny that 'Blue Spire' is the best of all with its deeply cut leaves and huge flower spikes.

Persicaria microcephala 'Red Dragon'

Type: hardy perennial
Soil & situation: moist but free-draining soil/full sun or part shade
North American hardiness zone: 5–8
Height: 60cm (24in)
Spread: 50cm (20in)
Grow for: dramatic foliage of various colours, the predominant being a burgundy maroon

The foliage of this plant is fairly extraordinary: the elongated heart-shaped leaves are stridently marked with a minty-white chevron, and the stems are bright red. The flowers are small, white and fairly insignificant and the foliage goes downhill when it puts its energy into flowering, so

Persicaria microcephala 'Red Dragon'

I think they are better removed. It does not spread fast and is in no way invasive as many of the bistorts tend to be. The most difficult thing I find with this plant is deciding where to fit it into the garden so it looks right. The habit and form imply that it is best in wilder parts, semi-naturalized, but the exotic colour does not lend itself to that treatment. I grow it adjacent to a grassy path in a narrowish border with some ferns, cyclamen and variegated euonymus. It seems to fit reasonably happily there. It is not as picky as to where it will grow as the colouring suggests and apparently is equally happy in raised beds, borders or containers. There are several other good persicarias. *P. bistorta* 'Superba' is one of my favourites: it is a handsome plant with mounds of large, soft-green leaves and long stems of abundant poker-like pink flowers produced all summer.

'Red Dragon' is a fairly recent introduction and I have only grown it for a couple of years. Up to now I have done nothing to it apart from removing the flowers and the usual initial watering to get it going. I think it is going to be one of those plants that generally does not need much doing anyway, just dividing if and when necessary. **BG**

Petroselinum sativum

CURLY-LEAFED PARSLEY

Type: hardy, short-lived perennial or biennial herb
Soil & situation: any soil/sun or shade/likes moisture
North American hardiness zone: 5–8
Height: first year to 30cm (12in), second year to 1m (3ft)
Spread: first year to 15cm (6in), second year to 60cm (24in)
Grow for: superb curly-leafed foliage plant; culinary herb

There is no herb more essential to a cook's garden. You can do without almost any other garnish, salading or flavour, but not parsley. Try a cold cooked leek in a parsley vinaigrette to see what I mean. It is also one of the first plants to produce fresh leaves in spring, which make a great tonic salad with curly kale. But then it is also such a lovely garnish to make your humble meal look more inviting; you can use the curly leaves as a soft cushioning bed for freshly picked strawberries in the punnet, too. This healthy-looking, verdant green plant is more than good enough to be a foliage plant in the flower garden.

The plant reached England in the Middle Ages and has been popular ever since. I reckon more parsley is used for garnishing (think butcher's display and restaurant food) than is actually eaten. The curly-leafed form was developed to prevent inadvertent poisoning by weeds such as fool's parsley, which resemble the flat-leafed form. The form Hamburg parsley is grown for its roots. In Italy a curly variety still exists as grown in Roman times and known to Pliny. We get both common and botanical names from the Greek *petros selinon*, rock celery, via Old French *perresil*.

Parsley is notoriously difficult to grow but does better if sown in summer not spring, in moist, warm soil. The plants do best when they're self-sown, usually choosing damp, partly shady sites. Dead-heading the plants and trimming them back encourages new growth and a longer life. Parsley needs sowing every mid-summer to ensure a continuous supply. It can suffer badly from carrot root fly and is then best grown under a horticultural fleece. **BF**

Petroselinum sativum

Peucedanum graveolens

Peucedanum graveolens (syn. *Anethum graveolens*)

DILL

Type: tender annual
Soil & situation: rich, moist soil/full sun to light shade
North American hardiness zone: annual
Height: 1m (3ft)
Spread: 15cm (6in)
Grow for: attractive ferny foliage; essential salad herb

I must have this plant as I need its sweet aniseed-like taste to go with my pickled gherkins, along with black peppercorns and a bay leaf; it's the flavour I crave. I also like dill in a mixed salad and as the herb to go with pickled fish, such as herring or gravadlax. And if the plant gets too big despite my depredations, I add the seed to my liqueurs as it is an old remedy for indigestion.

Very closely related to parsley and carrots, this is an ancient plant coming from North Africa and the Near East, which has long been cultivated. Our common name may come from the Norse *dilla*, to dull or soothe, as it was used in sedative mixtures. The botanical name comes from the Greek *peukedanon* because of its parsnip-like root. The Greeks called a different plant, *Pimpinella anisum*, anise, by the name *Anethum*, but now we apply it to dill instead. Don't you just love nomenclatural botanists???

Dill can be sown from early spring on well-drained soil in a sunny position. The early leaves are best in salads, the later in pickles and the seed needs saving by cutting the nearly ripe plants down and the ripening finished off under cover in a warm, dry place. Sow shallowly *in situ* in succession from early spring to mid-summer. In shade or damp dill moulds easily; it may hybridize with fennel so these two plants should be grown well apart if self-saving seed for sowing. The seeds as used in gripe water are harmless, but the sweet alcohol they are in is highly addictive and as strong as sherry. **BF**

Phaseolus 'Kingston Gold'
CLIMBING FRENCH BEAN

Type: half-hardy, annual vegetable
Soil & situation: sunny, sheltered site with free-draining soil; does not establish well in cold, wet soils
North American hardiness zone: annual
Height: 1.8m (6ft)
Spread: individual plants about 15cm (6in)
Grow for: tender, but tasty, ornamental variety that crops well, exceptionally early, and for a good period of time

This is a good-looking, good-tasting vegetable. The golden pods hang conspicuously, sometimes at eye level, for all the world to admire. The flowers are a creamy white. Margaret Robinson, from my favourite vegetable firm, W. Robinson and Son, recommends growing it with a dark purple flowering sweet pea on a hazel archway or some such structure. It must be a heady combination.

I am not a big fan of 'queer gear' vegetables that are extraordinary but taste pretty revolting, but these are extraordinarily good to look at and exceedingly good to eat. They will be cropping by mid-summer if you have them out by the end of spring, and what is more, you will still be picking a few in early autumn. The yields are heavy, and these beans are produced right from the bottom of the plant to the top. The pods are longer than normal French beans, you pick them when they are about 15–18cm (6–7in) long and you do not have to bend double to pick them either. They are tender – you only need to top and tail them – and they retain their gold colour when cooked, though if you pick them very small they go a pale green. Climbing French beans have a lot of advantages over bush types, especially in wet summers where the pods are less likely to be damaged by slugs and splashed by soil. Another very attractive climbing French bean, but without the copious yield, is 'Rob Splash'. The beans are yellow and beautifully marked with purple splashes.

Phaseolus 'Kingston Gold'

I find with all my beans that I get far better results if I grow them singly in pots until two or three true leaves are produced, and then I plant them out. Otherwise germination can be a bit of a gamble. Slugs, mice, birds, cats and, last but not least, wet, all play a part in varying degrees preventing me from getting my apple-pie rows. Protecting them with fleece outside, at the vulnerable stage, is a quicker method and certainly increases the establishment percentage markedly. Popping a few extra beans at the ends of the row for gapping up failures makes this system fail-safe. **BG**

Phaseolus vulgaris
FRENCH BEANS

Type: tender, annual vegetable
Soil & situation: moist, warm soil/full sun
North American hardiness zone: annual
Height & spread: variable
Grow for: climbing varieties make ornamental vines with pretty flowers and coloured pods, otherwise for the crop value

I grow several sorts of French beans. I love the tiny, pencil-shaped, wax pod-type of dwarf green bean that is served small without slicing and squeaks as you eat it if it is fresh and quickly steamed. I love the climbing French beans which are like runner beans but smaller and with smoother, firmer flesh; these can be colourful with purple flowers and pods. I also adore the drying dwarf French beans as these are such value. You sow them and apart from weeding all you do is lift the plants and hang them up until you want a casserole. Then you pod the beans, soak them overnight, add the bacon, tomato, onion and so on, and simmer all day; food of the gods, and you sing their praises after….

We had none of these beans in the UK until an early explorer named de Soto saw them growing together with sweet corn and squashes in fields in Central America. These were long cultivated there and not long after de Soto's discovery were welcome in the Old World where their many uses were soon appreciated. Now there are countless varieties for many purposes. The botanical name is from the Old Greek name for another almost totally unrelated bean!!!

Phaseolus vulgaris

French beans need a moist, humus-rich soil in a sunny, warm, sheltered spot. The climbing varieties must be given poles or supports. For fresh green beans keep picking regularly as the plants will go on producing more. For drying beans uproot the whole plant when the season ends and hang it to dry in a warm airy place. Sow only when the late spring frosts are over and the soil is warm, otherwise germination is poor. Apart from cold springs they are relatively problem free and being legumes enrich the soil. **BF**

Philadelphus spp.

Type: hardy, perennial shrub
Soil & situation: any soil/sun or shade
North American hardiness zone: 5–8
Height & spread: variable, from 1.2–3m (4–10ft)
Grow for: forget the blooms, it's their scent!

Philadelphus are too strongly scented for some people and not good in the house for many as the smell can be too much, ooh I love them. Gorgeous, heavy, orange-blossom fragrances: the original *P. coronarius* (mock orange) is the most powerful; *P.* 'Belle Etoile' has a peaches-and-cream lightness; *P.* 'Avalanche' is heavier, more fruit salad like; 'Virginal' more, well, virginal; and best of all, my own seedling, of course – to my mind anyway.

Native to southern Europe, there are a dozen species and the first, *P. coronarius*, was introduced to the UK in the 16th century and has often confusingly been called *Syringa*, the botanical name for lilac. They are also called the mock orange because their scent and appearance of smaller-flowered forms have been likened to those of the orange. *Philadelphus* is the Greek for brotherly love.

They survive almost anywhere on any soil and they like chalk, as long as it's not too dry. Once established they need no attention and can be pruned hard back after a few years to keep them compact, or the older shoots can be removed annually immediately after flowering. Seedlings are variable and worth growing; propagate the named varieties by autumn cuttings, which is on the whole easy. Apparently they can get devastating aphid attacks but thankfully these do little long-term harm. **BF**

John adds:
'Belle Etoile' is my favourite philadelphus. On a calm day the area surrounding a flowering shrub is heavy with its fragrance. It makes a fine display when planted in mixed, open woodland. Mulching in early spring will help to retain moisture close to the surface roots. It can be propagated by softwood cuttings in summer or hardwood cuttings outside in a sheltered site in late autumn or winter.

Like Bob, I also love *Philadelphus* 'Virginal', which will grow to a height and spread of 3m (10ft) with large, fully double, very fragrant, pure white flowers. Another favourite is 'Bouquet Blanc', with fragrant double or semi-double flowers in summer and a height of 2m (6½ft).

Philadelphus 'Belle Etoile'

Phlomis fruticosa
JERUSALEM SAGE

Type: hardy, perennial, semi-evergreen, lax shrub
Soil & situation: well-drained soil/sun
North American hardiness zone: 8–9
Height: 1–1.2m (3–4ft)
Spread: 1.2–2m (4–6½ft)
Grow for: attractive ever-grey foliage and bright yellow flowers in summer; AGM

This is a lovely plant for a dry site with poor soil facing into a hot sun, where it will thrive. I've found it goes well with tree lupins (see page 252) and indeed any grey-leafed plants, which mostly love similar conditions. I'm fortunate in that I can smell the rich aromatic aroma of the leaves and flowers, but apparently many people are allergic to it. It is usually ever-grey with me as I have my current one in a sheltered spot, which makes a good winter home for ladybirds, and in the first sunny days of spring they come out to sit on it like orange flower buds.

A native of the Levant, this is one of several dozen species and was brought back after the crusades from the Mediterranean and recorded as growing in England in 1596. The botanical name comes from the Greek for another plant entirely!!!

Not a very long lived shrub, it survives best on a dryish sunny bank with some shelter. It can be lightly trimmed after flowering. Jerusalem sage may be deciduous in cold districts and cut back down to the ground in the coldest spots, but often returns if the soil is light, sandy and well drained.

It can be grown from seed or by softwood summer or hardwood autumn cuttings in a cold frame. It may be problem free but its scent causes severe allergic reactions in some people, so grow it away from paths and patios. **BF**

Solanum crispum

Type: hardy, evergreen climber
Soil & situation: moist, well-drained, neutral to alkaline soil/full sun
North American hardiness zone: 8–9
Height: 4m (13ft)
Spread: over 2m (7ft)
Grow for: the impressive sight of this scrambling climber in flower, which is all summer long and then a month or so longer

If I ever found a sport of this plant I would name it 'Disobedient'! It is a shrub that likes to pretend it is a climber, but unless you are constantly tying in the strong shoots they zoom off at all angles bursting with flower at the tips. My method of control is to train in the main stems to timber trellis and thereafter let it do its own thing. It does it beautifully. After flowering I take control once again.

The 12cm (5in) dark green leaves may become deciduous when growing in cold areas. From summer to autumn the fragrant, dark mauve-blue flowers appear in dense, terminal clusters. Each flower is 3cm (1in) across with bright golden-yellow stamens.

Avoid exposed sites subject to cold winds. Planted against a sheltered, sunny wall in well-drained, fertile soil, it will quickly cover its allocated space. Water regularly from spring onwards. Annual pruning is essential. Shorten back the long shoots immediately after flowering. In winter prune them back to 10–15cm (4–6in) of the old wood. Propagation is by semi-ripe cuttings in a free-draining compost in late summer in a heated propagator. **JC**

Phlomis fruticosa

Phlox paniculata 'White Admiral'

Type: hardy, herbaceous perennial
Soil & situation: moist, fertile soil/sun or half shade
North American hardiness zone: 4–8
Height & spread: 90cm (36in)
Grow for: an immensely useful, tall-growing perennial which produces white flowers from mid- to late summer; does not require staking; AGM

There are many phlox to choose from, but this strong white phlox is a reliably good performer. It invariably contributes good long-lasting flashes of white and loads the summer air with clouds of fragrance. There are many other colours available – every shade of pink, red, purple, lavender-blue and orange-scarlet, and many other great varieties. *P. maculata* 'Alpha' (AGM) has lilac-pink flowers and is another favourite of mine. However, the fresh white flowers of 'White Admiral' against the strong green foliage look so outstanding in a border that I invariably end up using this plant again and again.

Generally phlox prefer soil which provides them with a good supply of moisture throughout the growing season and are least happy on an alkaline clay. So if your soil is on the thin side, beef it up with copious organic matter prior to planting. Eelworms are a pest – to avoid them propagate from root cuttings, rather than division or stem cuttings, and you will not have a problem. To prolong the flowering period it is worth cutting off the dying flowerheads and then they will produce sideshoots with yet more flowers.

Vigorously growing plants are more likely to produce the goods. They respond to irrigation and should not be overcrowded, so divide them every three or four years, leaving decent-sized hunks to make sure they flower in the first year. **BG**

Phormium 'Sundowner'

NEW ZEALAND FLAX

Type: hardy, evergreen perennial
Soil & situation: fertile, moist, well-drained soil/full sun
North American hardiness zone: 9–10
Height & spread: 2m (6½ft)
Grow for: this versatile, broad-leafed plant is good in the border or as a hedge; AGM

This is a tried and tested plant for adding shape and texture to the garden. Grown in the mixed border or in a large container there is instant impact. Planted in a row it forms an effective, informal hedge or screen.

It is clump forming with 1.2m (4ft) broad, upright, sword-like leaves which, close to the base, are folded to form a 'v' shape. They are purple-green with dark pink-red margins and cream stripes. In summer, enormous 2m (6½ft) high flower stalks shoot up from the centre of the clump with tubular, bright, yellow-green flowers. The green seedpods that turn black form at right angles to the stem. When ripe they twist open to reveal the shiny, black seeds.

Where there is a risk of heavy frost they will benefit from a deep, dry mulch of composted bark in winter. When planting, allow sufficient space for the plant to grow and form a striking large clump. Pull off the old, dead outer leaves when they turn a grey-brown colour.

Propagation is by seed sown in spring in a heated propagator. When transplanting seedlings take care not to damage the brittle roots. Large clumps may be divided in late spring by teasing pieces out, complete with roots. Replant as soon as possible without allowing the roots to dry out. **JC**

Phlox paniculata 'White Admiral'

Phormium 'Sundowner'

Photinia x *fraseri* 'Red Robin'

Type: frost-hardy, evergreen shrub
Soil & situation: moist, fertile, well-drained soil/full sun or partial shade
North American hardiness zone: 8–9
Height: 4m (13ft)
Spread: 5m (16ft)
Grow for: brilliant red leaves; AGM

There is nothing fickle about *Photinia* x *fraseri* 'Red Robin'. The new young leaves and shoots emerge in spring a bright, shiny red and retain their colour well into the summer. An actively growing mature plant can appear to be totally red for most of the season. Even in winter some mahogany-red remains on the younger leaves. The American-raised variety *P.* x. *f.* 'Birmingham' has coppery-red young leaves.

The 15–20cm (6–8in) long, leathery, dark evergreen leaves form a dense, compact screen for privacy, shelter or protection. When grown as a hedge or trained as a standard with a shaped head, it is important to clip over the young growths in early summer to allow new sideshoots to form and be hardened sufficiently to withstand winter frosts. It is tempting but unwise to put off the job in order to take advantage of the coloured foliage. Plant shaped, standard plants far enough apart to allow for an increase in the size of the head. Regular clipping restricts growth, but it doesn't stop it.

Cold winds and hard frosts may damage soft growth, spoiling the following year's display.

Photinia x *fraseri* 'Red Robin'

Feeding the plants with a high-potash fertilizer, such as a liquid tomato feed, in late summer will firm up the growth. Propagation is by semi-ripe cuttings in summer in a propagator with bottom heat. All photinias are prone to fireblight disease. Avoid planting where shrubs such as pyracantha have suffered. **JC**

Bunny adds:

There is not a huge range of good, large, structural evergreen shrubs in the garden, but this is one that I have used a lot. It is ideal for decorative screening purposes, but I have to admit I have mainly used it for impatient clients and have brought in ready grown and shaped ones which have been good, plump 3.5m (11½ft) specimens, with a stem girth of up to 25cm (10in), grown in Italy. I think the Italians have selected larger, more vigorous clones than we generally get in the UK, and of course the hotter summers speed up the growth rate. The shrubs establish surprisingly well when planted at this large size, tolerate the climate change and certainly can be less expensive than an inorganic, structural screen. They are often grown clipped into wide columns or mop-head standards, ideal for blocking out troublesome neighbours at first-floor level, and no planning permission required either! They look magnificent and can change the whole appearance of a garden in an instant.

Phygelius x *rectus* 'Salmon Leap'

Type: hardy, evergreen shrub
Soil & situation: fertile, moist, well-drained soil/full sun
North American hardiness zone: 8–9
Height: 1.2m (4ft)
Spread: 1.5m (5ft)
Grow for: a spectacular summer display of bright orange, tubular flowers; AGM

A very sensible plant. It has the good sense to hold its flowering stems at an angle resembling a fishing rod when reeling in a fish. This allows the pendent, tubular flowers to hang at an angle rather than directly down the stem of the plant, thus making a better display. It forms an upright, suckering plant with 10cm (4in) long, dark green leaves.

The bright orange, deeply lobed, long, tubular flowers are slightly curved. They are loosely arranged along 45cm (18in) high panicles in summer and autumn. Pruning out panicles which have finished flowering encourages a succession of flowers through the autumn. *P.* x *rectus* 'African Queen' produces pale red flowers with orange lobes and a yellow mouth. *P.* x *r.* 'Moonraker' has creamy-yellow flowers.

Avoid sites exposed to biting, cold winds. In gardens where the temperature is below freezing for long periods it can be treated as a herbaceous perennial. A mulch of bark will see it through the winter. In spring remove the previous year's stems to ground level.

Propagation is by removing rooted suckers in spring. They can be planted out where they are to flower or potted up for a season. Softwood cuttings taken in early summer should be over-wintered in a cold frame for the first season. **JC**

Phygelius x *rectus* 'Salmon Leap'

Physalis peruviana

Physalis peruviana (syn. *P. edulis*)

CAPE GOOSEBERRY

Type: tender, perennial, evergreen climber
Soil & situation: any soil/sun or light shade/under cover
North American hardiness zone: 8–10
Height & spread: 2m (6½ft)
Grow for: attractive downy leaves; small yellow flowers; interesting paper lantern-shaped edible fruits

This delicious fruit, rich in vitamin C, is not widely grown, mainly because when it is started off from seed it does crop in the autumn but very late and so the berries are not really sweet and ripe. If you grow it on or make new plants from cuttings these flower and crop much sooner in the year with a sweeter, riper fruit. I've got it in the border under cover and in pots. The fruits are truly ripe when they drop, which is still late in the year, and then they keep pristine inside their wrappers, eventually turning into little raisin-like dried fruits. A marvellous crop. There is a smaller sweeter sister, *Physalis pruinosa*/*P. pubescens* (ground cherry) which is an annual and crops outdoors. Its big sister, *P. ixocarpa*/*P. philadelphica* has tomato-sized, tomato-like fruits used like tomatoes. Why grow them? Well, they do not get blight!

The Cape gooseberry is closely related to the aubergine and the Chinese lantern, *P. alkengi*, known to the ancients, which does have an edible fruit and even steals the common name for its red, papery, lantern-like calyx. The true Cape gooseberry has a translucent white calyx. The generic name comes from the bladder, *physa* in Greek, which surrounds the sweet berry, and the Cape name for *P. peruviana* from their being much grown at the Cape of Good Hope, though they originate in South America.

Cape gooseberries need to be under cover in winter but can go outside in summer. It is best as a short-lived perennial, as fruits are then formed earlier in the year and ripen sweeter. These can be left on the plant, or allowed to drop off, yet remain clean and ripe for weeks – the fruit inside its personal paper bag remains unsullied by the dirt and mud on which it rests. If necessary the plant can be cut back hard in winter, to tidy it up or to keep it within its allotted space. It can be grown from seed planted in spring, or rooted from cuttings or layered at any time of year. Cape gooseberries do get some common greenhouse problems but still crop heavily. **BF**

Phytolacca americana

POKEWEED, RED INK PLANT

Type: hardy, herbaceous perennial
Soil & situation: fertile, moist soil/full sun or light shade
North American hardiness zone: 5–9
Height: 3m (10ft)
Spread: 1m (3ft)
Grow for: lovely flowers from mid-summer, followed by spectacular, 'corn-on-the-cob-like' berries

Phytolacca americana

My first plant arrived in the rockery about ten years ago as the result of a passing bird. Within weeks it was too large for the available space and was transferred to the herbaceous border. I have never been without a pokeweed since, rating it as good as most of its neighbours and better than some.

The erect, reddish stems carry large, lance-shaped, mid-green leaves which become tinged with purple in autumn. From mid-summer to mid-autumn the tiny pink or white flowers form 20–30cm (8–12in) long racemes, followed by a dense cylindrical mass of maroon-black berries.

Warning: the berries are toxic. Close up the plant exudes an unpleasant smell, but if planted at the back of the border this won't be obvious. Apparently native American Indians used to use the juice of the berry to write and draw. As it is deadly poisonous I hope they didn't lick their paint brush.

Pokeweed has thick, fleshy roots and dislikes being transplanted. Propagation is by seed sown in a propagator in early spring. Pot up the seedlings and keep containerized until planting out after all risk of frost is over. **JC**

Picea pungens 'Koster'

KOSTER'S BLUE SPRUCE

Type: hardy, evergreen conifer
Soil & situation: deep, moist, well-drained, neutral to acid soil/full sun
North American hardiness zone: 3–7
Height: 10m (33ft)
Spread: 5m (16ft)
Grow for: attractive blue-green, needle-like leaves; graceful habit with a conical shape; AGM

This is one of the best of the blue spruces suitable for the average-sized garden. The trouble is, it needs to be loved. Not pampered, but if it is totally ignored you will end up with a miserable, baldy, misshapen conifer.

It has an open, loose habit, allowing a view of the trunk. New growths open from tight, yellow-brown buds. Its sharply pointed new leaves are glaucous blue-green, but as they age they settle down to an attractive blue-green.

A young plant may produce two leading shoots. It is essential one of these is removed to prevent the shape of the tree being spoilt. Prune out the weakest shoot 1cm (½in) up from the joint, leaving the strongest stem to grow and form a

Picea pungens 'Koster'

leader. The side branches often grow at different rates. In order to form a conical shape it may be necessary to trim back long shoots in spring. *Picea pungens* 'Hoopsii' is slower growing with beautiful blue-white foliage.

Propagation is by grafting in winter. Red spider mite does serious damage to the foliage, turning it yellow and eventually brown. It never recovers, leaving the centre of the tree spoilt and dead looking. It attacks from late spring through to early autumn. Spraying with a recommended insecticide every three to four weeks in summer is the only control. **JC**

Pieris formosa var. *forrestii* 'Wakehurst'

Type: hardy, evergreen shrub
Soil & situation: moist, well-drained, humus-rich soil/full sun or light shade
North American hardiness zone: 7–9
Height: 5m (16ft)
Spread: 4m (13ft)
Grow for: an extremely handsome evergreen shrub with trusses of white flowers and vivid red leaves in spring; AGM

Even as a young plant this pieris earns its keep with masses of spring flowers and colourful young leaves. A mature plant can be tree-like, forming a mound of red and white in spring. The 10cm (4in) long, glossy, dark evergreen leaves are a brilliant red when young, gradually becoming bronze and finally green. Beautiful, 15cm (6in) long, pendent, terminal panicles of urn-shaped, white flowers appear at the same time as the red leaves.

An annual mulch of composted bark, leafmould or old compost will help retain moisture close to the surface where most of the fibrous roots remain. Mature plants may be successfully transplanted providing a large ball of soil contains the roots. After transplanting, water on a regular basis to prevent the roots drying out.

Avoid exposing the plant to cold, drying winds especially in late winter and early spring. There is no regular pruning needed, but if the shrub becomes too large or there are misshapen branches it can be cut in late spring. Try not to cause gaps in the outer covering of pieris as frost can penetrate and kill new growth.

Propagate using semi-ripe cuttings in late summer in a moist, peaty compost. Pinch out the growing tip of the rooted cutting to make it branch from the base of the plant. **JC**

Pieris formosa var. *forrestii* 'Wakehurst'

Pinus sylvestris 'Gold Coin'

Pinus sylvestris 'Gold Coin'
GOLDEN SCOTS PINE

Type: hardy, evergreen conifer
Soil & situation: well-drained soil/full sun
North American hardiness zone: 3–7
Height & spread: 5m (16ft)
Grow for: deep golden-yellow leaves in winter

There are those who think and say that the Scots pine is dull and drab. Don't listen to them, but if you have doubts then grow one of the yellow-leafed varieties. None of them make big trees, although labelling them dwarf is a bit risky.

Pinus sylvestris 'Gold Coin' starts off with good intentions to remain small, but in a fertile soil and a sheltered site it soon starts to put on 10–15cm (4–6in) of growth each year, in height and spread. In spring the needles are yellow-green, becoming grey green in summer and in early winter they turn to a deep golden-yellow. The twisted leaves are in pairs. Seen at 100m (330ft) in a snow-carpeted garden with a leaden sky it seems to light up the surrounding area. Plant in a soil where there is a decent root run. They are prone to blowing out of the ground where the top soil is shallow overlying chalk. Pruning may be necessary to keep the tree in shape. Occasionally it will throw out a strong sideshoot which quickly grows beyond the rest of the branches. Cut it back immediately to prevent it spoiling the branches close to it – it may cause needle drop due to congestion and a lack of light. Where two leaders appear on the same plant the weaker one should be removed in spring. Propagation is by grafting in winter. **JC**

Piptanthus nepalensis (syn. *P. laburnifolius*)
EVERGREEN LABURNUM

Type: hardy, semi-evergreen shrub
Soil & situation: fertile, well-drained soil/sun or partial shade/shelter from cold winds
North American hardiness zone: 9–10
Height: 2.5m (8ft)
Spread: 2m (6½ft)
Grow for: cheerful, bright yellow flowers; easy to grow and maintain

By no means rare, this evergreen laburnum is seldom seen in gardens. It is a good-value plant with its three palmate, lance-shaped, dark bluish-green leaflets, green-white on the underside. Pea-like, bright yellow, terminal racemes of flowers appear in late spring and early summer, followed by bright green seedpods up to 20cm (8in) long, which hang well into winter before turning brown and curling open to disperse the seeds.

In frost-prone areas it will enjoy a sheltered situation. Grown and trained against a warm, sunny red brick wall it will quickly fill its allocated space, adding colour and interest. It is a trouble-free plant with no pests or diseases to worry about. Pruning consists of removing any crossing branches which clutter up the centre, making the plant look untidy.

Once established it dislikes being transplanted. Tease out any congested roots before planting. It germinates easily from sweet pea-like seed without the need for stratification and will be happy in an alkaline soil. Softwood cuttings taken with a heel in summer root within a few weeks. **JC**

Piptanthus nepalensis

Pisum sativum 'Rondo'

Pisum sativum 'Rondo'
PEA

Type: half-hardy, annual climbing crop
Soil & situation: most moist soils/full sun to light shade
North American hardiness zone: annual
Height: 1m (3ft)
Spread: 15cm (6in)
Grow for: the sweetest full-size peas

I have long grown green peas as they are a gourmet crop; the petit pois type are especially good but they are fiddly to pick and pod, as the pods and peas are minute. 'Rondo' is a normal-size pea plant with a long pod with up to a dozen full-size and very sweet peas. Its pods hang in pairs, which makes picking easy, and they also pod easily. In taste and appearance it's similar to a famous pea I used to grow called 'Onward', though 'Rondo' is by far the sweeter.

Green peas are relatively modern. The Romans ate peas but these were usually as dried ones used in soups and stews; indeed peas have been dated at sites of about 8,000BC! The green pea as we know it arrived in 17th century Europe and began a craze; in 1696 peas were being taken in a manner seeming like addiction! The pea in question is a wrinkled seeded type which is not very hardy and will not over-winter, and is known as a marrowfat pea.

Peas need a moist soil preferably in full sun; they'll just grow in shade but not be sweet. They like a bit of lime in the soil but do not need feeding as they're legumes. Do pick these clean as they will grow on and give a few more pods if none are left to fully ripen. Sow in rows, from mid-spring until mid-summer, under bird protection; do not pre-soak seed but thoroughly wet the drill if the soil is dry. Water heavily when you see the flowers. Pods may get a maggot in the peas but early crops usually miss this. **BF**

Plectranthus argentatus
Plant of the Week (see page 225)

Polianthes tuberosa

Type: tender, tuberous perennial
Soil & situation: well-drained compost/full sun/under cover
North American hardiness zone: 8–10
Height: 60cm (24in)
Spread: 15cm (6in)
Grow for: the most powerfully fragrant flower spike of white waxy blooms; AGM

This is not an easy plant, as it takes a little care to coax the tubers into growth without rotting them and it is difficult to propagate. But goodness what a flower: a tall spike of waxy creamy-white flowers with the most powerful fragrance emanating from them in waves. I find the perfume addictive, almost carnal; it fills my tropical house and some friends find it decadent in its call to indulgence. In the open garden it is still wonderful, but not as imposing. This is a genus originating from Mexico with just one species. The name is the Greek for whitish flower. It has been a much-loved flower ever since Shelley described it as the 'sweet tuberose, the sweetest flower for scent that blows'.

Polianthes tuberosa

Tuberoses can be planted outdoors in sunny spots for the summer, but must be dried off and brought in for winter. They are very prone to cold and rotting off if damp in winter, but need copious moisture to get going in spring when they must be in the warm. They need a free-draining, gritty, leafmould-rich compost in big pots. They can go out for the summer but then the perfume is wasted and, anyway, they're better off in the conservatory, though some may find them overpowering. It is difficult to get hold of the seed and the small offsets rarely ripen well and take ages to reach flowering size, so go on, buy one – it's worth it. They are not pest prone but do suffer the odd attack. **BF**

Polygonatum multiflorum 'Striatum'
SOLOMON'S SEAL

Type: hardy, perennial rhizome
Soil & situation: fertile, humus-rich, well-drained soil/heavy or light shade
North American hardiness zone: 4–8
Height: 90cm (36in)
Spread: 45cm (18in)
Grow for: ideal for a shady position; arching stems; clusters of green-tipped, white flowers

A wonderfully, cheerful perennial for a woodland glade. The shoots push through the soil like the start of a crop of asparagus. They unfurl and continue to grow, sending out leaves. Once they decide to arch, the stems come into flower followed by fruit. Plant it close to the edge of a path where it can overhang and show off.

The lance-shaped, 5–10cm (2–4in) long, bright green leaves are striped and margined creamy-white and are arranged alternately along the stem. In late spring, clusters of two to six tubular, pendent, green-tipped, white flowers dangle from the leaf axils, followed by jet black spherical berries lined along the lower side of the arched stem.

Polygonatum multiflorum 'Striatum'

The common Solomon's seal, *Polygonatum* x *hybridum*, grows to 1.5m (5ft) in height with 20cm- (8in-) long, mid-green leaves and small, creamy-white flowers tipped green. The tubular flowers are waisted in the middle and are followed by blue-black berries.

Propagation is by ripe seed sown in autumn and over-wintered in a cold frame. Clumps can be divided in late spring. Lift the whole plant carefully to avoid damaging the emerging shoots. Tease out the rhizomes and pot up in a soil-based compost with added leafmould. Don't allow the rhizome to dry out. Greyish-white sawfly larvae have black heads and are a serious pest of Solomon's seal. They are capable of stripping the leaves, leaving bare stalks, but thankfully the plant will usually recover. The best control is to pick off the caterpillar-like pests. **JC**

Poncirus trifoliata

JAPANESE BITTER ORANGE

Type: hardy, deciduous shrub
Soil & situation: any well-drained soil/sun
North American hardiness zone: 5–9
Height & spread: 2m (6½ft)
Grow for: amazing green framework with enormous thorns; 5cm (2in) wide, white scented flowers and edible fruits

I first came across this plant in an old garden in winter; there was this peculiar shrubby mass of enormous thorns. I returned in spring to see the large orange-blossom flowers and smell their sweet scent; later the leaves came out but it failed to fruit. Sadly, so have both of mine which I have planted since; no matter, they are still fascinating plants. Apparently the American marines use this as a perimeter planting as it is said to keep out intruders up to the size of a jeep. Believe me, if you want a weird front hedge that makes a statement this is the one for you.

Poncirus comes from China and Japan where it is grown for the fruits, which make a delicious conserve. It is often used for rootstocks for other citrus and occasionally suckers can be detached. The generic name comes from the French for a citron-like plant.

It does well on most soils, even chalk, and is hardy and tough enough to be used for hedges. Only prune or clip immediately after flowering. It can be grown from seed, or by layering in spring; I have rooted cuttings. It has no common problems. **BF**

Poncirus trifoliata

Primula florindae

TIBETAN COWSLIP, GIANT COWSLIP

Type: hardy perennial
Soil & situation: shade, or sun where conditions remain moist/moist, deep, humus-rich soil
North American hardiness zone: 3–8
Height: to 1.2m (4ft)
Spread: 90cm (36in)
Grow for: long-lasting umbels of eye-catching, soft yellow flowers; AGM

This is a foolproof, robust and charming plant. It is ideal for naturalizing as it is a prolific self-seeder and spreads itself freely with amazing vigour where conditions are suitably moist. Just be careful that it does not swamp more fragile neighbours. It has bold, ovate, almost heart-shaped leaves which are shiny and can be up to 20cm (8in) long. However, if the moisture levels dry up these quickly become shrivelled and pathetic looking so, in dryer soils (and they will survive in normal garden soil), do make sure they get some shade. The large drooping clusters of funnel-shaped flowers are borne on stout stems in summer, and last for some time. Another great asset is the scent, which is bold and fruity. There are several other spring- and early summer-flowering primulas suitable for naturalizing in similar situations. *Primula japonica* 'Miller's Crimson' is smaller (60cm/24in), with strong crimson flowers. A good plant, too, and it can look effective mixed with *P. florindae.*

This is one of those welcome plants that, once you have planted it, you just let it do its own thing, particularly in a wild or naturalized part of the garden. Perhaps it may become over-dominant, which would entail removing clumps of self-sown seedlings, preferably when they are small and easy to deal with. If you want to propagate it, the simplest way is to get fresh seed from a friend and scatter it by hand. Alternatively transplant the seedlings as small as possible. **BG**

Primula florindae

Eucryphia x *intermedia* 'Rostrevor'

Type: hardy, evergreen tree
Soil & situation: moist, well-drained, acid soil/full sun or light shade
North American hardiness zone: 8–10
Height: 10m (33ft)
Spread: 6m (20ft)
Grow for: spectacular show of fragrant white flowers in summer and autumn. In August it is at its mid-season best, at least in my part of the world! AGM.

Rostrevor is a small village on the shores of Carlingford Lough in Co. Down, Northern Ireland. Squeezed between the sea and the Mourne Mountains it has a better than average climate for plant growth. Moist and mild is a wonderful combination for this tree. A mature tree has a broadly columnar habit and in full flower it is a spectacular sight.

The glossy, dark green leaves are pale green and glaucous on the underside with both simple and pinnate leaves carried on the same plant. In late summer and early autumn the pendulous, shallow, cup shaped, single flowers cover the tree, bending the slender stems. They are fragrant, ivory-white and up to 5cm (2in) across.

It deserves shelter from cold winds, which scorch the foliage and brown the flower buds before they open. Ideally positioned, the root area should be in shade with the head of the tree in full sun. A deep mulch of bark will help keep the root area cool.

Pruning is seldom necessary apart from removing any branches that spoil the overall shape. Propagation is by fresh seed sown in late autumn and over-wintered in a cold frame. Root semi-ripe cuttings in a gritty compost in summer, and grow on under glass until the spring. **JC**

Matt adds:
Trust my mate Cushnie to display his national bias yet again by picking a plant that comes from Co. Down! There's not even a whisper that there might be a choice, like the magnificent *Eucryphia* x *nymansensis* 'Nymansay' (below), which is taller and smothered with even larger flowers. 'Nymansay' came from Nymans garden in Sussex when seeds were sown in the hope of producing a hardier form; John's favourite was a spontaneous hybrid found in a garden. No wonder he approves; none of the work, but all the glory!

Primula vulgaris

Primula vulgaris
PRIMROSE

Type: hardy, herbaceous perennial
Soil & situation: most moist soils/light sun to heavy shade
North American hardiness zone: 4–7
Height & spread: 20cm (8in)
Grow for: large attractive leaves; primrose-yellow fragrant flowers in spring; AGM

Quintessential flowers of spring and early summer, to quote John Clare (1793–1864): 'Aye, flowers! The very name of flowers,/That bloom in wood and glen,/Brings Spring to me in Winter's hours,/And childhood's dreams again./The Primrose on the Woodlands lee/Was more than gold and lands to me.'

Primroses are part of my childhood, little harbingers of better weather to come, flowering from Christmas in sheltered hollows protected by the skeletons of deciduous trees from the screaming winds of a Norfolk winter. I still warm to them, indeed as I write this on a cold, bleak day with a wind howling gusts of snow there is a clump I can see from my window, such plucky little heroes – it's strange that yellow should be the colour of cowards when primroses are so valiant.

Part of our myth, folklore and once eaten in salads, the primrose is one of over 500 species of the northern hemisphere generally originating in hills, valleys and open deciduous woodlands. The primrose name comes from the medieval Latin, *prima rosa*, for first flower of spring, though it was not applied solely to this bloom initially; it was the early English botanist Parkinson who divided *Primula vulgaris*, the primrose, from *P. veris*, the cowslip. Primroses live on the sides of ditches, on the lower part of banks and at the base of damp walls. Cowslips prefer it out in the open, even in the middle of a meadow.

P. vulgaris prefers a loamy, leafmould-enriched, heavy soil with plentiful moisture, though not waterlogged. The clumps self-seed, so in moist dappled shade they may live forever. They can be grown from seed, which is considerably better when fresh, so they are best sown in summer; their roots can be divided in winter. Vine weevil is now a serious pest; kill it with the commercially available parasitic nematode watered on to wet soil. **BF**

Prostanthera cuneata
ALPINE MINT BUSH

Type: hardy (in all but the coldest areas), evergreen shrub
Soil & situation: moist, fertile, well-drained soil/full sun
North American hardiness zone: 9–10
Height: 60cm (24in)
Spread: 90cm (36in)
Grow for: mint-scented foliage; white flowers; AGM

When crushed, its foliage smells more like mint than mint does, with none of the bad habits of the herb (*Mentha*). When visitors smell it for the first time it quickly becomes a talking point.

Prostranthera cuneata forms a bushy, compact shrub. The small, rounded, glossy, mid-green leaves have rolled margins and are strongly aromatic when handled. The tube-shaped, white flowers have yellow and purple markings on the inside and form 20cm- (8in-) long racemes in spring and early summer.

It makes an interesting, informal, low, aromatic, evergreen hedge which should be clipped immediately after flowering. Hard pruning of older plants may kill the plant. It is easily propagated by softwood cuttings in a gritty compost under polythene in summer and it germinates readily from spring-sown seed. It is short lived when planted in a heavy, wet, clay soil and does not favour exposed sites and biting, cold winds. **JC**

Prostanthera cuneata

Prunus 'Amanogawa'

Prunus 'Amanogawa'

FLOWERING CHERRY

Type: hardy, deciduous tree
Soil & situation: moist, fertile, well-drained soil/full sun
North American hardiness zone: 6–8
Height: 7m (23ft)
Spread: 3m (10ft)
Grow for: pretty spring blossom; lovely foliage colours in spring and autumn; AGm

I have a 30-year-old-plant at the front of my house and every year it is in flower on 23 April, my elder son's birthday. The coloured ballons tied to the branches tend to take away from the display of flower. It forms a small columnar tree with stiff, upright branches. The 12.5cm (5in) long leaves open bronzy-yellow and turn mid-green during summer. In autumn they change again to deep red, orange and yellow. In spring clusters of soft pink, fragrant, semi-double flowers cover the tree. The branches are stiff, which means they hardly sway in the wind, allowing the blossom to remain for a longer period than other cherry trees.

It will branch naturally in the second or third year. Where two branches fork leaving a narrow 'v'-shaped angle, remove one shoot to eliminate the risk of the branches splitting later in life. If any pruning is required it should be carried out in summer when the spores of silver leaf disease are dormant.

If you want to be one up on the neighbours and you have the time and money plant two *Prunus* 'Amanogawa' 2m (6½ft) apart to form an arch over a path or entrance. Bend and tie the branches over wire hoops. It will look a treat at any time of the year and on my son's birthday it will be spectacular! **JC**

Prunus armeniaca

APRICOT

Type: hardy, deciduous tree
Soil & situation: well-drained soil, ideally a calcareous loam/warm sheltered position/against a sunny wall/cold greenhouse/cold winters and early springs
North American hardiness zone: 6–8
Height: up to 10m (33ft)
Spread: 3m (10ft)
Grow for: delicious fruit in large quantities a few years after planting; well-trained fan looking superb against a wall

When I was 20, I planted my first apricot fan and two or three years later was eating the most delicious fruit. The tree looked beautiful too against a south-facing, mellow-red brick wall next to the front door. I wondered why everybody did not grow them in the West Midlands. Now, in the East Midlands, I also have a thriving, productive tree. But as you move further north late frosts scupper the blossoms or small fruitlets. As the climate seems to be warming up, I think more gardeners should chance their arm and have a go, helped with the use of fleece and especially if they have a warm wall – a large fan will spread about 3.5m (11ft). They are self-fertile but tend to flower early, often in late winter, so if no insects are around hand pollination is recommended (though I have never had to do this).

Plant in late autumn, about 30cm (12in) away from the wall if you are training it that way. Tie the branches to horizontal wires, about 15cm (6in) apart, fixed to vine eyes. It is simplest to buy a ready-trained fan. These consist of a short, 30cm (12in) stem, usually with 8 to 12 branches radiating out from it. The even spacing of these 'spokes' helps to ensure the fruit get enough sun and warmth. When pruning a fan, the aim is to build up a series of fruiting spurs about 15cm (6in) apart along the length of the branches, so pinch back the sideshoots from the main branches in early summer, leaving 7.5cm (3in) of growth. Carry on tying in the extension to the main branch to keep the 'fan' shape. Beds at the base of walls tend to be dry places, so copious water in dry periods while the fruit is swelling will help. The yield from a fan can be 9kg (20lb), probably half that from a free-standing tree, except it might be all frosted from the latter. One sad warning – my apricot has recently suddenly died. They have a habit of doing this for no apparent reason, and apparently have done so since the time of Henry VIII, when they were introduced. I am not deterred and have ordered another. **BG**

Bob adds:
You have not had a good apricot until you have had one ripened on a warm wall in England. The flavour is exquisite – true, they are good anyway, but believe me the best comes off a wall. Fortunately they are fairly obliging as they fruit on shoots on old wood and can be easily trained on a wall on a permanent fan-shaped framework. This also allows easy protection of the blossom from the frosts which prevent apricots ever being much use as free-standing trees. This is a shame, as I have had over half a dozen sorts doing, or rather not doing, exactly that for nearly 20 years; meanwhile those on walls fruit every year. Apricots can also be grown in tubs and moved under cover for flowering and until fruiting is over, going outside in summer and winter, but the flavour is not as good as those on walls.

Prunus armeniaca 'Moorpark' is an old fruiting variety that has dubious credentials as a pure bred and is thought to be a hybrid with some plum blood, but it doesn't matter as it's very good anyway; it was found as a seedling from the older 'Nancy' ('Pèche de Nancy' from France) in 1760.

Ideally enrich and lime the soil in front of a warm, sunny wall and plant a fan-trained *P. a.* 'Moorpark' there. Prune by the book – buy one specially. When the tree is in flower, hang a blanket in front of it on frosty nights but remove it during the day. Keep the soil moist and thin heavy crops. You can grow them from seed but with variable results and little fruit – I know, it's a shame. Apricots suffer from few diseases but dieback is symptomatic and needs pruning out in spring; sometimes scale insects may attack but they can be cleaned off in winter.

Prunus armeniaca

Prunus avium
SWEET CHERRY, WILD CHERRY, GEAN

Type: hardy, perennial, deciduous bird food
Soil & situation: any soil/sun
North American hardiness zone: 4–8
Height & spread: 10m (30ft), twice that height in the wild or as seedlings
Grow for: very floriferous tree; red and yellow delicious fruits stolen by birds; AGM

I have grown many cherries as free-standing trees only to stand helpless as the birds steal the crop. I love birds and the fruits are a small price for their songs, but I want some too. So now I grow them on dwarfing rootstocks in a fruit cage. Sure, they eventually get too big, but until then I get crops, which I never have from the trees in the open. I've also tried sweet cherries in tubs and this works, keeping them inside while flowering and fruiting but back outdoors the rest of the time. However the quality was not as good as from the outdoor crop and not really worth the effort. Most of the best varieties need a pollinating partner but that's no problem – two sorts are better than one!

Cherries are the first tree fruits to ripen in the open garden and have been popular since antiquity. Ironically the name *avium* means of the birds! (The bird cherry is *Prunus padus* and of no culinary value.) Wild sweet cherries are known as geans or mazzards and are found in woods throughout the UK, but the cultivated forms are much improved. Our name cherry comes from the Greek *kerasos*, though this was probably for the sour morello sorts, *P. cerasus*.

Prunus avium

Ideally cherries want to be on a chalky, loamy soil and kept moist during the growing season; they are poor choices to have by fine lawns or drives as their roots run under the surface and bulge it. Most need a pollinator. They are by far the best on super-dwarfing stocks in a fruit cage. Do not prune unless diseased or damaged. The seedlings come up variable – I have a delicious mini cherry, all stone with a sweet pasty covering! The main problem is birds, black aphids merely tip-prune for you as the tip withers after an attack, saving you the effort of summer-pruning them. **BF**

Prunus cerasus

Prunus cerasus 'Morello'
MORELLO SOUR CHERRY

Type: hardy, perennial, deciduous bird food
Soil & situation: any soil/full sun or even shade
North American hardiness zone: 3–7
Height & spread: 5m (16ft)
Grow for: prolific white flowers in spring and gorgeous black fruits in summer; AGM

These are not sour; if they can be left on the bush long enough without the birds or damp getting them they are luscious and definitely sweet, well compared to a sloe – now that is sour! Sour cherries are not so watery sweet as sweet cherries and carry a much heavier, more aromatic flavour. This makes them perfect for cooked dishes where sweet cherries would be insipid. The bushes are also easier to keep small than sweet cherries, as they can be hard pruned more like blackcurrants; indeed this improves the crops.

Sour cherries were brought to us by the Romans, delighted us, and apparently were lost and re-introduced in the time of Henry VIII. They come from southwest Asia originally and, according to Pliny, the first was brought to Italy, thence to the town of Morello by Lucullus after his victory over Mithridates. They have been cross-bred with sweet cherries, and the epicure's choice, the Dukes, has such mixed blood.

Morellos like a chalky, rich, moist soil but can be grown in full sun or even in full shade; in the latter the fruits will be later and less sweet but there! As with sweet cherries a cage is essential. Morellos can and should be hard pruned, constantly replacing the old shoots by newer. I have had success growing this from seed but they are slow. The only problem is the birds. **BF**

Prunus domestica 'Victoria', 'Czar' and 'Marjorie's Seedling'
Plant of the Week (see page 311)

Prunus domestica x *P. insititia* 'Reine Claude de Bavay'
GREENGAGE

Type: hardy, deciduous tree
Soil & situation: most soils, provided they are not waterlogged or do not dry out too much/thin chalky soils will need heavy feeding/shelter from cold winds/no late frosts
North American hardiness zone: 5–8
Height & spread: to 6m (20ft), depending on rootstock
Grow for: one of the tastiest fruits around; attractive garden tree, especially when not grown on dwarfing rootstocks such as Pixy

Greengages are a type of plum and were introduced to Britain about 250 years ago by Sir William Gage. When ripe, they are far tastier than a normal plum with their sweet, almost melting, translucent flesh. Forget the ghastly stewed greengages at school, eat them fresh and there is little to rival them. Unfortunately, their yields are not high. 'Cambridge Gage' is an excellent variety, similar to the old one simply called 'Greengage', but gives heavier crops and is more reliable although it is not ideal for colder areas.

When we moved to our present house there was a decrepit 'plum' tree that never fruited. One autumn I emptied the contents of the chicken-house on its roots and the next year it was hung with beautiful green-gold, tasty fruit. They do, as I

Prunus domestica x *P. insititia*
'Reine Claude de Bavay'

found out, really appreciate rich, nitrogenous soils. When planting, avoid low-lying, frost-prone areas. Not all varieties are self-fertile so check this when you order. They can be shy to fruit because pollination can be disappointing – they tend to flower very early when few insects are about. Hand pollination can therefore be well worthwhile. Free-growing trees require little pruning: simply remove the dead wood and thin out the overcrowded growth. Do this in late spring or early summer. Although they can be trained as a fan against a wall, they need such hard, regular pruning that it is not that satisfactory. Brompton is a good rootstock, though quite vigorous up to 4m (13ft), and it resists suckering. With other rootstocks, the regular removal of suckers is necessary. **BG**

Bob adds:

The main reason for growing this plant is that you cannot find a good or ripe gage in the shops! I grow several: 'Golden Transparent Gage', 'Cambridge Gage' and 'Coe's Golden Drop'. They are all small green plums that turn yellow as they ripen and have a superb flavour, tart and yet almost honey-like. A flavour beyond the usual plum. They are candy when ripe off the tree, make delicious desserts and a divine conserve that is best with half ripe and half under-ripe gages. Gages need a warm sheltered spot and a rich, moist soil with plenty of lime. They are bushier than many plums but similarly resent pruning or training, and are best as orchard trees with a low, bushy head. *P. domestica* x *P. insititia* 'Reine Claude de Bavay' is self-fertile but does well with 'Victoria' as a pollinator. Seedlings come up but they are variable and slow to bear. These need to be budded onto a suitable rootstock, so the plant is best bought in. The major pest is wasp damage; other pests are minor by comparison, though silver leaf is a problem if they are pruned other than in summer.

Prunus insititia

DAMSON

Type: hardy, deciduous tree
Soil & situation: any soil/sun
North American hardiness zone: 5–8
Height & spread: 3m (10ft)
Grow for: it's just about impossible to find a good or ripe damson in the shops

I know I'm being greedy, but I've just got to have a damson as well as all the plums and gages. They are never eaten raw as dessert as they are bitter, but this goes with their spicy flavour to make a wonderful preserve that can be used as a jam on bread or as an accompaniment to cold meat or cheese. They make a powerful wine but best of all is damson liqueur made in the same way as sloe gin but with damsons, brown sugar and rum – the perfect winter tipple.

The damsons originally came from Damascus, were known to the Romans and have changed very little since. There used to be many sub-varieties but now only a few commonly survive such as the 'Shropshire' and the 'Merryweather'.

Damsons do not need the warm sheltered spot required by plums or gages, in fact they are so tough as to make a good windbreak. They do like a rich, moist soil with plenty of lime but will thrive on almost any. Damsons, like plums and gages, resent pruning or training and are likewise best as orchard trees with a low bushy head, but they are smaller, more compact and twiggier, which helps. They are self-fertile. Seedlings come up and are fairly true but slow to bear. Damsons are budded onto a suitable rootstock so they are best bought in. They seem to escape almost all the problems that affect plums and gages. **BF**

Prunus insititia

Prunus domestica

PLUMS – 'VICTORIA', 'CZAR' AND 'MARJORIE'S SEEDLING'

Type: hardy deciduous tree
Soil & situation: any soil/sun
North American hardiness zone: 5–8
Height: 6m (20ft)
Spread: 60–80cm (2–2½ft)
Grow for: you cannot find a good or ripe plum in the shops! September is a great month for plums after a lot of the soft fruits have disappeared and before the real glut of apples and pears.

I know I'm being greedy but I've just got to have all three, as they are so tasty and I love each of them. They are good for cooking or even as dessert, and make delicious jam when just under-ripe. 'Victoria' (left and top right) is the best but easy to find everywhere; it is a pointy plum with a red and yellow skin and sweet, yellow flesh. 'Czar' has the edge for preserves and has a reddish-purple skin and yellow flesh. 'Marjorie's Seedling' (below right) is valuable as it hangs late into autumn; it has a purple skin and tart, yellow flesh.

'Victoria' was allegedly a seedling found in Alderton, Sussex, southeast England, and introduced in about 1840. 'Czar' was raised by Thomas Rivers and first fruited in 1874, when the Czar of Russia was making a visit to the UK. 'Marjorie's Seedling' was first sold in Staffordshire, central England, of apparently local origin.

Plums need a warm, sheltered spot on a rich, moist soil with plenty of lime. They resent pruning or training and are best as orchard trees with a low bushy head. These three are all self-fertile. Seedlings come up and are variable and slow to bear fruit; they need to be budded on to a suitable rootstock so the plant is best bought in. The major pest is wasp damage; other pests are minor by comparison, though silver leaf disease is a problem if the trees are pruned other than in summer. **BF**

Prunus laurocerasus

Prunus laurocerasus
COMMON LAUREL, CHERRY LAUREL

Type: hardy, evergreen shrub
Soil & situation: any soil/sun or shade
North American hardiness zone: 6–8
Height & spread: 4m (13ft)
Grow for: prolific scented flowers in mid-spring; striking year-round foliage; a good screening plant; AGM

It is easy to overlook the good but commonplace. The common or cherry laurel is everywhere doing a fine job. As a hedge it makes a superb evergreen screen that is tough and hardy enough for most sites and will recover if cut back. In flower in spring it is a delight, with very strongly sweetly scented racemes of, admittedly, tiny, creamy-white blooms. It is even quite decorative in the autumn with its berries, which feed the birds and germinate about the garden. There are few shrubs so happy in shade or the drip from trees above them.

Introduced to the UK in 1576 this is not a native but an import from Asia Minor and Eastern Europe. It is such a useful plant with a dozen and a half different cultivars varying from the huge-leafed *Prunus laurocerasus* 'Magnoliifolia' to the sick-looking *P. l.* 'Variegata'. *P. l.* 'Otto Luyken' is reckoned to be the best form in leaf and flower but is a bit low growing for a hedge, for which *P. l.* 'Herbergii' is better, being erect and dense. It is probably rather obviously named as its leaves are like large *Laurus nobilis*, the classic laurel leaves, and it bears black, cherry-like fruits.

Laurels are long lived on well-drained soils but do not thrive on thin chalky soils. They will grow almost anywhere not completely dark or waterlogged. In mid-summer they ought to be trimmed with secateurs – if sheared the leaves on the cut branches brown and look miserable; mind you, I shear as they drop off soon enough. These can be grown from seed sown anytime, from layers they are easy and you can root autumn hardwood cuttings under a cloche. They suffer no usual problems but the leaves and fruits are poisonous, and they should not be burnt either. **BF**

Prunus persica 'Rochester'
PEACH

Type: hardy deciduous tree
Soil & situation: rich, moist soil/sun
North American hardiness zone: 5–8
Height & spread: 4m (13ft)
Grow for: gorgeous pink flowers in late winter and early spring; attractive willow-like foliage; enormous sweet fruits; AGM

Oh I adore peaches, I curse the spraying and wait in trepidation as they flower. (The frosts can be kept off with fleeces but so often these don't work and the fruitlets fall off.) Then the wait for weeks as the small fruits that do survive slowly swell, and the hope of sunshine for them to ripen. And then, in the good years, they are so large, so sweet, a bag full of syrup to melt in your mouth and down your front. In the bad years they are jam. I also grow them in big tubs which is the surest way of getting a crop, but they are just not so tasty as the outdoor ones.

Prunus persica 'Rochester'

Peaches probably came from China as there are many varieties there. They were known to Theophrastus in 322BC, and he gave them the origin of Persia, whence they get their specific botanical name. They are as often grown for their beautiful flowering forms as for their fruits, but for me it's the latter!

Peaches are short-lived trees. I fruit them as bush trees in warm sheltered spots but this is not easy in many parts of the UK. They are hard work to train on a wall or under cover as they need careful replenishment pruning. They can be grown in a large tub to be brought inside in early to mid-winter, when the warmth kicks the plant off and it flowers safe from the frosts and the leaves safe from the curl brought on by wet weather; once the fruits have ripened it can go back outside. Seeds do come true for garden purposes but should be of a local variety! Otherwise peaches are usually budded. They are even more short lived if they do not get treated for leaf curl. This is stopped by keeping the tree dry, or by spraying with Bordeaux or similar fungicide in late winter just as the buds start moving. **BF**

Prunus serrula
MAHOGANY-BARKED CHERRY

Type: hardy, round-headed, deciduous tree
Soil & situation: moist, well-drained, moderately fertile soil/full sun
North American hardiness zone: 6–8
Height & spread: 10m (33ft)
Grow for: shiny coppery-red bark in spring; AGM

This beautiful, ornamental Chinese cherry with its leaf colour, flower, fruit and amazing bark is good value for money. Imagine an old, highly polished, copper warming pan and you can just about conjure up the colour of mature bark on this tree. The outer bark is constantly peeling, or being pulled off by little fingers, to reveal the shiny, newly burnished, mahogany surface. The fawn circles of scars are lenticels contrasting with the bark.

The small, white flowers appear singly or in clusters of between two and four at the same time as the emerging 10cm- (4in-) long, tapered, dark green leaves. They are downy on the underside turning to a soft yellow in early autumn. The

Prunus serrula

small, red fruits are loved by blackbirds and disappear before they are fully coloured.

This cherry is not fussy as to soil type, succeeding on all but waterlogged ground. When purchasing the mahogany cherry make sure it has been bottom grafted. Top grafted trees won't have coloured bark on the main trunk. As with all cherries, prune in summer when the spores of silver leaf disease are dormant and can't enter the wound. **JC**

Prunus spinosa

BLACKTHORN, SLOE

Type: hardy, dense, deciduous, spiny, suckering shrub or small tree
Soil & situation: well-drained, moisture-retentive soil/sun or partial shade
North American hardiness zone: 5–9
Height & spread: 6m (20ft)
Grow for: white flowers in early or mid-spring; dark autumn fruits

In spring, the view from my office window is illuminated by blackthorn in bloom. Hedgerows forming billowing clouds of pure white flowers roll down the fields into the shallow valley below and punctuate roadsides dominated by hawthorn and holly. Its display matches any flowering cherry for impact and is a particularly welcome sight in dull early spring days. After the show, it merges with other foliage until autumn when it's decked with small dark fruits with an attractive blue 'bloom', which are harvested by keen-eyed collectors for winemaking or flavouring gin. It is widespread in UK hedgerows and occasionally as a woodland tree reaching 6m (20ft); the wood is extremely hard and was valued for making hay-rake teeth and Irish shillelaghs, once described as 'ancient Hibernian tranquillizers'! English country lore observes that a period of cold weather coincides with blackthorn flowering; it is known as a 'blackthorn winter'. They are an important food for several caterpillars, they attract bees and they are good for nesting birds.

Prunus spinosa 'Plena' has pretty, pure white, double flowers. The dark stems increase their impact. *P. s.* 'Purpurea' grows to 2m (6½ft) and has deep purple leaves and white flowers. It makes an excellent purple-leafed shrub.

Robust and tolerant of variable conditions it prefers sunshine or partial shade in well-drained, moisture-retentive soil, but tolerates clay to sandy soils and some chalk. Many *Prunus* species suffer from several pests and diseases, but sloes are so robust that they are usually unaffected. Propagate by seed, semi-ripe cuttings or suckers. Suckers are easiest – detach them in late winter. **MB**

Prunus spinosa

Prunus x *subhirtella* 'Autumnalis'

WINTER-FLOWERING CHERRY, AUTUMN CHERRY

Type: hardy, deciduous, spreading tree
Soil & situation: well-drained, moisture-retentive soil; thrives on chalk/sun
North American hardiness zone: 6–8
Height & spread: 8m (25ft)
Grow for: buds and blossom from mid-autumn to early spring; autumn colour; AGM

This is such a pretty tree. The slender, wand-like branches are clothed in green through spring and summer, but when the autumn leaves fall in a blaze of rich red and bronze, it takes on an altogether more subtle hue. Dainty flowers appear like clouds of swirling snowflakes among the branches, capturing the mood of the darker seasons. From mid-autumn to early spring the display ebbs and flows, depending on the weather; during mild periods, the tree can be filled with bloom and it's difficult to resist the temptation to cut a few sprigs to bring into the house. Plant it in the back garden and keep the secret to yourself or in the front against a dark background to highlight the pale flowers. Those passing by can share their beauty and it will bring a little warmth to cheer the winter gloom.

There are several forms of *P. subhirtella*, including 'Autumnalis Rosea' with deep pink flowers; 'Fukubana' with rose-madder flowers; and 'Pendula' which is a slender weeping tree flowering later, from early to mid-spring.

It likes a well-drained, moisture-retentive loam and thrives on chalk. It dislikes waterlogged conditions. Keep pruning to a minimum, remove dead, diseased, dying, crossing and rubbing branches or stems from mid-summer to early autumn to avoid silver leaf. Propagate by semi-ripe cuttings from mid-summer onwards. It comes under attack from aphids plus dieback and leaf spots, which are worse in wet seasons or if the plant is under stress. **MB**

Prunus x *subhirtella* 'Autumnalis'

Psidium cattleianum
STRAWBERRY GUAVA

Type: tender, evergreen shrub
Soil & situation: well-drained compost/sun/under cover in winter
North American hardiness zone: 10–11
Height & spread: 3m (10ft)
Grow for: scented if crushed, attractive, neat, evergreen leaves; cute, creamy, fragrant, paintbrush-like flowers; dark red strawberry-flavoured fruits

This is a little-known fruit, yet is so much better in many ways than the usual guava (see next entry). I grow both and although guava is more exotically perfumed, as a fruit I want to eat more of the strawberry guava. The dark red, almost purple-black skin hides a pure white flesh with annoying seeds but worth it for the strawberry-like taste. The jam is superb. It is surprising this is not more widely grown as it makes a decorative conservatory plant and is happy to go out on the patio in summer. A large tropical genus of 50 or so species with whitish, fragrant flowers and sometimes edible fruits.

The strawberry guava is almost hardy, indeed I have only killed three or four out of eight so far finding out. It likes a well-drained compost and is quite thirsty. It tends to over-crop and needs thinning if you want bigger fruits. It can be cut back hard in late winter and will regrow. The seeds can be sown any time in the warmth and are easy to grow on under cover. It suffers from few problems. **BF**

Psidium cattleianum

Psidium guajava

Psidium guajava
GUAVA

Type: tender, deciduous shrub
Soil & situation: well-drained compost/sun/undercover in winter
North American hardiness zone: 10–11
Height & spread: 3m (10ft)
Grow for: large laurel-like leaves; cute, creamy, fragrant, paintbrush-like flowers; very big, incredibly scented, creamy coloured fruits

This little-known fruit is occasionally seen in supermarkets or on ethnic stalls, where it is dry and mealy. Grown under cover in the UK it is more exotically perfumed than any other fruit and the fragrance will fill a large lecture hall – I know, I've done it. The yellow or red pulp inside the creamy skin is full of annoying seeds and the stringy texture could be improved, but the flavour is delicious. The jam is also excellent. The rough bark also sheds totally every year, leaving beautiful new bark as growth sets in again.

It is surprising the guava is not more widely grown as it makes a very decorative conservatory plant and is happy to go out on the patio in summer. It is quick and easy from seed, which is in every fruit at the supermarket. There are two main sorts of guava: the pear-shaped, which I prefer, and the apple-shaped, which has a greener skin and redder flesh but is otherwise similar.

Guava is almost hardy. It likes a well-drained compost and is unbelievably thirsty – in fact I reckon it's the thirstiest plant I grow. It tends to need thinning if you want bigger fruits. It can be cut back hard in late winter and will regrow. The seeds can be sown any time in the warmth and are easy to grow on under cover. It suffers from few problems other than mealy bugs, which can be controlled with sponging. **BF**

Ptelea trifoliata
HOP TREE, STINKING ASH, WATER ASH

Type: hardy, low, spreading, deciduous tree or large shrub
Soil & situation: fertile, well-drained, moisture-retentive soil/sun or partial shade
North American hardiness zone: 5–9
Height: 8m (25ft)
Spread: 4m (13ft)
Grow for: fragrance, foliage and unusual fruits

It's a signature of all members of the plant family Rutaceae that they have a strong odour from the essential oils found throughout the plant; rue, *Citrus*, *Choisya*, x *Citrofortunella* and *Ptelia* are all in this group. Look at a trilobed leaf against the light and you can see that it's dotted with oil glands that emit a fragrance, particularly if they are crushed or it's a hot sunny day. I say fragrance, you say odour; I say sweet, you say stink; it's one of those smells that people tend to feel strongly about! I like it, but then you should smell my aftershave!

Ptelea trifoliata

Clusters of small, yellowish, fragrant flowers appearing in early summer are followed by bitter-tasting, pale green, disc-shaped, winged fruits with a seed in the middle, which hang on the branches long after leaf fall and have been used as a substitute for hops. The unusual shape reminds me of something from outer space like the planet Saturn or the sherbet spaceships I used to eat as a child! They are excellent trees for shrub borders or as specimens in the garden with their spreading 'crown' and attractive foliage. *Ptelea trifoliata* 'Aurea' has soft yellow leaves which make a fine contrast to purple or dark green shrubs.

It prefers fertile, well-drained, moisture-retentive soil in full sun or partial shade, but tolerates most, including waterlogged soils. Prune in spring if necessary. Sow seeds in autumn or spring; take greenwood cuttings in early summer. **MB**

Pyracantha atalantioides

Pulmonaria 'Sissinghurst White'

Type: semi-evergreen perennial
Soil & situation: deep, rich moisture-retentive soils/shady position/will tolerate full sun
North American hardiness zone: 6–8
Height: 30cm (12in)
Spread: 45cm (18in)
Grow for: ground-cover plant with attractive spotted foliage; pure white spring flowers; AGM

I love the harmony of green and white in woodland or shady situations. It is always such a fresh and stunning combination. With this plant, you have just that – throughout the year there are its heavily spotted green and white leaves, and in addition, in spring you have its enchanting white flowers. Admittedly, only small rosettes of leaves are retained throughout the winter, but they are still a bonus. Thick clumps of new, hairy leaves come on the scene, just after the funnel-shaped white flowers have started to appear, in early spring.

Pulmonaria 'Sissinghurst White'

There are many other good lungworts; another favourite of mine is *Pulmonaria rubra*. It is also semi-evergreen, as is *P. saccharata*. *P. rubra* has lime-green new leaves that appear just after the salmon-red flowers make their appearance. They are unspotted but large, and look superb with the flowers in spring. This plant seems more tolerant of dry conditions than many other pulmonarias

When the flowers are going over it is worth shearing the entire plant to the ground, then handsome new foliage returns which will be more resistant to powdery mildew and look fresh for the rest of the summer. Plants respond well to dividing and replanting every three years or so after flowering. It is easily propagated by division or root cuttings in winter. **BG**

Pyracantha atalantioides
FIRETHORN

Type: hardy, evergreen conifer
Soil & situation: fertile, well-drained soil/full sun or partial shade
North American hardiness zone: 6–9
Height: 6m (20ft)
Spread: 3m (10ft)
Grow for: a mass of flowers in spring; clusters of berries in the autumn; makes a good hedge

As a free-standing plant this species would almost qualify as a tree. It forms a large, dense shrub plastered with flowers and then with fruit. Trained on a wall it quickly fills its allocated space.

The 7.5cm (3in) long, lance-shaped leaves are glossy and deep green. The panicles of white flowers appear in spring in sufficient numbers to cover the plant. They are followed in autumn by large clusters of bright orange-red berries. The berries will last well into the spring and may be still evident when the new flowers appear. If the old fruit trusses are still hanging, remove them to encourage new growth. In my experience the birds aren't particularly fond of these berries, but your feathered friends may have different tastes. *Pyracantha atalantioides* 'Aurea' is similar but has bright golden-yellow fruit.

P. atalantioides makes a great, dense, evergreen hedge – spiny enough to deter trespassers. Clip hedges in mid-summer. Trim shrubs for shape in winter and prune trained wall plants in spring, removing unwanted shoots before the flowers appear. After flowering, shorten the sideshoots to two to three buds from the older branches. Propagateby seed sown in autumn and stratified in a cold frame. Protect the top of the container to deter vermin. Semi-ripe cuttings root easily in summer in a heated propagator. Pot the rooted plants before they grow large. They dislike transplanting, so plant in their permanent place when small. Pyracanthas are prone to scab, which turns the fruit brown. Fireblight is a killer disease and this species is liable to come under attack. **JC**

Pyrus communis 'Doyenne du Comice'
PEAR

Type: hardy, deciduous tree
Soil & situation: rich, moist soil/sun
North American hardiness zone: 5–9
Height: 2m (6½ft)
Spread: 4m (13ft) wide espalier
Grow for: prolific white flowers in spring; large luscious juicy pears – better than you ever dreamt; AGM

I have chosen several apples, several plums, several grapes, but one pear. But what a pear: it is undoubtedly the supreme pear. There is none better and few even approach the wonderful 'Doyenne du Comice'. Pears from the shops are but street harlots to this courtesan of emperors, unforgettable for its flavour, perfume and the melting texture as the succulent flesh dissolves in your mouth to a lingering sweetness. Damn and they're all eaten until next autumn! You may have had a good pear from a shop and it will have been a 'Comice'. But I'll warrant you've never tasted home grown. They can get huge and really ripe.

Pyrus communis 'Doyenne du Comice'

So let them ripen late into the autumn keeping birds away with nets; wait until the first ripe ones fall, then gather them gently and keep them in a warm, humid place. Watch them carefully, as they yellow up and perfume, take them into the kitchen and don't delay eating them, as by the following day they will have gone over.

Pears are natives of Europe and were well known to the ancients; Pliny lists over 40 varieties! However for centuries the most popular way of enjoying pears was cooking them. It was not until the 17th century that improvement really started to happen and the modern luscious dessert pear was born. French and Belgian gardeners developed most of those we love today. 'Doyenne du Comice' was bred in 1849 in Angers, France.

Pears are long lived and have fibrous rootballs, which means you can take them with you as they can be moved even late in life. They require a warm spot with a moist soil. They do best as espalier-trained trees on a wall, with a summer and winter pruning. Pears need a pollinator – I grow a *P. c.* 'Beurre Hardy', but a 'Glou Morceau' or 'Docteur Jules Guyot' would do instead and they are all good. Pears are too variable, too vigorous, too big and too long before fruiting to try to grow them from seed, so why have I grown one? And it's fruited, a bit like a *P. c.* 'Conference'. Pears need working on dwarf stock so buy one ready worked. They are rarely troubled by pests and diseases, suffering far less than apples. **BF**

Pyrus salicifolia 'Pendula'
WEEPING WILLOW-LEAVED PEAR

Type: hardy, deciduous tree
Soil & situation: well-drained soil/sun
North American hardiness zone: 5–9
Height: 5m (16ft)
Spread: 4m (13ft)
Grow for: silvery foliage and attractive flowers in mid-spring; AGM

This is one of my favourite trees for the small garden, perhaps it is because the foliage always reminds me of After Eight mints. There is no other tree with foliage that has a soft sheen of minty green, apart from *Pyrus salicifolia*, the more upright species. The flowers too are very pretty, in clusters of creamy-white, with prominent dark anthers and, although somewhat camouflaged among the emerging foliage, they are a wonderful, uplifting sight. They are followed by tiny, rounded pears which seem somewhat incongruous on an ornamental plant. A few weeks after emerging, the leaves undergo a subtle transformation, losing the silvery covering from their upper surface. They are still the perfect foil for pastel-flowered climbers, particularly clematis like the deep carmine 'Ville de Lyon' that fades to mauve, the blue tones of 'Perle d'Azur' or the rich deep blue of 'Lasurstern'. The purple-leaved vine, *Vitis vinifera* 'Purpurea' (see page 319), also looks wonderful growing through this weeping pear. Athough I have often seen it planted in borders, it makes a fine specimen tree, with its curtain of leaves falling to the ground without the impediment of surrounding shrubs.

Pyrus salicifolia 'Pendula'

It needs an open, sunny positon and thrives in most soils except very dry or waterlogged ones. It is very robust, tolerating atmospheric pollution, drought and excessive moisture. Prune carefully to retain the weeping habit, thinning the 'crown' in winter to prevent it from becoming too dense and untidy. Propagate by grafting or budding in late winter. **MB**

Quercus ilex

EVERGREEN OAK, HOLM OAK, HOLLY-LEAVED OAK

Type: large, frost-hardy, evergreen tree
Soil & situation: a wide range of free-draining soils/useful for coastal or windy areas/dislikes extremely cold, inland areas
North American hardiness zone: 7–9
Height: up to 27m (90ft) but frequently less
Spread: to 20m (66ft)
Grow for: one of the most magnificent evergreen trees that grows in the UK; AGM

This is a highly useful, structural, evergreen plant that I have used in many different ways in many different gardens, including my own. The glossy, dark green leaves are pale green-grey beneath, some holly-like and some hardly toothed at all, depending on the clone, the growing conditions and the age. At its simplest, and if you have the space, it is a wonderful specimen tree with a lovely rounded head of branches which eventually become slightly hanging as it matures. Do not be too concerned about the height: it tolerates any amount of clipping, pruning and shaping. In smaller gardens they can be pruned to form useful mop-head trees like majestic giant bay trees, or as I have them, shaped into 4m (13ft) high sculptural pyramids. They will form stout architectural hedges, pleached screens (hedges on stilts) or may be clipped to form vertical 'walls' to blot out eyesores.

Quercus rubra

Quercus ilex

They are not so slow growing: plant them small, keep them weed- and grass free for a good metre (3ft plus) radius around their base, water them in dry summer periods, and you will be amazed at the rapid new growth in response. Perhaps use some proprietary shelter guard in the first few years till the roots get down and they have acclimatized to the wind. I think this system would get them to establish in colder inland areas too. The best time to clip them is mid- to late summer, after the first flush of growth. **BG**

Quercus rubra

RED OAK

Type: hardy, deciduous tree
Soil & situation: deep, fertile, well-drained, acid soil/full sun or partial shade
North American hardiness zone: 5–9
Height: 25m (80ft)
Spread: 18m (60ft)
Grow for: spectacular autumn leaf colour; AGM

There are so many good, reliable species of *Quercus* but with the red oak you have the bonus of outstanding autumn colour. It can vary from year to year, sometimes a lazy yellow-orange yet the following season a brilliant red.

It is a fast-growing tree with a spreading head. The 20cm (8in) long, dark green leaves have deeply cut lobes. In early autumn they turn to buttery-yellow, orange, red and pale brown. Small quantities of hemispherical acorns ripen in late autumn. The variety *Q. rubra* 'Aurea' is slower growing with bright golden-yellow leaves in spring which gradually revert to green in summer.

Pruning may be necessary in its early years to ensure a good spread of branches. In winter remove crossing stems and those creating a narrow angle. Young, well-grown plants may make up to 1.5m (5ft) of growth in a season. Propagation is by seed sown as soon as it is ripe in a cold frame. Plant up the seedlings during their first year. Alternatively the seed may be sown outside in a sheltered seedbed covered with fine wire mesh to prevent damage from mice and squirrels. **JC**

Vitis vinifera 'Purpurea'

Type: hardy, deciduous vine
Soil & situation: well-drained, marginally alkaline soil/sun or part shade
North American hardiness zone: 6–9
Height & spread: 7m (23ft)
Grow for: luscious foliage of purple leaves, at their richest at this time of year; liberally hung with ornamental black grapes in autumn; AGM

The leaves of this vine start off as a very pale purple-white and downy, then as they increase in size the purple colour intensifies until they are a good claret-purple before they fall. This slow but ever-changing colour enhances its appearance. Some purple-leaved plants have a heavy, heavy, look – very monotone and dark. This is has a dynamic look with subtle and unusual combinations of warm, pale lilac-greys, reds and purples all mingling together. The small purple-black grapes complete the picture in autumn. However, do not be tempted to indulge! They are no culinary treat – a feast for the eyes only. This plant is not a vigorous grower and may not reach anything like 7m (23ft), added to which it often seems to be unusually slow at getting going. In order to help it on its way expeditiously, cosset it with a warm wall. Better autumn colour is produced on poorer soils.

This is a versatile vine, suitable for pergolas, trellis, training through large shrubs or trees and, of course, for walls. If the allocated space is restricted, it can be pruned back to a permanent framework in mid-winter as for *V. coignetiae* (see page 393), or else you can leave it pretty much to its own devices, just cutting away any weak or dying growth in mid-winter. In mid-summer it may be necessary to cut back the odd long shoot that is straying too far. **BG**

Reseda odorata

Reseda odorata
MIGNONETTE

Type: nearly hardy annual
Soil & situation: any soil/sun
North American hardiness zone: annual
Height & spread: up to 30cm (12in)
Grow for: one of the sweetest pot or border plants

I love this old-fashioned, out-of-fashion plant. Sure it is about as unimpressive and as scruffy a thing as you could grow, with odd brownish-yellow flowers, but the perfume is something else – just too nice with no sickly overtones. Delightful. And you can be very cunning with it: if you grow a good specimen in a pot and keep deflowering it, meanwhile training the main stem to a stick, it will grow and become a shrubby little tree and the next year will be an amazing mass of fragrance that will literally fill the greenhouse or conservatory.

The botanical name comes from the Latin *resedo*, meaning to heal, as it was once used for bruises. It was first introduced to the UK in 1752 from France but it came from North Africa and was called Mignonette d'Egypte, 'little darling of Egypt', because Napoleon sent seed to Josephine from his Egyptian campaign. It is the only one of five dozen species from the Mediterranean region to have fragrance, but it more than makes up for the rest of them.

Sow any time from spring to late summer, in clean soil *in situ* in a warm, moist, sunny border. Thin the plants to about 20cm (8in) apart and they will flower from mid-summer until autumn. Sow in pots in autumn and over-winter under cover and they will flower in spring.

It suffers from no problems whatsoever, but do avoid the more highly bred cultivars with showy flowers and less scent. **BF**

Rhamnus alaternus 'Argenteovariegata'
VARIEGATED ITALIAN BUCKTHORN

Type: frost-hardy, evergreen shrub
Soil & situation: just about any soil/sun or part shade
North American hardiness zone: 7–9
Height: 5m (16ft)
Spread: 4m (13ft)
Grow for: a fairly fast-growing evergreen shrub; variegated foliage. AGM

This was one of the first variegated plants to be grown for commercial production, and this particular form has been recognized since the 17th century – strange to think Charles I might have come across it, as it does not look like an historical plant. As variegated plants go, it is difficult to improve on.

The leaves are fairly small, about 3cm (1in) long and narrow. They are a polished grey-green colour with irregular creamy-white margins. It is not a brash variegated plant, but quite subtle, though lively, not dissimilar to a hunkier version of *Euonymus fortunei* 'Silver Queen'. Its speed of growth and year-round appearance make it a valuable addition to a range of planting schemes.

Rhamnus frangula is the native alder buckthorn. It may form a small tree but more often is used as a shrub in natural, thicket-type plantings. It is not evergreen but when in berry is a beauty. The berries start red then change to black and when the plant displays both colours it is a fine sight. Apparently its wood makes the finest charcoal for gunpowder.

This plant does not move well and will form quite a substantial shrub if you let it, so try to get it in the right place first time. The only pruning required is the removal of unhealthy or overcrowded wood, to keep it within bounds. This can be carried out in late winter to early spring. **BG**

Rhamnus alaternus 'Argenteovariegata'

Rheum palmatum 'Bowles' Crimson'
CHINESE RHUBARB

Type: hardy, rhizomatous perennial
Soil & situation: moist, deep, humus-rich soil/sun or light shade
North American hardiness zone: 5–9
Height: 2.5m (8ft)
Spread: 1.8m (6ft)
Grow for: unbelievably huge leaves; striking flower spike; eye-catching form

I love big, leafy plants, especially those that have the decency to die down in winter, reappearing in spring with new, unfurling, banner-like leaves. A mature rheum plant forms a massive, thick, fleshy rootstock supporting many large 1m (3ft) long, palmate leaves. Coarsely toothed, with between three and nine lobes, they are dark green on the upper surface. The crimson underside of each leaf is covered in soft hairs. In early summer the plant sends up an enormous 1.8m (6ft) high, leafless flower spike made up of hundreds of small, star-shaped, deep crimson flowers.

This is a great perennial for growing close to or beside water. It loves the moisture and will repay your kindness with a memorable display of leaf and flower spike reflected in the water. It is tolerant of light shade and is a welcome addition to the woodland garden where it will light up a dappled glade.

An annual mulch of old, rotted farmyard manure in spring will encourage strong growth. Lift and divide the roots in spring, making sure there are fat buds on each root. Watch out for slug and snail damage to young, emerging leaves in spring. **JC**

Rheum palmatum 'Bowles' Crimson'

Rheum rhaponticum 'Victoria'

RHUBARB

Type: hardy, rhizomatous perennial
Soil & situation: any soil/sun or shade
North American hardiness zone: 3–7
Height: 1.2m (4ft)
Spread: 2.4m (7½ft)
Grow for: enormous leaves; red stalks; foamy pink and white flowerhead

Rheum rhaponticum 'Victoria'

Rhubarb is the first fruit of spring and is so sharp to the taste, yet such a pleasure when made into a crumble served with custard. The plant is often treated badly, yet still gives plenty of stalks. However, for the best stalks, treat it well. Start with a virus-free clone as it makes all the difference. And do remember to pull the stalks with a twist rather than cutting them so that they bleed less. The leaves make handy mulch mats.

Originally grown for its medicinal qualities, rhubarb as we know it is very much an English crop, not much admired elsewhere. It may have been unpopular until cheaper sugar enabled its use as a 'fruit', but its value as a gentle laxative was much appreciated in the 17th and 18th centuries. However the earliness of the crop gives it an advantage over other fruits, coming as it does months before most fresh fare. It grows wild in Siberia and did not reach Europe until 1608 when it was hoped to be a substitute for the dried *Rheum officinalis* imported from China. There are several other edible species more used for medicinal purposes. The names come from the Greek name *rheon*, for the drug, and *rha barbaron* for foreign rhubarb.

Ideally grow rhubarb in a sunny spot in a well-drained, well-composted soil where it will do well and be long lived. Give it a mulch of well-rotted muck every winter. Put a bottomless bin over it in late winter full of loose straw to force the shoots up. Remove the flowerhead spike before seed is set. Some rhubarbs such as 'Glaskin's Perpetual' can be grown from seed but usually the crowns and roots are split in late winter or early spring and sections with a good bud planted. Rhubarb suffers virtually no problems. **BF**

Rheum ribes

RHUBARB

Type: hardy, rhizomatous perennial
Soil & situation: moderately heavy soil/sun or partial shade
North American hardiness zone: 6–8
Height & spread: 1.5m (5ft)
Grow for: unusual leaves and flowers in late spring and early summer

This unusual plant is found in western Asia from Turkey to Iran in dry gorges and among rocks; it's a typically robust, rugged rhubarb with a tough woody rhizome. The leaves are large, grey green, warty and ribbed up to 40cm (16in) across; they look like sandpaper poppadoms that dry and rustle in the wind. The flowers appearing through the centre of the leaves are green and red, while the stems to 30cm (12in) are eaten raw or cooked by the people of Turkey and Iraq.

Leonhardt Rauwolf left Austria in 1573 to search for some of the plants mentioned by classical writers; while examining the cedars of Lebanon he found *Rheum ribes*, the 'true *Ribes* of the Arabians' and made a specimen for his herbarium. He noted its presence in a market and saw several piles of the roots of this rhubarb, 'hairy, almost two feet long, waiting to be shipped in large quantities to the Turks, especially the Sultan'; it was one of many species that were valued as a cathartic. One herbarium specimen at Oxford University Botanic Garden was noted as having been brought back from Lebanon and had been growing in Eltham, south London, since 1724.

It prefers a deep, fertile, moderate to heavy, humus-rich, moisture-retentive, well-drained soil in sun or partial shade. It thrives in clay and can be long lived. Propagate in autumn or spring from seed sown in a cold frame. Divide in autumn or early spring with at least one growth bud in each division. Pot up smaller divisions and grow on before planting out; larger divisions can be planted out immediately. It is prone to crown rot and can be damaged by slugs. **MB**

Rhododendron 'Christmas Cheer'

Type: hardy, evergreen shrub
Soil & situation: moist, well-drained, acid soil/light shade
North American hardiness zone: 6–8
Height & spread: 2m (6½ft)
Grow for: in mid-winter the mass of pale pink flowers brings welcome colour

While this variety of rhododendron doesn't live up to its name, it produces its flowers very early in the New Year. In a sheltered situation it is a mass of colour in mid-winter and will continue to flower until mid-spring. Even when the early blooms are damaged by frost there is a succession of others to follow. When pot-grown in a cool greenhouse or conservatory it will flower in time to provide 'Christmas cheer'. It forms a dense, compact plant with medium-sized foliage and trusses of 5cm (2in) long, funnel-shaped, pale pink flowers. When planting dig in as much leafmould and well-rotted farmyard manure as possible. Lighten heavy soil by adding coarse grit. All rhododendrons have their roots close to the surface of the ground so they dislike deep planting. An annual mulch of leafmould in spring helps to keep the surface roots moist.

Dead-heading immediately after flowering, before the seedpods appear, will allow flower buds to form for the following year. Remove the whole truss by snapping it off above the top pair of leaves. Take care not to damage the new shoots which will be produced on either side of the old flower stem. **JC**

Rhododendron 'Christmas Cheer'

Rhododendron 'Praecox'

Rhododendron 'Praecox'

Type: hardy, evergreen shrub
Soil & situation: moist, acid soil/sun or dappled shade
North American hardiness zone: 6–8
Height & spread: 1.3m (4½ft)
Grow for: colourful early flowers in late winter and early spring; AGM

I was walking in a garden when I saw it! There in a distant border, a glow of rose-purple pierced the gloom of a winter's day. I rushed over and grabbed the label and the writing confirmed what my eyes disbelieved, there, etched in white lettering were the words *Rhododendron* 'Praecox'. A rhododendron flowering in winter? I couldn't believe it but it was true! The young plant was smothered in clusters of wide, funnel-shaped flowers in twos and threes at the tips of the shoots. They were a much deeper colour in bud and looked superb highlighted by the deep green leaves. What an uplifting sight on a cold grey day! From the same parents comes 'Emasculum', the pale lilac-purple flowers alone or in pairs up to 3cm (1in) wide. Have a look inside the flower, it is sterile and has no, or aborted stamens. Taller and wider – to 1.8m (6ft)each way – it flowers two to three weeks later than *R.* 'Praecox'.

It needs moist, free-draining, acid soil in sunshine or dappled shade and must be protected from frost which damages the flowers. Improve the soil with peat substitute, leafmould or well-rotted organic matter. Mulch annually in spring; dead-head (if practical) after flowering using the forefinger and thumb rather than secateurs; keep moist in drought using rainwater. The flowers are vulnerable to frost so plant under the protection of trees or on a slope where cold air drains away. Propagate by cuttings in late summer from young shoots. **MB**

Rhodotypos scandens

Type: hardy, deciduous shrub
Soil & situation: any soil/sun or shade
North American hardiness zone: 5–8
Height: 2m (6½ft)
Spread: 1m (3ft)
Grow for: delicate white flowers from late spring to late summer

Some plants are regarded as rather coarse yet are amply redeemed by their positive features; *Rubus* x *tridel* 'Benenden' is one and *Rhodotypos scandens* is another. *R. scandens* is a close relative of bachelor's buttons (*Kerria japonica* 'Pleniflora') and was once known as *Kerria japonica alba*. In dull, green leaf it is barely given a second glance but in flower, oh, in flower, its character is simply transformed by the cloud of white 'butterflies' that cover it. Admire their shape and simplicity, the elegant curve of the silky smooth petals; even the sharply toothed leaves become the perfect, textured foil.

Suddenly the peasant becomes prince and the whole plant rejoices in harmony in its moment of fleeting glory. Then as the flowers fade, it declines into anonymity again and all that remains of its moment of splendour are shiny black berries. Next time you see it dull, green and dowdy, don't complain about its lack of finesse, just recall those moments of incomparable, fleeting beauty.

It is one of those plants that cheerfully endures the worst conditions. It is very hardy, tolerates any soil, heavy shade and low temperatures; you will often find it hidden in the corner of a woodland garden. Please don't abuse its good nature: provide dappled shade in well-drained, moisture-retentive soil, if you can. Prune after flowering, removing flowering stems to a vigorous outward-growing shoot and taking off a quarter of the older stems to the base. Feed with a slow-release general fertilizer in spring until established. It is easily propagated by hardwood cuttings in late winter. **MB**

Rhodotypos scandens

Rhus typhina 'Dissecta'

Rhus typhina 'Dissecta'

STAG'S HORN SUMACH

Type: hardy, deciduous tree
Soil & situation: moist, well-drained soil/full sun
North American hardiness zone: 3–8
Height: 3m (10ft)
Spread: 3–4m (10–13ft)
Grow for: brilliant autumn leaf colour with deep red fruit; AGM

Those who claim it to be a common plant should remember that is because it is popular. So what if it suckers? There will be even more magnificent autumn leaf colour and spare plants for friends. Sometimes called *R. t.* 'Laciniata', it forms a large, open, multi-branched plant. The young, velvety-red shoots resemble a stag's horns.

The 60cm (24in) pinnate leaves are made up of deeply cut, dark green leaflets. In autumn they explode into a brilliant orange-red colour which in dry ground, deepens with age, to scarlet. The 20cm- (8in-) long, erect panicles of green-yellow female flowers appear in summer and are followed by dense clusters of small, round, dark crimson fruit. While it will tolerate light shade, a position in full sun will ensure better autumn leaf colour.

Pruning back to older wood in late spring will generate new growth. Old, neglected plants may be hard pruned close to the ground. Strong shoots will grow from the base and may be thinned to avoid overcrowding. Give rejuvenated plants a high-potash liquid fertilizer, such as tomato feed, in late summer to harden up the new growths before the winter frosts.

Remove suckers by digging down to remove all of the roots otherwise they will reappear. Propagation is by seed in autumn. Semi-ripe cuttings root well in summer. Root cuttings inserted in compost in winter root quickly. Removing rooted suckers is the quickest and simplest foolproof method. **JC**

Ribes divaricatum

WORCESTERBERRY

Type: hardy, deciduous shrub
Soil & situation: any soil/sun or shade
North American hardiness zone: 3–7
Height & spread: 1.5m (5ft) by too much
Grow for: good informal hedge for anti-social demarcation line

God gave us worcesterberries for where barbed wire won't grow. This mean brute of a plant is superficially like a gooseberry bush without the softer, gentler aspects. It has horrible curved spikes of thorns prolifically covering every woody surface. It is a lax shrub with arching branches layering and multiplying into a witches' nest of suckers wherever they touch. It makes a wonderful informal hedge to put across a burglar prone fence or unwanted entrance way. The small flowers are insignificant but valuable to insects and the red gooseberry fruits make a delicious conserve – if you can pick them, that is....

The worcesterberry was always believed to be a native UK species or a natural hybrid, but it is now thought to be an American species or hybrid. This is a tough, hardy plant that will grow almost anywhere, but does best in full sun with good air circulation. It will live too long and is too self-fertile. Prune in late winter if you can get to the branches. Seed gives variable, often very thorny results but autumn hardwood cuttings are easy and layers work at almost any time of year. Worcesterberries suffer from the sawfly caterpillar, but it is best ignored as there are far too many thorns to even attempt to get rid of it. Mildew is not a problem. If you fall into a bush you may ask to be shot rather than pulled out without complete anaesthesia. **BF**

Ribes divaricatum

Ribes x *gordonianum*

Type: hardy, deciduous shrub
Soil & situation: any soil/sun or shade
North American hardiness zone: 6–8
Height & spread: 1.5m (5ft)
Grow for: masses of fiery red and yellow blooms early in spring; good autumn colour

I like *Ribes sanguineum*, the well-known flowering redcurrant, which is a good reliable early bloomer and marvellous for the first beneficial insects. Unfortunately the whole plant does have an aroma of cat pee, which many find offensive. *R.* x *gordonianum* is a hybrid that is more sweet smelling without the feline overtones, which makes it much more useful near the patio or front door. It also has a laxer habit which does take more space but is not so stiffly formal as its parent, *R. sanguineum*; it is thought to get this from its other alleged parent *R. odoratum* (see page 328). However the main reason I grow this shrub is for the flowers; coming a little later than the others, they burst into a blaze of beauty, each drooping fat raceme made of blooms a rich coppery-red on the outside with a yellow burning colour from within – stunning.

Ribes is a family made up of about 60 members and widely represented in both flower and fruit gardens. The botanical name may come from the Arabic *ribus* for acid, as most of the edible berries are very acid. Gordon was a London nurseryman who died in 1791; this plant was noticed as a seedling and introduced in 1837.

A tough, hardy plant that will grow almost anywhere, it can be pruned hard and will usually recover. As it is a hybrid, seed is not available but autumn hardwood cuttings are easy, or layer it at almost any time of year. It suffers from hardly any problems. **BF**

Ribes x *gordonianum*

Ribes grossularia 'Langley Gage'

Ribes grossularia 'Langley Gage'
GOOSEBERRY

Type: hardy, deciduous shrub
Soil & situation: any soil/sun or shade
North American hardiness zone: 6–8
Height & spread: 1.2m (4ft)
Grow for: masses of incredibly sweet white berries

God gave us gooseberries for where grapes won't grow. This old adage is so true: I struggle with grapes but the goosegogs just do it all so reliably. I have tasted countless and grown more than a dozen sorts myself, and none have been like those hard green bullets sold in the shops. In fact most gooseberries are green bullets initially, when they can be used to make good jams and tart tarts; however, if they are left to ripen they make fantastic dessert fruits every bit as good as dessert grapes. Of all of them this is my favourite, for though the berries are small they are honey sweet when they turn ivory-white. When they are ripe the contents liquefy and I bite the end off, suck out the sweet pulp and discard the skin.

Gooseberries should be the national fruit of the UK as we grow them far more than any other country. They were first mentioned in our records as being supplied to King Edward I in 1276 but we surely gathered them from the wild before then. We used to have competitions, which are still carried on in some places, to grow the biggest berries. These caused a great surge in the fruit's development, especially in the northwest of the UK, but the improvements reached their peak when one variety, 'London', won for decades on end from 1829 until 1867.

This is a tough, hardy plant that will grow almost anywhere, but does best in full sun with good air circulation. Plant three different ones as, although self-fertile, it does better with others. It will die after 15 years. Prune in late winter leaving an open framework which makes it easy to reach the fruit; i.e. leave branches at least a hand's breadth apart or you'll swear. Seed gives very variable, usually extremely thorny, results but autumn hardwood cuttings are easy or propagate by layers at almost any time of year. Remove lower buds from cuttings to give a bare leg.

Gooseberries suffer from a sawfly caterpillar best watched for and eliminated when small – look for leaves in late spring that have many tiny holes and squidge the tiny caterpillars before they split up. Mildew occurs but open pruning, watering, mulches and good air ventilation control this. **BF**

Ribes laurifolium

Type: hardy, spreading, evergreen shrub
Soil & situation: moist soil/sun or partial shade
North American hardiness zone: 7–9
Height: 1.2m (4ft)
Spread: 1.5m (5ft)
Grow for: pale green flowers in late winter

My first introduction to this unusual plant was in a newly planted winter border, outside the ancient Ice House at Kew. My attention was drawn to a low-growing, loosely branched shrub with leathery leaves, reddish-coloured young stems and greenish-white flowers. The colour would have rendered them inconspicuous if they had appeared at any other time of the year, but what was extraordinary was that the curious pendent racemes were disproportionately large and looked as though they had been squeezed out of the thin branches like thick globs of glue.

Ribes laurifolium

I believe this plant is at its best when young. The coarse foliage gives it character. Male and female flowers are on different plants and you need both sexes to produce the black berries. Male plants have larger flowers with longer racemes. I've discovered that it is enhanced when planted with *Skimmia japonica* 'Rubella' or plum-purple hellebores. It's not beautiful, just fascinating and certainly not a typical 'flowering currant'.

Give it an open or partially shaded site, away from scorching sunshine and sheltered from cold winds to prevent leaf damage. It needs moisture-retentive, well-drained soil. It is slow to moderate in speed of growth and can take several years to become established. Pruning is not necessary apart from the removal of old, bare stems to encourage new shoots from the base. Propagate from semi-ripe or hardwood cuttings with a heel. **MB**

Ribes nidigrolaria

JOSTABERRY, JOSTA

Type: hardy, deciduous shrub
Soil & situation: any soil/sun or shade, even boggy shade
North American hardiness zone: 6–8
Height & spread: 2m (6½ft)
Grow for: masses of incredibly tasty large red/ black currants

This hybrid plant takes up a lot of room; it crops heavily, often giving over 4.5kg (10lb) of fruit per plant; it is immune to all the problems that can attack gooseberries or blackcurrants; it is self fertile, easy to propagate and totally thornless. If you don't know it, you are missing out on the easiest crop of all. The fruits are large, red to black in colour and, although they are much like gooseberries, they have a blackcurrant flavour and make great jams and tarts.

The jostaberry or josta is a hybrid between a gooseberry and a blackcurrant. It has a higher vitamin C content than gooseberries and is more vigorous than either parent. It was developed by the Dutch only recently and has not yet become widely known. The plants are like blackcurrants but even bigger and tougher, hardy shrubs that will grow almost anywhere, they do best in full sun and on a rich, moist soil. They need to be left to grow unpruned with plenty of space as they have a lax habit, but they can be trained with perseverance. Seed gives variable results, but autumn hardwood cuttings are easy and inadvertent layers set themselves all the time. Do not remove lower buds from cuttings and plant deep to get multiple shoots from below ground level. Jostas suffer no problems other than bird losses – though this can, admittedly, lead to a wipe-out! Although the leaves look as if they have all had a disease it is their normal state. **BF**

Ribes nigrum

BLACKCURRANT

Type: hardy, deciduous shrub
Soil & situation: any soil/sun or shade, even boggy shade
North American hardiness zone: 5–7
Height & spread: 1.5m (5ft)
Grow for: masses of incredibly tasty fruits and scented foliage

Just writing this has got me craving some; I love blackcurrant jam, and if you don't grow these currants you don't know how good it can be. I pick the very biggest, sweetest berries first, then I roughly pick the rest not worrying too much how many sprigs or bits of leaf go in with the currants. I juice this rough-picked crop and having sieved it, I add in the choicest berries and organic sugar to make my conserve. It is almost like black cherry jam in the depth of flavour, but of course different with that blackcurrant aroma. Blackcurrants are also wonderful if dropped into sugar and rum in a bottle and then left to stand for a few months; once strained off this is as delicious as the jam.

Although a European native and common enough in the wild to have been gathered in a time of famine, blackcurrants were never much admired. They were picked for medicinal use, particularly for sore throats and were probably effective as they have a high vitamin C content. With the advent – from about the 18th century onwards – of cheap, plentiful sugar from the West Indies to sweeten their acidity, suddenly blackcurrants became popular as a jam for which they are now grown as a commercial crop. There are many varieties with almost no difference between them other than size and season.

Blackcurrants are tough, hardy plants that grow almost anywhere, but do best in full sun on a rich, moist soil. Plant three different ones as although self-fertile it does better with others. They need to be hard pruned: remove one third of the whole plant each year, taking the oldest branches out right down to the ground.

Seed gives variable, small-fruited results but autumn hardwood cuttings are unbelievably easy and layers work at almost any time of year. Do not remove lower buds from cuttings and plant deep to get multiple shoots from below ground level.

Blackcurrants do get mildew though not often badly, aphids can be a problem on the tips but worst of all they get big bud disease. The big buds can be pulled off in winter but the pest inside carries a virus disease to which the plants inevitably succumb. Thus it will not be worth growing the same plants after ten years or so as they deteriorate and it is better to replace them with new ones. **BF**

Ribes nigrum

Nicotiana sylvestris

Type: half-hardy annual
Soil & situation: moist soil/dappled shade or sun
North American hardiness zone: annual
Height: 1.5m (5ft)
Spread: 60cm (24in)
Grow for: stately form and fragrant flowers from mid-summer to autumn. On those hot, still evenings of early autumn the scent is a particular treat. AGM.

If you only plant one annual, this should be it. A classic since its introduction in 1898, it is stately and stylish with the imposing presence and aura of a plant that feels it should carry a royal warrant. It has a lush rosette of mid-green, broad basal leaves and tall stout stems topped with curved, pure white, narrow, trumpet-shaped flowers 8cm (3½in) long. They are clustered in dense cascades that combine to create a wonderful display of floral fireworks.

Despite its height it rarely needs staking and is wonderful in bold ranks at the back of a border, against a dark background like a yew hedge that highlights its beauty. There should be a perfectly placed bench nearby, where you can sit with a gin and tonic, close your eyes, relax and luxuriate in the light and warmth of the setting sun and savour the flowers' evening fragrance. Bliss!

It needs a fertile, rich, moist, well-drained soil in full sun or partial shade. Dig in plenty of well-rotted organic matter before planting. Plant in a sheltered position to prevent the fragrance from being lost on the breeze, along the edge of a path or by a window or door. For further ideas, see above.

Sow indoors from late winter to mid-spring. Sow the seed over the compost surface and press in lightly with a board. Water from below, using tepid water. Harden off and plant out when any danger of frost is over. Protect from slugs. Aphids are a problem. You should also beware of tobacco mosaic virus and destroy affected plants immediately. **MB**

Ribes odoratum

Ribes odoratum
BUFFALO CURRANT

Type: very hardy, deciduous shrub
Soil & situation: any soil/sun or shade
North American hardiness zone: 5–8
Height & spread: 1.5m (5ft)
Grow for: delicate leaf; pretty, scented, yellow flowers; edible fruit

As I said before, I like *Ribes sanguineum*, which is a good reliable early bloomer but is not sweet to smell. *R. odoratum* is an alternative: flowering a little later, it has a more delicate leaf of a light green, and the yellow primrose-like flowers have a delicious clove scent. I first came across it when working in old kitchen gardens and, at first, did not know why it was there. The reason it appeared in odd places is because it was used as a rootstock for other *Ribes*, such as gooseberries, which died and then the buffalo currant would appear instead. The black berries that sometimes set are reckoned edible and much esteemed, but I've not found them very good; perhaps the selected varieties available in America produce better fruit.

R. odoratum comes from North America, whence its common name, and was introduced to the UK in 1812. There is allegedly another similar form *R. aureum*, also called buffalo currant, with more golden leaves and edible berries.

This is a tough, hardy plant that will grow almost anywhere. It can be pruned hard and will usually recover. Seed is available and should be sown in spring, autumn hardwood cuttings are easy, or propagate by layering at almost any time of year. It suffers from hardly any problems. **BF**

Ribes rubrum
REDCURRANT

Type: hardy, deciduous shrub
Soil & situation: any soil/sun or shade
North American hardiness zone: 6–8
Height & spread: 2m (6½ft)
Grow for: scarlet, edible bird food

This is glorious to look at when in full fruit with masses of the brightest red berries. These are very acid, though if you net the bush and keep the birds and wet off they will hang into autumn, becoming sweeter. They can be juiced and made into wine, and their tart flavour makes other juices such as strawberry more tasty, as well as adding good colour, and they do the same for jams. If you want cherry, raspberry or strawberry jelly or jam to set, add redcurrant juice, and it's magic. The fruits are also great garnishes.

Ribes rubrum is a common native plant of Europe but it was not cultivated until the 16th century. Even then it was taken medicinally or as an apéritif because of the acid fruit. The arrival of cheap sugar made it more widely usable, but it is still only a minor crop. All red varieties are very similar, but there are white ones as well and these are excellent for making a clear acid jelly for a mint sauce or for embalming scented petals in; I do this with night-scented stock petals and the jelly retains the perfume until the gloom of winter calls for it.

R. rubrum is a tough, hardy, self-fertile plant that will grow almost anywhere; it even thrives on a shady wall. It can be pruned hard and will always recover, indeed it is excellent to practise on as it is very forgiving. Seed can be sown in spring with similar results to commercial varieties, autumn hardwood cuttings are easy, or it can be layered at almost any time of year. It suffers from hardly any problems except birds. If you don't net or cage your redcurrants you'll never get a single currant. Be warned – these go as fast as cherries. **BF**

Ribes rubrum

Ribes sanguineum 'White Icicle'

Ribes sanguineum 'White Icicle'

Type: hardy, deciduous shrub
Soil & situation: an easy shrub to grow in any fairly decent soil; a moisture-retentive but free-draining loam is ideal/full sun or part shade
North American hardiness zone: 6–8
Height: up to 2.5m (8ft)
Spread: 2m (6½ft)
Grow for: attractive, rich, juicy, green leaves; conspicuous white flowers in spring; AGM

I am not a fan of *Ribes sanguineum* generally, as I think it is dull for much of the year and am not even keen on it when in flower. But 'White Icicle' does definitely earn its keep. It is easy to grow, tolerates dry soils and has lively foliage which is a bright, almost yellow, green. The leaves seem to glow in a rather dull, semi-shaded spot. The charming flowers are large and a good, bright white, added to which the racemes are usually generously proportioned too. In spring it really comes into its own, flowering for a good long period and livening up the spring scene in a non-brash fashion, unlike its commoner stablemates.

This plant is easy to look after. After flowering you can cut back the old, flowering shoots to a strong bud. Once the shrub becomes well established it is worth thinning out the old growth – remove about a fifth of the old shoots by cutting them right back down to ground level. It is an exceptionally easy plant to propagate from hardwood cuttings in winter, but this variety is protected by Plant Breeders' Rights, so you cannot sell them for commercial gain. **BG**

Ribes speciosum
FUCHSIA-FLOWERED CURRANT

Type: hardy, semi-evergreen, free-standing or wall shrub
Soil & situation: well-drained, moisture-retentive soil/sun/shelter
North American hardiness zone: 7–9
Height & spread: 2m (6½ft)
Grow for: attractive foliage and dainty flowers in mid- and late spring; AGM

I often wonder if Archibald Menzies, the great plant collector, was as excited as I was when I first saw *Ribes speciosum* – the frisson of excitement has reverberated until this day! He discovered it on his travels as naturalist with Captain George Vancouver when he circumnavigated the world from 1791 to 1795. It's among the most elegant plants you'll ever see; the slender arching shoots are covered with red, gland-tipped bristles when young and tufts of shiny, round, lobed leaves seem to hover, like a cloud formation, along the top of the stems. Below, rows of tiny, rich red, fuchsia-like flowers hang like dainty pendant earrings along the branches. They are simply gorgeous, particularly when viewed through a magnifying glass, as are the tiny, bristly fruits. It is elegant and refined, everything about it is classy, so it's a real surprise to discover, (and do whisper it quietly) that it's a posh relative of…the gooseberry!

In mild climates grow it as a shrub or informal hedge; elsewhere, fan train along wires against a sunny wall. It may still lose its leaves in cold winters but is one of the earliest to break into leaf in late winter. It needs moderately fertile, free-draining soil. Use young shoots growing from the base to replace older stems and keep the plant vigorous. Prune in late summer, tie in new growth and remove in-growing shoots or any growing in the wrong direction. It propagates easily by layering; less so from semi-ripe cuttings. **MB**

Ribes speciosum

Ricinus communis 'Carmencita'

Ricinus communis
CASTOR OIL PLANT

Type: best treated as a half hardy annual
Soil & situation: moist, free-draining soil/sun
North American hardiness zone: annual
Height: 1.8m (6ft)
Spread: 1m (3ft)
Grow for: bold foliage

The oil from the seed of this plant kept the Victorians going and does the same for cars; it is an additive in the engine oil Castrol (hence the name). Ricin, found in the seed coat, is highly toxic and six times more powerful than cyanide; it is a potential weapon for terrorists, yet is useful in medicine and used to target cancerous cells. Why am I recommending this potentially damaging plant? Because you will not be daft enough to eat it, will take sensible precautions when using the plant and storing its seed; most importantly, you'll appreciate its fine architectural foliage and upright growth. The female flowers appearing at the tips of the flower spikes have a bold red stigma. Remember, the whole plant is toxic.

Here are some of its varieties. 'Carmencita Pink' has red stems, dark green leaves and bright, deep pink seedpods; 'Carmencita' has red stems, dark brown leaves, and red flowers and seedpods; and 'Gibsonii' has dark, red-veined leaves. The foliage of 'Impala' is bronze-green and it has dark red flowers and scarlet fruit. 'Zanzibarensis' has large, green-veined leaves.

In cooler climates, grow as an annual in fertile, humus-rich, well-drained soil in full sun. Plants on poor soils tend to produce smaller leaves. Soak seed for 24 hours before sowing in late spring and pot on before the plants become pot bound to prevent premature flower production. Plant out when danger of frost is passed. In mid- or late spring, remove any shoots to maintain the shape; dead-head regularly unless seeds are required. Red spider mite can be a problem. **MB**

Romneya coulteri

Romneya coulteri
CALIFORNIAN TREE POPPY, MATILIJA POPPY

Type: frost-hardy subshrub, usually grown as a perennial
Soil & situation: free-draining loam/sunshine/in colder areas an ideal position is by a sunny wall/ will withstand temperatures down to –10°C (14°F)
North American hardiness zone: 7–8
Height: 1–2.5m (3–8ft)
Spread: indefinite
Grow for: beautiful, elegant, papery, white flowers with yolk-yellow centres over a long period from summer to early autumn; glaucous foliage is an attraction too; AGM

This plant established rapidly on my thin soil, and although grown as a free-standing plant, has survived several winters so far. In my experience it has been easy to get going, but many gardeners find it awkward. I think establishing it from good, well-rooted plants in good-sized containers, at least 1 litre if not 3 litres, is the key. Their down-side is undoubtedly that if they take to you, they can rather overdo things and end up taking you over. In large drifts of perennials they can do this fairly extensively in a desirable fashion. They can jostle amongst other similar beings and produce a successful, thriving mix. Their habit is such that they look tremendous in that informal setting too.

Plant these poppies into ground that has been well prepared: deep digging with the incorporation of humus seems to help. If you want to limit these plants to a specific area, either surround them by shrubby plants to hold them back or else spade round them in spring – they hate root disturbance so this does limit them. In the autumn or spring cut down the top growth (most of this will be cut back by frost anyway) and the new growth in spring will produce highly attractive foliage. It is recommended that they are propagated by root cuttings in late winter or, usually more successfully, by removing suckers which have developed a good root mass in spring, together with some rootball if possible. **BG**

Rosa banksiae 'Lutea'
YELLOW BANKSIAN ROSE

Type: hardy, evergreen, shrub rose
Soil & situation: moist, acid soil/sun or dappled shade/sheltered position
North American hardiness zone: 7–9
Height & spread: 8m (25ft)
Grow for: fragrant flowers in late spring to early summer; AGM

Introduced in 1824 from China via the Calcutta Botanic Garden this elegant rose is named for Lady Dorothea Banks, the wife of Sir Joseph Banks, one of my horticultural heroes, the first 'unoffficial' director of Kew. A stunning specimen climbed the walls of a Victorian museum at Kew, and every year the topmost stems would squeeze through the gap in a second- floor sash window and bloom well before the rest of the plant. The slender shoots produce few spines and delicate leaves of up to five leaflets. The tiny, double, soft buttery-yellow flowers barely 2cm (3/4in) across with a slight fragrance of violets, appear in small clusters, creating a cloud of soft yellow in late spring to early summer.

All the cultivars given below are also fragrant. 'Alba Plena' has slightly larger, double, white flowers. It was introduced to Kew from a garden in Canton, China in 1807. 'Lutescens' has single, yellow flowers. 'Normalis' has single, creamy-white flowers. Ernest 'Chinese' Wilson discovered *R. b.* 'Lutea' in central and western China; it is common in glens and ravines, forming tangled scrambling masses over low trees and scrub.
It requires a warm position against a sheltered, sunny wall on moist, free-draining soil. It dislikes shade and is damaged by cold winds, making it unsuitable for shady gardens. It needs training against wires or other supports. Thin out old wood after flowering, tie in new growths in mid-autumn, and cut back frost-damaged shoots in mid-spring. Propagate by hardwood cuttings in late autumn. **MB**

Rosa banksiae 'Lutea'

Rosa 'Buff Beauty'

Rosa 'Buff Beauty'
BUSH ROSE

Type: hardy, deciduous, shrub rose
Soil & situation: most soils/sun or shade
North American hardiness zone: 6–9
Height: 1.5m (5ft)
Spread: to 3m (10ft)
Grow for: prolific, scented, apricot-buff coloured flowers all summer covering glossy dark foliage; reliable; AGM

This is the rose for those who want trouble-free gardening. It is incredibly healthy and makes all the others look miffy beside it. The foliage is glossy and dark. The plant is so floriferous that it covers its own foliage completely with masses of blooms. And it is repeat flowering with a main show in summer and another in autumn. The only drawback is somewhat brittle stems that are hard to train.

This is one of the hybrid musk roses now reclassified as a cluster-flowered shrub rose. I prefer the old grouping as it sounds better. These were developed after the First World War from *R. moschata* and with their shiny dark foliage and fragrance are good choices with members such as *R.* 'Moonlight' and the vigorous *R.* 'La Mortola'. Roses prefer a rich, heavy, moist soil that stays cool but never gets waterlogged. They will grow in shade but are rarely very long lived anywhere. This one does best as a free-standing shrub and can be fairly hard pruned. Deadheading is important, as is pruning out diseased wood. This is a hybrid and cannot be grown from seed, but autumn hardwood cuttings are easy. It does not get either blackspot or mildew attacks very often. **BF**

Rosa canina

COMMON BRIER, DOG ROSE

Type: deciduous, shrub or scrambling rose
Soil & situation: most soils/sunshine or dappled shade
North American hardiness zone: 3–7
Height: 4m (13ft)
Spread: 1.8m (6ft)
Grow for: attractive flowers and autumn/winter fruits

It may be the most common wild rose in the UK and a familiar sight in hedgerows and banks, but it is still charming and worthy of inclusion in wildlife areas or infomal hedging. I have planted some among a 'fruiting' hedge containing British natives like elder, hazel, honeysuckle, viburnum and sloe. I'm hoping that the local wildlife gives me a chance to share its bounty: hazelnuts, sloes for gin and elderberries for wine. Dog rose will clamber through nature's supporting cast presenting cascades of pale to blush-pink, sweetly scented flowers in early and mid-summer from arching thorny stems. They are followed in autumn by orange-red hips which are rich in vitamin C. The varied form of the sepals gave rise to a Latin riddle translated thus: 'Five brothers in one house are we, all in one little family, two have beards and two have none and only half a beard has one.' What am I? A dog rose!

Rosa canina hybridizes with all the other native species. 'Abbotswood', a chance hybrid (possibly with *R. gallica*), has scented, double pink flowers. 'Andersonii' is a deep pink, larger-flowered form with fewer thorns and bright red hips. 'Hibernica' (*R. pimpinellifolia* x *R. canina*) is massed with rose-pink flowers and long lasting hips.

R. canina is tolerant of most soils and sites, but dislikes waterlogging and needs sunshine or dappled shade. Prune to keep under control; older stems can be cut hard back in spring if needed. Propagate by seed in spring or hardwood cuttings in late winter. **MB**

Rosa canina

Rosa 'Charles de Mills'

Rosa 'Charles de Mills'

Type: hardy, deciduous, shrub rose
Soil & situation: fertile, moist, well-drained, loamy soil/full sun or light shade
North American hardiness zone: 4–9
Height: 1.5m (5ft)
Spread: 1.2m (4ft)
Grow for: unforgettable flower colour and perfectly formed blooms; AGM

The flowers of this stunning rose are unusual in shape, colour and fragrance. It is long lived and well behaved – what more could you want? The origins of this Gallica rose are unknown.

It forms an upright, bushy shrub with arching stems, barely capable of holding the heavy heads of flowers. The mid-green leaves remain fresh and clean for most of the season. In mid-summer the pink buds open to 10cm- (4in-) wide, fully double flowers with wavy magenta petals with small pink and white blotches. The open flowers have a slightly flattened appearance and are quartered. The heady fragrance is a little spicy.

Pruning, in early spring, consists of getting rid of the old stems as close to the base as possible and removing crossing branches. Applying a high-potash liquid fertilizer or foliar feed in summer will strengthen the flowering stems. Feed with a rose fertilizer containing trace elements in spring. Propagation is by hardwood cuttings inserted in open ground in early winter. **JC**

Rosa 'Cooperi'

Rosa 'Cooperi'

COOPER'S BURMESE ROSE

Type: frost-hardy semi-evergreen, climbing rose
Soil & situation: moisture-retentive, free-draining soil/sun/shelter
North American hardiness zone: 5–9
Height & spread: 10m (33ft)
Grow for: beautiful, single, white flowers from late spring to early summer

This rose was introduced to the UK by Roland Cooper who was Superintendent of the Maymyo Botanic Garden in the Shan Hills of Burma from 1921 to 1927, and later became curator of the Royal Botanic Garden in Edinburgh. He sent seeds of Burmese plants to Lady Wheeler Cuffe in Ireland who, in October 1921, gave seeds of an unnamed rose to Glasnevin, Dublin's National Botanic Gardens, and some of these must have been sent to Kew where a plant flowered in the 1930s. Cooper could not remember from where they were gathered, though they were sent so soon after his arrival that they were probably collected from a plant in Maymyo known as *Rosa gigantea* and is regarded as a hybrid between this and *R.laevigata*. Whatever its origins, it's a beautiful white rose with large, 10cm (4in) across, scented flowers and pale brown stems and glossy foliage, which makes the perfect background for the flowers. It may flower from mid-summer, depending on the seasonal weather.

This definitely is a rose for a warm, sunny, sheltered wall in suitable microclimates and the southern counties of the UK as it is fairly tender. It needs moisture-retentive, free-draining soil. Prune in spring to keep within its allotted space and to remove winter-damaged stems. Propagate by sowing seed in spring or taking hardwood cuttings in late winter. **MB**

Rosa 'Dublin Bay'

Type: hardy, deciduous, climbing rose
Soil & situation: fertile, moist, well-drained, loamy soil/full sun
North American hardiness zone: 5–9
Height & spread: 2.5m (8ft)
Grow for: can't beat this rose for its wonderful flowers covering a wall or trellis; AGM

Of all the climbing roses this is my long time favourite. Introduced in 1976 it has stood the test of time and is still widely available in catalogues when other 'fantastic' varieties haven't lasted a decade.

Strong stems carry an abundance of glossy, dark green leaves. The rich, crimson, fragrant flowers are fully double and beautifully formed with each petal slightly down turned. The colour is consistent with no fading or blemishes on the outside petals. It is repeat flowering, carrying blooms from early summer through to autumn. Like most roses it is tolerant of a range of soil types, preferring a heavy clay or loamy soil to light, sandy ground or, at the other extreme, waterlogged conditions. Roses cannot be planted where there have previously been roses. A condition known as soil sickness will result in weak growth on plants which will never succeed.

Rosa 'Dublin Bay'

Pruning involves the removal of dead or old stems and crossing branches. This climber has a habit of growing as a bush instead of sending up strong shoots. When this occurs, hard prune the stems and train in the new growth. Arching the shoots over and tying them to wall wires or trellis will result in many more flowering sideshoots. Dead-head regularly, cutting two leaves below the old flower. Remove suckers as they appear, pulling them off where they join the stem or root. Cutting will encourage more suckers to grow from the stump. Apply a rose fertilizer containing trace elements in spring and surface mulch with composted bark or old, well-rotted farmyard manure to retain moisture. Propagate by hardwood cuttings inserted in open ground in early winter. **JC**

Rosa 'Etoile de Hollande'

Rosa 'Etoile de Hollande'

SCENTED ROSE

Type: frost-hardy, deciduous, shrub rose
Soil & situation: most soils/sun or shade
North American hardiness zone: 5–9
Height: 1.5m (5ft)
Spread: to 2m (6½ft)
Grow for: heavily fragrant, large, dark red flowers

This is a poor doer compared to some, but the colour of the summer flowers is magnificent and the fragrance heavy and intoxicating. I feel compelled to bury my face in a ripe bloom – the perfume is almost edible. I often tear a bloom to pieces and use it in salads and rice puddings.

The hybrid tea group, to which this belongs, is relatively recent and one of the largest with over

Rosa 'Ferdinand Pichard'

3,500 varieties! They were originally said to have the fragrance of tea, which is not a great compliment, and they are also criticized as being scentless. One survey found that indeed a quarter had no scent but nearly as many were highly scented, so you just have to choose carefully. This beauty was introduced in 1919.

Ideally roses prefer a rich, heavy, moist soil that stays cool but never gets waterlogged. It will grow in shade if it is open but is rarely very long lived anywhere. Dead-heading is important, as is pruning out diseased wood. It gives most flowers as a bedding rose. It is a hybrid and cannot be grown from seed, but autumn hardwood cuttings are easy. This rose suffers the usual problems and is to be honest a bit miffy, but the fragrance more than makes up for it. **BF**

Rosa 'Ferdinand Pichard'

Type: hardy, deciduous shrub rose
Soil & situation: good, moist but well-drained soil/full sun or part shade
North American hardiness zone: 5–9
Height: 1.5m (5ft)
Spread: 1.2m (4ft)
Grow for: the most beautiful, repeat-flowering striped rose: flowers have a pink background which is splashed and striped with crimson, the pink gradually fading to white while the crimson flashes intensify; AGM

This is my favourite rose. If you saw it on a chintz tablecloth you would assume the designer had had a flight of fancy then, when you discovered it was real, you would assume that it was a weedy, picky number that was awkward to grow and permanently covered with black spot, mildew and the like. Not so! What is more, it has a good bushy shape and the foliage is a fresh, light green. It repeat flowers, the only striped rose apart from the diminutive rose, 'Stars 'n' Stripes', to do so. The flowers produce a good, old rose fragrance which, as with all perfumes, lingers longer if it is sited in a sheltered spot.

Like all roses, it performs far better if grown in a good, fertile soil. On planting, generous quantities of well-rotted manure and compost are advisable on all but the best soils. A good mulching of well-rotted manure helps each winter, though the inevitable weeds that come along for the ride are a pain. I have switched to chicken manure and a mulch of organic matter, such as produce from my shredder, in a bid to rid my garden of weeds. We can live in hope!

Dead-heading helps produce further blooms and improves appearances. Planting amongst other plants, rather than in designated rose gardens, makes a huge difference in helping to reduce the incidence of many common rose pests and diseases. Prune as for *R.* 'Marie Pavie' (see page 335). **BG**

Rosa 'Golden Celebration'

Type: hardy, deciduous, shrub or climbing rose
Soil & situation: sun or light shade/ideally a humus-rich, well-draining but moist soil with a pH of around 6.5/grows satisfactorily in more acid or alkaline soils
North American hardiness zone: 4–9
Height & spread: 1.2m (4ft)
Grow for: rich golden-yellow flowers; repeat flowers throughout the summer, fantastic fragrance; a good 'full' shape – the sort you would not want for yourself but love in a rose; AGM

This rose is one of the most magnificent of the 'English roses' which have been bred by my uncle, David Austin. These shrub roses have many characteristics of the old roses, i.e. form, character and growth, but they have the repeat-flowering habit and the wider colour range of modern roses – a useful combination of characteristics – good-looking and hardworking. I think that this is one of his finest. Firstly, and for me most importantly as I am often working in gardens with less than perfect soil, it does well wherever you plant it. In addition it has healthy growth, with ample foliage, few thorns and a good rounded, but slightly arching, shape; the perfume is 'a combination of a sauterne wine and strawberry' – you want to drink it in

Rosa 'Golden Wings'

deeply when you pass by; and the colour is a rich golden-yellow. As with many of the 'English roses', if planted against a wall or fence it will climb and can easily make 2.5m (8ft), especially in a warm position. It will form an excellent standard rose too.

As with all roses, regular dead-heading keeps them looking their best and also hastens the repeat flowering. If you wish to restrict the size of the plant you can cut back about 30cm (12in) of the plant at any time during the growing season. In countries with warmer, longer summers than the UK this works particularly well.

The pruning of this rose is simple, and best done in late winter. Firstly you remove all weak, dead, dying or diseased growth, then you reduce all the growth back by one-third to two-thirds its length. In colder climates than the UK this can be carried out just as the spring growth is starting. **BG**

Rosa 'Golden Wings'

Type: hardy, deciduou, modern shrub rose
Soil & situation: as for *Rosa* 'Golden Celebration' (see previous entry)
North American hardiness zone: 4–9
Height & spread: 1.5m (5ft)
Grow for: large, almost single, sulphur-yellow flowers throughout the summer and into mid-autumn; longer in warmer climates than mine! AGM

These, simple, charming, scented roses are produced on a spreading bush with many prickly stems, and good, pale green leaves. The flowers, which fade as they age, are up to 13cm (5in) across with conspicuous brown stamens in the centre which stand out beautifully against the yellow. There are few good single-flowering roses, despite the fact that nature made them that way, and yet they are indispensable in the garden, particularly in more natural areas. This productive rose has something of the charms of a wild species and so is ideal for the wilder areas. It will also make an excellent medium-height hedge, forming a pretty, impenetrable barrier, either mixed with other hedging plants or on its own.

Plant and mulch as for *R.* 'Ferdinand Pichard' (see page 333). This rose's habit does tend to be fairly open, rigid and poker-like. When you prune it, bear this in mind and try to encourage a more branching, bushier form by reducing the more stick-like growth. Dead-head as needed. **BG**

Rosa 'Gruss an Aachen'

Rosa 'Gruss an Aachen'

Type: frost-hardy, deciduous, shrub rose
Soil & situation: as for *Rosa* 'Golden Celebration' (see page 333)
North American hardiness zone: 5–9
Height & spread: 1m (3ft)
Grow for: excellent, repeat-flowering, small shrub rose which will bloom from early summer to mid-autumn; large and lovely pale pink, fading to white flowers; good bushy foliage

These are the 'white' roses which are grown in the White Garden at Hidcote, chosen no doubt, even though they do not strictly conform in colour, for their magnificent flowering performance. The blooms start off a pearly pink and later fade to a creamy white. The individual flowers are up to 8cm (3½in) across and deeply cupped. The petals, having a silky texture, have bags of typical 'old rose' character. The plant itself is a robust grower with an erect, but bushy, habit and dark green foliage. It will grow well even in less than perfect rose soils.

Treat this rose as for *R.* 'Golden Celebration' (see page 333) **BG**

Rosa longicuspis

Type: half-hardy, vigorous, semi-evergreen, rambling rose
Soil & situation: moist, free-draining soil/sun/shelter
North American hardiness zone: 5–9
Height: 10m (33ft)
Spread: 5m (16ft)
Grow for: attractive young shoots, leaves, flowers from mid-summer and fruits

The one in my garden is the true *Rosa longicuspis*, not *R. mulliganii* which is often sold under that name. This species, collected by Frank Kingdon-Ward in the Naga Hills of northeast India is also found in east Nepal and west China. It is very dense and vigorous; in spring you can almost see the stems growing, threatening to engulf anything in their path. I'm sure that somewhere in the middle of mine, Sleeping Beauty awaits her handsome prince! The stems, their hooked thorns (be warned, *longicuspis* means 'long pointed'!) and young leaves are an extraordinary reddish-brown when they first emerge with bronze-tinted young shoots, and look as though they have been dipped in lacquer. The leaves are made up of small, attractive, grey-green leaflets. The open clusters of as many as 15 single flowers, up to 5cm (2in) across, are cream in bud, opening to white, with yellow stamens and a banana fragrance. They are followed by orange-red fruits which decorate the plant through the winter.

It is slightly tender but flourishes in my Hertfordshire garden in a sheltered, east-facing location, on moisture-retentive, free-draining soil. Grown against a warmer, sunnier wall it would reach even greater heights. It enjoys clambering up trees or over buildings. Prune if necessary in spring to keep tidy. Beware of the thorns: use eye protection, wear gauntlets and a long-sleeved jacket! If possible, put the trimmings straight into a shredder before they can cause any harm. Propagate by seed in spring and hardwood cuttings in late winter. **MB**

Rosa longicuspis

Rosa 'Madame Alfred Carrière'

Rosa 'Madame Alfred Carrière'

Type: hardy, deciduous, climbing rose
Soil & situation: humus-rich, well-draining but moist soil/pH of around 6.5/grows best on a sunny wall, but performs well in any aspect
North American hardiness zone:
Height: 5m (16ft)
Spread: 3m (10ft)
Grow for: the best, reliable, repeat-flowering, hardy, white climber; AGM

This rose was bred in France by Schwartz and introduced in 1879. Sometimes the old ones are the best, and even today, most gardeners would agree that there is no rose as yet to rival its performance. The flowers, which are produced continually; are white flushed shell-pink, large and highly perfumed with a sweet, true rose scent. The foliage is bold and produced in copious amounts by this strong-growing climber, which will grow up to the eaves of a two-storey house on any aspect. It is also reliably free from disease. What more could you ask?

'Madame Alfred Carrière' does require fairly careful training. Her growth tends to be a little stiff and vertical so it may be necessary to encourage more horizontal growth. Although she is often seen growing against walls and is frequently at her finest in that position, she is also useful for growing over large pergolas, into an old tree or over an arbour. **BG**

Rosa 'Marie Pavie'

Type: hardy, dwarf polyantha rose
Soil & situation: will do better than many roses in less than favourable conditions/copes reasonably well on lighter, freer-draining soils/sunny position
North American hardiness zone: 5–9
Height & spread: 45cm (18in)
Grow for: non-stop, blush-white flowers in summer

The dwarf polyantha roses have *Rosa multiflora* in their parentage. *R. multiflora* is also the parent of many rambling roses and, as a result of this, their flowers are similar to those of a rambler. The dwarf polyanthas are very tough and hardy, as is *R. multiflora*, and as the parent name suggests they have an amazing capacity to produce copious blooms with continuous regularity. 'Marie Pavie' (sometimes also known as 'Marie Pavic') has tightly packed clusters of delicate, fresh, blush-white flowers which are one of the most appealing of this floriferous group – in both quality and quantity. The plant has an excellent bushy form so is highly useful for planting in groups to form good wedges of almost continuous summer colour in the front of borders.

Caring for this rose is generally as for *R.* 'Ferdinand Pichard' (see page 333). 'Marie Pavie', like most roses, benefits from annual pruning. For 'Marie Pavie' (and most repeat-flowering shrub roses), this is best carried out by initially removing any weak, dead or diseased growth. Remaining healthy growth can then be reduced by between one-third and two-thirds of its length. This is best done in winter or late winter, except in areas where very cold winters occur, when this should be carried out just as growth begins in spring. **BG**

Rosa 'Marie Pavie'

Rosa 'Mermaid'

Rosa 'Mermaid'

Type: half-hardy, semi-evergreen, climbing rose
Soil & situation: moist, free-draining soil/flourishes on sunny walls, tolerates shade
North American hardiness zone: 6–9
Height: 9m (30ft)
Spread: 6m (20ft)
Grow for: foliage and flowers from summer to autumn; AGM

This is often decribed as a classic, and rightly so. Choose its location carefully – it's a vigorous climber/rambler with long stems. The young wood is maroon coloured with large hooked thorns in pairs so it's a relief that regular heavy pruning isn't necessary. The foliage is rich glossy green, it is evergreen in shelter or warm climates but may lose its leaves in severe weather; this too should influence your choice of site. It flowers right through the summer into autumn, producing an almost constant stream of large, delicately fragrant, single flowers which can reach a massive 15cm (6in) across and are soft, rich lemon or sulphur-yellow with mahogany-coloured stamens. They seem to increase in quality and quantity as the season progresses, especially during warm summers. This really is a refined plant.

This is definitely a rose for a sheltered, sunny wall as it is slightly tender; however, it tolerates some shade with reduced performance. Do not plant in exposed positions where cold winds can cause dieback. Grow in moist, well-drained soil, and mulch in spring with well-rotted organic matter. Prune sparingly, to keep under control; remove old or frost-damaged wood in spring. Tie in shoots of wall-grown plants in autumn. Beware of the thorns: as with *R. longicuspsis,* wear eye protection, gauntlets and a long-sleeved jacket! If possible, put the trimmings straight into a shredder before they can do any harm. Propagate by hardwood cuttings in late autumn. Very disease resistant. **MB**

Rosa 'New Dawn'

Type: hardy climbing rose
Soil & situation: good moist, fertile but well-drained soil/ sun or part shade
North American hardiness zone: 5–9
Height & spread: 3m (10ft)
Grow for: excellent, repeat-flowering climber with pale pink, fragrant roses from summer to autumn; AGM

This was the first rose ever to receive a patent and nobody would go to all that trouble unless they had a gem. One of its outstanding assets is its repeat-flowering capacity. The pretty, pearly-pink flowers are produced in large clusters for a really long period. They smell good too, with a strong, sweet fragrance. The other asset is disease resistance. Its mass of shiny, mid-green leaves are produced in quantity and nearly always look in tip-top condition. Its habit is gently arching. Its use is not restricted to being trained up pillars, posts, walls, over low roofs and the like, as it can be grown as a hedge or pruned to form a free-standing shrub.

If you are training this climber up pillars, to avoid getting purely vertical growth, which can lead to flowers at the top only, it is recommended that the shoots are trained around the support in a spiral formation encouraging the roses to be produced along the stems.

A climbing rose is made up of the long main stems, which you train up and along the structure, and the short, sideshoots coming off the main stems which produce the flowers. As the main stems become crowded you remove the weakest, oldest ones, cutting them to about 30cm (12in) above ground, removing one or two main stems every one to three years. The sideshoots you just reduce back to about 7cm (2¾in). The best time to do this is late winter or early spring. For the first couple of years all you need to do (apart from watering in dry periods) is to remove dead and diseased growth and start tying it in to a support system. Otherwise dead-heading, annual mulching and regular feeding all help. **BG**

Rosa 'New Dawn'

plant of the week (see page 337)

Rosa 'Phyllis Bide'

Type: hardy, semi-evergreen, rambling rose
Soil & situation: good moist, fertile but well-drained soil/in sun or part shade
North American hardiness zone: 6–9
Height & spread: 2.5m (8ft)
Grow for: clusters of small flowers, repeat flowering; fragrant apricot-yellow flowers tinged with pink; AGM

This is a charming, dainty rambler that is ideal for growing up 2–3m (6½–10ft) supports such as pergolas, fences, tripods and similar structures. This rose will reach the top but will not go rampaging on to towering heights, getting out of hand; with a bit of help, it will flower from top to bottom. It is a vigorous grower with fairly lax, mid-green but shiny leaves. The sprays of small (5cm/2in) double flowers are produced in summer and will carry on flowering well into autumn.

It is worth enriching the soil with lots of well-rotted organic matter prior to planting. Watering in dry periods during the first couple of years after planting really helps get it going, especially if it is planted at the base of a house wall. Regular mulching and feeding always pay big dividends.

Rosa 'Phyllis Bide'

Generally you just leave rambling roses without pruning them, only removing old wood when it becomes too dense to encourage renewal. Otherwise just give them their head and let them go; the less you do, the better they are. If you do need to constrain their growth they can be pruned as you would a climber (see *R.* 'Golden Celebration, page 333). Dead-heading is also worthwhile. **BG**

Rosa rubiginosa

Rosa rubiginosa (syn. *R. eglanteria*)

SWEET BRIAR

Type: hardy, vigorous, climbing/rambling rose
Soil & situation: most soils/sun
North American hardiness zone: 4–9
Height: 3.5m (11ft)
Spread: 2.5m (8ft)
Grow for: fragrant foliage and delicate flowers

Few plants are grown specifically for the fragrance of their foliage but this is one of them. The upright, prickly stems are covered in dainty leaves composed of five to nine rounded leaflets deliciously scented of apples. Clusters of simple, clear pink flowers about 4cm (1½in) across punctuate the arching branches in mid-summer and are followed by bright red, oval fruits that last well into the winter. The fragrance is most intense after a shower of rain and whenever the atmosphere has been refreshed. If trained up trellising or grown near a window it can scent the whole house. It can be left free to scramble through a hedgerow or be the hedge itself growing up to 2.5m (8ft) tall, though it is usually kept smaller. It is better clipped each spring before growth begins to encourage young growth that exudes the strongest scent. It also makes a strong-growing shrub.

It has been cultivated for centuries and there were many varieties listed in 19th-century catalogues. Double-flowered hybrids have been cultivated since the 17th century, two raised before 1800 are still available and nurseries stock many varieties. It is one of the parents of the 'Penzance Briars' raised from 1884 onwards by Lord Penzance, who crossed this with other species and garden varieties.

Rosa rubiginosa can grow in a range of soils but prefers one that is moisture retentive and free draining; avoid waterlogged conditions. It flourishes in full sun but tolerates some shade. Propagate by seed in spring, hardwood cuttings in late winter. **MB**

Rosa rugosa 'Alba'

RAMANAS ROSE, HEDGEHOG ROSE

Type: hardy, deciduous, shrub rose
Soil & situation: moist, well-drained soil/full sun or partial shade
North American hardiness zone: 2–9
Height: 2–2.5m (6–8ft)
Spread: 2.5m (8ft)
Grow for: it makes the most perfect hedge

Grown as a hedge this plant is not only sturdy and dense but, in flower, is spectacular. This is a vigorous-growing rose with prickly stems. The dark green, leathery leaves are heavily wrinkled and made up of seven to nine leaflets, each 5cm (2in) long. The 10cm (4in) wide flowers are pure white opening from pink buds. Single, cupped, fragrant flowers with golden stamens appear from early summer to autumn. These are followed by large, tomato-shaped, orange-red hips.

Rosa rugosa 'Alba'

Rosa rugosa is not a fussy plant and will enjoy most soils except those which are waterlogged. Never plant in soil which has previously grown roses. Prune by cutting out the older stems as close to the ground as possible. Flowers are produced on new growths and two-year-old stems. Avoid the temptation to trim the plant lightly, as this causes the new growths to form higher up, close to where it was cut. Old, neglected hedges and individual plants can be rejuvenated by cutting the whole plant in winter or early spring to within 20cm (8in) of the ground. Water and feed with a high-nitrogen liquid fertilizer to get the plants going again. In late summer apply high-potash fertilizer to harden up the growth before winter.

Propagation is by seed, stratified over-winter and sown in spring. Some of the resulting plants will be white flowering but most will be mauve and shades of pink. Hardwood cuttings taken with a heel in winter will root outside in the open ground. **JC**

Rosa sericea subsp. *omeiensis* f. *pteracantha*

WINGED THORNED ROSE

Type: hardy, vigorous, upright, deciduous shrub rose
Soil & situation: moisture-retentive, free-draining soil/sun
North American hardiness zone: 6–9
Height: 3m (10ft)
Spread: 2.2m (7ft)
Grow for: attractive thorns and hips; flowers late spring to early summer

Rosa sericea subsp. *omeiensis* f. *pteracantha*, one of the longest names in plant taxonomy, is one of few plants grown for gorgeous thorns. They are flat, thin, wedge-shaped to 3cm (1in) or more long, and 2cm (3/4in) tall, forming 'wings' down the stems, which are covered with fine, soft bristles. This treasure should be carefully placed in the garden so that the morning or preferably the evening sun shines through the gorgeous translucent thorns when the effect lasts longer and they glow like rubies as the sun goes down. It is shade tolerant and suitable for planting in woodland glades, but should always be placed where it is spot-lit by the sun; the narrow, vase-shape of the plant makes it an excellent specimen shrub for lawns or borders too. One day I'd like to visit Mount Omei in China, home to some incredible plants, so I could see this glorious plant growing in its native habitat. Bliss!

Rosa sericea subsp. *omeiensis* f. *pteracantha*

The thorns are accompanied by delicate, pale grey, ferny foliage and small, single, white, four-petalled flowers with crimson and yellow edible hips. In late spring white flowers 5cm (2in) in diameter appear in loose clusters

It prefers free-draining, moisture-retentive soils but is tolerant of poorer conditions. The thorns are especially conspicuous on young, vigorous basal shoots; by the second year they are grey and woody. In spring, prune hard annually or biennially back to the base to encourage young growth and lots of thorns. Propagate by seed in spring or hardwood cuttings in late winter. **MB**

Rosa 'Sharifa Asma'

Type: hardy, deciduous, shrub rose
Soil & situation: As for *R.* 'Golden Celebration' (see page 333)
Height: 1m (3 ft)
Spread: 75cm (30in)
Grow for: almost continuous flowers, a beautiful delicate blush-pink that fades to near white on the outer petals as they age

This is an excellent 'English' rose. It copes very well in less-than-perfect rose-growing soils i.e. in the thinner, lighter types like mine. I like the continuity of flowering and the vigour of the plant, yet it has the good qualities of the old roses: the beauty and charm of the flower and the strong, fruity but sweet fragrance which is 'reminiscent of white grapes and mulberry'.

The flowers are shallow cups which relax into rosettes as they age. The growth is rather upright, and to make more of a bushy group it is worth planting three or five (if not more) in a tight group at about 50cm (20in) centres. As long as they have good food and moisture, close planting will not affect their performance. The blooms can occasionally be damaged by hot sun but this is rarely a problem in Britain.

Care for it as you would for *R.* 'Golden Celebration' (see page 333) **BG**

Rosa 'Sharifa Asma'

Rosa 'William Lobb'

Rosa 'William Lobb'

Type: hardy, deciduous, shrub rose
Soil & situation: most soils/sun or shade
North American hardiness zone: 4–9
Height & spread: 2.5m (8ft)
Grow for: prolific, heavily scented, dark crimson flowers in summer following scented mossy buds; AGM

Many roses have scented flowers but only a few are mossy. This rose produces a moss-like formation on the buds and tops of the flowering stems that has an incense-like perfume. I love to rub it on my fingers and sniff the delicious aroma as I walk the garden. Later the blooms are just as delightful. I have trained it along wires but it threatens to grow too heavy. Still I expect it to recover from a massacre of a pruning once every five or ten years.

This interesting group is descended from *Rosa centifolia*, which was the old Rose of Provence. These mossy types were first grown in the 18th century in England but every other country also claims them. They have lost the great popularity they enjoyed a hundred years ago when masses of varieties were grown. *R.* 'Nuits de Young' is one of the varieties available today.

Ideally roses prefer a rich, heavy, moist soil that stays cool but never gets waterlogged. It will grow in open shade, such as on an exposed wall. It is relatively long lived and flowers most easily as a free-standing shrub. Dead-heading is important, as is pruning out diseased wood. It is a hybrid and cannot be grown from seed, but autumn hardwood cuttings are easy. This rose does get pests and diseases, but you don't notice them, and its only real problem is that it gets too big for small gardens. **BF**

Matt adds:
I think that the 'old' roses are best, though there are exceptions, but I prefer species and older cultivars overall. I first saw this one at Chelsea Flower Show, its beautiful blooms against a buttermilk wall and the memory is still etched in my mind; it was a wonderful contrast I'd love to recreate. *R.* 'William Lobb' is vigorous and robust, like a tall shrub, and the flower clusters are so heavy that it arches to the ground, so it needs support of wires, trellis or placing at the back of a border where the long stems bend forward and mingle with other shrubs. It is a moss rose, the stems and buds covered with a bristly beard and there's something magical about the flower colour. It starts off purple, turns to magenta, then fades to violet-grey. As with all the best roses, there is a rich 'old-fashioned' perfume. This one is sometimes called 'Old Velvet'.

Rosa 'Zéphirine Drouhin'
CLIMBING ROSE

Type: hardy, deciduous, climbing rose
Soil & situation: most soils/sun or shade
North American hardiness zone: 6–9
Height: 3m (10ft)
Spread: unlimited, but probably 2m (6½ft)
Grow for: prolific, scented, silver-pink flowers in flushes from early summer to late autumn on thornless stems

Many roses are available in the pinky-red, semi-double format, but few have such a good fragrance and none are thornless. This alone makes 'Zéphirine Drouhin' a valuable rose, but add in the repeat flowering, the ease with which it can be trained to a shrubby or climbing habit and its ease of propagation and this is a real winner. I have many of these planted in my garden all from the same plant; those with a more moist site and good air flow get far fewer problems and a lot more flowers than those growing on dry walls.

This is one of the Bourbon roses, which all originated in the early 19th century from a cross between a Damask and a China rose. These were the first roses to be bred that flower several times in a year and this, combined with gorgeous fragrance, has made the whole group favourites, such as the superb 'Madame Isaac Pereire', 'Boule de Neige' and 'Souvenir de la Malmaison'. 'Kathleen Harrop' is a sport and definitely worth growing.

Ideally roses prefer a rich, heavy, moist soil that stays cool but never gets waterlogged. They will grow in shade but are rarely very long lived anywhere. Deadheading is important, as is pruning out diseased wood, but otherwise this rose gives most flowers if just trained up a pillar or tree and lightly pruned as the leaves fall; it can also be grown as a free-standing shrub. It is a hybrid and cannot be grown from seed, but autumn hardwood cuttings are easy. It suffers from aphid attacks, blackspot and mildew but who cares, it's thornless and scented. **BF**

Rosa 'Zéphirine Drouhin'

Rosmarinus officinalis
ROSEMARY

Type: frost-hardy, evergreen shrub
Soil & situation: well-drained, light soil/sun
North American hardiness zone: 7–10
Height & spread: 1m (3ft), possibly twice as much
Grow for: good neat evergreen for small informal hedge; gorgeous blue and white flowers in profusion and, of course, a useful culinary herb

There are few plants with such beauty all year round, with such amazing, if small, orchid-like flowers and such culinary appeal. (Mind you, I had a woman once ask me what was wrong with her rosemary as it was causing complaints when used with the lamb roasts – it turned out to be lavender!) Lavender is very similar, but rosemary is more upright and evergreen not ever-grey.

Rosemary is for remembrance – and for Romans, as they revered its culinary and medicinal uses. It is believed to have been brought to England by Edward III's wife. *Ros marinus* means dew of the sea, as it is found wild on sea cliffs of southern Europe

Rosmarinus officinalis 'Miss Jessopp's Upright'

Rosemary needs a well-drained, light soil in a sheltered spot otherwise it is short lived. It does not like the wind and in cold wet areas does best against a warm wall. It can be trimmed after flowering and will usually re-grow. The seed can be sown in spring or cuttings taken in spring or autumn. It does get cut back by hard frosts and recently has started to suffer from a form of dieback. **BF**

Rosmarinus officinalis 'Miss Jessopp's Upright'

Type: frost-hardy, evergreen shrub
Soil & situation: a range of soils/best in sharp draining, slightly limy soils/sun but tolerates part shade/dislikes winter wet/thrives in hot, dry conditions.
North American hardiness zone: 7–10
Height & spread: 2m (6½ft)
Grow for: multi-purpose plant: useful herb for culinary and other purposes; worth growing for foliage; using for topiary, hedging and in pots; pale blue flowers in mid-spring in large quantities; AGM

My rosemary is covered with masses of lovely blue flowers, today on St Valentine's Day, and has had a profusion for two or three weeks. It is in a pot outside my front door and everything in the courtyard is covered with a thick white frost. It is trained into a pyramid which, thanks to its natural upright habit, it was quick to achieve. As I am often away, it is an ideal pot plant. You can neglect it for a good two weeks, even in the height of summer, and it will hardly have noticed it is parched (though I always use huge pots and soak before I go). It is thought that rosemary was the original Christmas tree, being used long before the Norway spruce. Apparently if you bring a plant into the house on Christmas Eve, you have luck for the rest of the year. It does look charming in the house, especially when clipped to the romantic pyramid for 'Christmas card trees'. You can dress it up and even gild some of its leaves and the pot (as was often done in Victorian times). Cut off the gilded leaves later and then move it back outdoors to enjoy it in the garden till next Christmas.

Prune this plant after flowering to maintain a compact, bushy habit. Cuttings strike extremely easily, and can be taken as softwood or semi-ripe cuttings in the growing season. **BG**

Rubus fruticosus 'Bedford Giant'

BLACKBERRY

Type: hardy, deciduous, lax-stemmed shrub
Soil & situation: any soil/sun or shade
North American hardiness zone: 6–8
Height: 2m (6½ft)
Spread: to 10m (33ft)
Grow for: excellent fencing plant and delicious fruits

This is the plant for training on wires to keep out undesirables. It throws 10m (33ft) canes in a rich soil and these are prone to root and start new plants for free. There are more vigorous types still, such as *Rubus fruticosus* 'Himalayan Giant', but its canes are more brittle and harder to train onto wires. It not only makes an effective protective shield but is also good for wildlife who love the flowers and dry, safe centre. The fruits come early; they have a good flavour and are quite large and make excellent blackberry and apple jam, jelly and pie.

Although there are, theoretically, more than 250 species in the *Rubus* family there is no such thing as a pure-bred blackberry as they are all hybrids. This is one of the cultivated varieties. These were known to the Romans, who called them *Rubus*, but gathered them from the wild rather than growing them. Blackberry canes are very different to those of raspberry as the former are pliable, root at the tips easily and may live more than one year, while raspberry canes are stiff, do not root easily and usually die after fruiting.

Long lived, especially as it throws stems which root and grow almost anywhere on almost any soil. Prune out all the dead and old stems and tie the new onto wires after fruiting. The wires need to be strong with sturdy supports. The seedlings come up everywhere with variable results. The tips are layered in autumn and soon root to be planted out in spring. There are rarely any problems other than the vigour making it too big for small gardens. **BF**

Rubus fruticosus 'Bedford Giant'

Rubus hybrid
TAYBERRY

Type: perennial, deciduous, lax-stemmed shrub
Soil & situation: any soil/sun or shade
North American hardiness zone: 4–8
Height & spread: to 7m (23ft)
Grow for: huge delicious fruits

Although related to the blackberries this is not as vigorous and is more like a raspberry, except the stems are covered in very sharp prickles and thorns. I have grown almost every sort of berry and there are few that are this luscious; it is better eaten ripe and raw than any of the others. The berry can get as big as my thumb and is dark wine-purple in colour, aromatic and sweet, and once ripe it pulls off its plug like a raspberry. It is a significant improvement on all the other berries, and a good plant for cool, shady walls rather than needing the sunniest sites.

The tayberry was developed in Scotland and is like a much-improved loganberry. There are many hybrid berries, such as the loganberry, the veitchberry, the sunberry and the boysenberry, all of which are in between blackberries and raspberries in fruit and habit.

In the UK the tayberry is happiest in cool northern or western areas; I find it gets parched in full sun and wind here in East Anglia and my best berries are produced on the north side of a wooden panel fence. Prune out all the dead and old stems and tie the new onto wires after the old finish fruiting. The wires need to be strong with good supports. The seedlings come up everywhere with variable results. The tips are layered in autumn and soon root to be planted out in spring.

There are rarely any problems other than bird losses, which are heavy, so it needs be netted or caged. **BF**

Rubus hybrid

Rubus idaeus

Rubus idaeus
RASPBERRY

Type: hardy, perennial, deciduous, clump-forming thicket
Soil & situation: any soil/sun or shade
North American hardiness zone: 3–8
Height & spread: 3m (10ft) high clump
Grow for: most delicious fruits

Although related to the blackberries, raspberries are different. Their stiff canes support themselves and do not root easily at the tips, and they nearly always die after fruiting. Ripe raspberries usually leave their plug behind, making them more delectable than blackberries and the hybrids, which mostly pull off with the plug inside, and are more chewy. Raspberries can be eaten in quantity without the dire results of most fruits – I can testify to this. They also make the most brilliant jam, refreshing drinks and superb sorbets. They can be in fruit from early summer to well into late autumn if you have several varieties.

The name comes from the earlier *raspise*, which is possibly from the name for an old type of French red wine. Raspberries are common in the wild in northern European countries, where they are normally gathered rather than cultivated. In the USA they have their own series raised from their native raspberries rather than from our stocks.

In the UK raspberries are happiest in cool northern or western areas; they do not like hot, dry, thin or chalky soils and revel in a rich, moist loam. They are not long lived and deteriorate after eight years. Prune out all the dead old stems and tie the new onto wires after the old finish fruiting; for autumn fruiters remove all canes in mid-winter. Thinning new canes to a hand's breadth apart improves the quality of the crop. Supporting wires do not have to be very strong as they are only there to restrain the canes and stop them falling over. Raspberry seedlings come up everywhere with variable but usually acceptable results and any bit of root with a bud can be planted out in spring. Maggots are best avoided by growing autumn fruiters. Raspberry mosaic virus will creep in sooner or later, so eradicate any plants with mottled leaves. **BF**

Rubus phoenicolasius
JAPANESE WINEBERRY

Type: hardy, deciduous, arching shrub
Soil & situation: any soil/sun or shade
North American hardiness zone: 5–9
Height & spread: 4.5m (15ft)
Grow for: decorative russet stems; nice leaves; delicious, red, edible berry; pretty star-shaped calyces left after fruits

This is a rarity but should be common. It has a fruit you can just eat and eat and eat – good for parking children in front of to keep them occupied. Once the fruit has been picked, the white star-shaped calyces make the plant look in flower again. The stems are bristly rather than thorny and a colourful russet ruddy-brown; the leaves are decorative and a lovely lime-juice green. It is a shame the berries are not much use either as jam or juice, and I would love to cross this with a tayberry, but so far it has always come true from seed. The birds do not strip these berries as fast as many others – I think the birds reckon they are unripe blackberries.

Rubus phoenicolasius

The weird bit of the name is the Latin for purple hairs, which I suppose is close enough to its ruddy-brown hairs. It comes from Japan as the common name, for once correctly, indicates, though it is also found in China. It was brought to the UK in the 19th century and was more popular as an ornamental shrub than for its fruit, which is of little value other than as a fresh-picked delight.

The Japanese wineberry does well on almost any soil or site but looks best trained against a whitewashed wall. Prune out all the dead and old stems and tie the new onto wires after the old finish fruiting. The wires need be strong with good supports. The seedlings come true and the tips can be layered in autumn. There are rarely any problems other than it does self-seed rather abundantly. **BF**

Rudbeckia fulgida var. *sullivantii* 'Goldsturm'

Type: hardy, herbaceous perennial
Soil & situation: moist soil; tolerates clay/sun or partial shade
North American hardiness zone: 4–9
Height: 60cm (24in)
Spread: 45cm (18in)
Grow for: golden-yellow 'daisies' from late summer to autumn

This genus is named after Olof Rudbeck (1630–1702), who has been described as 'one of the greatest Swedes of all time', founder of Uppsala Botanic Garden in Sweden, and his son Olof the Younger, a friend of Linnaeus. Rudbeckias are among the most delightful and reliable of all late summer-flowering 'daisies'; when they are in flower, the sun shines every day. Like many other midsummer-flowering herbaceous plants, will tolerate clay and are high on the list of favourites to be planted in a new herbaceous border that I am planning for my garden.

Rudbeckia fulgida var. *sullivantii* 'Goldsturm' has a clump of hairy leaves and stems that are usually branched in the upper part. Each plant carries masses of bright yellow flowers with a small dark purple-brown (looks black) central cone. It makes a striking and desirable contrast that is further enhanced when they are planted with blue sea hollies, red hot pokers in orange and green, or crocosmias like the fiery red 'Lucifer' and apricot 'Star of the East'. *R. fulgida* var. *deamii* is similar but with smaller flowers. *R. occidentalis* 'Green Wizard' lacks the ray florets; the single dark cone is a novelty but has all the sex appeal of a bald woman. It is beloved by flower arrangers.

It does best on heavier, moisture-retentive soils, and where necessary dig in plenty of organic matter before planting. Mulch heavily with well-rotted organic matter and water if necessary during drought. Divide in spring every four to five years; sow seed in late spring to early summer to flower the following year. **MB**

Rudbeckia fulgida var. *sullivantii* 'Goldsturm'

Ruta graveolens

Ruta graveolens
COMMON RUE

Type: hardy, deciduous shrub
Soil & situation: well-drained soil/sun
North American hardiness zone: 5–9
Height & spread: 1m (3ft)
Grow for: prolific, though small, scented yellow flowers in summer on beautifully aromatic, fern-like, blue foliage

True blue foliage is rare, yet rue has a lovely leaf that is almost blue in varieties such as *Rue graveolens* 'Jackman's Blue' (see next entry). The soft ferny leaves have a delicious citrus-like scent, which is so strong that the leaves have often been used to keep pests away. Although it is poisonous and sometimes used as a medicinal herb, I came across it being eaten in France where it was used as a flavouring for cheese. I have often done the same since with no apparent harm but for the woes of the litigious I must insist you do not try it, especially if you are pregnant as rue is undoubtedly dangerous.

The botanical name is for bitterness, as is the common name. Rue was officially introduced in 1652 but was probably brought by the Romans as this herb, a native of southern Europe, has long been cultivated for its medicinal qualities. Rue has a big family; there are over five dozen other species, most of which are tender and carry the distinctive citrus-like scent in foliage and flower. There are another 600 in the family of Rutaceae, often similarly scented, such as choisya.

Rue is not long lived and less so if the soil is damp in winter or it is in shade. It can be trimmed back lightly in spring before the growth resumes and it is worth shearing off the flowerheads before they set seed. It can be grown from seed sown in pots in spring or rooted by summer cuttings in a coldframe. Rue suffers few problems but is strongly irritant to the skin and care should be taken with the foliage, especially in hot weather. It may self-seed. **BF**

Kniphofia caulescens

RED-HOT POKER

Type: hardy evergreen perennial
Soil & situation: fertile deep loam/sun or partial shade/young plants need protection with a mulch for their first winter
North American hardiness zone: 7–9
Height: up to 1.2m (4ft)
Spread: to 60cm (24in)
Grow for: striking, year-round, broad, grass-like, glaucous foliage; long-lasting stately spikes of cool coral and yellow flowers at any time in summer or autumn; AGM

For the most part I strongly favour hard-working plants. This, for sure, is one of those and I have never worked out why it is not more common. Perhaps because when you mention red-hot pokers a wide group of gardeners turn up their noses haughtily. But this one is streets ahead of your average red-hot poker. Apart from its dramatic, stately, long-lasting flowers – a subtle coral colour initially before fading up the spike to an unbrassy yellow as they age – their foliage is to die for. It is a good blue-green, does not look tatty even in late winter, spreads in generous basal rosettes with arching leaves and would be worth growing for that alone. I initially veered away from it, having been wrongly informed that it was tender. It certainly looks exotic but it thrives in my East Midlands patch, and I have never even given it so much as a protective mulch in winter.

To keep the foliage at its best, division of the plant every two to four years may be necessary. You do this in spring by breaking off pieces and replanting them with the foliage cut well back, but with some woody stem. **BG**

Ruta graveolens 'Jackman's Blue'

Ruta graveolens 'Jackman's Blue'

Type: hardy, evergreen herb/shrub
Soil & situation: well-drained soils in full sun/tolerates partial shade quite successfully/ requires gloves when handling – the sap contains feranocoumarins and blistering can be triggered by contact with skin
North American hardiness zone: 5–9
Height: 60cm (24in)
Spread: 50cm (20in)
Grow for: intense blue-grey foliage; divided, fern-like leaves; an excellent year-round plant; AGM

Ruta graveolens (see page 343) has been cultivated for hundreds of years for its intense flavour, which has been used in sausage – though probably not served with egg, chips and ketchup! A tea made from infusing the leaves has long been used as a stimulant. This herb is also believed to have magical properties, especially when acquired by theft. Tantalizing to think how this was most likely discovered by desperate sorcerers shinning up monastic walls by moonlight.

Thudding back to reality, though, I grow it simply for its magical appearance. It is supreme as a low hedge or edging plant, especially in parterres with an unusual twist, mixed with dwarf myrtles, germanders, Japanese hollies and other plants with fascinating backgrounds. It is most commonly used in mixed borders too, where it quickly establishes to form a good-looking presence in its first year.

If grown as a low hedge this plant will need cutting back once, possibly twice, during the growing season. Grown as a shrub, one good cut back will do the job. The main time to cut back is early spring and the existing growth should be cut back by half to two thirds. A second cut later on, to tidy up the first flush of growth, will help to form a really compact habit. This will probably be at the expense of the uninspiring flowers – no bad thing as the mustard-yellow colour with the blue of the foliage is not an asset anyway. Old shrubs that look past it can be renewed by hard cutting back to 15cm (6in) from the ground. If this fails, cuttings in late summer are a sure winner. **BG**

Salix alba subsp. *vitellina*

GOLDEN WILLOW

Type: hardy, deciduous tree, often maintained as a shrub
Soil & situation: grow best in deep, moist but well-drained soils/will tolerate a vast range of conditions, including impoverished ones/sun or partial shade
North American hardiness zone: 2–9
Height: 25m (80ft) as a tree, 1–2m (3–6½ft) as a shrub
Spread: 10m (33ft) as a tree
Grow for: spectacular fiery new growth with young stems a bright yellow-orange; will grow in extremely inhospitable conditions, wet or dry, so is highly useful for reclamation work; AGM

This is a stunning willow which comes into its own at the end of autumn when the dramatic-coloured stems, devoid of leaves, brighten up the winter landscape. I regularly use it in bold groups mixed with other willows of the same ilk, such as *S. alba* 'Chermesina', the scarlet willow, which has bright orange-scarlet young stems and *S. daphnoides*, the violet willow, whose purple-violet new stems are overlaid with a whitish bloom.

This is more sober than the previous two but attractive, nonetheless. Although all their maximum heights are tall, they are usually coppiced every other year to make sure the vigorous new stems are produced and so the height is kept at only 1–2m (3–6½ft). I think they look best in wilder parts of the garden, although you do see them in mixed borders, but they seem to me to be out of context when they jostle next to more refined neighbours. They are fabulous in marshy situations or on banks by water. They are also superb for creating living play areas around other play equipment as they form green den-making domains, which can be heavily trampled by hyperactive feet, but will always grow back providing they have established.

Assuming you want shrubs, not trees, coppice these plants a couple of years following planting and then about every other year. This simply entails cutting them back to about 10cm (4in) from ground level in spring. They are easy to grow from cuttings and these will take in open ground at pretty well any time of year, but hardwood cuttings in the dormant season are the norm. Willows have invasive roots, so do not plant them close to buildings or drains if you are going to let them form anything other than small shrubs. **BG**

Salix alba subsp. *vitellina* 'Britzensis'

Salix alba subsp. *vitellina* 'Britzensis'

RED-STEMMED WILLOW

Type: hardy, deciduous tree
Soil & situation: moist, well-drained, fertile soil/full sun
North American hardiness zone: 4–9
Height: 20m (66ft)
Spread: 10m (33ft)
Grow for: bright orange-red bark on new growths; yellow male catkins in spring; AGM

I think this variety is different enough from Bunny's choice (above) to merit a separate entry.

Viewed from a distance, against a dull wintery sky, the overall effect is of a stationary orange cloud. Up close the bark is as striking as that of dogwood (*Cornus alba*, see page 16).

Yellow male catkins, 5cm (2in) long, appear in spring together with the mid-green leaves, which are blue-green on the underside. It is, however, the bright orange-red bark which lifts this willow above most of the other species. As the tree grows the older bark becomes brown. With that in mind it is the fashion to prune (coppice) the branches hard every second year. They are cut close to the ground to encourage young, highly coloured growths. Every spring prune back hard and then feed with a high nitrogen fertilizer in early summer to help the growth. Left unpruned it will form an elegant tree with dyed hair.

A word of caution: avoid planting willows close to buildings or underground services, such as sewage pipes or drains. They have a vigorous root system capable of causing damage.

The simplest method of propagation is by hardwood cuttings. Large cuttings are easily rooted. It is not unusual to find large willows either side of a field entrance, where the farmer used willow branches as gate posts. They rooted and, in time, became matching trees. Like most willows, 'Britzensis' will tolerate wet ground and is happy with its roots close to the water's edge. It dislikes waterlogged soil, where it will be more prone to willow anthracnose disease. **JC**

Salix elaeagnos
HOARY WILLOW, ROSEMARY WILLOW

Type: hardy, deciduous shrub
Soil & situation: as for *Salix alba* subsp.*vitellina* (see page 346)
North American hardiness zone: 4–9
Height: 3–6m (10–20ft)
Spread: 5m (16ft)
Grow for: wonderful foliage, similar to an enlarged rosemary leaf; highly ornamental, yet tough plant very useful for 'lifting' native plantings in wilder parts of the garden or countryside

The leaf of this willow is about 10cm (4in) long by 5mm (1/4in) wide, the new growth is silver and hoary i.e. covered with short white hairs (like an old man with a soft stubble). Later on, the leaves become dark olive-green on top and silver-felted below. They are densely produced covering much of the rust-coloured stems. Small catkins are produced with or just before the leaves.

This really choice willow is less vigorous than many. I often use it for screening with other native plants (*Viburnum opulus, V. lantana, Ligustrum vulgare*) to form attractive thickets around compost heaps, play areas, children's gardens and the like. It can be maintained at a metre (3ft) high without wearing out or over-taxing your arm muscles, and yet will quickly achieve that height. It is a superb waterside shrub too.

Although these willows can be left to form a large shrub or small tree, they are often kept as busy shrubs so you can enjoy the foliage near to eye level. They can be maintained by cutting back to prevent them becoming too large. The best time to do this is early spring, and then you can really appreciate the new silvery foliage as it rapidly extends in the growing season. They are asy to propagate, the simplest method being putting hardwood cuttings, 15-30cm (6-12in) long or so, into open ground in the late autumn or winter. **BG**

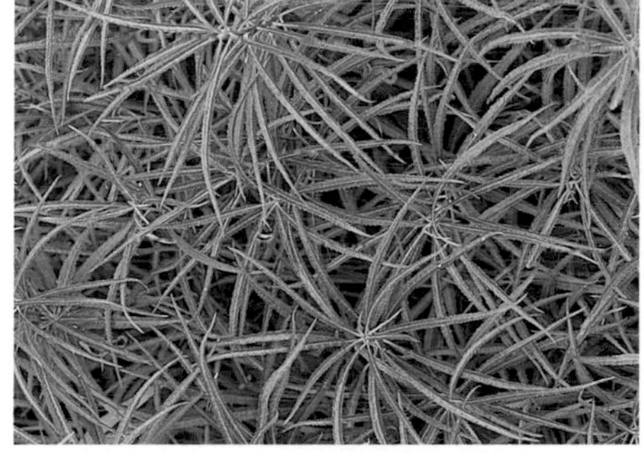
Salix elaeagnos

Salix gracilistyla 'Melanostachys'

Type: hardy, spreading, deciduous shrub
Soil & situation: moist, heavy soil/sun
North American hardiness zone: 5–8
Height: 3m (10ft)
Spread: 4m (13ft)
Grow for: 'black' catkins and brick-red anthers

Oh those catkins! How could you resist a willow with 'black' catkins and brick-red anthers? Just think about it, black and brick-red and appearing before the leaves too! Look at the picture – aren't you tempted? OK the anthers later turn yellow but it is still magnificent. This has to be one of the most stunning colour combinations in the plant world. I can't seem to find out much about its origins, apart from that it's also known as Kureneko, Kurome and Kuroyanagi, the leaves are thicker than the species and strongly veined, there is only a male clone in existence and it was introduced into Europe via Holland in 1950. Perhaps it appeared as a 'sport' somewhere in Japan, Korea or China where *Salix gracilistyla* has its home, or was spirited from Japan by an entrepreneurial Dutch nurseryman. The dearth of information adds to the magic of this mysterious, seductive plant so I will search no more and continue to wonder because one thing is certain – ignorance is bliss!

Salix gracilistyla 'Melanostachys'

Prune after flowering to keep within its allotted space. Propagate by 30cm (12in) hardwood cuttings of one-year-old wood in spring. It is prone to anthracnose. Brown spots occur on the leaves, which fall early, and cankers appear on the shoots. Affected parts must be cut out, and don't forget to sterilize your secateurs by wiping with a cloth impregnated with methylated spirits after use. Regular sprays with Bordeaux mixture or copper fungicide starting when the leaves unfold should give some control; rake up and dispose of fallen leaves. It is worse in wet seasons. **MB**

Salix viminalis
COMMON OSIER, HEMP WILLOW

Type: hardy, deciduous shrub or small tree
Soil & situation: as for *Salix alba* subsp.*vitellina* (see page 346)
North American hardiness zone: 4–9
Height: 6m (20ft) or more, but often maintained as a shrub
Spread: 5m (16ft)
Grow for: best willow for weaving into living or dead willow structures: arbours, dens, arches, fences

This willow was traditionally grown for basket-making and so has extremely pliable shoots. It is a large, vigorous willow with long, narrow, typical willow leaves. They are a flat green above and covered with fine hairs below. It is not especially ornamental as a shrub, so if you are growing it to produce cuttings, site it somewhere natural where it will fit it agreeably. Once woven into something it is obviously transformed.

I have used this willow for weaving all sorts of structures, including a crocodile which was a key element in my children's play area when they were small. For growing willow fences it is a gem. You can form a wide assortment of different lattice shapes or weaving styles with it, introducing an element of originality. One of my favourites was a living woven serpentine fence, on the same lines as those amazing crinkle-crankle walls.

To grow this plant commercially for cutting production, they are grown on a short leg, about 30cm (12in) high, and then cut back to that every year, rather like a mini-pollarded willow. They produce lots of wands or cuttings which grow from the top of the leg, ready for cutting and using at leaf fall, usually at the end of autumn. For good cutting production a moist, fertile soil obviously produces good long cuttings, well over 1m (3ft) long if not 2m (6½ft). When making growing structures, which can be done any time in the dormant season I insert the long (up to 3m/10ft) cuttings in their final position, just deep enough in the ground to make them stable, maybe 15cm (6in). Having woven the structure I want, I water the new cuttings in during dry periods and maintain bare earth, as opposed to vegetation around the base, to facilitate establishment. The new growth on the structures needs frequent cutting back, often three times in the growing season, to prevent it becoming a mass of verdant willow shoots. **BG**

Salix viminalis

Salvia glutinosa

Salvia glutinosa
JUPITER'S DISTAFF

Type: hardy, herbaceous perennial
Soil & situation: not demanding, but does appreciate a moister soil than many sages/some shade/will grow in full sun
North American hardiness zone: 5–8
Height: 90cm (36in)
Spread: 60cm (24in)
Grow for: attractive, yellow flowers from summer to late autumn; a good plant for naturalizing in semi-shaded, wilder areas; good, bushy foliage, with yellow-green heart-shaped leaves

I am ashamed to say that I grew this plant for a couple of years before I realized what a quiet star it is – the flowers in no way jump out at you. They are carried in tall spikes and are a soft, pale yellow with red-brown spots on the hooded top lip and red-brown stripes on the lower lip. They attract many species of bumble-bees and you do notice early on that the large, branched flower spikes are very sticky indeed. I grow it in a dry, sunny position, not the ideal position, but this was done out of total ignorance – I just gave it what I thought most sages liked – but it does well, flowering on and on. Now I am going to try some in a more natural setting, letting it naturalize in spangled clumps amongst ferns, luzulas, liberties and foxgloves in light shade and moister conditions. I think I will like it even better there. I cut this plant back in the early winter, and otherwise do very little to it. It can be propagated from softwood cuttings in early summer, which root very quickly, or from seed sown in spring. **BG**

Salvia indica 'Indigo Spires'

Type: tender perennial
Soil & situation: frost-free conditions during winter/good drainage/full sun
North American hardiness zone: 5–9
Height: up to 1.5m (5ft)
Spread: 50cm (20in)
Grow for: a see-through, floriferous plant with deep indigo-blue flowers from early summer till late autumn

I adore many of the more subtle, tender sages, but 'Indigo Spires' is my all-time favourite. It was raised in 1979, at the Huntingdon Botanic Garden in California. I plant generous quantities of them in my Cambridgeshire courtyard garden, dangerously early in late spring (standing by with fleece in the event of a late frost) and they flower pretty much from late spring to late autumn. The plant has a gentle, lax air about it; the pretty blue flowers are studded at intervals up the long, lean stems, giving a soft, gentle colour – none of this brash, bold and in-your-face stuff. I grow them threaded through lower clumps of perennials, and they waft around on their own with no staking. It is possible that this may not be the case if you are the lucky owner of deep, fertile loam as opposed to my poor, thin offering.

Salvia indica 'Indigo Spires'

Being a tender perennial, this plant does necessitate higher levels of care but gives real value in return. I lift them just before the first frosts and pot them up, keeping them in a frost-free greenhouse over winter. I keep them on the dry side and check them over every so often, removing any mouldy stems. In addition I take cuttings from the parent plants in late summer, to ensure I have a good supply of young plants too. Cuttings will root quickly and easily at any time in the growing season. Apparently excess nitrogen results in sparse flowering. **BG**

Salvia involucrata 'Bethellii'

Salvia involucrata 'Bethellii'

Type: tender perennial
Soil & situation: well-drained loam/sun/preferably winter protection
North American hardiness zone: 7–10
Height: up to 1.5m (5ft)
Spread: to 1m (3ft)
Grow for: pinky-magenta flowers from late spring till autumn; AGM

This plant is a bit of an exhibitionist. It is a showy but stately plant with attractive, almost glabrous leaves, vaguely purplish on the underside. The non-stop flowers come in unbranched racemes and are curious in that they produce a large, fat, terminal bud which sits at the end of the flower spike on top of lots of densely-packed flowers.

One year I grew them in semi-shade under a line of pleached trees, in soil that is packed with dense tree roots. They still surprised me with a fair quantity of flowers although they did take a few weeks longer to get into their stride. Another year I left some out over winter and they survived to tell the tale. However, I will not repeat the experiment as they took a long time to come into growth and it was late summer before they flowered.

Most of the time I give them what they like best – sun and free-draining soil – and they never succumb to disease, never need staking and are definitely star performers that I would not want to be without.

Before the frosts these salvias need lifting, potting up and then keeping in a frost-free greenhouse over winter. Alternatively, new cuttings can be taken any time in the summer, kept in frost-free conditions over winter and planted out the following spring after the frosts. **BG**

Salvia officinalis
SAGE

Type: hardy, semi-evergreen shrub
Soil & situation: well-drained soil/sun
North American hardiness zone: 5–8
Height & spread: 1m (3ft)
Grow for: attractive, aromatic, grey foliage; scented purple flowers; culinary herb

I could not be without sage, both for its delicious scent and pleasing appearance when young and tidy, and for its use in the kitchen. I must have a sage and onion stuffing with my home-grown roast chicken, indeed I like it more than the meat. I always put a little fresh sage in my salads and the flowers are an essential part of one of the best of my liqueurs. It's also much visited by all sorts of insects when in flower.

Salvia is the Latin for safe and well, or good health, as this plant was thought to keep you healthy, and the name became corrupted into the modern equivalent. It is an enormous genus with over 500 species, many native to southern Europe. It is reputed to be the herb to eat for a long life, though it was used originally to hide the flavour of over-ripe meat.

Salvia officinalis

Sage is quite long lived in a well-drained, sunny site but gets rather leggy and scrappy, and if you cut it back it rarely regrows satisfactorily. In fact the best way to treat it is to replace it every few years with another. Sage can be grown from seed in spring but named varieties must be rooted or layered, which is easier; indeed, the whole plant can be earthed up in spring and then divided the next year. Sage rarely suffers any problems. **BF**

Salvia officinalis 'Purpurascens'

Salvia officinalis 'Purpurascens'
PURPLE SAGE

Type: hardy, evergreen subshrub
Soil & situation: sunny, well-drained soil/will tolerate a lightly shaded position/will not cope with heavy, cold soils.
Height: up to 80cm (32in)
Spread: 1m (3ft)
North American hardiness zone: 5–8
Grow for: rich, purple-mauve toned foliage which brings it into a class of its own; useful aromatic herb; spikes of blue-mauve flowers in early summer; AGM

This is a first-rate foliage plant when grown well and looking in the peak of condition. The young leaves are purple and as they age they turn green-grey, maintaining the purple veining and edging. The undersides have distinctive purple veining, which stands out against a grey backdrop. To keep these plants looking good they must be clipped lightly in spring to encourage new, well-coloured growth and to neaten them up. Also, being fast growers they are not in their prime of life for long and I think they are best replaced with new plants every four or five years, depending on your soil. They are easy to grow from cuttings and grow fast, making quite a statement after just one year of growth. The golden form, *S.officinalis* 'Icterina' (AGM), is superb too, but *S. officinalis* 'Tricolor' (AGM), with its colourful white, pink and purple foliage is tender, and really needs planting out each year. These plants are not good in cold, damp conditions, and suffer with wet periods followed by sharp cold nights. Cuttings root quickly and should be taken in the growing season, providing a stock of replacement plants as necessary. Regular replacement of plants, combined with an annual haircut in spring, will ensure they do their best. **BG**

Salvia patens

Type: frost-hardy to tender perennial
Soil & situation: moist but well-drained soil/sun or half shade
North American hardiness zone: 8–9
Height: generally 75cm (30in) but up to 1m (3ft)
Spread: 60cm (24in)
Grow for: strong Oxford-blue flowers from mid-summer to mid-autumn; AGM

Salvia patens

I love the depth of blue of these flowers, though because you do not often get more than one or two blooms flowering on each flower spike at a time, the overall effect is not overpowering. In order to create real impact I like to use several plants together, preferably in repeated groups. They will flower from mid-summer to mid-autumn, enabling you to see out the growing season with a bang. Their ovate to triangular leaves are mid-green, hairy top and bottom and are a good, relaxed foil to the flowers. I cannot quite fathom their degree of hardiness – they have been known to withstand temperatures of –7°C (19°F) in the wet, but die in –6°C (21°F) in drier conditions.

These plants do not flower well in baking hot summers, so do not be discouraged if one year its performance dips – it might be the temperature. Trim in late summer to neaten them up and encourage them to flower more profusely. If you do not want to take a chance and leave them out well-mulched over winter, you can treat them as you would a dahlia, as these too form tubers, albeit small ones, which you can lift and store over winter. Alternatively they are simple to grow from seed or from cuttings taken in mid-summer, allowing time for the tuberous roots to become established before the winter. **BG**

Salvia rutilans (syn. *S. elegans* 'Scarlet Pineapple')

PINEAPPLE SAGE

Type: tender, semi-evergreen shrub
Soil & situation: well-drained compost/full sun/undercover
North American hardiness zone: 8–10
Height: 60cm (24in)
Spread: 1.2m (4ft)
Grow for: pineapple-scented foliage and brilliant crimson-scarlet flowers

This stunner is too tender for most gardens though it may survive like a fuchsia, coming again from its roots. However it really is worth growing, and as it roots easily it can be propagated in the autumn and the small plants over-wintered undercover to be put out for the next summer. The scent of the heart-shaped leaves is amazing and they are sensually soft to the touch; the exquisite crimson flowers are fantastic set against the verdant green of the foliage. *Rutilans* means reddish, because of the flowers. The plant's origins are unknown but it appeared in the UK during the Victorian age and became very popular. We still grow other salvias as tender bedding plants.

Pineapple sage must have a warm, well-drained site or it will die promptly the first winter; on a wall with some protection it may come from the roots again. It can be grown as a conservatory specimen easily, though gets big and straggly so really needs constant replacement with newer stock. This is a species so can be grown from spring-sown seed but cuttings and layers are not difficult in summer in a coldframe. Under cover it does act as a magnet for whitefly! **BF**

Salvia rutilans

Salvia sclarea var. *turkestanica*

Plant of the Week (see page 201)

Sambucus nigra 'Aurea'

GOLDEN ELDER

Type: hardy, deciduous shrub
Soil & situation: any soil/anywhere
North American hardiness zone: 6–8
Height: 6m (20ft)
Spread: 5m (16ft)
Grow for: prolific, scented, white foamy flowers in late spring; striking yellow foliage; AGM

I have seen black elder growing as a weed from the tea plantations of Sri Lanka to the wild bush of Jamaica, it is a real survivor. In my garden it comes up everywhere as the birds spread the seeds and it is infuriatingly vigorous! The black berries of the standard form are excellent for jelly, though often giving me stomach ache as a kid when I ate them raw. I love the smell of the flowers and often cook them in batter, but they must be fresh or they taste fishy. I've selected the 'Aurea' form as a garden plant as this is one of the toughest of golden-foliage plants, and it is not so prolifically fruited as the wild form so you get fewer seedlings everywhere.

Related to the honeysuckles, there are 40 other species around the world. It was known to the ancients and used for both medicine and magic. The hollow stems were used as pipes, and by little boys to make pop-guns, the hollow trunks to make bigger instruments – *Sambucus* comes from the Greek *sambuca*, a harp.

Elders will grow almost anywhere but thrive on a moist site and even in quite dense shade; they do well on chalky soils. This yellow-leafed form does best in light shade as it may scorch in full sun. It needs pruning to keep it small and can be cut back hard each year, removing all the old wood. The wild form comes from seed, the variegated and yellow forms are unbelievably easy from autumn cuttings. Prone to aphid attacks, this is otherwise no problem save the self-seeding everywhere. **BF**

John adds:
The variety *Sambucus nigra* 'Guincho Purple' is spectacular with its dark green leaves turning to blackish-purple and then red in autumn. The pink-tinged panicles of flowers appear to have been stained with red wine and are carried on purple stalks. A striking plant for the large border.

Sambucus nigra 'Aurea'

Sanguinaria canadensis

Sanguinaria canadensis
CANADIAN BLOODROOT

Type: hardy, rhizomatous perennial
Soil & situation: moist, humus-rich soil/dappled shade
North American hardiness zone: 3–8
Height: 10cm (4in)
Spread: 30cm (12in) or more
Grow for: delicate white flowers from mid- to late spring; attractive leaves

This delicate-looking gem is very hardy. The heart- to kidney-shaped, blue-green leaves with scalloped margins and prominent red veins on the underside emerge folded, then open up to 30cm (12in) across. Before they do, the very short-lived white flowers have already opened. Just a breath of wind and the petals are quickly lost; if not, they remain on the plant for a month.

The orange-red sap, thought to be natural anti-freeze, is visible in the red leaf stems. It contains the active ingredient sanguinarine. Indians living by Lake Superior used it for cancer treatment. In the 1950s Dr J. W. Fell developed a paste based on bloodroot extract to treat cancers; it was placed on the tumour daily and when it became encrusted he made incisions, packed it with paste and within 2–4 weeks it was destroyed, falling out after 7–14 days, leaving a sore that rapidly healed. His results, mainly on breast cancer, detailed remissions if not cures. A revival of the technique was being used in 1977 – I'm not sure if it still is today.

Sanguinaria canadensis f. *multiplex* is a mass of petals. Each time I have seen it there is always a cluster around the plant and it has plenty to spare! *S. c.* 'Early Form' flowers in early to mid-spring. 'Jerry Flintoff' has semi-double flowers. *S. c.* f. *multiplex* 'Plena' (double bloodroot) has short-lived, double, white flowers. Check the plant regularly when flowering is anticipated.

It is ideal for a sheltered woodland garden and needs humus-rich soil in dappled shade or even full sun with adequate moisture. It spreads very slowly but can be naturalized in grass or under deciduous trees. Divide in late summer just after the leaves fully mature. **MB**

Morus nigra

BLACK MULBERRY

Type: hardy deciduous tree
Soil & situation: sheltered and sunny position/fertile soil
North American hardiness zone: 5–9
Height: 12m (40ft)
Spread: 15m (50ft)
Grow for: architectural form; attractive, bold, heart-shaped leaves; edible, bitter-sweet (but more sweet than bitter) raspberry-like fruits maturing in late summer. Like many plants in this book, it could have been allocated to almost any month, but the fruits are luscious at this time of year – and for weeks before and after; AGM

A mature mulberry tree conveys an almost magical feel to a garden. It gives it an ancient, old-established feel with its gnarled bark and often eccentric outline. Mulberries are fairly fast-growing trees and their characteristic habit does make them look prematurely aged, so maybe the next generation will relish them too. The leaves appear in late spring/early summer and are often not fully out till summer. They cast heavy shade, but even so grass thrives relatively well underneath the canopy and they fall early, most having gone by late autumn.

Paving under the canopy does not look good, as the small fruits will start to drop in summer and carry on ceaselessly until autumn, applying their intense colour to the hard surface below.

If you are keen on the fruit, which can be delicious when mature (about the size of a large loganberry) and fully ripe (when black), order a named selection that produces fine, juicy fruits as opposed to small, seedy, ones. An excellent form is 'Large Black', another is 'King James'. They are vegetatively propagated and will fruit when about six or seven years old.

When the leaves fall, the tree's other qualities come to the fore – the beautiful, warm, rough-textured bark and the architectural form.

Propagate by hardwood cuttings 18cm (7in) long in autumn, with a heel of two-year-old wood, in open ground in a shady spot. Larger cuttings are also successful. Train the tree with a clear stem of about 1.5m (5ft). It may take three or four years before the tree develops feathers, or sideshoots, which then can then be cut back. Once you have this clear stem, you simply let the tree mature. The naturally weeping habit may involve removing some lower limbs – cut these back when the tree is fully dormant to avoid the bleeding sap. Other pendent branches can be propped, and these props can add to the old, gnarled feel of the tree. **BG**

Santolina chaemaecyparissus

Santolina chaemaecyparissus (syn. *S. incana*)

COTTON LAVENDER, LAVENDER COTTON

Type: hardy, evergreen shrub
Soil & situation: well-drained, sandy soil/sun
North American hardiness zone: 6–9
Height & spread: 60cm (24in)
Grow for: delicate, finely divided, ever-grey, aromatic foliage and pretty yellow flowers in mid-summer; AGM

This is one of the best edging plants as it makes a change from the lavender and box you see everywhere doing the same job. The silvery, lacy foliage has a delightful perfume and as I hate to throw away the prunings I use them underfoot as a strewing herb in my sheds and stores. The French call it *garde-robe*, for it is supposed to be good at keeping out clothes moths, but it certainly did not keep them out of my attic where I hung it with some old clothes which are now only fit for making dapper scarecrows.

Introduced to the UK in the 16th century from the Mediterranean, this has about a dozen closely related and similar species. It was given its common name of cotton lavender or lavender cotton from its habit of growth and white woolly appearance. It was considered a good herb for feeding children to cleanse them of worms. The botanical name comes from the Old Latin *sanctum linum,* meaning holy flax.

Santolina needs a well-drained soil in full sun. It is not long lived and some spares should be kept at all times, as it may be lost in a wet or hard winter. Shear back lightly in early spring just before growth starts. It is easy to propagate from cuttings taken with a heel in mid-summer or autumn and can be grown from spring-sown seed. **BF**

Santolina rosmarinifolia subs. *rosmarinifolia* 'Primrose Gem'

COTTON LAVENDER

Type: frost-hardy, evergreen shrub
Soil & situation: thin, well-drained soil (often alkaline)/sunny position
North American hardiness zone: 6–9
Height: 60cm (24in)
Spread: 1m (3ft)
Grow for: aromatic, finely divided evergreen foliage; responds well to regular shearing so is an often-used component of knot gardens; beautiful pale lemon-yellow flowers in massive quantities in mid-summer; AGM

The feathery foliage of this santolina is a refreshing, bright green that seems to have a lot of life about it. Somehow I find that some of the very silver-white forms can look rather flat by comparison. The knobbles of pale flowers are formed at the end of long stalks. This is a useful, rapid-impact plant and one well worth propagating up and then having at the ready to plug gaps in early spring. It will quickly fill out in one summer providing you plant at quite close intervals, about 20cm (8in). The only disadvantage with close planting (assuming you have propagated your own plants) is that they can suffer in dry periods. But as this plant relishes those conditions, it is not often a problem.

The foliage of this plant looks good throughout the year, except of course, when you have just cut it back in spring. It can seem a shame to lay into a fine-looking plant when others around it are looking far less bouncy, but it must be done otherwise it will start to flop and sprawl, exposing bare, leggy stems. Cut it back hard to 15–20cm (6–8in) from the ground. If you have an old specimen, cutting back into the old wood can be fatal, so take cuttings first. Young specimens will spring back to life and in about eight weeks time will look better than new. After flowering, the faded flower shoots must be removed and any long shoots shortened to neaten the plant. To propagate take semi-ripe cuttings in summer; they are quick, easy and successful. **BG**

Santolina rosmarinifolia subsp. *rosmarinifolia* 'Primrose Gem'

Saponaria officinalis

Saponaria officinalis
BOUNCING BET, SOAPWORT

Type: hardy, herbaceous perennial
Soil & situation: any soil/sun or shade/preferably moist
North American hardiness zone: 3–9
Height: 60cm (24in)
Spread: 2m (6½ft)
Grow for: sprawling, straggly, cottage-garden delight with scented pink or white flowers; useful for wild, damp areas

Traditionally the leaves were boiled to extract the soapy sap. I've tried it and it worked, but be warned it is very irritant to the skin although quite effective on clothes. The books say this plant grows erect – don't believe them it flops everywhere. However it is an endearing troublemaker: the floppiness is bad enough but it runs underground when happy, popping up everywhere. The flowers are deliciously scented though, the double forms the more so and it is a delightful thing to put in difficult spots, but not if you like neatness and order.

Saponaria officinalis is a native wild flower and its name comes from the Latin for soap. There are 30 more species, mostly native to Europe. It was not used so much for washing people as wool, though it was a treatment for skin infections and the root extracts were used in medicines.

In a damp garden you'll never get rid of soapwort regardless of the soil; it even survives in my dry garden under a Leylandii hedge. Basically it is a tough plant; it can be trimmed but never trained so is better for the informal or wild garden. The wild forms come from seed sown any time and the roots can be divided whenever if kept moist. The only problem is this is a thug in tart's clothing! **BF**

Sarcococca confusa
Plant of the Week (see page 403)

Satureja hortensis
SUMMER SAVORY

Type: hardy, annual herb
Soil & situation: any soil/sun to light shade
North American hardiness zone: annual
Height: 30cm (12in)
Spread: 20cm (8in)
Grow for: brilliant flavour; good dwarf edger

This is not unattractive and makes a good, heather-like edging plant for low beds, but it is as a culinary herb that it shines. Summer savory, and don't be fooled by the coarse and rough perennial winter form, is the herb for savoury dishes. I put it in almost everything that is not actually sweet and I think it goes especially well with dried bean casseroles. It is easy to dry and retains its flavour well. Grow plenty, as once you've tried it you'll want more.

Well known and well loved by all the ancient Mediterranean people for its culinary uses, it retains its ancient name of *Satureia* or *Satyreia* as it was reputed to have aphrodisiacal properties; well maybe it does, I use a lot in my cooking and I certainly need a muzzle....

Although summer savory can be grown as temporary edging in the ornamental or herb garden, it deserves a place in the vegetable plot. A poor soil will do but moist and in full sun is preferable. Harvest just before flowering; if cut back hard, a second flush of growth can be induced with a good watering. Sow, preferably *in situ*, in mid-spring. I have never known it suffer any problem other than poor germination in cold years, so use a cloche at first. **BF**

Satureja hortensis

Saxifraga 'Ruth Draper'

Saxifraga 'Ruth Draper'
SAXIFRAGE

Type: hardy, evergreen perennial
Soil & situation: moist, humus-rich, very well-drained, neutral to alkaline soil/light shade
North American hardiness zone: 2–6
Height: 3cm (1in)
Spread: 20cm (8in)
Grow for: an attractive ground-coverer for summer show in crevices

Previously known as *Saxifraga oppositifolia* 'Ruth Draper', it is not very big, but in this case size doesn't matter. Accustomed to Arctic conditions, it will flower readily in well-drained soil .

Mat forming, with rosettes of tiny, stiff, dark green leaves on branching stems. The single, cup-shaped, rose-pink flowers appear in early summer on very short stems and may flower spasmodically until the autumn. This cheerful little saxifrage is ideal for growing in crevices in a rockery or scree bed where the drainage is good. It is not a rampant grower, making it a good choice for a stone trough or shallow pan.

Top dress with a surface mulch of riddled leaf mould in spring and water the plants in summer to prevent the soil drying out. If grown in the open, the afternoon, summer sun will scorch the foliage. Propagation is by fresh seed sown in the autumn and over-wintered in a cold frame. Individual rosettes can be rooted as cuttings in late spring and early summer. Remove the lower leaves and insert the cuttings in a peat-based compost with additional well-washed, coarse grit. **JC**

Euonymus europeaus 'Red Cascade'

SPINDLE BUSH

Type: hardy, deciduous shrub or small tree
Soil & situation: any soil, but flourishes on chalk/full sun or light shade
North American hardiness zone: 4–7
Height: 3m (10ft)
Spread: 2.5m (8ft)
Grow for: brilliant autumn colour and unusual fruits; AGM

You may well have passed this green-stemmed shrub with arching branches and narrowly oval, mid-green leaves without even realizing it. For much of the year the spindle bush crouches in the hedgerows playing its annual game of hide-and-seek, then suddenly in autumn it erupts into life. First there's an explosion of bright red leaves, then in a quick-fire burst of momentum it stuns a gasping crowd with one of nature's more psychedelic moments. 'Bravo,' they cry as masses of unusual pink fruits split to reveal bright orange seeds that are attractive to birds. 'More,' they plead, and pendulous, bronzed and red *Euonymus europeaeus* 'Thornhayes' takes to the stage, accompanied by a pallid-fruited *E. e.* f. *albus*. Finally, *E. e.* 'Aucubifolius' with mottled yellow and white leaves saunters forward, 'He looks so ill,' some whisper. 'Don't worry,' comes the reply, 'he'll be in the pink by autumn.' 'It's true,' they all agree, 'when it comes to it the euonymus is really far from anonymous'!

It needs full sun or partial shade, and in the former it must have more moisture. It thrives in almost any well-drained soil, particularly on chalk. The easiest way to propagate is from nodal cuttings, which root well. It can suffer from mildew and is a host to the black bean aphid, which attacks broad beans, nasturtiums, philadelphus and dahlias.

The wood was once used for making skewers and toothpicks; the fruits were strongly purgative and sometimes baked, powdered and rubbed into the hair as a remedy for head-lice. **MB**

Scabiosa 'Chile Black'
PINCUSHION FLOWER

Type: hardy, herbaceous perennial
Soil & situation: well-drained soil/preferably alkaline or neutral with moderate fertility/ sun/tolerates part shade
North American hardiness zone: 3–9
Height & spread: 60cm (24in)
Grow for: near-black to dark wine-coloured flowers speckled with cream anthers in the summer; an uncommon but extremely useful colour shade; a vigorous and easy plant to grow, except on heavy soils

It is always interesting to grow something a little out of the ordinary and this curious colour is different. I use it particularly with other wine and purple plants but it looks great with strong orange tones too. This is a fairly vigorous plant, though it has a sparse habit, so it is more successful to plant several plants close together to achieve more impact. The flowers never come in huge volumes, so the effect is subtle.

It is well worth dead-heading this plant, then the succession of flowers will last for over a month if not two. It is not long lived, and to maintain good healthy plants it is best to divide them every three or four years. To propagate it you can take basal cuttings or divide. **BG**

Scabiosa 'Chile Black'

Schisandra rubriflora

Schisandra rubriflora
MAGNOLIA VINE

Type: hardy, deciduous climber
Soil & situation: well-drained, fertile soil/sun or dappled shade
North American hardiness zone: 7–9
Height & spread: 10m (33ft)
Grow for: attractive buds, flowers in mid- and late spring, and fruit

This twining, woody climber with aromatic bark, slender red shoots and lance-shaped leaves, which turn yellow in autumn, is believed to be a relative of the magnolia. Look at the fragrant flowers, appearing in late spring, and there are some similarities. The buds, resembling ripe cherries, open to dark crimson flowers, to 3cm (1in) across. To obtain fruit, male and female plants must be grown; several nurseries have been sexing their schisandras and now stock both male and female plants. The scarlet, fleshy fruits ripening by early autumn hang in clusters up to 15cm (6in) long. In their native habitat, they are eaten fresh or dried. No please, I insist, after you!

Schisandra grandiflora has aromatic bark, leathery leaves with conspicuous veins and white to pale pink flowers in late spring and early summer. The shiny, edible, red fruits packed together in a tight, bright, cluster are very ornamental.

They need fertile, well-drained, moisture-retentive loam in sun or dappled shade, preferring slightly acid soils but tolerating some alkalinity. Dig in plenty of well-rotted organic matter before planting, mulch in spring and water in dry spells. Prune in late winter to remove dead wood and keep to their allocated space. Grow as a wall plant twining up wires, up a post or through trees or large shrubs. Propagate by semi-ripe cuttings in summer, layers in autumn, suckers or seed. They are susceptible to aphids. **MB**

Schizanthus x *wisetonensis*
POOR MAN'S ORCHID

Type: half-hardy or tender annual
Soil & situation: most soils/sun or under cover
North American hardiness zone: annual
Height & spread: 50cm (20in)
Grow for: attractive ferny foliage; unbelievable mass of amazing flowers; good for diligent kids

Who could not fall in love with this beauty, as even if badly grown she still produces the most beautifully exotic flowers just not in such great profusion? A well-grown, good specimen is a magnificent sight. The common name is so apt as there really is no other plant that can give such a display, yet is so cheap and easy. The only downside is that it's neither scented nor edible. The botanical name is from the Greek *schizo*, meaning to divide, and *anthos*, flower, as the corolla is deeply cut. There are several related species, mostly from South America, but the modern selected hybrids are far superior.

Schizanthus needs a sunny spot on a warm bed to be used for summer bedding, or grow it in a pot or planter and have it on the patio. It should be started off under cover in mid-spring and planted out in early summer, or grown on and kept in pots, ideally sowing the best selection for whichever purpose. With careful culture in a heated greenhouse, sown late with much nipping out, the very dwarf, squat plants can be produced with a mass of flowers for Christmas. It suffers no problem other than it seems almost surreal in bloom. **BF**

Schizanthus x *wisetonensis*

Scilla peruviana

Scilla peruviana
SQUILL

Type: Frost-hardy bulbous perennial
Soil & situation: very free-draining soil/sun
North American hardiness zone: 8–9
Height: 30cm (12in)
Spread: 30cm (12in) or more
Grow for: dramatic buds and flowers in late spring and early summer

It's comforting to know that Carl Linnaeus, the Father of Botanical Latin, had occasional bad days at the office. He named this plant *Scilla peruviana* when it's actually from the Mediterranean!

The rounded flowerhead on a mid-green stem elongates into a dense cone of up to a hundred violet-blue, starry flowers punctuated with yellow anthers, then dries to become a florist's dream! The rosette of waxy, long, green leaves becomes rather untidy by the time they flower but is easy to ignore. When my bulbs come into bloom I'm reminded of the wonderful flower market in Funchal, Madeira, the 'island of flowers', where I bought them. The market is a buzzy, bustling place where 'Belladonna' lilies, strelitzias and orchids abound and it's overflowing with clamouring customers all eager to buy plants. Arrive early and visit the fruit market upstairs which is packed with exotics, such as balloon-sized avocados, then go to the fish market and see the scary-looking espada fish that is hauled up from the deep. My *Scilla peruviana* is packed full of happy memories! Look out also for the white-flowered *S. peruviana* 'Alba'.

Plant in autumn at the base of a sunny wall or fence with the tips just below the soil surface or grow in pots of well-drained compost in cooler climates. In needs a sunny position on very free-draining, moderate to poor soil; richer conditions bring more leaf rather than flower. Where necessary, encourage flowering with sulphate of potash in autumn or early spring. Divide and re-plant congested clumps in spring. **MB**

Scrophularia auriculata 'Variegata'
VARIEGATED FIGWORT

Type: hardy, herbaceous perennial
Soil & situation: moist or wet soil/sun or part shade
North American hardiness zone: 5–9
Height: up to 75cm (30in)
Spread: 60cm (24in)
Grow for: an attractive foliage plant which quickly makes an impact

When I gardened on moisture-retentive, heavy loam, this plant was a firm favourite. It has ovate leaves with wavy margins which are picked out in broad irregularly creamy-white variegations. This striking foliage grows rapidly from basal evergreen or semi-evergreen rosettes. It will easily make 75cm (30in) of growth in a season, forming a good bushy clump and as such is a highly useful filler. It flowers in mid- to late summer; the yellowish-green flowers are insignificant. In favourable conditions where there is no shortage of water, this plant will stay looking in its prime until well into early autumn. In dryer conditions its charms, sadly, will be well over a month or two before this. Another way to enjoy this plant is as cut foliage – the stems last for a long time in water and are an unusual but showy and versatile favourite of florists.

To keep this plant looking good, remove the flowers as soon as they start to appear, otherwise the foliage goes downhill fast. Its leaves are also very attractive to slugs, capsid bugs and the mullein shark caterpillar, unfortunately, but they will quickly recover if you have to cut them down to size once in a while. **BG**

Scrophularia auriculata 'Variegata'

Cyclamen europaeum (syn. *C. odoratum*)

CYCLAMEN

Type: hardy, evergreen corm
Soil & situation: well-drained, moist soil/light sun to shade
North American hardiness zone: 5–9
Height & spread: 15cm (6in)
Grow for: gorgeous evergreen leaves, gorgeous flowers, gorgeous scent! The best choice if you want cyclamens in autumn; AGM

Cyclamens are wonderful for their resistance to pests and diseases; their beautiful, marbled, heart-shaped leaves each with the most exquisite, finely executed pattern; the delicately sculptured flowers (up to a hundred of them per plant in a long flowering season); and the fantastic scent – this plant has it all. Shame it is not ten times bigger!

The name comes from the Greek word for circular. Cyclamens are native to Europe and were once so common that they were used as pig fodder – well, I guess the pigs dug them up, in fact – thus its old name of sowbread. It has an odd, spherical seed capsule held near the crown by a 'spring' made of old flower stalk.

It needs a moist, rich, limy, friable soil in dappled shade under a deciduous tree. Plant *C. europaeum* deeper than for other cyclamen at 10cm (4in), and dress with bonemeal in spring. I grow them from seed taken from my most scented plants; they take several years to reach flowering size. Small seedlings can be found around older plants and moved when tiny. Plant corms smooth side down. Unlike most other cyclamen, plant this one in spring. And presumably avoid having pigs visit. **BF**

Sedum telephium subsp. *maximum* 'Atropurpureum'

Sedum spectabile

Plant of the Week (see page 289)

Sedum telephium subsp. *maximum* 'Atropurpureum'

Type: hardy, herbaceous perennial
Soil & situation: light free-draining soils/neutral to slightly alkaline soils are more suitable than acid ones/full sun
North American hardiness zone: 4–9
Height: 45cm (18in)
Spread: 25cm (10in)
Grow for: superb, dark purple stems and glaucous, dark purple leaves; flowers in late summer to early autumn; AGM

I highly rate this fleshy plant for its decidedly useful, dark purple foliage, the leaves being succulent, oval, but slightly scalloped too. It has quite an open-spreading habit, which lends itself to being grown in an area of gravel, or mulched with a chipping, with other unusual-looking plants such as *Euphorbia myrsinites* (see page 95). It is also good in borders, contrasting especially well with strong, juicy limes. The purple leaves are good in border situations but best when growing out of a sea of low ground cover. The flowers are a pinky-red, with orange-red centres and are small, star-shaped and carried in sprays.

It needs little attention apart from cutting back at the end of the year. Dividing it up when it becomes congested, every three or four years, helps to promote its flowering capacity. Propagation is simple from cuttings. **BG**

Sempervivum arachnoideum

HOUSELEEK

Type: hardy, evergreen perennial
Soil & situation: barely any soil/sun
North American hardiness zone: 5–8
Height: 3cm (1in)
Spread: 5cm (2in)
Grow for: weird cactus or dahlia flower-like plant for dry spots with little or no soil; occasional odd red flowers in clusters on stalks; rosettes of leaves and a strange cobweb of white hairs at the leaf tips; AGM

I like all the houseleeks, from the standard ones found on roofs to the coloured ones such as *Sempervivum* 'Rubine', but most of all this delightful beauty which makes its own spider's web joining together the tips of the pointed leaves, amazing. I love their low-maintenance requirements and have them not on my roof where I cannot see them, but growing in lumps of timber and rock as garden ornaments.

Native to southern Europe, it was known to the ancients – *semper vivum* is the Latin for 'always alive'. The usual form, *S. tectorum*, grows naturally on roofs, and was believed to protect the abode from lightning. Strangely this is now shown to be valid as points do discharge the accumulating electrical force, diffusing the risk – the same principle as for the modern lightning rod.

Houseleeks require almost no soil, or water, or attention; once old and congested they will flower and die rosette by rosette, slowly, and the dead ones can be removed and the others will fill in the gap. It can be grown from seed but is much quicker from offsets. Birds can devastate an old clump, ruining it in their search for worms; tie it down with black plastic netting or grow under wire cloches. **BF**

Sempervivum arachnoideum

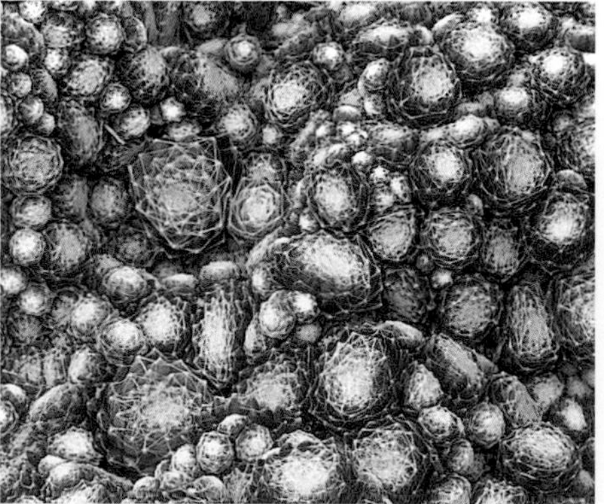

Skimmia japonica subsp. *reevesiana growing with snowdrops*

Skimmia japonica subsp. *reevesiana*

Type: hardy, evergreen shrub
Soil & situation: moist, humus-rich, well-drained soil/light or deep shade
North American hardiness zone: 9–10
Height & spread: 1m (3ft)
Grow for: clusters of red berries; aromatic foliage; tiny white flowers

Sexually this plant is confused. It's a hermaphrodite, with male and female flowers on the same plant, so doesn't require a partner for the production of berries. It forms a low, compact mound with narrow, 7cm (2¾in) long, mid-green leaves with a pale margin. The terminal panicles of white flowers appear in late spring and are followed by egg-shaped, mat, bright crimson-red berries. They will remain on the shrub through the winter and are often still looking good when the next season's flowers appear.

It will not succeed in ground which dries out or in an alkaline soil, but it thrives in city gardens and industrial pollution. Pruning is not usually necessary. Propagation is by semi-ripe cuttings in mid-summer. Rooting is speeded up with bottom heat in a propagator. Occasionally the base of the cutting will callus over, forming a large growth rather than roots. Scrape this off and start again. It will root the second time. Take care not to damage the brittle, white roots when potting. **JC**

Skimmia japonica 'Veitchii'

Skimmia japonica 'Veitchii'

Type: hardy, evergreen shrub
Soil & situation: good, fertile soil/grows particularly well in light shade/will cope with a sunny position. This is a female clone and in order to produce the fruiting berries, it is necessary to plant a male clone with it, such as *Skimmia japonica* 'Rubella'
North American hardiness zone: 7–9
Height & spread: 70cm (27½in)
Grow for: superb, large bunches of vivid red fruit from late summer and still looks good until early summer the following year; eye-catching panicles of fragrant white flowers in spring; evergreen foliage which looks smart throughout the year

Skimmias, in common with many evergreens, are not the fastest growers, but this is a vigorous female clone. The leaves are particularly broadly ovate, and the habit of growth is fairly upright. Although the flowers are scented, the male forms tend to have a stronger fragrance (the equivalent of men's feet in the plant world but in a desirable form!). So when choosing your male clone to accompany this berrying stunner, go for *S. japonica* 'Rubella': the pretty flower buds stand up proudly and are a deep chintz pink, as are the margins of the leaf. If you are pushed for space, settle for *S. japonica* 'Robert Fortune', as this has both male and female flowers on the same plant.

In sunny positions you get more flowers, but the leaves can become rather yellow and scorched. Ideally plant in light shade or plant some big bruiser nearby to shade it for you. You can propagate it from cuttings in early summer or from seed sown in spring, but of course, the resulting plant will be different from the parent. **BG**

Smilacina racemosa
Plant of the Week (see page 161)

Solanum crispum
Plant of the Week (see page 297)

Solanum laxum 'Album' (syn. *S. jasminoides* 'Album')
WHITE-FLOWERED POTATO VINE

Type: half-hardy, semi-evergreen, climbing shrub
Soil & situation: reasonably well-drained but moist fertile soil/sun or part shade/may need some protection in colder areas until well established/flowers most profusely on a warm, sunny wall
North American hardiness zone: 8–9
Height: 6m (20ft)
Spread: 2m (6½ft)
Grow for: vigorous, climber with long climbing stems; flowers from summer to autumn/highly fragrant, beautiful, white flowers; AGM

Do not be put off by this elegant beauty's common name – it is the same family, of course, but not so down-to-earth. It is one of my favourite climbers, mainly because of the profusion of elegant, star-shaped flowers and obvious anthers borne over an incredibly long period. These are then followed by black fruit. In the East Midlands I find the foliage is pretty much evergreen as opposed to semi-evergreen. Despite a series of heavy frosts, gales and snow, it is still hanging on thickly now, at the end of winter, with its glossy, dark green, oval leaves. It is 3–4m (10–13ft) high now, and it is about five years old. It is a fast grower too and, to please impatient clients, I need a few of these up my sleeve.

Solanum laxum 'Album'

You do need to support this climber with a trellis, system of wires or whatever. As far as pruning goes you cut back the sideshoots to within three or four bueds of the established, permanent framework, and thin out any overcrowded shoots as necessary. This is best done after flowering. **BG**

Solanum tuberosum 'Dunluce'
POTATO, EARLY CROP

Type: half-hardy, herbaceous vegetable
Soil & situation: most soils/sun
North American hardiness zone: annual
Height: 60cm (24in)
Spread: 30cm (12in)
Grow for: there are no potatoes like new potatoes; your own are the freshest and taste the best, and this is the finest variety

I love my new potatoes and grow them for more than half the year round, enjoying them forced from early to mid-spring until the outdoor lot crop in early summer and go on until late summer, when the main crop potatoes arrive (they make better chips). If you want the maximum crop of earlies, go for 'Rocket' instead, but if you want supreme flavour, grow 'Dunluce'.

Members of a wide family with many edible and many poisonous members, potatoes would not be allowed by governmental edict if found today; they would be classed as an illegal poisonous drug. Greened potatoes, the seedpods and the foliage actually are all potentially deadly! Coming from South America these originated in the high mountain valleys of Peru and have been much bred and selected to give the modern forms. 'Dunluce' is an 'early' and is very different to a 'main' crop (see *Solanum tuberosum* 'King Edward', next entry). Earlies crop early so miss the dreaded blight most years; many can be stored but they give light yields.

Although earlies can be grown outdoors at about 30cm (12in) apart they are much better grown under cloches, in a cold frame or in a greenhouse in pots, as then they give really early crops. Put the sets into pots at fortnightly intervals from early winter to early spring, also under cloches from late winter, and plant outdoors for summer crops from early to late spring. Ideally chit the later plantings beforehand by standing them in an egg tray in a frost-free, light place until they are used. Leave all the sprouts on the sets and plant them rose end (more eyes or sprouts on it and not the little bit of old stem)up. The only real problem is frost! **BF**

Solanum tuberosum 'King Edward'

Solanum tuberosum 'King Edward'

POTATO, MAIN CROP

Type: half-hardy, herbaceous vegetable
Soil & situation: most soils/sun
North American hardiness zone: annual
Height: 1m (3ft)
Spread: 60cm (24in)
Grow for: there are no potatoes like home-grown potatoes and this is finest of the main crop varieties

I love my potatoes and grow more than a couple of dozen varieties every year. There are more reliable and heavier-cropping sorts such as 'Remarka', some with better texture for salads such as 'Charlotte', but few match 'King Edward' for flavour and all-round kitchen use.

Main crops are very different to earlies and the two lines diverged years ago. Earlies are bred to be quick and many especially to grow under cover; main crops are bred to give the maximum yield of good storing potatoes. Thus, they necessarily take a longer season to finish and need to be growing into autumn for the biggest crops. But they still need planting early, though they do not need chitting (see previous entry). However, the shoots are reduced to three at planting so as to get fewer but bigger tubers. This variety was originally a chance seedling of unknown parentage found in Northumberland and called 'Fellside Hero' for some years until re-introduced as 'King Edward' in 1902.

Main crops need a richer soil than earlies so include plenty of well-rotted manure, give them full sun. Plant the sets rose end up (see previous entry), removing all the shoots bar three, and further apart than earlies. Water generously when you see the flowers. Remove the flowers. Earth up the plants to prevent the swelling tubers seeing the light and greening. Dig on a drying day when the haulms have died down, dry the tubers for an hour or so before packing in paper sacks and storing in a cool, dark, frost-free place. Slugs are always a problem; baiting them with old potatoes cut into chips works well. Blight is a problem in many areas and few sprays work well – try prayer.
BF

Solidago 'Goldenmosa'

GOLDEN ROD, AARON'S ROD

Type: hardy, woody perennial
Soil & situation: moderately fertile, sandy, well-drained soil/full sun
North American hardiness zone: 5–9
Height: 90cm (36in)
Spread: 45cm (18in)
Grow for: bright yellow summer and autumn colour in the herbaceous border; AGM

I have fond memories of this plant. It was one of the first perennials I grew when I was a boy. Powdery mildew was a problem then and, while there is an improvement in the varieties, the mildew hasn't gone away.

It forms a vigorous, bushy plant with stiff, upright stems. The 10cm- (4in-) long, wrinkled, yellow-green leaves become sparse further up the stem. The conical panicles of tiny, bright yellow, mimosa-like flowers appear in late summer and early autumn. They are in great demand as a golden backdrop in flower arrangements. *Solidago* 'Loddon Gold' has a similar habit of growth with deep yellow, autumn flowers.

Remove the flowerheads after flowering to prevent self-sown seedlings appearing as weeds all over the garden. Clumps should be divided in spring every two to three years. The oldest centre portion becomes woody with few shoots and should be discarded. The outer growths can be teased apart, complete with roots, and planted out in the border or potted up. **JC**

Solidago 'Goldenmosa'

Sophora japonica

Sophora japonica
JAPANESE PAGODA TREE

Type: hardy, deciduous tree
Soil & situation: open sunny site with well-drained soil/will tolerate fairly thin soils
North American hardiness zone: 5–9
Height: up to 30m (100ft)
Spread: to 20m (66ft)
Grow for: a very elegant tree with several assets: attractive foliage; large panicles of creamy-white flowers in late summer till early autumn on mature trees; AGM

This tree is too rarely grown. It is similar to *Robinia pseudoacacia,* but I think far more useful: partly because it does not grow to such a massive size, and partly because it doesn't suddenly drop huge branches without warning; it does not sucker either; and because its leaves remain green and fresh on the tree, a good month after the robinias have lost theirs. So if you are looking for a tree that is fast-growing with very handsome divided leaves that look translucent with the sun through them and has a shapely, rounded head, then go for this. I did not add its flowering qualities: these are amazing too – huge fragrant flowers in the late autumn – but these are not produced on young trees. Be magnanimous and someone else will be able to enjoy these.

Establish the tree as for *Acer capillipes* (see page 22). Otherwise there is little care apart from removing dead, damaged and diseased wood. **BG**

Sorbus cashmiriana

Type: hardy, deciduous tree
Soil & situation: an open position in moist, well-drained, fertile soil/sun or partial shade
North American hardiness zone: 5–7
Height: 8m (25ft)
Spread: 7m (23ft)
Grow for: spring flowers; autumn and winter fruits; AGM

This is one of the prettiest trees for the small garden. It has a neat, open habit with leaves comprising 17–19 small serrated leaflets. In late spring, it's decked with flat clusters of soft pink flowers 18cm (7in) across, which are replaced by loose, hanging, pale green fruits made prominent in autumn when they become shiny and white. White fruits have the advantage of being ignored by birds and remain well into winter long after leaf fall and slowly moulder away.

It was introduced to the UK in the 1930s and is a native of the sub-alpine zones of the western Himalayas, including the area known as Baltistan, which you would have never heard of a few years ago but which is now famous for its Balti curries. Next time you have one, share it with your sorbus and give it a pungent reminder of home in what is now northern Pakistan. Other white-flowered sorbus include *S. hupehensis* and *S. prattii,* another fine small tree.

It prefers a good, moist soil and makes an ideal specimen tree for lawns. Plant a small group, if you have the space. Prune in winter to maintain the shape or remove dead, diseased, dying, crossing, weak and rubbing branches. Grow from seed chilled over winter and sown in spring. Sadly, it is susceptible to fire blight, but this should not deter you from planting this fabulous tree in areas where the disease does not occur. **MB**

Sorbus cashmiriana

Sorbus sargentiana

ROWAN TREE

Type: hardy, deciduous tree
Soil & situation: deep, moist, fertile, well-drained soil/full sun
North American hardiness zone: 5–7
Height & spread: 10m (33ft)
Grow for: year-round interest – autumn leaf colour, flowers, berries and buds. I plumped for October because the autumn leaf colour is perhaps its greatest attribute, but it was a close-run thing. AGM.

This is my favourite sorbus and I am not likely to change my mind. It has the ability to show off for 12 months of the year.

The 35cm (14in) long, dark green, pinnate leaves turn orange-red and then a brilliant crimson in autumn. Even after leaf fall they lay out the red carpet. Large 20cm (8in) wide clusters of white flowers are produced in early summer followed by bunches of bright red berries. If left alone by the birds they will last well into winter. Finally, to complete the year, the short, stout shoots carry large, sticky, deep red buds like those of the horse chestnut. These open in spring as young, red-tinted leaves.

It is not fussy as to location but dislikes alkaline or waterlogged soil. When grown in light shade the autumn leaf colour is less intense. Occasionally it will send up erect branches forming a narrow angle where they join. Remove the weaker branch before it becomes large. If left to grow, the branches may split apart when mature, spoiling the shape of the tree.

Propagation is by budding on to *Sorbus aucuparia* rootstock in summer or grafting in winter. It is possible to root softwood cuttings in summer, but there is a low success rate. It will not come true from seed. **JC**

Sorbus 'Joseph Rock' November

Type: hardy, upright, deciduous tree
Soil & situation: well-drained, fertile soil; short-lived on chalk/prefers sun or partial shade
North American hardiness zone: 7–8
Height & spread: 10m (33ft) x 7m (23ft), occasionally more
Grow for: attractive form, flowers, autumn colour, fruits. Another plant that is special over several seasons of the year, but again autumn colour and fruit carried the day.

Words can't express how much I adore this plant. If I had the chance, I'd cover the country with *Sorbus* 'Joseph Rock' then you could love it too! I remember the first one I ever planted outside a bank in Leicester and ever since then it's been my favourite tree! Sorbus are real 'value for money' plants with four seasons of interest, which makes them invaluable for the garden. There are flowers in spring, foliage in summer, fruits and colour in autumn, and sculptural shape and form in winter; *S.* 'Joseph Rock' is the best! It's a rowan of unknown parentage and is probably a natural hybrid that came from seed collected by Joseph Rock in China 1932. Thank you Dr Rock!

It is upright with a compact 'crown' and leaves composed of 15–19 narrowly oblong, sharply toothed leaflets. They are the perfect backcloth for the white flowers up to 10cm (4in) across that appear in late spring. In summer, it's decorated with fresh green foliage and clusters of up to 50 fruits, which start off pale green, become creamy-yellow, and turn primrose-yellow as they mature. The fruits remain on the tree, untouched by birds until long after leaf fall. They mingle with the rich autumn colour of the tree when ablaze with orange-red and purple, then re-emerge to illuminate winter with a soft buttery glow.

Sow seed in spring. Prune in winter to retain shape. Unfortunately it is highly susceptible to fire blight, but should be planted widely in areas where this does not occur. **MB**

Sorbus 'Joseph Rock'

Plant of the Week (see page 369)

Sorbus reducta

DWARF ROWAN

Type: hardy, deciduous shrub
Soil & situation: humus-rich, well-drained, neutral to acid soil/full sun or partial shade
North American hardiness zone: 5–8
Height: 1–1.2m (3–4ft)
Spread: 2m (6½ft)
Grow for: glossy leaves; clusters of white flowers; red berries turning to white; AGM

Size matters, and it is size that stops this sorbus being a tree. It has all the attributes of a good rowan, including brilliant autumn leaf colour, flowers and fruit in early winter.

A free-suckering shrub with stiff, upright branches, it will quickly colonize large areas. The 10cm (4in) long, pinnate, glossy, dark green leaves turn to red and finally purple before leaf fall. Clusters of small white flowers appear in late spring and are followed by spherical, deep red berries which turn white in early winter. A super shrub for the larger rockery where it can be contained within bounds.

It is totally hardy, well capable of withstanding cold winds and prolonged frost. Propagation is by transplanting suckers. There seems to be a strain in circulation which doesn't produce many berries. It would be a pity to plant it as the berries help to make this a special shrub. The birds leave mine alone until well into the New Year but that is no guarantee your feathered friends won't be really greedy or hungry. **JC**

Sorbus reducta

Spartium junceum

Sorbus sargentiana

Plant of the Week (see page 367)

Spartium junceum

SPANISH BROOM

Type: frost-hardy, deciduous shrub
Soil & situation: well-drained, alkaline soil/full sun
North American hardiness zone: 8–10
Height & spread: 3m (10ft)
Grow for: a mass of yellow in summer; AGM

Rabbits love this plant even more than I do, I stop short of eating it. The first three plants were devoured, so the fourth was better protected than Fort Knox and is a mass of colour every year. It seems to be trying to flower for the others as well. It forms an upright shrub with slender, dark green stems. Small quantities of tiny, dark green leaves, silky on the underside, furnish the stems. From early summer to mid-autumn the plant smothers itself in 45cm (18in) long terminal racemes of flower. Pea-like, golden-yellow flowers are sweetly scented. They are followed by 8cm (3½in) long, flat, brown seedpods. Trained on wires, against a red or brown brick wall, close to an opening window provides two of the senses, sight and smell, with a treat. It thrives in coastal gardens and on thin soils overlying chalk.

Pruning consists of removing straggly branches in spring. Old plants can be cut down close to the ground and will grow away flowering within two years. Propagation is by seed in spring or sown fresh and over-wintered in a cold frame. They dislike being moved so thin out seedlings when they are small and transplant before they become large. **JC**

Spiraea japonica 'Goldflame'

Type: hardy, deciduous shrub
Soil & situation: moist, fertile, well-drained soil/full sun
North American hardiness zone: 4–9
Height & spread: 1m (3ft)
Grow for: wonderful foliage colour; brings structure to the garden

There are spiraea that inspire and this, for me, is one of them. It lies dormant all winter with no hint of its beauty. Then, in spring, it bursts into life with a collection of leaf colours to make a painter's overalls look jaded. It seems to grow in two stages. Firstly it quickly forms a compact mound and stays about the same size for a season or two. Then it takes off, forming a dense, twiggy clump 1m (3ft) high.

The leaves emerge bronze-red, turning to a bright, buttery-yellow, while the next batch of new leaves provides a contrast in colour. In summer they become mid-green with occasional splashes of yellow. Dark pink flowers appear in summer at the tips of that year's growth. A similar variety, *Spiraea japonica* 'Golden Princess', retains its golden foliage through the summer, turning red in autumn.

I manage to fit *S. j.* 'Goldflame' into almost all of my landscape designs and love to plant it in groups of five or six spaced about 1m (3ft) apart. When pruning a group of them I cheat, clipping 50 per cent of them hard to within 10cm (4in) of the base of the plant. These produce maximum leaf colour. The remainder are lightly pruned resulting in early leaves with less colour on bigger plants. The following year I hard prune the other half.

Propagation is easy. Take small, softwood cuttings in early summer and root them around the edge of a pot of gritty compost. Cover with a clear plastic bag. They will root within weeks ready for potting on before autumn and their leaf fall. **JC**

Spiraea japonica 'Goldflame'

Stachys byzantina 'Big Ears'

Stachys byzantina 'Big Ears'

LAMB'S TONGUE, LAMB'S TAIL, LAMB'S EARS, WOOLLY BETONY

Type: hardy perennial
Soil & situation: well-drained, reasonably fertile soil/prefers sunshine
North American hardiness zone: 4–8
Height: 1m (3ft)
Spread: 60cm (24in)
Grow for: one of the most good-natured and tolerant of the silver-leaved plants with bold, attractive leaves and little tendency to flower

I think the common form of this plant was my favourite as a child, as like many children, I adored the furry leaves. But as a professional gardener, I quickly became disenchanted with it as after flowering it disintegrates into a messy mixture of spent flower stalks and miserable leaves. Then my mother gave me a clump of 'Big Ears' and my affection was reawakened. This form has larger, cleanly-shaped, silvery, felted leaves that form a very decorative carpet. It does flower, but much less so than the ordinary form, and so the foliage keeps looking neat for most of the growing season. In the coldest winter months it does not totally disappear, but keeps some almost respectable-looking leaves. *S. b.* 'Silver Carpet' is a better-known form which only occasionally flowers, and as such is neater and better than the common form, but the foliage does not compare with 'Big Ears'.

This plant needs little looking after apart from dividing up old clumps every so often – this is also one of the best ways to propagate it. It is worthwhile removing any flower spikes as soon as they start to rise as it helps to keep the plant at its best. Some forms, particularly 'Silver Carpet', are prone to mildew, but dividing the clumps more frequently can help to prevent this. **BG**

Stachyurus praecox

Type: hardy, medium to large, deciduous shrub
Soil & situation: moist, humus-rich soil/sun or partial shade/shelter
North American hardiness zone: 7–9
Height: 2m (6½ft)
Spread: 3m (10ft)
Grow for: yellow flowers in late winter and early spring; occasional autumn colour; AGM

Nature possesses an array of unusual colour combinations. Take the flowers of *Stachyurus praecox* for instance: they are an unfamiliar tone of yellow with a slight limy tint and unless my eyes are deceiving me, the purity of colour makes them almost iridescent. They hang in ranks of stiff, gravity-defying flower spikes to 7cm (2¾in) long from reddish-brown, leafless stems. The two colours may not be a combination for your lounge, but it's perfect to brighten up a dull grey winter's day!

Tiny, bell-shaped flowers are formed the previous year, maturing in autumn before leaf fall but not opening until late winter or early spring, depending on the weather. The species is hermaphrodite but there is a selection *S. p.* 'Gracilis' with female flowers. *S. p.* var. *matsuzakii* has thicker, pale green stems and larger leaves. The yellow flowers open later too, in mid-spring and it's only suitable for mild climates.

S. praecox needs sun or partial shade and shelter, particularly in cold areas where it can be trained against a wall as the flowers can be damaged by frost. Any soil will do, but cool, humus-rich, acid soil is favoured and it is also lime tolerant. Prune after flowering, remove dead, diseased, dying, crossing, rubbing or weak wood at the base; it soon regenerates. Thin out congested specimens. Tie in the strongest growth of wall shrubs after flowering, replacing the framework regularly using young growth at the base. Propagate by layering or semi-ripe cuttings with a heel from mid-summer to early autumn. **MB**

Stachyurus praecox

Sternbergia lutea

Sternbergia lutea
AUTUMN DAFFODIL

Type: hardy, bulbous perennial
Soil & situation: free-draining, alkaline soil/sun
North American hardiness zone: 7–9
Height: 20cm (8in)
Spread: 30cm (12in)
Grow for: bright yellow, goblet-shaped flowers at the start of autumn

It's found in the Mediterranean on or near cultivated land in dry scrub and rocky grassy slopes. The cheerful golden-yellow, goblet-shaped flowers that appear in early autumn, accompanied by contrasting narrow, glossy green, strap-like leaves, look like crocuses but are members of the Amaryllis family. Lift a slab from the patio or plant them among grey foliage plants like sage or lavender, but make sure the bushes don't overshadow the bulbs; they need a good baking in summer.

Sternbergia sicula is a smaller version, with flower stems only 5–7cm (2–2¾in) tall. The narrow dark green leaves have a pale central stripe. *S. clusiana* has large flowers with greenish-yellow goblets appearing from early to late autumn before the strap-shaped, grey-green leaves. It is not totally reliable but worth trying at the base of a sunny wall.

It needs very free-draining, neutral to alkaline soil and full sunshine; the base of a sunny wall is ideal. Plant in autumn immediately after buying about 10cm (4in) deep and the same apart, watered in if the soil is dry. They may take a year or two to settle before flowering. Once established, they are better left undisturbed to grow into clumps for the most effective display. Lift and divide clumps after a few years in late summer or late spring while the leaves are green or they will become shy of flowering; a light feed of sulphate of potash in autumn and spring helps this too. **MB**

Stipa gigantea
SPANISH OAT GRASS

Type: hardy, evergreen or semi-evergreen perennial
Soil & situation: any reasonable, well-drained soil/sun
North American hardiness zone: 7–10
Height: up to 2.5m (8ft), leaves 75cm (30in)
Spread: 1m (3ft)
Grow for: an essential flowering grass, with strong form and a lasting presence; straw-yellow flowers for most of the winter; evergreen leaves; sends up its bold panicles in late spring; AGM

All the stipas are natives of the expansive grasslands of the world, particularly meadows, prairies and steppes. So consider this when choosing your site, giving them sun and reasonable drainage. This giant is one of the most spectacular as a specimen plant, with its huge, airy, oat-like, bristly spikelets soaring above the lower foliage. Yet it is quite delicate and see-through, so is equally useful for threading through lower plants to create a tracery effect. It will slowly form spreading, grey-green leafy clumps, which are a year-round asset. It is fairly drought resistant and will soak up any amount of sun. Unfortunately it tends not to seed around, more is the shame, as home-grown seed does not tend to be fertile.

The old flowering spikelets usually tend to start falling to bits at the onset of the harder winter weather, and at this point, usually after Christmas, they can be snipped off to tidy them up. They look fantastic covered in frost and in some years can be left on a good while. The easiest way to propagate this plant is from imported seed, as when it is propagated by division the plants seem slow to establish. Seed is best sown in autumn and left to be exposed to frost. **BG**

Stipa gigantea

Styrax japonicus

Styrax japonicus
SNOWBELL, JAPANESE SNOWBELL

Type: hardy, deciduous, large shrub or small tree
Soil & situation: moist, well-drained, acid soil/sheltered position in full sun to partial shade
North American hardiness zone: 6–8
Height: 10m (33ft)
Spread: 8m (25ft)
Grow for: dainty and delicate flowers in early summer; good winter form; AGM

The snowbell, an elegant, graceful tree, has spreading fan-like branches covered with clusters of fragrant, pure white, bell-shaped, pendent flowers in June (often earlier). It is better planted where their exquisite beauty can be appreciated from below. A bank is ideal, overhanging a path or simply lie on the ground below with a glass of chilled Chablis, and look up – then you can enjoy two of life's greatest pleasures! Once the oval to elliptic leaves turn yellow or red and fall in autumn, the stems provide winter interest. The bark is marked with fissures revealing orange-brown inner layers and the branches, forming a dense mound, look spectacular when covered with frost.

Styrax japonicus Benibana Group 'Pink Chimes' with pale pink flowers, is better than the similar *S. japonicus* 'Roseus'. *S. j.* 'Fargesii' is more tree-like with slightly larger leaves and flowers. 'Emerald Pagoda' (or 'Sohuksan') has larger flowers than the species, thicker petals and the leaves are leathery and deeper green. 'Carillon' is one of the prettiest weeping trees; to 5m (16ft) x 2.5m (8ft). Train the leading shoot vertically for extra height.

It needs a sheltered position, in sun or partial shade (ideally protected from morning sun; young shoots can be damaged by late-spring frosts), on moist, free-draining, acid soil. Add leafmould or peat substitute to the ground before planting. The bark may split if planted in cold or exposed locations. Remove dead, diseased, dying and damaged wood in winter. Propagate from seed or layering. **MB**

Symphytum 'Hidcote Blue'

Type: hardy, evergreen perennial
Soil & situation: pretty well any soil/easy and undemanding/full sun or deep shade
North American hardiness zone: 3–9
Height: 45cm (18in)
Spread: indefinite
Grow for: a neat mound of lush, evergreen leaves; pretty red buds open to mid-blue flowers which later fade to white; nearly unbeatable plant for rapidly colonizing difficult areas

I use sheets of this plant all around my cesspit – most exciting – but the point of the story is that the pit has four large concrete covers, each one a good one and a half square metres (five square feet) in size, and I had planted the comfrey immediately after one visit from the emptying lorry, however, the next time the man came to empty it he could not find the covers as the comfrey had totally camouflaged it! I do admit I leave the emptying interval longer than I should, a good 12 months, but even so it is magic. The plants have obviously not rooted into the slabs but spread out over them. I also use this same comfrey to form neat circles around the base of my old fruit trees in the orchard' where the solid rings of dark green look almost sculptural. It is a superb plant with great uses. Apart from this gem there are several other comfreys I am keen on too. One is *Symphytum* x *uplandicum* 'Variegatum' which is no thug but very striking with its handsome green leaves, edged with white. 'Hidcote Blue' will spread but if you grow it surrounded by grass, then there is no problem in containing it as the mower does it for you. Otherwise, you can simply spade round it. When I want it to spread in a new area, I just divide it up into small clumps and re-plant at virtually any time of year. **BG**

Symphytum 'Hidcote Blue'

Symphytum officinale

Symphytum officinale
COMFREY

Type: hardy, herbaceous perennial
Soil & situation: damp soil/sun or shade
North American hardiness zone: 3–9
Height: 1.5m (5ft)
Spread: 1.2m (4ft)
Grow for: good-looking leaves; tall stems with many small purple flowers; excellent for making liquid feed; attracts bees

Although it is very useful to me as I rot down the leaves and stalks to make a liquid feed, I would grow comfrey anyway as I like its rugged enthusiasm and the buzz of bees about its flowers. It is also an exceptionally useful plant for filling shady banks, the edges of ditches and many other damp spots with little sun.

This is a native European plant often eaten in times of famine and by those seeking relief from arthritis, but this is now discouraged as apparently if you feed rats almost nothing else they get sick on it, surprise surprise. *Symphytum* is the ancient Greek name for this plant, even then known as a wound healer. The common name may come from the Latin *conferva*, for grow together, as it has always been used to make poultices to help knit bones and heal flesh. The infamous comfrey tea is simply comfrey leaves rotted under water and diluted down to tea colour before using as a feed; it is similar to commercial tomato feed in constituents and ideal for most plants in pots.

It prefers a damp, rich soil and will grow on the sides of rank ditches in sun or shade. Once you have it you've got it for good! The species can be grown from seed but any bit of root takes almost any time. No problems other than tenaciousness if it's no longer wanted. **BF**

Syringa velutina (syn. *S. palibiniana*)
KOREAN LILAC

Type: hardy, deciduous shrub
Soil & situation: most soils/full sun or very light shade
North American hardiness zone: 4–7
Height & spread: 2.5m (8ft) x 2m (6½ft), eventually
Grow for: neat compact shrub with velvety leaves and a profusion of pinky-purple panicles of scented flowers in early summer

Many of the lilacs are lovely plants but they are no longer popular despite their gorgeous flowers and heavy scents. This pretty little shrub remains compact and yet is covered with flowers, even when young. These are pinky-lilac in colour and sweetly scented, but not as cloying as say the old double white. It makes a nice combination with the Persian lilac, *Syringa* x *persica*, and the small-leafed *S. microphylla*, giving you three shades of flower all on compact shrubs, but *S. velutina* is the best of them.

Syringa comes from the Greek for pipe as it has hollow stems. Botanists once grouped *Syringa* with *Philadelphus* (see page 295), but the two are now considered separate genera. The name lilac comes from the Arabic or Persian for bluish flower and *velutina* describes the somewhat velvety leaves.

Syringa velutina

Most lilacs like a moist, leafmould-rich soil but they will grow almost anywhere, even on chalky soils; they revel in sun, but can cope with shade although will flower less. It is worth removing seedheads as the flowers wither. This variety is compact and should not need pruning. It cannot be easily grown from seed but spring-softwood cuttings taken with a heel may take under mist, eventually. It suffers no common problems. **BF**

Syringa vulgaris 'Katherine Havemeyer'

Syringa vulgaris 'Katherine Havemeyer'
LILAC

Type: hardy, deciduous shrub or small tree
Soil & situation: fertile, well-drained, neutral to alkaline soil/full sun
North American hardiness zone: 4–7
Height: 7m (23ft)
Spread: 6m (20ft)
Grow for: early summer fragrance for alkaline soil; AGM

Of all the plants that can and can't be grown on different soils I really do feel sorry for people who are unable to grow lilac. It dislikes acid conditions and while those same gardeners revel in a whole range of ericaceous plants, including rhododendrons, pieris and camellias, the absence of lilac leaves a gaping hole, metaphorically.

It has an upright habit with 10cm (4in) long, heart-shaped, mid-green leaves. In late spring and early summer it produces dense, compact, panicles of very fragrant, double, lavender-blue flowers fading to light pink. In bud they are deep purple. In fact, the term 'very fragrant' is hardly adequate. Some flowers go beyond that and, for me, lilac is off the scale. Perhaps 'not heavy but heavenly' is more apt.

Prune in late winter to remove crossing branches. Old, neglected plants may be pruned hard into the old wood and will respond well with new growth. Dead head after flowering, especially in the first few years after planting. Where the plant produces extra-strong summer growth the stems should be cut back to half their length. When planted in shade it will struggle to reach the light, becoming straggly with all its flowers at the top of the plant. Lilac loves a humus-rich soil and a deep, annual winter mulch will be beneficial. For me the easiest method of propagation is by layering in early summer. **JC**

Syringa vulgaris 'Madame Lemoine'

Type: hardy, deciduous shrub
Soil & situation: well-drained, fertile soil/preferably neutral or alkaline/needs full sun to flower well
North American hardiness zone: 4–7
Height & spread: 7m (23ft)
Grow for: wonderful, fragrant, large, double, white flowers from late spring to early summer; AGM

Syringa vulgaris 'Madame Lemoine'

I used to be indifferent to lilacs, I think because I had seen so many grown as specimen trees in front gardens looking dull, almost oppressive, for most of the year. My interest in them was awakened when one day I was searching for a picture for the jacket of my first book. We came upon a neglected glade lined with lilacs in full glory and the long grass under the canopy was strewn with wild flowers. This was it! The decision was unanimous, the owners agreed and we arranged to return in a few days with the photographer. But it was not to be. The thoughtful owners (unbeknown to us) had cut all the grass and the idyllic illusion was shattered. Lilacs do look wonderful in more natural settings, and the compact, but very large white flowers of 'Madame Lemoine' look especially well against the multitude of fresh greens in spring gardens. I recommend using white clematis to extend the flowering period. They are ideal for intertwining amongst the mid-green, heart-shaped leaves, bringing the canopy to life a second time.

It is not necessary to prune lilacs every year, though it is worth removing the dead flowerheads as they look brown and well past it, as they go over. It is also generally agreed that dead-heading newly planted lilac prevents fruit forming, so helps them establish. Otherwise prune the shrubs after flowering when they become too crowded, to thin out the dead and older wood. Old plants can be renovated by cutting hard back as they respond favourably. This lilac is one of those that roots easily from cuttings. These are best taken with a heel, just as the wood is just starting to ripen. When purchased they are sometimes grafted which can lead to suckering. These need removing. **BG**

Tagetes patula
FRENCH MARIGOLD

Type: half-hardy annual
Soil & situation: any soil/sun or light shade
North American hardiness zone: annual
Height & spread: 30cm (12in)
Grow for: neat compact plant with verdant, fern-like foliage, a pungent smell that keeps pests away and ghastly orange flowers which clash with most colour schemes

The organic gardener has to grow these as they are so useful. I have them by the greenhouse doors and at the gates of my vegetable plot. I mix them with tomatoes and valuable crops and am convinced they deter many pests. And their roots have exudates that depress levels of pestilential soil nematodes. And they look really good all summer, it's just a shame about their colour.

Tagetes patula

They are not French at all, nor is the bigger African marigold from Africa. In fact 20-odd species of *Tagetes* marigold are from Central America, mostly Mexico. They are named after Tages, a god of the earth.

French marigolds are good as bedding in most soils and sites, but not heavy shade or cold. They do well in pots and containers. As a half-hardy annual they are best started off in the warmth early in spring and planted out as soon as the frosts are over. **BF**

Tamarix tetrandra
TAMARISK

Type: hardy, deciduous shrub
Soil & situation: well-drained soil/moist if not coastal/full sun
North American hardiness zone: 5–9
Height & spread: 3m (10ft)
Grow for: a mass of blooms; AGM

When you first grow this shrub there is a temptation to treat it as less than hardy. The foliage and flower suggests a fragile plant, but it is tough enough to enjoy seaside conditions. I have an eight-year-old plant which has flowered, without fail, every year since it went in.

The pale green, needle-like, ferny foliage appears in late spring on thin, arching, purple-brown shoots. In mid- to late spring lateral racemes of four-petalled, light pink flowers appear on the previous year's wood before the leaves. When grown on light soils at the coast it can withstand strong winds, making a first-class and attractive windbreak. On inland sites protect it from cold winds and choose a moist, free-draining soil. *Tamarix ramosissima* is another excellent species for seaside conditions, flowering on the new growth in late summer and autumn.

Prune immediately after flowering, cutting back to healthy buds. Old, neglected plants may be rejuvinated by a severe cutting into the old, gnarled wood, which will re-sprout by the following summer. Remove half of the branches in the first year. Feed with a balanced fertilizer during summer and cut the remaining branches the following season. Propagate by semi-ripe cuttings in summer or hardwood cuttings outside in winter. **JC**

Tamarix tetrandra

Rhus glabra 'Laciniata' November

SMOOTH SUMACH

Type: hardy, deciduous shrub or small tree
Soil & situation: moist, well-drained soil/sun
North American hardiness zone: 2–8
Height: 3m (10ft)
Spread: indefinite
Grow for: flamboyant autumn colour; plume-like seedheads in winter, but the autumn colour wins out to make it a choice for November

This plant is a rough diamond. Rough – it has toxic sap and the suckers can take over your garden; diamond – it radiates warmth from spring to autumn in gratitude to the gardener for overlooking its shortcomings and allowing it space to shine. In leaf, the dainty, fern-like fronds projecting at a sharp angle from the smooth, spreading stems create an exotic, tropical ambience – the picture below shows it in a mixed planting with *Ricinus communis, Eucalyptus gunnii* and *Phormium* 'Sundowner'.

Autumn brings a transformation as it responds to the needs of gardeners when the weather becomes damp and chilling. Stand in its warming glow and you can almost hear the twigs crackling and feel the heat from the glorious shimmering leaves that fall around the plant like a pool of fire, before finally fading away.

It prefers moist, well-drained, moderately fertile soil in full sun. Control suckers by creating a barrier of paving slabs or thick polythene around the plant and grow in containers; or allow it to exert its right to roam; the impact is magnificent!

Prune in winter to keep within its allotted space. If you prune last year's growths to within 3–5cm (1–2in) of a framework of older wood or back to the base like a dogwood (see *Cornus alba*, page 17) and thin to leave the strongest growths, it produces fewer, broader leaves, up to 1m (3ft) long. Remove suckers by clearing the soil and pulling them from the roots. Propagate from suckers cut from the roots in winter.

Warning: the sap can cause dermatitis, so avoid skin contact. Wear gloves, a long-sleeved top and long trousers when pruning; do not burn the wood. **MB**

Taxus baccata
COMMON YEW, ENGLISH YEW

Type: hardy, evergreen tree
Soil & situation: wide range of conditions/acid and alkaline soils/grows more successfully in well-drained soils than in heavy, water-retentive ones, where it becomes susceptible to fungal root rots/shade/sun
North American hardiness zone: 7–8
Height: up to 15m (50ft), rarely to 27m (90ft), but can be maintained at just 30cm (12in)
Spread: to 10m (33ft)
Grow for: the best evergreen hedge, with its fine, dense texture; is not so slow growing if it is given the correct care; highly useful for topiary, arches, arbours and the like; with patience, forms a magnificent tree; AGM

I plant yew to form the garden structure more than any other plant as it conveys an air of permanence, forming magnificent boundaries which look like dark green walls. I have found that it will grow as fast as many deciduous rivals but the secret is to water it copiously in dry periods during the summer months. This is something that people rarely do, as its hatred of badly drained, heavy soil is legendary. I first found this out in my own garden. On one side of my garden I have three sections of yew hedging backing onto my vegetable garden, on the other side the three sections are mirror images, backing onto my nuttery. The yew plants in with the vegetables are irrigated regularly, inadvertently along with the runner beans, courgettes and lettuces. This section formed a dense, above eye-level screen in less than eight years, while the other one grew at the speed generally expected, that of a boy from birth onwards. So do not be fobbed off with faster-growing alternatives – if this is what you really crave, go for it. It does not have to form a high hedge. My uncle, David Austin, uses it as a low 30cm (12in) hedge to edge around the front of his rose garden where it looks extremely smart and makes a change from box. Surprisingly he cuts it once a year. A word of warning: yew is toxic so watch nearby grazing animals and warn children about berries.

Taxus baccata

If planted as a hedge I plant a double staggered row unless I need a really wide hedge, in which case I use a triple staggered row. I plant far closer than many people recommend – at 50cm (20in) centres with 50cm (20in) between the rows. If your drainage is poor, it is essential to get this right before you plant, or opt for something else. I do not add copious amounts of muck into the trench but tend to add a mulch in successive springs, as this helps reduce the moisture loss. Feed is then washed down to the roots rather than away from the roots, which happens if you put muck in the base of the trench. Keep any grass a good 60cm (24in) from the base of the plant as grass roots steal precious moisture. Clip once a year in summer (at Hidcote they do it virtually 12 months a year due to the sheer volume) and just clip the sides till you have the height you want and then do the tops – such a great feeling when you do this for the first time. Your garden seems suddenly to come of age! **BG**

Taxus baccata 'Fastigiata Aurea'
Plant of the Week (see page 389)

Tecophilaea cyanocrocus
CHILEAN BLUE CROCUS

Type: hardy, bulbous corm
Soil & situation: rich, sandy, free-draining soil/sun
North American hardiness zone: 7–9
Height: 10cm (4in)
Spread: 25cm (10in)
Grow for: blue flowers from early to mid-spring

Tecophilaea cyanocrocus

What a magnificent name! It commemorates Tecophilaea Villotti, an Italian botanical artist, and I wonder if her beauty equalled this glorious vision in deep gentian-blue. Yet beauty has its perils: this priceless treasure is now thought to be extinct in the wild because of over-grazing and over-collecting; when you're so irresistibly beautiful, everyone wants a piece of the action! Conservationists from the Royal Botanic Gardens, Kew, are managing ongoing projects with their colleagues in Chile to re-establish plants at selected sites, yet I suspect their beauty will always be their downfall.

They are only worth risking outdoors in mild parts of the UK where they combine well with silver-foliaged plants. Plant corms about 5cm (2in) deep in rich, sandy, well-drained soil in sunshine; dig in grit or sharp sand if necessary and cover the surface with coarse gravel for protection. After flowering they become dormant; allow them to dry out but not 'bake' or the corms will desiccate. The safer alternative is to grow them in pots of gritty compost in a cool greenhouse; always keep the label with the pot! *Tecophilaea cyanocrocus* 'Leichtlinii' has paler, clear blue flowers with large white centres and *T. cyanocrocus* 'Violacea' has deep purplish flowers.

Pollinate the flowers with a soft brush and sow the seed in autumn when it is ripe. After germination, keep seedlings in a pot in a cold frame until they are large enough to plant out. They too will die back in summer but take care to not let them dry out completely. They produce some offsets; lift and replant when they are dormant. **MB**

Teucrium fruticans
TREE GERMANDER, SHRUBBY GERMANDER

Type: first-hardy, evergreen shrub
Soil & situation: well-drained soils/prefers neutral or slightly alkaline soil/needs a warm, sunny position
North American hardiness zone: 8–9
Height: up to 2m (6½ft)
Spread: up to 4m (13ft)
Grow for: aromatic foliage; attractive silver-grey green and felted leaves; pale blue flowers throughout the summer

This is a stunning small shrub which looks very Mediterranean. It is good towards or at the front of the border, where if you want to reform its naturally rather lax habit you can shape it up as required to produce a more rounded, compact dome. The leaves have great appeal all through the year, a neat, ovate- to lance-shape about 2cm (¾in) long and are woolly-white underneath with square-shaped stems to match. The pretty, pale blue flowers are borne in loose racemes. The form *Teucrium fruticans* 'Azureum' has darker blue flowers which look really special against the grey. Unfortunately it is slightly more tender but is worth growing on in a large pot till it is a more robust size for coping with cold, and then planting out in spring.

Prune this plant in spring as growth begins, removing any dead or weak growth and trimming it to produce more compact growth. It will cope well with hard pruning if required to renovate older, leggy plants. Propagation is by seed or is easy from softwood or semi-ripe cuttings. **BG**

Teucrium fruticans

Thalictrum delavayi

Thalictrum delavayi 'Hewitt's Double'
MEADOW RUE

Type: hardy, herbaceous perennial
Soil & situation: moist soil, sun or dappled shade
North American hardiness zone: 5–9
Height: 1.2m (4ft)
Spread: 60cm (24in)
Grow for: foliage and delicate flowers from early to late summer; AGM

This wonderfully light and airy plant has mounds of delicate, frothy, grey-green foliage and shimmering clouds of tiny, double, lilac flowers with pale yellow, petal-like stamens, resembling minute pompoms. It looks so pretty and fragile, you'd think that a strong gust of wind would shatter the plant and blow the fragments away. *Thalictrum delavayi* has graceful clusters of purple flowers with long creamy-yellow stamens. There is a white-flowered form called 'Album' which was introduced from China but has become naturalized in the UK.

To ensure that the more exotic species don't take all of the glory, I'm delighted that there are some 'garden worthy' species native to the UK. *T. minus* has delicate fresh green leaves and tiny heads of creamy-green flowers with prominent hanging stamens. It is found in chalky places on cliffs and banks throughout the UK and prefers limy soil. There is a selection called *T. m.* 'Adiantifolium' with delicate, tiny leaves like a maidenhair fern and small, creamy-green flowers. *T. alpinum* has green-flushed, purple flowers, with long yellow anthers. As its name suggests, it comes from mountainous areas. *T. flavum* subsp. *glaucum* has sulphur-yellow flowers and blue-green finely cut leaves and stems. This is a subspecies of the native meadow rue.

Grow in moist, humus-rich soil in sun to partial shade. Before planting dig in plenty of well-rotted organic matter if necessary; cut back stems and mulch in autumn; water during drought. Divide when new growth starts in spring. Susceptible to powdery mildew in dry conditions; slugs can be a problem. **MB**

Thuja occidentalis 'Rheingold'

Type: hardy, evergreen conifer
Soil & situation: moist, well-drained soil/full sun
North American hardiness zone: 3–7
Height: 3m (10ft)
Spread: 2.5m (8ft)
Grow for: golden-yellow foliage in summer, coppery-orange in winter; AGM

This is one of my favourite conifers for year-round colour. In summer it is golden-yellow but in winter the foliage turns to a warm coppery-orange. When grown in an exposed site its winter cloak can be deep bronze.

The foliage often causes arguments and confusion. There are two distinct forms: juvenile leaves, which are soft and ferny and usually to be found at the base of a young plant, and the rest of the plant, which is made up of normal adult foliage. As the plant matures it becomes conical or pyramidal in shape, losing the juvenile growth. Avoid soil contaminated with perennial weeds, which will smother the plant, causing the foliage to brown. Plant in a well-prepared hole with rotted farmyard manure worked into the soil. Tease out the rootball and spread the roots. Water as necessary during the first year after planting. A surface mulch of composted bark will help retain moisture in summer. **JC**

Thuja occidentalis 'Rheingold'

Thymus spp.

Plant of the Week (see page 249)

Thymus serpyllum 'Minimus'

MINIMUS THYME

Type: hardy, evergreen perennial
Soil & situation: free-draining soil, preferably calcareous/sun
North American hardiness zone: 4–9
Height: 5mm (1/4in)
Spread: to 20cm (8in)
Grow for: a ground-hugging, aromatic plant that keeps healthy-looking foliage throughout the year; smothered in pinky-mauve flowers for several weeks in the summer

This is a hard-working, highly desirable, completely prostrate thyme with tiny leaves. It is ideal for using in paving areas, perhaps in large squares to form a chequerboard pattern or perhaps in bold stripes. It quickly forms dense mats of green, which will tolerate a certain amount of walking on, providing living paving for 12 months of the year. When it comes into flower in early summer, it transforms into a mass of enchanting pink flowers, which, due to their abundant production of nectar, will be alive with bees. Of course there are many different types of *Thymus serpyllum* (the wild thyme), such as 'Goldstream' with variegated leaves, and 'Snowdrift' with white flowers, both which are excellent too, but I find the minimus thyme the most useful creeping one.

Thymus serpyllum 'Minimus' *in Bunny's Herbalist Garden for the 1998 Chelsea Flower Show.*

Tiarella wherryi

This plant thrives in conditions with really sharp drainage, otherwise it will die out in wet winters. So do make sure you lighten the soil if necessary. It also prefers calcareous soils. If you want to establish respectably sized areas of it, I find it useful to plant it into completely weed-free substrate (such as sterilized compost) to avoid intensive weeding before it has completely covered the ground. After flowering, trimming back is advisable, which rejuvenates the plant. Propagation is very simple and cuttings can be taken in spring or summer. **BG**

Tiarella wherryi

FOAMFLOWER

Type: hardy, herbaceous perennial
Soil & situation: moist, humus-rich soil/dappled shade
North American hardiness zone: 5–9
Height: 25cm (10in)
Spread: 15cm (6in)
Grow for: flowers from mid-spring to late summer; ornamental foliage; AGM

This pretty little plant proves that small is beautiful. It forms a neat cushion of ivy leaf-shaped foliage that is velvety and moss-green with brown markings along the central vein. Delicate pale pink buds in dainty spikes open to reveal tiny flowers, their long stamens creating a shimmering haze; every one is a twinkling star! Beth Chatto, the knowledgeable and discerning plantswoman, grows it alongside *Ophiopogon planiscapus* 'Nigrescens', the emerald velvet foliage contrasting with the black leaves. *Tiarella* is from the Greek word *tiara* or small crown, referring to the shape of the seed capsule.

There have been many selections from this and other species, chosen for their colour and the marking on their leaves; many are spreading. *Tiarella wherryi* 'Bronze Beauty' has dark, red-bronze leaves, turning darker in winter. *Tiarella* 'Skid's Variegated' has cream-mottled, pink-tinted foliage. *T.* 'Ninja' has deeply lobed leaves with a central blotch of dark chocolate which become almost totally plum-purple in winter. 'Heronswood Mist' was a chance seedling found at the legendary Heronswood Nursery in Washington state, USA. The foliage is marbled and blotched in cream and pink – a spectacular plant! *T. polyphylla* is a good gap filler with marbled leaves and pink flowers.

They need cool, moist, humus-rich soil in shade. Dig in plenty of well-rotted organic matter if necessary before planting. Cut back foliage and mulch in spring. They dislike waterlogging in winter. Sow seed of species in spring or as soon as ripe; divide in spring. Slugs can damage the leaves. **MB**

Trachelospermum jasminoides
STAR JASMINE

Type: frost-hardy, evergreen, twining climber
Soil & situation: well-drained, moisture-retentive, free-draining soil/sun/shelter
North American hardiness zone: 7–10
Height & spread: 9m (30ft)
Grow for: glossy leaves and fragrant waxy flowers from mid- to late summer; AGM

This plant provided one of my life's most memorable moments! I was visiting a garden in the centre of Blandford Forum in Dorset, when I was overwhelmed with a glorious scent that encapsulated the heady sensation of summer. There several metres away, bathed in sunshine was the most wonderful *Trachelospermum jasminoides* I have ever seen. How thankful I am that it was introduced by Robert Fortune from Shanghai in 1844 – what a wonderful legacy!

The oval, glossy, dark green leaves provide the perfect contrast to the pure white, waxy flowers 3cm (1in) across that are produced from mid- to late summer. It is hardy in all but the coldest parts of the UK, where it needs the protection of a conservatory or can be grown in a container and taken outdoors in summer. Train it up canes or grow it through a trellis.

T. asiaticum reaches 6m (20ft) each way. Its flowers are creamy white with a buff yellow centre, it is neater and more compact but less fragrant and, in my opinion, is not quite as beautiful. The leaves of the varieties listed below become crimson with winter's chilling touch. *T. jasminoides* 'Japonicum' is vigorous, grows taller and has larger leaves; the leaves of *T. j.* 'Variegatum' are splashed and margined with creamy white; *T. j.* 'Wilsonii' has attractively veined leaves.

Trachelospermum jasminoides

Grow in well-drained, moderately moisture-retentive soil in a sheltered, sunny position. Dig in plenty of well-rotted organic matter before planting, mulch in spring and feed with general fertilizer. Lightly prune in spring to remove dead or weak growth or to keep within its allotted space. Propagate by semi-ripe cuttings in late summer and layering. **MB**

Bunny adds:
Do not be put off by the hardiness zone – I have found this plant perfectly hardy in my East Midlands garden for a good ten years now. I did put up some fleece to keep off a few degrees of frost during cold nights in the first winter, but have not bothered since. It is my favourite climber, and I regularly use it on many schemes. Not only is it smart looking but it grows fast too. The leaves are up to 8cm (3½in) long, an oval-lanceolate shape and mine colours up very strongly in the winter. Right now (late winter) it is a strong ruby-red nearly all over. This is on a south wall, whereas the ones on a shadier, east-facing wall are still a smart racing green. As you may notice I have gone big on this splendid plant. I am training them quite formally up to the top of the ground floor windows along an elegant-looking Georgian part of the house. The scent penetrates the keyhole of the front door reminding you, that if only you opened the door, the whole room would be filled with fragrance. I have seen ready-made arches of this plant imported from Italy, which you can just 'pop over' your front door to form an evergreen, sweet-smelling entrance – no planning needed but deep pockets essential. They are quick growing, so get the extra satisfaction of training your own!

Trachycarpus fortunei
Plant of the Week (see page 383)

Tricyrtis formosana
TOAD LILY

Type: hardy, rhizomatous perennial
Soil & situation: moist, well-drained, humus-rich soil/partial or deep shade
North American hardiness zone: 6–9
Height: 90cm (36in)
Spread: 45cm (18in)

Tricyrtis formosana

Grow for: happy in deep shade; an interesting, different-looking flower; AGM

This is a very useful perennial for planting in deep shade. It is late flowering with a most unusual flower, shaped like a starfish. The erect, soft hairy stems tend to zigzag with 10cm (4in) long, lance-shaped leaves. They are dark green with purple-green spots on the surface. The upward facing, 3cm (1in) wide flowers appear in autumn.They are pinkish-purple on a white background, with red-purple spots on the inside and white stigmas with red spots. The base of the tepals is a pale yellow.

I can grow this plant in a peat bed with no added soil where it quickly spreads by underground stolons. Avoid areas exposed to biting, cold, drying winds. Apply an annual deep mulch of coarse bark every winter after flowering is finished. Propagation is by seed sown as soon as it is ripe and over-wintered in a cold frame with protection from frost. Young plants may be planted out after all risk of frost is over. Divide established clumps in early spring before growth starts. Take precautions against slugs and snails in spring as the new shoots appear. **JC**

Trachycarpus fortunei November

CHUSAN PALM, HEMP PALM

Type: evergreen palm
Soil & situation: tolerates a range of soils/appreciates free drainage conditions/full sun or partial shade/looks best in a place free from strong winds, which lacerate the foliage
North American hardiness zone: 8–9
Height: 20m (66ft)
Spread: 2.5m (8ft), trunk diameter to 1m (3ft)
Grow for: the air of tropical luxuriance conveyed by its exciting, huge – up to 1.2m (4ft) – evergreen fan-shaped leaves; will tolerate temperatures down to –10°C (14°F). Few plants look this good at this time of year; AGM

I have grown this palm in my East Midlands courtyard for a good ten years or so. The plants are in huge pots and too massive to move now, but they have 'lived out' from the word go when they were under a foot high, so that is not a problem. Now one of them strokes its leaves against my first-floor bedroom window in breezy weather. Visitors often arrive and on encountering my palms remark on what an amazingly warm courtyard it must be. No way! It is just that these palms are far tougher than most people think. They grow well in containers too, looking even more dramatic in massive pots, and have amazingly small root systems compared to their height. On one job we had to transplant one with a digger; it was about 4m (13ft) high, but the roots were hardly 60cm (24in) in diameter. It transplanted very easily, which is nearly always the case with these great plants.

These could be protected with fleece in the early years if you are planting them in colder areas. Good, free-draining conditions undoubtedly help them get through cold periods. No pruning is required apart from cutting off any of the lower leaf bases to make the trunk more visible as it is curious clothed with the fibrous remains of the old leaf bases. The yellow flowers (interesting and odd, but not what I would call beautiful) grow on quite young plants in huge quantities in terminal panicles and sometimes male and female flowers occur on the same tree. The fruits are like dark, midnight-blue marbles. They freely seed around and this is an easy way to propagate them. **BG**

Trollius x *cultorum* 'Lemon Queen'

GLOBEFLOWER

Type: hardy, herbaceous perennial
Soil & situation: moist, damp soil/sun or partial shade
North American hardiness zone: 5–8
Height: 1m (3ft)
Spread: 60cm (24in)
Grow for: attractive leaves and bold flowers from late spring to mid-summer

I love these big bold buttercups with their deeply cut leaves and globular flowers like giant lollipops. Forget your temperamental flouncy summer specials, these yeomen of the garden are tough, no-nonsense herbaceous plants with attractive leaves and cheerful flowers. Robust and jolly, they are happy to wallow up to their knees in damp soil by ponds or streams, in boggy borders or naturalized in meadows and drink all day! The flowers, up to 6cm (2½in) across, appear from late spring to mid-summer. There are some wonderful selections, but the clear tones of *Trollius* x *cultorum* 'Lemon Queen' are just perfect, although 'Alabaster', which flowers slightly ahead of the others, with clear, pale yellow blooms, 7cm (3in) across, is not far behind. From the Swiss-German name *Trollblume*, Latinized as *Trollius flos* or rounded flower, it's linked to the Middle English *troll*, to trundle or roll. You'd expect them to come rolling home!

There are about 30 cultivars of *T.* x *cultorum* available, most flowering from mid-spring to early summer. 'Commander-in-Chief' has large, glowing orange flowers. 'Golden Monarch' has warm orange flowers, 'Fire Globe' (also known as 'Feuertroll') is rich orange-yellow and the early-flowering 'Heleos' has orange globes. 'Orange Princess' has wonderful, large, double, orange-gold flowers in late spring and early summer. 'Superbus' has greeny-yellow flowers from late spring to mid-summer.

Trollius x cultorum 'Lemon Queen'

They need moist, deep, fertile, preferably heavy soil that never dries out; happy in full sun or shade or wet, heavy clay. Cut back in spring and mulch with well-rotted organic matter. Divide in spring or immediately after flowering. **MB**

Tropaeolum 'Strawberries and Cream'

Tropaeolum 'Strawberries and Cream'

NASTURTIUM

Type: hardy, annual climber
Soil & situation: impoverished, moist, well-drained soil/full sun
North American hardiness zone: annual
Height: 20–30cm (8–12in)
Spread: 30cm (12in)
Grow for: a lovely-looking plant – and every bit edible

All parts of this plant are edible. I wonder if I am starting to write like Bob Flowerdew! Its leaves are spicy, the seeds, which can be pickled, are hot and the flowers are colourful in salads.

The 5cm (2in) wide, rounded, light green leaves have wavy edges. The flowers are produced from summer to autumn with long spurs and creamy-yellow petals each with a red blotch at the base. They are double and up to 5cm (2in) across. *Tropaeolum* 'Strawberries and Cream' is a non-trailing variety ideal for annual bedding or growing in containers on a patio.

When grown in 'poor' soil without nutrients they flower more readily. Fertile soils produce more leaves at the expense of flowers. Where the soil is fertile feed with a high-potash liquid fertilizer weekly to encourage more flowers. Seed can be sown in late spring *in situ*. Propagation is by seed which is quick to germinate. Tip cuttings can be rooted in a gritty compost in early summer and over-wintered in a cool greenhouse. **JC**

Tulipa 'Artist'

Type: hardy, bulbous perennial
Soil & situation: fertile, well-drained soil/full sun/shelter from strong winds
North American hardiness zone: best treated as an annual with the bulbs lifted each year
Height: 45cm (18in)
Spread: 15cm (6in) for a single plant
Grow for: an impressive display when planted en masse; AGM

I love tulips. My favourites are the long-stemmed varieties that stand on parade, proud and to attention. The mid-green, lance-shaped leaves of *Tulipa* 'Artist' (which belongs to the Viridiflora Group) are lower than the flowerheads. The single flowers are cup shaped, appearing in late

Tulipa 'Artist'

spring. Before they fully open the petal margins are crimped and salmon-pink with a greenish-purple stripe on the outside of each petal. When fully open the inside of each flower is green flushed salmon-pink. It makes a wonderful display when the bulbs are planted in a mass in the border or as a mixed planting underplanted with yellow wallflowers. An added bonus is that they make excellent, long-lasting cut flowers.

After flowering remove the dead heads before they set seed. Allow the foliage to yellow before cutting it down. Lifting the bulbs isn't essential but there is more chance of losing them to slugs or rot if they are left in the ground over winter. Avoid planting in wet ground. Plant at least 10–15cm (4–6in) deep and space the bulbs 8cm (3½in) apart. Tulips may be planted out as late as November. Earlier planting may encourage the disease tulip fire. **JC**

Tulipa 'Magier'

Plant of the Week (see page 177)

Tulipa 'Queen of Night'

Type: hardy, bulbous perennial
Soil & situation: good garden loam/sunny position
North American hardiness zone: 3–8
Height: 60cm (24in)
Spread: 15cm (6in) for a single plant
Grow for: dark purple, velvety flowers in late spring

I first saw these tulips growing in the late John Codrington's front garden: they were planted with equal quantities of white tulips, and generous masses of them were threaded through extensive clumps of low-growing, cottage-garden plants. This exuberant planting almost totally filled the space between the cottage and the road, a width of about 8m (25ft).

These tulips are such a bold, yet subtle colour, that you can afford to be equally bold with your planting and make quite a statement. They are ideal for using in repeated clumps, to stock all those spare gaps that will later be filled with expanding foliage or plants not yet in place. The first year you plant them they are tall, but if you leave them *in situ* they are usually slightly shorter with smaller flowers in subsequent years. I prefer them like this. Either way, they give several weeks of colour.

Tulipa 'Queen of Night'

For a simpler life, you can leave these tulips *in situ*, rather than treating them as bedding tulips. Whichever way you choose, plant them by early winter (or if you are desperate up until early spring) and do plant them deeply, with a good 20cm (8in) of soil above them. This helps to prevent slug damage and also helps them give a better performance in subsequent years, as does a good summer baking. Plant them about 10cm (4in) apart. **BG**

Ulex europeaus 'Flore Pleno'

Plant of the Week (see page 111)

Vaccinium corymbosum

HIGHBUSH BLUEBERRY

Type: very hardy, deciduous shrub
Soil & situation: moist, acid soil/sun/shelter
North American hardiness zone: 3–7
Height: 1.5m (5ft)
Spread: unpruned to over 4m (13ft)
Grow for: pretty flowers in late spring to early summer; edible fruit in mid- to late summer; and brilliant autumn colour; AGM

I still can't decide which stirs my passions more, their autumn leaves aflame in tones of red and yellow, or a bowl heaped with delicious blueberries, submerged in lashings of cream!

Pretty white flowers, like dainty lampshades appear in late spring and early summer and are pleasing to the eye, but it is the blue-black fruit that makes my heart beat faster. Grow at least two varieties for a worthwhile crop.

Will it be *Vaccinium* 'Bluecrop', the top all rounder with brilliant autumn colour, heavy crops and good drought resistance; *V.* 'Earliblue' with its eye-catching autumn colour and moderate crops; or *V.* 'Herbert' who's more subdued in autumn but with an unbeatable flavour? The choice is yours! Blueberry pies, blueberry muffins, blueberries with blueberries and yet more cream! Stand aside, strawberries, your reign is over; all hail, blueberries, king of summer fruit!

Blueberries need shelter, sunshine or light shade and a moist, free-draining soil with a pH of 4–5.5. Grow in raised beds or pots in a 50:50 mix of ericaceous compost and grit. Water with rainwater and never let the soil dry out. Feed with ericaceous plant food and mulch to 15cm (6in) deep with sawdust, bark or ericaceous compost. Harvest every four to five days.

Prune in early spring; two-to-three-year-old wood is the most productive. In the first two years remove weak, diseased or damaged shoots and fruit buds; thereafter cut out old wood at the base or to strong outward facing shoots. Propagate by semi ripe cuttings. Protect the fruit from birds using netting. **MB**

Vaccinium corymbosum

Bob adds:
I never used to grow blueberries, then I got a taste for them with yoghurt so now I have to grow them. Despite living in a dry village on a lime-filled, sandy soil they have proved fairly easy in large containers; these are usefully carried into the greenhouse or fruit cage for getting the ripening fruits away from the birds. They also like company, as the more plants I get the more each one bears as they seem to need cross-pollinators although are theoretically self-fertile.

Blueberries are not water plants but marginals, i.e. they like wet, not waterlogged, soil, and can drown! Otherwise they are easy in any acid soil or compost and need no special treatment. Ideal for the edge of a ditch or pond or under a rainwater drainpipe. They will become parched in a hot dry place but do not crop well in heavy shade. They can be sown in winter or divided in early spring; alternatively, with some care, summer softwood cuttings can be rooted. They suffer no special problems other than a dislike for both lime and lime-filled, chlorinated tapwater.

Veratrum album
FALSE HELLEBORE

Type: hardy, herbaceous perennial
Soil & situation: most soil/partial sun to heavy shade
North American hardiness zone: 5–9
Height: 1.2m (4ft)
Spread: 30cm (12in)
Grow for: attractive, ribbed, hosta-like leaves and a tall spike of green outside white inside, small flowers

Veratrum album

I am fond of poisonous plants. I started as a child, probably with unpleasant motives, and still find them fascinating. Although every part of the false hellebore is toxic, it is a beautiful stately plant with few problems and combines well, under an arch of laburnum and yew, with monkshood and foxgloves in a little corner dedicated to matrimonial harmony.

Veratrum is the Old Latin name as this plant was known to the Romans. It was long used as a pesticide for killing obstinate pests such as gooseberry sawfly caterpillars but is now obsolete. There are a few other species, all of which make stately garden plants, though they are not in favour at the time of writing – possibly due to their poisonous properties!

It seems to grow almost anywhere though is happiest in dappled shade with a moist, leafmould-enriched soil. It can be tidied after flowering to prevent seed setting, though this is unusual. It can be grown from seed but is slow to germinate and grow. Old plants can be divided in autumn or spring. It is slug immune, so should be grown among hostas to confuse them. **BF**

Verbascum bombyciferum 'Polarsommer'

Type: biennial to perennial
Soil & situation: dry, free-draining soil/sun
North American hardiness zone: 4–8
Height: up to 1.8m (6ft)
Spread: up to 1m (3ft)
Grow for: a fun plant that will self-seed but not so prolifically as to become a nuisance; brightens up an area of gravel, paving or border; saucer-shaped, pale yellow flowers throughout the summer on the large candelabra-shaped spikes; huge basal rosettes of the young plants which maintain their presence throughout the winter

There are several different verbascums to choose from. This one has exceptional foliage – rosettes of silver-grey, woolly leaves in its first year, which are set off by its pale flowers. It has strong growth so the flower spikes do not need supporting unless grown on very rich soil. It is an architectural plant I would not want to be without and invariably settles into pleasantly surprising, new spots each year. For instance, one year in my garden it formed a strong line all the way along the north side of a massive stone barn. Happily it has remained there, although I would have thought it was too cool and dark, providing a highlighted band of dazzling silver amongst the gravel. Of all the plants which require little maintenance, this must be one of the most eye-catching.

Verbascum bombyciferum 'Polarsommer'

My husband loathes this plant, as on returning home late from work, he accidentally brushes his dark suit against it in the dark, and only notices when colleagues comment on his woolly appearance the next morning.

This plant requires little attention apart from, perhaps, the removal of the flower spike after it has set seed, assuming you wish to produce more. Even the dead spikes do not look unattractive and in frost they are positive stars. They are short-lived though and generally die after flowering, but I find it safe just to let them carry on and do their own thing, as self-sown seedlings can usually be relied upon to be similar to type. Alternatively, seed can be sown in late spring or early summer. If sown earlier it may flower in its first year. Root cuttings may also be taken in winter. **BG**

Verbascum nigrum
DARK MULLEIN

Type: hardy, semi-evergreen perennial
Soil & situation: infertile, well-drained, alkaline soil/full sun
North American hardiness zone: 5–8
Height: 90cm (36in)
Spread: 60cm (24in)
Grow for: tall spikes of orange-yellow flowers in summer

I surprised myself when I first decided to recommend this mullein. Normally I extol the virtues of the giant *Verbascum olympicum* and *V. bombyciferum*, and rightly so. However, the dark mullein wins on flower colour and ultimate size. It isn't an embarrassment in a windy autumn when other taller types need support.

The mid-green, long-stalked, scalloped basal leaves form a rosette. They can be 15–45cm (6–18in) long, becoming smaller up the flowering stem. The slender, upright racemes of flowers, up to 60cm (24in) long, appear in summer and early autumn. The saucer-shaped flowers are deep orange-yellow with violet-coloured filaments and are clustered tightly on the stem. They open at different times, appearing in batches up and down the stalk.

Mulleins tolerate impoverished soil and will germinate and grow in the cracks in the patio or path. In fertile soil they tend to become large and more liable to wind damage. They are not long-lived perennials, often dying after the second year of flowering. Propagation is by seed in early summer. Pot up the seedlings and plant out the following spring to flower the same year. Every year since the millennium all my mulleins have suffered from moth caterpillar attacks. The simple remedy has been to pick them off and introduce them to a heavy boot. **JC**

Verbascum nigrum

Viburnum carlesii

Viburnum carlesii

Type: hardy, deciduous shrub
Soil & situation: moisture-retentive soil/sun or partial shade
North American hardiness zone: 5–8
Height & spread: 2m (6½ft)
Grow for: pink buds and domed clusters of white, fragrant flowers from mid- to late spring

This compact, dense shrub is impeccably attired in oval, irregularly toothed leaves, which often turn red in autumn. Domed flowerheads appear from mid to late spring, the clusters of bright pink buds bursting open, revealing white- or pink-flushed flowers with a strong daphne-like fragrance followed by red fruits that ripen to black.

This genteel plant has inspired several selections and hybrids all with the same glorious perfume. 'Aurora' has red buds and pale pink flowers. Its young leaves are light green, some flushed with copper. 'Charis' is vigorous, the buds are red, and the flowers pink fading to white. 'Diana' is also vigorous with red buds, but the young leaves have chocolate tints. Many argue that the hybrids are more beautiful. *Viburnum* x *burkwoodii* (*V. carlesii* x *V. utile*) is a medium-sized evergreen, with clusters of fragrant pink flowers from mid-winter (if it is mild) but usually mid- to late spring. It is hardy, beautiful and easy to raise from semi-ripe cuttings. *V.* x *carlcephalum* (*V. carlesii* x *V. macrocephalum*) is deciduous with flower clusters up to 15cm (6in) across which are impressive but rather overpowering. It often has good autumn colour. *V.* x *juddii* (*V. bitchiuense* x *V. carlesii*) is a floriferous, small- to medium-sized shrub which is robust and less susceptible to the attentions of aphids.

Prune after flowering to retain the shape. Propagate by softwood cuttings and evergreens from semi-ripe in summer. Viburnum aphid damages the leaves of *V. carlesii* which stay distorted for the rest of the season. Spray colonies before they disfigure the leaves. **MB**

Viburnum davidii

Type: hardy, evergreen shrub
Soil & situation: moist, well-drained soil/full sun or light shade
North American hardiness zone: 7–9
Height & spread: 1.5m (5ft)
Grow for: attractive evergreen foliage and winter fruit; AGM

For a reliable winter show plant a group of three, spaced 2m (6½ft) apart. It forms a dome-shaped, compact plant with 15cm (6in) long, shiny, dark green leaves. They are marked with three, deep, parallel veins.

Panicles of small, tubular, white flowers appear in late spring and are followed in autumn by clusters of metallic, deep blue fruits which will remain on the plant for most of the winter months. It is necessary to grow male and female plants together to guarantee fruit.

Pruning is not normally necessary once the framework of branches has been achieved. Propagation is by seed sown in autumn in a cold frame and over-wintered. Semi-ripe cuttings taken in late summer will root in a heated propagator. **JC**

Viburnum davidii

Taxus baccata 'Fastigiata Aurea'

GOLDEN IRISH YEW

Type: evergreen tree
Soil & situation: well-drained, fertile soil/any position
North American hardiness zone: 7–8
Height: after ten years 2m (6½ft) and eventually to 8m (25ft)
Spread: 60cm (24in)
Grow for: good looks all year round, so it's particularly welcome in the botanical doldrums of mid-winter.

If you want a plant that will behave itself and scorn any maintenance, then grow this yew. It retains its golden-yellow foliage for 12 months of the year, and becomes bright yellow in a sunny site. An added bonus is, being female, it produces dusky red fruit which contrast with the gold. It will retain its linear leaves to ground level with stiff upright shoots, giving the tree its columnar appearance. This yew makes a wonderful dot plant in a bed of low-growing heathers or is perfect for giving stature to a rock area.

Like most yews, it will tolerate acid or alkaline soil situated in full sun or a shaded site. It prefers a well-drained, fertile soil. If necessary old, sprawling yew trees may be rejuvenated to their former glory by pruning hard in spring, followed by regular watering and liquid feeds.

Warning: every part of the plant, with the exception of the seed coat, is poisonous. It is recommended that it isn't planted in the vicinity of grazing animals. **JC**

Viburnum farreri

Viburnum farreri

Type: hardy, deciduous shrub
Soil & situation: fertile, moist, well-drained soil/full sun or partial shade
North American hardiness zone: 6–8
Height: 3m (10ft)
Spread: 2.5m (8ft)
Grow for: clusters of very fragrant flowers; bright red fruit; AGM

This beautiful shrub used to be called *Viburnum fragrans*. It was a much better and more descriptive name and I wouldn't dream of correcting anyone who hasn't heard of the new one.

It forms an erect shrub with 10cm (4in) long, young bronze leaves, turning dark green and finally a rich red-purple in autumn. Dense clusters of very fragrant, white or white tinged pink, tubular flowers are produced in late autumn, before leaf fall, and throughout the winter. Small, vivid red fruits follow. *V. farreri* 'Candidissimum' has pure white flowers followed by bright yellow fruit. The young leaves are pale green, turning mid-green.

An annual mulch of composted bark in spring will conserve moisture close to the plant's surface roots. Pruning of young plants is seldom necessary. Old, neglected plants can be hard pruned in spring. Cut half the old branches with flaking bark as close to the ground as possible to encourage new shoots from the base. The following year cut the remaining branches. Propagation is by semi-ripe cuttings in mid-summer. Cover them with horticultural fleece until they are rooted. Don't transplant newly rooted cuttings until the following spring before they come into leaf. **JC**

Viburnum opulus

GUELDER ROSE, WATER ELDER

Type: hardy, deciduous shrub
Soil & situation: damp soil/dry soils too/sunny or light shade/will tolerate shadier sites
North American hardiness zone: 4–8
Height: 5m (16ft)
Spread: 4m (13ft)
Grow for: attractive but unassuming plant; ideal for use in woodlands, hedgerows and thickets where a more natural landscape is required; white flowers in late spring/early summer

This thicket-forming shrub produces rather showy flowers, white, lace-cap-like, up to 8cm (3½in) across and reminiscent of hydrangeas. They appear in late spring to early summer. The dark green leaves are usually three-lobed and maple-like, and colour up in autumn to burning reds and purples. Bright, glistening, red, fleshy fruits are produced in autumn and are on display well into winter. It is an easy plant to grow. I find it tolerates extremes from virtual hardcore to bogs and, although native, it looks pretty and ornamental. It is useful mixed into broad, natural plantings, perhaps to form a woodland edge or screen for some children's play area. Onc established it will recover from trampling or being used as a general stalking ground.

I also use *Viburnum lantana*, the wayfaring tree, for these types of spaces. It is perhaps more ornamental, the leaves are very different – broadly ovate, pale creamy-green and velvety when they come out – as are the young shoots. It is not so versatile in wet areas as *V. opulus*, but tolerates very shallow, limy, exposed conditions without batting an eyelid.

On planting these tough natives, I make sure there is no weed competition till they are well established. In wilder areas, weed control can take the simplest, least expensive method: many sheets of old newspaper, hidden and kept in place with grass clippings. I plant them bare-rooted in autumn or late winter, trim them right back to 50cm (20in) from the ground and never bother with rabbit-proof guards. I often mix them up, in groups of threes and fives, in native hedges with *Acer campestre, Crataegus monogyna, Ligustrum vulgare* and a little wild rose and holly, with the hawthorn (*Crataegus*) forming maybe 40 per cent, as it knits it all firmly together. A wonderful, colourful, natural, countryside boundary. **BG**

Viburnum rhytidophyllum

Type: hardy, evergreen shrub
Soil & situation: fertile, moist, well-drained soil/full sun or partial shade
North American hardiness zone: 6–8
Height: 5m (16ft)
Spread: 4m (13ft)
Grow for: large deeply veined evergreen leaves and late spring flowers

'Big and bold' sums up this useful evergreen. Generally trouble free, it quickly forms a dense screen for privacy or shelter. The 20–25cm (8–10in) long, lance-shaped leaves have wavy edges. They are glossy, dark green and deeply veined. Large, terminal clusters of small white flowers are produced in late spring, followed by bright red fruit ripening to shiny black.

It is tolerant of most soils except the extremes of wet and dry. Provide young plants with shelter from cold, drying winds. It dislikes being transplanted so it is better to purchase small container-grown plants. Apply a deep mulch of composted bark in autumn.

Viburnum opulus

Viburnum rhytidophyllum

Pruning where necessary to thin out crowded branches should be completed before spring. Cut old branches to ground level to encourage new strong shoots from the base. Propagation is by semi-ripe cuttings in summer. Shorten the leaves by half to reduce transpiration until the cuttings form roots. Pot the young rooted plants up the following spring. **JC**

Vicia faba 'Stereo'

BROAD BEAN

Type: half-hardy, annual vegetable
Soil & situation: best on deep, fairly heavy but well-drained land/acceptable crops on a wide range of soils
North American hardiness zone: annual
Height: 50cm (20in)
Spread: 60cm (24in)
Grow for: a milder taste than many conventional broad beans; is delicious cooked or raw

I am a big broad bean fan and grow quite a quantity of different types: dwarf ones, such as this; Longpods, which are very hardy; and Windsors, which have broader pods and more flavour. The sweeter, more delicate flavour of 'Stereo' makes it stand out from the crowd in terms of flavour, but in stature it is smaller. This means staking is usually unnecessary. It is a good bean in terms of productivity too, though due to the short pods you usually only get five or six beans in one pod, and they are small and whitish. There is no way I would ever tire of broad beans, but for those more easily bored there are different ways to enjoy them. You can pick them small (no bigger than your little finger), cook them in their shells and eat pod and all – delicious but extravagant with the young pods. Another favourite way is to remove the 'jackets' from the bean itself, revealing a shinier, darker bean which you usually cook unless the bean is young, and then you can use them in salads. I like them raw best of all.

These shorter-podded beans do better with a spring sowing as opposed to an autumn one. They can be sown at about three-week intervals from early to late spring. Early spring sowings will probably have more losses in terms of actual plants, but the resulting yields will be higher because of the extra growing time gained. Fleece helps tremendously in beefing up success rates, especially for early sowings. It certainly prevents the birds from hoiking out the seeds too. Black bean aphids are a nuisance, congregating on the growing tip in mid-summer. They are dealt with by pinching out the top of the plant (about 7cm/2¾in) as the early beans start to develop. **BG**

Vicia faba 'Stereo'

Vinca minor

LESSER PERIWINKLE

Type: hardy, evergreen ground cover
Soil & situation: one of the most tolerant plants/ will grow in any soil, in any aspect/extremely tolerant of temperature extremes
North American hardiness zone: 4–9
Height: 10–20cm (4–8in)
Spread: indefinite
Grow for: colonizing ground; attractive bright blue flowers from spring to early summer and from then on at odd intervals till the autumn

When you look at this plant in the garden centre your heart probably won't leap into your mouth with excitement. But when you see sheets of it studded with its penetratingly blue flowers and mixed in with a few other old favourites such as foxgloves and bluebells in a modest, lightly-shaded orchard, then I reckon it might well do. It is such an obliging plant, and does not take over, as its big brother, *Vinca major*, does. It looks well furnished, with small, neat, trailing shoots that root as they go. It is perfect for growing with many bulbs as it takes your eye off the decaying foliage of plants such as erythroniums, daffodils and the like. In short, it is one of those plants that is common, dead common, but that is because it is good – use it well and it is stunning. If you like something a little on the flash side then opt for *Vinca minor* 'Argenteovariegata' (AGM) with creamy-white, variegated leaves.

Needless to say, there really is not much you have to do to this plant. For ground cover, I usually plant at a rate of 8 per square metre or square yard, making sure the ground is as weed free as possible first. Plants in full sun flower best. I would normally grow them by division just popping in any shoot with roots where you intend it to go, anytime from autumn to spring. Or, if I was shorter of material, cuttings taken virtually anytime of year will grow but semi-ripe cuttings in summer are quickest. **BG**

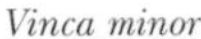

Vinca minor

Vinca minor 'Atropurpurea'

Vinca minor 'Atropurpurea'
LESSER PERIWINKLE

Type: hardy, herbaceous perennial
Soil & situation: most soils/sun or shade
North American hardiness zone: 4–9
Height: 20cm (8in)
Spread: indefinite
Grow for: swirling stems and flowers from spring to autumn; AGM

At some point in their careers, most gardeners have used ultra-vigorous evergreen *Vinca major* 'Variegata'. Freely available in garden centres, you can buy as many as you want, the flower colour is tempting and well, it seems like a good idea at the time. There's plenty of time to repent at leisure when you're stumbling through 'spaghetti'; few have not been upended by its looping, rolling stems. It's fine for naturalizing on banks or when wandering through woodlands but in genteel borders, never!

Consider instead one of its enthusiastic but more civilized relatives. *V. minor* understands all of your needs, is more refined yet still ground covering, and floriferous yet more discreet. Its trailing shoots and fine glossy leaves offer the perfect background for the beautiful flowers.

Here are some of its varieties: 'Blue Cloud', 'Blue Drift', 'Blue Moon', 'Azurea Flore Pleno' provide a myriad of shades of blue, but 'Gertrude Jekyll', 'Alba' and 'Bowles' White' with pink buds all produce white flowers.

The variegated leaf forms are 'Argenteovariegata' with creamy margins and 'Alba Variegata' with a yellow edge. My favourite is 'Atropurpurea': the flowers are a deep-plum purple or, if you prefer, a deep burgundy – which, of course, I do!

It may become invasive but cutting back hard in early spring keeps it under control. Choose the planting location carefully and allow it space to spread. It flourishes in full sun, where it will flower prolifically, or partial shade in any soil except those that are very dry. Divide from autumn to spring. Stems naturally root at the nodes. **MB**

Viola odorata
ENGLISH VIOLET, SWEET VIOLET

Type: hardy, semi-evergreen, spreading, perennial rhizome
Soil & situation: moist, well-drained, humus-rich soil/full sun or partial shade
North American hardiness zone: 6–9
Height: 20cm (8in)
Spread: 40cm (16in)
Grow for: dainty, sweetly scented flowers from late winter to early spring

This little gem is native to southern England and widely spread throughout England and Wales although less so in Scotland and Ireland. The Victorians used bunches of violets as a love token and at funerals, which meant the plant was always in demand. It is ironic that in the wild, white rather than violet is the most common colour. Sweet violet is a great standby for the cottage border and makes an early splash of colour in the wild garden.

Viola odorata

The runners or stolons spread rapidly, rooting as they go with long-stalked, bright green, heart-shaped rosettes of leaves. The sweetly scented, solitary flowers are carried on 5–10cm (2–4in) stalks from late winter until late spring. Usually white, there are forms with violet, purple, lilac or pink flowers. In milder areas the plant may flower again in the autumn.

There is no difficulty propagating this plant as it freely seeds all over the garden and can become a bit of a weed – but a nice one. Large clumps may be divided in autumn or in colder areas in spring.

For such harmless and useful plants they suffer a lot of ailments. Slugs, snails, red spider and greenfly love them and they can be affected by rust and powdery mildew. **JC**

Vitex agnus-castus
CHASTE TREE, MONKS' PEPPER

Type: hardy, open, spreading, aromatic, deciduous shrub
Soil & situation: well-drained soil/sun
North American hardiness zone: 6–9
Height & spread: 8m (25ft)
Grow for: leaves and late autumn flowers

This is a very pretty shrub; the leaves are made up of dark green, rounded leaflets that line the elegant, grey, downy shoots. The flowers are a beautiful soft lilac to dark blue on slender spikes up to 18cm (7in) long and appear at the tip of the current year's shoots in early and mid-autumn. *Vitex agnus-castus* 'Alba' has white flowers. *V. negundo* is similar but with smaller violet-blue flowers.

This aromatic native of the Mediterranean and southwest and central Asia grows in riverbeds often with tamarisk and oleander and is said to have been cultivated in the UK since 1570. The Greeks knew it as *agnos*, or chaste, and it was the symbol of chastity in ancient Greece, though the seeds were also used to treat venereal disease – presumably after the chaste became chased! It is still used as a hormone regulator for women.

Vitex agnus-castus

Pliny, the Roman natural historian (AD 23–79), spoke of using the plant to promote menstruation, purge the uterus and encourage the flow of milk in new mothers; recent research suggests that he may well have been right.

It needs shelter and sunshine on free-draining soil. It flowers best on sunny walls after a long hot summer. Once the framework has been established, prune back the previous summer's growth to two to three buds from the old wood in early spring once the danger of frost is over. Grow from seed in autumn or spring, or semi-ripe cuttings in summer. **MB**

Vitis coignetiae

Type: hardy, deciduous climber
Soil & situation: humus-rich, neutral to alkaline soil/sun or partial shade
North American hardiness zone: 5–9
Height & spread: 15m (50ft)
Grow for: architectural foliage and brilliant autumn colour

This spectacular plant challenges the Russian vine for vigour and easily beats it for beauty. It is a woody climber, with twining tendrils. The young shoots are covered with a loose grey down and the huge leathery, very shallowly three- to five-lobed, heart-shaped leaves, to 30cm (12in) diameter, are just magnificent. Sunken veins create a rough texture on the upper surface, underneath there's thick rusty-brown felt that feels like suede. Forget the insignificant green flowers in the summer and the small, black, inedible grapes with a purple bloom appearing in autumn – they don't even make wine! Admire instead the spectacular autumn colour creating a colourful cloak of scarlet, mahogany and orange; bathed in autumn sunshine, its awesome! When planting, ensure you have enough space, grow it along a wall, let it wrap its tendrils round the branches and shin up the tallest trees, but beware of growing it over your house: it will disappear!

It needs well-drained, humus-rich, preferably neutral to alkaline soil in full sun or partial shade. The best colours are on poorer soil or a restricted root run where the plant is grown 'hard'; do not let the soil dry out or the leaves will be smaller. Prune to keep it within its allotted space (oh, yes?) by shortening the young shoots in summer. It is difficult to propagate – try layering in autumn. It may suffer from powdery mildew and honey fungus. **MB**

Bunny adds:
The leaves of this plant are such a visual treat – I like them situated on a horizontal surface at eye level, so you can ogle them at close quarters. My mother has sited one perfectly in her garden, on a rather tumbled-down, low stone wall that surrounds an old pig sty.

Although I agree with Matt that the berries are not tasty in their raw form, in Japan I regularly drink a juice made from them. It is the best juice in the world, sort of bitter sweet. I would think quantities of sugar must be added. Next time I'll get the label translated.

Vitis coignetiae needs a good, hefty support system to carry its considerable weight. The permanent framework of the plant becomes a feature in its own right, beautifully gnarled and knobbly.

To renovate, you could risk cutting it all down to 30–45cm (12–18in) and then selecting the strongest three or four shoots that are produced from each stem to develop the new structure, cutting out the rest. Ideally, to shock the plant less, you would thin out over two or three years, reducing the older stems by a half, removing weak and dead growth, and thinning half of the remaining stems to about 5–10cm (2–4in).

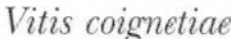

Vitis coignetiae

Vitis vinifera 'Muscat Hamburg'

Vitis vinifera 'Muscat Hamburg'

GRAPE, UNDER COVER

Type: hardy, deciduous climber
Soil & situation: rich compost/sun
North American hardiness zone: 6–9
Height: 2.2m (7ft)
Spread: 60cm (24in)
Grow for: attractive climber with typical vine leaves colouring well in autumn; insignificant scented flowers, but the tastiest dessert grape

I grow many indoor grapes, now mostly in tubs as those in the ground have been too much effort to control and rife with problems. Those in containers just keep on cropping year after year with just a spring top dressing. I grow nearly a dozen and a half indoor varieties, and most are excellent, bearing bigger sweeter fruits than outdoor sorts, and out of all of these 'Muscat Hamburg' (not 'Black Hamburg', which is good but not as good) is the finest flavoured; a black oval fruit with a spicy aromatic, sweet flavour.

Indoor grapes are a peculiarly European development that occurred during the Victorian period when hot houses were common. Most vines are far too vigorous for modern, small greenhouses or conservatories unless grown in containers; this allows them to be kept compact and by spending winter outdoors most pests and diseases are eliminated.

Ideally do not grow an indoor grape in the border inside or out but in a container. This reduces the pruning, the pests and diseases and ensures reliable crops every year. Plant in big tubs of rich compost and grow in full sun trained up poles. These will be very long lived; mine are still cropping after two decades in the same tubs! In autumn prune back all the growth leaving just a stub of each with a couple of buds on a short framework and put the tubs out for the winter. In spring bring the tubs inside. In summer tie six shoots to the pole, removing the rest; later cut them off when they reach the top, and nip out sideshoots. Cuttings can be taken in autumn. The only common problems are wasps and there's nothing you can do about those. **BF**

Vitis vinifera 'Phoenix'

Type: hardy, deciduous climber
Soil & situation: reasonably fertile but well-drained soil with a pH between 6 and 7.5/warm, sunny wall or trained on a support system
North American hardiness zone: 6–9
Height: it can grow a good 4m (13ft) in a season, depending on the rootstock
Spread: indefinite
Grow for: good disease-resistant variety; ideal for an amateur; grapes are delicious for eating, but it is commercially grown for winemaking

I have only grown this vine for about six months but it has been highly recommended to me by Simon Day, a leading viticulturalist, and several others who have been growing vines commercially for many years. It is a fairly new variety (it was registered in Germany in 1984) and has been grown experimentally in the UK from the early 1990s, but in the last three or four years has really gained in popularity, as growers and amateurs are realizing its potential. It is outstanding for gardeners because of its disease resistance and because it has delicious grapes which ripen to a lovely, pale, golden colour. Of all the wine varieties, they are one of the tastiest to eat (more delicious than any I have ever bought from a supermarket). They are about as large as the smallest supermarket eating grape and they do have pips, but the skin is not tough.

Too rich a soil encourages masses of vegetative growth as opposed to fruit. I grow my vines trained up walls where they look wonderful as well as being highly productive. They can of course also be grown over pergolas, arches and garden fences, all to great effect. You can choose between several different systems of training them: the Double Guyot system is quite popular but it depends what best suits you and your structure. This variety is vigorous, so do make sure that your trellis, wires or support system is man enough to cope with it, otherwise you can end up carrying out excessive summer pruning and canopy management. If you want to pick the grapes to eat then leave them on the vine longer than you would normally, as this allows the acid level to drop. **BG**

Vitis vinifera 'Purpurea'

Plant of the Week (see page 319)

Vitis vinifera 'Siegerrebe'

GRAPE, OUTDOOR

Type: hardy, deciduous climber
Soil & situation: low lime soil/sun
North American hardiness zone: 6–9
Height & spread: unlimited
Grow for: attractive climber with typical vine leaves colouring well in autumn; insignificant scented flowers and some of the best tasting rosy-red grapes you have ever tried

I adore grapes; I went grape picking as a student and love wine too. But I prefer the fresh juice and can drink much more of it. I grow many outdoor grapes, over a dozen and a half, but few are much good most years in the open. Some varieties such as *Vitis* 'Boskoop Glory' are reliable but not well flavoured; many others, like the *V.* 'Strawberry Grape', crop well but taste poor. However, *V. vinifera* 'Siegerrebe' is not a bad cropper given a warm site, it comes early and is staggeringly delicious! A red fruit with a spicy aromatic flavour and very sweet.

Grapes are the one of oldest plants in cultivation and are mentioned in the book of Genesis. Thought to have been brought to the UK by the Romans, grapes were only sporadically cultivated here until recent times when new varieties made it possible to grow outdoor grapes without a wall or cloches – though good results still come more often with the aid of a wall! This variety is used to make an excellent wine – I've had some from a vineyard in Devon.

Ideally put an outdoor grape on a warm wall in full sun; otherwise train it on poles and wires to get as much sun as possible. It will be very long lived, so do a good job on the supports and siting. Prune back all the new growth in autumn, leaving just a stub of each with a couple of buds on the framework. In summer nip out all shoots to five leaves after a bunch and thin the bunches by half. Cuttings can be taken in autumn. The only common problems are cold, wet summers, wasps and birds and you can do ****** all about all save the last. **BF**

Watsonia 'Stanford Scarlet'

Watsonia 'Stanford Scarlet'

Type: half-hardy, cormous perennial
Soil & situation: open, gritty, well-drained soil/full sun
North American hardiness zone: 9–10
Height: 80–120cm (32–48in)
Spread: 15cm (6in)
Grow for: long, sword-like foliage; striking orange-red flowers; excellent form

Watsonias are strikingly beautiful with their tall, symmetrical spikes of brightly coloured flowers which are held horizontally to the stem. They resemble gladiolus with panache.

The mid-green, sword-like leaves are up to 1m (3ft) long, not reaching the height of the flower spike. In late spring and early summer, each unbranched spike carries up to 12 tubular, orange-red flowers. When fully open, the tepals are spread wide. Watsonia is native to South Africa, where in the wild it grows in areas prone to bush fires, appearing immediately after a burn. Where they can be left in the ground mulch them with wood ash after the foliage has died down or top dress container-grown plants. They will love it.

Plant the corms 15cm (6in) deep, at the base of a sheltered, sunny wall in a very free-draining soil. Protect them from frost and in a few years they will form a clump. They will flower better if they are left undisturbed. In less ideal situations the corms should be lifted in autumn and stored in a dry, frost-free place over the winter for planting out in spring. Propagation is by division in autumn. When grown from seed it may take five years to produce flowering-sized corms.

Watsonia pillansii flowers in summer and autumn with branched spikes bearing up to 20 tubular, bright orange-pink flowers. **JC**

Weigela middendorffiana

Weigela middendorffiana

Type: hardy, deciduous shrub
Soil & situation: fertile, well-drained soil/partial shade
North American hardiness zone: 5–7
Height & spread: 1.5m (5ft)
Grow for: showy, bell-shaped flowers surrounded by bright green foliage

When you are used to shades of pink and red there is something nice about a change of colour and this weigela does it with panache. When mature it forms an upright shrub with the older branches arching. The 8cm (3½in) long, pointed, bright green leaves turn golden-brown in autumn. The bell-shaped, sulphur-yellow flowers have conspicuous, dark orange markings on the lower lobes and are continually produced from mid-spring until mid summer.

It prefers to be planted in a sheltered situation in partial shade and protected from cold winds. When grown in full sun the flowers quickly fade to a pale yellow. Prune after flowering by cutting back shoots which have flowered to strong, healthy buds lower down the stem. Old plants may be rejuvenated by removing a third of the oldest branches as close to the soil level as possible. New strong shoots will be produced from the base. Continue to prune over a three-year period until all the old branches have been replaced with flowering shoots.

Propagation is easy using softwood cuttings in early summer. Pot the rooted plants before autumn to ensure there is a root run through the compost. Hardwood cuttings taken in winter root well outside in a sheltered position. They will be ready for planting out the following winter. **JC**

Acer pensylvanicum

SNAKE-BARK MAPLE, MOOSE WOOD

Type: hardy, deciduous tree
Soil & situation: moist, well-drained loam; dislikes chalk/prefers a sheltered position
North American hardiness zone: 3–7
Height & spread: 6m (20ft); occasionally as tall as 10m (33ft)
Grow for: compact profile; autumn colour; beautiful bark in winter, which is why I have allocated it to December; AGM.

It was love at first sight when I saw this gorgeous tree with her elegant upswept branches and a fine cloak of large trilobed leaves; she simply oozes grace and style. Stepping into the limelight in autumn, she coyly sheds her soft yellow garments to reveal delicately marked, 'snake skin' stems. The silvery-white pattern, highlighted by the jade-green background, is intense on young growth and she looks stunning basking in the spotlight of the low winter sun. Her relative *Acer pensylvanicum* 'Erythrocladum' is more glamorous but not as robust. A stunning, candy-pink when young, she fades to orange-red with age; it's the difference between a real and fake tan! A restorative face-lift by hard pruning every other year brings back much of her appeal, but as far as I'm concerned, *A. pensylvanicum* with her charm and lasting beauty is the ultimate 'it' tree!

It needs a cool, moist, well-drained, acid soil and must be protected from scorching sunlight and cold winds. Plant at the same level as it is in the pot; water well until settled in. Young plants are cheaper to buy and establish more rapidly than mature ones.

Prune only if necessary when branches are small, in early summer or late autumn; don't prune in spring or the cuts will bleed. Propagation is by sowing seed of the species in spring after a period of chilling over winter. Drought and frost cause bark splitting and late frosts can damage the shoot tips. Plant in a sheltered spot. It can suffer from coral spot; remove affected stems with sharp secateurs. **MB**

Wisteria sinensis

Wisteria sinensis 'Alba'

Wisteria sinensis

CHINESE WISTERIA

Type: hardy, deciduous, twining climber
Soil & situation: deep, moist, well-drained soil/full sun
North American hardiness zone: 5–8
Height: 9m (30ft)
Spread: to 1.5m (5ft) or more
Grow for: trailing garlands of fragrant flowers

If you have been putting off planting a wisteria because those you have seen have grown all over their support and are totally bare of flower then read on. They are one of the most spectacular flowering climbers, fully hardy in all but the coldest of gardens. The secret of success is in the pruning and that is easily explained.

The mid-green, pinnate leaves are carried on twining stems. In late spring and early summer the plant is smothered in 30cm (12in) long, pendent racemes of fragrant, pea-like, lilac-blue to white flowers, which are followed in autumn by 15cm (6in) long, velvety green, bean-like seedpods. The variety *W. s.* 'Sierra Madre' has very fragrant, lavender-blue flowers flushed white. *W. s.* 'Alba' has long, pendent racemes of pure white flowers.

Given support, wisteria is ideal for growing on a sunny wall. At planting don't enrich the soil with manure, which will encourage growth at the expense of flowers. Avoid a cold, windy site.

Prune twice a year. In summer cut the new side-shoots back to four or five leaves from the older branches. In winter further reduce these shoots to two or three buds. At the same time, shorten the main leading shoots to leave 1m (3ft) of new growth. This builds up a framework of branches with lots of short 'spurs' which carry the flowers. Wisterias scrambling through trees are not pruned. I have no difficulty rooting layers. After 18 months they are ready to plant out or pot up.

How do you tell a Chinese wisteria from a Japanese wisteria? Easy. *Wisteria sinensis* (Chinese) twines anti-clockwise. *W. floribunda* (Japanese) twines clockwise. **JC**

Yucca filamentosa 'Bright Edge'

ADAM'S NEEDLE

Type: hardy, evergreen shrub
Soil & situation: well-drained soil/sunny position
North American hardiness zone: 5–10
Height: 75cm (30in)
Spread: 1.5m (5ft)
Grow for: architectural plant with striking dark green leaves edged with yellow stripes; AGM

This is a stemless yucca and has several good attributes. It always looks striking and smart, with its erect, brightly coloured, lance-shaped leaves. This is in part due to its degree of hardiness. *Y. filamentosa* is hardy to about –15°C (5°F) and so it takes an extremely severe winter to make it suffer. When I first realized its robustness, I was surprised – it looks such an exotic beast. Tall panicles of creamy-white flowers, rising to about 1.2m (4ft), are produced in mid- to late summer. They are pretty dramatic and remain looking good for a fair few weeks. And, usefully for impatient gardeners, they bloom at a young age.

In many situations I like the plain green *Yucca filimentosa* as much as, if not more than, its rather brash-looking, gold and green relative. Particularly when it comes to flowering, the simplicity of the plain green looks more stylish, with just the green and white coming into play. As ever, it all depends on the effect you are driving at.

With many yuccas the tips of the leaves are very pointed, so if you have young children it is worth cutting off the tips of the leaves as soon as they – children or plants – arrive. As they tolerate dry conditions and are so hardy, *Y. filimentosa* are perfect container plants. They often look better raised up nearer to eye level and are extremely tolerant of negligence, for those that tend to be idle with the watering can. Propagate by removing rooted suckers in spring or by root cuttings in winter. **BG**

Yucca filamentosa 'Bright Edge'

Yucca gloriosa

Yucca gloriosa
SPANISH DAGGER

Type: frost-hardy, evergreen shrub
Soil & situation: well-drained soil/full sun
North American hardiness zone: 7–10
Height & spread: 2m (6½ft)
Grow for: its form, foliage and flowers; AGM

Yucca gloriosa grows in at least five locations in my garden. I love its shape, leaves and flowers. I have one particular plant with an attitude problem. It insists on sending up enormous flower spikes in mid- to late autumn. When they do manage to flower there is often a coating of frost on the flowers. It has carried on like this for 12 to 15 years and even managed to be in full bloom one Christmas.

When mature it forms an erect shrub with thick, bare stems. The broad, sword-like leaves with dangerously sharp points are clustered near the top of the branches. The young leaves are blue-green maturing to dark green. The 5cm (2in) long, pendent, bell-shaped, ivory-white flowers are often tinged with purple. They are carried on stiff, 2m (6½ft) long, upright panicles during late summer and autumn.

After flowering remove the whole stalk, cutting it as close to the leaf rosette as possible. I have never seen seed form and I'm told it is necessary to pollinate the flowers by hand. Where there are people, especially children, coming in contact with the leaves it is necessary to remove the sharp tips. This is easily done with nail clippers and it will never be noticed. Remove the dying leaves as they yellow by pulling downwards from the stem one at a time.

Y. gloriosa hates wet ground. At planting time incorporate extra coarse grit to the planting hole. Choose a sheltered site in full sun. Propagation is by seed sown in spring in a propagator. Rooted suckers may be carefully removed in spring and potted up for a year before planting out in the garden. Root cuttings may be taken in winter and rooted in a free-draining compost. **JC**

Zaluzianskya capensis
NIGHT OR CAPE PHLOX

Type: half-hardy annual
Soil & situation: any soil/sun
North American hardiness zone: annual
Height: 30cm (12in)
Spread: 15cm (6in)
Grow for: prolific, scented, white flowers opening in the evening

Night phlox is slightly heather-like until the flowers appear; these resemble campions rather than phloxes and are chocolate-brown inside, opening purest white in the cool of the evening and giving off an addictive lemony-vanilla fragrance that is so intoxicating. Named after a 16th-century botanist from Prague, this South African beauty is little known, which is probably because it comes at the end of the catalogue. There are three dozen species.

Night phlox is good as bedding in most soils and sites but not heavy shade or cold. It does well in pots and containers. As a half hardy-annual it is best sown in the warmth early in spring and planted out as soon as the frosts are over. Do not take pots into a warm room to enjoy their perfume, as they lose it inside. **BF**

Zaluzianskya capensis

Zaluzianskya ovata

Zaluzianskya ovata
SOUTH AFRICAN PHLOX

Type: half-hardy perennial
Soil & situation: moist, free-draining soil/sun
North American hardiness zone: 9–10
Height: 25cm (10in)
Spread: 60cm (24in)
Grow for: beautiful flowers from early summer to mid-autumn

I once met a beautiful woman who ate chocolate and wore raspberry; I'm sure she would adore this plant. Like a tiny jewel, each facet glistening, the deep raspberry-red bud unfurls revealing pure white, saucer-shaped flowers with heart-shaped petals backed with that same sumptuous colour. They shy away from bright sunlight, opening only when the light is low; in early morning, on dull days or at dusk when glistening in the twilight, the night air is laden with their sweet and sensuous perfume. I planted mine by a window so the fragrance of romance drifted through; yours may be on a moonlit terrace or by a tranquil pool; choose carefully, then linger long, and dream of tropical climes.

Z. ovata 'Semonkong' from Lesotho is hardier, flowers for longer, is less compact and becomes straggly later in the season. *Z. capensis* (see previous entry) is taller with narrower lobes and is good as a gap-filler in the front of the border.

All need a warm, sheltered position on moist, humus-rich, free-draining soil; water well in summer. Dead-head regularly and they will flower until the first frosts. Cut back hard after flowering. They are not frost hardy, so lift and pot up in autumn or grow in containers and over-winter in a cool, bright, frost-free place. Plants are short lived; propagate regularly from tip cuttings in summer, over-winter under glass and plant out when danger of frost has passed. Prone to botrytis in damp conditions. **MB**

Zantedeschia aethiopica 'Crowborough'
ARUM LILY

Type: hardy, tuberous perennial
Soil & situation: humus-rich, moist soil/full sun
North American hardiness zone: 8–10
Height: 90cm (36in)
Spread: 45cm (18in)
Grow for: elegant spathes; arrow-shaped glossy foliage; makes a big impression in a clump; AGM

I have mixed feelings about the arum lily. I appreciate its tolerance of wet, boggy conditions, making it ideal for the pool edge. I love the pure white, upturned trumpet-shaped spathe. Against that, it is associated with funerals. Although that hasn't stopped me planting six or seven clumps in various areas of my garden.

Zantedeschia aethiopica 'Crowborough'

It quickly forms a clump, remaining evergreen in mild locations. The 45cm (18in) long, glossy, dark green leaves are arrow shaped. They stand almost vertical well into autumn. The wide-throated, ivory-white spathes with a long, golden spadix are produced in succession from late spring through to mid-summer. *Z. a.* 'Green Goddess' has a similar habit of growth but its flowers are pale green with a white-and-green-splashed throat. Very striking. Arums are great as cut flowers, lasting for long periods in water.

It may be used as a marginal plant in the pond tolerating up to 30cm (12in) of water. In the border it dislikes soils which dry out in summer. In gardens prone to frosts the foliage will die down in winter. It is advisable to cover the crown with a deep mulch of bark or straw, which can be removed when risk of frost is past. Propagation is by division in spring. Take care not to damage the fleshy roots. **JC**

Zea mays
SWEET CORN

Type: half-hardy annual crop
Soil & situation: rich, moist soil/sun
North American hardiness zone: annual
Height: 3m (10ft)
Spread: 60cm–1m (2–3ft)
Grow for: architectural statuesque plants with cobs of delicious sweet kernels; some with decorative colours

Sweet corn has to be fresh to be really sweet, and I mean fresh; I run in with the cobs and throw them into the already boiling water. You don't believe me – well pick one half an hour early and another and boil them immediately and you'll see the difference. I grow lots of varieties, which is hard as they need to be kept apart, but they are all delicious. There are also some ornamental cultivars with coloured cobs and of course popcorn.

Originally grown by the American Natives there are no wild species known but countless cultivars. They grew it as one of three sisters, planting sweet corn, squashes and beans in hillocks together, which is an early example of effective companion gardening. It gets its name from the Greek for another cereal entirely!

Sweet corn needs a moist soil enriched with a handful of chicken pellets or similar. A dead fish is traditional. Give full sun as any shade leads to no cobs. Water heavily and grow in a block, not a long row, to ensure (wind) pollination, and do not mix varieties or plant them adjacently. In the warmer parts of the UK you can sow *in situ* in late spring or early summer and hope to get a crop; in colder regions it is best started under cover in individual pots and planted out after the last frosts. Other than our miserable summers and two-legged rats (adults of the species *Homo criminalis*) there are no problems with sweet corn. **BF**

Zea mays

Zingiber officinale

Zingiber officinale
GINGER

Type: tender rhizomatous perennial
Soil & situation: well-drained compost/dappled shade to light sun/under cover
North American hardiness zone: 10–11
Height: 60cm (24in) vertical blade
Spread: 60–120cm (2–4ft)
Grow for: curiosity and as a crop

I love to grow anything I can eat or sniff and this is a real challenge; not so much in the maintenance but just to get it going. Then it needs a long season to do well, so it has to be started in late winter when the light is a bit too low. None the less, most years I make my own stem ginger in syrup for Christmas and have plenty of root ginger for my cooking. I use ginger and garlic in most fried dishes as the former offsets the bad breath engendered by the latter.

Ginger was known to the ancients; it originated on the Pacific rim and from there went to central Asia; indeed the name comes from the Indian via the Greek and Latin. It was brought to England by the Romans and it is in many old Anglo-Saxon recipes. Traded since as one of the most important spices, it was sea-faring merchants' search for its roots that led to the discovery of the rest of the world. Galangal (*Alpinia officinarum*) is very similar but actually a different plant.

Grow in a gritty, rich, moist compost. It needs to be in bright light but full sun parches it, so I find it does well at the back of the greenhouse. The initial root needs warmth to spur it into growth and the tall grass-like stems do not seem to do much. However, in autumn they die down and if they are in a big pot you will find a much bigger root or hand. If it is harvested while the leaves are still green it is more succulent and known as stem ginger, which you can preserve in sugar syrup. Other than needing warmth, ginger is fairly easy once it gets going. **BF**

Sarcococca confusa

CHRISTMAS BOX, SWEET BOX

Type: hardy, evergreen shrub
Soil & situation: humus-rich, moist, well-drained soil/deep or partial shade
North American hardiness zone: 6–9
Height: 2m (6½ft)
Spread: 1m (3ft)
Grow for: the most incredible winter fragrance from clusters of small, white flowers; happy in shade. I couldn't feature the Christmas box in any other month! AGM.

This perfectly behaved shrub deserves to be planted in every garden in the country. There is no excuse. It is small, evergreen and trouble free, with flowers, fruit and the most exquisite winter fragrance imaginable. You don't have to bury your nose in the flowers: you can be 6m (20ft) away and its perfume will still stop you in your tracks.

It forms a bushy shrub with 5cm (2in) long, glossy, dark green leaves. The tiny, pure white, very fragrant flowers appear in winter in clusters of five. They are followed by shiny black fruit. Other species include *Sarcococca hookeriana*, which is similar and grows to 1.5m (5ft); and *S. humilis*, which has fragrant, white flowers tinged with pink, and is more compact, growing to 60cm (24in).

In gardens where the soil remains moist in summer *S. confusa* may be grown in sun, otherwise it will perform best in deep shade and is ideal in woodland. Providing it is sheltered from cold, drying winds, the Christmas box will grow against a shady wall or fence.

Older plants can become straggly. In spring, after flowering is finished, remove any long growths that are spoiling the shape. Propagation is by seed, sown in spring, in pots outside. Semi-ripe, 5cm (2in) long cuttings taken in late summer will root in a peaty compost. Grow the rooted plants in a container for a year before planting out in the ground. **JC**

Some Practical Tips

Planting

When planting trees dig a big hole – do not be mean, make it wide and deep, break up the subsoil but do not mix it with the topsoil. Do not put loads of fertilizer or much else in the hole! It is better to apply muck, fertilizer and so on as mulches in later years than to confine it to the planting hole now, as the roots will not need it for a year or two. Hammer in the stake to support the tree. Spread out the roots in their natural layers as you refill the hole, tread the soil in firmly, embedding each root in its own portion. Make sure the tree is not buried too deep or too shallow – set it to its original level, indicated by a dirty mark on the trunk. After refilling and refirming the soil, tie the tree to the supporting stake, then mulch around it well and keep a big circle weed free for the first year or three. It is far better to plant into moist soil, i.e. ground that was well watered previously, than to water the holes just before or worse, to water on top.

Planting out shrubs is much the same as for trees, but without the need for a stake or as careful teasing out of roots. Obviously the smaller the shrublet the smaller the hole needs be, but bigger holes are always worth the effort and smaller plants well planted soon outgrow bigger ones no matter how well the latter are treated. The same goes for herbaceous plants. However, as these grow much smaller and so are planted more densely than most shrubs, their entire bed should be prepared and enriched before planting. Herbaceous plants usually look better grouped in threes, fives and sevens. Biennials and bedding plants should be treated as herbaceous plants with their whole bed prepared and enriched beforehand and they will need more assiduous watering to help them establish as they are often moved when in growth. Many annuals do not perform well if their soil is rich and do best sown *in situ* in poor soil; only a few do not resent being transplanted. Bulbs are fussy about how they are planted – requirements vary enormously from species to species, so read the instructions on the packet carefully or seek the advice of an expert.

Watering

Water control is crucial. Too little and the plants desiccate, too much and their roots drown; unfortunately the symptoms are the same in both cases with drooping, flagging leaves. In pots it is safest to keep the compost only just moist, if not actually dry all winter, and then to water more and more generously as the year warms up. Rather than pouring water on top to run through the container, you may immerse pots in water and then drain them, but *never, ever* leave any specimen standing in water unless you want to lose it! In hot weather big plants in small pots need watering at least three times daily. Plants in the ground need watering from the day they are planted if the weather and soil are dry, the more so if it is also windy. It is almost impossible to over-water plants in the ground, especially during the growing season. Foliage, bog and salad plants need even more water than most other groups if they are to perform well. If you must skimp on watering, leave out the lawn and concentrate on the plants.

Soil type

Your basic soil type will affect your success with many sorts of plants. If it's a sticky, heavy clay you may drown plants in water-filled planting holes, but, once tempered, clay will produce luxuriant growth and is best suited to permanent planting such as trees, shrubs and bog gardens. In a chalky soil you will not be able to grow acid-loving lime-haters such as heathers or camellias, and you will need to feed and water often. In a sandy soil you will probably be able to grow acid-loving plants and will also need to feed and water often. In most common garden, loamy soils you can grow the majority of plants fairly well and weeds most luxuriantly. To improve all soil types add more organic material as muck and compost and mulch really heavily.

If you don't know whether your soil is acid or alkaline, assume it is alkaline unless everyone around you is growing rhododendrons. **BF**

Pests and Diseases

Pests and diseases can be controlled by chemical sprays, good hygiene and management, or by using 'biological controls', natural predators that parasitize or prey on the pest.

Following these few simple rules will improve your chances of producing healthy plants:

• Check plants regularly, preferably daily, for signs of pests and diseases; treat them before they become established and spread to nearby plants.

• Provide good growing conditions so that your plants are strong, healthy and disease resistant. Choose disease-resistant cultivars where possible.

• Encourage natural predators to your garden, such as lacewings, ladybirds and blue tits to control aphids. Provide an 'anvil' stone so that song thrushes can smash snail shells and eat the contents. Encourage hedgehogs.

• Use environmentally friendly sprays and physical barriers such as horticultural fleece to control pests and diseases.

• Buy a specialist book to help you identify problems correctly.

• Use companion planting and sacrificial crops to discourage predators. Bob Flowerdew's *Complete Book of Companion Planting*, also published by Kyle Cathie, will tell you all you need to know!

• Legislation governing chemical controls is constantly changing, so check what's available at your retailer and always follow the manufacturer's instructions. Most controls either work on contact or are translocated through the sap system.

Here is some basic advice on combating specific pests and diseases mentioned in this book.

Pests

Aphids are sap sucking and come in many colours and sizes. Many have summer and winter hosts; others, like viburnum aphid, are specific to a particular group. They debilitate and disfigure young growth, transmit viruses and secrete 'honeydew', encouraging sooty mould (see below). Don't overfeed with nitrogen.

Use contact or translocated organic or inorganic sprays, physical barriers such as horticultural fleece and encourage predators like ladybirds, lacewings and blue tits.

Woolly aphids hide among the cracks and crevices in the bark of pyracantha, cotoneaster and apples, and are covered with a white, protective 'wool'. It can be cleaned off with a scrubbing brush and water, blasted off with a hose (taking care not to damage the plant tissue), hanging bird food in the tree so that the birds waiting their turn at the feeding station feed on the nearest available insects, or spraying.

Lily beetles are bright red with black heads. The larvae cover themselves with excrement as a protection from predators – it's revolting but effective! Adults and larvae eat leaves, flowers and seedpods, devastating lilies and fritillarias. They appear from spring until autumn and are becoming more widespread throughout Britain. Pick off the adults by hand – they tend to drop off the leaf just as you are about to pick them up, so cup your hand and place it below the leaf to catch them or temporarily cover the ground below with white plastic so that they are easy to spot once they fall. Alternatively, spray with contact insecticide or wipe off the larvae by hand – or get someone else to do it!

Asparagus beetles appear from late spring and eat the leaves and bark from the stems, which then turn yellow and die. They're black with six yellow blotches on their back. There are two generations between late spring and autumn. Seek and destroy by burning over-wintering asparagus stems, remove by hand or spray at dusk so that bees are not affected.

Flea beetles are shiny beetles about 2mm (1/12in) long that jump off the leaves when disturbed; there are several species, appearing from late spring to mid-summer, that leave anything from rocket to stocks covered in tiny holes that can 'check' growth or kill. Cover with horticultural fleece, use contact insecticide.

Capsid bugs are pale green and about 6mm (1/4in) long with toxic saliva that disfigures leaves and shoot tips and causes puckering on apples and other fruit. Check plants regularly from late spring to late summer and spray with contact insecticide.

Mealy bugs look like tiny woodlice covered in white fluff. Spray with insecticidal soap or use biological control indoors.

Carrot fly leaves the roots of carrots and its relatives riddled with holes. There are three generations between late spring and early autumn. Grow resistant varieties such as 'Sytan' or 'Flyaway', surround the crops with barriers, cover with horticultural fleece, thin crops on damp days or sow in clusters at the final spacing, thus reducing the need to thin the crops.

Whitefly cluster on the underside of leaves to suck the sap, flying up when disturbed. They also produce 'honeydew' that encourages black, disfiguring sooty mould (see below). Use contact or translocated sprays, physical barriers or biological control.

Big bud affects a number of plants, most commonly currants. The buds become swollen and fail to develop because they are packed with microscopic mites. These can be found at any time of year. The disease is most serious on blackcurrants; remove affected stems immediately and, in bad cases, destroy the whole plant.

Caterpillars may be solitary or in clusters. Many are alarmingly voracious; some, like those of 'webber' moths, cover themselves with a fine web to protect themselves from predators. Sawfly larvae are eating machines that can defoliate plants at an alarming rate, particularly Solomon's seal (*Polygonatum* spp.) and berberis. Larger specimens such as the caterpillars of grey, yellow and black mullein moth can be picked off by hand; prune out the affected stems of plants attacked by webber moths or spray with the biological control *Bacillus thuringiensis*. Make sure that you spray the pests and not butterfly caterpillars – *Bacillus thuringiensis* is non-selective. Other caterpillars can damage fruit, notably the codling moth, the 'maggot' in your apples. Pheromone traps catch enough males on isolated trees to reduce the population; otherwise spray in early summer before the caterpillars enter the developing fruit.

Two-spotted or red spider mites are tiny and difficult to spot with the naked eye; they are a problem in summer, or all year round under glass. A magnifying glass reveals all! Symptoms include mottling and fine webbing over the leaf. Increase humidity; use contact or translocated sprays or biological control.

Scale insects hide under a protective hemispherical shell on leaves and stems, sucking sap and secreting 'honey dew'. Spray with translocated insecticide, soft soap or use biological controls.

Eelworms are microscopic nematodes living within the plant with a variety of hosts from narcissus to onion and phlox. Others nibble root hairs and transmit viruses. Affected narcissus have distorted leaves and stems; onions become stunted, swollen and may rot; phlox have swollen, stunted stems that often split. Dispose of affected plants immediately; do not grow vulnerable plants on infected sites, buy 'clean' stock, rotate crops.

Slugs and snails damage leaves, shoots and flowers. Pick them off by hand, encourage predators, remove decaying organic matter, use traps, barriers and biological controls.

Wasps damage soft fruit such as plums, but on apples and pears cause secondary damage, usually after the birds have taken their pick. Protect ripening fruit with netting or bags made from old nylon tights or muslin. Destroy nests but remember too that wasps they are valuable predators of aphids and help the gardener.

Vine weevil adults are black with orange spots and cut notches from the edge of leaves, particularly on plants such as rhododendrons. The larvae are white, fat and slightly curved, and eat the roots of a wide range of plants, especially in containers; the worst damage is between autumn and mid-spring. Use biological controls or physical barriers, squash adults, use drench or compost containing imidacloprid.

Diseases

Black spot appears as dark blotches on rose leaves with yellowing patches – in severe cases they join together and can defoliate plants. Spray, rake up and destroy infected leaves, prune out infected wood in winter and destroy, mulch in autumn and grow resistant cultivars. It is worse in damp seasons.

Grey mould comes in several guises and includes peony wilt. Fuzzy, grey fungal growth appears on infected parts; any soft tissue of living and dead plant material is vulnerable. Isolate dead and injured plants before they become infected, prune back infected areas to healthy growth, remove all plant debris immediately, spray with fungicide.

Coral spot appears as orange pustules on dead and sometimes on living material. Remove infected parts back to healthy material immediately the disease appears and burn; destroy garden debris that harbours the disease.

Blight appears in several forms. Potato blight causes browning and collapsing of the plant, tubers become rotten and evil smelling. Spray with copper-based fungicide, grow resistant varieties; also affects tomatoes. The symptoms of box blight are yellowing leaves and death; remove affected plants immediately. Fire blight leaves the flowers, foliage and stems looking as though they have been too close to a bonfire. It affects Rosaceae with apple-like fruit, including *Sorbus* and *Cotoneaster* spp., though some varieties are more susceptible than others. Remove infected parts immediately, cutting well back into healthy wood, sterilize tools after use, burn pruned material.

Honey fungus causes die back on susceptible plants from trees to perennials; honey-coloured mushrooms appear at the base of the plant in autumn; white mycelium (fungus roots) can be found below the bark at the base of woody plants; 'boot lace' rhizomorphs are found in the ground. Grow non-susceptible plants, install physical barriers, remove all stumps and as much root as possible from felled or infected trees. Keep plants healthy and stress free.

Iris ink disease is so called because of the blue-black streaks that appear on the bulb. The whole bulb may turn black and rot and any foliage is striped yellow with red tints. Dispose of bulbs immediately, grow plants in a new location.

Leaf spots can be bacterial or fungal; bacterial spots often have a bright yellow 'halo', fungal spots may join together, forming patches. Both show that plants are under stress or have other problems. Remove infected leaves, rake them up and dispose of them at the end of the season, improve plant health. Treat fungal spots with fungicide.

Powdery mildew appears like a whitish powdery layer on leaves; young shoots may distort and fruit is blemished. Encourage air circulation, keep plants well watered, prune out affected branches immediately, avoid high-nitrogen fertilizers, spray with fungicide, grow resistant varieties.

Silver leaf affects notably plums and cherries (*Prunus* spp.). The symptoms are silvering of the leaves, failure to leaf in spring and 'die back'; stems more than 2.5cm (1in) wide have a central reddish stain. The fungus enters through pruning cuts or damage. Prune vulnerable plants throughout the summer months, never in winter. Some control may be gained by pruning infected boughs to at least 15cm (5in) past stained wood or by using biological control.

Tulip fire causes emerging foliage to wither, distort and become mouldy. Buds may develop but not open; if they do flower the petals are blotched. Horrible! Remove infected plants immediately, buy from a reputable source, do not plant tulips on the site for three years.

Willow anthracnose is manifested by curling yellowing leaves that fall early; stems are covered with rough cankers and may die back. It is worse in wet seasons. Fungus over-winters in the cankers, on bud scales and leaves. Prune out infected stems immediately and rake up leaves. Bordeaux mixture may help.

Green alga covers the surface of the leaves and the sunless side of trees and shrubs, particularly in damp areas; if it becomes unsightly, it can be rubbed off or washed off with slightly soapy water. Improve air circulation and reduce dampness.

Sooty mould is a black fungus that lives on the sugary exudate from scale, whitefly, aphids, mealy bug and other 'suckers'. Treat the cause, then wipe off the mould carefully with a soft, damp, slightly soapy cloth.

Phytophthora root rot causes rotting at the collar of woody plants, foliage is sparse and becomes yellow, stems die back; often the whole plant dies. Look at the roots: affected fibrous roots are dead, others discoloured. Remove the bark at the base and you will find a reddish-brown stain. Remove and destroy infected plants and the soil around them, improve drainage.

Rots can be bacterial or fungal. Bacterial such as *Brassica* bacterial soft rot affects roots, fruits, tubers and rhizomes. Discoloured areas develop, then sink as the rot spreads. The bacteria enter via wounds and are spread by pruning tools. Infection spreads rapidly; destroy damaged tissue immediately and disinfect tools.

Fungal rots such as brown rots are manifested by soft brown rotting tissue; fruits fall off or become 'mummified'. Avoid damage to plants, remove infected material immediately and prune out mummified fruits with a small portion of wood.

Rusts appear on leaves and stems as bright orange or brown pustules; infected parts often wither and die. Some have alternative hosts for the winter; others only one. Remove infected leaves, spray, grow resistant varieties.

Scabs can appear on potatoes or apples and fit their description perfectly. Apples crack or split, are small or misshapen, affected leaves fall early. It can occur on any apple or relative. Rake up fallen leaves, prune out cracked or scabby shoots; grow resistant varieties.

Viruses stunt and distort the whole plant – leaves develop streaks or mosaic patterns, flowers develop colour breaks, some plants are simply weakened, not showing external symptoms. Plants affected include cucumbers and tobacco. Viruses can be spread by sap-sucking insects. Dispose of affected plants, buy virus-free stock, control sap-sucking insects, do not plant similar varieties in the same location, wash hands and tools after use, don't propagate from infected plants. **MB**

Pruning

The difference between simply cutting a plant and pruning it properly is knowledge and common sense. Anyone can cut a shrub or tree, but to prune it you need to understand the plant's reaction to the treatment. If you bear in mind that pruning promotes growth you will naturally go easy with the cutting equipment.

Throughout this book there are many examples of shrubs which can be rejuvenated by a hard pruning, leaving the stumps of branches. Escallonias, rhododendrons and *Taxus* (yew) will recover fully from such drastic action. Where time allows it is easier on the plant and the eye if you work on them over a two-year period, cutting 50 per cent of the old stems in the first year. But dish out the same treatment to a lavender or *Cytisus* (broom) and it will probably die. Another group of plants does not require pruning other than to restrict their size or to change the shape: camellias, pieris, kalmias, magnolias and azaleas are happy to grow and flower year after year without input from the owner.

The golden rule with all pruning is to remove any diseased or rubbing branches first. After that, try to retain the shape of the plant without it becoming one-sided or gappy.

With small branches try to prune immediately above a bud, sloping the cut so that water will run away from the bud. Always make a clean cut with a sharp blade. Where a saw has left roughened bark, smooth it by trimming with a knife. When diseased branches are removed, clean the blade before cutting healthy wood.

The majority of shrubs deserve and in some cases demand an annual prune to encourage flowers, leafy growth, coloured bark or fruit. With these plants it is necessary to know and recognize their habit of growth. When they flower and the age of the stems they flower on are crucial to the type and time of pruning:

• Winter-flowering deciduous shrubs do not normally need to be pruned except to remove diseased branches or those that are growing towards the centre of the plant.

• Those that flower in spring and early summer should be pruned as soon as flowering is finished. First remove any diseased or thin shoots, then cut all the branches that flowered back to within a few buds of the base. Leave the new shoots to flower next year.

• Prune late summer-flowering shrubs in spring when all risk of frost has passed. Again, remove diseased and thin shoots and prune out last year's flowering shoots, allowing the new shoots to grow away and flower next year.

• Evergreen shrubs should be pruned in early summer to avoid any risk of frost damage. Again, the priority is to remove diseased, thin and spindly shoots, and to maintain a balanced and attractive shape.

A few specific examples:

Forsythias flower early in the year on growth made the previous summer. Prune immediately after they have finished flowering, removing all of the branches which produced blossom. The new shoots will grow during the summer and flower next spring.

Bush roses flower on this year's growth but as they are prone to spring frost damage do not prune them until spring; they will then come into flower from mid-summer onwards.

Apple trees fruit best on wood which is at least two years old. In spring last year's growths should be shortened by half to encourage more shoots. The remainder of the stem will produce fruit buds in winter and fruit the following summer.

Wisterias are best pruned twice each year. Cut the excess new growth in summer, leaving 10–15cm (4–6in). Sideshoots will form. In winter shorten the hardening stems back to 5–7cm (2–3in). Flower buds will appear on the remaining stem.

To thicken a young hedge, clip it lightly in late spring. This causes the stems to form sideshoots. After a few cuts there will be an extensive branch system.

The young growths of the red stemmed ***Cornus alba* 'Sibirica'** have the best colour and are most visible in winter after leaf fall. In early spring cut all the branches to within a few centimetres of soil level. They will quickly regrow with good colour for the coming winter. Gather up the prunings and shred or burn them. **JC**

Propagation

Being naturally frugal, I got into propagation at an early age, but apart from saving huge sums of money, it has other big benefits too. It totally changes the way you approach planting design because it enables you to grow larger quantities of plants, encouraging you to plant generous interlocking drifts or repeated groups of one plant. Almost inevitably the overall effect is far more cohesive than the spotty results often achieved by garden-centre buyers who are able to indulge in only one of each type. It also, especially in the case of box, can prevent you importing noxious diseases that inevitably come with certain plants.

The simplest methods of propagation are seed, cuttings and division. Division is generally the easiest: you dig up the clump that is to be divided and either tease it apart by hand or prise it using two garden forks. Replant as soon as possible in weed-free soil and water the plants in to settle the soil around the roots.

If you are propagating from seed, far better success rates are achieved if you can sow seeds with some protection from the elements and pests, such as in a greenhouse, cold frame or on the window sill. The majority of my spring vegetable seed I now get going inside first, as external factors can be so extreme at this time of year. I tend not to use seed trays – having little spare time, I go for the most time-efficient method possible. I find the special dried pellets, such as the Jiffy-7, which come in reusable plastic trays, extremely easy to use. You soak the peat and coir pellets in their trays for 30 minutes and then sow one or two seeds per cell, thinning them out to one after germination. As soon as I see the plants roots at the base of the pellet, I start hardening them off (putting them outside for longer and longer each day) to acclimatize them to the real world; then I plant them out as soon as the temperature permits. The little netting bag they come in is left intact and degrades quickly in the soil. To water them I tend to soak the entire tray, every few days or as necessary. Many plants need warmer temperatures for germination (but not necessarily high light levels), but will not tolerate lower light levels as soon as leaves start to emerge, so if your window sill is overloaded you can put the trays near a radiator initially and then move them to a cooler, lighter place once they have germinated.

Propagating by cuttings is extremely simple for many plants, but like many things it can be made complicated. You can take softwood cuttings, from fresh new growth, semi-ripe cuttings from the later growth when the shoots are starting to firm at the base or hardwood cuttings later on towards the end of the year. Some plants are best taken as basal cuttings (through the base of the young shoot where it joins the parent branch, cutting through the slight swelling); heeled cuttings (formed by tugging off the young shoot complete with a small piece of parent plant that can be trimmed up); nodal cuttings (immediately below a leaf bud); or internodal (between two leaf buds). There are other types too, but these four will cover many, many plants. I almost invariably take heeled or nodal cuttings, which are quick, simple and effective. Once detached from the plant the softer, younger growth will wilt quickly, so have a plastic bag ready to put the cuttings in as soon as you take them, keeping them well away from sunlight.

I find a mix of 50 per cent grit and 50 per cent compost works well as a rooting medium for most plants and I generally use seed trays and put the cuttings fairly close together – depending on the size of the material, I will often get a hundred or so cuttings from one seed tray. You can put many, easily rooted cuttings straight into the soil outside, but I still find them easier to handle in trays.

Once you have inserted the cuttings into the tray, softwood cuttings or more difficult subjects may require a plastic bag over the container and/or being kept in a shaded place initially, to keep the cuttings in good condition. I also mist them with a mist sprayer, if they look on the point of flagging. The cold frame or greenhouse is the ideal place for rooting cuttings, but many work outside too. I rarely use hormone powder because its shelf life is quite short and most months I will be taking cuttings of something and I am not organized enough to have fresh supplies to hand. It does seem to speed up rooting and improve success rate in some cases, but I compensate by taking larger quantities to allow for possible failures.

Many other factors affect success too. The vigour of the parent plant is a significant one, so if it is an old favourite on its last legs that you want to retain, give it a good boost with feed, water and murmur a few sweet nothings to it to encourage it to put on a great spurt of new life ready for you to take advantage of, rather than selecting some slothful old shoot. Bottom heat – wonderful term – speeds things up no end, and you can achieve this by running soil-warming cables through the compost, or buying a special metal tray which heats up to stand the seed trays on. (Also handy for speeding up germination). This is my latest toy, and my success rates are very satisfying. Bottom heat is well worth putting on your Christmas list.

There are other ways of propagating – grafting, which is largely used for trees; and layering, which is particularly useful for climbers and involves encouraging a branch to shoot by covering it with soil while it is still attached to the parent plant, are just two of many to which there is not space to do justice here. All fascinating, but requiring a bit more expertise and less used than cuttings and seeds. Even so, they are well worth having a go at, just to see what amazing things you can do with plants. Micropropagation is becoming increasingly popular, but is limited to specialists with the necessary knowledge and equipment. **BG**

Index of Plants by Type

Plants are listed in ascending order of height. Some plants occur in more than one category.

Index of Plants by Common Name

Photographic Acknowledgements

Key
AL = Andrew Lawson
AZ = A–Z Botanical Collection
CN = Clive Nicholls
EC = Eric Crichton
HA = Heather Angel
GP.com = GardenPhotos.com
GPL = Garden Picture Library
GWI = Garden World Images
Holt = Holt Studios International Ltd
JB = Jonathan Buckley
JF = John Fielding
JG = John Glover
JH = Jerry Harpur
MHa = Marcus Harpur
MH = Marijke Heuff
LeSM = Le Scanff-Mayer
MM = Marianne Majerus
PH = Photos Horticultural
PPW = Plant Portraits Worldwide
SH = Sunniva Harte
SaxH = Saxon Holt
SO = S & O Mathews

t = top
b = bottom
c = centre
l = left
r = right

page 1 JB (Great Dixter, East Sussex; design: Christopher Lloyd); 2/3 MH; 4/5 (l) JG; 7 MH (Barnsley House); 11 CN (Eastgrove Cottage, Worcester); 12 EC; 15 JB (Great Dixter; design: Christopher Lloyd); 16 MM; 17 JB (Lady Farm, Somerset; design: Judy Pearce); 18 (l) JG; (r) JH; 19 (l) MM; (r) JG; 20 (l) GPL/Neil Holmes; (r) MHa; 21 (l) MM; (c) Holt/Jean Hall; 22 (l) JG; (c) JG (RHS Garden, Wisley); (r) JG; 23 (l) JG; (r) EC; 24 Holt/ Nigel Cattlin; 25 PH; 26 (tl) AL; (bl) JB; (r) JB; 27 (l) PH; (r) JB (Glen Chantry, Essex); 28 (l) MM; (c) MH; (r) JB (Great Dixter; design: Christopher Lloyd); 29 (l) JG; (r) AZ/ Adrian Thomas; 30 (l) JB; (c) PH; (r) GPL/Neil Holmes; 31 (l) GPL/Jerry Pavia; (r) JG; 32 JH; 33 JG; 34 (l) Oxford Scientific Films; (r) JG; 35 (l) JG; (r) GPL/Rex Butcher; 36 (l) GP.com/Judy White; (r) CN; 37 (l) PH; (c) GPL/François de Heel; (r) JB; 38 (l) MM (design: Piet Oudolf); (tr) Nigel Cattlin; (br) GPL/Christopher Fairweather; 39 (l) JG; (r) GPL/Bob Challinor; 40 GPL/Steven Wooster; 41 MHa; 42 (l) MM; (r) JB (Glen Chantry; design: Sue & Wol Staines); 43 (l) GPL/Christopher Fairweather; (r) JH; 44 (l) JG; (c) MM; (r) JG; 45 (l) MM; (r) SO; 46 (l) PH; (r) MHa; 47 (l) PH; (c) SaxH; (r) AL; 48; (l) MM; (c) AL; (r) SaxH; 49 (l) JG; (c) MHa; (r) JB (Perch Hill; design: Sarah Raven); 50; (l) LeSM (les Jardins de Bellevue); (r) JH; 51 (l) JB (Great Dixter; design: Christopher Lloyd); (r) JB; 52 (l) MHa (design: Beth Chatto); (r) MM; 53 (tl) MM; (bl) JG; (r) PH; 54 JG; 55 SaxH; 56 (l) MM; (r) EC; 57 (l) SH; (r) SH; 58 (l) GWI; (c) GPL/Howard Rice; (r) JG; 59 (l) EC; (r) AZ/Adrian Thomas; 60 MHa; 61 MHa; 62 (l) JH; (r) PH; 63 (l) GPL/ Howard Rice; (r) PPW; 64 (l) JB; (r) Andrea Jones; 65 GPL/Michael Howes; 66 JB (Great Dixter); 67 JG; 68 JG; 69 (tr) JH; (br) JH; 70 Holt/ Richard Anthony; 71 (l) JG; (r) JB; 72 (l) GPL/ Jerry Pavia; (r) GPL/Neil Holmes; 73 (l) GPL/Sunniva Harte; (c) JB (Alan Titchmarsh's Garden); (r) PH; 74 GPL/Sunniva Harte; 75 JB (Hinton Ampner, Hampshire); 76 (l) PPW; (c) JG; (r) JB; 77 (l) JG; (r) JG; 78 JG; 79 (tr) JG; (br) JG; 80 (l) PH; (r) MHa; 81 (l) JG; (c) JB; (r) GPL/ Didier Willery; 82 (l) GPL/Howard Rice; (c) JG; 83 (l) Richard Bloom; (c) AL; (r) JG; 84 (l) MHa; (r) JH; 85 (l) JB; (r) GPL/Christi Carter; 86 GPL/ Howard Rice; 87 GPL/David Cavagnaro; 88 (l) JG; (r) S&O (Hilbarn House); 89 (l) JG; (c) JH (design: Beth Chatto); (r) MH; 90 (l) JH; (c) JG; (r) JH; 91 (l) JB; (r) JB (Upper Mill Cottage, Kent; design: David & Mavis Seeney); 92 (l) JG; (r) JB (Hollington Herbs, Berks; design: Simon Hopkinson); 93 (l) JH; (r) GPL/John Ferro Sims; 94 MH; 95 JB (design: Beth Chatto); 96 (l) Bob Flowerdew; (r) JB (Ketley's, East Sussex; design: Helen Yemm); 97 (l) Jane Nichols; (r) GPL/Howard Rice; 98 (l) JG; (c) JG; (r) JG; 99 (l) JB (Great Dixter); (r) JB (Glen Chantry; design: S & W Staines); 100 (l) MM; (c) Holt/Primrose Peacock; (r) PH; 101 JG; 102 (l) MM; 103 SaxH; 104 (l) GPL/Christi Carter; (r) JG; 105 (l) Holt/Nigel Cattlin; (r) GPL/Howard Rice; 106 (l) GPL/Densey Clyne; (r) PH; 107 (l) MM; (c) MM; (r) JG; 108 (l) JG; (r) LeSM (Ellebore, France); 109 (l) JG; (r) MM; 110 Oxford Scientific Films/Geoff Kidd; 111 Sunniva Harte; 112 (l) GPL/JG; (r) JG; 113 (l) JG; (tr) JH; (br) CN; 114 (l) JH (design: Beth Chatto); (r) MM (RHS Garden, Wisley); 115 (l) Andrea Jones Location Photography; (r) JB (RHS Garden, Wisley); 116 (l) LeSM; (r) John Cushnie; 117 (l) SaxH; (r) LeSM; 118 LeSM (Les Jardins du Prieuré Notre Dame d'Orsan Maisonnais (18) France); 119 Bob Gibbons; 120 (l) SO; (tr) Holt/Willem Harinck; (br) MM; 121 (l) MHa; (r) JH; 122 (l) PH; (c) JG; (r) PH; 123 (l) JG; (r) MH; 124 (tr) MM; (br) Derek St Romaine; 125 (l) EC; (r) Andrew N. Gagg's PHOTO FLORA; 126 JB (design: Beth Chatto); 127 GPL/Howard Rice; 128 (l) CN; (r) JF; 129 (l) MM; (r) JB (Great Dixter); 130 (l) MHa; (r) JB (Glen Chantry); 131 (l) PH; (c) PH; (r) LeSM; 132 (l) JB; (r) CN (Stourton House, Wilts); 133 (l) PH; (c) JH; (r) JG; 134 JB (design: Beth Chatto); 135 HA; 136 (l) JB (Abbey Dore, Herefordshire); (c) MM (r) JH; 137; (l) GPL/Lamontagne; (r) MM; 138 JH; 139 (l) GPL/Philippe Bonduel; (r) MHa; 140 (l) JB; (c) PH; (r) JB; 141 (l) JG; (r) GP.com/Judy White; 142 (l) JG; (r) GPL/David England; 143 (l) SaxH; (r) GPL/LeSM; 144 Michael Howes; 145 EC; 146 (l) Holt/Alan & Linda Detrick; (c) MHa; (r) MM; 147 (l) JH; (r) GPL/Mark Bolton; 148 (l) CN; (c) MHa; (r) JB (Sissinghurst); 149 (l) MH; (r) GP.com/Graham Rice; 150 (l) GPL/J S Sira; (r) MHa; 151 (l) MM (Urn Cottage, Charfield; design: Lesley Rosser; (r) GPL/Lamontagne; 152 JG; 153 LeSM (Jardin des Fournials Ossart-Maurières, France); 154 (l) JG; (r) JB (design: Beth Chatto; 155 (l) GP.com/ Graham Rice; (r) LeSM; 156 (l) GPL/ Lamontagne; (c) JH; (r) JG; 157 (l) CN; (c) JG; (r) JH; 158 (l) CN; (r) MHa (design: Beth Chatto); 159 (l) MM; (r) MHa; 160 LeSM (Les Jardins de Bellevue); 161 MM; 162 (l) PH; (r) PH; 163 (l) GPL/Didier Willery; (c) JG; (r) JB (Great Dixter); 164 (l) GPL/Henk Dijkman; (r) Holt/Nigel Cattlin; 165 (l) MM; (r) GPL/Marie O'Hara; 166 (l) CN; (c) JG; (r) PH; 167 (c) MM; (r) GPL/Brian Carter; 168 (l) JG; (c) GPL/Juliette Wade; (r) PH; 169 (c) JB (RHS Garden, Wisley); (r) MH; 170 JB; 171 JG; 172 (l) PH; (c) MM; 173 (l) JB; (c) CN (design: Jill Billington); (r) GPL/Steven Wooster; 174 (l) MHa; (r) JF; 175 (l) JB; (r) JG; 176 GPL/Chris Burrows; 177 MM; 178 (l) JB (Glen Chantry); (r) SaxH; 179 (l) JG; (c) MM; (r) PH; 180 (l) MM; (r) JG; 181 (l) JB; (r) JB (Magdalen College, Oxford); 182 (l) JB; (c) JG; (r) GPL/Sunniva Harte; 183 (l) AL; (r) JG; 184 GPL/Howard Rice; 185 (l) JH; (r) JH; 186 (l) MHa; (c) PH; (r) MM; 187 (l) JG; (r) MM; 188 (l) JG; (c) JG; (r) MHa; 189 (l) JB; (r) JG; 190 (l) JH; (c) JB; 191 (l) JB; (c) SaxH; (tr) LeSM; (br) JG; 192 GPL/Christi Carter; 193 GPL/Stephen Robson; 194 (l) PH; (c) SaxH; (r) JG; 195 (l) PH; (r) MM (Chesil Beach); 196 (l) GPL/Howard Rice; (r) JB; 197 (l) PH;

(r) JG; 198 (l) MHa (RHS Garden, Wisley); (c) JG; (r) PH; 199 (l) GPL/Sunniva Harte; (r) EC; 200 JH; 201 MM; 202 (l) SaxH; (r) JF; (r) GPL/Jerry Pavia; 203 MM; 204 (l) EC; (r) CN; 205 (l) MHa; (c) GPL/Howard Rice; (r) GPL/Jerry Pavia; 206 (l) JG; (c) AZ/Martin Land; (r) CN; 207 (c) GPL/J S Sira; (r) JH; 208 JB; 209 LeSM (Les Jardins de Bellevue (76) France); 210 (l) GWI; (c) Holt/Nigel Cattlin; (r) JB; 211 (l) SO; (r) JG; 212 (l) GPL/Howard Rice; (c) MM; 213 (l) A Young; (r) GPL/Howard Rice; 214 (l) GPL/Lamontagne; (r) JB; 215 (l) PH; (c) anon (r) JB (Great Dixter); 216 JB; 217 JH; 218 (l) SO; (r) GPL/Jerry Pavia; 219 (l) GWI; (r) JG; 220 (l) JG; (c) GPL/Howard Rice; (r) MHa; 221 MHa; 222 (l) JH; (c) JH; (r) JG; 223 (l) JG; (r) JB (Glen Chantry); 224 JG; 225 JB (Coton Manor, Northants; design: Susie Pasley-Tyler); 226 (l) AL; (c) PH; (r) GWI; 227 (l) SaxH; (r) PH; 228 (l) Thompson & Morgan; (r) JG; 229 (l) SaxH; (r) MHa; 230 (l) GPL/David Russell; (c) JG; (r) LeSM (Les Jardins de Bellevue (76) France); 231 (l) MHa; (r) JB (Great Dixter); 232 JG; 233 JH; 234 (l) Geoff Hayes; (c) JG; (r) JG; 235 (c) JG; (r) JG; 236 (l) Holt/Bob Gibbons; (c) GPL/Howard Rice; (r) JG; 237 (l) JH; (r) JG; 238 (l) JG; (r) JF; 239 (l) JB; (r) GPL/Brian Carter; 240 MH; 241 JB; 242 (l) JG; (r) PH; 243 (l) JG; (c) MH (design: Beth Chatto); (r) JG; 244 (l) JG; (r) JB; 245 (l) JH; (r) PH; 246 (l) JG; (c) JG; (r) MM; 247 (l) JB (East Ruston, Old Vicarage, Norfolk; design: Alan Gray & Graham Robeson; (r) LeSM; 248 CN; 249 Geoff Hayes; 250 (l) JG; (r) MHa; 251 (l) GPL/Didier Willery; (c) JG; (r) GPL/Neil Holmes; 252 (l) GPL/LeSM; (r) SO; 253 (l) JH; (r) GPL/LeSM; 254 (l) GWI; (r) JG; 255 (l) SO; (r) JG; 256 JG; 257 SO; 258 (l) GPL/Brian Carter; (r) JG; 259 (l) LeSM (Domaine de St Jean de Beauregard); (r) JG; 260 (l) AZ/Nick Wiseman; (r) PH; 261 (c) JB; (r) MHa; 262 (c) PH; (r) GPL/Sunniva Harte; 263 (l) EC; (c) MM; (r) EC; 264 CN; 265 (tr) GPL/Brigitte Thomas; (br) GPL/David Cavagnaro; 266 (l) JG; (c) EC; 267 (tl) SaxH; (bl) MM; (r) SaxH; 268 (l) GP.com/Judy White; (c) PH; (r) JB (Great Dixter); 269 (tr) PH; (br) MM; 270 (l) JB (RHS Garden, Wisley); (r) EC; 271 (l) EC; (r) LeSM; 272 JB (design: Gay Wilson); 273 JG; 274 (l) JH; (r) GPL/Erika Craddock; 275 (l) JG; (c) PH; (r) PH; 276 (l) JB (Great Dixter); (c) GPL/Jerry Pavia; (c) MH; 277 (l) JB (Ketley's, East Sussex; design: Helen Yemm); (r) JG; 278 (l) GPL/Jerry Pavia; (r) CN; 279 (l) MM; (r) JH; 280 MM; 281 JG; 282 (l) GWI; (c) MM (design: Tom Stuart-Smith); 283 (tl) SaxH; (bl) GPL/Sunniva Harte; (r) JG; 284 (l) JG; (c) CN; (r) JG; 285 (l) LeSM (Les Jardins de Bellevue (76) France); (r) AZ/Carol Casselden; 286 (l) JG; (c) MM; (r) MHa; 287 (l) JB (Great Dixter); (r) JF; 288 JG; 289 JB; 290 (l) JG; (r) JB (design: Anthony Goff); 291 (l) PH; (r) EC; 292 (l) AL; (c) MM; 293 (l) MM; (c) MH; (r) MM; 294 (l) PH; (r) GP.com/Judy White; 295 (l) MHa; (c) JH; 296 JG; 297 JB; 298 (l) SaxH; (c) PH; (r) JH; 299 (l) JG; (c) JG; (r) PH; 300 (l) MM; (r) PH; 301 (l) EC; (c) CN; (r) GPL/JG; 302 (l) GWI; (c) GPL/David Cavagnaro; 303 (l) PH; (c) MHa; (r) JB; 304 AL; 305 SO; 306 (l) PH; (r) JG; 307 (l) MHa; (r) AL; 308 (l) LeSM; (c) JG; 309 (l) PH; (r) JG; 310 PH; 311 (tr) SO; (br) JG; 312 (l) GPL/Micky White; (c) EC; 313 (l) MM; (c) JG; (r) MHa; 314 (l) GPL/Philippe Bonduel; (c) Holt/Inga Spence; (r) GPL/Jerry Pavia; 315 (l) MHa; (r) PH; 316 (l) JB (Great Dixter); (r) EC; 317 (l) JG; (r) MHa; 318 Holt/Primrose Peacock; 319 GPL/Howard Rice; 320 (l) EC; (r) MHa; 321 (l) JB; (c) PH; 322 (l) JG; (r) JG; 323 (l) GWI; (c) MM; (r) PH; 324 (l) PH; (c) GPL/Sunniva Harte; (r) EC; 325 leSM; 326 JG; 327 JB; 328 (l) GPL/Howard Rice; (c) MM; (r) SaxH; 329 (l) GPL/Howard Rice; (r) JB (Great Dixter); 330 (l) JH; (c) JG; (r) JG; 331 (l) GPL/J S Sira; (r) LeSM; 332 (l) GPL/David Russell; (c) EC; (r) GPL/David Askham; 333 MM; 334 (l) SaxH; (c) LeSM; (r) PH; 335 (l) MM; (c) David Austin Roses Ltd; (r) PH; 336 JB (design: Jackie McLaren); 337 MM; 338 (l) GPL/J S Sira; (c) GWI; (r) JB (Lady Farm, Somerset; design: Judy Pearce); 339 (c) JB (Hollington Herbs); (r) JG; 340 (l) JB (Perch Hill; design: Sarah Raven); (r) JB (design: Robin Green & Ralph Cade); 341 (l) MHa; (r) PH; 342 (l) JG; (c) JG; (r) MM; 343 (l) AL; (r) JB; 344 JB; 345 JB; 346 (l) JG; (c) MHa; 347 (c) GPL/Mark Bolton; (r) PH; 348 (l) SO; (c) Holt/Bob Gibbons; (r) JG; 349 (l) LeSM; (c) Geoff Hayes; (r) MHa; 350 (l) JG; (r) JG; 351 (l) EC; (r) EC; 352 MM; 353 Wildlife Matters; 354 (l) Geoff Hayes; (r) PH; 355 (l) GPL/Didier Willery; (c) Holt; (r) PH; 356 MM; 357 GPL/JG; 358 (l) MM; (c) GPL/J S Sira; (r) PH; 359 (l) MM; (r) PH; 360 AL; 361 SO; 362 (l) MHa; (c) JG; (r) JG; 363 (l) GPL/Howard Rice; (c) GP.com/Graham Rice; 364 (l) PH; (r) JG; 365 (l) JG; (r) CN; 366 AL; 367 JH; 368 MM; 369 PH; 370 (l) PH; (c) JH; (r) JG; 371 (l) GPL/J S Sira; (r) MM; 372 (l) GPL/Neil Holmes; (r) JB (design: Judy Pearce); 373 (l) MH; (c) GPL/Neil Holmes; (r) SaxH; 374 (l) GPL/Neil Holmes; (c) JG; (r) EC; 375 (c) JG; (r) JH; 376 JG; 377 JB; 378 (l) JG; (r) GPL/Howard Rice; 379 (l) MM; (c) JF; (r) JG; 380 (l) MM (The Herbalist Garden, RHS Chelsea 1998; design: Bunny Guinness); (r) GPL/J S Sira; 381 (l) MM; (r) JB (design: David & Mavis Seeney); 382 JG; 383 MM; 384 (l) JB; (c) JF; (r) JB; 385 (c) JH; (r) AZ/Gary Newport; 386 (l) AZ/Lino Pastorelli; (r) MM (design: Tom Stuart-Smith); 387 (l) GPL/Neil Holmes; (c) GPL/Howard Rice; (r) SaxH; 388 GPL/Steven Wooster; 389 (tr) JG; (br) GPL/Gillian McAlmont; 390 (l) JB; (r) JB; 391 (l) JH; (r) JG; 392 (l) JG; (c) MM; 393 (l) Robin B. Cushman; (r) JG; 394 Holt/Jean Hall; 395 (l) SO; (r) MHa; 396 EC; 397 CN; 398 (l) GPL/ JG; (c) GPL/JG; (r) PH; 399 (l) JH; (r) GWI; 400 (l) MHa; (r) MHa; 401 (l) MHa; (r) Holt/Inga Spence; 402 JG; 403 LeSM (Les Jardins de Bellevue (76) France)